Visit classzone.com and get connected

Online resources provide instruction, practice, and learning support correlated to your text.

- **Misconceptions database** provides solutions for common student misconceptions about science and their world.
- **Professional development links,** including SciLinks, offer additional teaching resources.
- **Animations and visualizations** help improve comprehension.
- **Math Tutorial** helps strengthen students' math skills.
- **Flashcards** help students review vocabulary.
- **Test practice** prepares students for assessments.

Gain immediate access to *ClassZone*'s teacher resources.

MCDTCOWDMISSZ

Use this code to create your own username and password.

Also visit *ClassZone* to learn more about these innovative and updated online resources.

- eEdition Plus Online
- Content Review Online

McDougal Littell

TEACHER'S EDITION

McDougal Littell

CALIFORNIA

Science

FOCUS ON EARTH SCIENCES

The Earth System

The Changing Earth

Earth's Surface

Ecology and Resources

Science Content Standards for California Public Schools reproduced by permission, California Department of Education, CDE Press, 1430 N Street, Suite 3207, Sacramento, CA 95814.

Printed in the United States of America.

ISBN13: 978-0-618-64098-0

ISBN10: 0-618-64098-3 2 3 4 5 6 7 8 VJM 09 08 07

Internet Web Site: http://www.mcdougallittell.com

McDougal Littell Science

Effective Science Instruction Tailored for Middle School Learners

Focus on Earth Sciences Teacher's Edition Contents

McDougal Littell Science

Each book in this three-book *McDougal Littell Science* Series emphasizes concepts from one science—earth, life, or physical—while integrating concepts from the other two sciences.

- Carefully sequenced units and chapters that consistently connect new learning to prior knowledge
- Focused integration of selected concepts from other sciences and technology
- Complete Student Resource Handbooks in every book

Focus on Earth Sciences

Unit 1 ▶ The Earth System
1. Energy and Change
2. Energy in the Earth System
3. Weather Patterns
4. Weather Fronts and Storms

Unit 2 ▶ Earth's Surface
5. Views of Earth Today
6. Minerals and Rocks
7. Erosion and Deposition

Unit 3 ▶ The Changing Earth
8. Plate Tectonics
9. Earthquakes
10. Mountains and Volcanoes

Unit 4 ▶ Ecology and Resources
11. Ecosystems and Biomes
12. Interactions Within Ecosystems
13. Natural Resources
14. Human Impact on Ecosystems

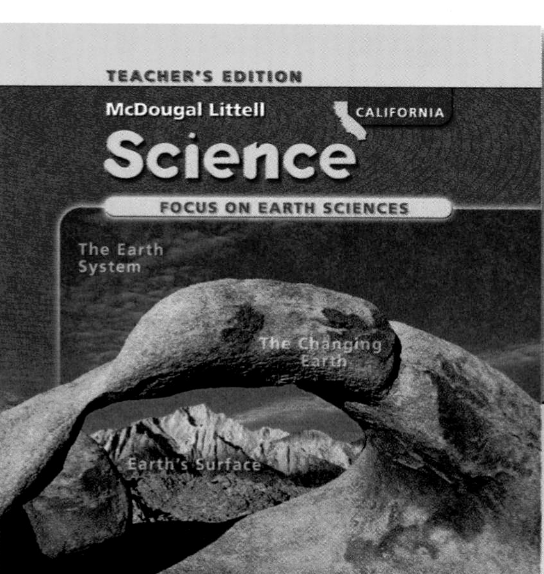

Focus on Life Sciences

Unit 1 ▶ Cells and Heredity
1. The Cell
2. How Cells Function
3. Cell Division
4. Patterns of Heredity

Unit 2 ▶ Earth and Life History
5. Views of Earth's Past
6. Evolution of Living Things
7. Classification of Living Things

Unit 3 ▶ Structure and Function in Living Systems
8. Systems in Organisms
9. Reproduction
10. Movement and Forces
11. Fluids, Pressure, and Circulation

Unit 4 ▶ Physical Principles in Hearing and Vision
12. Sound
13. Light
14. Optics

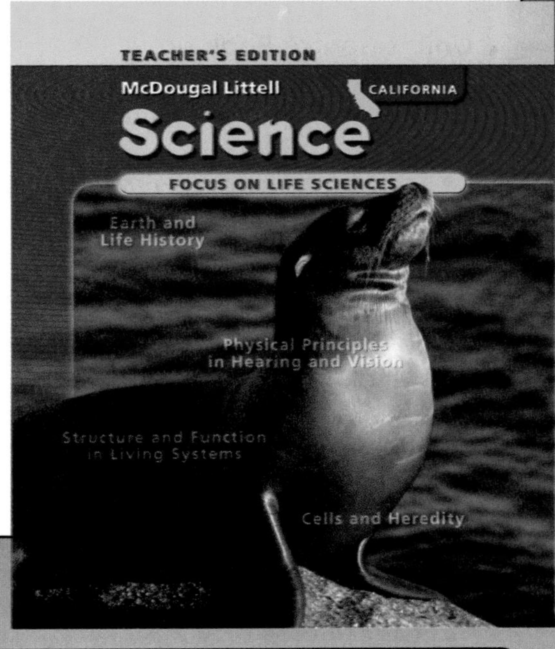

Focus on Physical Sciences

Unit 1 ▶ Motion and Forces
1. Motion
2. Forces
3. Gravity, Elastic Forces, and Friction
4. Density and Buoyancy

Unit 2 ▶ The Structure of Matter
5. Properties of Matter
6. States of Matter
7. Atomic Structure and the Periodic Table

Unit 3 ▶ Chemical Interactions
8. Chemical Bonds and Compounds
9. Chemical Reactions
10. Solutions
11. Chemistry of Living Systems

Unit 4 ▶ Space Science
12. Earth, Moon, and Sun
13. Our Solar System
14. Stars, Galaxies, and the Universe

Teaching Resources

A wealth of print and technology resources helps you adapt the program to your teaching style and to the specific needs of your students.

Book-Specific Print Resources

Unit Resource Book provides all of the teaching resources for the unit organized by chapter and section.

- Family Letters
- *Scientific American Frontiers* Video Guide
- Unit Projects
- Lesson Plans
- Reading Study Guides (Levels A and B)
- Spanish Reading Study Guides
- Challenge Readings
- Challenge and Extension Activities
- Reinforcing Key Concepts
- Vocabulary Practice
- Math Support and Practice
- Investigation Datasheets
- Chapter Investigations (Levels A, B, and C)
- Additional Investigations (Levels A, B, and C)
- Summarizing the Chapter

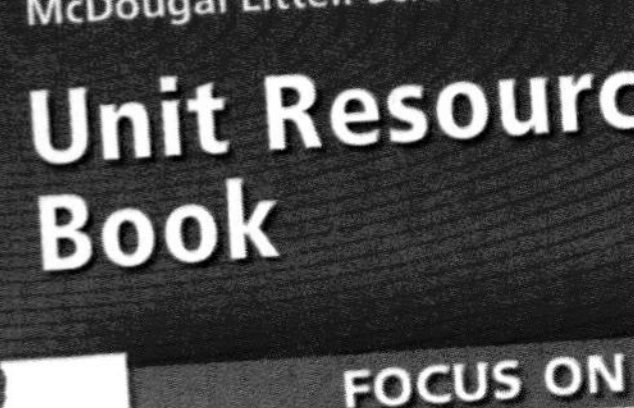

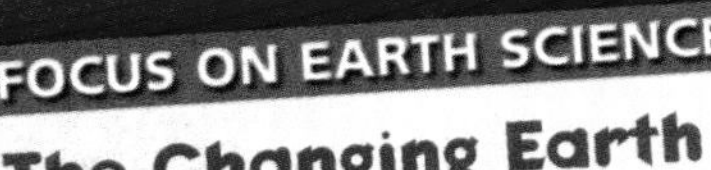

Assessment Book with Benchmark Tests contains complete resources for assessing student knowledge and performance.

- Chapter Diagnostic Tests
- Section Quizzes
- Chapter Tests (Levels A, B, and C)
- Alternative Assessments
- Unit Tests (Levels A, B, and C)
- Benchmark Tests (1–4)

Transparency Book includes instructional visuals for each chapter.

- Three-Minute Warm-Ups
- Note-Taking Models
- Daily Vocabulary Scaffolding
- Chapter Outlines
- Big Idea Flow Charts
- Chapter Teaching Visuals

Standards Review and Practice Book

California Modified Lesson Plans for English Learners

California Lab Manual

Note-Taking/ Reading Study Guide

Spanish Note-Taking/ Reading Study Guide

Program-Wide Print Resources

Science Toolkit

City Science

Visual Glossary

Multi-Language Glossary

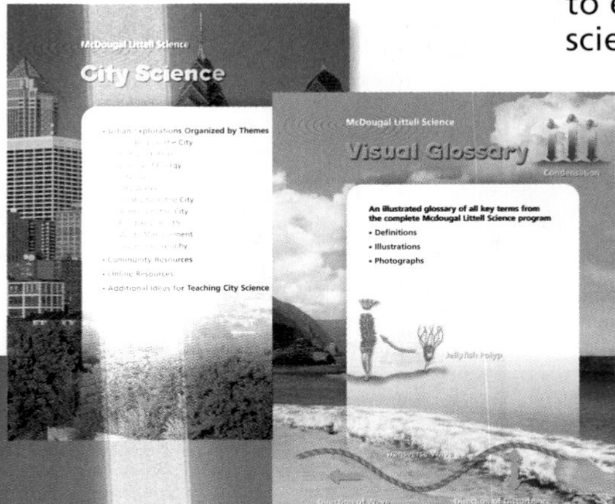

English Learners Package

***Scientific American Frontiers* Video Guide**

How Stuff Works Express
This quarterly magazine offers opportunities to explore current science topics.

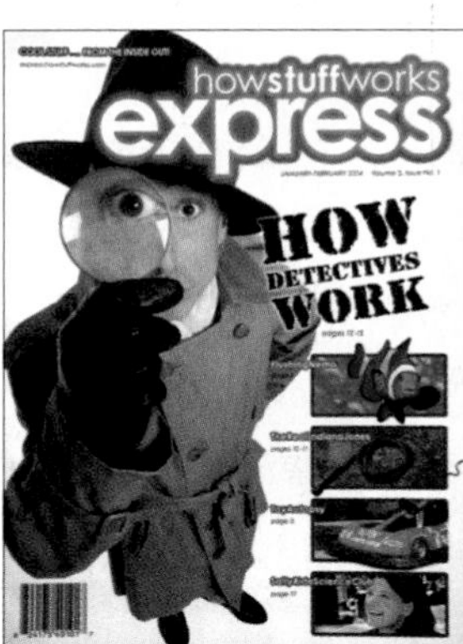

Technology Resources

***Scientific American Frontiers* Video Program**
Each specially tailored segment from this award-winning PBS series correlates to a unit; available on VHS and DVD.

Audio CDs Complete chapter texts read in both English and Spanish

Lab Generator CD-ROM
A searchable database of all activities from the program plus additional labs for each unit; includes labs in Spanish; edit and print your own version of labs

Test Generator CD-ROM

eEdition CD-ROM

EasyPlanner CD-ROM

Content Review CD-ROM

Power Presentations CD-ROM

Online Resources

- ClassZone.com
- Content Review Online
- eEdition Plus Online
- EasyPlanner Plus Online
- eTest Plus Online

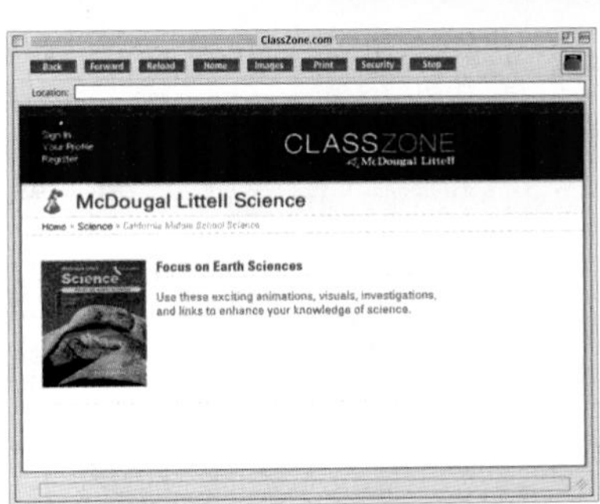

Research-Based Solutions for Your Classroom

The distinguished program consultant team and a thorough, research-based planning and development process assure that *McDougal Littell Science* supports all students in learning science concepts, acquiring inquiry skills, and thinking scientifically.

Standards-Based Instruction

Concepts and skills were selected based on careful analysis of California Science Content Standards.

California Science Standards

As you read and study your science book this year, you'll be learning many of the ideas described in the California Science Standards. The standards that you will concentrate on are listed here.

Following each standard is an explanation of what it means and how you will learn about it. References to chapters tell you where you'll begin to study the content in the standard. Many standards refer to several chapters. That's because you will read and study information presented in several chapters in order to understand a standard fully. By the end of the year, you will have learned the content of these California Science Standards.

Focus on Earth Sciences

Plate Tectonics and Earth's Structure

Standard 6.1: Plate tectonics accounts for important features of Earth's surface and major geologic events.

Standard 6.1.a	What It Means to You
Students know evidence of plate tectonics is derived from the fit of the continents; the location of earthquakes, volcanoes, and midocean ridges; and the distribution of fossils, rock types, and ancient climatic zones.	The theory of plate tectonics explains how the major features on Earth's surface formed and why geologic events such as earthquakes happen. It states that Earth's lithosphere is broken into huge plates that move and change in size over time. You will learn how scientists developed this theory by noticing evidence such as the shapes of the continents and how they appear to fit together. **(Chapters 8, 9, and 10)**

Standard 6.1.b	What It Means to You
Students know Earth is composed of several layers: a cold, brittle lithosphere; a hot, convecting mantle; and a dense, metallic core.	You will learn the properties of Earth's layers. The lithosphere is made up of Earth's crust, a thin layer of cool rock, and the top of the mantle. The top of the mantle is cool and hard. The rest of the mantle is made of rock that is hot and soft enough to flow slowly. Below the mantle is the outer core, a layer of molten metals. The inner core, which is at Earth's center, is made up of very hot but solid metals. **(Chapters 2, 6, 8, 9, and 10)**

Standard 6.1.c	What It Means to You
Students know lithospheric plates the size of continents and ocean move at rates of centimeters per year in response to movement in the mantle.	The lithosphere is broken into slabs of rock called plates. They fit together like a jigsaw puzzle on Earth's surface. Underneath the plates is the asthenosphere, a layer of soft, hot rock. You will learn that rock in the asthenosphere moves slowly by convection, a motion that transfers heat energy. Convection in the asthenosphere allows the plates to move over Earth's surface. **(Chapters 8 and 10)**

CA2 McDougal Littell Science

CHAPTER 2

Energy in the Earth System

the BIG idea

The Sun is the major source of energy for Earth's atmosphere and surface.

Key Concepts

SECTION 1 The Earth system has four major parts. Learn about the parts of the Earth system and how they shape the planet's surface.

SECTION 2 The Sun provides energy to the Earth system. Learn how uneven heating of Earth by the Sun is one cause of the seasons.

SECTION 3 Energy is transferred within the Earth system. Learn how solar energy powers the water cycle and affects weather and climate.

California ClassZone

CLASSZONE.COM

Chapter 2 online resources: Content Review, three Visualizations, three Resource Centers, Math Tutorial, Test Practice

38 Unit 1: The Earth System

Place an outdoor thermometer in an empty paper cup, and place the cup in a freezer. Check the thermometer every three minutes and record the time it takes for the temperature to reach 0°C (32°F). Remove the cup from the freezer. After it returns to room temperature, fill the cup with soil and repeat the experiment.

Observe and Think How long did it take for the temperature to reach 0°C each time? Why might there have been a difference?

What Is Climate? Code: MDL012

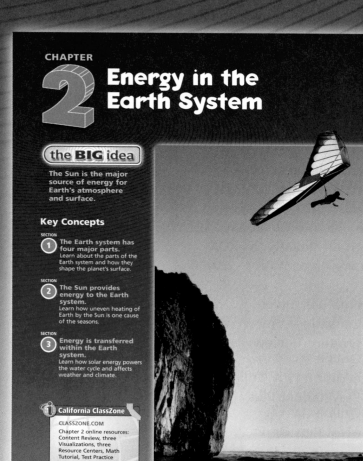

Chapter 2: Energy in the Earth System 39

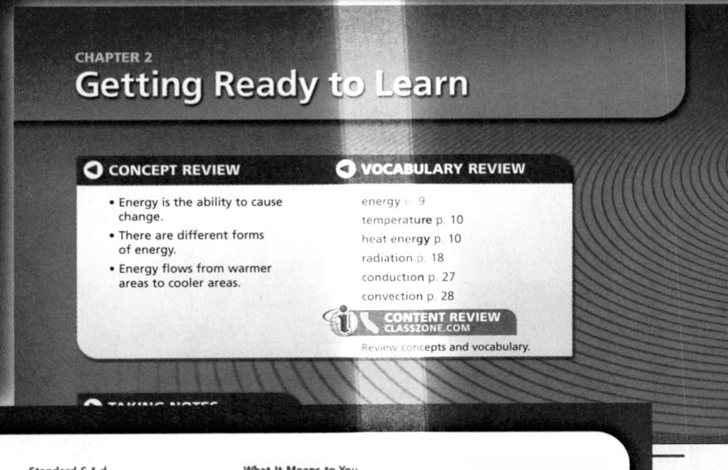
CHAPTER 2

Getting Ready to Learn

CONCEPT REVIEW

- Energy is the ability to cause change.
- There are different forms of energy.
- Energy flows from warmer areas to cooler areas.

VOCABULARY REVIEW

energy p. 9
temperature p. 10
heat energy p. 10
radiation p. 18
conduction p. 27
convection p. 28

CONTENT REVIEW CLASSZONE.COM

Review concepts and vocabulary.

Effective Instructional Strategies

McDougal Littell Science incorporates strategies that research shows are effective in improving student achievement. These strategies include

- Note taking and nonlinguistic representations (Marzano, Pickering, and Pollock)
- A focus on big ideas (Kame'enui and Carnine)
- Background knowledge and active involvement (Project CRISS)

Robert J. Marzano, Debra J. Pickering, and Jane E. Pollock, *Classroom Instruction That Works: Research-Based Strategies for Increasing Student Achievement* (ASCD, 2001)

Edward J. Kame'enui and Douglas Carnine, *Effective Teaching Strategies That Accommodate Diverse Learners* (Pearson, 2002)

Project CRISS (Creating Independence Through Student-Owned Strategies)

Standard 6.1.d	What It Means to You
Students know that earthquakes are sudden motions along breaks in the crust called faults and that volcanoes and fissures are locations where magma reaches the surface.	A fault is a break in the lithosphere where blocks of rock move past each other. An earthquake is a shaking of the ground caused by a sudden movement along a fault. You will learn that magma is rock that is so hot it is melted and can flow. A volcano is an opening in Earth's crust through which magma can erupt. **(Chapter 10)**

Standard 6.1.e	What It Means to You
Students know major geologic events, such as earthquakes, volcanic eruptions, and mountain building, result from plate motions.	Most major earthquakes, volcanic eruptions, and mountain-building events happen where one tectonic plate meets another. Plates can move apart, push together, or scrape past each other. One plate can sink beneath another plate. Mountains can form as rocks crumple and fold. **(Chapters 8, 9, and 10)**

Standard 6.1.f	What It Means to You
Students know how to explain major features of California geology (including mountains, faults, volcanoes) in terms of plate tectonics.	You will learn how the movement of tectonic plates has shaped the geologic features of California. For example, the San Andreas Fault is where the Pacific Plate and the North American Plate are scraping past each other. Mount Shasta is a volcano that has formed in an area where the Pacific Plate is sinking underneath the edge of the North American Plate. **(Chapters 8, 9, and 10)**

Standard 6.1.g	What It Means to You
Students know how to determine the epicenter of an earthquake and know that the effects of an earthquake on any region vary, depending on the size of the earthquake, the distance of the region from the epicenter, the local geology, and the type of construction in the region.	The focus of an earthquake is the place underground where rocks first begin to move. The epicenter is the place on the surface directly above the focus. You will learn that scientists can locate an earthquake's epicenter by analyzing seismic waves recorded at three locations. **(Chapter 9)**

California Science Standards CA3

The parts of the Earth system are connected.

VOCABULARY
Remember to make a frame game diagram for each vocabulary term.

A terrarium is a simple example of a **system**—an organized group of parts that work together to form a whole. To understand a system, you need to see how all its parts work together. This is true for a small terrarium, and it is true for planet Earth.

Both a terrarium and Earth are closed systems. They are closed because matter, such as soil or water, cannot enter or leave. However, energy can flow into or out of the systems. Light and heat can pass through the glass of the terrarium. In the same way, sunlight and heat enter and leave the Earth system through the atmosphere.

The Earth system is made up of four connected parts. These parts are the atmosphere (Earth's air), the hydrosphere (Earth's waters), the biosphere (Earth's living things), and the geosphere (Earth's interior and its rocks and sediments). Each of these parts is an open system because both matter and energy move into and out of it. The four open systems work together to form one large, closed system called Earth.

Chapter 2: **Energy in the Earth System 41**

Comprehensive Research, Review, and Field Testing

An ongoing program of research and review guided the development of *McDougal Littell Science.*

- Program plans based on extensive data from classroom visits, research surveys, teacher panels, and focus groups
- All Student Edition activities and labs classroom-tested by middle school teachers and students
- All chapters reviewed for clarity and scientific accuracy by the Content Reviewers
- Selected chapters field-tested in the classroom to assess student learning, ease of use, and student interest
- Independent randomized control study for learner verification

Content Organized Around Big Ideas

Each chapter develops a big idea of science, helping students to place key concepts in context.

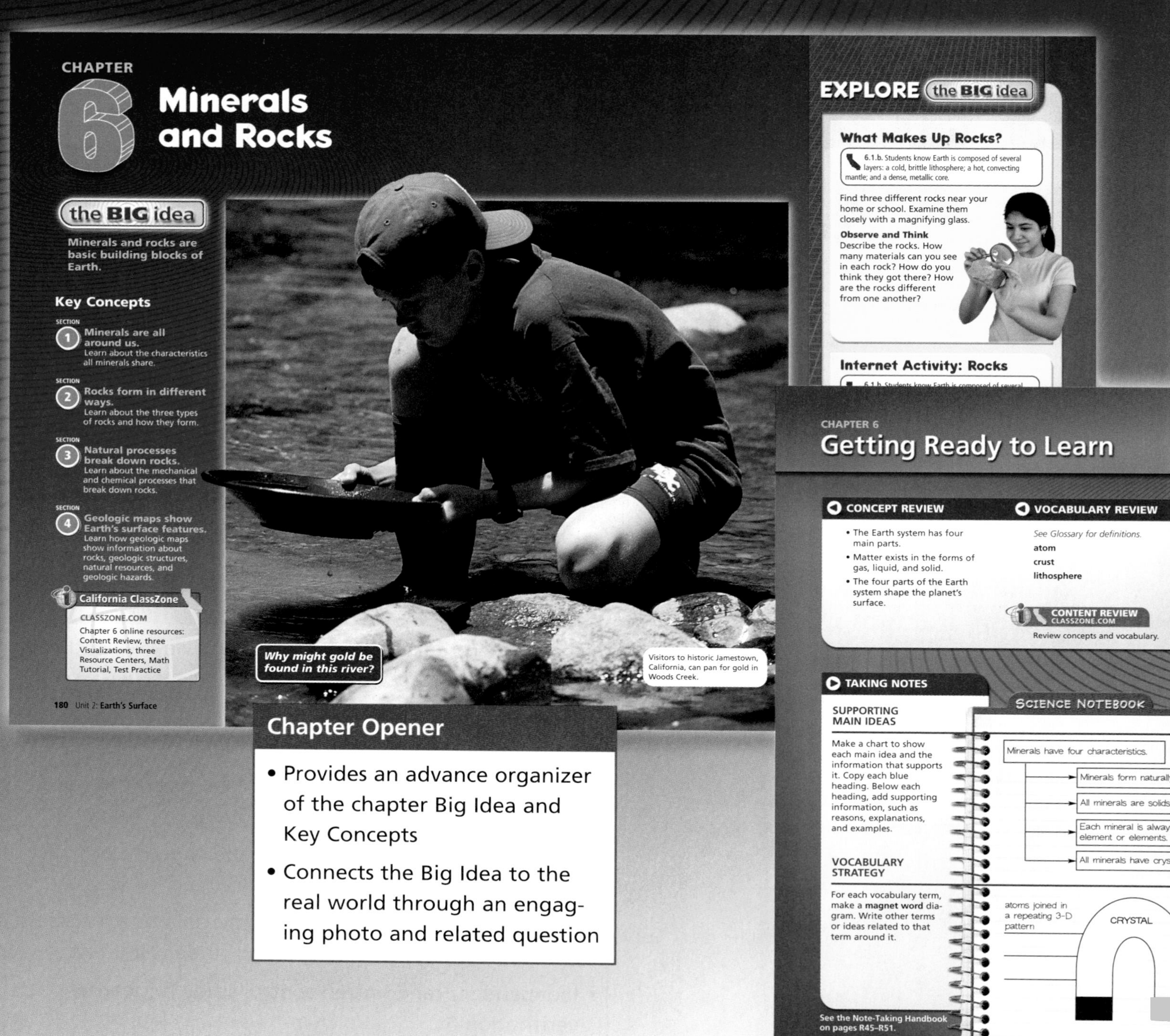

CHAPTER 6

Minerals and Rocks

the BIG idea

Minerals and rocks are basic building blocks of Earth.

Key Concepts

SECTION 1 **Minerals are all around us.** Learn about the characteristics all minerals share.

SECTION 2 **Rocks form in different ways.** Learn about the three types of rocks and how they form.

SECTION 3 **Natural processes break down rocks.** Learn about the mechanical and chemical processes that break down rocks.

SECTION 4 **Geologic maps show Earth's surface features.** Learn how geologic maps show information about rocks, geologic structures, natural resources, and geologic hazards.

California ClassZone

CLASSZONE.COM

Chapter 6 online resources: Content Review, three Visualizations, three Resource Centers, Math Tutorial, Test Practice

Why might gold be found in this river?

Visitors to historic Jamestown, California, can pan for gold in Woods Creek.

180 Unit 2: Earth's Surface

EXPLORE the BIG idea

What Makes Up Rocks?

6.1.b. Students know Earth is composed of several layers: a cold, brittle lithosphere; a hot, convecting mantle; and a dense, metallic core.

Find three different rocks near your home or school. Examine them closely with a magnifying glass.

Observe and Think Describe the rocks. How many materials can you see in each rock? How do you think they got there? How are the rocks different from one another?

Internet Activity: Rocks

CHAPTER 6

Getting Ready to Learn

CONCEPT REVIEW

- The Earth system has four main parts.
- Matter exists in the forms of gas, liquid, and solid.
- The four parts of the Earth system shape the planet's surface.

VOCABULARY REVIEW

See Glossary for definitions.

atom
crust
lithosphere

CONTENT REVIEW CLASSZONE.COM

Review concepts and vocabulary.

TAKING NOTES

SUPPORTING MAIN IDEAS

Make a chart to show each main idea and the information that supports it. Copy each blue heading. Below each heading, add supporting information, such as reasons, explanations, and examples.

VOCABULARY STRATEGY

For each vocabulary term, make a **magnet word** diagram. Write other terms or ideas related to that term around it.

See the Note-Taking Handbook on pages R45–R51.

SCIENCE NOTEBOOK

Minerals have four characteristics.

Minerals form naturally.

All minerals are solids.

Each mineral is always element or elements.

All minerals have crysta

atoms joined in a repeating 3-D pattern

CRYSTAL

182 Unit 2: Earth's Surface

Chapter Opener

- Provides an advance organizer of the chapter Big Idea and Key Concepts
- Connects the Big Idea to the real world through an engaging photo and related question

Visual Summary

- Summarizes Key Concepts using both text and visuals
- Reinforces the connection of Key Concepts to the Big Idea

6 Chapter Review

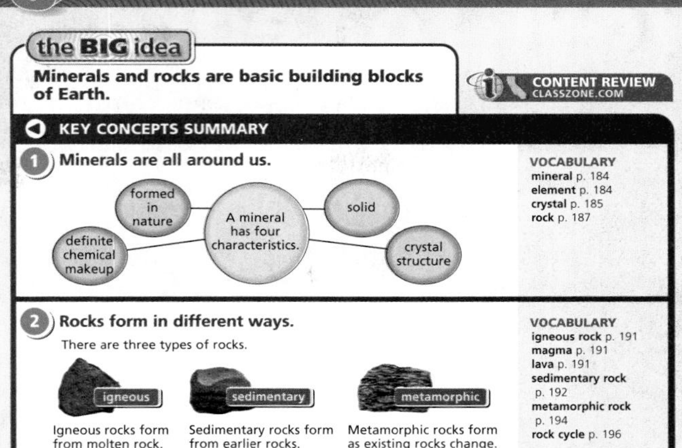

the BIG idea

Minerals and rocks are basic building blocks of Earth.

CONTENT REVIEW CLASSZONE.COM

KEY CONCEPTS SUMMARY

1 Minerals are all around us.

VOCABULARY
mineral p. 184
element p. 184
crystal p. 185
rock p. 187

2 Rocks form in different ways.

There are three types of rocks.

Igneous rocks form from molten rock. Sedimentary rocks form from earlier rocks. Metamorphic rocks form as existing rocks change.

VOCABULARY
igneous rock p. 191
magma p. 191
lava p. 191
sedimentary rock p. 192
metamorphic rock p. 194
rock cycle p. 196

3 Natural processes break down rocks.

Over time, **mechanical weathering** breaks a rock into smaller pieces.

Chemical weathering affects exposed rock surfaces.

VOCABULARY
geologic cycle p. 199
weathering p. 199
mechanical weathering p. 200
chemical weathering p. 202

4 Geologic maps show E

Geologic maps show
- types and ages of rocks
- geologic structures
- resources and hazards

Reviewing Vocabulary

On a separate sheet of paper, write a sentence or two describing the relationship between the two terms.

1. mineral, crystal
2. magma, lava
3. intrusive, extrusive
4. igneous rock, metamorphic rock
5. geologic cycle, weathering
6. mechanical weathering, chemical weathering
7. geologic map, topographic map

Reviewing Key Concepts

Multiple Choice *Choose the letter of the best answer.*

8. A crystal structure is characteristic of **(6.6)**
   a. an element
   b. a rock
   c. magma
   d. a mineral

9. How is it possible for two different minerals to have the same chemical composition? **(6.6)**
   a. They have different crystal structures.
   b. One is formed only by organisms.
   c. Only one is a rock-forming mineral.
   d. They have different appearances.

ntinually

allization?

Thinking Critically

Use the map and key to answer the next seven questions. **(6.7.f)**

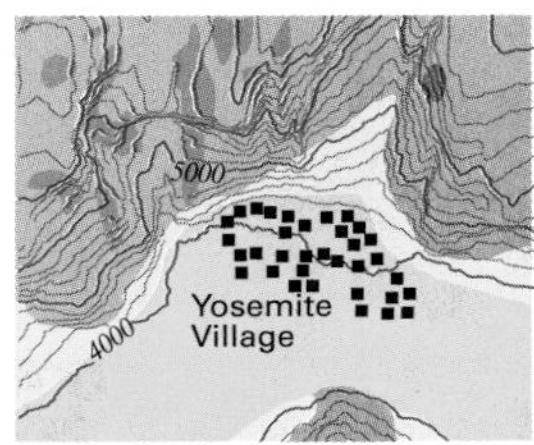

Sediment or Rock Type	Approximate Age
Sediment deposits mainly left by streams	0–2 million years
Sediment deposits made up of rocks fallen from cliffs	0–10,000 years
Igneous rock: granodiorite	88 million years
Igneous rock: granodiorite	93 million years
Igneous rock: granite and granodiorite	102 million years
Metamorphic rock formed from sedimentary rock	144–206 million years

20. **APPLY** Which two types of maps have been combined to make this map? **(6.7.f)**
21. **APPLY** From what type of rock did the metamorphic rock form?
22. **INTERPRET** All of the igneous rocks have large mineral crystals. Did they form from magma or from lava? Explain.
23. **CALCULATE** What is the difference in age between the youngest and oldest types of igneous rock?
24. **SYNTHESIZE** Why are sediments likely to be found at the lowest elevations? **(6.2.a)**
25. **DRAW CONCLUSIONS** The age of the sediment deposits left by streams is given as a range. What is a likely reason why it is not given as a single age? **(6.2.b)**
26. **SYNTHESIZE** How might weathering processes help form the sediment deposits made up of rocks fallen from cliffs? **(6.2.a)**
27. **HYPOTHESIZE** Thick layers of halite are mined near Detroit, Michigan. At one time, seawater covered the area. Write a hypothesis that explains how the halite formed there. **(6.7.a)**
28. **COMPARE AND CONTRAST** How does mechanical weathering differ from chemical weathering? How are the two processes similar? **(6.2.a)**
29. **SYNTHESIZE** A cycle is a series of events or actions that repeats regularly. Describe a cycle that involves living things. **(6.2.a)**

the BIG idea

30. **ANALYZE** Minerals are basic components of planets such as Earth and Mars. Other planets in our solar system, such as Jupiter and Saturn, are called gas giants because they are made up mainly of the gases hydrogen and helium. They do not have solid surfaces. Do you think that minerals are basic components of gas giants? Why or why not? **(6.6)**
31. **INFER** Minerals make up much of Earth. People use minerals as sources of many materials, such as metals. Some metals are used to make machine parts or build houses. How would your life be different if minerals that contain metals were rare in Earth's crust? **(6.6.c)**
32. **SYNTHESIZE** Use your knowledge of the rock cycle and weathering to explain why loose pieces of gold might be found in a river.

UNIT PROJECTS

If you need to do an experiment for your unit project, gather the materials. Be sure to allow enough time to observe results before the project is due.

Section Opener

- Highlights the Key Concept
- Connects new learning to prior knowledge
- Previews important vocabulary

KEY CONCEPT

6.1 Minerals are all around us.

CALIFORNIA Content Standard

Background for 6.1.b. Students know Earth is composed of several layers: a cold, brittle lithosphere; a hot, convecting mantle; and a dense, metallic core.

BEFORE, you learned
- Earth is made of layers
- Earth's outermost rocky layer is the crust

NOW, you will learn
- About the characteristics of minerals
- How minerals are classified into groups
- Which mineral group is most common

VOCABULARY
mineral p. 184
element p. 184
crystal p. 185
rock p. 187

EXPLORE Minerals (6.1.b)

What are some characteristics of a mineral?

PROCEDURE

1. Sprinkle some table salt on a sheet of colored paper. Look at a few grains of the salt through a magnifying glass. Then rub a few grains between your fingers.
2. In your notebook, describe all the qualities of the salt that you observe.
3. Examine the rock salt in the same way and describe its qualities in your notebook. How do the two differ?

MATERIALS
- colored paper
- table salt
- rock salt
- magnifying glass

WHAT DO YOU THINK?

Salt is a fairly common mineral in Earth's crust. From your observations of salt, what do you think are some characteristics of minerals?

Minerals and rocks are part of daily life.

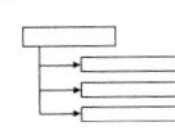

SUPPORTING MAIN IDEAS
Enter this blue heading in a chart and record supporting information.

You use minerals all the time. Every time you turn on a microwave oven or a TV, you depend on minerals. The wires that carry electric current are made of copper, which is a mineral. Table salt, or halite (HAL-YT), is another mineral that you use in your everyday life.

Earth's lithosphere is made of rocks. As you will read later in this chapter, almost all rocks are made of minerals. People use rocks in many ways. If you look at large buildings, you might see that parts of their outside walls are made of rocks. Sometimes you can see minerals in the rocks. In a museum, you might see statues and other artworks carved from rocks.

The Big Idea Questions

- Help students connect their new learning back to the Big Idea
- Prompt students to synthesize and apply the Big Idea and Key Concepts

Many Ways to Learn

Because students learn in so many ways, *McDougal Littell Science* gives them a variety of experiences with important concepts and skills. Text, visuals, activities, and technology all focus on Big Ideas and Key Concepts.

Considerate Text

- Clear structure of meaningful headings
- Information clearly connected to main ideas
- Student-friendly writing style

Oceanic-Oceanic Subduction

An **oceanic-oceanic subduction** occurs where one plate with oceanic crust sinks under another plate with oceanic crust. The older plate sinks because it is colder and denser than the younger plate. When the older crust reaches the asthenosphere, it melts in the intense heat. Two main features form at oceanic-oceanic subductions: deep-ocean trenches and island arcs.

Deep-Ocean Trenches These trenches are like deep canyons that form in the ocean floor as a plate sinks. Most deep-ocean trenches are found in the Pacific Ocean. One example is the Mariana Trench. There, the Pacific Plate is sinking under the Philippine Plate. This trench is the deepest place in the world's oceans. It extends nearly 11,000 meters (36,000 ft) into the sea floor.

Island Arcs Chains of volcanic islands form on the top plate, parallel to a deep-ocean trench. As oceanic crust of the sinking plate melts, magma rises through the top plate. Over time, the flows build up a series of islands. Island arcs include the Philippine Islands, the Aleutian Islands of Alaska, and the islands of Japan.

Visuals That Teach

- Information-rich visuals directly connected to the text
- Thoughtful pairing of diagrams and real-world photos
- Reading Visuals questions to support student learning

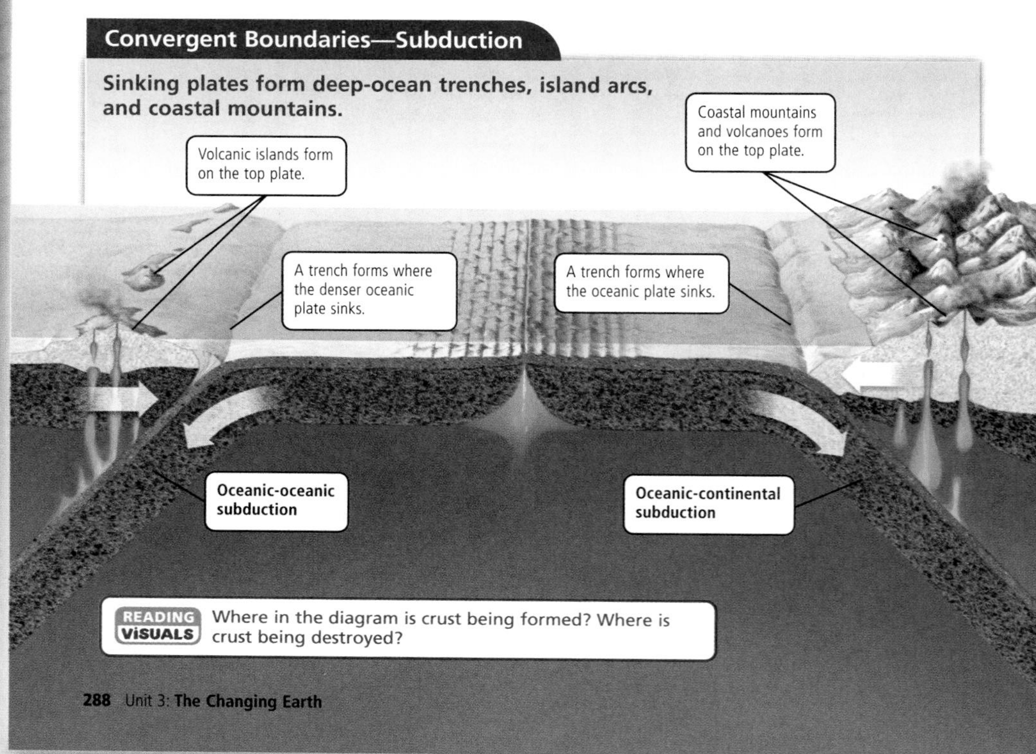
Convergent Boundaries—Subduction
Sinking plates form deep-ocean trenches, island arcs, and coastal mountains.
Volcanic islands form on the top plate.
Coastal mountains and volcanoes form on the top plate.
A trench forms where the denser oceanic plate sinks.
A trench forms where the oceanic plate sinks.
Oceanic-oceanic subduction
Oceanic-continental subduction
READING VISUALS Where in the diagram is crust being formed? Where is crust being destroyed?
288 Unit 3: The Changing Earth

Oceanic-Continental Subduction

An **oceanic-continental subduction** occurs when ocean crust sinks under continental crust, as shown in the diagram on page 288. The oceanic crust sinks because it is colder and denser than the continental crust. At these sites, deep-ocean trenches and coastal mountains form.

Deep-Ocean Trenches Some of the world's youngest trenches are in the eastern Pacific Ocean. Here, the Pacific Plate is sinking under the North American Plate. As the oceanic crust moves, it often causes underwater earthquakes.

Coastal Mountains As oceanic crust sinks under a continent, the continental crust buckles to form a range of mountains. Like island arcs, these mountains are parallel to a deep-ocean trench. Some of these mountains are volcanoes, which form as melted oceanic crust rises through the top plate.

The Cascade Mountains in California, Oregon, and Washington are coastal mountains. They formed as the Juan de Fuca Plate began sinking under the North American Plate. Some of these peaks, such as Mount St. Helens in Washington, are active volcanoes.

Why do deep-ocean trenches form at both types of subduction?

Explore what happens along plate boundaries.

INVESTIGATE Convergent Boundaries

How can you model converging plates?

Tectonic plates move so slowly and are so large that it is hard to see exactly how they move. Use what you know to design models showing subduction.

DESIGN YOUR OWN

SKILL FOCUS
Designing models (6.1.e)

MATERIALS
- clay in three or more colors
- poster board
- marker pens

TIME
30 minutes

PROCEDURE

1. Design your models using the materials listed. You can use the diagrams on pages 287–288 as a guide.
2. Add more clay to your models if you need it.

WHAT DO YOU THINK?

- Describe how your models worked. You can draw a picture of each model to go along with your description.
- How well did your models represent each type of zone? Did each model work? Why or why not?
- How would you modify your designs now that you have seen the results?

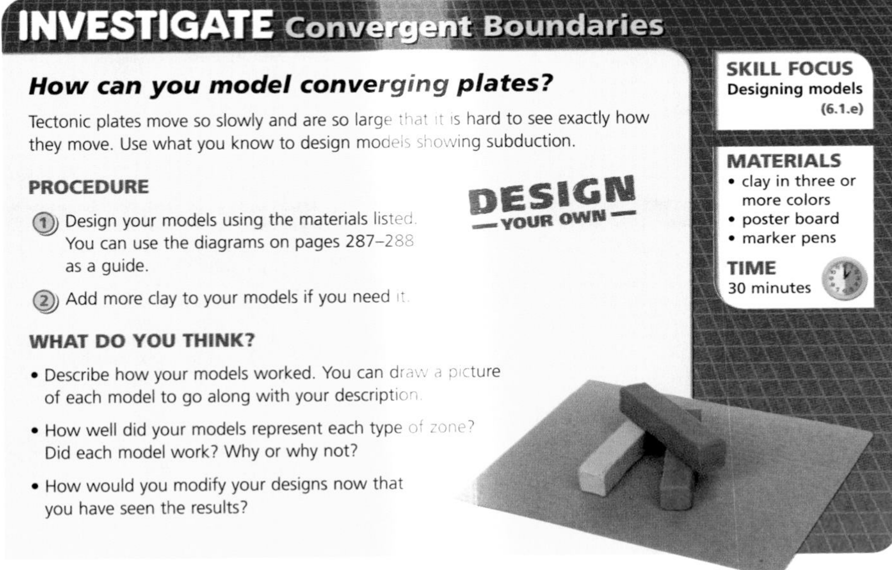

Integrated Technology

- Interaction with Key Concepts through Simulations and Visualizations
- Easy access to relevant Web resources through Resource Centers and SciLinks
- Opportunities for review through Content Review and Math Tutorials

Hands-on Learning

- Activities that reinforce Key Concepts
- Skill Focus for important inquiry and process skills
- Multiple activities in every chapter, from quick Explores to full-period Chapter Investigations

Differentiated Instruction

A full spectrum of resources for differentiating instruction supports you in reaching the wide range of learners in your classroom.

6.1 INSTRUCT

Teach the Standards

Lithosphere 6.1.b

In this section: Students build on what they know about the layers of Earth by learning in detail about minerals and rocks, which make up the lithosphere. Ask students to describe the lithosphere in their own words and contrast it with the mantle beneath it.

previously taught: Earth's layers, p. 44

future opportunities: plate tectonics, pp. 267–268; earthquakes, p. 303

Teach Difficult Concepts

Many texts state that one of the characteristic of minerals is that they are inorganic, not derived from living organisms. This is not strictly accurate because many living organisms produce minerals to form their shells, bones, and other hard parts. However, a substance that forms only by an organic process cannot be considered a mineral. For example, sugar forms organically; it never forms inorganically (without a process involving a living organism). Therefore, sugar is not a mineral, even though it has all of the other required characteristics. A substance must form from an inorganic process as well to be considered a mineral.

Teacher Demo

Place a handful of sugar on a sheet of colored paper and a handful of salt next to it. Ask whether both materials are minerals. Explain that the sugar is not a mineral but the salt is. All sugar comes from plants, which are living organisms. Thus, sugar is an organic product. Salt does not come from a living organism. It precipitates out of water.

Ongoing Assessment

Identify the characteristics of minerals.

Ask: What characteristics does ice have that make it a mineral? *It forms in nature, is a solid, has a definite chemical makeup, and has a crystal structure.*

184 Unit 2: Earth's Surface

Minerals have four characteristics.

A mineral can be so small that you need a microscope to see it, or it can be large. No matter what size a mineral is, it has four characteristics. A **mineral** is a substance that

- forms in nature
- is a solid
- has a definite chemical composition
- has a crystal structure

Forms in Nature

A

Minerals are formed by natural processes. Every type of mineral can form in nature by processes that do not involve living organisms. A few minerals can also be produced by organisms as part of their shells or bones.

B

Minerals form in many ways. Halite can form when water evaporates in a shallow part of the ocean, leaving behind the salt it contained. Many types of minerals develop when molten rock cools. Talc, a mineral that can be used to make baby powder, forms inside Earth as high pressure and temperature cause changes in solid rock.

READING TIP: *Molten rock* refers to rock that has become so hot that it has melted.

Solid

A mineral is a solid—that is, it has a definite volume and a rigid shape. Volume refers to the amount of space an object takes up. For example, a golf ball has a smaller volume than a baseball, and a baseball has a smaller volume than a basketball.

A substance that is a liquid or a gas is not a mineral. However, in some cases its solid form is a mineral. For example, liquid water is not a mineral, but ice is.

Definite Chemical Composition

REMINDER: You may remember *compound* from compound words—words formed by joining together smaller words: *note* + *book* = *notebook*. Likewise, a chemical compound has two or more elements joined together.

Each mineral has a definite chemical makeup: it consists of a specific combination of atoms of certain elements. An **element** is a substance that contains only one type of atom. In turn, an atom is the smallest particle an element can be divided into.

Look at the illustration on page 185. You can see that some substances, including the minerals gold and copper, consist of just one element. However, most minerals are compounds, substances that consist of several elements in specific proportions. Notice that halite has one atom of sodium for every atom of chlorine.

184 Unit 2: Earth's Surface

Atoms in Minerals

The mineral copper is made up of only copper atoms.

The mineral halite is made up of equal numbers of sodium and chlorine atoms.

READING VISUALS: How do the diagrams show that copper consists of only one element and halite is a compound?

Crystal Structure

If you look closely at the particles of ice that make up frost, you will notice that they have smooth, flat surfaces. These flat surfaces form because of the arrangement of atoms in the ice, which is a mineral. This arrangement is a characteristic of minerals. It is the structure of a **crystal**, a solid in which the atoms are arranged in an orderly, repeating three-dimensional pattern.

C

Each mineral has its own type of crystal structure. In some cases, two minerals have the same chemical composition but different crystal structures. For example, both diamond and graphite consist of just one element—carbon. But the arrangements of the carbon atoms in these two minerals are not the same. Therefore, they have different crystal structures and very different properties. Diamonds are extremely hard and have a brilliant sparkle. Graphite is soft, gray, and dull.

CHECK YOUR READING: Why do graphite and diamond have different properties?

In nature, a perfect crystal is rare. One can grow only when a mineral is free to form in an open space. This condition rarely exists within Earth's crust. The amount of space available for growth influences the shapes and sizes of crystals. Most crystals have imperfect shapes because their growth was limited by other crystals that formed next to them. But even though most crystals do not have perfect shapes, their atoms are still arranged in orderly crystal structures.

Chapter 6: Minerals and Rocks

DIFFERENTIATE INSTRUCTION

More Reading Support

A How do minerals form? *by natural processes*

B Does a mineral exist as a solid, a liquid, or a gas? *solid*

English Learners This section has a number of phrasal verbs, such as *takes up* (p. 184) and *make up* (p. 185). English learners may read these phrases incorrectly by combining the meanings of the two words. Provide some synonyms for these phrasal verbs. If necessary, have students draw a sketch that helps them remember the meanings.

DIFFERENTIATE INSTRUCTION

More Reading Support

C How can two minerals have the same chemical composition and still be different minerals? *They can have different crystal structures.*

Advanced Explain chemical formulas to students. Th chemical formula of copper is Cu, and that of halite is N The proportion of an element in a compound is indicate number following the element symbol, such as H_2O for v Have students use a mineral identification book to explai chemical formulas of minerals mentioned in this chapter.

Challenge and Extension, p. 78

Teacher's Edition

- More Reading Support for below-level readers
- Strategies for below-level and advanced learners, English learners, and inclusion students

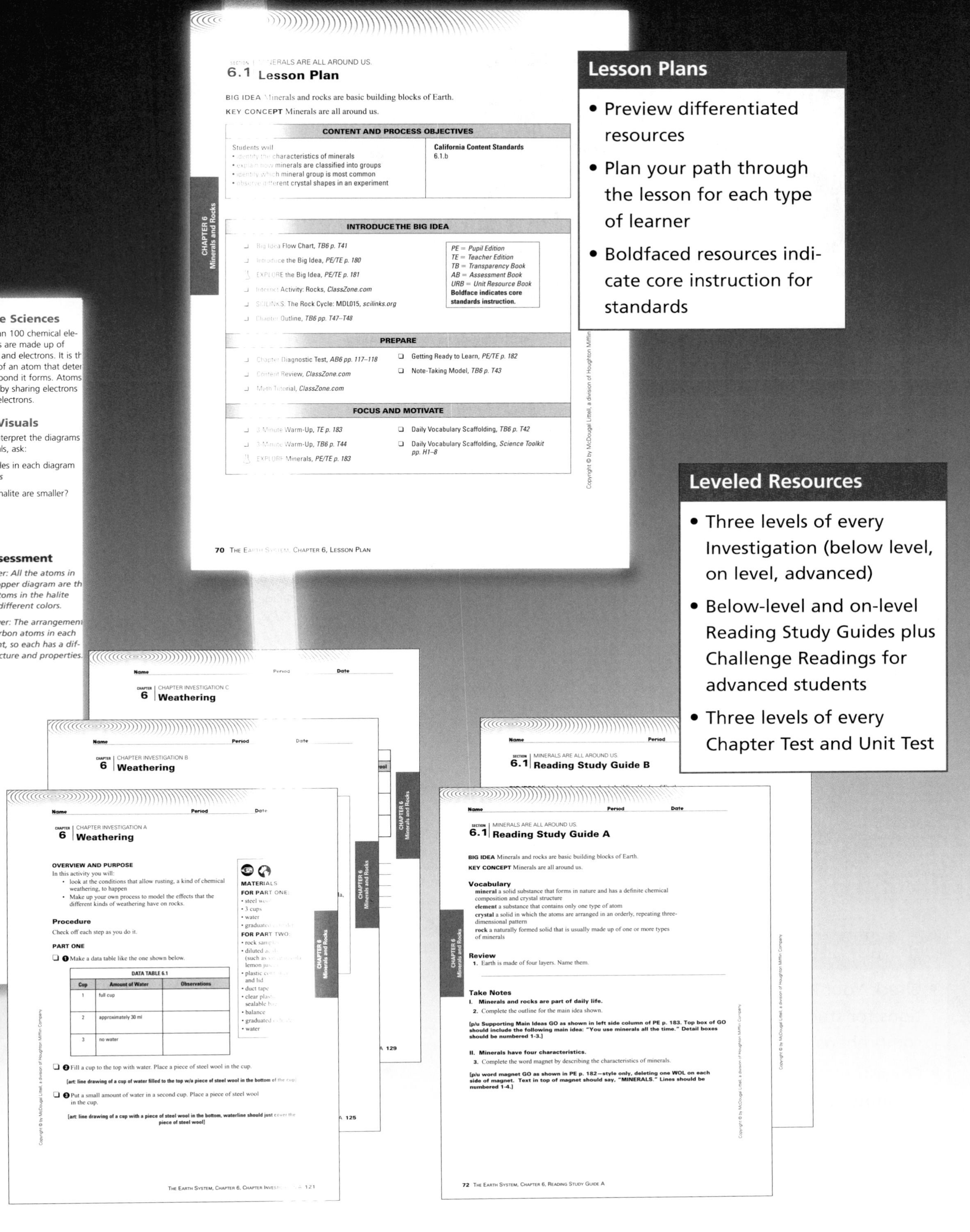

SECTION 6.1 MINERALS ARE ALL AROUND US.

6.1 Lesson Plan

BIG IDEA Minerals and rocks are basic building blocks of Earth.

KEY CONCEPT Minerals are all around us.

CONTENT AND PROCESS OBJECTIVES	
Students will • characteristics of minerals • minerals are classified into groups • mineral group is most common • crystal shapes in an experiment	**California Content Standards** 6.1.b

INTRODUCE THE BIG IDEA

- Flow Chart, *TB6 p. T41*
- the Big Idea, *PE/TE p. 180*
- EXPLORE the Big Idea, *PE/TE p. 181*
- Activity: Rocks, *ClassZone.com*
- SCILINKS: The Rock Cycle: MDL015, *scilinks.org*
- Outline, *TB6 pp. T47–T48*

PE = Pupil Edition
TE = Teacher Edition
TB = Transparency Book
AB = Assessment Book
URB = Unit Resource Book
Boldface indicates core standards instruction.

PREPARE

- Diagnostic Test, *AB6 pp. 117–118*
- Review, *ClassZone.com*
- Tutorial, *ClassZone.com*
- Getting Ready to Learn, *PE/TE p. 182*
- Note-Taking Model, *TB6 p. T43*

FOCUS AND MOTIVATE

- Warm-Up, *TE p. 183*
- Warm-Up, *TB6 p. T44*
- EXPLORE Minerals, *PE/TE p. 183*
- Daily Vocabulary Scaffolding, *TB6 p. T42*
- Daily Vocabulary Scaffolding, *Science Toolkit pp. H1–8*

CHAPTER 6 Minerals and Rocks

Copyright © by McDougal Littell, a division of Houghton Mifflin

70 THE EARTH SYSTEM, CHAPTER 6, LESSON PLAN

the Sciences

e than 100 chemical ele-
atoms are made up of
ons, and electrons. It is th
ture of an atom that deter
d of bond it forms. Atoms
ither by sharing electrons
ing electrons.

m Visuals

nts interpret the diagrams
inerals, ask:

e circles in each diagram
atoms

s in halite are smaller?

Assessment

nswer: All the atoms in
he copper diagram are th
he atoms in the halite
two different colors.

Answer: The arrangemen
of carbon atoms in each
ferent, so each has a dif-
structure and properties.

Name Period Date

CHAPTER 6 CHAPTER INVESTIGATION C **Weathering**

Name Period Date

CHAPTER 6 CHAPTER INVESTIGATION B **Weathering**

Name Period Date

CHAPTER 6 CHAPTER INVESTIGATION A **Weathering**

OVERVIEW AND PURPOSE
In this activity you will:
- look at the conditions that allow rusting, a kind of chemical weathering, to happen
- Make up your own process to model the effects that the different kinds of weathering have on rocks.

Procedure
Check off each step as you do it.

PART ONE

1. Make a data table like the one shown below.

DATA TABLE 6.1

Cup	Amount of Water	Observations
1	full cup	
2	approximately 30 ml	
3	no water	

2. Fill a cup to the top with water. Place a piece of steel wool in the cup.
[art: line drawing of a cup of water filled to the top w/a piece of steel wool in the bottom of the cup]
3. Put a small amount of water in a second cup. Place a piece of steel wool in the cup.
[art: line drawing of a cup with a piece of steel wool in the bottom, waterline should just cover the piece of steel wool]

MATERIALS
FOR PART ONE
- steel wool
- 3 cups
- water
- graduated

FOR PART TWO
- rock samples
- diluted
- plastic
- duct tape
- clear plastic sealable
- balance
- graduated
- water

CHAPTER 6 Minerals and Rocks

THE EARTH SYSTEM, CHAPTER 6, CHAPTER INVESTIGATION A 121

Name Period

SECTION 6.1 MINERALS ARE ALL AROUND US. **Reading Study Guide B**

Name Period Date

SECTION 6.1 MINERALS ARE ALL AROUND US. **Reading Study Guide A**

BIG IDEA Minerals and rocks are basic building blocks of Earth.
KEY CONCEPT Minerals are all around us.

Vocabulary
mineral a solid substance that forms in nature and has a definite chemical composition and crystal structure
element a substance that contains only one type of atom
crystal a solid in which the atoms are arranged in an orderly, repeating three-dimensional pattern
rock a naturally formed solid that is usually made up of one or more types of minerals

Review
1. Earth is made of four layers. Name them.

Take Notes
I. **Minerals and rocks are part of daily life.**
2. Complete the outline for the main idea shown.

[p/u Supporting Main Ideas GO as shown in left side column of PE p. 183. Top box of GO should include the following main idea: "You use minerals all the time." Detail boxes should be numbered 1-3.]

II. **Minerals have four characteristics.**
3. Complete the word magnet by describing the characteristics of minerals.

[p/u word magnet GO as shown in PE p. 182—style only, deleting one WOL on each side of magnet. Text in top of magnet should say, "MINERALS." Lines should be numbered 1-4.]

CHAPTER 6 Minerals and Rocks

72 THE EARTH SYSTEM, CHAPTER 6, READING STUDY GUIDE A

Lesson Plans

- Preview differentiated resources
- Plan your path through the lesson for each type of learner
- Boldfaced resources indicate core instruction for standards

Leveled Resources

- Three levels of every Investigation (below level, on level, advanced)
- Below-level and on-level Reading Study Guides plus Challenge Readings for advanced students
- Three levels of every Chapter Test and Unit Test

Effective Assessment

McDougal Littell Science incorporates a comprehensive set of resources for assessing student knowledge and performance before, during, and after instruction.

Diagnostic Tests

- Assessment of students' prior knowledge
- Readiness check for concepts and skills in the upcoming chapter

Teach from Visuals

Note that the two rocks pictured are examples of a common type of rock and an unusual type of rock. To help students interpret the visual, ask:

- How does the obsidian differ in appearance from the gabbro? *The obsidian appears more uniform in color and texture than the gabbro. The obsidian looks glassy, and the gabbro looks grainy.*
- How does this difference in appearance reflect their compositions? *The obsidian is a natural glass and contains no minerals. Gabbro is made up of several types of minerals, which results in grains of different colors.*

Ongoing Assessment

CHECK YOUR READING *Answer: A mineral always has the same composition, but rocks do not.*

6.1 ASSESS & RETEACH

Assess

Section 6.1 Quiz, p. 119

Reteach

- Hold up a sample of a mineral, such as a piece of chalk. Ask students what four characteristics it has that make it a mineral. List the four characteristics on the board and ask volunteers to explain each one.
- Hold up a common rock (make sure the rock is not limestone or another carbonate). Ask students what group the minerals in the rock most likely belong to. Have students explain what silicates contain and why they are the most common mineral group in Earth's crust.

Technology Resources

Have students visit **ClassZone.com** for reteaching of Key Concepts.

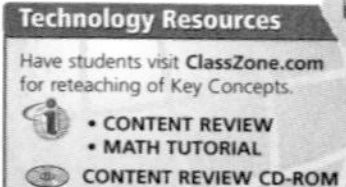

- CONTENT REVIEW
- MATH TUTORIAL

CONTENT REVIEW CD-ROM

READING TIP

Proportions show relationships between amounts. For example, a quartz crystal always has the same proportion of oxygen atoms to silicon atoms: two oxygen atoms for every silicon atom.

The structure of rocks is different from that of minerals. A mineral is always made of the same elements in the same proportions. All minerals have an orderly crystal structure. However, the proportion of different minerals in a certain type of rock may vary. Also, the minerals in a rock can be all jumbled together.

CHECK YOUR READING How are minerals different from rocks?

Gabbro, like most rocks, is made up of several types of minerals.

Obsidian is an unusual rock because it contains no minerals.

A few types of rocks are made up of one type of mineral. A few contain no minerals at all. Limestone, for example, can be made up entirely of the mineral calcite. Obsidian (ahb-SIHD-ee-uhn) is a rock that contains no minerals. It is made of natural glass, which is not a mineral because it does not have a crystal structure.

Coal is another rock that does not have a crystal structure. It is made up of the remains of ancient plants that were buried and pressed into rock. Coal started forming millions of years ago in swamps. As plants died, their remains fell on the remains of earlier plants. Then other materials buried the plant remains. Over time, the weight of the materials above pressed the plant remains into coal. You will read in Chapter 13 how people use coal as an energy source.

6.1 Review

KEY CONCEPTS

1. What are the four characteristics of a mineral? (6.1.b)
2. How are minerals classified? (6.1.b)
3. What is the most common group of minerals? What percentage of the crust do they make up? (6.1.b)

CRITICAL THINKING

4. **Classify** Can oil and natural gas be classified as minerals? Why or why not?
5. **Apply** When a piece of quartz is heated to a very high temperature, it melts into a liquid. Is it still a mineral? Why or why not?

CHALLENGE

6. **Interpret** You can see perfect crystals lining the inside of certain rocks when they are broken open. How do you think the crystals were able to form?

ANSWERS

1. A mineral forms in nature, is a solid, has a definite chemical makeup, and has a crystal structure.

2. Scientists classify minerals into groups on the basis of their chemical makeups.

3. The silicate group is the most common, and these minerals make up about 90% of the crust.

4. Oil and natural gas cannot be classified as minerals, because they are not solids, do not form crystals, and do not have a definite chemical makeup.

5. Melted quartz is not a mineral, because it is not a solid.

6. The minerals had room to grow into perfect crystals because the rocks are hollow.

Reviewing Vocabulary

On a separate sheet of paper, write a sentence or two describing the relationship between the two terms.

1. mineral, crystal
2. magma, lava
3. intrusive, extrusive
4. igneous rock, metamorphic rock
5. geologic cycle, weathering
6. mechanical weathering, chemical weathering
7. geologic map, topographic map

Reviewing Key Concepts

Multiple Choice *Choose the letter of the best answer.*

8. A crystal structure is characteristic of (6.6)
   a. an element
   b. a rock
   c. magma
   d. a mineral
9. How is it possible for two different minerals to have the same chemical composition? (6.6)
   a. They have different crystal structures.
   b. One is formed only by organisms.
   c. Only one is a rock-forming mineral.
   d. They have different appearances.
10. The rock cycle shows how rocks continually (6.1.b)
    a. increase in size
    b. increase in number
    c. become more complex
    d. change over time
11. Which kind of rock forms by recrystallization? (6.1.b)
    a. intrusive igneous
    b. extrusive igneous
    c. sedimentary
    d. metamorphic
12. Rock salt is an example of a sedimentary rock that develops from dissolved minerals as (6.1.b)
    a. water evaporates
    b. magma cools
    c. sediments break down
    d. sand settles in water
13. The force of expanding water in the cracks and pores of a rock is an example of (6.2.a)
    a. chemical weathering
    b. mechanical weathering
    c. oxidation
    d. crystallization
14. The breakdown of rock by acidic water is an example of (6.2.a)
    a. chemical weathering
    b. mechanical weathering
    c. oxidation
    d. crystallization
15. Three factors that affect the rate of weathering are (6.2.a)
    a. microorganisms, plants, and animals
    b. weather, landforms, and rainfall
    c. surface area, rock composition, and climate
    d. texture, color, and pore space
16. The term *geologic structure* refers to (6.1.b)
    a. types and ages of rocks
    b. characteristics of minerals
    c. patterns of weathering in rocks
    d. features of rocks and relationships among rocks

Short Answer *Write a short answer for each question.*

17. Why aren't all solids minerals? Include the term *crystal structure* in your answer. (6.6)
18. What is the difference between a rock and a mineral? (6.1.b)
19. Compare the distribution of rock types at Earth's surface with their distribution in the entire crust. How are any differences related to processes that take place in the rock cycle? (6.1.b)

Ongoing Assessment

- Check Your Reading questions for student self-check of comprehension
- Consistent Teacher's Edition prompts for assessing understanding of Key Concepts

Section and Chapter Reviews

- Focus on Key Concepts and critical thinking skills
- A full range of question types and levels of thinking

Leveled Chapter and Unit Tests

- Three levels of test for every chapter and unit
- Same Big Ideas, Key Concepts, and essential skills assessed on all levels

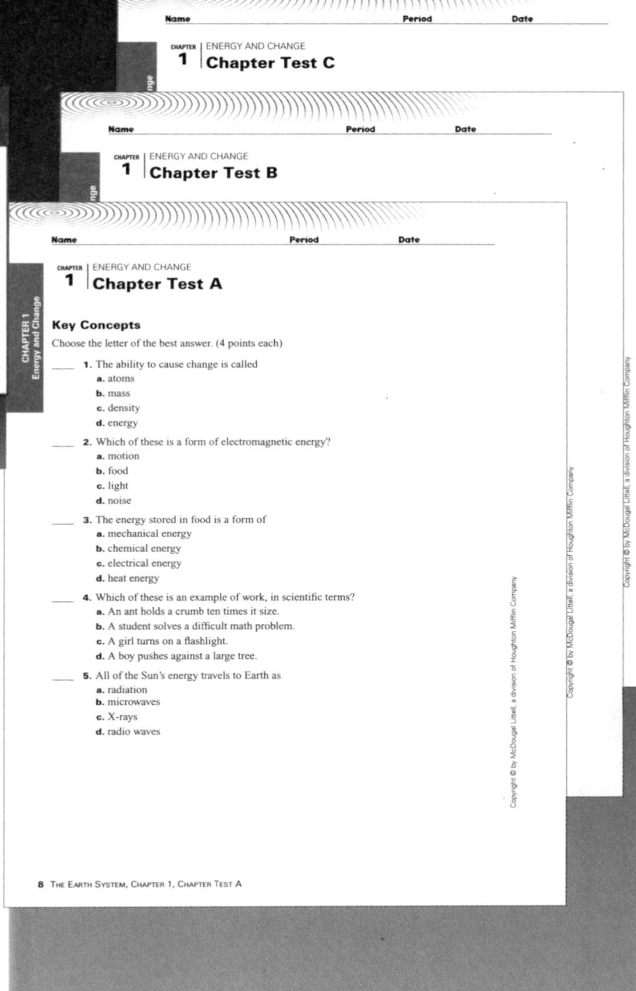
Name Period Date

CHAPTER 1 | ENERGY AND CHANGE
Chapter Test C

Name Period Date

CHAPTER 1 | ENERGY AND CHANGE
Chapter Test B

Name Period Date

CHAPTER 1 | ENERGY AND CHANGE
Chapter Test A

Key Concepts

Choose the letter of the best answer. (4 points each)

____ 1. The ability to cause change is called
a. atoms
b. mass
c. density
d. energy

____ 2. Which of these is a form of electromagnetic energy?
a. motion
b. food
c. light
d. noise

____ 3. The energy stored in food is a form of
a. mechanical energy
b. chemical energy
c. electrical energy
d. heat energy

____ 4. Which of these is an example of work, in scientific terms?
a. An ant holds a crumb ten times it size.
b. A student solves a difficult math problem.
c. A girl turns on a flashlight.
d. A boy pushes against a large tree.

____ 5. All of the Sun's energy travels to Earth as
a. radiation
b. microwaves
c. X-rays
d. radio waves

CHAPTER 1 Energy and Change

Copyright © by McDougal Littell, a division of Houghton Mifflin Company

8 The Earth System, Chapter 1, Chapter Test A

Thinking Critically

Use the map and key to answer the next seven questions. (6.7.f)

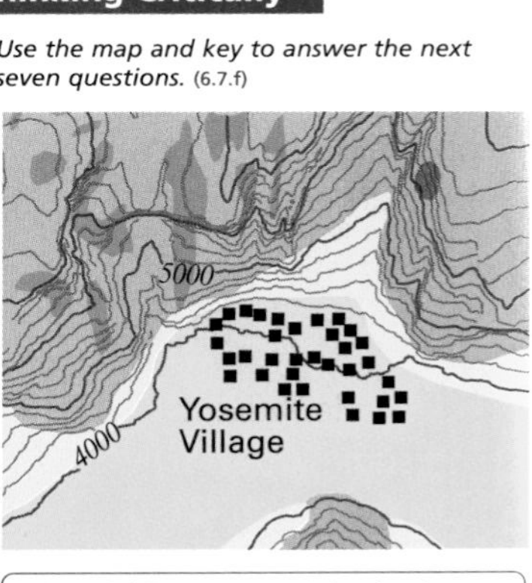

Sediment or Rock Type	Approximate Age
Sediment deposits mainly left by streams	0–2 million years
Sediment deposits made up of rocks fallen from cliffs	0–10,000 years
Igneous rock: granodiorite	88 million years
Igneous rock: granodiorite	93 million years
Igneous rock: granite and granodiorite	102 million years
Metamorphic rock formed from sedimentary rock	144–206 million years

20. **APPLY** Which two types of maps have been combined to make this map? (6.7.f)

21. **APPLY** From what type of rock did the metamorphic rock form?

22. **INTERPRET** All of the igneous rocks have large mineral crystals. Did they form from magma or from lava? Explain.

23. **CALCULATE** What is the difference in age between the youngest and oldest types of igneous rock?

24. **SYNTHESIZE** Why are sediments likely to be found at the lowest elevations? (6.2.a)

25. **DRAW CONCLUSIONS** The age of the sediment deposits left by streams is given as a range. What is a likely reason why it is not given as a single age? (6.2.b)

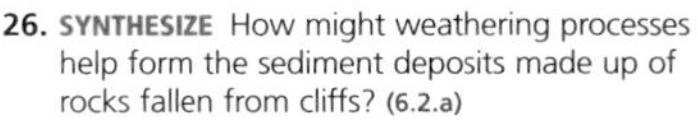

26. **SYNTHESIZE** How might weathering processes help form the sediment deposits made up of rocks fallen from cliffs? (6.2.a)

27. **HYPOTHESIZE** Thick layers of halite are mined near Detroit, Michigan. At one time, seawater covered the area. Write a hypothesis that explains how the halite formed there. (6.7.a)

28. **COMPARE AND CONTRAST** How does mechanical weathering differ from chemical weathering? How are the two processes similar? (6.2.a)

29. **SYNTHESIZE** A cycle is a series of events or actions that repeats regularly. Describe a cycle that involves living things. (6.2.a)

30. **ANALYZE** Minerals are basic components of planets such as Earth and Mars. Other planets in our solar system, such as Jupiter and Saturn, are called gas giants because they are made up mainly of the gases hydrogen and helium. They do not have solid surfaces. Do you think that minerals are basic components of gas giants? Why or why not? (6.6)

31. **INFER** Minerals make up much of Earth. People use minerals as sources of many materials, such as metals. Some metals are used to make machine parts or build houses. How would your life be different if minerals that contain metals were rare in Earth's crust? (6.6.c)

32. **SYNTHESIZE** Use your knowledge of the rock cycle and weathering to explain why loose pieces of gold might be found in a river.

UNIT PROJECTS

If you need to do an experiment for your unit proj-

216 Unit 2: **Earth's Surface**

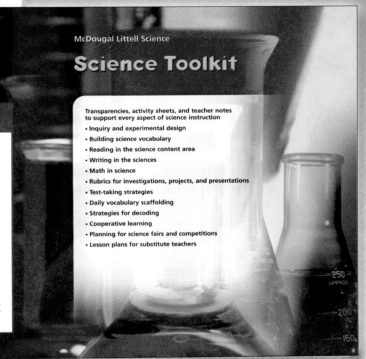

Rubrics

- Rubrics in Teacher's Edition for all extended-response questions
- Rubrics for all Unit Projects
- Alternative Assessment with rubric for each chapter
- A wide range of additional rubrics in the Science Toolkit

McDougal Littell Science

Transparencies, activity sheets, and teacher notes to support every aspect of science instruction

- Inquiry and experimental design
- Building science vocabulary
- Reading in the science content area
- Writing in the sciences
- Math in science
- Rubrics for investigations, projects, and presentations
- Test-taking strategies
- Daily vocabulary scaffolding
- Strategies for decoding
- Cooperative learning
- Planning for science fairs and competitions
- Lesson plans for substitute teachers

Meeting the Needs of English Learners

Nancy Siddens
Consulting Editor, English for Speakers of Other Languages, McDougal Littell

The Challenge

Although the English learner population has grown dramatically throughout Grades K–12, its greatest challenges are at the middle and high school levels. At these levels, the gap between students' English language abilities and the level at which they need to perform is much greater than it is at elementary grade levels. Also, at these levels the educational focus has traditionally been on developing content knowledge, not on developing reading or other language basics. It is estimated that learners need one to three years to develop basic communication skills in English, but five to seven years to develop competency in academic English. Although the task of developing competency in academic English is difficult and lengthy, the study of content should help develop that competency. There are methods of teaching content that have been shown to best meet the needs of English learners. These methods can be used with all students, and everyone may benefit from their approaches.

Make the Most of Instructional Materials

McDougal Littell Science provides components specifically designed to meet the needs of English learners:

- Quick Reference English Learner Strategies for Science
- Multi-Language Glossary
- Spanish Reading Study Guide
- Audio Readings in English and in Spanish
- Spanish Assessment

Many components intended for use by all students may be especially helpful for English learners. All lessons in *McDougal Littell Science* support the research-based methods for teaching content to English learners, such as connecting new information to prior knowledge; making content comprehensible through visuals, audio, and labs; identifying the objectives at the beginning of the lesson; and clarifying key vocabulary and language.

Use Research-Supported Methods for Teaching Content

It has become increasingly important to use teaching methods that are supported by research. Legislative requirements demand proven methods that support teachers in meeting the needs of their students. The three instructional approaches outlined below have been proved by research to be helpful for enabling English learners to access content knowledge. For a more intensive look at each, please refer to the sources cited at the end of this article.

Teach the Text Backwards

Teach the Text Backwards is an approach identified by the Center for Applied Linguistics and summarized by Judy Jameson in an article available on their Web site. Teach the Text Backwards frontloads information for students and gives them a familiarity with concepts prior to asking them to read text presenting information in detail. A summary follows.

Step 1 **Do selected applications based on the material.** Activate students' prior knowledge. If students have studied a related concept earlier, use an activity or lab that links that content knowledge to the new material. Connect new concepts to familiar concepts in their daily lives, explaining the connection.

Step 2 **Discuss the material in class.** Preview key ideas and the vocabulary and language structures used to discuss them.

Step 3 **Answer the study questions at the end of the section.** Preview questions in the Section Review and clarify their meaning before students read the text. Have students use those questions to focus their reading. If they are overwhelmed by the complete lesson, they can at least read for the answers to these questions.

Step 4 **Read the text.** After this preparation, have students read the text.

Cognitive Academic Language Learning Approach (CALLA)

The Cognitive Academic Language Learning Approach was researched and developed by Anna Uhl Chamot and J. Michael O'Malley at George Washington University. This method for lesson planning and delivery encompasses all student needs, from introduction to assessment. A CALLA lesson plan includes five recursive steps.

1. **Preparation** Determine clear objectives for the lesson and provide them to students. Outline language objectives that support the content.
2. **Presentation** Access students' prior knowledge, suggest and explain learning strategies, and make content comprehensible by using visual, verbal, and modeling clues. Check student comprehension frequently.
3. **Practice** Provide authentic opportunities for students to practice their knowledge. Interaction and communication are critical for developing language. Reteach as needed.
4. **Expansion** Provide opportunities to apply new knowledge to students' lives through projects that expand on that knowledge. Relate material to their personal, family, or community culture.
5. **Evaluation** Provide formal and alternative forms of assessment. Have students summarize material both orally and in writing. Also use other types of activities, such as having students reflect on their learning in learning logs and then evaluating the strategies they used.

Sheltered Instruction Observation Protocol (SIOP)

The Sheltered Instruction Observation Protocol provides comprehensive guidelines for lesson planning. Researchers Jana Echevarria, Debra Short, and Mary Ellen Vogt compiled teaching methods that appeared to be effective with English learners, organized them into a formalized protocol for teaching, and tested their effectiveness with the help of the Center for Applied Linguistics. The SIOP method includes eight components. The three components with asterisks (*) are considered most critical for English learners.

1. **Preparation** Prepare clearly defined content and language objectives. Adapt the delivery of content to all levels of student proficiency. Provide meaningful practice of language and content concepts.
2. **Building Background*** Link new concepts explicitly to students' background experience and past learning. Emphasize key vocabulary and language.
3. **Comprehensible Input*** Use a variety of techniques to introduce and clarify concepts, such as illustrations, audio, charts, summary outlines, and labs. Clearly explain tasks, and accommodate classroom speech to students' proficiency levels. Check comprehension frequently.
4. **Strategies** Introduce learning strategies to students, with opportunities to use them. Scaffold lessons, providing a variety of support, such as using questions at different levels of language and thinking.
5. **Interaction*** Group students to support language and content objectives. Provide frequent opportunities for interaction and discussion.
6. **Practice/Application** Provide hands-on activities; integrate language skills into each lesson.
7. **Lesson Delivery** Pace the lesson appropriately for students' levels of ability, and clearly support content and language objectives. Engage students 90–100 percent of the time, as learning is an active task.
8. **Review/Assessment** Provide a comprehensive review of key vocabulary and content concepts. Provide regular feedback and frequent assessment of comprehension.

References

Chamot, A. U., and J. M. O'Malley. *The CALLA Handbook.* Reading, MA: Addison-Wesley, 1991.

Echevarria, J., M. E. Vogt, and D. J. Short. *Making Content Comprehensible for English Learners: The SIOP Model.* Boston, MA: Allyn and Bacon, 2000.

Jameson, Judy. "Teach the Text Backwards: A Practical Framework Which Helps ESOL Students Understand Textbooks." *From Theory to Practice*, Number 7. Tampa, FL: The Region XIV Comprehensive Center, Center for Applied Linguistics, 1999.

Teaching Academic Vocabulary in Science

By Mary Lou McCloskey and Lydia Stack

A key concern for secondary science students—particularly for English learners (ELs) and students whose reading is below grade level—is their requirement for vocabulary development. As if learning English weren't challenging enough, ELs have more than one type of English language to acquire. They must learn the language of everyday conversation—which most ELs achieve successfully in one to two years—and they must also become proficient in a very different academic language. Academic language uses more complex organizational structures than spoken language; different, more complex, grammatical structures; and very different and vastly increased vocabulary—vocabulary that students are rarely exposed to outside of academic reading. English learners require at least five years of exposure to academic English to score, on average, like English-only speakers (Brown, Cummins & Sayers, 2006; Hakuta, Butler & Witt, 1999; Thomas & Collier, 2002). The challenge for secondary content teachers is to find the best ways to accelerate learning the academic vocabulary ELs must have to be successful in secondary school.

What is vocabulary? Under the umbrella of vocabulary, we include:

- words and word families (words with various prefixes, suffixes, and alternate forms)
- idioms
- word combinations such as challenging phrasal verbs (e.g., *go into, go on, go over*).

What does it mean to learn a word? Knowing a word is not at all simple—it implies knowing many things about a word: literal meanings, possible multiple meanings, connotations, ways words can be used syntactically (what grammar works with the words), semantic associates (synonyms, antonyms, categories), words with closely connected meanings, collocations (words and sequences with which a word is commonly used), and when and in what discourse context the word is used (Carlo, et al, 2004, Folse, 2004). Because learning a word is so complex, just memorizing a synonym is not sufficient for full understanding. Rather, learners require multiple deep encounters with the word. For academic vocabulary learning, this must happen with many terms that learners will encounter almost exclusively in academic reading and discussions in school.

Why focus on academic vocabulary? Because academic vocabulary is related to the ability to comprehend higher-level texts (García, 1991; National Reading Panel, 2000), researchers have given particular attention to academic vocabulary as a valuable focus for improving EL learning. Coxhead, for example, compiled a list of 570 academic word families that appear frequently in academic works across a wide range of content areas. Carlo, et al (2004) found that teaching a set of useful academic terms along with word analysis and vocabulary development strategies in a context of meaningful use and cooperative learning led to both increased vocabulary knowledge and improved reading comprehension on the part of both ELs and English-proficient students. For science study, ELs will need support and instruction with both the general academic words as in Coxhead's Academic Word list (e.g., *access, benefit, chart, design*) and the content-specific words of science (e.g., *igneous, sedimentary, metamorphic*).

What vocabulary and strategies should we teach? We must pay careful attention to selecting highly useful, important, and representative words for close focus and development of deep understanding, but more importantly to developing learners' strategies for solving new words themselves. Effective strategies include focus on

- **Word parts** Students must learn how words are made up of and transformed by prefixes, suffixes, and combined words (*atmosphere, hydrosphere, biosphere, geosphere; arrange, rearrange, arrangement*), and the meanings of prefixes and suffixes.
- **Multiple meanings** ELs need to understand that words have multiple meanings and to learn these multiple meanings. Words can have both multiple meanings at the conversational level (What do you *mean*? Don't be *mean*!) and specific meanings in a scientific or mathematical context (The *mean* difference is 0.5.).
- **Context cues** Using context cues is difficult for ELs and below-level readers, who already understand fewer words and less of the context than proficient English readers. They need modeling, explicit instruction, scaffolding, and practice to learn to use contextual cues to deduce word meanings.
- **Dictionary and glossary skills** Learners need support in knowing *how* and *when* to look up words in

English dictionaries, glossaries, bilingual dictionaries, and technological tools. Contrary to common belief, using their first language can often help ELs learn new words very efficiently, so they might sometimes choose a bilingual dictionary rather than an English-English dictionary, and teachers might sometimes simply provide a translation to help them learn a new term quickly. Using a dictionary unnecessarily can interrupt the reading process and interfere with comprehension, so students should be encouraged to look up words selectively, looking up only words that are central to understanding the passage. If they can acquire the word more quickly another way (e.g., preteaching, translation from a peer, page glosses, glossary, etc.), they should use the shortcut. If new words do not seem central to meaning, students should skip over them, later checking their comprehension to make sure they didn't miss anything important.

- **Cognates** Students who speak other languages should develop their ability to explore cross-language relationships to understand the meanings of new words. Many scientific terms, based on Latin, are similar across Romance languages such as French, Spanish, Italian, Romanian—as well as English. Other languages "borrow" or adapt similar terms for scientific use. Learners must also be alert to the false cognates that can lead them astray.
- **Learning strategies** Help students learn to take responsibility for their own learning, from planning and organizing (When, where, and how will I study vocabulary? How will I organize my words?), to choosing which words to learn. They also need rationale, support, and motivation to expand exposure through reading, listening, writing, and speaking beyond class (Nation, 2001).

What are the best ways to develop vocabulary?

- **Help learners attend to vocabulary.** Help them to notice new words, to recognize when it is important to determine the meaning of new words, and to relate new words to ones they know (Nation, 2001).
- **Select important words.** Exploit these words to develop word analysis and vocabulary development strategies. *The Compleat Lexical Tutor* includes many tools for analyzing texts to find key academic words and high-frequency words.
- **Teach vocabulary directly as one strand of teaching.** Use clear, simple, brief explanations of new terms. Translations are very helpful. Present vocabulary and develop vocabulary development strategies in meaningful, purposeful contexts. Be aware that too much information too soon is confusing to ELs. As you teach, address only a limited amount of information at a time.
- **Promote deep processing.** The amount and strength of learning depends on the quality of mental processing that occurs when students interact with a word and with peers. After they study key words, for example, you might ask pairs or small groups to discuss questions like, "Each group has a rock. Observe and describe the features of the rock. What do you infer about how the rock was created? If this rock were subjected to metamorphosis, how would it change?" Prepare students for such a discussion: teach the language needed, model appropriate use of the language, and provide structured practice before expecting students to carry out the task independently.
- **Promote repeated, spaced retrieval.** Learners need to retrieve words they have learned occasionally in order to retain them. Increased space between later repetitions works best. Expect only limited learning from single meetings with a word, with gradual increase in depth of understanding with multiple retrievals.
- **Promote learner independence.** As ELs and below-level readers develop their skills, gradually release the responsibility for vocabulary learning to them.

How can you support vocabulary development in science? Keep in mind that teaching science to ELs and below-level readers must involve teaching language as well. Academic vocabulary and scientific terminology must become part of every lesson. Students' comprehension depends on their vocabulary understanding, so you will usually need to pre-teach key academic and scientific terms before learners read them or use them independently. Students won't learn a word in one introduction; they will need to re-access and retrieve new terms frequently. Do not assume that learners understand even the general academic words you use. Check understanding frequently, and develop ways to make your own language—and the text—comprehensible to your students.

Selected Academic Vocabulary

The following list contains 60 of the most frequently used academic vocabulary that will appear in the *McDougal Littell Science* text. The words were pulled from the Academic Word List by Averil Coxhead, (2000), published in TESOL Quarterly 34. Go online to Coxhead's website for more common academic vocabulary words: <http://language.massey.ac.nz/staff/awl/index.shtml>

affect
analyze
approach
area
assess
assume
available
benefit
category
complex
component
concept
conclude
consist
constant
consume
data
define
demonstrate
design
distinct
estimate
evaluate
evident
factor
feature
focus
formula
function
indicate
individual
interpret
involve
item
maintain
major
normal
occur
perceive
percent
period
positive
previous
process
range
region
relevant
require
research
resource
respond
section
select
similar
source
specific
strategy
structure
transfer
vary

Resources

Brown, K., Cummins, J. & Sayers, D. (2006). *From grade expectations to great expectations: Rethinking literacy instruction and technology in today's diverse classrooms.* Boston: Allyn & Bacon.

Carlo, M. S., August, D., McLaughlin, B, Snow, C. E., Dressler, C, Lippman, D. N., Lively, T. J., & White, C. E. (2004). Closing the gap: Addressing the vocabulary needs of English-language learners in bilingual and mainstream classrooms. *Reading Research Quarterly, 39*:2, 188-215.

Coxhead, A. (2000, summer). A new academic word list. *TESOL Quarterly 34*:2.

Coxhead, A. *The compleat lexical tutor.* <http://132.208.224.131/>

Folse, K. (2004). *Vocabulary myths: Applying second language research to classroom teaching.* Ann Arbor, MI: University of Michigan Press.

García, G. E. (1991). Factors influencing the English reading test performance of Spanish-speaking Hispanic students. *Reading Research Quarterly,* 26, 371-392.

Hakuta, K, Butler, Y.G., & Witt, D. (2000). *How long does it take English learners to attain proficiency?* Santa Barbara: University of California Linguistic Minority Research Institute.

Nation, I.S.P. (Ed.) (1994). *New ways in teaching Vocabulary.* Alexandria, VA: TESOL.

Nation, I.S.P. (2001). *Learning vocabulary in another language.* Cambridge University Press, Cambridge.

National Institute of Child Health and Human Development. (2000). *The report of the National Reading Panel. Teaching children to read: An evidence-based assessment of the scientific literature on reading and its implications for reading instruction.* Washington DC: U.S. Government and Printing Office. <http://www.nationalreadingpanel.org/Publications/publications.htm>

Stahl, S. A. & Fairbanks, M. (1986). The effects of vocabulary instruction: A model-based meta-analysis. *Review of Educational Research, 56*:72-100.

Thomas, W.P, & Collier, V.P. (2002). *A national study of school effectiveness of language minority students' long-term academic achievement.* Santa Cruz, DA: center for Research on Education, Diversity and Excellence, University of California – Santa Cruz. <http://repositories.cdlib.org/crede/finalrpts/1_1_final/>

Group Work in the Science Classroom

Group work is a valuable real-world skill that helps students develop and master important communication and team-building skills. The strength of a group is often in the differences between members of the group. However, students need practice with different formats of group work in order to become effective team members. Achieving the balance among several variables, including student personalities, time management, and academics can be challenging for you as a teacher. To ease your task, work at teaching students how to organize themselves to work best as a group, how to modify their behavior to support the group's effort, and how to participate effectively and respectfully in a discussion. When students are able to manage their own group dynamics, they are more likely to have a positive experience.

Assigning roles to individuals within a group is an effective technique to teach students how to work together. It helps limit the behavior of more outgoing students and requires less outgoing students to participate; it also empowers students and allows them to feel as though they are a connected and important member of the group.

Each type of group work is a little different. Prior to the first time students work in a particular type of group, spend time introducing them to the structure of the group, the different roles and the responsibilities that come with each role, and your expectations of their behavior during group work. The first time students do a particular type of group work, some of their time is spent learning the process. Start with a simple activity to teach students the process, and scale up to more complex tasks.

Role of the Teacher

1. **Prepare students for group work.** Discuss the goals and objectives of the task, your expectations for behavior, time to be spent, limits and rules you set.
2. **Assign students roles within the groups.** Make group assignments random and form new groups as you do new activities. Distribute appropriate role sheets from the Science Toolkit. As the year progresses, let students select roles.
3. **Guide the process.**
   - Circulate around the room and regularly check the progress of each group.
   - Be available to answer questions and to redirect groups when they are off-task.
   - Offer positive reinforcement when groups and individuals are staying on task.
   - Anticipate potential stumbling blocks for students and be ready to help.
   - Encourage participation and good listening; discourage domination within the group.
4. **Provide closure.** After group work, pull the class together and discuss what was learned. For labs, you might share group results on the board and compare them. Make sure students understand the point of the lab. Also discuss the process: what worked well with the groups and what did not. Get the class to commit to improving the group work process.

Role of the Student

The Science Toolkit contains copymasters for each type of group work in *Section J, Cooperative Learning*. Copy and distribute by the specific type of group work:

- **Classroom group work:** For tasks during lessons such as reading passages in the text or analyzing a video or demonstration, use *J3: Group Roles; J4 Discussion Roles; J7 Jigsaw Activities; J8 Think, Pair, Share Activities; J10 Cooperative Activities.*
- **Lab group work:** When time is an issue, break up the lab into parts and have students actively participate in managing the time needed to complete each part. Use *J6 Guidelines for Cooperative Lab Work.*
- **Project group work:** Make sure students know your product expectations (give a rubric if possible) and how much time they have to complete the project. Emphasize that every individual should do an equal amount of work. Use *J5 Project Roles; J9 Group Project Progress Report.*

California Science Content Standards at a Glance

CHAPTER	1	2	3	4
Plate Tectonics and Earth's Structure				
6.1 Plate tectonics accounts for important features of Earth's surface and major geologic events. As a basis for understanding this concept:				
6.1.a *Students know* evidence of plate tectonics is derived from the fit of the continents; the location of earthquakes, volcanoes, and midocean ridges; and the distribution of fossils, rock types, and ancient climatic zones.				
6.1.b *Students know* Earth is composed of several layers: a cold, brittle lithosphere; a hot, convecting mantle; and a dense, metallic core.		2.1		
6.1.c *Students know* lithospheric plates the size of continents and oceans move at rates of centimeters per year in response to movements in the mantle.				
6.1.d *Students know* that earthquakes are sudden motions along breaks in the crust called faults and that volcanoes and fissures are locations where magma reaches the surface.				
6.1.e *Students know* major geologic events, such as earthquakes, volcanic eruptions, and mountain building, result from plate motions.				
6.1.f *Students know* how to explain major features of California geology (including mountains, faults, volcanoes) in terms of plate tectonics.				
6.1.g *Students know* how to determine the epicenter of an earthquake and know that the effects of an earthquake on any region vary, depending on the size of the earthquake, the distance of the region from the epicenter, the local geology, and the type of construction in the region.				
Shaping Earth's Surface				
6.2 Topography is reshaped by the weathering of rock and soil and by the transportation and deposition of sediment. As a basis for understanding this concept:				
6.2.a *Students know* water running downhill is the dominant process in shaping the landscape, including California's landscape.				
6.2.b *Students know* rivers and streams are dynamic systems that erode, transport sediment, change course, and flood their banks in natural and recurring patterns.				
6.2.c *Students know* beaches are dynamic systems in which the sand is supplied by rivers and moved along the coast by the action of waves.				
6.2.d *Students know* earthquakes, volcanic eruptions, landslides, and floods change human and wildlife habitats.		2.1		

5	6	7	8	9	10	11	12	13	14
			8.1, 8.2, 8.3, 8.4	9.1, 9.2	10.1				
	6.1, 6.2		8.1, 8.2, 8.3	9.1	10.1, 10.2				
			8.2		10.1				
			8.3	9.1, 9.3	10.2				
			8.3, 8.4	9.1, 9.2	10.1, 10.2				
			8.2, 8.4	9.1	10.1				
				9.2					
5.2	6.2, 6.3	7.1, 7.2, 7.4							
		7.2							
		7.3							
		7.1, 7.2, 7.3		9.3	10.3				

Standards at a Glance

CHAPTER	1	2	3	4
Heat (Thermal Energy) (Physical Science)				
6.3 Heat moves in a predictable flow from warmer objects to cooler objects until all the objects are at the same temperature. As a basis for understanding this concept:				
6.3.a *Students know* energy can be carried from one place to another by heat flow or by waves, including water, light and sound waves, or by moving objects.	1.1, 1.3			4.2
6.3.b *Students know* that when fuel is consumed, most of the energy released becomes heat energy.	1.1			
6.3.c *Students know* heat flows in solids by conduction (which involves no flow of matter) and in fluids by conduction and by convection (which involves flow of matter).	1.3			
6.3.d *Students know* heat energy is also transferred between objects by radiation (radiation can travel through space).	1.2	2.2, 2.3		
Energy in the Earth System				
6.4 Many phenomena on Earth's surface are affected by the transfer of energy through radiation and convection currents. As a basis for understanding this concept:				
6.4.a *Students know* the Sun is the major source of energy for phenomena on Earth's surface; it powers winds, ocean currents, and the water cycle.		2.2, 2.3	3.2, 3.3, 3.4	
6.4.b *Students know* solar energy reaches Earth through radiation, mostly in the form of visible light.	1.2	2.2		
6.4.c *Students know* heat from Earth's interior reaches the surface primarily through convection.		2.3		
6.4.d *Students know* convection currents distribute heat in the atmosphere and oceans.	1.3	2.2, 2.3		4.3
6.4.e *Students know* differences in pressure, heat, air movement, and humidity result in changes of weather.		2.3	3.1, 3.2, 3.3, 3.4	4.1, 4.2, 4.3, 4.4
Ecology (Life Science)				
6.5 Organisms in ecosystems exchange energy and nutrients among themselves and with the environment. As a basis for understanding this concept:				
6.5.a *Students know* energy entering ecosystems as sunlight is transferred by producers into chemical energy through photosynthesis and then from organism to organism through food webs.	1.1			
6.5.b *Students know* matter is transferred over time from one organism to others in the food web and between organisms and the physical environment.				
6.5.c *Students know* populations of organisms can be categorized by the functions they serve in an ecosystem.				
6.5.d *Students know* different kinds of organisms may play similar ecological roles in similar biomes.				
6.5.e *Students know* the number and types of organisms an ecosystem can support depends on the resources available and on abiotic factors, such as quantities of light and water, a range of temperatures, and soil composition.				

5	6	7	8	9	10	11	12	13	14
				9.2, 9.3					
			8.2		10.3				
					10.3				
						11.1, 11.3			
						11.12, 11.3			
							12.1, 12.2		
						11.4			
						11.1	12.1, 12.2, 12.3		14.1, 14.2

Standards at a Glance

CHAPTER	1	2	3	4
Resources				
6.6 Sources of energy and materials differ in amounts, distribution, usefulness, and the time required for their formation. As a basis for understanding this concept:				
6.6.a *Students know* the utility of energy sources is determined by factors that are involved in converting these sources to useful forms and the consequences of the conversion process.				
6.6.b *Students know* different natural energy and material resources, including air, soil, rocks, minerals, petroleum, fresh water, wildlife, and forests, and know how to classify them as renewable or nonrenewable.				
6.6.c *Students know* the natural origin of the materials used to make common objects.				
Investigation and Experimentation				
6.7 Scientific progress is made by asking meaningful questions and conducting careful investigations. As a basis for understanding this concept and addressing the content in the other three strands, students should develop their own questions and perform investigations. Students will:				
6.7.a Develop a hypothesis.		**2.2**	**3.3**	
6.7.b Select and use appropriate tools and technology (including calculators, computers, balances, spring scales, microscopes, and binoculars) to perform tests, collect data, and display data.	**1.1**		**3.3**	**4.4**
6.7.c Construct appropriate graphs from data and develop qualitative statements about the relationships between variables.	**1.2**			**4.4**
6.7.d Communicate the steps and results from an investigation in written reports and oral presentations.	**1.1**	**2.2**	**3.3**	**4.4**
6.7.e Recognize whether evidence is consistent with a proposed explanation.		**2.2**	**3.3**	
6.7.f Read a topographic map and a geologic map for evidence provided on the maps and construct and interpret a simple scale map.				
6.7.g Interpret events by sequence and time from natural phenomena (e.g., the relative ages of rocks and intrusions).				
6.7.h Identify changes in natural phenomena over time without manipulating the phenomena (e.g., a tree limb, a grove of trees, a stream, a hillslope).				

5	6	7	8	9	10	11	12	13	14
					10.3			13.1, 13.2, 13.3	14.2, 14.3
								13.1, 13.2, 13.3	14.1, 14.2, 14.3
5.1								13.1, 13.2, 13.3	14.3
			8.1, 8.2	9.3	10.2				14.3
	6.3	7.2				11.1	12.1		
	6.3					11.4	12.1. 12.2		
5.2	6.3	7.2	8.2	9.3	10.2	11.1	12.1	13.4	14.3
			8.2						14.3
5.1, 5.2, 5.3	6.4								
	6.3	7.1, 7.3	8.2, 8.3, 8.4		10.1				
		7.3, 7.4				11.4	12.3		

Correlations to California Science Content Standards

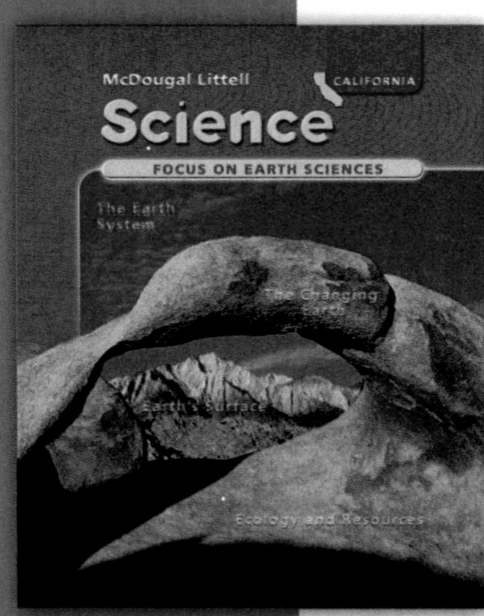

The science curriculum in grade six emphasizes the study of earth sciences. Students at this age are increasing their awareness of the environment and are ready to learn more. The standards in grade six present many of the foundations of geology and geophysics, including plate tectonics and earth structure, topography, and energy. The material is linked to resource management and ecology, building on what students have learned in previous grades. Unless students take a high school earth science class, what they learn in grade six will be their foundation for earth science literacy.

—*Science Framework for California Public Schools.*
Adopted by the California State Board of Education.
Copyright © 2004 the California Department of Education.

Standards	Primary Citations	Supporting Citations
PLATE TECTONICS AND EARTH'S STRUCTURE		
6.1 Plate tectonics accounts for important features of Earth's surface and major geologic events. As a basis for understanding this concept:		
6.1.a ***Students know*** **evidence of plate tectonics is derived from the fit of the continents; the location of earthquakes, volcanoes, and midocean ridges; and the distribution of fossils, rock types, and ancient climatic zones.**	**PUPIL/TEACHER EDITION** 268–269, 270, **270–275,** 278–279, **281**, 282–285, **286–292, 302,** 338 Benchmark Tests: 3.1, 3.2, 3.3, 4.1 CA Standards Review and Practice: 1–2	**PUPIL/TEACHER EDITION** CA15, 45, 47, 206–207, 218–221, 275 (#1–2), 284 (#2), 292 (#3), 293, 295 (#7–11, 17), 309, 327 (#11, 14), 328 (#24), 329, 330–333, 337, 339, 349, R56–R57, R64–R65 **PRINT COMPONENTS** **Unit Resource Books:** The Changing Earth: 9–10, 15–18, 21, 24–31, 34–43. 46–54, 71–81, 84–92, 103 **Modified Lesson Plans for English Learners:** 30–31, 33–34, 37 **Lab Manual:** 150–152, 157–161, 163 **TRANSPARENCIES/TECHNOLOGY** **Unit Transparency Books:** The Changing Earth, T57–T64 **Lab Generator:** Magnetic Reversals; Convergent Boundaries; Magnetic Patterns on the Ocean Floor; Subduction Zone Earthquakes **Content Review:** 8.1–8.4, 9.1, 10.1 **Power Presentations:** 8.1–8.4, 9.1, 10.1
6.1.b ***Students know*** **Earth is composed of several layers: a cold, brittle lithosphere; a hot, convecting mantle; and a dense, metallic core.**	**PUPIL/TEACHER EDITION** **44,** 45, 197, **263, 265–267,** 268, 268–269, **273,** 274, 279, 281, 299, 301, **303** Benchmark Tests: 1.1, 2.1, 2.2, 3.4, 4.2 CA Standards Review and Practice: 3–4	**PUPIL/TEACHER EDITION** 151, 153, 181, 183, 186, 188 (#1–3), 190, 197 (#1–3), 215 (#10–12,16,18–19), 217, 269 (#1–3), 276–277, 281, 284 (#1), 327 (#15), 329 (#29), 365 (#4) **PRINT COMPONENTS** **Unit Resource Books:** The Earth System: 74, 76, 80–81; Earth's Surface: 7–8, 72–80, 83–89; The Changing Earth: 13–21, 34–35, 40, 43, 62–81, 84 **Modified Lesson Plans for English Learners:** 8, 22–23, 30–32, 34, 37–38 **Lab Manual:** 73, 123, 149, 153–160 **TRANSPARENCIES/TECHNOLOGY** **Unit Transparency Books:** The Changing Earth, T57–T64 **Lab Generator:** Convection Currents and Plate Movement; Magnetic Reversals; Magnetic Patterns on the Ocean Floor; Earth's Different Layers; Geosphere's Layers; Crystal Shape **Content Review:** 2.1, 6.1, 6.2, 8.1–8.3, 9.1, 10.1, 10.2 **Power Presentations:** 2.1, 6.1, 6.2, 8.1–8.3, 9.1, 10.1, 10.2

Citations in blue indicate hands-on activities. Bold face indicates core standards instruction.

The Pupil Edition is also available online and on DVD. Audio Readings of the Pupil Edition are available in English and Spanish. The Teacher's Edition is available on DVD.

Correlations to California Science Content Standards

Standards	Primary Citations	Supporting Citations
6.1.c ***Students know*** **lithospheric plates the size of continents and oceans move at rates of centimeters per year in response to movements in the mantle.**	**PUPIL/TEACHER EDITION** **273–274,** 276–277, **285,** 340 Benchmark Tests: 3.5, 3.6 CA Standards Review and Practice: 5–6	**PUPIL/TEACHER EDITION** 275 (#3), 278, 295 (#12, 18), 296 (#32), 315 **PRINT COMPONENTS** Unit Resource Books: The Changing Earth: 24–31, 34–40, 60–61, 66–69 Modified Lesson Plans for English Learners: 30–31, 37 Lab Manual: 150, 153–156 **TRANSPARENCIES/TECHNOLOGY** Unit Transparency Books: The Changing Earth, T57–64 Lab Generator: Convection Currents and Plate Movement Content Review: 8.1, 8.2, 10.1 Power Presentations: 8.1, 8.2, 10.1
6.1.d ***Students know*** **that earthquakes are sudden motions along breaks in the crust called faults and that volcanoes and fissures are locations where magma reaches the surface.**	**PUPIL/TEACHER EDITION** 299, **301,** 302, **303–305,** 335, 346, **346–348, 350–352,** 354–355 Benchmark Tests: 3.7, 3.8, 4.3 CA Standards Review and Practice: 7–8	**PUPIL/TEACHER EDITION** 47, 258–261, 282–284, 290, 296 (#20), 305 (#2,3), 323 (#1), 327 (#12), 328 (#17, 21), 329, 353 (#2–3), 365 (#7–10, 12,15), 366 (#17, 20, 24–26, 28), 367 **PRINT COMPONENTS** Unit Resource Books: The Changing Earth: 1–8, 34–35, 40, 84–92, 107, 114, 117–119, 131–140, 155–156, 157–162, 182–186, 191–199 Modified Lesson Plans for English Learners: 34, 38 Lab Manual: 161, 169–172 **TRANSPARENCIES/TECHNOLOGY** Unit Transparency Books: The Changing Earth, T65–T81 Lab Generator: Faults; Make Your Own Volcano; Modeling Magma Movement; Earthquake Depths Content Review: 9.1, 10.2 Power Presentations: 9.1, 10.2 SAF Video: Paradise Postponed

Standards	Primary Citations	Supporting Citations
6.1.e ***Students know*** **major geologic events, such as earthquakes, volcanic eruptions, and mountain building, result from plate motions.**	**PUPIL/TEACHER EDITION** **283–284,** 286, **287–289,** 289, **302–303,** 303, **304–305,** 337, 337–339, **340–342, 342, 343–344, 349** Benchmark Tests: 3.9, 3.10, 3.11, 4.4 CA Standards Review and Practice: 9–10	**PUPIL/TEACHER EDITION** 218–221, 282, 284 (#3), 292 (#1–2), 293, 295 (#13–16), 296 (#19, 21, 25, 32), 297, 301, 305 (#1), 306, 309, 314 (#2), 335, 344 (#2–3), 345, 353 (#1), 365 (#5–6, 13), 366 (#22–23, 27, 29–30), 367 **PRINT COMPONENTS** Unit Resource Books: The Changing Earth: 1–6, 34–35, 36–40, 43, 46–54, 84–85, 86–92, 103, 131–138, 144–152, 155–162, 200–201 Modified Lesson Plans for English Learners: 32–34, 37–38 Lab Manual: 150, 152, 161, 163, 169–172, 173 **TRANSPARENCIES/TECHNOLOGY** Unit Transparency Books: The Changing Earth Lab Generator: Convergent Boundaries; Faults; Fault–Block Mountains; Subduction Zone Earthquakes; Earthquake Depths Content Review: 8.3, 8.4, 9.1, 10.1, 10.2 Power Presentations: 8.3, 8.4, 9.1, 10.1, 10.2
6.1.f ***Students know*** **how to explain major features of California geology (including mountains, faults, volcanoes) in terms of plate tectonics.**	**PUPIL/TEACHER EDITION** **290,** 291, **302,** 344 Benchmark Tests: 3.12, 3.13, 3.14, 4.5 CA Standards Review and Practice: 11–12	**PUPIL/TEACHER EDITION** 175, 274–275, 289, 296 (#26–31), 303, 305, 309, 328 (#26), 344 (#1), 365 (#14) **PRINT RESOURCES** Unit Resource Books: The Changing Earth: 46–52, 54, 84–92, 144–150, 152 Modified Lesson Plans for English Learners: 33–34, 37 Lab Manual: 151, 161 **TRANSPARENCIES/TECHNOLOGY** Unit Transparency Books: The Changing Earth, T57–T72 Lab Generator: Convergent Boundaries; Faults; Fault–Block Mountains; Earthquake Depths; Subduction Zone Earthquakes Content Review: 8.4, 9.1, 10.1 Power Presentations: 8.4, 9.1, 10.1

Correlations to California Science Content Standards

Standards	Primary Citations	Supporting Citations
6.1.g ***Students know*** **how to determine the epicenter of an earthquake and know that the effects of an earthquake on any region vary, depending on the size of the earthquake, the distance of the region from the epicenter, the local geology, and the type of construction in the region.**	PUPIL/TEACHER EDITION **307–314,** 315–318 Benchmark Tests: 3.15, 3.20 CA Standards Review and Practice: 13–14	PUPIL/TEACHER EDITION 309, 314 (#1), 319–322, 323 (#3), 324, 327 (#7–8), 328 (#18, 23, 25) PRINT COMPONENTS Unit Resource Books: The Changing Earth: 95–104, 107–119, 122–130 Modified Lesson Plans for English Learners: 35–36 Lab Manual: 162–163, 165–168 TRANSPARENCIES/TECHNOLOGY Unit Transparency Books: The Changing Earth, T65–T72 Lab Generator: Subduction Zone Earthquakes; How Structures React in Earthquakes Content Review: 9.2, 9.3 Power Presentations: 9.2, 9.3
SHAPING EARTH'S SURFACE		
6.2 **Topography is reshaped by the weathering of rock and soil and by the transportation and deposition of sediment. As a basis for understanding this concept:**		
6.2.a ***Students know*** **water running downhill is the dominant process in shaping the landscape, including California's landscape.**	PUPIL/TEACHER EDITION 194, **199–202,** 203, **225–226,** 226, 227–228, 230, 230–235, **236–237,** 245, **245–246,** 247–250, 249 Benchmark Tests: 2.3, 2.4, 3.16, 4.6 CA Standards Review and Practice: 15–16	PUPIL/TEACHER EDITION 151, 153, 168–169, 192–193, 203 (#3), 204–205, 215 (#13–15), 216 (#25–26), 223, 229 (#1–2), 235 (#1), 250 (#1–2), 251, 253 (#9, 11, 20–21), 255 PRINT COMPONENTS Unit Resource Books: Earth's Surface: 9–10, 31–32, 50–58, 90, 143–151, 154–161, 175–188, 191–210; Ecology and Resources: 23, 25, 31 Modified Lesson Plans for English Learners: 24, 26–27, 29 Lab Manual: 115–118, 124, 135–137, 139–146 TRANSPARENCIES/TECHNOLOGY Unit Transparency Books: Earth's Surface, T41–T56 Lab Generator: Topographical Maps; Sediment Layers; Weathering; Erosion; Creating Stream Features; Kettle Lake Formation; Rivers Change the Land Content Review: 6.3, 7.1, 7.2, 7.4 Power Presentations: 6.3, 7.1, 7.2, 7.4

Standards	Primary Citations	Supporting Citations
6.2.b ***Students know*** **rivers and streams are dynamic systems that erode, transport sediment, change course, and flood their banks in natural and recurring patterns.**	PUPIL/TEACHER EDITION **230–233, 236–237** Benchmark Tests: 2.5, 2.6, 2.7, 2.8, 2.9, 3.17, 3.18 CA Standards Review and Practice: 17–18	PUPIL/TEACHER EDITION 235 (#1–2), 253 (#12–15), 255 PRINT COMPONENTS Unit Resource Books: Earth's Surface: 154–161, 164–169, 172, 186–188, 191–210 Modified Lesson Plans for English Learners: 27 Lab Manual: 139–145 TRANSPARENCIES/TECHNOLOGY Unit Transparency Books: Earth's Surface, T49–56 Lab Generator: Creating Stream Features; Rivers Change the Land Content Review: 7.2 Power Presentations: 7.2
6.2.c ***Students know*** **beaches are dynamic systems in which the sand is supplied by rivers and moved along the coast by the action of waves.**	PUPIL/TEACHER EDITION **238–240, 240, 241–242, 244** Benchmark Tests: 2.11, 2.12, 2.13, 4.7 CA Standards Review and Practice: 19–20	PUPIL/TEACHER EDITION 186–187, 223, 243 (#1), 253 (#16, 22), 255 PRINT COMPONENTS Unit Resource Books: Earth's Surface: 164–172, 186–188, 209–210 Modified Lesson Plans for English Learners: 28 Lab Manual: 136 TRANSPARENCIES/TECHNOLOGY Unit Transparency Books: Earth's Surface, T49–56 Lab Generator: Longshore Drift Content Review: 7.3 Power Presentations: 7.3

Correlations to California Science Content Standards

Standards	Primary Citations	Supporting Citations
6.2.d ***Students know*** **earthquakes, volcanic eruptions, landslides, and floods change human and wildlife habitats.**	**PUPIL/TEACHER EDITION** 211, 231, **232, 316,** 317, **318–319, 322–325, 324–325, 356–359, 359, 360** Benchmark Tests: 1.2, 2.14, 2.16, 3.19, 3.21, 3.22 CA Standards Review and Practice: 21–22	**PUPIL/TEACHER EDITION** 45–46, 211, 227–229, 229 (#3), 253 (#10, 23–24), 255, 258–261, 306, 320–321, 323 (#2), 362 (#1–3), 365 (#11,16), 366 (#18–19, 21), 367 **PRINT RESOURCES** Unit Resource Books: The Earth System: 79, 228–234, 236, 252–253; Earth's Surface: 112–113, 143–151, 154–161; The Changing Earth: 107–119, 122–130, 165–166, 167–168, 169–174 Modified Lesson Plans for English Learners: 25–28, 36, 39 Lab Manual: 126, 135, 165–168, 174–175 **TRANSPARENCIES/TECHNOLOGY** Unit Transparency Books: Earth's Surface, T49–T56; The Changing Earth, T65–T72 Lab Generator: How Structures React in Earthquakes; Mudflows; Landslide Areas; Erosion; Creating Stream Features Content Review: 7.1–7.3, 9.3, 10.3 Power Presentations: 7.1–7.3, 9.3, 10.3 SAF Video: Paradise Postponed

Standards	Primary Citations	Supporting Citations
HEAT (THERMAL ENERGY) (PHYSICAL SCIENCE)		
6.3 Heat moves in a predictable flow from warmer objects to cooler objects until all the objects are at the same temperature. As a basis for understanding this concept:		
6.3.a ***Students know*** **energy can be carried from one place to another by heat flow or by waves, including water, light and sound waves, or by moving objects.**	PUPIL/TEACHER EDITION **10, 11, 19–20,** 22–23, 124–125, **309–311, 318, 472–475** Benchmark Tests: 1.3, 1.4, 1.5, 3.23, 3.24 CA Standards Review and Practice: 23–24	PUPIL/TEACHER EDITION CA13, 7, 9, 14, 15 (#2), 16–17, 23, 26–27, 39, 72–75, 122, 126, 307, 312–313, 314 (#3), 315, 316, 324–325, 327 (#9–10), 328 (#20, 27–29), 329, 477–478, 479 (#1), 482 (#13–15) PRINT COMPONENTS Unit Resource Books: The Earth System: 13–21, 31, 51–59, 69–70, 217–222, 224, 225; The Changing Earth: 95–101, 104, 107–116, 122–130; Ecology and Resources: 178–190, 193–210 Modified Lesson Plans for English Learners: 3–5, 35, 50 Lab Manual: 61, 65–72, 100, 165–168, 213–220 TRANSPARENCIES/TECHNOLOGY Unit Transparency Books: The Earth System: T1–T8; The Changing Earth, T65–T72; Ecology and Resources, T97–104 Lab Generator: Energy; Energy Conversions; Energy Transfer; Ice; How Structures React in Earthquakes Content Review: 1.1, 9.2, 13.4 Power Presentations: 1.1, 9.2, 13.4
6.3.b ***Students know*** **that when fuel is consumed, most of the energy released becomes heat energy.**	PUPIL/TEACHER EDITION **12, 14–15,** 16–17 Benchmark Tests: 1.6, 1.7 CA Standards Review and Practice: 25–26	PUPIL/TEACHER EDITION CA18–CA19, 9–10, 13, 15 (#3) PRINT COMPONENTS Unit Resource Books: The Earth System: 13–19, 51–63, 69–70 Modified Lesson Plans for English Learners: 3–5 Lab Manual: 65–68 TRANSPARENCIES/TECHNOLOGY Unit Transparency Books: The Earth System, T1–T8 Lab Generator: Energy Conversions Content Review: 1.1 Power Presentations: 1.1

Correlations to California Science Content Standards

Standards	Primary Citations	Supporting Citations
6.3.c ***Students know*** **heat flows in solids by conduction (which involves no flow of matter) and in fluids by conduction and by convection (which involves flow of matter).**	PUPIL/TEACHER EDITION **26, 26–31,** 32, **273–274,** 361–362 Benchmark Tests: 1.8 CA Standards Review and Practice: 27–28	PUPIL/TEACHER EDITION 11, 32 (#1–3), 33, 37, 39, 72–75, 56–59, 263, 265, 276–277 PRINT COMPONENTS Unit Resource Books: The Earth System: 35–48, 51–54, 64–70, 73, 120, 128: The Changing Earth: 24–25, 27, 29, 31, 66–69, 75–78 Modified Lesson Plans for English Learners: 7, 31 Lab Manual: 63, 69–72, 153–160 TRANSPARENCIES/TECHNOLOGY Unit Transparency Books: The Earth System, T1–T8; The Changing Earth, T57–T64 Lab Generator: Insulators; Convection Currents and Plate Movement; Observing Convection Content Review: 1.3, 8.2 Power Presentations: 1.3, 8.2
6.3.d ***Students know*** **heat energy is also transferred between objects by radiation (radiation can travel through space).**	PUPIL/TEACHER EDITION **18, 18–19, 22–23, 23, 24** Benchmark Tests: 1.9, 3.24 CA Standards Review and Practice: 29–30	PUPIL/TEACHER EDITION 48–51, 51, 55 (#1), 56–57, 59, 65, 72–75, 150 PRINT COMPONENTS Unit Resource Books: The Earth System: 24–32, 60–70, 73, 84–89, 91, 102, 111–119; Earth's Surface: 1–4 Modified Lesson Plans for English Learners: 6, 9 Lab Manual: 62, 77–80 TRANSPARENCIES/TECHNOLOGY Unit Transparency Books: The Earth System, T1–T8 Lab Generator: Energy Transfer; Solar Energy; Modeling Solar Energy; Heating and Cooling Rates Content Review: 1.2, 2.2 Power Presentations: 1.2, 2.2 SAF Video: All That Glitters

Standards	Primary Citations	Supporting Citations
ENERGY IN THE EARTH SYSTEM		
6.4 **Many phenomena on Earth's surface are affected by the transfer of energy through radiation and convection currents. As a basis for understanding this concept:**		
6.4.a ***Students know*** **the sun is the major source of energy for phenomena on Earth's surface; it powers winds, ocean currents, and the water cycle.**	PUPIL/TEACHER EDITION 48, **59,** 60–61, 64–65, 83, 83–84, **93,** 128, 380 Benchmark Tests: 1.10, 3.25 CA Standards Review and Practice: 31–32	PUPIL & TEACHER & eEDITION CA13, 23, 24, 51, 56–57, 66 (#2), 71, 99 (#1), 102–103, 106 (#1), 109 (#13, 23), 110 (#25–30, 40), 111, 330–333, 385, 391 PRINT COMPONENTS Unit Resource Books: The Earth System: 31, 84–89. 91–92, 95–101, 103, 115–118, 129, 144–149, 152, 155–160, 178–180; Ecology and Resources: 233 Modified Lesson Plans for English Learners: 9, 10, 13–14 Lab Manual: 62, 73–74, 77–80 TRANSPARENCIES/TECHNOLOGY Unit Transparency Books: The Earth System, T9–T24 Lab Generator: Energy Transfer; Solar Energy; Modeling Solar Energy Content Review: 2.2, 2.3, 3.3, 3.4 Power Presentations: 2.2, 2.3, 3.3, 3.4
6.4.b ***Students know*** **solar energy reaches Earth through radiation, mostly in the form of visible light.**	PUPIL/TEACHER EDITION 19–20, **21–22,** 25, 48 Benchmark Tests: 1.11, 1.12, 4.8 CA Standards Review and Practice: 33–34	PUPIL/TEACHER EDITION CA13, 23, 24 (#1–2), 49–50, 51, 56–57, 148–151 PRINT COMPONENTS Unit Resource Books: The Earth System: 24–32, 69–70, 84–90, 111–119; Earth's Surface: 1–4 Modified Lesson Plans for English Learners: 6, 8 Lab Manual: 62, 77–80 TRANSPARENCIES/TECHNOLOGY Unit Transparency Books: The Earth System, T1–T16 Lab Generator: Energy Transfer, Solar Energy; Modeling Solar Energy Content Review: 1.2, 2.2 Power Presentations: 1.2, 2.2 SAF Video: All That Glitters

Correlations to California Science Content Standards

Standards		Primary Citations	Supporting Citations
6.4.c	***Students know*** **heat from Earth's interior reaches the surface primarily through convection.**	PUPIL/TEACHER EDITION **58,** 59, **361–363** Benchmark Tests: 1.13 CA Standards Review and Practice: 35–36	PUPIL/TEACHER EDITION CA13, 269, 282 PRINT COMPONENTS Unit Resource Books: The Earth System: 95. 97, 99, 124–127 Modified Lesson Plans for English Learners: 10, 39 Lab Manual: 81–84 TRANSPARENCIES/TECHNOLOGY Unit Transparency Books: The Earth System, T9–T16; The Changing Earth, T73–T80 Lab Generator: Observing Convection Content Review: 2.3, 10.3 Power Presentations: 2.3, 10.3
6.4.d	***Students know*** **convection currents distribute heat in the atmosphere and oceans.**	PUPIL/TEACHER EDITION **30–31, 62–63,** 65–66 Benchmark Tests: 1.14, 1.15, 2.18, 3.26 CA Standards Review and Practice: 37–38	PUPIL/TEACHER EDITION 28–29, 29, 36 (#25–26), 37, 52–55, 55 (#2–3), 66 (#3), 89, 91, 128–130, 130, 132 (#1), 143 (#17–22) PRINT COMPONENTS Unit Resource Books: The Earth System: 35–40, 42, 43, 46–48, 69–70, 95, 97, 99, 103, 120–128, 130, 228–233, 235, 236 Modified Lesson Plans for English Learners: 7, 10, 17 Lab Manual: 63, 101, 81–84 TRANSPARENCIES/TECHNOLOGY Unit Transparency Books: The Earth System, T1–T16 Lab Generator: Density; Updrafts; Observing Convection Content Review: 1.3, 2.3, 4.3 Power Presentations: 1.3, 2.3, 4.3

Standards	Primary Citations	Supporting Citations
6.4.e ***Students know*** **differences in pressure, heat, air movement, and humidity result in changes of weather.**	**PUPIL/TEACHER EDITION** 2–5, 5, 62–63, **79,** 80–81, 81, **83–84,** 85, 89, **90,** 92–94, 102–103, 103, **118–121,** 123, 123–129, 131 Benchmark Tests: 1.16, 1.17, 1.18, 2.19, 2.20, 2.21, 3.27, 4.9 CA Standards Review and Practice: 39–40	**PUPIL/TEACHER EDITION** 50–51, 65, 77, 62 (#1–3), 86–88, 90 (#1–3), 91, 95, 95–99, 99 (#2–3), 100–101, 104–105, 106 (#2–3), 107, 109 (#9–12, 14–22, 24), 110 (#31–32, 39), 111, 113, 115, 115–117, 117, 121 (#1–3), 122, 127 (#1–3), 132 (#2–3), 134, 137, 139 (#2), 140–141, 143 (#9–10, 12–13, 16–17, 19–21), 385 **PRINT COMPONENTS** Unit Resource Books: The Earth System: 1–6, 96, 98, 100–103, 106–107, 133–141, 144–152, 155–163, 166–175, 184–203, 206–214, 217–223, 225, 228–233, 239–244, 249–251, 254–261, 263–273 Modified Lesson Plans for English Learners: 11–18 Lab Manual: 75, 85–99, 104–110 **TRANSPARENCIES/TECHNOLOGY** Unit Transparency Books: The Earth System, T17–T32 Lab Generator: Relative Humidity; Condensation; Precipitation; Coriolis Effect; Heating and Cooling Rates; Air Pressure; Air Masses; Design a Weather Center; Hurricane Hugo; Estimating Wind Speed Content Review: 3.1–3.4, 4.1–4.4 Power Presentations: 3.1–3.4, 4.1–4.4 SAF Video: Dust Busting
ECOLOGY (LIFE SCIENCE)		
6.5 **Organisms in ecosystems exchange energy and nutrients among themselves and with the environment. As a basis for understanding this concept:**		
6.5.a ***Students know*** **energy entering ecosystems as sunlight is transferred by producers into chemical energy through photosynthesis and then from organism to organism through food webs.**	**PUPIL/TEACHER EDITION** **380, 386,** 390, **390–393,** 393, **394–397** Benchmark Tests: 4.10 CA Standards Review and Practice: 41–42	**PUPIL/TEACHER EDITION** CA16, 9, 11, 375, 377, 396 (#1), 407 (#8, 15–16), 408 (#17,20), 411 **PRINT COMPONENTS** Unit Resource Books: The Earth System: 13–19; Ecology and Resources: 13–20, 34–42, 57–59 Modified Lesson Plans for English Learners: 40–42 Lab Manual: 188 **TRANSPARENCIES/TECHNOLOGY** Unit Transparency Books: Ecology and Resources, T81–T88 Lab Generator: Decomposers Content Review: 11.1–11.3 Power Presentations: 11.1–11.3

Correlations to California Science Content Standards

Standards	Primary Citations	Supporting Citations
6.5.b ***Students know*** **matter is transferred over time from one organism to others in the food web and between organisms and the physical environment.**	PUPIL/TEACHER EDITION **384, 384–387, 387, 388, 391–393, 393, 394–396** Benchmark Tests: 4.11, 4.12 CA Standards Review and Practice: 43–44	PUPIL/TEACHER EDITION CA15, CA17, 2–5, 43, 70 (#20–21), 370–373, 388 (#1–3), 397, 407 (#9–10, 14), 408 (#28), 411, 425 PRINT COMPONENTS Unit Resource Books: The Earth System: 1–4, 73, 75, 79, 81–82; Ecology and Resources: 1–4, 23, 28–31, 34–42, 81, 95–103, 106–112, 114, 117–119, 140 Modified Lesson Plans for English Learners: 41–42 Lab Manual: 187–188, 199 TRANSPARENCIES/TECHNOLOGY Unit Transparency Books: Ecology and Resources, T81–T88 Lab Generator: Carbon; Decomposers; Species Interactions Content Review: 11.2, 11.3 Power Presentations: 11.2, 11.3 SAF Video: Dust Busting; Prairie Comeback
6.5.c ***Students know*** **populations of organisms can be categorized by the functions they serve in an ecosystem.**	PUPIL/TEACHER EDITION 415, **422–423,** 424–429 Benchmark Tests: 4.13 CA Standards Review and Practice: 45–46	PUPIL/TEACHER EDITION 393, 411, 413, 416, 419 (#1–3), 425, 429 (#1–3), 439 (#7, 9–11, 13–15), 440 (#19, 22, 24), 441–445 PRINT COMPONENTS Unit Resource Books: Ecology and Resources: 41, 85–92, 95–101, 103, 115–119, 131–140 Modified Lesson Plans for English Learners: 44–45 Lab Manual: 188, 199, 205–208 TRANSPARENCIES/TECHNOLOGY Unit Transparency Books: Ecology and Resources, T89–T96 Lab Generator: Decomposers; Species Interactions: Prey Survival Content Review: 12.1–12.2 Power Presentations: 12.1–12.2

Standards	Primary Citations	Supporting Citations
6.5.d ***Students know*** **different kinds of organisms may play similar ecological roles in similar biomes.**	**PUPIL/TEACHER EDITION** **398** **Benchmark Tests:** 4.14 **CA Standards Review and Practice:** 47–48	**PUPIL/TEACHER EDITION** 399–405, 405 (#1–3), 407 (#12), 408 (#18–19, 21, 23), 409, 440 (#16–17), 442–445 **PRINT COMPONENTS** **Unit Resource Books:** Ecology and Resources: 45–51, 54, 57–59 **Modified Lesson Plans for English Learners:** 43 **TRANSPARENCIES/TECHNOLOGY** **Unit Transparency Books:** Ecology and Resources, T81–T88 **Content Review:** 11.4 **Power Presentations:** 11.4
6.5.e ***Students know*** **the number and types of organisms an ecosystem can support depends on the resources available and on abiotic factors, such as quantities of light and water, a range of temperatures, and soil composition.**	**PUPIL/TEACHER EDITION** **378–381,** 414–419, 431, **431–433,** 433, 492, 494–495 **Benchmark Tests:** 4.15, 4.16, 4.17, 4.18 **CA Standards Review and Practice:** 49–50	**PUPIL/TEACHER EDITION** 43, 330–333, 370–373, 373, 377, 381 (#1–3), 382–383, 403, 407 (#7, 13), 408 (#22, 24–27), 409, 420–421, 430, 434–436, 436 (#1, 3), 437, 439 (#6, 8, 12), 440 (#18, 20, 25), 442–445, 487, 498, 506 **PRINT COMPONENTS** **Unit Resource Books:** The Earth System: 73–79, 87; Ecology and Resources: 1–6, 13–20, 45–54, 57–59, 62–82, 85–92, 95–101, 103, 106–114, 117–119, 122–130, 140, 215–221, 224, 227–235, 238–243, 248–250 **Modified Lesson Plans for English Learners:** 40, 45–46, 51 **Lab Manual:** 189, 191–198, 200–204 **TRANSPARENCIES/TECHNOLOGY** **Unit Transparency Books:** Ecology and Resources, T81–T96 **Lab Generator:** Testing Soil; Climate; The Water Cycle; Environmental Conditions; Limiting Factors; Particles in the Air **Content Review:** 11.1, 12.2, 12.3, 14.1 **Power Presentations:** 11.1, 12.2, 12.3, 14.1 **SAF Video:** Prairie Comeback

Standards		Primary Citations	Supporting Citations
RESOURCES			
6.6	**Sources of energy and materials differ in amounts, distribution, usefulness, and the time required for their formation. As a basis for understanding this concept:**		
6.6.a	***Students know*** **the utility of energy sources is determined by factors that are involved in converting these sources to useful forms and the consequences of the conversion process.**	PUPIL/TEACHER EDITION **451–453, 454,** 462, **463,** 464, **471–479,** 512 Benchmark Tests: 4.19, 4.20, 4.21, 4.22 CA Standards Review and Practice: 51–52	PUPIL/TEACHER EDITION 12–13, 330–333, 447, 456 (#2), 467–468, 468, 469, 479 (#1–3), 480–481, 483 (#9, 11, 13–17, 20), 484 (#22, 24, 26, 36), 485, 504 (#2), 498–502, 507, 514–515, 517 (#10, 12–13, 15), 518 (#23–23), 519 PRINT COMPONENTS Unit Resource Books: Ecology and Resources: 144–150, 153, 156–164, 167–175, 178–197, 202–212, 227–232, 235, 238–243, 246–247, 253–271 Modified Lesson Plans for English Learners: 47–50, 52–53 Lab Manual: 211–215, 225–232 TRANPARENCIES/TECHNOLOGY Unit Transparency Books: Ecology and Resources, T97–T104 Lab Generator: Mining; Conservation; Wind Power; Solar Houses; Cleaning Oil Spills; Pollutants on the Move Content Review: 10.3, 13.1–13.4, 14.2, 14.3 Power Presentations: 10.3, 13.1–13.4, 14.2, 14.3

Standards	Primary Citations	Supporting Citations
6.6.b ***Students know*** **different natural energy and material resources, including air, soil, rocks, minerals, petroleum, fresh water, wildlife, and forests, and know how to classify them as renewable or nonrenewable.**	**PUPIL/TEACHER EDITION** 449, **450, 451,** 452, **455,** 457, 471–476, 497, 503, 506–513 Benchmark Tests: 2.22, 4.23, 4.24, 4.25, 4.26 CA Standards Review and Practice: 53–54	**PUPIL/TEACHER EDITION** 210, 373, 447, 456 (#1), 466, 466–469, 469 (#1–3), 483 (#7–8, 18–19), 484 (#21, 23, 25, 27, 35, 37), 489, 492, 492–493, 498, 504 (#1, 3), 505, 513 (#1,2), 517 (#11), 518 (#20–22, 25), R66–R75 **PRINT COMPONENTS** Unit Resource Books: Ecology and Resources: 7–8, 144–153, 156–162, 164, 167–173, 211–212, 215–220, 222–224, 227–235, 238–243, 245, 248–250, 271–272 Modified Lesson Plans for English Learners: 47–49, 51–53 Lab Manual: 210, 212, 221, 223 **TRANSPARENCIES/TECHNOLOGY** Unit Transparency Books: Ecology and Resources, T97–T112 Lab Generator: Fossil Fuels Distribution; Water Usage; Particles in the Air Content Review: 13.1–13.3, 14.1–14.3 Power Presentations: 13.1–13.3, 14.1–14.3
6.6.c ***Students know*** **the natural origin of the materials used to make common objects.**	**PUPIL/TEACHER EDITION** **159, 455–456, 458, 458–459** Benchmark Tests: 4.27, 4.28 CA Standards Review and Practice: 55–56	**PUPIL/TEACHER EDITION** 216 (#28), 449, 456 (#3), 460–461, 464 (#1–3), 465, 483 (#10), 485, 506, R66–R75 **PRINT COMPONENTS** Unit Resource Books: Earth's Surface: 20–21, 104–110; Ecology and Resources: 144–150, 153, 156–162, 164, 167–173, 175, 211–212, 244 Modified Lesson Plans for English Learners: 48–49, 53 Lab Manual: 61 **TRANSPARENCIES/TECHNOLOGY** Unit Transparency Books: Ecology and Resources, T97–T104 Lab Generator: California Natural Resources Content Review: 13.2, 13.3, 14.3 Power Presentations: 13.2, 13.3, 14.3

Correlations to California Science Content Standards

Standards		Primary Citations	Supporting Citations
INVESTIGATION AND EXPERIMENTATION			
6.7	**Scientific progress is made by asking meaningful questions and conducting careful investigations. As a basis for understanding this concept and addressing the content in the other three strands, students should develop their own questions and perform investigations. Students will:**		
6.7.a	**Develop a hypothesis.**	**PUPIL/TEACHER EDITION** 5, **56, 100, 269, 276, 324, 354, 480, 514** Benchmark Tests: 1.19 CA Standards Review and Practice: 57–58	**PUPIL/TEACHER EDITION** CA20–CA22, CA29, 23, 65, 216 (#24), R3, R29 **PRINT COMPONENTS** Unit Resource Books: The Earth System: 9–10, 111, 115, 120, 124, 188, 197; Earth's Surface: 130, 134, 200, 204; The Changing Earth: 62, 66, 71, 75, 122, 126, 131, 135, 182, 186, 191, 195; Ecology and Resources: 72, 76, 131, 135, 193, 197, 202, 206, 210, 253, 257, 262, 266 Lab Manual: 17–20, 45, 49, 53, 57, 77, 81, 91, 153, 157, 165, 169, 177, 181, 213, 217, 225 **TRANSPARENCIES/TECHNOLOGY** Science Toolkit: A21–22, A41–A42 Lab Generator: Modeling Solar Energy; Relative Humidity; Convection Currents and Plate Movement; Observing Convection; Modeling Rock Formation; How Structures React to Earthquakes; Earthquake Depths; Magnetic Patterns on the Ocean Floor; Make Your Own Volcano; Modeling Magma Movement; Rivers Change the Land; Estimating Wind Speed; The Water Cycle; Prey Survival; Wind Power; Solar Houses; Cleaning Oil Spills; Pollutants on the Move
6.7.b	**Select and use appropriate tools and technology (including calculators, computers, balances, spring scales, microscopes, and binoculars) to perform tests, collect data, and display data.**	**PUPIL/TEACHER EDITION** 16–17, 100–101, **140–141, 204–205,** 236–237, 382–383, **420–421,** 480–481, **R12–R19** Benchmark Tests: 3.28 CA Standards Review and Practice: 59–60	**PUPIL/TEACHER EDITION** CA23, CA24–CA25, 261 **PRINT COMPONENTS** Unit Resource Books: The Earth System: 51–63, 184–200, 202, 239–244, 254–262; Earth's Surface: 43–44, 59–67, 69, 121–128; The Changing Earth: 7–8, 9–10, 79, 120–121, 180–181; Ecology and Resources: 19, 62–71, 122–130, 193–201; 254–261, 262, 273 Lab Manual: 3–12, 14–16, 53–56, 65–68, 91–94, 103–106, 127–130, 139–142, 201–204, 213 **TRANSPARENCIES/TECHNOLOGY** Lab Generator: Energy Conversions; Relative Humidity, Design A Weather Center; Weathering; Estimating Wind Speed; Wind Power; Air Pressure; Testing Soil; Environmental Conditions; Creating Stream Features

Standards	Primary Citations	Supporting Citations
6.7.c Construct appropriate graphs from data and develop qualitative statements about the relationships between variables.	PUPIL/TEACHER EDITION 23, **140–141, 251,** 403, **420–421, 425, 470, 481, R23–R27** Benchmark Tests: 1.20 CA Standards Review and Practice: 61–62	PUPIL/TEACHER EDITION 67, 519 (#3) PRINT COMPONENTS Unit Resource Books: The Earth System: 31, 62, 66, 109–110, 256, 261; Earth's Surface: 189–190; The Changing Earth: 139; Ecology and Resources: 52, 102, 122, 191–192, 201, 204, 208 Lab Manual: 21–26, 31–36, 41–42, 47, 51, 55, 58, 62, 103–106, 189 TRANSPARENCIES/TECHNOLOGY Science Toolkit: A17–A20, A33–34, E1–E6, E11–16 Lab Generator: Energy Transfer; Solar Energy; Insulators; Design a Weather Center; Earthquake Depths; Climate; Environmental Conditions; Wind Power; Solar Houses; Species Interactions
6.7.d Communicate the steps and results from an investigation in written reports and oral presentations.	PUPIL/TEACHER EDITION **5, 16–17, 56–57, 100–101, 140–141, 168–169, 204–205, 236–237, 276–277, 324–325, 354–355, 373, 382–383, 420–421, 480–481, 514–515, R33–R34** Benchmark Tests: 2.17 CA Standards Review and Practice: 63–64	PUPIL/TEACHER EDITION 72–75, CA23, CA29, 261 PRINT RESOURCES Unit Resource Books: All Units: 5–10, All Chapter Investigations Lab Manual: 29–30, 39–40, 47, 51, 55, 65–72, 77–84, 91–98, 103–110, 115–122, 127–134, 139–146, 153–160, 165–172, 177–184, 191–198, 201–208, 213–220, 225–232 TRANSPARENCIES/TECHNOLOGY Science Toolkit: A23–A24, A35–A38, D12–D35 Lab Generator: All Chapter Investigations
6.7.e Recognize whether evidence is consistent with a proposed explanation.	PUPIL/TEACHER EDITION **56–57, 100–101, 261, 276–277, 514–515, R7** Benchmark Tests: 4.29, 2.23 CA Standards Review and Practice: 65–66	PUPIL/TEACHER EDITION CA20, CA29 PRINT RESOURCES Unit Resource Books: The Earth System: 3–4, 114, 118, 123, 127, 187, 191; The Changing Earth: 5–6, 66–69; Ecology and Resources: 256, 260, 265, 268 Lab Manual: 17–18, 37–38, 48, 52, 56, 58, 77–84, 91–94, 153–156, 225–232 TRANSPARENCIES/TECHNOLOGY Science Toolkit: A39–A40 Lab Generator: Modeling Solar Energy; Observing Convection; Relative Humidity; Convection Currents and Plate Movement; Cleaning Oil Spills; Pollutants on the Move

Standards		Primary Citations	Supporting Citations
6.7.f	**Read a topographic map and a geologic map for evidence provided on the maps and construct and interpret a simple scale map.**	PUPIL/TEACHER EDITION 5, 151, 156–158, **159, 163,** 164, **164–165, 166,** 167, 168–169, 178 (#19–23), 179, 211, **R76** Benchmark Tests: 2.10, 2.15, 2.25, 3.30, 4.30 CA Standards Review and Practice: 67–68	PUPIL/TEACHER EDITION 155, 160–162, 162 (#1–3), 167 (#1–3), 170–174, 174 (#1–3), 175, 177 (#9–18), 178 (24–25, 31–33), 261 PRINT COMPONENTS Unit Resource Books: The Earth System: 7–8; Earth's Surface: 5–6, 13–18, 20–21, 22, 25–30, 31–32, 35–40, 41, 42, 45–47, 48–49, 50–68, 104–105, 109, 110, 111, 140; The Changing Earth: 9–10 Modified Lesson Plans for English Learners: 19–21, 25 Lab Manual: 113–114, 115–118, 125 TRANSPARENCIES/TECHNOLOGY Unit Transparency Books: Earth's Surface, T33–40 Lab Generator: California Natural Resources; Topographical Maps; Make a Map by Triangulation; Landslide Areas Content Review: 5.1, 5.2, 5.3, 6.4 Power Presentations: 5.1, 5.2, 5.3, 6.4
6.7.g	**Interpret events by sequence and time from natural phenomena (e.g., the relative ages of rocks and intrusions).**	PUPIL/TEACHER EDITION **191–197,** 199, **200–204,** 204–205, **205, 225,** 238, 244, **270–275,** 278–284, **292, R62–R63** Benchmark Tests: 2.24 CA Standards Review and Practice: 69–70	PUPIL/TEACHER EDITION 128–129, 341, 344 PRINT COMPONENTS Unit Resource Books: Earth's Surface: 83–91, 94–101, 121–129, 130–138; The Changing Earth: 24–31 Modified Lesson Plans for English Learners: 23–24, 31 Lab Manual: 127–130 TRANSPARENCIES/TECHNOLOGY Unit Transparency Books: Earth's Surface, T41–48; The Changing Earth, T57–64 Lab Generator: Weathering; Modeling Rock Formations Content Review: 6.2, 6.3, 8.2 Power Presentations: 6.2, 6.3, 8.2

Standards	Primary Citations	Supporting Citations
6.7.h Identify changes in natural phenomena over time without manipulating the phenomena (e.g., a tree limb, a grove of trees, a stream, a hillslope).	**PUPIL/TEACHER EDITION** 238, **239–240,** 240, **241–243,** 244, **248–249,** 249, **250–251,** 297, 373, 403, 434–435 Benchmark Tests: 3.29 CA Standards Review and Practice: 71–72	**PUPIL/TEACHER EDITION** 243 (#2–3), 250 (#3), 254 (#26–31, 35), 436 (#2) **PRINT COMPONENTS** Unit Resource Books: Earth's Surface: 171–172; Ecology and Resources: 9–10, 112 Lab Manual: 136–137 **TRANSPARENCIES/ TECHNOLOGY** Unit Transparency Books: Earth's Surface, T49–T56; Ecology and Resources, T89–T96 Lab Generator: Longshore Drift; Kettle Lake Formation Content Review: 7.3, 12.3

CALIFORNIA SCIENCE CONTENT STANDARDS

Lesson-by-Lesson Correlations

Section or Feature	Standard
Unifying Principles	6.1.a, 6.3.b, 6.4.a, 6.4.c, 6.5.a, 6.5.b
The Nature of Science	6.7.a, 6.7.b, 6.7.d, 6.7.e
The Nature of Technology	6.7.b
Using the Tools of Science	6.7.a, 6.7.b, 6.7.d, 6.7.e
Unit 1 The Earth System	
Frontiers in Science Dust in the Air	6.4.e, 6.5.b, 6.7.f, 6.7.a, 6.7.d
Chapter 1 Energy and Change	
1.1 Change occurs as energy is transferred.	6.3.a, 6.3.b, 6.5.a, 6.7.b, 6.7.d
1.2 Radiation transfers energy.	6.3.d, 6.4.b, 6.7.c
1.3 Heat energy flows from warmer to cooler areas.	6.3.a, 6.3.c, 6.4.d
Chapter 1 Review/Standards-Based Assessment	6.3.c, 6.4.d
Math in Science Visible Light	6.4.b, Math 6.NS.1.1
Science on the Job Cooking and Heat	6.3.c
Chapter 2 Energy in the Earth System	
2.1 The Earth system has four major parts.	6.1.b, 6.2.d
2.2 The Sun provides energy to the Earth system.	6.3.d, 6.4.a, 6.4.b, 6.4.d, 6.7.a, 6.7.d, 6.7.e
2.3 Energy is transferred within the Earth system.	6.3.d, 6.4.a, 6.4.c, 6.4.d, 6.4.e
Chapter 2 Review/Standards-Based Assessment	6.4.a
California Close-Up An Earth-Moving Force	6.1.a, 6.1.d, 6.1.g
Math in Science Carbon Dioxide Levels	6.7.c, Math 6.MS.1.1
Timelines in Science Temperature and Heat	6.3.a, 6.3.c, 6.3.d, 6.7.d

Section or Feature	Standard
Chapter 3 Weather Patterns	
3.1 Air pressure varies in the atmosphere.	6.4.e
3.2 The atmosphere has wind patterns.	6.4.a, 6.4.e
3.3 Most clouds forms as air rises and cools.	6.4.a, 6.4.e, 6.7.a, 6.7.b, 6.7.d, 6.7.e
3.4 Water falls to Earth's surface as precipitation.	6.4.a, 6.4.e
Chapter 3 Review/Standards-Based Assessment	6.4.a, 6.4.e
Math in Science Navigate the Jet Stream	6.4.d, 6.4.e, Math 6.NS.2.3
Extreme Science Caught Inside a Thunderhead	6.4.e
Chapter 4 Weather Fronts and Storms	
4.1 Weather changes as air masses move.	6.4.e
4.2 Low-pressure systems can become storms.	6.3.a, 6.4.e
4.3 Vertical air motion can cause severe storms.	6.4.d, 6.4.e
4.4 Weather forecasters use advanced technologies.	6.4.e, 6.7.b, 6.7.c, 6.7.d
Chapter 4 Review/Standards-Based Assessment	6.4.d, 6.4.e
Math in Science Movement of a Front	6.4.e, Math 6.NS.1.2, Math 6.AF.2.2
Think Science What Type of Weather Buried This Truck?	6.2.d
Unit 2 Earth's Surface	
Frontiers in Science Remote Sensing	6.1.b, 6.2.a, 6.3.d, 6.4.b, 6.7.f
Chapter 5 Views of Earth Today	
5.1 Maps and globes are models of Earth.	6.6.c, 6.7.f
5.2 Topographic maps show the shape of the land.	6.2.a, 6.7.d, 6.7.f
5.3 Technology is used to map Earth.	6.7.f
Chapter 5 Review/Standards-Based Assessment	6.7.f

Lesson-by-Lesson Correlations

Section or Feature	Standard
Math in Science How Far Is It?	6.7.f, Math 6.NS.1.3
California Close-Up The Big Picture	6.1.f
Chapter 6 Mineral and Rocks	
6.1 Minerals are all around us.	6.1.b
6.2 Rocks form in different ways.	6.1.b, 6.2.a, 6.7.g
6.3 Natural processes break down rocks.	6.2.a, 6.7.b, 6.7.c, 6.7.d, 6.7.g
6.4 Geologic maps show Earth's surface features.	6.7.f
Chapter 6 Review/Standards-Based Assessment	6.1.b, 6.2.a
Math in Science Minerals in Rocks	Math 6.NS.2.4
Connecting Sciences Coral Polyps Rock!	6.5.b
California Close-Up Gold Fever!	6.6.c
Timelines in Science The Story of Fossils	6.1.a, 6.1.e
Chapter 7 Erosion and Deposition	
7.1 Processes wear down and build up Earth's surface.	6.2.a, 6.2.d, 6.7.g
7.2 Moving water shapes the land.	6.2.a, 6.2.b, 6.2.d, 6.7.b, 6.7.d
7.3 Waves and wind shape land.	6.2.c, 6.2.d, 6.7.g, 6.7.h
7.4 Glaciers carve land and move sediments.	6.2.a, 6.7.h
Chapter 7 Review/Standards-Based Assessment	6.2.a, 6.2.b, 6.2.c, 6.2.d, 6.7.h
California Close-Up The Changing Shoreline	6.2.c
Math in Science Snow Line Elevation and Latitude	6.2.a, 6.7.c, Math 6.MR.2.4

Section or Feature	Standard
Unit 3 The Changing Earth	
Frontiers in Science Studying Volcanoes with Satellites	6.1.d, 6.2.d, 6.7.b, 6.7.d, 6.7.e, 6.7.f
Chapter 8 Plate Tectonics	
8.1 Earth has several layers.	6.1.a, 6.1.b, 6.7.a
8.2 Continents change position over time.	6.1.a, 6.1.b, 6.1.c, 6.1.f, 6.3.c, 6.7.a, 6.7.d, 6.7.e, 6.7.g
8.3 Plates move apart.	6.1.a, 6.1.b, 6.1.d, 6.1.e, 6.7.g
8.4 Plates converge or scrape past each other.	6.1.a, 6.1.e, 6.1.f, 6.7.g
Chapter 8 Review/Standards-Based Assessment	6.1.a, 6.1.c, 6.1.d, 6.1.e, 6.1.f, 6.7.h
Math in Science Tracking Tectonic Plates	6.1.a, 6.1.c, Math 6.NS.2.2, Math 6.NS.2.3
Think Science What on Earth is Happening Here?	6.1.e
Chapter 9 Earthquakes	
9.1 Earthquakes occur along faults.	6.1.a, 6.1.b, 6.1.d, 6.1.e, 6.1.f
9.2 Earthquakes release energy.	6.1.a, 6.1.e, 6.1.g, 6.3.a
9.3 Earthquake damage can be reduced.	6.1.d, 6.1.g, 6.2.d, 6.3.a, 6.7.a, 6.7.d
Chapter 9 Review/Standards-Based Assessment	6.1.a, 6.1.b, 6.1.d, 6.1.f, 6.1.g, 6.3.a
Extreme Science When Earth Shakes	6.1.e, 6.2.d
Math in Science Earthquake Energy	6.1.a, 6.1.c, Math 6.NS.2.3, Math 6.NS.2.6
Timelines in Science History of the Earth System	6.1.a, 6.4.a, 6.5.e, 6.6.a
Chapter 10 Mountains and Volcanoes	
10.1 Movement of rock builds mountains.	6.1.a, 6.1.b, 6.1.c, 6.1.e, 6.1.f, 6.7.g
10.2 Volcanoes form as molten lava erupts.	6.1.b, 6.1.d, 6.1.e, 6.7.a, 6.7.d
10.3 Volcanoes affect Earth's land, air, and water.	6.2.d, 6.3.c, 6.4.c, 6.6.a
Chapter 10 Review/Standards-Based Assessment	6.1.b, 6.1.d, 6.1.e, 6.1.f, 6.2.d

Lesson-by-Lesson Correlations

Section or Feature	Standard
Math in Science Comparing Mountain Heights	6.1.e, Math 6.SD.1.1, Math 6.SD.1.4
California Close-Up In Hot Water!	6.4.c
Unit 4 Ecology and Resources	
Frontiers in Science Ecosystems on Fire	6.5.b, 6.5.e, 6.6.b, 6.7.d, 6.7.h
Chapter 11 Ecosystems and Biomes	
11.1 Ecosystems support life.	6.5.a, 6.5.e, 6.7.b, 6.7.d
11.2 Matter cycles through ecosystems.	6.5.b
11.3 Energy flows through ecosystems.	6.5.a, 6.5.b
11.4 Biomes contain many ecosystems.	6.5.d, 6.7.c, 6.7.h
Chapter 11 Review/Standards-Based Assessment	6.5.a, 6.5.b, 6.5.d, 6.5.e
Math in Science Temperature and the Water Cycle	6.2.a, 6.3.c, Math 6.NS.2.3
Connecting Sciences Biomagnification	6.5.b
Chapter 12 Interactions Within Ecosystems	
12.1 Groups of living things interact within ecosystems.	6.5.c, 6.5.e, 6.7.b, 6.7.c, 6.7.d
12.2 Organisms can interact in different ways.	6.5.c, 6.5.e, 6.7.c
12.3 Ecosystems are always changing.	6.5.e, 6.7.h
Chapter 12 Review/Standards-Based Assessment	6.5.c, 6.5.d, 6.5.e
Think Science Where Are the Salamanders?	6.5.e
Math In Science Number of Births and Populations	6.5.e, Math 6.NS.2.1
Timelines in Science Wilderness Conservation	6.5.c, 6.5.d, 6.5.e

Section or Feature	Standard
Chapter 13 Natural Resources	
13.1 Natural resources support human activity.	6.6.a, 6.6.b, 6.6.c
13.2 Minerals and rocks are nonrenewable resources.	6.6.a, 6.6.b, 6.6.c
13.3 Resources can be conserved and recycled.	6.6.a, 6.6.b, 6.6.c
13.4 Resources can be converted to useful forms.	6.3.a, 6.6.a, 6.6.b, 6.7.a, 6.7.b, 6.7.c, 6.7.d
Chapter 13 Review/Standards-Based Assessment	6.3.a, 6.6.a, 6.6.b, 6.6.c
California Close-Up Feeling Thirsty?	6.6.b
Science on the Job Geometry for Gems	6.6.c
Math in Science Tracking Contaminants	6.7.c, Math 6.MR.2.4
Chapter 14 Human Impact on Ecosystems	
14.1 Human population growth presents challenges.	6.5.e, 6.6.b
14.2 Human activities affect the environment.	6.5.e, 6.6.a, 6.6.b
14.3 People are working to protect ecosystems.	6.6.a, 6.6.b, 6.6.c, 6.7.a, 6.7.d, 6.7.e
Chapter 14 Review/Standards-Based Assessment	6.6.a, 6.7.c
California Close-Up Burn On!	6.5.e
Math in Science How Much Water?	6.6.b, Math 6.MG.1.2, Math 6.MG.1.3
California Resources	
Student Resource Handbooks	6.7.a, 6.7.b, 6.7.c, 6.7.d, 6.7.e
Appendix	6.1.a, 6.6.b, 6.6.c, 6.7.f, 6.7.g

Unit 1 *The Earth System* Pacing Guide

The following pacing guide gives suggested times for covering the units and chapters of McDougal Littell Science in 166 days of classroom teaching, allowing the remaining time for review, testing, and special projects. All of the 6th grade California Science Content Standards are covered in these materials.

	CLASSROOM INSTRUCTION		CALIFORNIA CONTENT STANDARDS
	TOTAL TIME (MINUTES)	HANDS-ON ACTIVITIES (MINUTES)	
Frontiers in Science: Dust in the Air	45		6.4e, 6.5b, 6.7a, 6.7d, 6.7f
Chapter 1 Energy and Change			
Explore the Big Idea	50	50	6.3.a
1.1 Change occurs as energy is transferred.	105	15	6.3.a, 6.3.b, 6.5.a, 6.7.b
Chapter Investigation	45	40	6.3.a, 6.3.b, 6.4.d, 6.7.b, 6.7.d
1.2 Radiation transfers energy.	115	25	6.3.d, 6.4.b, 6.7.c
1.3 Heat energy flows from warmer to cooler areas.	115	25	6.3.a, 6.3.c, 6.4.d
Chapter 1 Review/Standards-Based Assessment	45		6.3.c, 6.4.d
Chapter 2 Energy in the Earth System			
Explore the Big Idea	20	20	6.4.e
2.1 The Earth system has four major parts.	105	15	6.1.a, 6.1.b, 6.1.d, 6.1.g, 6.2.d
2.2 The Sun provides energy to the Earth system.	110	20	6.3.d, 6.4.a, 6.4.b, 6.4.d, 6.7.a, 6.7.e
Chapter Investigation	45	40	6.3.d, 6.4.a, 6.4.b, 6.7.a, 6.7.d, 6.7.e
2.3 Energy is transferred within the Earth system.	120	30	6.3.d, 6.4.a, 6.4.c, 6.4.d, 6.4.e, 6.7.c
Chapter 2 Review/Standards-Based Assessment	45		6.3.d, 6.4.a, 6.4.b, 6.4.d
Timelines in Science: About Temperature and Heat	45		6.3.a, 6.3.c, 6.3.d, 6.7.d
Chapter 3 Weather Patterns			
Explore the Big Idea	30	30	6.3.a, 6.3.c
3.1 Air pressure varies in the atmosphere.	115	25	6.4.e
3.2 The atmosphere has wind patterns.	110	20	6.4.a, 6.4.d, 6.4.e
3.3 Most clouds form as air rises and cools.	105	15	6.4.a, 6.4.e, 6.7.a, 6.7.b, 6.7.d, 6.7.e
Chapter Investigation	45	40	6.4.e, 6.7.a, 6.7.b, 6.7.d, 6.7.e
3.4 Water falls to Earth's surface as precipitation.	105	15	6.4.a, 6.4.e
Chapter 3 Review/Standards-Based Assessment	45		6.4.a, 6.4.e
Chapter 4 Weather Fronts and Storms			
Explore the Big Idea	25	25	6.4.e
4.1 Weather changes as air masses move.	130	40	6.4.e
4.2 Low-pressure systems can become storms.	110	20	6.3.a, 6.4.e
4.3 Vertical air motion can cause severe storms.	110	20	6.2.d, 6.4.d, 6.4.e
4.4 Weather forecasters use advanced technologies.	100	10	6.4.e, 6.7.b, 6.7.c
Chapter Investigation	45	40	6.4.e, 6.7.b, 6.7.d
Chapter 4 Review/Standards-Based Assessment	45		6.3.d, 6.4.a, 6.4.b, 6.4.d
Total Days for Unit	**47**	**13**	

Unit 2 *Earth's Surface* Pacing Guide

	CLASSROOM INSTRUCTION TOTAL TIME (MINUTES)	HANDS-ON ACTIVITIES (MINUTES)	CALIFORNIA CONTENT STANDARDS
Frontiers in Science: Remote Sensing	45		
Chapter 5 Views of Earth Today			
Explore the Big Idea	40	40	6.2.a, 6.1.b
5.1 Maps and globes are models of Earth.	130	40	6.6.c, 6.7.f
5.2 Topographic maps show the shape of the land.	100	10	6.2.a, 6.7.f
Chapter Investigation	45	40	6.2.a, 6.7.d, 6.7.f
5.3 Technology is used to map Earth.	90		6.1.f, 6.7.f
Chapter 5 Review/Standards-Based Assessment	45		6.7.f
Chapter 6 Minerals and Rocks			
Explore the Big Idea	30	30	6.1.b
6.1 Minerals are all around us.	120	30	6.1.b
6.2 Rocks form in different ways.	120	30	6.1.b, 6.2, 6.2.a, 6.7.g
6.3 Natural processes break down rocks.	110	20	6.2, 6.2.a, 6.5.b, 6.7.b, 6.7.c, 6.7.d, 6.7.g
Chapter Investigation	45	40	6.2, 6.7.b, 6.7.c, 6.7.d
6.4 Geologic maps show Earth's surface features.	110	20	6.6, 6.7.f
Chapter 6 Review/Standards-Based Assessment	45		6.1.b, 6.2.a
Timelines in Science: The Story of Fossils	45		
Chapter 7 Erosion and Deposition			
Explore the Big Idea	20	20	6.2.a, 6.2.c
7.1 Processes wear down and build up Earth's surface.	115	25	6.2.a, 6.2.d, 6.7.g
7.2 Moving water shapes land.	100	10	6.2.a, 6.2.b, 6.2.d, 6.7.b
Chapter Investigation	45	40	6.2.a, 6.2.b, 6.7.b, 6.7.d
7.3 Waves and wind shape land.	105	15	6.2.c, 6.2.d, 6.7.g, 6.7.h
7.4 Glaciers carve land and move sediments.	125	35	6.2.a, 6.7.c, 6.7.h
Chapter 7 Review/Standards-Based Assessment			6.2.a, 6.2.b, 6.2.c, 6.2.d, 6.7.h
Total Days for Unit	**36**	**10**	

Unit 3 *The Changing Earth* Pacing Guide

	CLASSROOM INSTRUCTION TOTAL TIME (MINUTES)	HANDS-ON ACTIVITIES (MINUTES)	CALIFORNIA CONTENT STANDARDS
Frontiers in Science: Studying Volcanoes with Satellites	45		6.1.d, 6.2.d, 6.7.b, 6.7.d, 6.7.e, 6.7.f
Chapter 8 Plate Tectonics			
Explore the Big Idea	30	30	6.1.b, 6.3.c
8.1 Earth has several layers.	120	30	6.1.a, 6.1.b, 6.7.a
8.2 Continents change position over time.	110	20	6.1.a, 6.1.b, 6.1.c, 6.1.f, 6.3.c, 6.7.a, 6.7.d, 6.7.e, 6.7.g
Chapter Investigation	45	40	6.1.c, 6.3.c, 6.6.a, 6.7.c, 6.7.d
8.3 Plates move apart.	125	35	6.1.a, 6.1.b, 6.1.c, 6.1.d, 6.1.e, 6.7.g
8.4 Plates converge or scrape past each other.	130	40	6.1.a, 6.1.e, 6.1.f, 6.7.g
Chapter 8 Review/Standards-Based Assessment	45		6.1.a, 6.1.c, 6.1.d, 6.1.e, 6.1.f, 6.7.h
Chapter 9 Earthquakes			
Explore the Big Idea	25	25	6.1.b, 6.1.d
9.1 Earthquakes occur along faults.	115	25	6.1.a, 6.1.b, 6.1.d, 6.1.e, 6.1.f, 6.2.d
9.2 Earthquakes release energy.	120	30	6.1.a, 6.1.c, 6.1.e, 6.1.g, 6.3.a
9.3 Earthquake damage can be reduced.	100	10	6.1.d, 6.1.g, 6.2.d, 6.3.a
Chapter Investigation	45	40	6.1.d, 6.2.d, 6.3.a, 6.7.a, 6.7.d
Chapter 9 Review/Standards-Based Assessment	45		6.1.a, 6.1.b, 6.1.d, 6.1.f, 6.1.g, 6.3.a
Timelines in Science: History of the Earth System	45		6.1.a, 6.4.a, 6.5.e, 6.6.a
Chapter 10 Mountains and Volcanoes			
Explore the Big Idea	25	25	6.1.d, 6.1.e
10.1 Movement of rock builds mountains.	115	25	6.1.a, 6.1.b, 6.1.c, 6.1.e, 6.1.f, 6.7.g
10.2 Volcanoes form as molten lava erupts.	100	10	6.1.b, 6.1.d, 6.1.e, 6.7.a
Chapter Investigation	45	40	6.1.d, 6.7.a, 6.7.d
10.3 Volcanoes affect Earth's land, air, and water.	115	25	6.2.d, 6.3.c, 6.4.c, 6.6.a
Chapter 10 Review/Standards-Based Assessment			6.1.b, 6.1.d, 6.1.e, 6.1.f, 6.2.d
Total Days for Unit	**35**	**10**	

Unit 4 *Ecology and Resources* Pacing Guide

	CLASSROOM INSTRUCTION TOTAL TIME (MINUTES)	HANDS-ON ACTIVITIES (MINUTES)	CALIFORNIA CONTENT STANDARDS
Frontiers in Science: Ecosystems on Fire	45		6.5.b, 6.5.e, 6.6.b, 6.7.d, 6.7.h
Chapter 11 Ecosystems and Biomes			
Explore the Big Idea	30	30	6.5.a
11.1 Ecosystems support life.	100	10	6.5.a, 6.5.e, 6.7.b
Chapter Investigation	45	40	6.5.e, 6.7.b, 6.7.d
11.2 Matter cycles through ecosystems.	115	25	6.5.b
11.3 Energy flows through ecosystems.	130	40	6.2.a, 6.3.c, 6.5.a, 6.5.b
11.4 Biomes contain many ecosystems.	110	20	6.5.b, 6.5.d, 6.7.c, 6.7.h
Chapter 11 Review/Standards-Based Assessment	45		6.5.a, 6.5.b, 6.5.d, 6.5.e
Chapter 12 Interactions Within Ecosystems			
Explore the Big Idea	20	20	6.5.a, 6.5.c
12.1 Groups of living things interact within ecosystems.	90		6.5.c, 6.5.e, 6.7.b, 6.7.c
Chapter Investigation	45	40	6.5.e, 6.7.b, 6.7.c, 6.7.d
12.2 Organisms can interact in different ways.	120	30	6.5.c, 6.5.e, 6.7.c
12.3 Ecosystems are always changing.	130	40	6.5.e, 6.7.h
Chapter 12 Review/Standards-Based Assessment	45		6.5.c, 6.5.d, 6.5.e
Timelines in Science: Wilderness Conservation	45		6.5.c, 6.5.d, 6.5.e
Chapter 13 Natural Resources			
Explore the Big Idea	55	55	6.6.a, 6.6.b
13.1 Natural resources support human activity.	105	15	6.6.a, 6.6.b, 6.6.c
13.2 Minerals and rocks are nonrenewable resources.	125	35	6.6.a, 6.6.b, 6.6.c
13.3 Resources can be conserved and recycled.	120	30	6.6.a, 6.6.b, 6.6.c
13.4 Resources can be converted to useful forms.	90		6.4.a, 6.4.e
Chapter Investigation	45	40	6.6.a, 6.7.a, 6.7.c, 6.7.d
Chapter 13 Review/Standards-Based Assessment	45		6.3.a, 6.6.a, 6.7.a, 6.7.c
Chapter 14 Human Impact on Ecosystems			
Explore the Big Idea	30	30	6.5.e
14.1 Human population growth presents challenges.	130	40	6.5.e, 6.6.b
14.2 Human activities affect the environment.	90		6.5.e, 6.6.a, 6.6.b
14.3 People are working to protect ecosystems.	105	15	6.6.a, 6.6.b, 6.6.c, 6.7.a, 6.7.e
Chapter Investigation	45	40	6.6.a, 6.7.a, 6.7.d, 6.7.e
Chapter 14 Review/Standards-Based Assessment	45		6.6.a, 6.7.c
Total Days for Unit	**48**	**13**	

Planning the Chapter

Complete planning support precedes each chapter.

Previewing Content

- Section-by-section science background notes for each chapter
- Common Misconceptions notes

CHAPTER

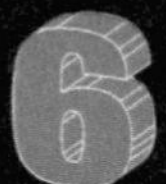

Minerals and Rocks

Earth Science
UNIFYING PRINCIPLES

PRINCIPLE 1	PRINCIPLE 2	PRINCIPLE 3	PRINCIPLE 4
Heat energy inside Earth and radiation from the Sun provide energy for Earth's processes.	Physical forces, such as gravity, affect the movement of all matter on Earth and throughout the universe.	Matter and er among Earth's soil, atmosphe and living thi	

Unit:
Earth's Surface
BIG IDEAS

CHAPTER 5 Views of Earth Today	CHAPTER 6 Minerals and Rocks	CHAPTER 7 Erosion and Deposition
Modern technology has changed the way we view and map Earth.	Minerals and rocks are basic building blocks of Earth.	Water, wind, and ice shape Earth's surface.

CHAPTER 6
KEY CONCEPTS

SECTION 1	SECTION 2	SECTION
Minerals are all around us. 1. Minerals and rocks are part of daily life. 2. Minerals have four characteristics. 3. Minerals are grouped according to composition. 4. Most rocks are made of minerals.	**Rocks form in different ways.** 1. Our world is built of rocks. 2. Rocks are classified by how they form. 3. Rocks can change into other types of rocks.	**Natural proces down rocks.** 1. Weathering features over 2. Mechanical physical char 3. Chemical we the mineral 4. Weathering rates.

The Big Idea Flow Chart is available on p. T41 in the **TRANSPARENCY BOOK.**

Content

SECTION

Minerals are all around us. pp. 183–189

1. Minerals have four characteristics.
Minerals are the building blocks of most rocks. Minerals differ from **rocks** by having uniform compositions and orderly internal structures. The four characteristics of minerals are explained in the following chart:

Four Characteristics of Minerals

SECTION 2

1. Ou
Ear
last
suc
um
are

Previewing Content

SECTION

Natural processes break down rocks. pp. 199–205

1. Weathering helps change Earth's features over time.
Weathering is the process by which natural forces break down rock into particles called *sediments*. The two main types of weathering are mechanical and chemical. **Mechanical weathering** involves a physical change in a rock. **Chemical weathering** changes the composition of rock.

2. Mechanical weathering produces physical changes in rocks.
The agents of mechanical weathering include
- ice wedging
- pressure release
- plant root growth
- abrasion

When water freezes in the cracks and pores of rocks, it expands, and ice breaks apart the rocks. Pressure release occurs when intrusive rocks are pushed to the surface; pressure on the rock is released and layers or sheets of rock gradually break off.

Plants can take root in cracks of rocks and wedge the cracks open. Moving water can break up rocks by abrasion, which is the process of wearing down an object by friction.

3. Chemical weathering changes the mineral composition of rocks.
When certain minerals in rock react with air and water, they dissolve or are changed into different minerals. For example, small amounts of atmospheric carbon dioxide can react with precipitation to form a weak acid. This acidic rainwater can move through soil and break down minerals in rocks.

4. Weathering occurs at different rates.
When a rock is broken down, more of its surface area is exposed to air and water. As surface area increases, rates of weathering increase. Rates of weathering vary for different types of rocks—the igneous rock granite, for example, weathers more slowly than a softer rock, such as limestone. Because water is needed for chemical weathering to occur, and heat increases the rate of chemical weathering, chemical weathering occurs faster in wet, hot regions than it does in cold, dry regions.

SECTION 4
Geologic maps show Earth's surface features. pp. 206–213

1. Geologic maps show information about rocks at and near Earth's surface.
A **geologic map** is a type of map that shows geologic features at or near Earth's surface for a specific region. The features can include the types and ages of rocks, as well as geologic structures such as fracture patterns within rock layers, the direction and angle at which rock layers are tilted, and faults.

2. Geologic maps show information about resources and hazards.
Geologic maps are useful for evaluating potential resources and hazards that might be present in an area. Some examples of resources are oil or valuable minerals. Some examples of hazards are volcanoes (along with lava flow), landslides, and earthquakes.

Common Misconceptions

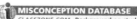

MISCONCEPTION DATABASE
CLASSZONE.COM Background on student misconceptions

DENSITY OF WATER Students may think that the density of water does not change when it freezes. In fact, when water freezes, it becomes less dense as it expands. This is why ice is a powerful agent of mechanical weathering—water in the pores of rocks can freeze, expand, and split rocks apart.

TE This misconception is addressed on p. 200.

CHANGES IN ROCKS Some students might think that rocks do not change or break down over time by natural processes. They may not understand that smaller stones are the result of larger rocks breaking apart or that something so seemingly strong and unchanging as a boulder can be dissolved or broken apart by something so seemingly "weak" as water.

TE This misconception is addressed on p. 201.

Previewing Chapter Resources

- Section-by-section listing of all print and technology resources
- Correlations to California Science Content Standards

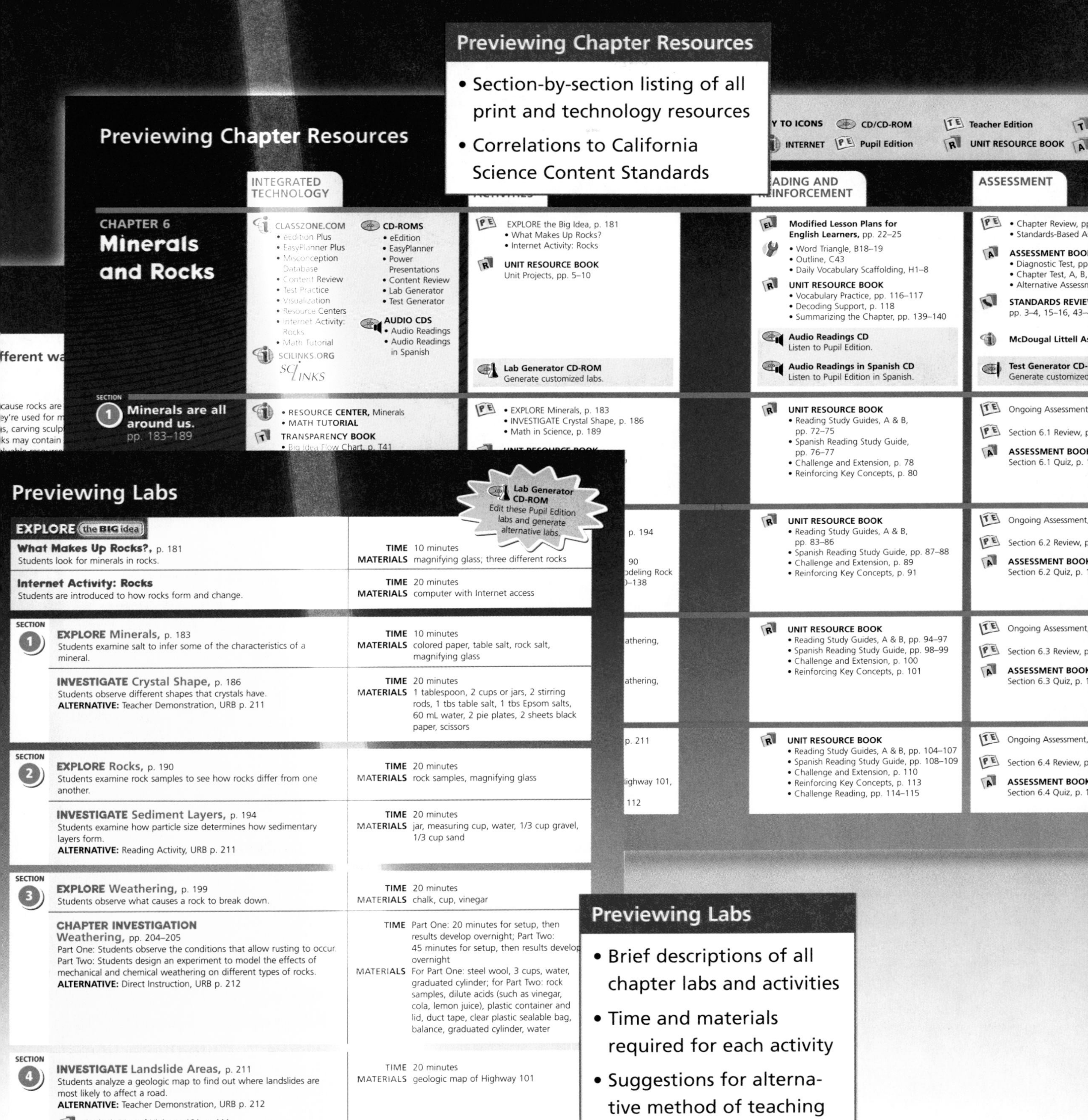

Previewing Chapter Resources

KEY TO ICONS: CD/CD-ROM · INTERNET · Pupil Edition · Teacher Edition · UNIT RESOURCE BOOK

	INTEGRATED TECHNOLOGY	ACTIVITIES	READING AND REINFORCEMENT	ASSESSMENT
CHAPTER 6 **Minerals and Rocks**	CLASSZONE.COM • eEdition Plus • EasyPlanner Plus • Misconception Database • Content Review • Test Practice • Visualization • Resource Centers • Internet Activity: Rocks • Math Tutorial SCILINKS.ORG **CD-ROMS** • eEdition • EasyPlanner • Power Presentations • Content Review • Lab Generator • Test Generator **AUDIO CDS** • Audio Readings • Audio Readings in Spanish	EXPLORE the Big Idea, p. 181 • What Makes Up Rocks? • Internet Activity: Rocks **UNIT RESOURCE BOOK** Unit Projects, pp. 5–10 **Lab Generator CD-ROM** Generate customized labs.	**Modified Lesson Plans for English Learners,** pp. 22–25 • Word Triangle, B18–19 • Outline, C43 • Daily Vocabulary Scaffolding, H1–8 **UNIT RESOURCE BOOK** • Vocabulary Practice, pp. 116–117 • Decoding Support, p. 118 • Summarizing the Chapter, pp. 139–140 **Audio Readings CD** Listen to Pupil Edition. **Audio Readings in Spanish CD** Listen to Pupil Edition in Spanish.	• Chapter Review, pp. • Standards-Based Ass **ASSESSMENT BOOK** • Diagnostic Test, pp. • Chapter Test, A, B, & • Alternative Assessme **STANDARDS REVIEW** pp. 3–4, 15–16, 43–44 McDougal Littell Ass **Test Generator CD-R** Generate customized
SECTION 1 **Minerals are all around us.** pp. 183–189	• RESOURCE CENTER, Minerals • MATH TUTORIAL **TRANSPARENCY BOOK** • Big Idea Flow Chart, p. T41	• EXPLORE Minerals, p. 183 • INVESTIGATE Crystal Shape, p. 186 • Math in Science, p. 189	**UNIT RESOURCE BOOK** • Reading Study Guides, A & B, pp. 72–75 • Spanish Reading Study Guide, pp. 76–77 • Challenge and Extension, p. 78 • Reinforcing Key Concepts, p. 80	Ongoing Assessment, Section 6.1 Review, p. **ASSESSMENT BOOK** Section 6.1 Quiz, p. 1
		p. 194 … 90 … odeling Rock …–138	**UNIT RESOURCE BOOK** • Reading Study Guides, A & B, pp. 83–86 • Spanish Reading Study Guide, pp. 87–88 • Challenge and Extension, p. 89 • Reinforcing Key Concepts, p. 91	Ongoing Assessment, Section 6.2 Review, p. **ASSESSMENT BOOK** Section 6.2 Quiz, p. 12
		athering, … athering,	**UNIT RESOURCE BOOK** • Reading Study Guides, A & B, pp. 94–97 • Spanish Reading Study Guide, pp. 98–99 • Challenge and Extension, p. 100 • Reinforcing Key Concepts, p. 101	Ongoing Assessment, Section 6.3 Review, p. **ASSESSMENT BOOK** Section 6.3 Quiz, p. 12
		p. 211 … ighway 101, … 112	**UNIT RESOURCE BOOK** • Reading Study Guides, A & B, pp. 104–107 • Spanish Reading Study Guide, pp. 108–109 • Challenge and Extension, p. 110 • Reinforcing Key Concepts, p. 113 • Challenge Reading, pp. 114–115	Ongoing Assessment, Section 6.4 Review, p. **ASSESSMENT BOOK** Section 6.4 Quiz, p. 12

Previewing Labs

Lab Generator CD-ROM: Edit these Pupil Edition labs and generate alternative labs.

	Activity	Time / Materials
EXPLORE the BIG idea	**What Makes Up Rocks?,** p. 181 Students look for minerals in rocks.	TIME 10 minutes MATERIALS magnifying glass; three different rocks
	Internet Activity: Rocks Students are introduced to how rocks form and change.	TIME 20 minutes MATERIALS computer with Internet access
SECTION 1	**EXPLORE Minerals,** p. 183 Students examine salt to infer some of the characteristics of a mineral.	TIME 10 minutes MATERIALS colored paper, table salt, rock salt, magnifying glass
	INVESTIGATE Crystal Shape, p. 186 Students observe different shapes that crystals have. **ALTERNATIVE:** Teacher Demonstration, URB p. 211	TIME 20 minutes MATERIALS 1 tablespoon, 2 cups or jars, 2 stirring rods, 1 tbs table salt, 1 tbs Epsom salts, 60 mL water, 2 pie plates, 2 sheets black paper, scissors
SECTION 2	**EXPLORE Rocks,** p. 190 Students examine rock samples to see how rocks differ from one another.	TIME 20 minutes MATERIALS rock samples, magnifying glass
	INVESTIGATE Sediment Layers, p. 194 Students examine how particle size determines how sedimentary layers form. **ALTERNATIVE:** Reading Activity, URB p. 211	TIME 20 minutes MATERIALS jar, measuring cup, water, 1/3 cup gravel, 1/3 cup sand
SECTION 3	**EXPLORE Weathering,** p. 199 Students observe what causes a rock to break down.	TIME 20 minutes MATERIALS chalk, cup, vinegar
	CHAPTER INVESTIGATION Weathering, pp. 204–205 Part One: Students observe the conditions that allow rusting to occur. Part Two: Students design an experiment to model the effects of mechanical and chemical weathering on different types of rocks. **ALTERNATIVE:** Direct Instruction, URB p. 212	TIME Part One: 20 minutes for setup, then results develop overnight; Part Two: 45 minutes for setup, then results develop overnight MATERIALS For Part One: steel wool, 3 cups, water, graduated cylinder; for Part Two: rock samples, dilute acids (such as vinegar, cola, lemon juice), plastic container and lid, duct tape, clear plastic sealable bag, balance, graduated cylinder, water
SECTION 4	**INVESTIGATE Landslide Areas,** p. 211 Students analyze a geologic map to find out where landslides are most likely to affect a road. **ALTERNATIVE:** Teacher Demonstration, URB p. 212 Geologic Map of Highway 101, p. 111	TIME 20 minutes MATERIALS geologic map of Highway 101

Additional INVESTIGATION, Modeling Rock Formation, A, B, & C, pp. 130–138; Teacher Instructions, pp. 211–212

Chapter 6: Minerals and Rocks 179D

Previewing Labs

- Brief descriptions of all chapter labs and activities
- Time and materials required for each activity
- Suggestions for alternative method of teaching each lab

Planning the Lesson

Point-of-use support for each lesson provides a wealth of teaching options.

1. Prepare

- Concept and vocabulary review
- Note-taking and vocabulary strategies

2. Focus

- Set Learning Goals
- 3-Minute Warm-Up

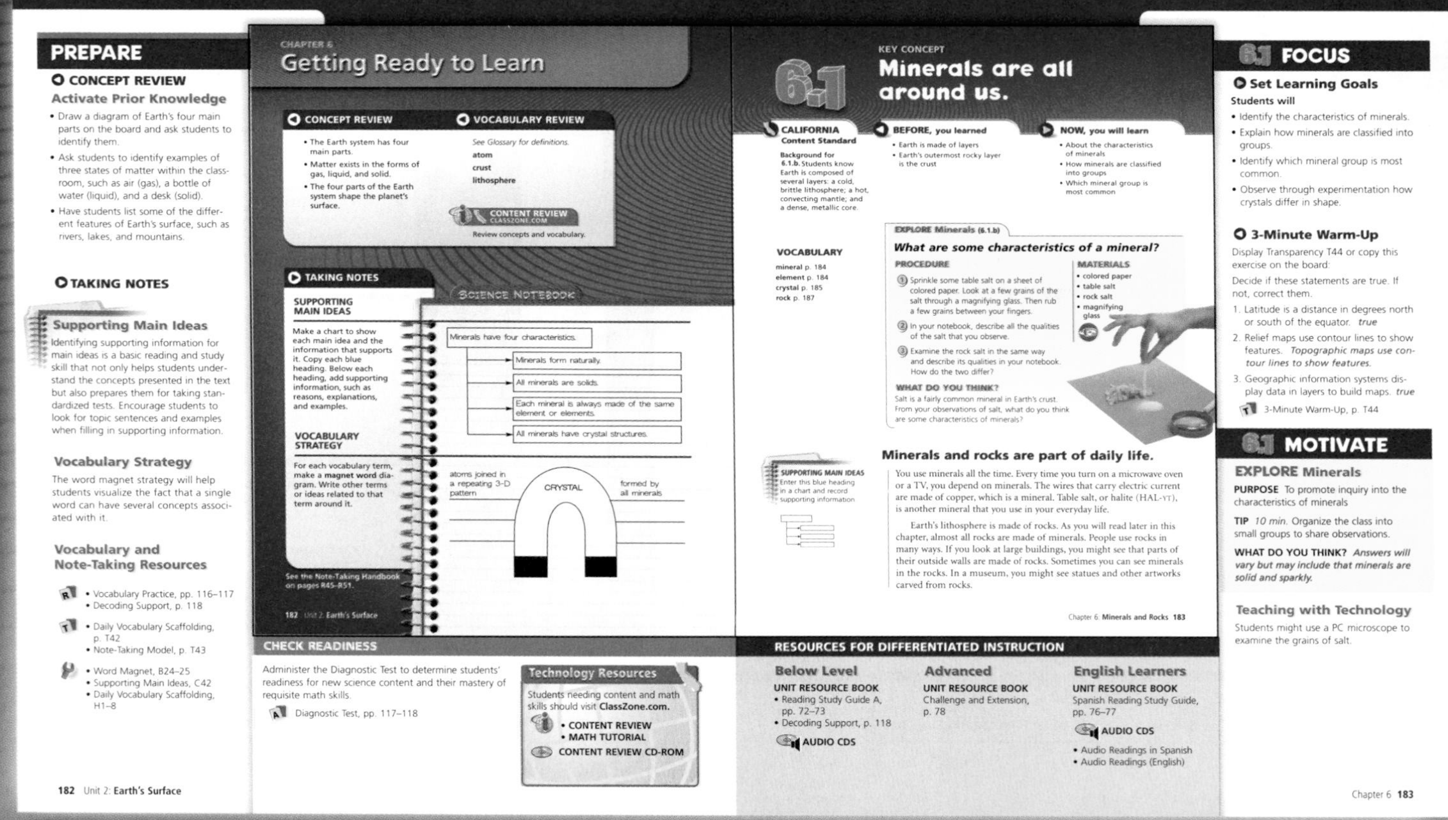

PREPARE

CONCEPT REVIEW

Activate Prior Knowledge

- Draw a diagram of Earth's four main parts on the board and ask students to identify them.
- Ask students to identify examples of three states of matter within the classroom, such as air (gas), a bottle of water (liquid), and a desk (solid).
- Have students list some of the different features of Earth's surface, such as rivers, lakes, and mountains.

TAKING NOTES

Supporting Main Ideas

Identifying supporting information for main ideas is a basic reading and study skill that not only helps students understand the concepts presented in the text but also prepares them for taking standardized tests. Encourage students to look for topic sentences and examples when filling in supporting information.

Vocabulary Strategy

The word magnet strategy will help students visualize the fact that a single word can have several concepts associated with it.

Vocabulary and Note-Taking Resources

- Vocabulary Practice, pp. 116–117
- Decoding Support, p. 118
- Daily Vocabulary Scaffolding, p. T42
- Note-Taking Model, p. T43
- Word Magnet, B24–25
- Supporting Main Ideas, C42
- Daily Vocabulary Scaffolding, H1–8

CHAPTER 6

Getting Ready to Learn

CONCEPT REVIEW

- The Earth system has four main parts.
- Matter exists in the forms of gas, liquid, and solid.
- The four parts of the Earth system shape the planet's surface.

VOCABULARY REVIEW

See Glossary for definitions.

atom

crust

lithosphere

CONTENT REVIEW CLASSZONE.COM

Review concepts and vocabulary.

TAKING NOTES

SUPPORTING MAIN IDEAS

Make a chart to show each main idea and the information that supports it. Copy each blue heading. Below each heading, add supporting information, such as reasons, explanations, and examples.

VOCABULARY STRATEGY

For each vocabulary term, make a magnet word diagram. Write other terms or ideas related to that term around it.

See the Note-Taking Handbook on pages R45–R51.

SCIENCE NOTEBOOK

Minerals have four characteristics.

Minerals form naturally.

All minerals are solids.

Each mineral is always made of the same element or elements.

All minerals have crystal structures.

atoms joined in a repeating 3-D pattern

CRYSTAL

formed by all minerals

182 Unit 2: Earth's Surface

CHECK READINESS

Administer the Diagnostic Test to determine students' readiness for new science content and their mastery of requisite math skills.

Diagnostic Test, pp. 117–118

Technology Resources

Students needing content and math skills should visit ClassZone.com.

- CONTENT REVIEW
- MATH TUTORIAL

CONTENT REVIEW CD-ROM

182 Unit 2: Earth's Surface

KEY CONCEPT

6.1 Minerals are all around us.

CALIFORNIA Content Standard

Background for 6.1.b. Students know Earth is composed of several layers: a cold, brittle lithosphere; a hot, convecting mantle; and a dense, metallic core.

BEFORE, you learned

- Earth is made of layers
- Earth's outermost rocky layer is the crust

NOW, you will learn

- About the characteristics of minerals
- How minerals are classified into groups
- Which mineral group is most common

VOCABULARY

mineral p. 184

element p. 184

crystal p. 185

rock p. 187

EXPLORE Minerals (6.1.b)

What are some characteristics of a mineral?

PROCEDURE

1. Sprinkle some table salt on a sheet of colored paper. Look at a few grains of the salt through a magnifying glass. Then rub a few grains between your fingers.
2. In your notebook, describe all the qualities of the salt that you observe.
3. Examine the rock salt in the same way and describe its qualities in your notebook. How do the two differ?

MATERIALS

- colored paper
- table salt
- rock salt
- magnifying glass

WHAT DO YOU THINK?

Salt is a fairly common mineral in Earth's crust. From your observations of salt, what do you think are some characteristics of minerals?

SUPPORTING MAIN IDEAS

Enter this blue heading in a chart and record supporting information.

Minerals and rocks are part of daily life.

You use minerals all the time. Every time you turn on a microwave oven or a TV, you depend on minerals. The wires that carry electric current are made of copper, which is a mineral. Table salt, or halite (HAL-YT), is another mineral that you use in your everyday life.

Earth's lithosphere is made of rocks. As you will read later in this chapter, almost all rocks are made of minerals. People use rocks in many ways. If you look at large buildings, you might see that parts of their outside walls are made of rocks. Sometimes you can see minerals in the rocks. In a museum, you might see statues and other artworks carved from rocks.

Chapter 6: Minerals and Rocks 183

RESOURCES FOR DIFFERENTIATED INSTRUCTION

Below Level

UNIT RESOURCE BOOK

- Reading Study Guide A, pp. 72–73
- Decoding Support, p. 118

AUDIO CDS

Advanced

UNIT RESOURCE BOOK

Challenge and Extension, p. 78

English Learners

UNIT RESOURCE BOOK

Spanish Reading Study Guide, pp. 76–77

AUDIO CDS

- Audio Readings in Spanish
- Audio Readings (English)

6.1 FOCUS

Set Learning Goals

Students will

- Identify the characteristics of minerals.
- Explain how minerals are classified into groups.
- Identify which mineral group is most common.
- Observe through experimentation how crystals differ in shape.

3-Minute Warm-Up

Display Transparency T44 or copy this exercise on the board:

Decide if these statements are true. If not, correct them.

1. Latitude is a distance in degrees north or south of the equator. *true*
2. Relief maps use contour lines to show features. *Topographic maps use contour lines to show features.*
3. Geographic information systems display data in layers to build maps. *true*

3-Minute Warm-Up, p. T44

6.1 MOTIVATE

EXPLORE Minerals

PURPOSE To promote inquiry into the characteristics of minerals

TIP *10 min.* Organize the class into small groups to share observations.

WHAT DO YOU THINK? *Answers will vary but may include that minerals are solid and sparkly.*

Teaching with Technology

Students might use a PC microscope to examine the grains of salt.

Chapter 6 183

3. Motivate

- Engaging entry into the section
- Explore activity or Think About question

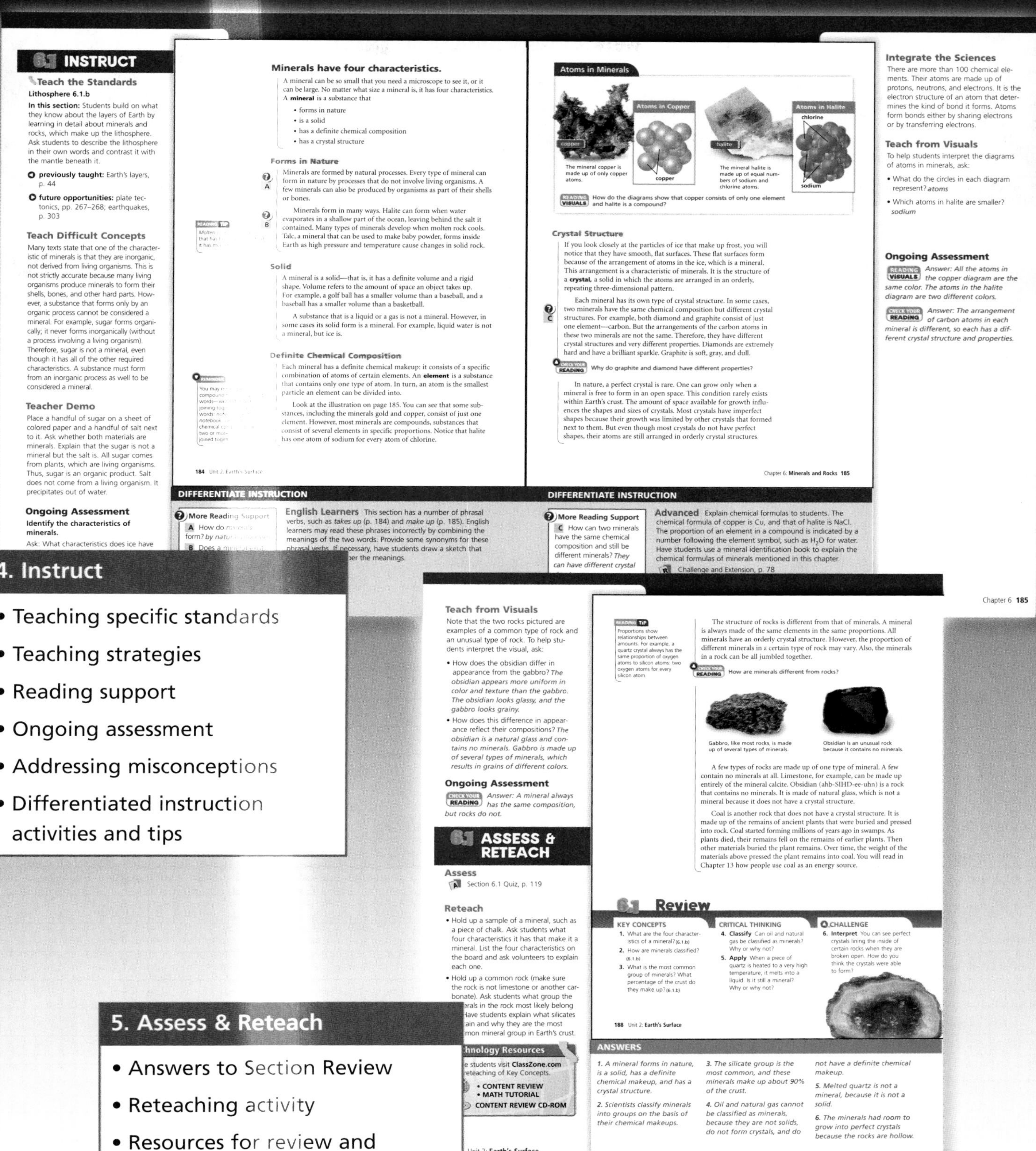
4. Instruct
• Teaching specific standards
• Teaching strategies
• Reading support
• Ongoing assessment
• Addressing misconceptions
• Differentiated instruction activities and tips
5. Assess & Reteach
• Answers to Section Review
• Reteaching activity
• Resources for review and assessment

Lab Materials List

The following charts list the consumables, nonconsumables, and equipment needed for all activities. Quantities are per group of four students. For consumable materials required in more than one lab, the quantity per group is the quantity needed for all labs in total. Lab aprons, goggles, water, books, paper, pens, pencils, and calculators are assumed to be available for all activities.

Materials kits are available. For more information, please call McDougal Littell at 1-800-323-5435.

Consumables

Description	Quantity per Group	Explore *page*	Investigate *page*	Chapter Investigation *page*
aluminum foil	18"	7	23	16
apple	1		45	
bag containing an assortment of items	1	489		
balloon	5	39, 77	81, 85	
bead, medium yellow	3		463	
bead, small blue, green, red	14		463	
can, empty aluminum with holes	1			16
can, metal	1		81	
caramel rice cake	1			16
cardboard, 4" x 4"	4		130	
cardboard, 10 cm x 10 cm	20		425	
cardboard, 12" x 12"	4	7		354
cardboard, thin, 15 cm x 15 cm	1			324
cardboard, stiff	1		117	
cardboard juice container, half-gallon	1			168
celery, leafy stalk	1	487		
chalk	1 piece	199		
clay, modeling	5 bricks	245	249	16, 168, 324
clay, modeling, in three or more colors	3 or more	337	289	
clear plastic sealable bag	1			204
clear plastic sheet (transparency)	1			168
cloth, cotton or felt	3" x 3"			100
cola	12 oz			204
cornstarch	40 mL			514
cotton ball	8			514
cotton rag	1			514
crouton	1			16
cup, clear plastic	18	29, 199, 265, 299, 431, 487	65, 117, 268	204
cup, foam	5		130	
cup, plastic	4	447	23	
cup, waste	1		29	
cup, paper	5	39	433	354

Description	Quantity per Group	Explore *page*	Investigate *page*	Chapter Investigation *page*
dish soap	40 mL			514
dowel rod, 1/4" diameter	12"			16
effervescent antacid tablet	1	346		
egg, hard-boiled and peeled	1	79		
feather	1			514
file folder	one half			480
film canister	1	346		
food coloring, red and blue	2 each	265, 487	117, 130	168, 276
fruit, slices	3		393	
garden soil	1 cup		393	
gravel	4.5 cups	194	65, 249, 268	354
hot dog	1	7		
ice cube containing sand and gravel	1	245		
ice cubes	18	115	126, 249	
leaves	3		393	
lemon juice	12 oz			204
matches, wooden	8	79	95	16, 276
milk carton, 1 pint	1			100
newspaper	2	316, 337		
newspaper weather map	1	134		
oatmeal box (with slit cut in side)	1	278		
oil, cooking	1 mL	7		
oil, vegetable	40 mL			514
paper, 8.5" x 11"	7	123, 155, 458, 466	14, 230, 270	
paper, black, 3" x 11"	2	447		
paper, black, 8" x 8"	4	186	51	
paper, black, 8.5" x 11"	1			420
paper, colored, 8.5" x 11"	1	183		
paper, squares, 3 cm x 3 cm	200		425	
paper, striped, 8.5" x 11"	1			278
paper clip, large	11	230		16
paper clip, small	1			480
paper, fastener, brass	1			480
paper, graph, 10" x 12"	4		403, 425	56, 140
paper napkins, square	6	286		
paper towel	3	245		420, 514
pebble	1	390		
pH test strip	2			382
pie plate, aluminum	4	186, 223		16
pill bug	6			420
pint carton	1			480
plant, potted	1	375		
plant, small potted	1	384		

Description	Quantity per Group	Explore *page*	Investigate *page*	Chapter Investigation *page*
plaster of Paris	375 mL			354
plastic bag, clear	1	384		
plastic container and lid	1			204
plastic knife	1	487		
plastic spoon	1	265		
plastic wrap, black and white	12"		23	
plastic wrap, clear, 16" long	3	115		
plastic wrap, 6" x 6"	2	447		
poster board, 11" x 17"	1		289	
pushpin	1			480
rice cake, caramel	1			16
rubber band	9	447	23, 81	100, 382
rubbing alcohol	40 mL			514
salt, Epsom	1 tbs	186		
salt, rock	3 oz	183		
salt, table	1.2 oz	183, 186, 265	117, 126	
sand	23.5 lb	316, 390	194, 249	236, 514
sand and gravel mixture	16 oz	223		
seashell, whole or pieces	1 oz		387	
seaweed	1 oz			514
seeds, radish	30		433	
shoebox lid	1			420
soil	2 lb, 6 oz	39	226	
soil, dry	1/2 cup			382
soil, dried sample	400 mL			382
soil, garden	1 cup		393	
soil, potting	2 cups	506	433	
spaghetti, dry	1 box			168
sponge	4	263		276, 514
steel wool	1 pad			204
stirring stick	2		268	354
stones	1/4 cup		393	
straw, clear	1		29, 81	480
string	42"	77	281	480
string, 3 different colors, each piece 60 cm long	180 cm		309	
sugar	1 1/4 tsp	431		
tape, transparent	80 cm	384	14, 51, 81, 230, 309	168, 278
tape, masking	1 roll		281, 303	16
tape, masking	126"		393, 425	480
tape, black	1 roll		51	204
tealight candles	2			276
tray, metal, 9" x 12" x 2"	2	226		

Description	Quantity per Group	Explore *page*	Investigate *page*	Chapter Investigation *page*
tube, cardboard (from paper towel roll)	1		51	
turmeric	1 tsp			514
thread	15 cm		14	
vinegar	16 oz	199		204
vinegar, white	1.5 oz		387	
washer	1	316		
water, hot	250 mL	26		
water, cold	100 mL	26		
water, room temperature	4 Tbsp		95	168
water, warm	900 mL	115, 431		
wild bird seed mix with sunflower seeds	1 lb		463	
window screening, 5" x 5"	1			382
wooden beads, colored	3 or 4 dozen		268	
wooden craft stick	1	301		
yarn	20'			514
yeast, dry	1 1/2 tsp	431		

Nonconsumables

Description	Quantity per Group	Explore *page*	Investigate *page*	Chapter Investigation *page*
balance, triple beam	1			16, 204
bar magnet	1		281	
barometer	1			140
beaker, 500 mL	1	26	117	514
beaker, 200 mL	1	26		
beaker, 100 mL	1		117, 387	514
block of wood, rectangular	2		303	
books	2 or 3		240	
bowl, 2 qt	1 or 2	39, 115, 390		100
bottle, glass	1	7, 39, 79		
bottle, 1L, clear plastic with cap	1		95, 393	
bottle, 2L, plastic	1			382
brick	2			276
bucket	1			236
calculator	1	466	492	
checkers	10	335		
clock with second hand	1			382, 420
coin	1	7	240	
container, 9" x 12", clear	1		130	

Description	Quantity per Group	Explore *page*	Investigate *page*	Chapter Investigation *page*
cup, glass	2	186		
eyedropper	1		130	
fan, small desktop	1			480
flashlight	1	83, 299		56
glass baking dish, rectangular	1			276
globe	1	83		
graduated cylinder, 50 mL	1			16, 204
graduated cylinder, 250 mL	1			382
hand mirror	1	92		
jar, 1 qt, glass with lid	1	194		382
lamp, desk, incandescent	1	18	14	420
lamp, table	2		468	
light bulb, fluorescent	1		468	
light bulb, incandescent	1		468	
marker, colored	1	431	14, 303, 393	420
magnetic compass	1			140
magnifying glass	1	183, 190		
measuring cup	1	194, 431, 506		
measuring spoon, 1 teaspoon	1	431		
measuring spoon, 1/2 teaspoon	1	431		
measuring spoon, 1/4 teaspoon	1	431		
meter stick	1			56
mortar and pestle	1		387	
pan, aluminum baking, 9" x 12"	1		463	514
paper punch	1			480
pen, felt-tip	1	466	85, 281, 468	
pens, variously colored	3 or 4	270		
pen, washable color	1	164	281	
pen, erasable color	1			168
pencil	1	77, 155, 466	433, 468	
pencil, wooden, No. 2	1	458		
pencil, wooden, No. 4	1	458		
pencil, colored	2		403, 425	
pitcher, 64 oz	1			236
plant pot with tray	2	506		
pot, metal, 2 quart	1	263		
protractor	1			56, 354

Description	Quantity per Group	Explore *page*	Investigate *page*	Chapter Investigation *page*
psychrometer	1			140
pushpins	3 or 4			276
quarter (25 cent coin)	1			480
ring stand, with ring	1			16
rock	1	390		
rock, flat	1	316		
rock samples	1	190		204
ruler	1	83, 431	65, 81, 309, 433	100, 168, 236, 324, 354, 382
ruler, metric	1			480
scissors	1	186, 270	14, 23, 81, 117, 309, 393	100, 168, 276, 278, 324, 382, 480
shake table	1			324
shoebox	3	115		
sieve	1			236
sink with drain	1			236
skewer, wooden	1	7		
stream table, with hose attachment or recirculating pump	1			236
sea-floor model	1		281	
spoon	1			514
spring toy	1	307		
stirring rod	2	186		
stopper, cork	1	7		16
stopwatch	1	26, 377, 506	23	480
tablespoon	1	186	95	
thermometer	1	26, 39, 377, 477	23, 51, 65, 468	16, 100, 140
toy top	1	123		
tray, 8" x 8" x 2"	1		249	
wood blocks	2	337		236
wood blocks, triangular	3		342	
wood blocks, rectangular	3	337		

Unit Resource Book Datasheet

Description	Quantity per Group	Explore *page*	Investigate *page*	Chapter Investigation *page*
Map, Earthquake	1		309	
Map, Geological Map of CA Hwy 101			211	
Map, Mount Rainier Mudflows	1		359	
Map, U. S. Fossil Fuels Distribution	1		455	
Map, California Natural Resources	1		159	
Map, California Precipitation	1		103	
Relative Humidity Chart	1			100
Texture Flow Chart	1			382
Water Use Datasheet	1		492	

McDougal Littell

CALIFORNIA

Science

FOCUS ON EARTH SCIENCES

The Earth System

The Changing Earth

Earth's Surface

Ecology and Resources

Science Content Standards for California Public Schools reproduced by permission, California Department of Education, CDE Press, 1430 N Street, Suite 3207, Sacramento, CA 95814.

Printed in the U.S.A.

ISBN 13: 978-0-618-64094-2
ISBN 10: 0-618-64094-0 2 3 4 5 6 7 8 VJM 09 08 07

Internet Web Site: http://www.mcdougallittell.com

Science Consultants

Chief Science Consultant

James Trefil, Ph.D. is the Clarence J. Robinson Professor of Physics at George Mason University. He is the author or co-author of more than 25 books, including *Science Matters* and *The Nature of Science*. Dr. Trefil is a member of the American Association for the Advancement of Science's Committee on the Public Understanding of Science and Technology. He is also a fellow of the World Economic Forum and a frequent contributor to *Smithsonian* magazine.

Rita Ann Calvo, Ph.D. is Senior Lecturer in Molecular Biology and Genetics at Cornell University, where for 12 years she also directed the Cornell Institute for Biology Teachers. Dr. Calvo is the 1999 recipient of the College and University Teaching Award from the National Association of Biology Teachers.

Kenneth Cutler, M.S. is the Education Coordinator for the Julius L. Chambers Biomedical Biotechnology Research Institute at North Carolina Central University. A former middle school and high school science teacher, he received a 1999 Presidential Award for Excellence in Science Teaching.

Instructional Design Consultants

Douglas Carnine, Ph.D. is Professor of Education and Director of the National Center for Improving the Tools of Educators at the University of Oregon. He is the author of seven books and over 100 other scholarly publications, primarily in the areas of instructional design and effective instructional strategies and tools for diverse learners. Dr. Carnine also serves as a member of the National Institute for Literacy Advisory Board.

Linda Carnine, Ph.D. consults with school districts on curriculum development and effective instruction for students struggling academically. A former teacher and school administrator, Dr. Carnine also co-authored a popular remedial reading program.

Sam Miller, Ph.D. is a middle school science teacher and the Teacher Development Liaison for the Eugene, Oregon, Public Schools. He is the author of curricula for teaching science, mathematics, computer skills, and language arts.

Donald Steely, Ph.D. serves as principal investigator at the Oregon Center for Applied Science (ORCAS) on federal grants for science and language arts programs. His background also includes teaching and authoring of print and multimedia programs in science, mathematics, history, and spelling.

Vicky Vachon, Ph.D. consults with school districts throughout the United States and Canada on improving overall academic achievement with a focus on literacy. She is also co-author of a widely used program for remedial readers.

iii

Content Reviewers

John Beaver, Ph.D.
Ecology
Professor, Director of Science Education Center
College of Education and Human Services
Western Illinois University
Macomb, IL

Donald J. DeCoste, Ph.D.
Matter and Energy, Chemical Interactions
Chemistry Instructor
University of Illinois
Urbana-Champaign, IL

Dorothy Ann Fallows, Ph.D., MSc
Diversity of Living Things, Microbiology
Partners in Health
Boston, MA

Michael Foote, Ph.D.
The Changing Earth, Life Over Time
Associate Professor
Department of the Geophysical Sciences
The University of Chicago
Chicago, IL

Lucy Fortson, Ph.D.
Space Science
Director of Astronomy
Adler Planetarium and Astronomy Museum
Chicago, IL

Elizabeth Godrick, Ph.D.
Human Biology
Professor, CAS Biology
Boston University
Boston, MA

Isabelle Sacramento Grilo, M.S.
The Changing Earth
Lecturer, Department of the Geological Sciences
San Diego State University
San Diego, CA

David Harbster, MSc
Diversity of Living Things
Professor of Biology
Paradise Valley Community College
Phoenix, AZ

Richard D. Norris, Ph.D.
Earth's Waters
Professor of Paleobiology
Scripps Institution of Oceanography
University of California, San Diego
La Jolla, CA

Donald B. Peck, M.S.
Motion and Forces; Waves, Sound, and Light; Electricity and Magnetism
Director of the Center for Science Education (retired)
Fairleigh Dickinson University
Madison, NJ

Javier Penalosa, Ph.D.
Diversity of Living Things, Plants
Associate Professor, Biology Department
Buffalo State College
Buffalo, NY

Raymond T. Pierrehumbert, Ph.D.
Earth's Atmosphere
Professor in Geophysical Sciences (Atmospheric Science)
The University of Chicago
Chicago, IL

Brian J. Skinner, Ph.D.
Earth's Surface
Eugene Higgins Professor of Geology and Geophysics
Yale University
New Haven, CT

Nancy E. Spaulding, M.S.
Earth's Surface, The Changing Earth, Earth's Waters
Earth Science Teacher (retired)
Elmira Free Academy
Elmira, NY

Steven S. Zumdahl, Ph.D.
Matter and Energy, Chemical Interactions
Professor Emeritus of Chemistry
University of Illinois
Urbana-Champaign, IL

Susan L. Zumdahl, M.S.
Matter and Energy, Chemical Interactions
Chemistry Education Specialist
University of Illinois
Urbana-Champaign, IL

Safety Consultant

Juliana Texley, Ph.D.
Former K–12 Science Teacher and School Superintendent
Boca Raton, FL

English Language Advisor

Judy Lewis, M.A.
Director, State and Federal Programs for reading proficiency and high risk populations
Rancho Cordova, CA

iv

California Teacher Reviewers

Bill Bruce
Tenaya Middle School
Fresno, CA

Mark J. Handwerker, Ph.D.
Erle Stanley Gardner Middle School
Temecula, CA

Jack Castro
William Sheppard Middle School
San Jose, CA

Sandy Steinburg
Winston Churchill Middle School
Carmichael, CA

Bernice Filerman, Ph.D.
Bell Gardens High School
Bell Gardens, CA

California Panel Members and Lab Evaluators

Al Brofman
Tehipite Middle School,
Fresno, CA

Jenifer Cox
Sylvan Middle School,
Citrus Heights, CA

Ann Marie Lynn
Amelia Earhart Middle School,
Riverside, CA

Barbara Newell
Charles Evans Hughes Middle School,
Long Beach, CA

Greg Pirolo
Golden Valley Middle School,
San Bernardino, CA

Nancy Stubbs
Sweetwater Union Unified
School District,
Chula Vista, CA

Lori Walker
Audubon Middle School &
Magnet Center,
Los Angeles, CA

v

Teacher Panel Members

Carol Arbour
Tallmadge Middle School,
Tallmadge, OH

Patty Belcher
Goodrich Middle School,
Akron, OH

Gwen Broestl
Luis Munoz Marin Middle School,
Cleveland, OH

John Cockrell
Clinton Middle School,
Columbus, OH

Linda Culpepper
Martin Middle School,
Charlotte, NC

Melvin Figueroa
New River Middle School,
Ft. Lauderdale, FL

Doretha Grier
Kannapolis Middle School,
Kannapolis, NC

Robert Hood
Alexander Hamilton Middle School,
Cleveland, OH

Scott Hudson
Covedale Elementary School,
Cincinnati, OH

Loretta Langdon
Princeton Middle School,
Princeton, NC

Carlyn Little
Glades Middle School,
Miami, FL

James Minogue
Lowe's Grove Middle School,
Durham, NC

Kathleen Montagnino-DeMatteo
Jefferson Davis Middle School,
West Palm Beach, FL

Joann Myers
Buchanan Middle School,
Tampa, FL

Anita Parker
Kannapolis Middle School,
Kannapolis, NC

Laura Pottmyer
Apex Middle School,
Apex, NC

Lynn Prichard
Williams Middle Magnet School,
Tampa, FL

Jacque Quick
Walter Williams High School,
Burlington, NC

Robert Glenn Reynolds
Hillman Middle School,
Youngstown, OH

Stacy Rinehart
Lufkin Road Middle School,
Apex, NC

Theresa Short
Abbott Middle School,
Fayetteville, NC

Rita Slivka
Alexander Hamilton Middle School,
Cleveland, OH

Marie Sofsak
B F Stanton Middle School,
Alliance, OH

Sharon Stull
Quail Hollow Middle School,
Charlotte, NC

Donna Taylor
Bak Middle School of the Arts,
West Palm Beach, FL

Sandi Thompson
Harding Middle School,
Lakewood, OH

Teacher Lab Evaluators

Andrew Boy
W.E.B. DuBois Academy,
Cincinnati, OH

Jill Brimm-Byrne
Albany Park Academy,
Chicago, IL

Gwen Broestl
Luis Munoz Marin Middle School,
Cleveland, OH

Michael A. Burstein
The Rashi School,
Newton, MA

Trudi Coutts
Madison Middle School,
Naperville, IL

Larry Cwik
Madison Middle School,
Naperville, IL

Esther Dabagyan
Le Conte Middle School,
Los Angeles, CA

Jennifer Donatelli
Kennedy Junior High School,
Lisle, IL

Melissa Dupree
Lakeside Middle School,
Evans, GA

Carl Fechko
Luis Munoz Marin Middle School,
Cleveland, OH

Paige Fullhart
Highland Middle School,
Libertyville, IL

Sue Hood
Glen Crest Middle School,
Glen Ellyn, IL

William Luzader
Plymouth Community Intermediate School,
Plymouth, MA

Ann Min
Beardsley Middle School,
Crystal Lake, IL

Aileen Mueller
Kennedy Junior High School,
Lisle, IL

Nancy Nega
Churchville Middle School,
Elmhurst, IL

Oscar Newman
Sumner Math and Science Academy,
Chicago, IL

Lynn Prichard
Willimas Middle Magnet School,
Tampa, FL

Jacque Quick
Walter Williams High School,
Burlington, NC

Stacy Rinehart
Lufkin Road Middle School,
Apex, NC

Seth Robey
Gwendolyn Brooks Middle School,
Oak Park, IL

Kevin Steele
Grissom Middle School,
Tinley Park, IL

vi

MCDOUGAL LITTELL SCIENCE

Focus on Physical Sciences

vii

eEdition

UNIT 1
The Earth System

Unit Features

What different forms of energy are shown in this photograph? page 6

3 Weather Patterns 76

the BIG idea

Some features of weather have predictable patterns.

4 Weather Fronts and Storms 112

the BIG idea

The interaction of air masses causes changes in weather.

Visual Highlights

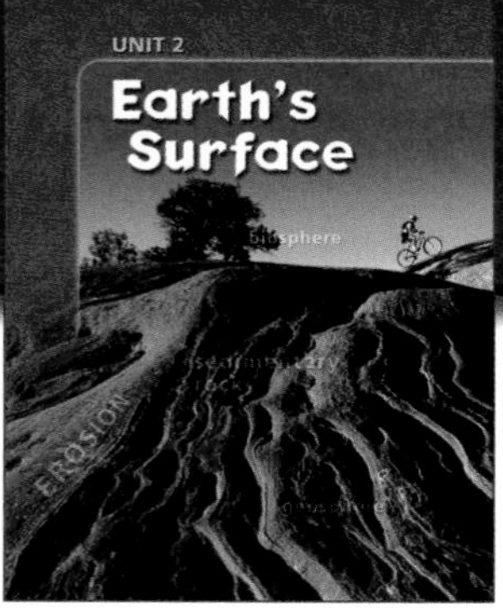

eEdition

UNIT 2

Earth's Surface

Unit Features

5 Views of Earth Today 152

the BIG idea

Modern technology has changed the way we view and map Earth.

How can gold be separated from other minerals and rocks in a river? page 180

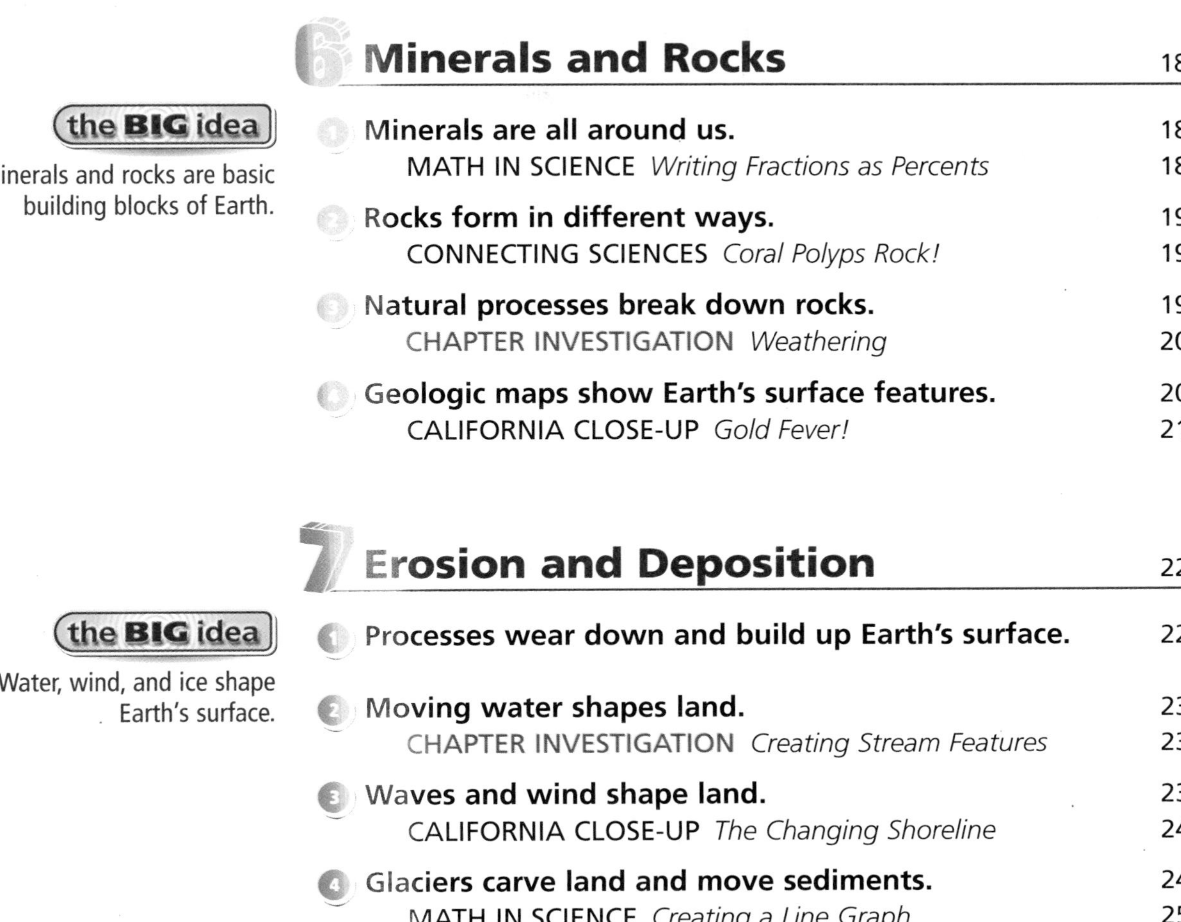

Minerals and Rocks 180

the BIG idea

Minerals and rocks are basic building blocks of Earth.

Erosion and Deposition 222

the BIG idea

Water, wind, and ice shape Earth's surface.

Visual Highlights

eEdition

UNIT 3
The Changing Earth

Unit Features

What might have made this huge crack in Earth's surface? page 262

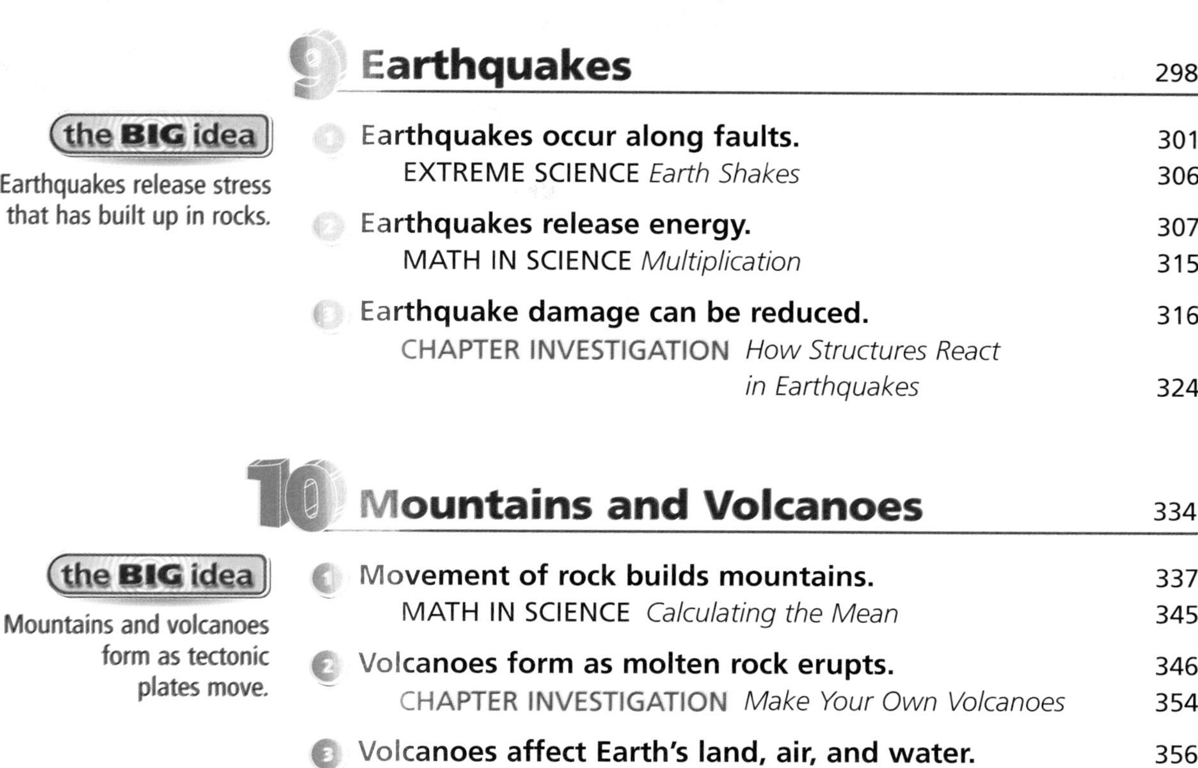

9 Earthquakes 298

the BIG idea

Earthquakes release stress that has built up in rocks.

10 Mountains and Volcanoes 334

the BIG idea

Mountains and volcanoes form as tectonic plates move.

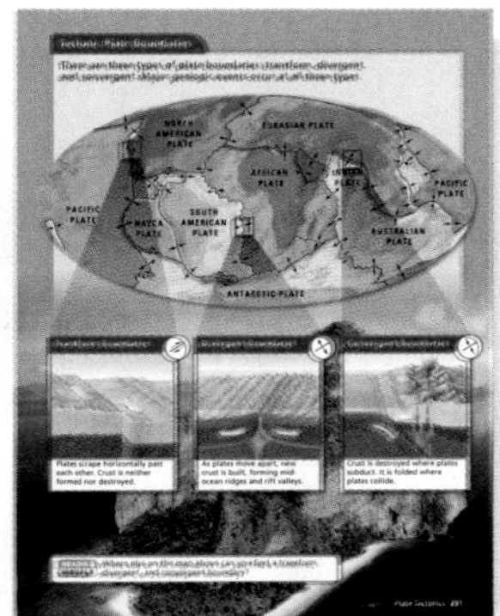

Visual Highlights

xiii

eEdition

UNIT 4
Ecology and Resources

Unit Features

11 Ecosystems and Biomes 374

the BIG idea

Matter and energy together support life within an environment.

How many living and nonliving things can you identify in this photograph? page 374

xiv

12 Interactions Within Ecosystems 410

the BIG idea

Living things within an ecosystem interact with each other and the environment.

13 Natural Resources 446

the BIG idea

Society depends on natural resources for energy and materials.

14 Human Impact on Ecosystems 486

the BIG idea

Humans and human population growth affect the environment.

Visual Highlights

Features

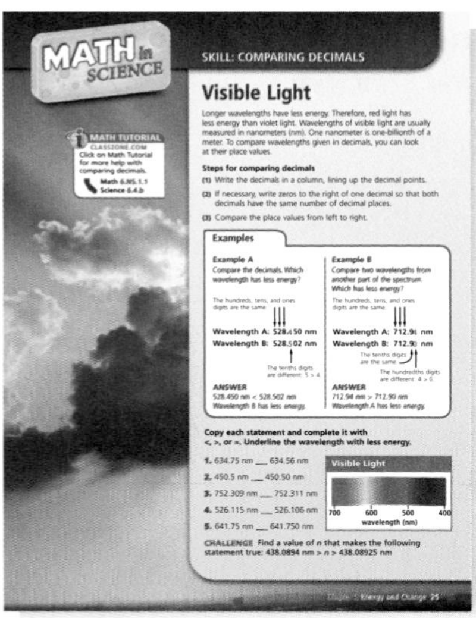

Math in Science

Think Science

Connecting Sciences

Science on the Job

Extreme Science

California Close-Up

Frontiers in Science

Timelines in Science

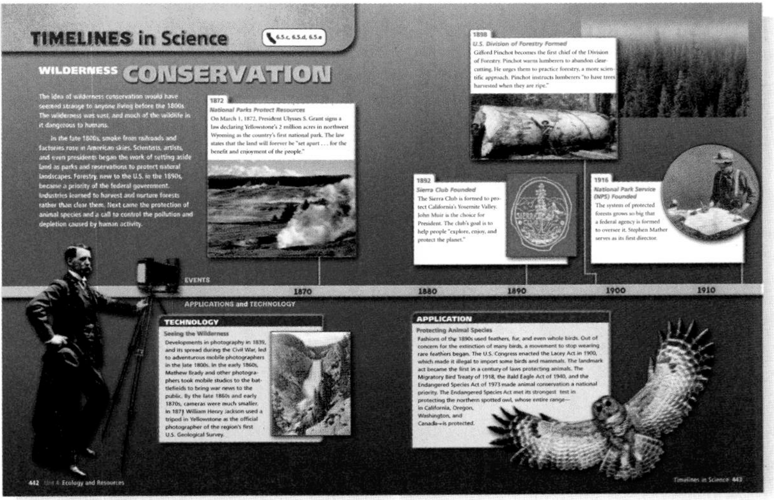

xvii

Internet Resources @ ClassZone.com

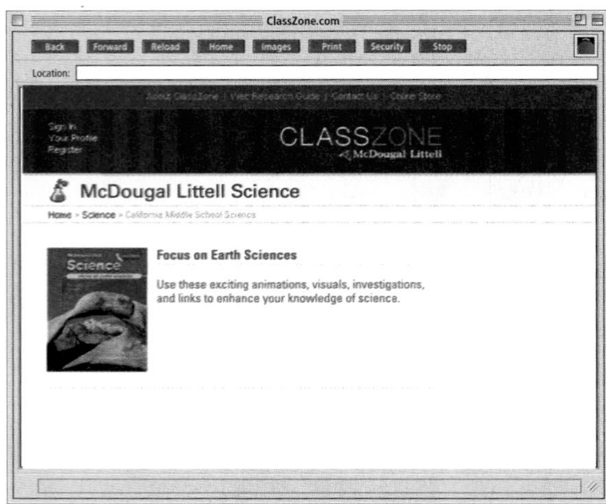

Simulations

Visualizations

Career Centers

Resource Centers

Math Tutorials

NSTA SciLinks

Codes for use with the NSTA SciLinks site may be found on every chapter opener.

Content Reviews

There is content review for every chapter at ClassZone.com.

Test Practice

There is test practice for every chapter at ClassZone.com.

Explore the Big Idea

Chapter Opening Inquiry

Each chapter opens with hands-on explorations that introduce the chapter's Big Idea.

Chapter Investigations

Full-Period Labs

The Chapter Investigations are in-depth labs that let you form and test a hypothesis, build a model, or sometimes design your own investigation.

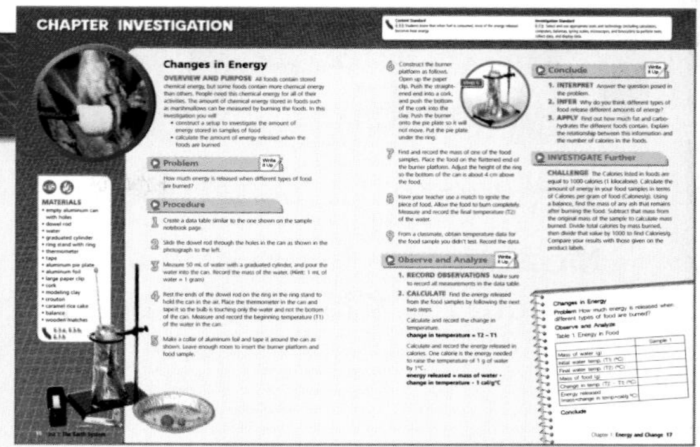

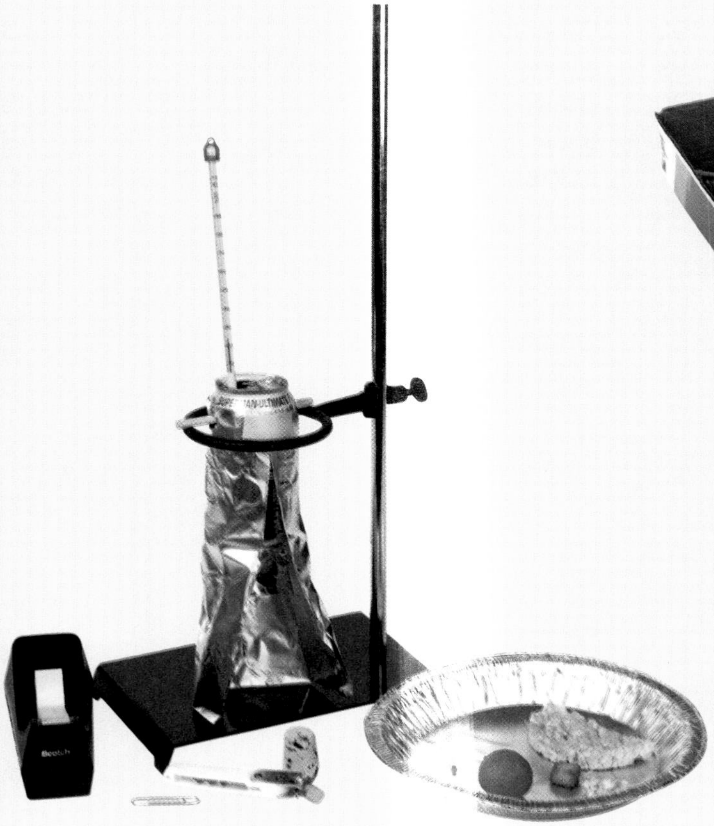

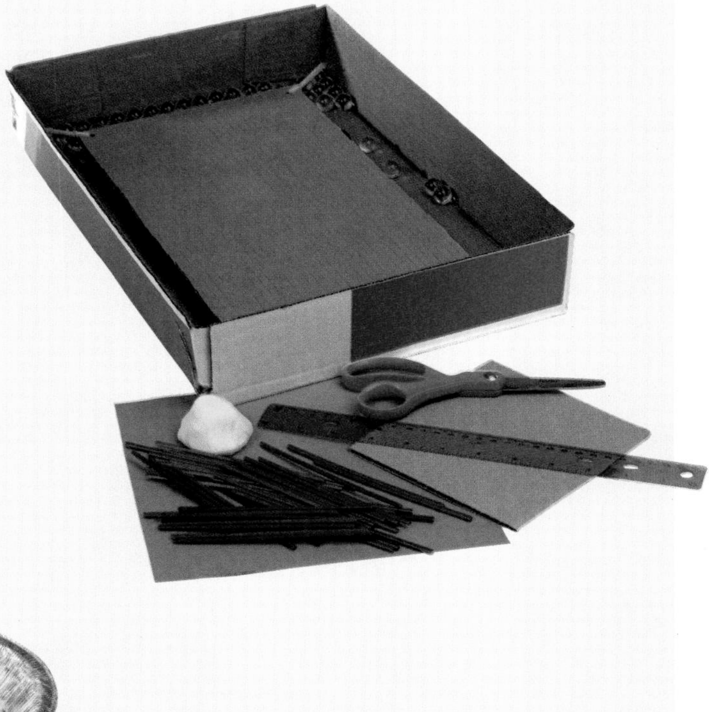

Explore

Introductory Inquiry Activities

Most sections begin with a simple activity that lets you explore the Key Concept before you read the section.

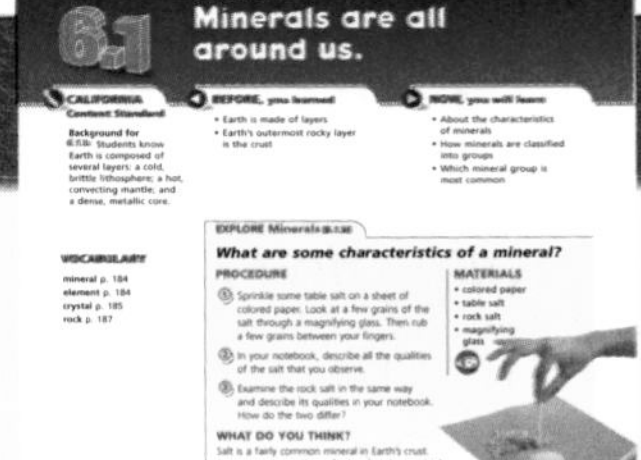

The Earth System

Earth's Surface

The Changing Earth

Ecology and Resources

Investigate

Skill Labs

Each Investigate activity gives you a chance to practice a specific science skill related to the content that you're studying.

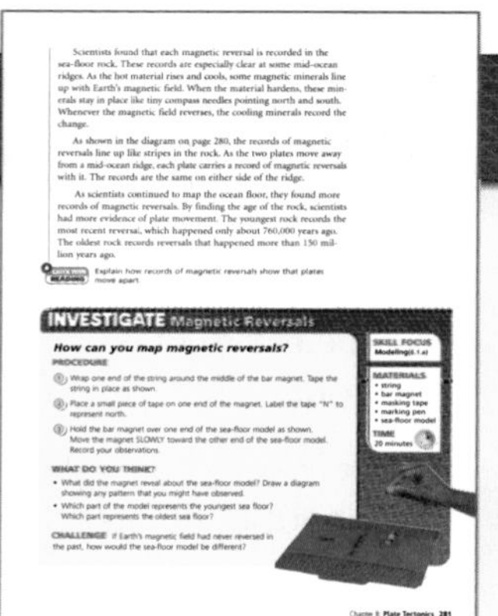

Scientists found that each magnetic reversal is recorded in the sea-floor rock. These records are especially clear at some mid-ocean ridges. As the hot material rises and cools, some magnetic minerals line up with Earth's magnetic field. When the material hardens, these minerals stay in place like tiny compass needles pointing north and south. Whenever the magnetic field reverses, the cooling minerals record the change.

As shown in the diagram on page 280, the records of magnetic reversals line up like stripes in the rock. As the two plates move away from a mid-ocean ridge, each plate carries a record of magnetic reversals with it. The records are the same on either side of the ridge.

As scientists continued to map the ocean floor, they found more records of magnetic reversals. By finding the age of the rock, scientists had more evidence of plate movement. The youngest rock records the most recent reversal, which happened only about 760,000 years ago. The oldest rock records reversals that happened more than 150 million years ago.

Explain how records of magnetic reversals show that plates move apart.

INVESTIGATE Magnetic Reversals

How can you map magnetic reversals?

PROCEDURE

1. Wrap one end of the string around the middle of the bar magnet. Tape the string in place as shown.
2. Place a small piece of tape on one end of the magnet. Label the tape "N" to represent north.
3. Hold the bar magnet over one end of the sea-floor model as shown. Move the magnet SLOWLY toward the other end of the sea-floor model. Record your observations.

WHAT DO YOU THINK?

- What did the magnet reveal about the sea-floor model? Draw a diagram showing any pattern that you might have observed.
- Which part of the model represents the youngest sea floor? Which part represents the oldest sea floor?

CHALLENGE If Earth's magnetic field had never reversed in the past, how would the sea-floor model be different?

SKILL FOCUS
Modeling (6.1.a)

MATERIALS
- string
- bar magnet
- masking tape
- marking pen
- sea-floor model

TIME
20 minutes

Chapter 8: Plate Tectonics 281

CA1

California Science Standards

As you read and study your science book this year, you'll be learning many of the ideas described in the California Science Standards. The standards that you will concentrate on are listed here.

Following each standard is an explanation of what it means and how you will learn about it. References to chapters tell you where you'll begin to study the content in the standard. Many standards refer to several chapters. That's because you will read and study information presented in several chapters in order to understand a standard fully. By the end of the year, you will have learned the content of these California Science Standards.

Focus on Earth Sciences

Plate Tectonics and Earth's Structure

Standard 6.1: Plate tectonics accounts for important features of Earth's surface and major geologic events.

Standard 6.1.a	What It Means to You
Students know evidence of plate tectonics is derived from the fit of the continents; the location of earthquakes, volcanoes, and midocean ridges; and the distribution of fossils, rock types, and ancient climatic zones.	The theory of plate tectonics explains how the major features on Earth's surface formed and why geologic events such as earthquakes happen. It states that Earth's lithosphere is broken into huge plates that move and change in size over time. You will learn how scientists developed this theory by noticing evidence such as the shapes of the continents and how they appear to fit together. **(Chapters 8, 9, and 10)**

Standard 6.1.b	What It Means to You
Students know Earth is composed of several layers: a cold, brittle lithosphere; a hot, convecting mantle; and a dense, metallic core.	You will learn the properties of Earth's layers. The lithosphere is made up of Earth's crust, a thin layer of cool rock, and the top of the mantle. The top of the mantle is cool and hard. The rest of the mantle is made of rock that is hot and soft enough to flow slowly. Below the mantle is the outer core, a layer of molten metals. The inner core, which is at Earth's center, is made up of very hot but solid metals. **(Chapters 2, 6, 8, 9, and 10)**

Standard 6.1.c	What It Means to You
Students know lithospheric plates the size of continents and ocean move at rates of centimeters per year in response to movement in the mantle.	The lithosphere is broken into slabs of rock called plates. They fit together like a jigsaw puzzle on Earth's surface. Underneath the plates is the asthenosphere, a layer of soft, hot rock. You will learn that rock in the asthenosphere moves slowly by convection, a motion that transfers heat energy. Convection in the asthenosphere allows the plates to move over Earth's surface. **(Chapters 8 and 10)**

Standard 6.1.d	What It Means to You
Students know that earthquakes are sudden motions along breaks in the crust called faults and that volcanoes and fissures are locations where magma reaches the surface.	A fault is a break in the lithosphere where blocks of rock move past each other. An earthquake is a shaking of the ground caused by a sudden movement along a fault. You will learn that magma is rock that is so hot it is molten and can flow. A volcano is an opening in Earth's crust through which magma can erupt. **(Chapter 10)**

Standard 6.1.e	What It Means to You
Students know major geologic events, such as earthquakes, volcanic eruptions, and mountain building, result from plate motions.	Most major earthquakes, volcanic eruptions, and mountain-building events happen where one tectonic plate meets another. Plates can move apart, push together, or scrape past each other. One plate can sink beneath another plate. Mountains can form as rocks crumple and fold. **(Chapters 8, 9, and 10)**

Standard 6.1.f	What It Means to You
Students know how to explain major features of California geology (including mountains, faults, volcanoes) in terms of plate tectonics.	You will learn how the movement of tectonic plates has shaped the geologic features of California. For example, the San Andreas Fault is where the Pacific Plate and the North American Plate are scraping past each other. Mount Shasta is a volcano that has formed in an area where the Pacific Plate is sinking underneath the edge of the North American Plate. **(Chapters 8, 9, and 10)**

Standard 6.1.g	What It Means to You
Students know how to determine the epicenter of an earthquake and know that the effects of an earthquake on any region vary, depending on the size of the earthquake, the distance of the region from the epicenter, the local geology, and the type of construction in the region.	The focus of an earthquake is the place underground where rocks first begin to move. The epicenter is the place on the surface directly above the focus. You will learn that scientists can locate an earthquake's epicenter by analyzing seismic waves recorded at three locations. **(Chapter 9)**

Shaping Earth's Surface

Standard 6.2: Topography is reshaped by the weathering of rock and soil and by the transportation and deposition of sediment.

Standard 6.2.a	What It Means to You
Students know water running downhill is the dominant process in shaping the landscape, including California's landscape.	Running water is the major force shaping the landscape on Earth. You will use a stream table to demonstrate how water erodes land and deposits sediment. You will learn about water's ability to shape shorelines and form drainage basins, divides, floodplains, deltas, and caverns. **(Chapters 6 and 7)**

Standard 6.2.b	What It Means to You
Students know rivers and streams are dynamic systems that erode, transport sediment, change course, and flood their banks in natural and recurring patterns.	Flowing water picks up sediment and deposits it in a new place. You will learn that streams form complex drainage systems as they flow toward the ocean. **(Chapters 2 and 7)**

Standard 6.2.c	What It Means to You
Students know beaches are dynamic systems in which the sand is supplied by rivers and moved along the coast by the action of waves.	Streams deposit sediment as they slow down when they flow into the ocean. Waves and ocean currents move this sediment along the shore, forming sandy beaches. Shorelines are shaped by the action of water, currents, and wind. **(Chapter 7)**

Standard 6.2.d	What It Means to You
Students know earthquakes, volcanic eruptions, landslides, and floods change human and wildlife habitats.	Powerful natural processes can cause earthquakes, volcanic eruptions, landslides, and floods. These events in turn can cause severe damage and loss of life. You will learn how people can reduce the damage caused by these natural events by learning to predict where they are likely to happen and by building different types of structures. **(Chapters 1, 2, 7, 9, and 10)**

Heat (Thermal Energy) (Physical Sciences)

Standard 6.3: Heat moves in a predictable flow from warmer objects to cooler objects until all the objects are at the same temperature.

Standard 6.3.a	What It Means to You
Students know energy can be carried from one place to another by heat flow or by waves, including water, light and sound waves, or by moving objects.	Energy is the ability to cause change. Energy moves from one place to another when objects change in temperature. It also travels in waves, such as radiation from the Sun. You will learn how energy moves through the Earth system, making it possible for organisms to live and grow. **(Chapters 1, 2, 9, 10, and 13)**

Standard 6.3.b	What It Means to You
Students know that when fuel is consumed, most of the energy released becomes heat energy.	Every time energy changes form, some of it changes into heat. For example, in a light bulb, not all of the electrical energy is changed into light. Some useful energy is lost as heat. **(Chapters 1 and 13)**

Standard 6.3.c	What It Means to You
Students know heat flows in solids by conduction (which involves no flow of matter) and in fluids by conduction and convection (which involves flow of matter).	Conduction is the process that moves energy from one object to another when they are touching. Convection is also a process that moves energy from place to place, but it occurs in materials that are able to flow, such as gases and liquids. **(Chapters 1, 2, 8, 10, and 13)**

Standard 6.3.d	What It Means to You
Students know heat energy is also transferred between objects by radiation (radiation can travel through space).	Energy in the form of electromagnetic waves is called radiation. You will learn about different forms of radiation, such as visible light, microwaves, and x-rays, and how people use them to improve everyday life. **(Chapters 1, 2, and 13)**

Energy in the Earth System

Standard 6.4: Many phenomena on Earth's surface are affected by the transfer of energy through radiation and convection currents.

Standard 6.4.a	What It Means to You
Students know the sun is the major source of energy for phenomena on Earth's surface; it powers winds, ocean currents, and the water cycle.	Almost all of the energy around you comes from the Sun. This energy can be transferred within the Earth system. You will learn that solar energy powers the water cycle, weather, and climate. **(Chapters 2 and 3)**

Standard 6.4.b	What It Means to You
Students know solar energy reaches Earth through radiation, mostly in the form of visible light.	The Sun's energy travels to Earth in electromagnetic waves called radiation. You will learn that visible light—light that the eye can see—is only a small part of the electromagnetic spectrum. **(Chapters 1 and 2)**

Standard 6.4.c	What It Means to You
Students know heat from Earth's interior reaches the surface primarily through convection.	Heat is generated deep inside Earth. You will learn that convection currents transfer heat from the Earth's interior toward the surface. Evidence of this internal heat can be seen at hot springs, geysers, and erupting volcanoes. **(Chapters 2 and 13)**

CA5

Standard 6.4.d	What It Means to You
Students know convection currents distribute heat in the atmosphere and oceans.	A convection current is a pattern of circulation in which a material is heated and rises in one area, and then sinks in another area. You will learn the effects of convection currents on weather, ocean currents, and tectonic plate movement. **(Chapters 1, 2, and 4)**

Standard 6.4.e	What It Means to You
Students know differences in pressure, heat, air movement, and humidity result in changes of weather.	Weather is the condition of Earth's atmosphere at a particular time and place. You will learn that moving air masses cause changes in weather. High-pressure systems bring fair weather, while low-pressure systems tend to bring stormy weather. **(Chapters 2, 3, and 4)**

Ecology (Life Sciences)

Standard 6.5: Organisms in ecosystems exchange energy and nutrients among themselves and with the environment.

Standard 6.5.a	What It Means to You
Students know energy entering ecosystems as sunlight is transferred by producers into chemical energy through photosynthesis and then from organism to organism through food webs.	A producer is any organism that takes in energy from the Sun and stores it in food as chemical energy. You will learn that food webs and food chains are models that show feeding relationships among organisms in an ecosystem. **(Chapter 11)**

Standard 6.5.b	What It Means to You
Students know matter is transferred over time from one organism to others in the food web and between organisms and the physical environment.	In an ecosystem, energy is transferred from one organism to the next as organisms eat or are eaten. You will learn that the remains of dead plants and animals become the organic matter in soil. The process of decay adds valuable raw materials to the ecosystem. **(Chapter 11)**

Standard 6.5.c	What It Means to You
Students know populations of organisms can be categorized by the functions they serve in an ecosystem.	Scientists group living things according to shared characteristics. Organisms can also be grouped according to the functions they perform in an ecosystem. You will learn about predators and prey, along with other ways in which organisms interact. **(Chapter 12)**

Standard 6.5.d	What It Means to You
Students know different kinds of organisms may play similar ecological roles in similar biomes.	Biomes are large geographic regions that have similar climates, plants, and animals. You will learn about both land and marine biomes and the organisms that live there. **(Chapter 11)**

Standard 6.5.e	What It Means to You
Students know the number and types of organisms an ecosystem can support depends on the resources available and on abiotic factors, such as quantities of light and water, a range of temperatures, and soil composition.	Abiotic factors are nonliving parts of an ecosystem. The combination of different abiotic factors in an ecosystem determines the types of organisms that the ecosystem can support. **(Chapters 11 and 12)**

Resources

Standard 6.6: Sources of energy and materials differ in amounts, distribution, usefulness, and the time required for their formation.

Standard 6.6.a	What It Means to You
Students know the utility of energy sources is determined by factors that are involved in converting these sources to useful forms and the consequences of the conversion process.	Natural resources are energy sources, organisms, or substances found in nature that people use. You will learn the benefits and costs of using certain resources, such as fossil fuels. For example, burning coal produces heat but also releases material that pollutes the air. **(Chapters 10, 13, and 14)**

Standard 6.6.b	What It Means to You
Students know different natural energy and material resources, include air, soil, rocks, minerals, petroleum, fresh water, wildlife, and forests, and know how to classify them as renewable or nonrenewable.	Renewable resources can be replaced in nature at about the same rate that they are used. Nonrenewable resources exist in fixed amounts or are used up faster than they can be replaced. You will learn how scientists are developing alternative energy sources, such as solar and wind energy. **(Chapters 13 and 14)**

Standard 6.6.c	What It Means to You
Students know the natural origin of the materials used to make common objects.	Fossil fuels, minerals, and plants are used in many everyday items, such as cars, glass, clothing, toothpaste, and paint. You will learn the common uses of many natural materials in technology, industry, and the arts. **(Chapters 13 and 14)**

Investigation and Experimentation

Standard 6.7: Scientific progress is made by asking meaningful questions and conducting careful investigations.

Standard 6.7.a	What It Means to You
Develop a hypothesis.	A hypothesis is a tentative explanation for something you observe. You will perform investigations to test hypotheses. Your findings will either support or not support your original hypothesis. **(Chapters 2, 3, 8, 9, 10, 13, and 14)**

Standard 6.7.b	What It Means to You
Select and use appropriate tools and technology (including calculators, computer, balances, spring scales, microscopes, and binoculars) to perform tests, collect data, and display data.	Design Your Own and other investigations allow you to choose the materials and procedures for testing an idea. This will help you develop scientific habits of mind, such as asking questions and sharing results. **(Unit projects and investigations throughout)**

Standard 6.7.c	What It Means to You
Construct appropriate graphs from data and develop qualitative statements about the relationships between variables.	Scientists must choose the best way to record and communicate their data. You will show the results of your investigations as drawings, narratives, graphs, or tables. The type of graph you choose depends on your independent variable. **(Investigations throughout)**

Standard 6.7.d	What It Means to You
Communicate the steps and results from an investigation in written reports and oral presentations.	Scientists must describe their findings so others are able to reproduce them. As part of interpreting the results of an investigation, you will write an answer to a problem statement. **(Investigations throughout)**

Standard 6.7.e	What It Means to You
Recognize whether evidence is consistent with a proposed explanation.	After performing an investigation, scientists interpret the results to determine if they support the hypothesis. You will do the same in the conclusion stage of an investigation. **(Chapters and investigations throughout)**

Standard 6.7.f	What It Means to You
Read a topographic map and a geologic map for evidence provided on the maps and construct and interpret a simple scale map.	A scale map relates distances on the map to actual distances on Earth's surface. A topographic map shows the shape of land using contour lines. A geologic map shows geologic features of Earth's surface, including rock types. You will learn to read and interpret all three types of maps. **(Chapters 5 and 6)**

Standard 6.7.g	What It Means to You
Interpret events by sequence and time from natural phenomena (e.g., the relative ages of rocks and intrusions).	Some natural events leave evidence about the order in which they happened. You will learn how to interpret such evidence. For example, older layers of sediment are covered by younger layers. The types of plants and animals in an area change as environmental conditions change. **(Chapters throughout)**

Standard 6.7.h	What It Means to You
Identify changes in natural phenomena over time without manipulating the phenomena (e.g., a tree limb, a grove of trees, a stream, a hillslope).	Natural processes change landscapes and landforms. For example, you will learn how waves and currents shape rock formations and shorelines over time. You will learn how the movement of energy causes change. **(Chapters throughout)**

Introducing Science

Scientists are curious. Since ancient times, they have been asking and answering questions about the world around them. Scientists are also very skeptical of the answers they get. They carefully collect evidence and test their answers many times before accepting an idea as correct.

In this book you will see how scientific knowledge keeps growing and changing as scientists ask new questions and rethink what was known before. The following sections will help you get started.

What Is Science?

Science is the systematic study of all of nature, from particles too small to see to the human body to the entire universe. However, no individual scientist can study all of nature. Therefore science is divided into many different fields. For example, some scientists are biologists, others are geologists, and still others are chemists or astronomers.

All the different scientific fields can be grouped into three broad categories: earth science, life science, and physical science.

- Earth science focuses on the study of our planet and its place in the universe; it includes the fields of geology, oceanography, meteorology, and astronomy.
- Life science focuses on the study of living things; it includes the fields of cell biology, botany, ecology, zoology, and human biology.
- Physical science focuses on the study of what things are made of and how they change; it includes the fields of chemistry and physics.

McDougal Littell Science, Focus on Earth Sciences

McDougal Littell Science, Focus on Earth Sciences, explores the Earth where you live but includes some life science and physical science as well. In this book you will first learn about where Earth gets its energy and how that energy appears—in sunshine, wind, and storms for example. Then you'll learn about Earth's surface, what it's made of, and how land and water structures get built up and worn down. You will see how Earth's surface can change suddenly, through earthquakes, mountain building, and volcanoes. Finally you will see how living things together with Earth make up ecosystems, and how humans fit into the whole Earth system.

Unifying Principles

As you learn, it helps to have a big picture of science as a framework for new information. *McDougal Littell Science* has identified unifying principles from each of the three broad categories of science: earth science, life science, and physical science. These unifying principles are described on the following pages. However, keep in mind that the broad categories of science do not have fixed borders. Earth science shades into life science, which shades into physical science, which shades back into earth science.

On the next few pages, look for the four unifying principles of earth science:

- Heat energy inside Earth and radiation from the Sun provide energy for Earth's processes.
- Physical forces, such as gravity, affect the movement of all matter on Earth and throughout the universe.
- Matter and energy move among Earth's rocks and soil, atmosphere, waters, and living things.
- Earth has changed over time and continues to change.

the BIG idea

Each chapter begins with a big idea. Keep in mind that each big idea relates to one or more of the unifying principles.

What is Earth Science?

Earth science is the study of Earth's interior, its rocks and soil, its atmosphere, its oceans, and outer space. For many years scientists studied each of these topics separately. Recently, however, they have started to look more and more at the connections among the different parts of Earth—its oceans, atmosphere, living things, rocks and soil, even other planets in the solar system and stars and galaxies far away. Through these studies scientists have learned more about Earth and its place in the universe.

The lava pouring out of this volcano in Hawaii is liquid rock that was melted by heat energy under Earth's surface.

UNIFYING PRINCIPLES of Earth Science

Heat energy inside Earth and radiation from the Sun provide energy for Earth's processes.

You are always surrounded by different forms of energy, such as heat energy or light. **Energy** is the ability to cause change. All of Earth's processes need energy to occur. A process is a set of changes that leads to a particular result. For example, **evaporation** is the process by which liquid changes into gas. A puddle on a sidewalk dries up through the process of evaporation. The energy needed for the puddle to dry up comes from the Sun.

Earth's interior is very hot. It is so hot that the solid rock there is able to flow very slowly—a few centimeters each year. In a process called **convection**, hot material rises, cools, then sinks until it is heated enough to rise again. Convection of hot rock carries heat energy up to Earth's surface. There it provides the energy to build mountains, cause earthquakes, and make volcanoes erupt.

Earth receives energy from the Sun as **radiation**—the energy that moves in the form of certain types of waves. Visible light is one type of radiation. Energy from the Sun causes winds to blow, ocean currents to flow, and water to move from the ground to the atmosphere and back again.

Physical forces, such as gravity, affect the movement of all matter on Earth and throughout the universe.

What do the stars in a galaxy, the planet Earth, and your body have in common? For one thing, they are all made of matter. **Matter** is anything that has mass and takes up space. Rocks are matter. You are matter. Even the air around you is matter. Matter is made of tiny particles called atoms that are too small to see through an ordinary microscope.

Everything in the universe is also affected by the same physical forces. A **force** is a push or a pull. Forces affect how matter moves everywhere in the universe. One force you experience every moment is **gravity**, which is the attraction, or pull, between two objects. Gravity pulls you to Earth and Earth to you; gravity is the force that causes objects to fall downward toward the center of Earth, and the force that keeps objects in orbit around planets and stars.

Friction is the force that resists motion between two surfaces that are pressed together. You feel friction when you rub your finger across a table or a piece of sandpaper. There are many other forces at work on Earth and throughout the universe. Magnetic fields exert forces. A contact force occurs when one object pushes or pulls on another object by touching it.

You see Earth changing all of the time. Rain turns dirt to mud, and a dry wind turns the mud to dust. Many changes are small and can take hundreds, thousands, or even millions of years to add up to much. Other changes are sudden and can destroy in minutes a house that had stood for many years.

UNIFYING PRINCIPLES of Earth Science, continued

Matter and energy move among Earth's rocks and soil, atmosphere, waters, and living things.

Think of Earth as a huge system, or an organized group of parts that work together. Within this system, matter and energy move among the different parts. The four major parts of Earth's system are the

- **atmosphere,** which includes all the air surrounding the solid planet
- **geosphere,** which includes all of Earth's rocks and minerals, as well as Earth's interior
- **hydrosphere,** which includes oceans, rivers, lakes, every drop of water on or under Earth's surface, and water in the air
- **biosphere,** which includes all living things on Earth.

It's easy to see how matter moves within the Earth system. When water in the atmosphere falls as rain, it becomes part of the hydrosphere. When an animal drinks water from a puddle, the water becomes part of the biosphere. When rainwater soaks into the ground, it moves through the geosphere. As the puddle dries up, the water becomes part of the atmosphere again.

Earth has changed over time and continues to change.

Events are always changing Earth's surface. Some events, such as the building or wearing away of mountains, occur over millions of years. Others, such as earthquakes, occur within seconds. A change can affect a small area or an entire continent, such as North America.

Scientists learn about Earth's past by examining the evidence they find in rock layers and by observing processes now occurring. Evidence from rocks and fossils along the edges of continents shows that all continents were once joined and then moved apart over time. A **fossil** is the trace of a once-living organism. Fossils show that new types of plants and animals develop, and others, such as dinosaurs, die out. **Climate**—the long-term weather patterns of an area—may also change. Scientists are studying how changes in climates around the world might affect Earth in this century.

What is Life Science?

Life science is the study of living things. As you study life science, you will observe and read about a variety of organisms, from huge redwood trees to the tiny bacteria that cause sore throats. But life science is not simply about learning the names of millions of organisms. It includes big ideas to help us understand how all these living things interact with their environment. Life science is the study of characteristics and needs that all living things have in common. It's also a study of changes, both daily changes and changes that take place over millions of years. It's the study of how living things depend on Earth and its resources.

A moose chomps on the leaves of a plant. This ordinary event involves many interactions among living and nonliving things within the forest.

UNIFYING PRINCIPLES of Life Science

All living things share common characteristics.

Despite the variety of living things on Earth, there are certain characteristics common to all. The basic unit of life is the **cell**. Any living thing, whether it has one cell or many, is described as an **organism**. All organisms are characterized by

- organization—the way the organism's body is arranged
- growth—the way that an organism grows and develops over its lifetime
- reproduction—the way that an organism produces offspring like itself
- response—the ways an organism interacts with its surroundings

All living things share common needs.

All living things have three basic needs: energy, materials, and living space. These needs must be met for the organism to stay alive. Energy enables an organism to carry out all the activities of life. The body of every organism needs water and other materials. Water is important because most of the chemical reactions in a cell take place in water. Organisms also require other materials. Plants, for example, need carbon dioxide to make energy-rich sugars, and most living things need oxygen. Living space is the environment in which an organism gets the energy and materials it needs.

Living things meet their needs through interactions with the environment.

The **environment** is everything that surrounds a living thing. This includes other organisms as well as nonliving factors, such as rainfall, sunlight, and soil. Any exchange of energy or materials between the living and nonliving parts of the environment is an interaction. Plants interact with the environment by capturing energy from sunlight and changing that energy into chemical energy that is stored in sugar. Animals can interact with plants by eating the plants and getting energy from the sugars that plants have made.

The types and numbers of living things change over time.

A **species** is a group of living things so closely related that they can produce offspring together that can also reproduce. Scientists have named about 1.4 million different species. The great variety of species on Earth today is called **biodiversity**. Different species have different characteristics, or **adaptations**, that allow the members of that species to get their needs met in a particular environment. Over the millions of years that life has existed on Earth, new species have come into being and others have disappeared. The disappearance of a species is called **extinction**. Studying fossils of extinct organisms is one way that scientists have of seeing how living things have changed over time.

What is Physical Science?

Physical science is the study of what things are made of and how they change. It combines the studies of both physics and chemistry. Physics is the science of matter, energy, and forces. It includes the study of topics such as motion, light, and electricity and magnetism. Chemistry is the study of the structure and properties of matter. It especially focuses on how substances change into different substances.

You cannot "use up" energy. Even though a camp stove's fuel may be gone and a flashlight's battery is no longer functioning, the energy they provided has not disappeared. It has only changed forms.

UNIFYING PRINCIPLES of Physical Science

Matter is made of particles too small to see.

The tiny particles that make up all matter are called **atoms**. Atoms are so tiny that they are far too small to see even through a powerful microscope. In fact, an atom is more than a million times smaller than the period at the end of this sentence. There are more than 100 basic kinds of matter called **elements**. The atoms of any element are all alike but different from the atoms of any other element.

Matter changes form and moves from place to place.

You see objects moving and changing all around you. All changes in matter are results of atoms moving and combining in different ways. Regardless of how much matter may change, however, under ordinary conditions it is never created or destroyed. Matter that seems to disappear merely changes into another form of matter.

Energy changes from one form to another, but it cannot be created or destroyed.

All the changes you see around you depend on energy. **Energy**, in fact, means the ability to cause change. Using energy means changing energy. But energy is never created or destroyed, no matter how often it changes form. This fact is known as the **law of conservation of energy**. The energy you may think you've lost when a match has burned out has only been changed into other forms of energy.

Physical forces affect the movement of all matter on Earth and throughout the universe.

A **force** is a push or a pull. Every time you push or pull an object, you are applying a force to that object, whether or not the object moves. There are several forces—several pushes or pulls—acting on you right now. All these forces are necessary for you to do the things you do, even sitting and reading. **Gravity** keeps you on the ground. Gravity also keeps the Moon moving around Earth, and Earth moving around the Sun. **Friction** is the force that opposes motion. The friction between the bottoms of your shoes and the floor makes it possible for you to walk without slipping. Too much friction between a heavy box and the floor makes it hard to push the box across the floor.

CA19

The Nature of Science

You may think of science as a body of knowledge or a collection of facts. More important, however, science is an active process that involves certain ways of looking at the world.

Scientific Habits of Mind

Scientists are curious. They ask questions. A scientist who finds an unusual rock by the side of a river would ask questions such as, "Did this rock form in this area?" or "Did this rock form elsewhere and get moved here?" Questions like these make a scientist want to investigate.

Scientists are observant. They look closely at the world around them. A scientist who studies rocks can learn a lot about a rock just by picking it up, looking at its color, and feeling how heavy it is.

Scientists are creative. They draw on what they know to form possible explanations for a pattern, an event, or an interesting phenomenon that they have observed. Then scientists put together a plan for testing their ideas.

Scientists are skeptical. Scientists don't accept an explanation or answer unless it is based on evidence and logical reasoning. They continually question their own conclusions as well as the conclusions suggested by other scientists. Scientists only trust evidence that can be confirmed by other people or other methods.

Scientists use seismographs to observe and measure vibrations that move through the ground.

This scientist is collecting a sample of melted rock from a hot lava flow in Hawaii.

Science Processes at Work

You can think of science as a continuous cycle of asking and seeking answers to questions about the world. Although there are many processes that scientists use, all scientists typically do the following:

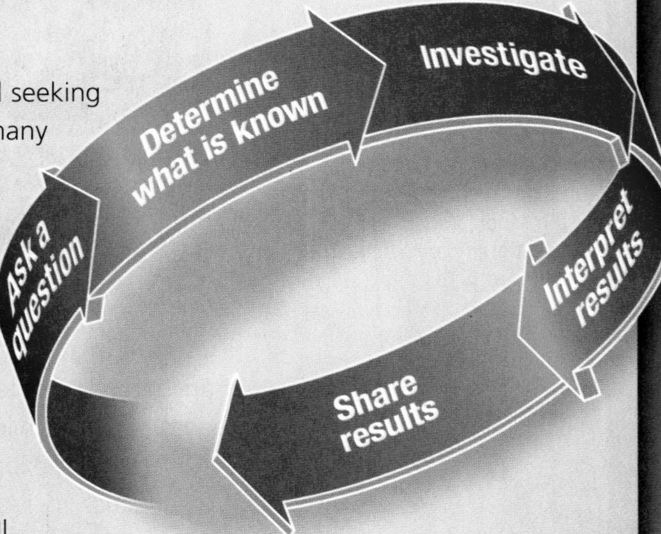

- Observe and ask a question
- Determine what is known
- Investigate
- Interpret results
- Share results

Observe and Ask a Question

It may surprise you that asking questions is an important skill. A scientific investigation may start when a scientist asks a question. Perhaps scientists observe an event or a process that they don't understand, or perhaps answering one question leads to another.

Determine What Is Known

When beginning an inquiry, scientists find out what is already known about a question. They study results from other scientific investigations, read journals, and talk with other scientists. The scientist who is trying to figure out where an unusual rock came from will study maps that show what types of rocks are already known to be in the area where the rock was found.

CA21

Investigate

Investigating is the process of collecting evidence. Two important ways of doing this are experimenting and observing.

An **experiment** is an organized procedure to study something under controlled conditions. For example, the scientist who found the rock by the river might notice that it is lighter in color where it is chipped. The scientist might design an experiment to determine why the rock is a different color on the inside. The scientist could break off a small piece of the inside of the rock and heat it up to see if it becomes the same color as the outside. The scientist would need to use a piece of the same rock that is being studied. A different rock might react differently to heat.

A scientist may use photography to study fast events, such as multiple flashes of lightning.

Rocks, such as this one from the Moon, can be subjected to different conditions in a laboratory.

Observing is the act of noting and recording an event, characteristic, or anything else detected with an instrument or with the senses. A scientist makes observations while performing an experiment. However, some things cannot be studied using experiments. For example, streaks of light called meteors occur when small rocks from outer space hit Earth's atmosphere. A scientist might study meteors by taking pictures of the sky at a time when meteors are likely to occur.

Forming hypotheses and making predictions are two other skills involved in scientific investigations. A **hypothesis** is a tentative explanation for an observation or a scientific problem that can be tested by further investigation. For example, the scientist might make the following hypothesis about the rock from the beach:

The rock is a meteorite, which is a rock that fell to the ground from outer space. The outside of the rock changed color because it was heated up from passing through Earth's atmosphere.

A **prediction** is an expectation of what will be observed or what will happen. To test the hypothesis that the rock's outside is black because it is a meteorite, the scientist might predict that a close examination of the rock will show that it has many characteristics in common with rocks that are already known to be meteorites.

Interpret Results

As scientists investigate, they analyze their evidence, or data, and begin to draw conclusions. **Analyzing data** involves looking at the evidence gathered through observations or experiments and trying to identify any patterns that might exist in the data. Scientists often need to make additional observations or perform more experiments before they are sure of their conclusions. Many times scientists make new predictions or revise their hypotheses.

Scientists use computers to gather and interpret data.

Scientists make images such as this computer drawing of a landscape to help share their results with others.

Share Results

An important part of scientific investigation is sharing results of experiments. Scientists read and publish in journals and attend conferences to communicate with other scientists around the world. Sharing data and procedures gives scientists a way to test each others' results. They also share results with the public through newspapers, television, and other media.

The Nature of Technology

When you think of technology, you may think of cars, computers, and cell phones. Imagine having no refrigerator or radio. It's difficult to think of a world without the products of what we call technology. Technology, however, is more than just devices that make our daily activities easier. Technology is the process of using scientific knowledge to design solutions to real-world problems.

Science and Technology

Science and technology go hand in hand. Each depends upon the other. Even a device as simple as a thermometer is designed using knowledge of the ways different materials respond to changes in temperature. In turn, thermometers have allowed scientists to learn more about the world. Greater knowledge of how materials respond to changes in temperature helped engineers to build items such as refrigerators. They have also built thermometers that could be read automatically by computers. New technologies lead to new scientific knowledge and new scientific knowledge leads to even better technologies.

The Process of Technological Design

The process of technological design involves many choices. What, for example, should be done to protect the residents of an area prone to severe storms such as tornadoes and hurricanes? Build stronger homes that can withstand the winds? Try to develop a way to detect the storms long before they occur? Or learn more about hurricanes in order to find new ways to protect people from the dangers? The steps people take to solve the problem depend a great deal on what they already know about the problem as well as what can reasonably be done. As you learn about the steps in the process of technological design, think about the different choices that could be made at each step.

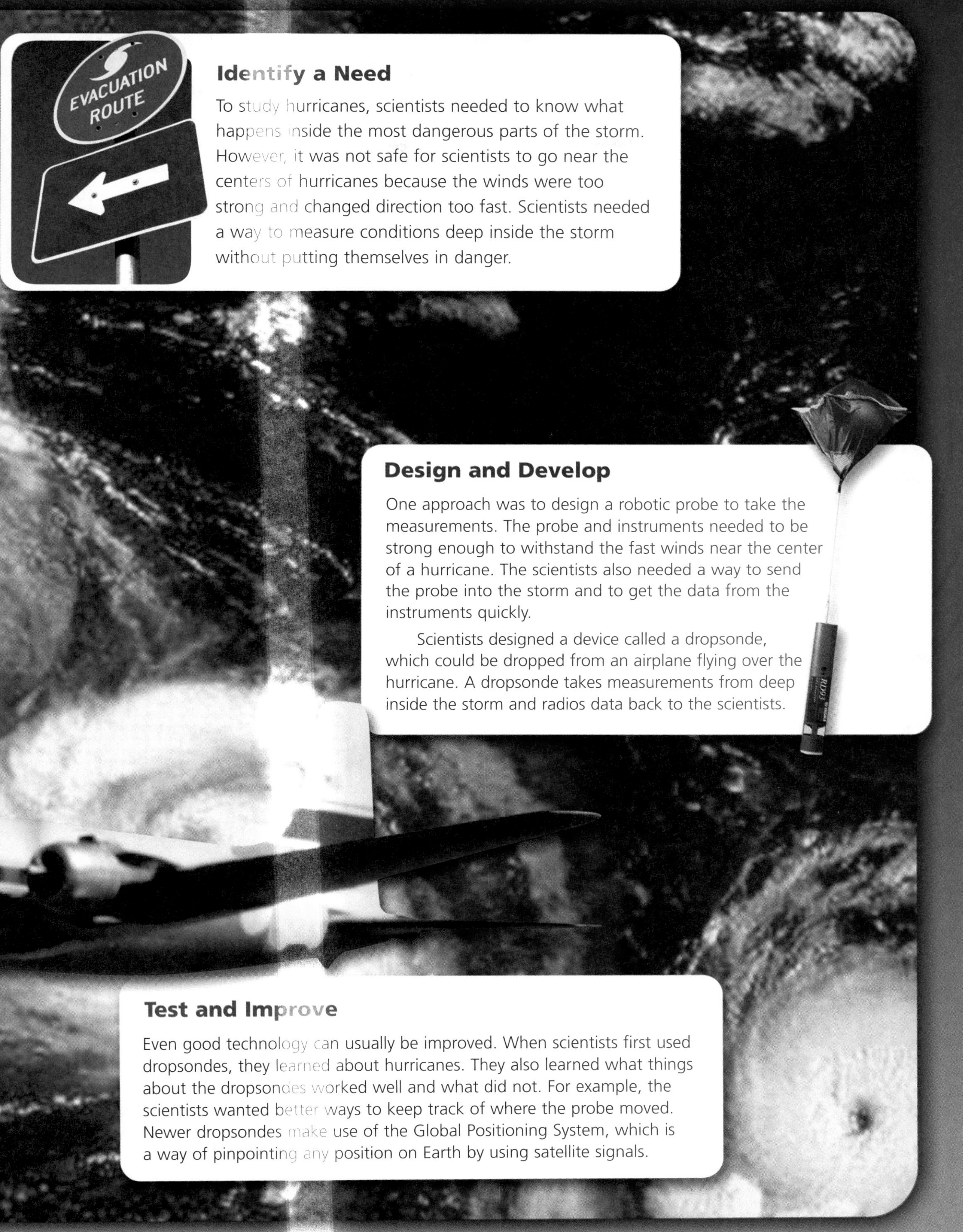

Identify a Need

To study hurricanes, scientists needed to know what happens inside the most dangerous parts of the storm. However, it was not safe for scientists to go near the centers of hurricanes because the winds were too strong and changed direction too fast. Scientists needed a way to measure conditions deep inside the storm without putting themselves in danger.

Design and Develop

One approach was to design a robotic probe to take the measurements. The probe and instruments needed to be strong enough to withstand the fast winds near the center of a hurricane. The scientists also needed a way to send the probe into the storm and to get the data from the instruments quickly.

Scientists designed a device called a dropsonde, which could be dropped from an airplane flying over the hurricane. A dropsonde takes measurements from deep inside the storm and radios data back to the scientists.

Test and Improve

Even good technology can usually be improved. When scientists first used dropsondes, they learned about hurricanes. They also learned what things about the dropsondes worked well and what did not. For example, the scientists wanted better ways to keep track of where the probe moved. Newer dropsondes make use of the Global Positioning System, which is a way of pinpointing any position on Earth by using satellite signals.

Using the Tools of Science

You can learn about science by doing it. Doing science includes trying experiments or making observations so that you see for yourself what happens. For example, activities such as growing plants, measuring acid in rainwater, looking at live cells under a microscope, and trying to make an object fly are the exciting parts of science. These are the reasons people become scientists.

Safety First!

apron

goggles

disposal

electrical safety

chemical safety

fire safety

sharp objects

heating safety

fumes

poison

gloves

To do any experiments, think safety first! You may think it is unnecessary to wear goggles or plastic gloves—and sometimes it is unnecessary. But beakers break and spill, even if the materials are not dangerous. Why take a chance? You can prevent injuries or ruined clothes by taking simple precautions. Remember, we never plan for things to go wrong, but accidents happen!

The investigations and explorations in this book have safety symbols next to them when needed. Some have to do with what you wear—goggles, apron, gloves. Some warn of fire and heat dangers; some concern safety when working with electricity. Others caution you about chemicals, sharp objects, disposing of materials, or working with animals. Look at the safety rules and symbols on page R10. Become familiar with them. Look for them before you do an activity, and take the necessary precautions.

Measuring

Scientists use the International System (SI) for measurements of length, volume, mass, and temperature. The units in the SI system are metric, based on multiples of ten. These are different from the units we use in the United States, but most countries and all scientists use them. Once you learn the SI system, you will become part of the international community.

Measuring Length In science, meters and centimeters, not yards, feet, and inches, are used to measure length. A meter is about a yard. Within the metric system you change units by multiplying or dividing by powers of 10. For example,

1 centimeter (cm) = .01 meter (m), or 1/100 of a meter

1 millimeter (mm) = .001 meter (m), or 1/1000 of a meter

The prefix tells you how large or small each measurement is. You can easily change units to and from the SI units. See page R20 for help in changing units of the metric system.

graduated cylinder

Measuring Volume The metric system measures volume in liters, not gallons. If you buy a 2 liter bottle of soda, it is about half a gallon in U.S. units. In a lab, it is more precise to measure 20 milliliters than to measure 1 teaspoon. Remember that 1 liter (L) = 1000 milliliters (mL). The prefix *milli-* means "one thousandth." When you measure the volume of a liquid, use a graduated cylinder and read the volume in mL, or milliliters. Each milliliter equals 1 cm^3.

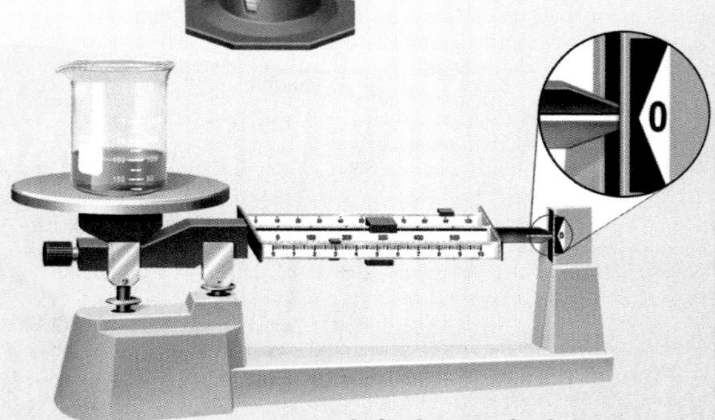

triple-beam balance

Measuring Mass Mass is measured in grams, not pounds. By now you can guess that 1 kilogram (kg) = 1000 grams (g). A pound is a measure of weight, and weight is not the same as mass. In SI units, weight is measured in newtons. To measure mass, you use a double-pan balance or a triple-beam balance.

Measuring Temperature There are three systems of temperature measurement in the International System: Kelvin, Celsius, and Fahrenheit. Usually in science class you will use Celsius, not Fahrenheit or Kelvin. The Celsius system uses one hundred degrees between the freezing and the boiling point of water, 0–100° C. The Fahrenheit system, which we commonly use in the United States, goes from 32° to 212° F freezing to boiling point. Again, since it's based on 10's, the Celsius scale is easier to use.

double-pan balance

Why Bother?

Why do all scientists need to use standard tools and measurements? They do this so that others can reproduce their experiments. Remember that scientists are a skeptical bunch—they don't believe what they hear until they try it themselves. To try an experiment that someone else has done, you have to have exact measurements. One drop more of a solution can make a huge difference in the results! One temperature degree higher and the whole experiment might fail!

Reproducibility is the only way scientists accept each other's work. Hypotheses have to be tested over and over again. If the results are different every time the experiment is done, then the hypothesis is not supported.

You need to use the scientific method every time you do an investigation. The scientific method varies according to the kind of investigation you're doing. The next two pages walk you through a lab. How do you make a hypothesis? How do you set up a test for it? How do you interpret your results? **Turn the page to find out.**

Conducting an Investigation

The fun part of science is "doing" science. You "do" science when you conduct your own investigations, collect your own data, and reach your own conclusions. You will practice using scientific methods whenever you do an investigation. Your method will change depending on what you are investigating. Sometimes you will observe and collect data. Sometimes you will make a model to see how things work. Sometimes you will conduct an experiment.

Modeling Solar Energy

OVERVIEW AND PURPOSE In this investigation you will model how the amount of solar energy received at one place changes throughout a year and during a day. You will model the amount of solar energy received at different times as you

- point a light source at different angles to a surface
- determine how the amount of energy received at a location changes during a summer day

Problem

Make sure you understand the purpose of your investigation. What are you trying to model or find out?

Problem Write It Up

How does the angle of light affect the amount of solar energy a location receives at different times of year?

Hypothesis

A hypothesis is a tentative explanation of what will happen and why it may happen. You base your hypothesis on what you know and a bit of educated guessing. You might not be right, but you test it to see. Set it up as a 3-part **if-then-because** statement:

1. **If** I model a high angle of light on my paper like summer sunshine, (What you'll do)
2. **then** the light on the paper will be brighter, (Your prediction)
3. **because** the higher angle concentrates the energy in a smaller area. (Your reason)

Hypothesize Write It Up

After performing step 4, write a hypothesis to explain how the angle of sunlight affects the amount of solar energy your locatio receives. Your hypothesis should take the form of an "If . . . , then . . . , because . . ." statement.

Procedure

Read the entire procedure before you begin. This procedure helps everyone do exactly the same thing. Then follow it step by step. Record your data accurately as you go.

Procedure

PART ONE

1. Mark an X near the center of the graph paper. Shine the flashl onto the paper from about 30 cm straight above the X—at a angle of 90° to the surface. Estimate the length of the spot of l
2. Shine the flashlight onto the X at different angles. Measure record the angles. Keep the flashlight at the same distance. Record the estimated length of the spot of light at the angl
3. Repeat step 2, but observe just one square near the X. Write down what happens to the brightness of the light as you change the angle. The brightness shows how much energy the area receives from the flashlight.
4. Think about the temperatures at different times of year at your location, and then write your hypothesis.

step 2

90°

56 Unit 1: The Earth System

Measure and Calculate

In order to collect data in this experiment, you need to use a protractor and subtraction. You will figure out your latitude and the angle that you need to shine the flashlight.

Content Standard
6.4.b Students know solar energy reaches Earth through radiation, mostly in the form of visible light.

Investigation Standard
6.7.a Develop a hypothesis.

PART TWO

5 Find from your teacher the latitude of your location. You will use this information to calculate the Sun's noontime elevation at your location on June 21, the first day of summer.

6 Subtract the latitude of the tropic of Cancer, which is at 23.5° north, from your latitude.

7 Subtract the number you calculated in step 6 from 90°. Your result is the Sun's noontime elevation in degrees above the horizon in your location on the first day of summer.

8 Point the light at the X on the graph paper. Move the flashlight in an arc from one side of the graph paper to the other. The maximum angle of the flashlight above the paper should be the angle you calculated in step 7. The movement of the flashlight represents the apparent movement of the Sun across the sky.

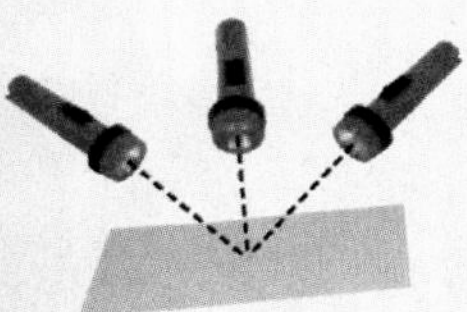

9 Observe how the brightness of the light near the X changes as you move the flashlight through the arc.

Observe and Analyze

Write It Up

1. **RECORD** Draw the setup of your materials in each part of the investigation. Organize your notes.
2. **ANALYZE** Describe how the angle of the flashlight in step 2 affected the spot of light. Which angle concentrated the light into the smallest area?

Record Observations

Write all your data so others can copy your experiment. Draw your setup. Measure your angles and the length of the spot. In some experiments, you can graph your data.

3. **EVALUATE** In Part Two, what part of the flashlight arc represented sunrise? noon? sunset?
4. **COMPARE** Compare the brightness of light your area receives during a day at noon and at sunset.

Conclude

Write It Up

1. **EVALUATE** Why do areas closer to the equator receive more solar energy?
2. **APPLY** Why are you more likely to get a sunburn at noon than at sunrise?
3. **INTERPRET** Do your results support your hypothesis? Explain why or why not.

Conclude

Draw conclusions from your experiment. Was your hypothesis supported? What did you learn from the experiment?

INVESTIGATE Further

CHALLENGE Compare the brightness of a day in summer and a day in winter at your location. Determine the total difference in latitude between your location and the latitude of the tropic of Capricorn (23.5° south). Subtract the total from 90°. The result is the noontime elevation of the Sun in your area on the first day of winter. Repeat Part Two using this maximum angle.

Modeling Solar Energy
Problem How does the angle of light affect the amount of solar energy a location receives at different times of year?
Hypothesize
Observe and Analyze
Table 1. Angle of Light and Brightness

Angle of Light (°)	Length of Spot (cm)	Brightness
15		
30		
45		

UNIT 1

The Earth System

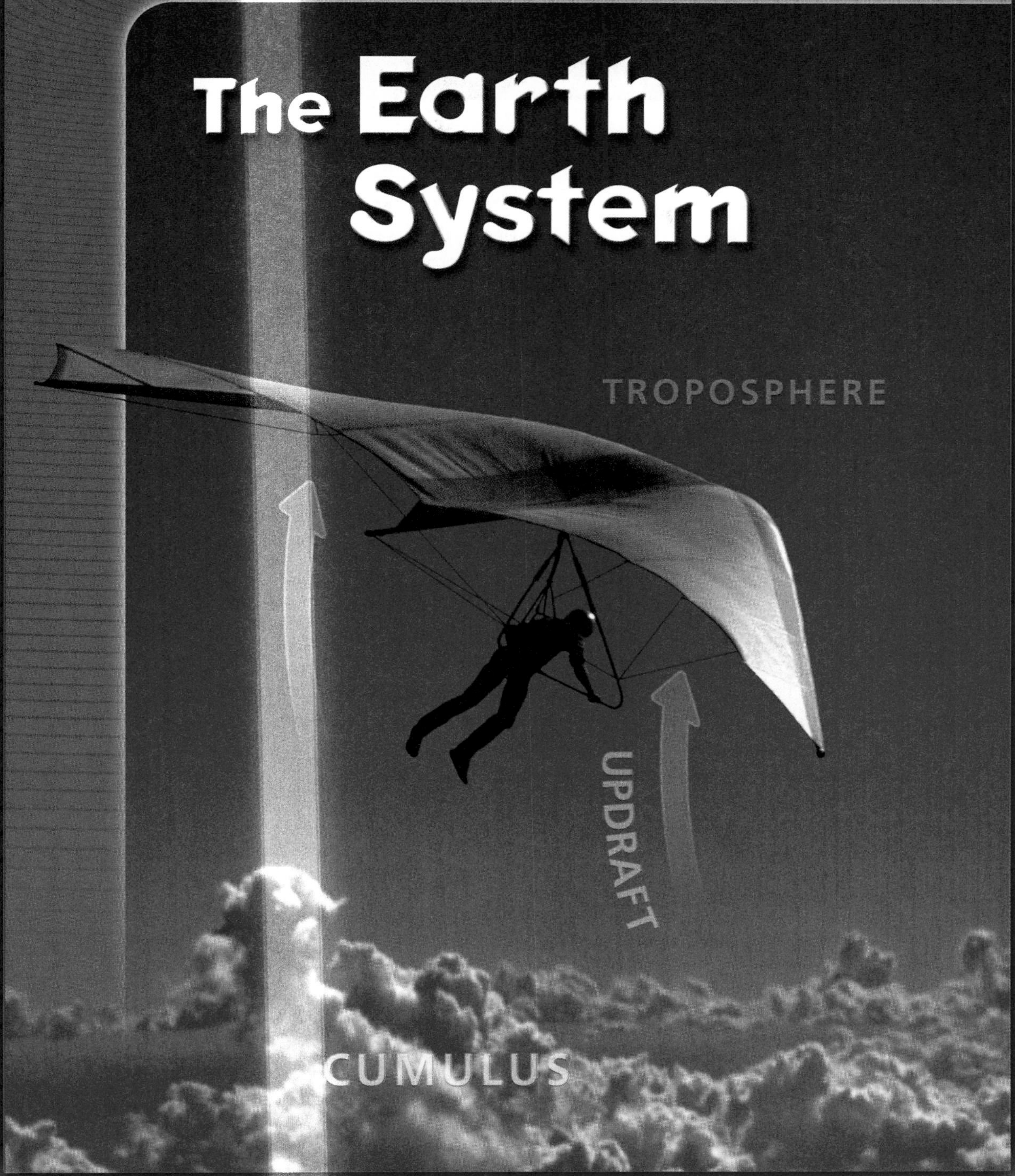

TROPOSPHERE

UPDRAFT

CUMULUS

Contents Overview

Unit 1 Scientific Background

Below is an in-depth look at some subtopics of the concepts presented in this unit.

ENERGY AND CHANGE: Potential and Kinetic Energy

Scientists classify energy into two categories: potential and kinetic. All the various forms of energy, such as mechanical, chemical, electrical, and sound, can be classified as some combination of potential and kinetic energy.

Potential Energy The stored energy an object possesses, such as in its molecular bonds, or as a result of its position in a gravitational field, is potential energy. It is energy that can be—but has not yet been—released. A boulder at the edge of a cliff has gravitational potential energy. A stretched rubber band has stored mechanical energy. When it snaps, its potential energy is released. Both food and fuels contain potential chemical energy in the bonds that hold their atoms and molecules together.

Kinetic Energy The energy an object possesses as a result of its motion is kinetic energy. Because all matter consists of atoms and molecules that are in motion, all objects and substances that are seemingly at rest have kinetic energy as well. This energy is referred to as internal kinetic energy. The movement of electrical charges through a wire and the movement of air particles as sound waves in a concert hall are examples of kinetic energy.

Temperature is a measure of the average kinetic energy of the atoms and molecules of a substance. A higher temperature indicates more internal energy. Units used to measure temperature include Kelvin. The Kelvin scale begins at absolute zero, ice melts at 273 K (0°C, 32°F), and water boils at 373 K (100°C, 212°F).

Kinetic Molecular Theory The relationship between physical composition of a gas and such properties as temperature and pressure is described by kinetic molecular theory. A gas consists of atoms and molecules that are in constant, random motion. The atoms and molecules have kinetic energy because they are moving. The faster they move, the higher the temperature of the gas. A temperature value in Kelvin is directly proportional to the average kinetic energy of the atoms and molecules of a substance. Therefore, if the temperature value in Kelvin of a substance increases by a factor of two, then the average kinetic energy of the atoms and molecules of the substance has doubled.

ENERGY IN THE EARTH SYSTEM: Earth's Energy Budget

Earth's energy budget, or radiation budget, includes all gains of incoming energy and all losses of outgoing energy. The balance of incoming solar energy and the energy reflected or re-radiated to space keeps Earth at a fairly constant average surface temperature of about 15°C (59°F).

Balancing the Energy Budget What would happen if the Earth system did not maintain a balanced energy budget? The Earth system would heat up if the amount of incoming solar energy were greater than the amount of energy eventually sent back into space. On the other hand, the Earth system would cool down if the amount of incoming solar energy were less than the amount of outgoing energy. Such a change occurs when Earth enters an ice age.

During a year, the incoming solar energy reaching Earth's surface is balanced by the outgoing thermal infrared energy emitted through the atmosphere. This is true for Earth as a whole, not for specific regions. The equatorial region receives more energy than is emitted to space, and polar regions emit more energy to space than they receive from the Sun. The transport of heat from the equator toward the poles accounts for this apparent paradox.

Measuring Energy NASA uses satellite instruments to measure and track Earth's incoming and outgoing energy. The Space Shuttle Challenger launched the first Earth Radiation Budget Satellite (ERBS) in 1984. Instruments on weather satellites launched by the National Oceanic and Atmospheric Administration also provide data on incoming energy from the Sun and outgoing energy from Earth.

The Greenhouse Effect Earth's atmosphere is largely transparent to solar energy in the visible part of the electromagnetic spectrum. Much of this energy is absorbed by Earth's surface and released at longer wavelengths as infrared radiation. Greenhouse gases such as water vapor, carbon dioxide, and methane absorb this outgoing terrestrial radiation. The gases then re-radiate the infrared radiation in all directions, including out into space and back toward Earth's surface. By slowing the escape of heat energy to space, greenhouse gases keep Earth's average surface temperature about 33°C higher than it would otherwise be. This process is known as the greenhouse effect.

The analogy between a greenhouse and the action of greenhouse gases is somewhat misleading. Like the atmosphere, glass in a greenhouse is transparent to visible light. The glass absorbs and re-radiates outgoing terrestrial infrared energy. However, the main way that a greenhouse traps heat is by blocking the escape of warmed air by convection. No such process blocks convection in the atmosphere.

WEATHER PATTERNS: Seasonal Changes in Atmospheric Circulation

Since the amount of solar radiation received by the northern and southern hemispheres changes with the seasons, the location of pressure zones and global winds also varies with the seasons. The main pressure zones and their accompanying winds move an average of about 10 to 15 degrees in latitude during the year. Their seasonal migration affects the precipitation and other weather conditions in many areas.

Locations of Pressure Zones In the doldrums, the region that surrounds the equator, is a low-pressure zone called the equatorial low. Because the trade winds of the northern and southern hemispheres converge in this zone, it is also called the intertropical convergence zone (ITCZ). In the horse latitudes, which are about 30° north and 30° south of the equator, is a zone of high pressure called the subtropical high. Although these pressure systems are commonly called zones, in actuality, landmasses break them up into low- and high-pressure cells.

Seasonal Migration in the Northern Hemisphere In summer in the Northern Hemisphere, the ITCZ and the subtropical highs move north or toward the North Pole, following the Sun. The subtropical highs grow stronger and expand in the summer. In the winter, the ITCZ and the subtropical highs move south toward the equator, again following the Sun. The subtropical highs become weaker and smaller in the winter.

The polar jet stream follows a similar migration pattern. It moves north in the summer and south in the winter. It blows stronger in the winter than in the summer. The polar jet stream is closely associated with the polar front, which is the boundary between the cold easterlies from the poles and the warmer westerlies from the horse latitudes.

Effects on Weather in California The summertime movement of a subtropical high to the north brings generally dry weather to the west coast of California. In the winter, when the subtropical high and the polar jet stream move south, the region has cooler, rainy weather.

WEATHER FRONTS AND STORMS: Mid-latitude Cyclones

Although many people use the word cyclone as another name for a tornado, the term actually refers to a large area of low pressure with rotating winds and rising air. A tornado also has rotating winds, but it is both smaller in scale and more violent than a cyclone. The winds of a cyclone blow inward in a counterclockwise direction in the Northern Hemisphere and a clockwise direction in the Southern Hemisphere.

The mid-latitude cyclones are large areas of low pressure that occur between 30 degrees and 60 degrees in latitude. Most of the United States lies within this latitude range, and mid-latitude cyclones produce the majority of the stormy weather in the country. The mid-latitude cyclones generally move from west to east.

Development of a Cyclone In the United States, a cyclone typically begins to develop along the boundary between a warm, moist air mass from the Gulf moving northward and a cold, dry air mass from Canada moving southward. The leading parts of these air masses wrap around a center of low pressure. As the winds circle inward, the warm, moist air rises. Then clouds typically form and precipitation occurs. Eventually, all the warm air rises and cooler air replaces it, eliminating the temperature and pressure difference in the lower atmosphere. Then the winds slow, and the cyclone dies out.

Cyclonic Weather Conditions On a satellite weather map, a cyclone appears as a cloud pattern shaped like a comma. Most cyclones pass over a region in about two to four days. In this short time, however, sudden changes in weather conditions are common. The passage of a mid-latitude cyclone over the middle of the United States can generate thunderstorms that produce heavy rain, hail, and sometimes a tornado. Such severe thunderstorms are most likely to occur in the spring.

FRONTIERS in Science

VIDEO SUMMARY

SCIENTIFIC AMERICAN FRONTIERS

"Dust Busting" is a 10-minute video that takes viewers underwater in the Caribbean Sea to observe a mysterious coral disease. Alan Alda introduces the work of three scientists who find evidence that the coral die-off links to dust storms in Northwest Africa.

The scientists collect evidence to support their hypothesis that African dust caused the coral disease. First, diseased coral samples from six islands reveal the same threadlike fungus. Second, the fungus is gene-mapped and found to match an African strain of the soil fungus *aspergillus*. Third, the scientists use space shuttle photography to view huge storm clouds that carried soil across the Atlantic. Fourth, the scientists filter the Caribbean air for dust, and again find the same *aspergillus*.

Finally, scientists drill core samples of boulder coral representing 30 years' worth of growth. In the lab, the core samples are dissolved, leaving a residue. They find high soil content trapped in the coral that lived during the peak years of the dust storms.

California Content Standards

6.4.e Students know differences in pressure, heat, air movement, and humidity result in changes of weather.

6.5.b Students know matter is transferred over time from one organism to others in the food web and between organisms and the physical environment.

FRONTIERS in Science

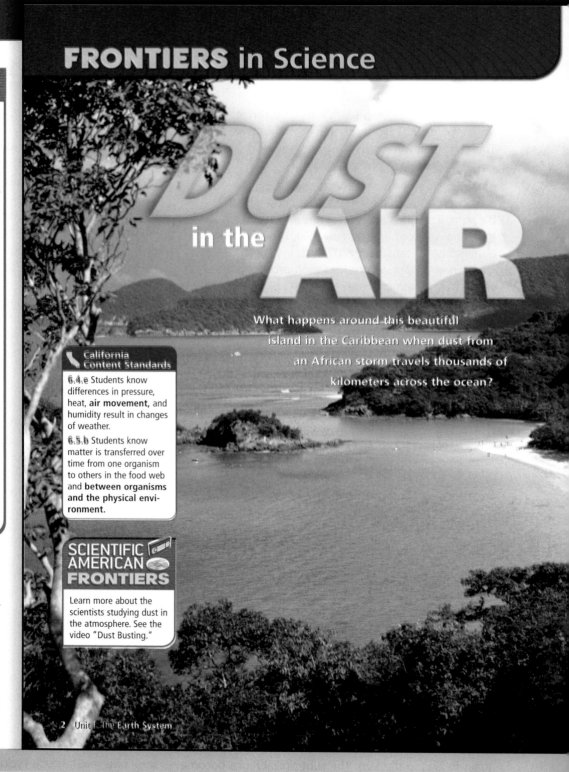

DUST in the AIR

What happens around this beautiful island in the Caribbean when dust from an African storm travels thousands of kilometers across the ocean?

California Content Standards

6.4.e Students know differences in pressure, heat, **air movement,** and humidity result in changes of weather.

6.5.b Students know matter is transferred over time from one organism to others in the food web and **between organisms and the physical environment.**

SCIENTIFIC AMERICAN FRONTIERS

Learn more about the scientists studying dust in the atmosphere. See the video "Dust Busting."

2 Unit 1: The Earth System

ADDITIONAL RESOURCES

Technology Resources

Scientific American Frontiers Video: *Dust Busting:*
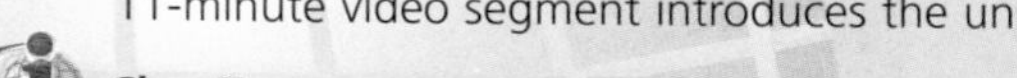
11-minute video segment introduces the unit.

ClassZone.com
CAREER LINK, careers in meteorology

Guide student viewing and comprehension of the video:

 Video Teaching Guide, pp. 1–2; Video Viewing Guide, p. 3; Video Wrap-Up, p. 4

Scientific American Frontiers Video Guide, pp. 33–36

Unit projects procedures and rubrics:

 Unit Projects, pp. 5–10

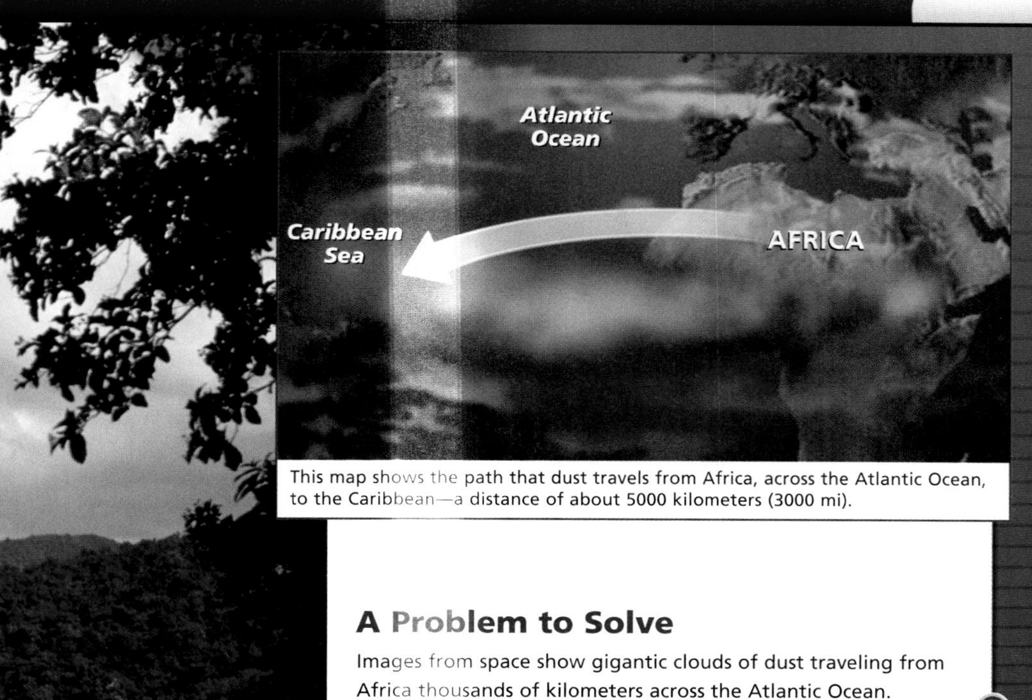

This map shows the path that dust travels from Africa, across the Atlantic Ocean, to the Caribbean—a distance of about 5000 kilometers (3000 mi).

A Problem to Solve

Images from space show gigantic clouds of dust traveling from Africa thousands of kilometers across the Atlantic Ocean. Weather reports in the Caribbean warn listeners about African dust storms. Coral and manatees in Caribbean waters show signs of disease. Are these events connected? (?) A

Each year, natural events and human activities together send as much as 2 billion metric tons of material into the skies. Once dust enters the atmosphere, it moves with the other materials in the air.

But how do Earth's surface processes and the movement of air relate to diseased coral? Teams of scientists studied diseases in living things around the Caribbean. In addition, they examined satellite photographs and recorded when dust storms occurred. After analyzing these data, they hypothesized that materials in African dust were affecting living things in the Caribbean. (?) B

Satellite images show us how far dust can travel in the atmosphere. Experiments on air samples let scientists look at dust up close. Tests reveal that atmospheric dust includes many substances, including living material. As often happens in science, this new knowledge raises more questions. Could the living material in dust grow in a distant location? Could a fungus that lives in African soil end up in Caribbean waters?

FOCUS

Set Learning Goals

Students will

- Examine some effects of dust storms.
- Determine how dust particles in the air can be analyzed.
- Design an experiment to explore atmospheric changes.

Remind students that frontiers are undeveloped fields for discovery or research, and that the "Dust Busting" video shows real scientists gathering and analyzing data to ask questions and find answers. Have students look at the visuals and title on the first two pages and predict what questions the scientists are trying to answer.

INSTRUCT

Scientific Process

After students have read p. 3, ask: What problem did scientists attempt to solve? *Could dust from Africa cause disease in Caribbean coral?* What scientific processes or skills did scientists use to solve the problem? *ask a question, hypothesize*

Teach from Visuals

Ask students how the photographs of dust storms support the scientists' hypothesis. *They show that dust from the African storm did reach the Caribbean.*

DIFFERENTIATE INSTRUCTION

More Reading Support

A What organisms are diseased in the Caribbean? *coral and manatees*

B What may have caused the diseases? *dust from Africa*

Below Level Have students use a globe or world map to locate the Caribbean Islands and the western coast of Africa. Have students trace the path of the dust across the Atlantic Ocean.

Scientific Process

Ask students to identify the parts of the scientific process described on this page. *investigate and interpret results*

Data Collection

Have students describe several ways the scientists collected data to support their hypothesis. *The scientists collected air samples during dust storms in the Caribbean, collected dust from the air, filtered air to trap dust, placed dust on nutrients, and looked for growth.*

Interpret Results

Make a table on the board using the following heads: "Helpful effects" and "Harmful effects." Have students fill in the effects of the African dust in the proper column. For guidance, tell them to use both the visuals and text. Point out that the cause is the dust from Africa; they are now evaluating its effects.

Helpful effects	Harmful effects
bits of metal: iron nourishes plants	fungi: cause disease in coral, sea fans
	bacteria: cause rapid growth of red algae, which hurts manatees, others

Integrate the Sciences

Aspergillus fungi belong to a group known as imperfect fungi. There are several species. *Aspergillus niger* is a fuzzy black type that grows on old jams or jellies. *Aspergillus flavus* grows on stale bread or stored grains. Some species of *aspergillus* are used to make antibiotics.

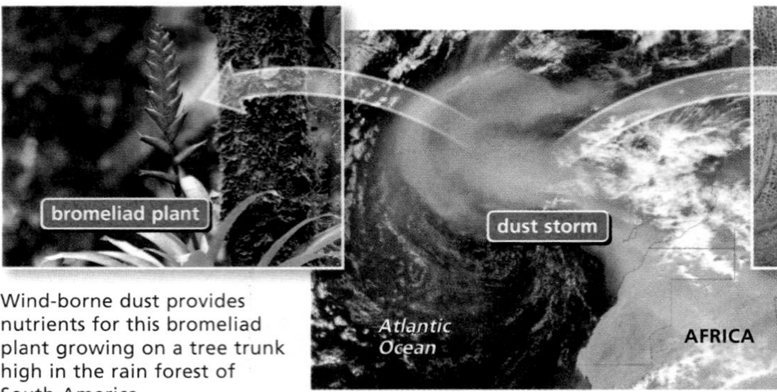

Wind-borne dust provides nutrients for this bromeliad plant growing on a tree trunk high in the rain forest of South America.

The huge dust storm shown in this satellite image carries both destructive fungus spores and life-sustaining nutrients across the Atlantic.

Fungus spores carried on dust particles have infected sea-fan corals growing on this reef near the island of St. John in the Caribbean Sea.

Answers Hidden in Dust

To explore these questions, scientists in the Caribbean gather air samples during dust storms. They collect dust from high in the air and from locations closer to Earth's surface. To collect the samples, scientists pull air through a paper filter, trapping the dust. Once they have caught the dust, the scientists are ready to perform tests to see what's really in the tiny particles. C

In the laboratory, researchers place dust samples on top of nutrients in petri dishes. Then they see if anything in the dust grows. Recent studies have shown that dust samples collected over the Caribbean contained African fungi and bacteria. More importantly, scientists saw that, even after their long voyage through the atmosphere, the living materials were able to grow.

View the "Dust Busting" segment of your *Scientific American Frontiers* video to learn about the detective work that went into solving the mystery of sea-fan disease.

IN THIS SCENE FROM THE VIDEO Biologist Ginger Garrison shows diseased coral to host Alan Alda.

MYSTERY SOLVED Sea fans are an important part of the Caribbean coral-reef community, but in the 1970s they began to die off. Recently marine biologist Garriet Smith was surprised to discover that a common soil fungus, called aspergillus, was killing the sea fans. But how could a soil fungus reach an undersea reef?

The answer came from geologist Gene Shinn, who knew that global winds carry dust from Africa to the Caribbean. When Shinn read about Smith's research, he hypothesized that aspergillus might be arriving with African dust. Shinn teamed up with Smith and biologist Ginger Garrison to test the hypothesis. They collected Caribbean air samples during an African dust event and cultured dust from the samples. Aspergillus grew in their very first cultures.

DIFFERENTIATE INSTRUCTION

More Reading Support

C How did scientists catch the African dust? *by pulling air through a paper filter*

D Why did scientists put the dust on top of nutrients? *to see what grew*

English Learners Use this opportunity to remind students of the meaning of scientific process words such as *hypothesize* and *analyze*. Also, review potentially unfamiliar terms or phrases such as *air samples, dust samples,* and *biologist*. In addition to reading these words and phrases in the text, students will hear them in the video.

Dust from Africa also contains tiny bits of metals, such as iron. The soil and atmosphere in the Caribbean are enriched by iron carried in African dust. Beautiful plants called bromeliads get the iron they need directly from the atmosphere.

Unfortunately, some of the materials found in the dust samples could be harmful to living things, such as manatees and corals. One of the fungi found in Caribbean dust samples is *Aspergillus sydowii,* which may cause diseases in sea fans and other corals. In addition, the dust contains bacteria that may speed the growth of toxic red algae, which can be harmful to manatees and other ocean animals.

Strong Connections

Dust storms affect the entire planet. On April 6–8, 2001, soils from the Gobi Desert in Mongolia and China blew into the air, creating a massive dust cloud. Satellite images showed the cloud traveling eastward. A few days later people in the western United States saw the sky turn a chalky white.

Such observations of atmospheric dust show us how events in one part of the planet can affect living and nonliving things thousands of kilometers away in ways we might not have imagined.

UNANSWERED Questions

Tiny particles of atmospheric dust may have huge effects. Yet the more we learn about the makeup and nature of dust, the more questions we have.

- How do dust storms affect human health?
- What can dust tell us about climate change?
- How can we use information about dust storms to predict climate change?
- How do materials in dust change ecosystems?

UNIT PROJECTS

As you study this unit, work alone or with a group on one of these projects.

TV News Report (6.4.e)

Prepare a brief news report on recent dust storms, using visuals and a script.

- Research dust storms that have occurred recently. Find out how they were related to the weather.
- Copy or print visuals, and write and practice delivering your report. Then make your presentation.

Map the Dust (6.7.f)

Make a map showing how dust arrives in your area or another location.

- Find out what the dust contains and how it moved there. Collect information from atlases, the Internet, newspapers, and magazines.
- Prepare your map, including all the areas you need to show. Include a key, a title, and a compass rose.

Design an Experiment (6.7.a, 6.7.d)

Design an experiment to explore how the atmosphere has changed. Research the forms of evidence scientists gather about the state of our atmosphere.

- Pick one question to investigate in an experiment. Write a hypothesis.
- List and assemble materials for your experiment. Create a data table and write up your procedure.
- Demonstrate or describe your experiment for the class.

Learn about careers in meteorology.

UNANSWERED Questions

Have students read the questions and think of some of their own. Remind them that scientists always end up with more questions—that inquiry is the driving force of science.

- With the class, generate on the board a list of new questions.
- Students can add to the list after they watch the *Scientific American Frontiers* Video.
- Students can use the list as a springboard for choosing their Unit Projects.

UNIT PROJECTS

Encourage students to pick the project that most appeals to them. Point out that each is long-term and will take several weeks to complete. You might group or pair students to work on projects, and in some cases guide student choice. Some of the projects have student choice built into them. Each project has two worksheet pages, including a rubric. Use the pages to guide students through criteria, process, and schedule.

 Unit Projects, pp. 5–10

REVISIT concepts introduced in this article:

Chapter 2
- parts of the Earth system, pp. 41–47
- movement of energy in the Earth system, pp. 58–67

Chapter 3
- global wind patterns, pp. 83–91

Chapter 4
- movement of air masses and storm systems, pp. 115–127

DIFFERENTIATE INSTRUCTION

More Reading Support

E What nutrients do plants obtain from the African dust? *iron*

F The dust contains bacteria that can speed the growth of what? *toxic red algae*

Differentiate Unit Projects Projects are appropriate for varying abilities. Allow students to choose the ones that interest them most. Encourage them to vary the products they produce throughout the year.

Below Level Encourage students to try "TV News Report."

Advanced Encourage students to complete "Design an Experiment."

CHAPTER

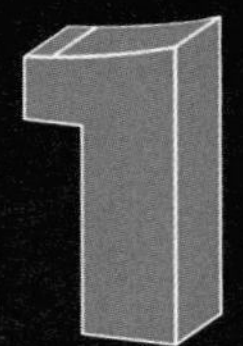

Energy and Change

Earth Science UNIFYING PRINCIPLES

PRINCIPLE 1
Heat energy inside Earth and radiation from the Sun provide energy for Earth's processes.

PRINCIPLE 2
Physical forces, such as gravity, affect the movement of all matter on Earth and throughout the universe.

PRINCIPLE 3
Matter and energy move among Earth's rocks and soil, atmosphere, waters, and living things.

PRINCIPLE 4
Earth has changed over time and continues to change.

Unit: The Earth System BIG IDEAS

CHAPTER 1
Energy and Change
Waves and heat flow transfer energy.

CHAPTER 2
Energy in the Earth System
The Sun is the major source of energy for Earth's atmosphere and surface.

CHAPTER 3
Weather Patterns
Some features of weather have predictable patterns.

CHAPTER 4
Weather Fronts and Storms
The interaction of air masses causes changes in weather.

CHAPTER 1 KEY CONCEPTS

SECTION 1

Change occurs as energy is transferred.

1. Life requires energy.
2. Energy has many forms.
3. Energy moves from one place to another.
4. Energy can change from one form to another.

SECTION 2

Radiation transfers energy.

1. Radiation travels in waves.
2. Earth receives radiation from the Sun.

SECTION 3

Heat energy flows from warmer to cooler areas.

1. Heat flow is a transfer of energy.
2. Heat flow by conduction requires contact.
3. Heat flow by convection involves a flow of matter.
4. Heat energy can be transferred in different ways at the same time.

The Big Idea Flow Chart is available on p. T1 in the **TRANSPARENCY BOOK.**

Previewing Content

SECTION

Change occurs as energy is transferred. pp. 9–17

1. Life requires energy.
Plants, animals, and other living things need **energy** to sustain life.

2. Energy has many forms.
Some of the principal forms that energy can take include:

- **mechanical energy**—the energy an object has due to its motion or position
- **sound energy**—energy that travels in waves produced by a vibrating objecct
- **chemical energy**—energy stored in the bonds that hold molecules together
- **electromagnetic energy**—visible light, x-rays, and other forms of energy emitted as radiation
- **heat energy**—the total energy of motion of the particles in an object

3. Energy moves from one place to another.
Energy is always on the move. Energy from the Sun travels to Earth and is used by plants to make food. The transfer of heat from one object to another is also a way energy moves. Heat always travels from warmer to cooler objects.

4. Energy can change from one form to another.
Chemical energy in an automobile's fuel changes form once the car is started. The energy becomes mechanical energy that makes the car move. Some of the mechanical energy turns into sound energy as the engine parts move. Although energy changes form, its total amount remains constant. According to the law of **conservation of energy**, energy can neither be created nor destroyed.

SECTION

Radiation transfers energy. pp. 18–25

1. Radiation travels in waves.
The light you see is one form of electromagnetic energy, or **radiation.** The light travels to your eyes in the form of **waves.** Similarly, other kinds of electromagnetic energy travel in waves. That energy forms the **electromagnetic spectrum**, comprising radiation from the shortest to the longest **wavelengths.**

2. Earth receives radiation from the Sun.
Radiation from the Sun takes about eight minutes to reach Earth. Once the radiation reaches the surface, a portion of it is reflected, but the land and oceans absorb much of it. As people use up fossil fuels, such as petroleum and natural gas, experts are looking to use the power of the Sun's radiation as an alternative energy source.

Common Misconceptions

ENERGY AND MATTER Students may think that everything that exists is matter, including heat, light, and electricity. Matter has mass and takes up space, whereas energy does not.

 This misconception is addressed on p. 10.

MISCONCEPTION DATABASE
CLASSZONE.COM Background on student misconceptions

DISPLACEMENT OF MATTER Students may conceive of waves as the motion of matter from one place to another. Although matter can move in a wave, it is not permanently displaced. Rather, it is energy—not matter—that is transferred in a wave.

 This misconception is addressed on p. 20.

Previewing Content

SECTION

Heat energy flows from warmer to cooler areas. pp. 26–33

1. **Heat flow is a transfer of energy.**
The movement of heat energy is called heat flow. Energy transfers from warmer objects to colder objects. On a cold day, people wear clothes that retard the transfer of heat from their bodies to the colder air.

2. **Heat flow by conduction requires contact.**
Conduction is the transfer of energy from one object to another and requires direct contact. The heat flow always moves from the warmer object to the colder one. Atoms and molecules with greater energy collide with other atoms and molecules and transfer some of their energy. Solids tend to conduct heat energy better than liquids and gases because their particles are more tightly packed. Metals are often good conductors. Materials such as wood and paper are poor conductors and are called insulators.

3. **Heat flow by convection involves a flow of matter.**
Convection occurs only in materials like gases and liquids that are able to flow. The colder part of a fluid becomes denser as molecules move closer together, and it tends to sink. Correspondingly, the warmer, less dense part rises. This process causes a flow within the material. Convection plays an important part in Earth's weather. Uneven heating of the planet creates **convection currents** of hot and cold air in the atmosphere. People who fly hang gliders take advantage of those currents to stay aloft.

4. **Heat energy can be transferred in different ways at the same time.**
Heat from a fire can transfer energy by radiation, conduction, and convection all at the same time. When wood burns, it gives off energy as radiation—visible light and infrared energy. Heat from the fire also warms the surrounding air by conduction. The warmed air helps establish a current in the air that warms the room by convection.

Common Misconceptions

MISCONCEPTION DATABASE

CLASSZONE.COM Background on student misconceptions

HEAT Some students may think that heat is a fluid that literally flows from one object to another and that heat and cold are different, rather than being at opposite ends of an energy flow. Heat is the flow of energy from a warm substance to a cooler substance.

This misconception is addressed on p. 27.

DIRECTION OF HEAT FLOW Because students have often heard that heat rises, they may think that heat only travels upward. Heat can transfer energy in all directions, depending upon the process that is involved.

This misconception is addressed on p. 30.

Previewing Labs

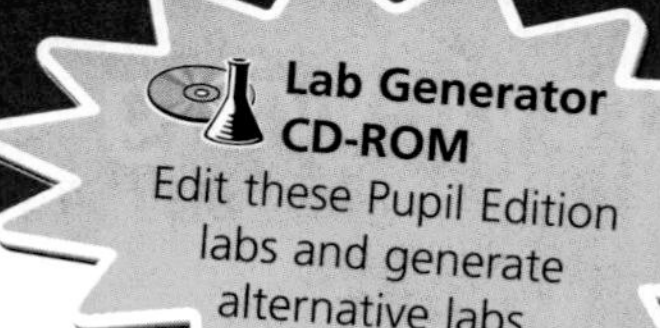

EXPLORE the BIG idea		
	A Penny for Your Energy, p. 7 Students explore the transfer of energy from a warm object to a cold object.	**TIME** 10 minutes **MATERIALS** cold glass bottle, cooking oil, coin
	Hot Dog! p. 7 Students use a solar-energy collector to cook a hot dog.	**TIME** 40 minutes **MATERIALS** cardboard, aluminum foil, wooden skewer, hot dog, two corks
SECTION 1	**INVESTIGATE Energy,** p. 14 Students observe one way that energy can change its form. **ALTERNATIVE:** Reading Activity, URB p. 274	**TIME** 15 minutes **MATERIALS** paper, marker, scissors, thread, tape, desk lamp
	CHAPTER INVESTIGATION Changes in Energy, pp. 16–17 Students investigate the amount of energy stored in different kinds of food by constructing a simple calorimeter and burning food samples. **ALTERNATIVE:** Teacher Modeling, URB p. 274	**TIME** 40 minutes **MATERIALS** empty aluminum can with holes, dowel rod, water, graduated cylinder, ring stand with ring, thermometer, tape, aluminum pie plate, aluminum foil, large paper clip, cork, modeling clay, crouton, caramel rice cake, balance, wooden matches
SECTION 2	**EXPLORE Radiation,** p. 18 Students hold their hands near a lit and an unlit light bulb to learn about radiation.	**TIME** 5 minutes **MATERIALS** lamp
	INVESTIGATE Energy Transfer, p. 23 Students observe how the color of a solar-energy collector affects the amount of energy collected. **ALTERNATIVE:** Reading Activity, URB p. 274	**TIME** 20 minutes **MATERIALS** 2 plastic cups, white and black plastic to cover cups, 2 rubber bands, scissors, 2 thermometers, stopwatch, aluminum foil
SECTION 3	**EXPLORE Conduction,** p. 26 Students observe the direction in which energy is transferred through direct contact between objects at different temperatures.	**TIME** 10 minutes **MATERIALS** 500 mL beaker, hot tap water, cold water, 2 thermometers, stopwatch, 200 mL beaker
	INVESTIGATE Density, p. 29 Students attempt to layer three different liquids in a cup to infer why liquids form layers. **ALTERNATIVE:** Teacher Demonstration, URB p. 274	**TIME** 15 minutes **MATERIALS** 3 solutions—A, B, and C—provided by teacher, clear straw, waste cup

R **Additional INVESTIGATION,** Insulators, A, B, & C, pp. 60–68; Teacher Instructions, pp. 274–275

Previewing Chapter Resources

CHAPTER 1
Energy and Change

INTEGRATED TECHNOLOGY

CLASSZONE.COM
- eEdition Plus
- EasyPlanner Plus
- Misconception Database
- Content Review
- Test Practice
- Simulations
- Resource Centers
- Math Tutorial

SCILINKS.ORG

SCiLINKS

CD-ROMS
- eEdition
- EasyPlanner
- Power Presentations
- Content Review
- Lab Generator
- Test Generator

AUDIO CDS
- Audio Readings
- Audio Readings in Spanish

LABS AND ACTIVITIES

EXPLORE the Big Idea, p. 7
- A Penny for Your Energy
- Hot Dog!

UNIT RESOURCE BOOK
- Family Letter, p. vii
- Spanish Family Letter, p. viii
- Unit Projects, pp. 5–10

Lab Generator CD-ROM
Generate customized labs.

SECTION

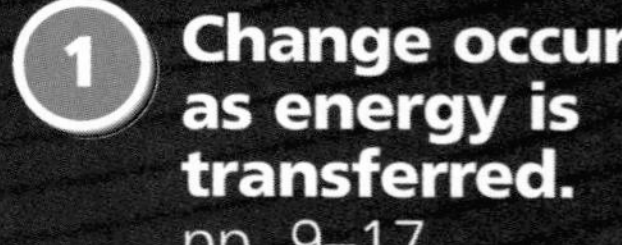

1 Change occurs as energy is transferred.
pp. 9–17

Lesson Plan, pp. 11–12

Integrated Technology

- **RESOURCE CENTER,** Energy Use
- **SIMULATION,** Lifting Virtual Weights

TRANSPARENCY BOOK
- Big Idea Flow Chart, p. T1
- Daily Vocabulary Scaffolding, p. T2
- Note-Taking Model, p. T3
- 3-Minute Warm-Up, p. T4
- "Changes in Forms of Energy" Visual, p. T6

Labs and Activities

- INVESTIGATE Energy, p. 14
- CHAPTER INVESTIGATION, Changes in Energy, pp. 16–17

UNIT RESOURCE BOOK
- Datasheet, Energy, p. 20
- CHAPTER INVESTIGATION, Changes in Energy, pp. 51–59

SECTION

2 Radiation transfers energy.
pp. 18–25

Lesson Plan, pp. 22–23

Integrated Technology

RESOURCE CENTER, Electromagnetic Spectrum

TRANSPARENCY BOOK
- Daily Vocabulary Scaffolding, p. T2
- 3-Minute Warm-Up, p. T4

Labs and Activities

- EXPLORE Radiation, p. 18
- INVESTIGATE Energy Transfer, p. 23
- Math in Science, p. 25

UNIT RESOURCE BOOK
- Datasheet, Energy Transfer, p. 31
- Math Support, p. 49
- Math Practice, p. 50

SECTION

3 Heat energy flows from warmer to cooler areas.
pp. 26–33

Lesson Plan, pp. 33–34

Integrated Technology

- **RESOURCE CENTER,** Convection Currents
- **SIMULATION,** Convection Currents

TRANSPARENCY BOOK
- Big Idea Flow Chart, p. T1
- Daily Vocabulary Scaffolding, p. T2
- 3-Minute Warm-Up, p. T5
- Chapter Outline, pp. T7–T8

Labs and Activities

- EXPLORE Conduction, p. 26
- INVESTIGATE Density, p. 29
- Science on the Job, p. 33

UNIT RESOURCE BOOK
- Datasheet, Density, p. 42
- Additional INVESTIGATION, Insulators, A, B, & C, pp. 60–68

KEY TO ICONS

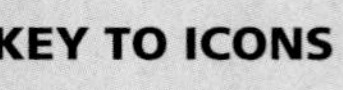 INTERNET

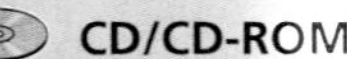 CD/CD-ROM

 Pupil Edition

 Teacher Edition

 UNIT RESOURCE BOOK

 TRANSPARENCY BOOK

 ASSESSMENT BOOK

 STANDARDS REVIEW AND PRACTICE

SCIENCE TOOLKIT

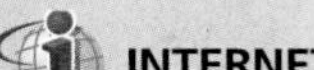

READING AND REINFORCEMENT	ASSESSMENT	STANDARDS
 **Modified Lesson Plans for English Learners,** pp. 3–7  • Magnet Word, B24–25 • Supporting Main Ideas, C42 • Daily Vocabulary Scaffolding, H1–8  **UNIT RESOURCE BOOK** • Vocabulary Practice, pp. 46–47 • Decoding Support, p. 48 • Summarizing the Chapter, pp. 69–70  **Audio Readings CD** Listen to Pupil Edition.   **Audio Readings in Spanish CD** Listen to Pupil Edition in Spanish. 	 • Chapter Review, pp. 35–36 • Standards-Based Assessment, p. 37  **ASSESSMENT BOOK** • Diagnostic Test, pp. 3–4 • Chapter Test, A, B, & C, pp. 8–19 • Alternative Assessment, pp. 20–21  **STANDARDS REVIEW AND PRACTICE,** pp. 23–30, 33–34, 37–38, 59–60  **McDougal Littell Assessment System** 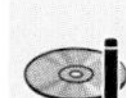 **Test Generator CD-ROM** Generate customized and Spanish tests.	California Content Standards 6.3.a, 6.3.b, 6.3.c, 6.3.d, 6.4.b, 6.4.d, 6.7.b, 6.7.c, 6.7.d See p. 6 for the standards.
UNIT RESOURCE BOOK • Reading Study Guide, A & B, pp. 13–16 • Spanish Reading Study Guide, pp. 17–18 • Challenge and Extension, p. 19 • Reinforcing Key Concepts, p. 21	 Ongoing Assessment, pp. 9–13, 15  Section 1.1 Review, p. 15  **ASSESSMENT BOOK** Section 1.1 Quiz, p. 5	California Content Standards 6.3.a, 6.3.b, 6.5.a, 6.7.b, 6.7.d
 **UNIT RESOURCE BOOK** • Reading Study Guide, A & B, pp. 24–27 • Spanish Reading Study Guide, pp. 28–29 • Challenge and Extension, p. 30 • Reinforcing Key Concepts, p. 32	 Ongoing Assessment, pp. 18–22, 24  Section 1.2 Review, p. 24  **ASSESSMENT BOOK** Section 1.2 Quiz, p. 6	California Content Standards 6.3.d, 6.4.b, 6.7.c
 **UNIT RESOURCE BOOK** • Reading Study Guide, A & B, pp. 35–38 • Spanish Reading Study Guide, pp. 39–40 • Challenge and Extension, p. 41 • Reinforcing Key Concepts, p. 43 • Challenge Reading, pp. 44–45	Ongoing Assessment, pp. 27–30, 32  Section 1.3 Review, p. 32  **ASSESSMENT BOOK** Section 1.3 Quiz, p. 7	California Content Standards 6.3.c, 6.4.d

Previewing Resources for Differentiated Instruction

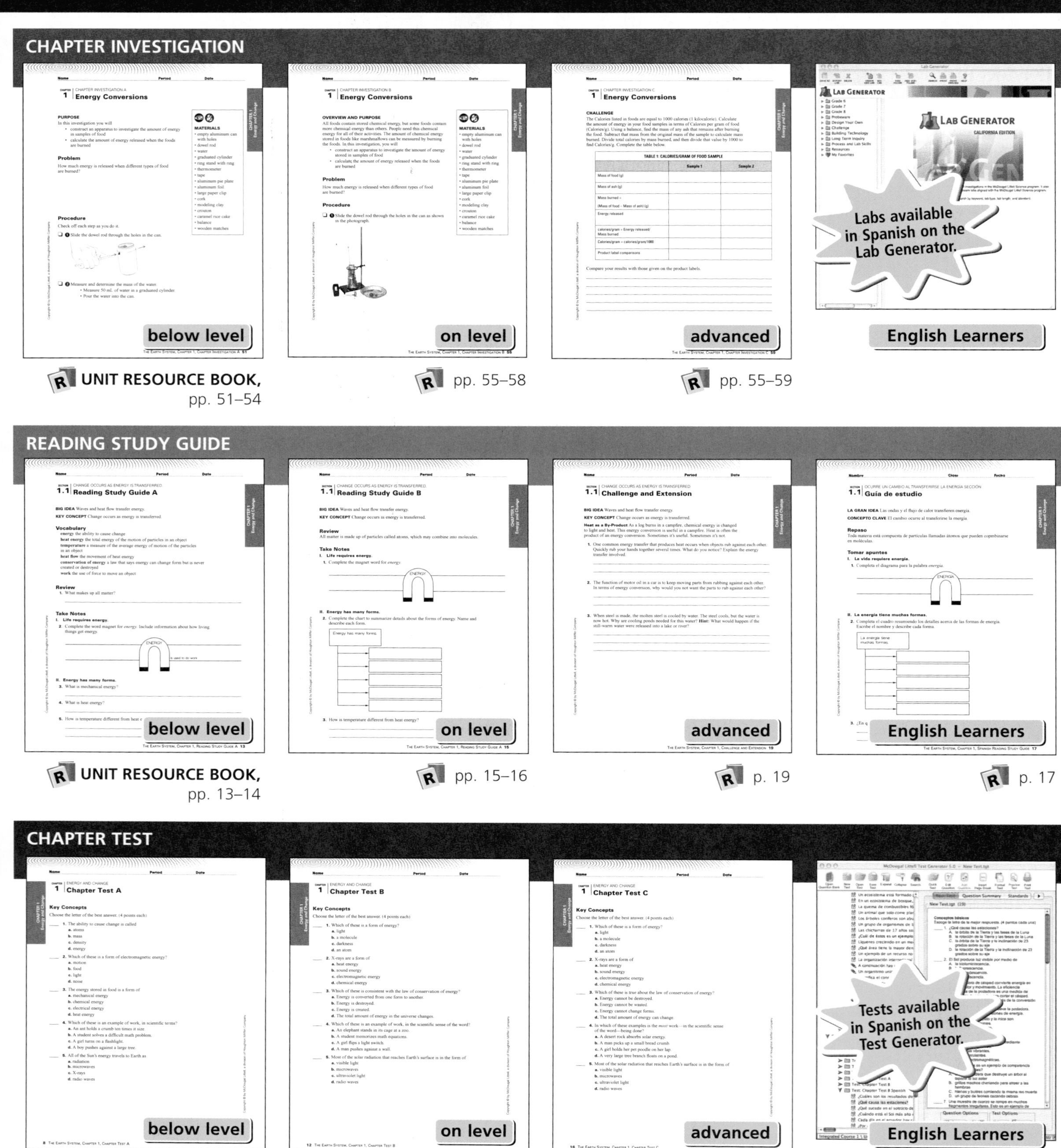

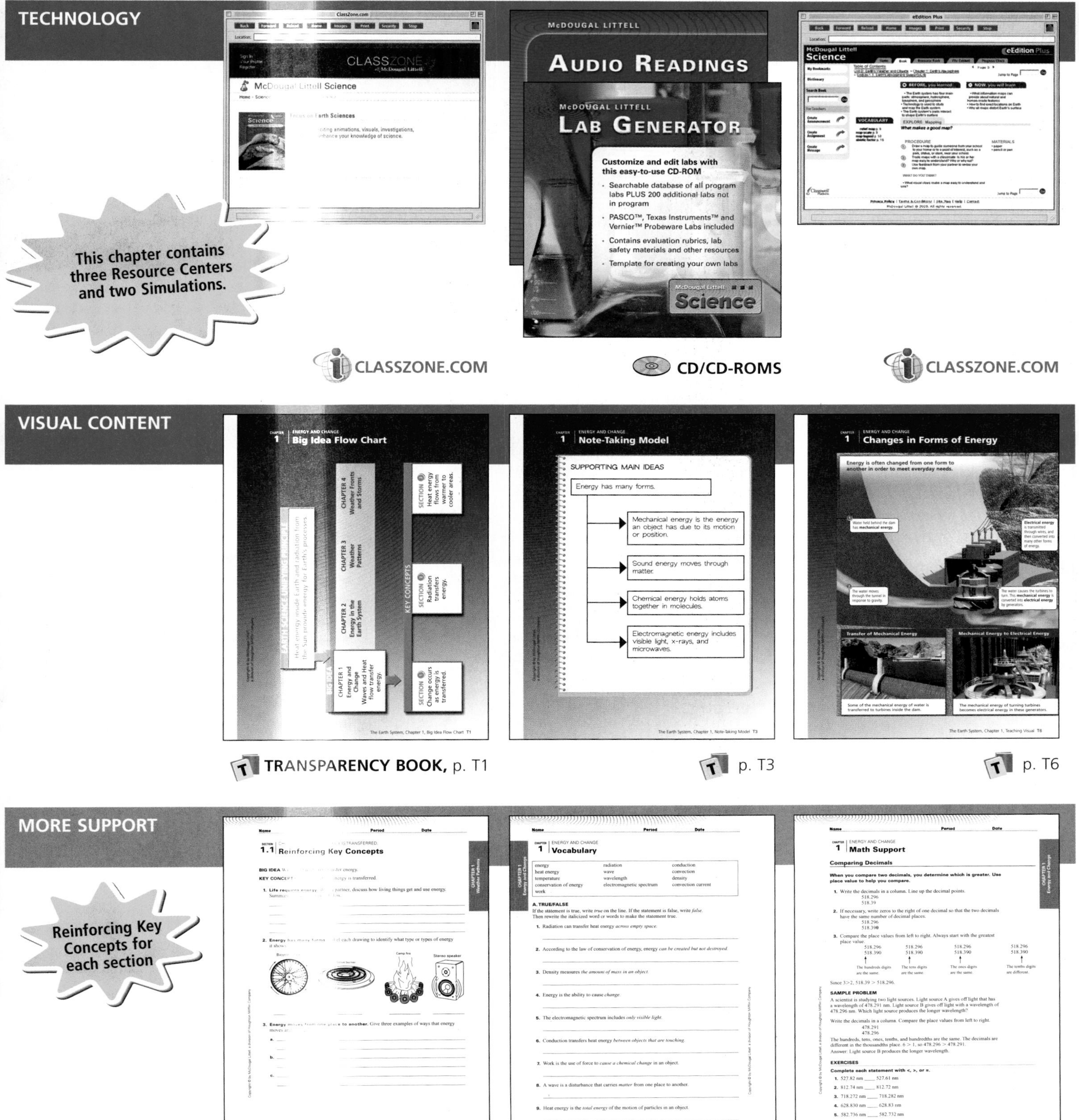

TECHNOLOGY
This chapter contains three Resource Centers and two Simulations.
McDougal Littell
Audio Readings
McDougal Littell
Lab Generator
Customize and edit labs with this easy-to-use CD-ROM
Searchable database of all program labs PLUS 200 additional labs not in program
PASCO™, Texas Instruments™ and Vernier™ Probeware Labs included
Contains evaluation rubrics, lab safety materials and other resources
Template for creating your own labs
McDougal Littell Science
CLASSZONE.COM
CD/CD-ROMS
CLASSZONE.COM
VISUAL CONTENT
Big Idea Flow Chart
Note-Taking Model
Changes in Forms of Energy
TRANSPARENCY BOOK, p. T1
p. T3
p. T6
MORE SUPPORT
Reinforcing Key Concepts for each section
Reinforcing Key Concepts
Vocabulary
Math Support
UNIT RESOURCE BOOK, p. 21
pp. 46–47
p. 49

CHAPTER 1 Energy and Change

INTRODUCE

the BIG idea

Have students look at the photograph of the cyclists and discuss how the question in the box links to the Big Idea:

- Which forms of energy are involved in riding a bicycle?
- Which activities that you participate in require energy?
- Which forms of energy do these activities require?

California Content Standards

6.3.a Students know energy can be carried from one place to another by heat flow or by waves, including water, light and sound waves, or by moving objects.

6.3.b Students know that when fuel is consumed, most of the energy released becomes heat energy.

6.3.c Students know heat flows in solids by conduction (which involves no flow of matter) and in fluids by conduction and by convection (which involves flow of matter).

6.3.d Students know heat energy is also transferred between objects by radiation (radiation can travel through space).

6.4.b Students know solar energy reaches Earth through radiation, mostly in the form of visible light.

6.4.d Students know convection currents distribute heat in the atmosphere and oceans.

6.7.b Select and use appropriate tools and technology (including calculators, computers, balances, spring scales, microscopes, and binoculars) to perform tests, collect data, and display data.

CHAPTER

Energy and Change

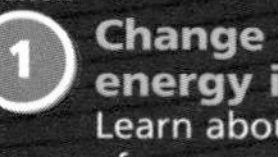

Waves and heat flow transfer energy.

Key Concepts

SECTION

Change occurs as energy is transferred.
Learn about different forms of energy and how energy can change from one form to another.

SECTION

Radiation transfers energy.
Learn about radiation and the electromagnetic spectrum.

SECTION

Heat energy flows from warmer to cooler areas.
Learn how the processes of conduction and convection transfer heat.

California ClassZone

CLASSZONE.COM

Chapter 1 online resources: Content Review, two Simulations, three Resource Centers, Math Tutorial, Test Practice

What different forms of energy are shown in this photograph?

INTERNET PREVIEW

CLASSZONE.COM For student use with the following pages:

Review and Practice
- Content Review, pp. 8, 34
- Math Tutorial: Comparing Decimals, p. 25
- Test Practice, p. 37

Activities and Resources
- Resource Centers: Energy Use, p. 12; Electromagnetic Spectrum, p. 21; Convection Currents, p. 30
- Simulations: Lifting Virtual Weights, p. 15; Convection Currents, p. 32

Forms of Energy
Code: MDL063

EXPLORE the BIG idea

A Penny for Your Energy

6.3.a Students know energy can be carried from one place to another by heat flow or by waves, including water, light and sound waves, or by moving objects.

Chill an empty glass bottle. Immediately complete the following steps. Rub a drop of cooking oil around the rim of the bottle. Place a coin on the rim so the oil forms a seal between the coin and the bottle. Wrap your hands around the bottle.

Observe and Think What happened to the coin? What do you think caused this to happen?

Hot Dog!

6.3.a Students know energy can be carried from one place to another by heat flow or by waves, including water, light and sound waves, or by moving objects.

Cover a piece of cardboard with aluminum foil. Bend it into the shape of a U. Poke a wooden skewer through a hot dog and through each side of the cardboard. Push corks over both ends of the skewer so the cardboard does not flatten out. Place your setup in direct sunlight for 30 minutes.

Observe and Think
What happened to the hot dog?
Propose an explanation for what happened.

NSTA scilinks.org SCILINKS
Forms of Energy **Code: MDL063**

EXPLORE the BIG idea

These inquiry-based activities are appropriate for use at home or as a supplement to classroom instruction.

A Penny for Your Energy

PURPOSE To introduce students to the concept of energy transfer. Students will see how heat causes air to expand and pop the coin off the rim of the bottle.

TIP *10 min.* Make sure the coin forms a tight seal on the bottle.

Answer: The coin popped off the bottle. Hand warmth caused the air in the bottle to expand and force off the bottle top.

REVISIT after p. 11.

Hot Dog!

PURPOSE To introduce students to the concepts of energy and waves. Students use aluminum foil to collect energy from the Sun. The energy is reflected off the foil and cooks the hot dog.

TIP *40 min.* Make sure the corks are tightly secured to the ends of the wooden skewer and that the aluminum foil stays bent in a U shape.

Answer: The hot dog was warmed and perhaps cooked. The Sun's energy was reflected off the aluminum foil as waves and cooked the hot dog.

REVISIT after p. 23.

TEACHING WITH TECHNOLOGY

If students have a temperature probe, they can measure temperature changes in burning food on p. 16.

If students have a conductivity probe, they can measure the conductivity of the water on p. 26.

PREPARE

CONCEPT REVIEW

Activate Prior Knowledge

- Draw a diagram of an atom on the board. Tell students that atoms are made up of protons, neutrons, and electrons. Ask students to identify the protons, neutrons, and electrons in the diagram.
- Use a desk lamp and a globe to show how Earth receives light and energy from the Sun.
- Ask students which processes that occur on Earth need energy. Have them name three to five processes, such as the weather, the movement of continents, or life. Then discuss how each process depends on energy.

TAKING NOTES

Supporting Main Ideas

Ask students to use their charts to develop well-written paragraphs about the main ideas in the chapter. Let them know that they can add information to what is in the charts to develop the paragraphs. Tell them they may want to use linking words such as *also* and *additionally* to connect ideas. Students might also want to note the significance of the information in the charts by using terms such as *most important, first,* or *starting with.*

Vocabulary Strategy

Ask students to use the information in their magnet word diagrams to help them write one sentence for each of the new words.

Vocabulary and Note-Taking Resources

- Vocabulary Practice, pp. 46–47
- Decoding Support, p. 48

- Daily Vocabulary Scaffolding, p. T2
- Note-Taking Model, p. T3

- Magnet Word, B24–25
- Supporting Main Ideas, C42
- Daily Vocabulary Scaffolding, H1–8

CHAPTER 1

Getting Ready to Learn

CONCEPT REVIEW

- All matter is made of tiny particles called atoms.
- Earth receives energy from the Sun.
- All of Earth's processes need energy to occur.

VOCABULARY REVIEW

See Glossary for definitions.

atom
force
matter
molecule

Review concepts and vocabulary.

TAKING NOTES

SUPPORTING MAIN IDEAS

Make a chart to show each main idea and the information that supports it. Copy each blue heading, which is a main idea. Below it, add supporting information, such as reasons, explanations, and examples.

VOCABULARY STRATEGY

Draw a **magnet word** diagram for each new vocabulary term. Around the magnet write words and ideas related to the term.

See the Note-Taking Handbook on pages R45–R51.

SCIENCE NOTEBOOK

Energy has many forms.
- Mechanical energy is the energy an object has due to its motion or position.
- Sound energy moves through matter.
- Chemical energy holds atoms together in molecules.
- Electromagnetic energy includes visible light, x-rays, and microwaves.

ENERGY
- ability to cause change
- has many forms
- can change forms
- is used to do work

8 Unit 1: The Earth System

CHECK READINESS

Administer the Diagnostic Test to determine students' readiness for new science content and their mastery of requisite math skills.

 Diagnostic Test, pp. 3–4

Technology Resources

Students needing content and math skills should visit **ClassZone.com.**

- **CONTENT REVIEW**
- **MATH TUTORIAL**

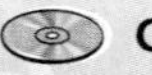 **CONTENT REVIEW CD-ROM**

KEY CONCEPT

1.1 Change occurs as energy is transferred.

CALIFORNIA Content Standards

6.3.a Students know energy can be carried from one place to another by heat flow or by waves, including water, light and sound waves, or by moving objects.

6.3.b Students know that when fuel is consumed, most of the energy released becomes heat energy.

BEFORE, you learned

- Matter is made of atoms, which may combine to make molecules
- Volume refers to the amount of space an object takes up
- Mass is a measure of how much matter an object contains

NOW, you will learn

- About some forms of energy
- How energy moves from place to place
- How energy can change from one form to another

VOCABULARY

energy p. 9
heat energy p. 10
temperature p. 10
heat flow p. 11
conservation of energy p. 14
work p. 15

THINK ABOUT

From what source do animals get their energy?

The California dogface butterfly (*Zerene eurydice*) is the state insect of California. When the butterfly is an adult, it feeds on flower nectar. Where do you think the butterfly gets the energy it needs to fly from flower to flower?

SUPPORTING MAIN IDEAS Support the main idea about life and energy with details and examples.

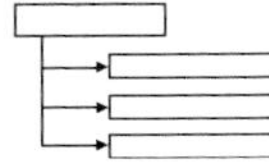

Life requires energy.

All living things need energy to live and grow. **Energy** is the ability to cause change. A redwood tree needs energy to produce new branches and leaves. A whale needs energy to swim through the ocean. You need energy for all of your activities, including eating, exercising, and even sleeping.

All living things get energy from food. Plants use energy from sunlight to make their own food. Using this energy, plants combine carbon dioxide from the air, and water from the soil, into sugars. Plants store these sugars for future use. Animals, including people, get energy by eating plants or by eating other animals that ate plants. When you eat a baked potato or a slice of chicken, you are gaining energy that originally came from sunlight.

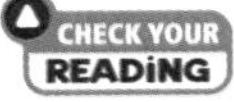

CHECK YOUR READING Where does the energy you need for talking or for playing basketball originally come from?

1.1 FOCUS

Set Learning Goals

Students will

- Know that there are different forms of energy.
- Explain how energy can move from one place to another.
- Know how energy can change forms.
- Observe how energy changes from one form into another.

3-Minute Warm-Up

Display Transparency 4 or copy this exercise to the board.

Are these statements true? If not, correct them.

1. Molecules join together to form different kinds of atoms. *Atoms combine to form molecules.*
2. You can determine an object's volume by weighing it. *An object's volume is the amount of space an object takes up without regard to its weight.*
3. An object's mass can be determined by how much matter it contains. true

3-Minute Warm-Up, p. T4

1.1 MOTIVATE

THINK ABOUT

PURPOSE To introduce the concept that energy powers life

DISCUSS Where do you get the energy you need to walk to school?

Sample answer: I get energy from sleep and food.

Ongoing Assessment

Know that there are different forms of energy.

Ask: Where do plants get energy to make food? Where do animals get the energy they need to live? *Plants get energy from sunlight; animals get the energy from eating plants or other animals*

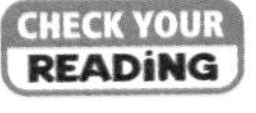

CHECK YOUR READING *Answer: The energy comes from the food a person eats.*

RESOURCES FOR DIFFERENTIATED INSTRUCTION

Below Level

UNIT RESOURCE BOOK

- Reading Study Guide A, pp. 13–14
- Decoding Support, p. 48

AUDIO CDS

Advanced

UNIT RESOURCE BOOK

Challenge and Extension, p. 19

English Learners

UNIT RESOURCE BOOK

Spanish Reading Study Guide, pp. 17–18

AUDIO CDS

- Audio Readings in Spanish
- Audio Readings (English)

1.1 INSTRUCT

Teach the Standards

Movement of energy 6.3.a

In this section: Help students understand that energy can take different forms, including mechanical, sound, chemical, electromagnetic, and heat; change from one form to another; and move from one place to another by heat flow or by waves.

future opportunities: electromagnetic spectrum, pp. 20–21; ocean currents, p. 63, p. 65; seismic waves, pp. 307–311; food web, pp. 394–396

Address Misconceptions

IDENTIFY Ask: Is light a substance? If students say yes, they may hold the misconception that energy is a form of matter, that is, an object.

CORRECT Have students list the properties that matter must have. Discuss whether light and other forms of energy have mass and volume.

REASSESS Ask students to write a short paragraph differentiating between an object and a property of an object. Ask: Which is energy? *a property of an object*

Technology Resources

Visit **ClassZone.com** for background on common student misconceptions.

MISCONCEPTION DATABASE

Ongoing Assessment

CHECK YOUR READING *Answer: Heat energy is the total energy of the motion of an object's particles; temperature measures the average amount of energy of the motion of an object's particles.*

Energy has many forms.

Energy takes many forms and has many different effects. For example, a bird uses energy to fly. The energy of wind causes leaves to flutter. All forms of energy have one important point in common: they cause changes to occur. Some of the many types of energy are described below.

Drummers use mechanical energy to produce sound, which is another form of energy.

Mechanical Energy The energy that an object has due to its motion or position is mechanical energy. For example, a basketball tossed in the air has mechanical energy as a result of its motion and its position above the ground.

Sound Energy Sound energy moves through matter such as air and water. When sound energy reaches you, your ears change it to electrical signals that are sent to your brain. You hear a sound when your brain processes the signals.

Chemical Energy Recall that matter is made up of atoms and molecules. The energy that holds atoms together in molecules is chemical energy. Your body uses chemical energy stored in food. As you digest food, its molecules break apart. They release chemical energy. Chemical energy is also released when wood or gasoline burns.

Electromagnetic Energy Electromagnetic energy includes visible light, x-rays, and microwaves. The energy that comes from the Sun is electromagnetic energy. Unlike sound energy, electromagnetic energy can move through empty space. You will read more about electromagnetic energy later in this chapter.

Heat Energy The atoms and molecules in matter are always moving. Even the atoms and molecules in a solid object are always moving back and forth over tiny distances. An object's **heat energy** is the total energy of the motion of particles in the object. Heat energy is also called thermal energy.

In this fiberglass factory, chemical energy from fuel is used to produce heat energy, which, in turn, melts the materials used to make glass. The melted glass releases electromagnetic energy and heat energy.

Heat energy and temperature are closely related. But they are not the same. **Temperature** is a measure of the average amount of energy of motion of the particles in an object. Temperature is measured using a thermometer.

Consider a liquid, such as hot cocoa, that has a high temperature. The particles that make up the liquid are moving very fast. On average, their energy of motion is high. The cocoa feels hot. Now consider a drink, such as a fruit smoothie, that has a low temperature. The particles in the liquid are moving more slowly. On average, their energy of motion is lower. The smoothie feels cold.

CHECK YOUR READING What is the relationship between temperature and heat energy?

DIFFERENTIATE INSTRUCTION

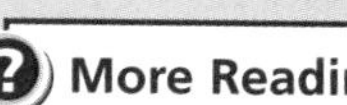

More Reading Support

A What type of energy does a thrown baseball have? *mechanical energy*

B Visible light is a form of what kind of energy? *electromagnetic energy*

English Learners/Below Level English learners and below-level students may need help distinguishing between different forms of energy. Create a table on the board, and list the different forms of energy. Work with the class to create a simple definition of each energy form. Then list an example of each form of energy. Have students copy the chart into their notebooks.

Movement of Energy

Energy from the Sun can be transferred to plants and then to animals. Living things require this movement of energy.

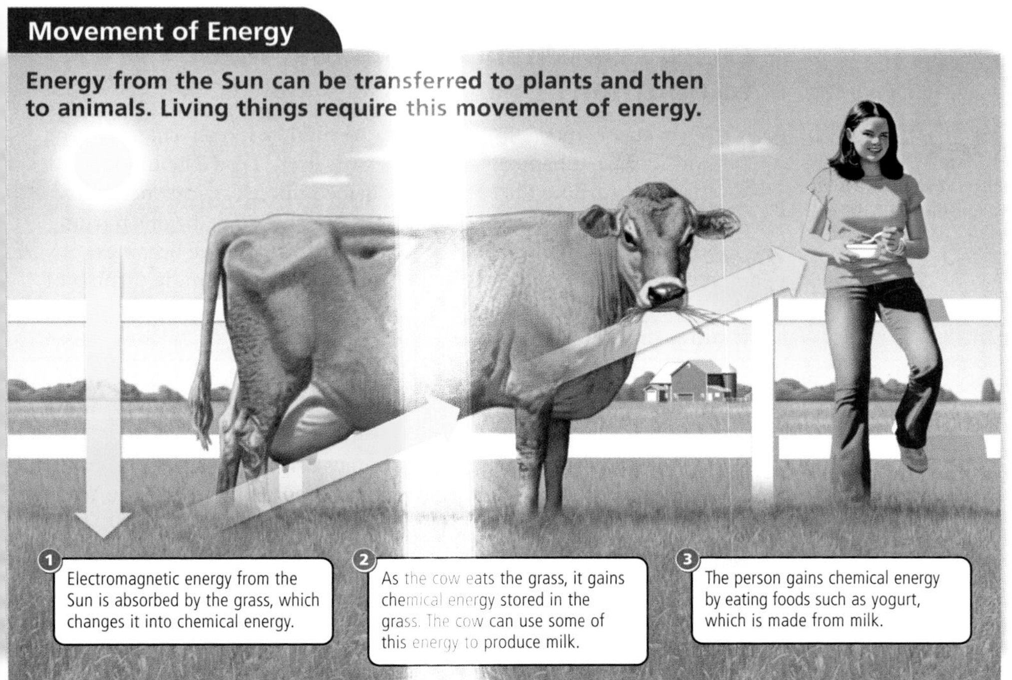

1 Electromagnetic energy from the Sun is absorbed by the grass, which changes it into chemical energy.
2 As the cow eats the grass, it gains chemical energy stored in the grass. The cow can use some of this energy to produce milk.
3 The person gains chemical energy by eating foods such as yogurt, which is made from milk.

Energy moves from one place to another.

The illustration above shows some of the ways that energy moves. Energy from the Sun is transferred to plants on Earth's surface. When animals such as cows eat the plants, some of the plants' energy is transferred to them. Milk from the cows can be turned into dairy products such as yogurt, ice cream, and cheese. Some of the energy in the food is transferred to the person who eats it.

Energy can also move from one object to another because of differences in temperature. The movement of heat energy is called **heat flow.** Suppose ice cubes are placed in a pitcher of warm lemonade. At first, the lemonade and the ice cubes have different temperatures. But the warm lemonade transfers heat energy to the cold ice cubes. The lemonade loses heat energy, so its temperature decreases. The ice gains energy, so its temperature rises. Eventually, the temperature of everything in the pitcher is the same. Heat energy always flows from warmer to cooler objects. If energy flowed in the opposite direction—from cooler to warmer—the ice would get colder and the lemonade would get hotter.

CHECK YOUR READING In which direction does heat flow always transfer energy?

EXPLORE the BIG idea

Revisit "A Penny for Your Energy" on p. 7. Have students explain what happened and why.

Teach from Visuals

To help students interpret the "Movement of Energy" visual, ask:

- Which kind of energy comes from the Sun? *electromagnetic energy*
- Which kind of energy does the grass convert that into? *chemical energy*
- Which kind of energy does a cow gain from eating grass? *chemical energy*
- Which kind of energy does a person gain from eating products made from milk? *chemical energy*

Ongoing Assessment

Explain how energy can move from one place to another.

Ask: From where do plants get energy to make food? How does heat flow in a glass of water with ice cubes? What does the heat do in the glass? *Plants get energy from the Sun to make food. In a glass of water, heat flows from the water to the ice cubes. The heat raises the temperature of the ice cubes and causes them to melt.*

CHECK YOUR READING *Answer: Heat flow always transfers energy from hotter to colder objects.*

DIFFERENTIATE INSTRUCTION

More Reading Support

C From where do plants get energy to grow? *the Sun*

D Why does ice melt in a warm glass of lemonade? *It gains energy and its temperature rises.*

Inclusion Help students understand mechanical energy. Use pictures to illustrate objects exerting mechanical energy through motion and position. Provide students with copies of sports magazines. Ask students to identify pictures that contain examples of mechanical energy. Examples may include a quarterback throwing a football or a basketball player shooting a freethrow.

Teacher Demo

Perform the following demonstration to help students visualize how energy can change from one form to another. Take a magnifying glass and a piece of white paper to an area near a window in your classroom. Place the paper in a metal container or in glass cookware, and focus the magnifying glass so that it casts sunlight on the paper. Note what happens to the paper after some time has elapsed. Ask students to describe what happened and how it happened. What was the original form of energy? To which form of energy did it change? (Note: After the experiment, extinguish the paper with water.) *Electromagnetic energy was changed to heat energy.*

Develop Critical Thinking

Scientists use the power from flowing water to make electricity. How else can electricity be made? Which forms of energy are being converted to electrical energy in your examples? *Answers may vary but may include: burning fossil fuels such as coal and petroleum—chemical energy is being converted; capturing solar energy—electromagnetic energy is being converted*

Ongoing Assessment

Answer: Students' examples may vary.

Energy can change from one form to another.

Learn about ways in which people use energy.

E

When energy moves from one place to another, it often changes form. Consider what happens when a person starts a car. The mechanical energy of turning the key is transformed into electrical energy that starts the engine. As the car's engine starts, gasoline begins burning. Some of the chemical energy released by the gasoline becomes mechanical energy used to make the car move. From the turning of the key to the movement of the car, energy has changed form at least three times.

Gasoline contains energy that changed form long ago. Gasoline is made from oil, a fossil fuel. A fossil fuel is a fuel formed from the remains of plants and animals that lived millions of years ago. The energy stored in the plants and animals originally came from sunlight. The remains of the plants and animals eventually became oil. You will read more about how fossil fuels form in Chapter 13.

Provide your own example of energy changing form.

Uses of Energy

People have developed ways to change energy from one form to another for many purposes. Some ways that energy changes form are described below. As you read each description, follow the process in the illustrations on page 13. You will see how energy that is stored in water held behind a dam is changed into electrical energy.

1. The water behind the dam has mechanical energy because of its position above Earth's surface. The water flows downward in response to the pull of gravity.
2. Some of the water flows through a tunnel within the dam.
3. Some of the mechanical energy of the moving water is transferred to the turbines, causing them to turn. Mechanical energy of the moving turbines is changed into electrical energy by electrical generators.
4. Electrical energy is transported away from the dam through wires. The electrical energy is changed into different forms of energy and is used in many different ways. For example, at a concert or a play, electrical energy is changed into light and heat by lighting systems. It is changed into sound energy by sound systems.

CALIFORNIA Focus

Shasta Dam, shown above, is on the Sacramento River. Water passing through the dam is used to produce some of the electricity supplied to California.

F

As you can see, energy changes form several times in the production of electrical energy. Every time that energy changes form, some of it becomes heat energy. The energy that becomes heat energy is usually not useful. Therefore, every time energy in the dam changes form, some useful energy is lost because it has become heat energy.

12 Unit 1: The Earth System

DIFFERENTIATED INSTRUCTION

More Reading Support

E What kind of energy is used by cars to move? *mechanical energy*

F What kind of energy is transported away from dams by wires? *electrical energy*

Advanced Remind students that heat is often a by-product of energy transfer. Have students make a list of various processes that transfer energy and create heat as a by-product. Ask students to hypothesize what happens to the heat at the end of the process. Then have students research these processes and determine whether their hypotheses were correct.

Challenge and Extension, p. 19

Changes in Forms of Energy

Energy is often changed from one form to another in order to meet everyday needs.

Transfer of Mechanical Energy

Some of the mechanical energy of water is transferred to turbines inside the dam.

Mechanical Energy to Electrical Energy

The mechanical energy of turning turbines becomes electrical energy in these generators.

READING VISUALS How many different transfers of energy are described in this diagram?

DIFFERENTIATE INSTRUCTION

Below Level Give groups of students a sheet of paper, and have them draw a diagram showing a dam on a river and a nearby city. On the diagram, have them show how water stored behind the dam eventually moves through it to become electrical energy to power the city. Tell them to use the illustrations on page 13 to guide their work.

Teach from Visuals

To help students interpret the "Changes in Forms of Energy" visual, ask:

- Give one reason why water behind the dam has mechanical energy. *The water behind the dam is held high above the ground.*
- What role does gravity play in changing the mechanical energy? *It pulls the water downhill.*
- Why does the water cause the turbines to turn? *The force of the water flowing downhill causes the turbines to turn.*
- What converts the energy from mechanical to electrical? *generators*

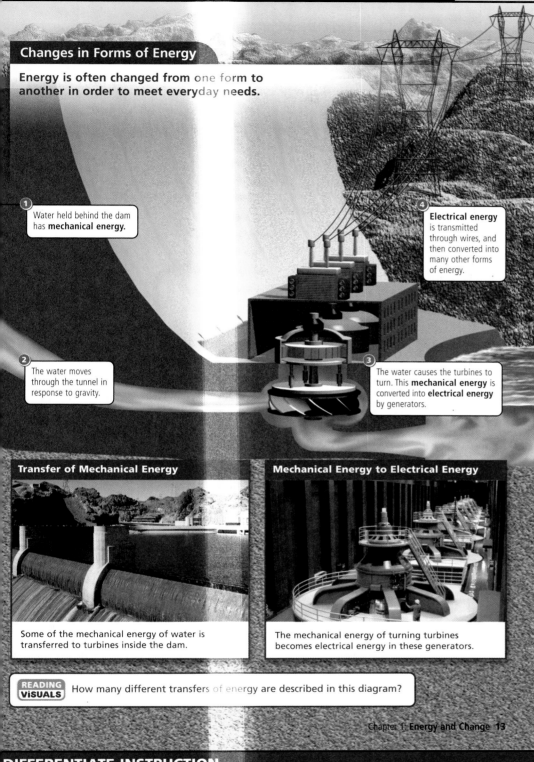
The visual "Changes in Forms of Energy" is available as T6 in the Transparency Book.

Real World Example

The Hoover Dam does more than provide electric power to a large portion of the southwestern United States. It also prevents the lower Colorado River from flooding each spring, provides water for irrigation, and helps form an artificial lake (Lake Mead). During dam construction, the Colorado River was diverted through four concrete tunnels. At one time, Hoover Dam, which was completed in 1936, was the largest hydroelectric plant in the world.

Ongoing Assessment

Know how energy can change forms.

Ask: How does mechanical energy change into electrical energy in the visual? *Mechanical energy from moving water turns turbines; turbines drive generators that convert mechanical energy into electrical energy.*

READING VISUALS *Answer: mechanical to electrical, electrical to other forms*

INVESTIGATE Energy

PURPOSE Observe how energy changes form

TIPS *15 min.*

- Close windows and air conditioning or heating vents during this lab so the spiral is not affected by strong movements of air.
- Perform this activity in different parts of the room if air currents are causing the spiral to move before the lamp is turned on.

WHAT DO YOU THINK? *The spiral turns. The energy changed from electromagnetic energy to mechanical energy.*

CHALLENGE *The movement of air in the room or vibrations in the object to which the spiral is attached would affect the spiral.*

 Datasheet, Energy, p. 20

Technology Resources

Customize this student lab as needed. Print rubrics to assess student lab reports.

 **Lab Generator CD-ROM**

Social Studies Connection

Flowing water can be captured and its energy turned into electricity. That energy is called *hydroelectric power.* The prefix *hydro-* comes from a Greek word meaning "water." Hydroelectric power is prized because it is a renewable form of energy—rainfall restores the source of the power. Most hydroelectric power is generated by dams built along rivers. About 10 percent of the electricity used in the United States comes from hydroelectric power.

INVESTIGATE Energy

How can you observe energy changing form?

SKILL FOCUS
Observing (6.3.a)

PROCEDURE

1. Mark and cut a spiral pattern in a piece of paper.
2. Cut a 15 cm piece of thread and tape one end to the center of the spiral.
3. Adjust the lamp to shine straight at the ceiling.
4. Fasten the thread to an object above the lamp so that the spiral hangs about 10 cm above the light bulb. Wait for the spiral to stop moving. Then turn on the lamp. **CAUTION: Don't let the paper touch the bulb!**

WHAT DO YOU THINK?

- What happened to the spiral after you turned on the light?
- In what sense has the energy changed form?

CHALLENGE In addition to the heat from the lamp, what conditions in the room might affect the spiral?

MATERIALS
- paper
- marker
- scissors
- thread
- tape
- desk lamp

TIME
15 minutes

Conservation of Energy

No matter how energy is transferred or changes form, all of the energy is still present. The total amount of energy never changes. This fact is described by the law of **conservation of energy,** which states that energy can change from one form to another, but it is never created or destroyed. For example, in a light bulb, electrical energy is changed into light and heat. The heat given off by a light bulb is usually not useful energy. So the amount of useful energy is less. But the total amount of energy is still the same. **G**

Recall what happens when a car is started. Gasoline begins to burn in the car's engine. The car gains energy as some of the chemical energy from the fuel becomes mechanical energy. The energy from the fuel is used to make the car move. If more gas is not sent to the engine, the car soon stops moving. **H**

The car also slows down or stops when the driver uses the brake system. This causes the car's mechanical energy to change form. There is friction between the car's wheels and the ground and also between the brake system and the wheels. Friction causes mechanical energy to change into heat energy. Eventually, most of the energy released by the fuel becomes heat energy. But the overall amount of energy is still the same. It has just changed form or moved to a different place.

DIFFERENTIATED INSTRUCTION

More Reading Support

G What never happens to energy? *It is never created or destroyed.*

H What kind of energy does most of the gasoline fuel of a car eventually become? *heat energy*

Alternative Assessment Have students use a computer graphics program to illustrate the description of energy in a car on this page. Ask them to include in their illustration one additional way that energy and a car interact.

Energy and Work

In science, **work** is the use of force to move an object some distance. A force is a push or a pull. In scientific terms, solving a crossword puzzle does not require work. However, filling out the puzzle with a pencil is work, because you are moving the pencil.

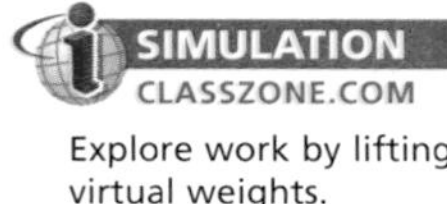
SIMULATION CLASSZONE.COM
Explore work by lifting virtual weights.

Work transfers energy. You do work on objects when you move them. For example, you do work when you pick up a piece of paper. When you pick up the paper, you transfer some of your energy to it. Objects can also do work. Water in a river does work as it carries fallen leaves downstream. A bowling ball does work when it knocks down bowling pins.

In the photograph, the woman is holding a large box. When she lifted the box, she did work on it. She applied a force that acted in the same direction as the motion of the box. The force was applied in an upward direction, and the box moved upward. What if she stood still while holding the box? She would not be doing work on the box, even if her muscles got tired. She must be moving the box to do work on it.

CHECK YOUR READING Give an example of applying a force to do work.

1.1 Review

KEY CONCEPTS

1. Give an example of how energy causes change.
2. What is heat energy? How is it different from temperature? (6.3.a)
3. Describe the changes in energy that take place when a person starts a car.

CRITICAL THINKING

4. **Synthesize** Describe two of the types of energy that are involved when a person beats on a drum with drumsticks.
5. **Apply** Is work being done by a person who is reading a book? Explain.

CHALLENGE

6. **Analyze** Explain how the heat and light produced by burning wood originally come from the Sun.

ANSWERS

1. Sample answer: Energy can cause trees to produce new branches and leaves.

2. the total energy of motion of particles in an object; the average amount of energy of motion of the particles in an object.

3. Mechanical energy changes to electrical (turning the key) to chemical (burning gasoline) to mechanical (moving the car).

4. Mechanical energy is used to beat on the drum; sound energy is produced.

5. Yes. A person reading a book uses energy to turn pages.

6. The Sun gives off electromagnetic energy. Trees on Earth use that energy to grow. The trees convert the electromagnetic energy into stored chemical energy. When wood burns, it releases its stored energy as heat and light—energy it originally received from the Sun.

Ongoing Assessment

CHECK YOUR READING *Sample answer: Lifting a sandwich to my mouth to eat it is work.*

EXPLORE the BIG idea

Have students relate the section to the Big Idea.

 Reinforcing Key Concepts, p. 21

1.1 ASSESS & RETEACH

Assess

 Section 1.1 Quiz, p. 5

Reteach

Have students recall the different forms of energy and how they can change to other forms. Ask them to create a table with three columns and three rows. In the first column, have them list three different forms of energy. In the second column, have them list a way that each form of energy might move from one place to another. In the third column, have them list the resulting new form of energy. *Column 1: mechanical; electromagnetic; heat; Column 2: hitting a baseball; microwaves passing into food; heat spreading throughout a stove's coils; Column 3: sound energy from the bat hitting the baseball; heat results from food absorbing the microwaves; the coils heat and emit electromagnetic energy in the form of light.*

Technology Resources

Have students visit **ClassZone.com** for teaching of Key Concepts.

 CONTENT REVIEW

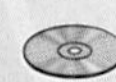 CONTENT REVIEW CD-ROM

CHAPTER INVESTIGATION

Focus

PURPOSE To investigate the amount of energy that is released when different types of food are burned

OVERVIEW Students will use an apparatus to trap the energy released from different food samples when they burn. Students will collect data and calculate the amount of energy each food contained. They will find the following:

- The water in the can traps the energy that is released by the burning food.
- The temperature increase in the water is greater when burning foods that are high in fats than when burning foods that are high are carbohydrates.
- Fats contain more energy than carbohydrates.

Lab Preparation

- Students can bring many of the materials, such as aluminum cans, from home.
- Construct the apparatus before class.
- Prior to the investigation, have students read the investigation and prepare their data tables. You may wish to copy and distribute datasheets and rubrics.

 UNIT RESOURCE BOOK, pp. 51–59

 SCIENCE TOOLKIT, F14

Lab Management

- Warn students not to eat the food samples.

SAFETY Advise students with long hair to tie it back. Students wearing long, loose sleeves should roll them up. Desks should be cleared of all nonessential and flammable materials.

INCLUSION Use a thermometer with large numbers so that students with visual impairments can easily read it.

Teaching with Technology

Have students use a temperature probe to record temperature changes.

CHAPTER INVESTIGATION

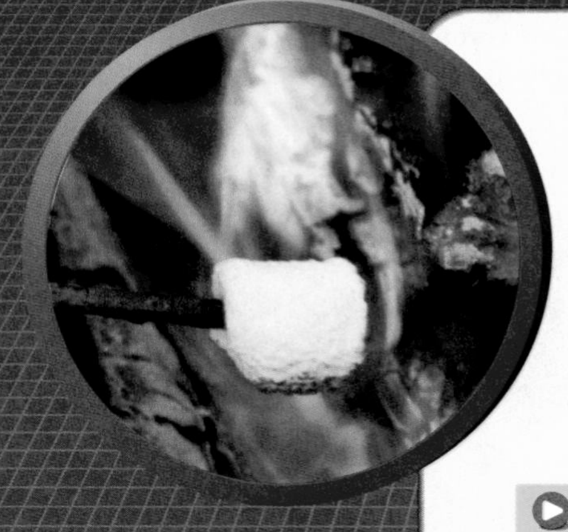

Changes in Energy

OVERVIEW AND PURPOSE All foods contain stored chemical energy, but some foods contain more chemical energy than others. People need this chemical energy for all of their activities. The amount of chemical energy stored in foods such as marshmallows can be measured by burning the foods. In this investigation you will

- construct a setup to investigate the amount of energy stored in samples of food
- calculate the amount of energy released when the foods are burned

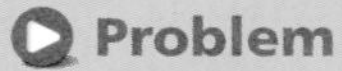 

Problem

How much energy is released when different types of food are burned?

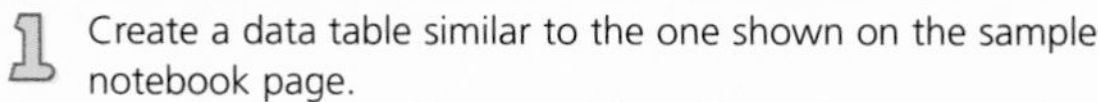

Procedure

1. Create a data table similar to the one shown on the sample notebook page.
2. Slide the dowel rod through the holes in the can as shown in the photograph to the left.
3. Measure 50 mL of water with a graduated cylinder, and pour the water into the can. Record the mass of the water. (**Hint:** 1 mL of water = 1 gram)
4. Rest the ends of the dowel rod on the ring in the ring stand to hold the can in the air. Place the thermometer in the can and tape it so the bulb is touching only the water and not the bottom of the can. Measure and record the beginning temperature (T1) of the water in the can.
5. Make a collar of aluminum foil and tape it around the can as shown. Leave enough room to insert the burner platform and food sample.

MATERIALS

- empty aluminum can with holes
- dowel rod
- water
- graduated cylinder
- ring stand with ring
- thermometer
- tape
- aluminum pie plate
- aluminum foil
- large paper clip
- cork
- modeling clay
- crouton
- caramel rice cake
- balance
- wooden matches

6.3.a, 6.3.b, 6.7.b

16 Unit 1: **The Earth System**

INVESTIGATION RESOURCES

 CHAPTER INVESTIGATION, Changes in Energy

- Level A, pp. 51–54
- Level B, pp. 55–58
- Level C, p. 59

Advanced students should complete Levels B & C.

 Writing a Lab Report, D12–13

Technology Resources

Customize this student lab as needed or look for an alternative. Print rubrics to assess student lab reports.

 **Lab Generator CD-ROM**

Content Standard
6.3.b Students know that when fuel is consumed, most of the energy released becomes heat energy.

Investigation Standard
6.7.b Select and use appropriate tools and technology (including calculators, computers, balances, spring scales, microscopes, and binoculars) to perform tests, collect data, and display data.

6 Construct the burner platform as follows. Open up the paper clip. Push the straightened end into a cork, and push the bottom of the cork into the clay. Push the burner onto the pie plate so it will not move. Put the pie plate under the ring.

step 6

7 Find and record the mass of one of the food samples. Place the food on the flattened end of the burner platform. Adjust the height of the ring so the bottom of the can is about 4 cm above the food.

8 Have your teacher use a match to ignite the piece of food. Allow the food to burn completely. Measure and record the final temperature (T2) of the water.

9 From a classmate, obtain temperature data for the food sample you didn't test. Record the data.

Observe and Analyze

Write It Up

1. **RECORD OBSERVATIONS** Make sure to record all measurements in the data table.
2. **CALCULATE** Find the energy released from the food samples by following the next two steps.

   Calculate and record the change in temperature.
   change in temperature = T2 – T1

   Calculate and record the energy released in calories. One calorie is the energy needed to raise the temperature of 1 g of water by 1°C.
   energy released = mass of water · change in temperature · 1 cal/g°C

Conclude

1. **INTERPRET** Answer the question posed in the problem.
2. **INFER** Why do you think different types of food release different amounts of energy?
3. **APPLY** Find out how much fat and carbohydrates the different foods contain. Explain the relationship between this information and the number of calories in the foods.

INVESTIGATE Further

CHALLENGE The Calories listed in foods are equal to 1000 calories (1 kilocalorie). Calculate the amount of energy in your food samples in terms of Calories per gram of food (Calories/g). Using a balance, find the mass of any ash that remains after burning the food. Subtract that mass from the original mass of the sample to calculate mass burned. Divide total calories by mass burned, then divide that value by 1000 to find Calories/g. Compare your results with those given on the product labels.

Changes in Energy
Problem How much energy is released when different types of food are burned?
Observe and Analyze
Table 1. Energy in Food

	Sample 1
Mass of water (g)	
Initial water temp. (T1) (°C)	
Final water temp. (T2) (°C)	
Mass of food (g)	
Change in temp. (T2 – T1) (°C)	
Energy released (mass•change in temp.•cal/g °C)	

Conclude

Observe and Analyze

1. *See students' data tables. Sample data: Rice snack (Sample 1): mass of water 50 g; T1 20°C; T2 24°C; Crouton (Sample 2): mass of water 50 g; T1 20°C; T2 32°C. Mass of food will depend on the size of the sample.*
2. *For the sample data, the rice cake produced 200 calories and the crouton produced 600 calories.*

Conclude

1. *The amount of energy released from foods depends on the nutrients in the foods.*
2. *Some types of foods store more energy than others do. Fats release more energy than carbohydrates because they store more energy than carbohydrates.*
3. *Fats contain more calories than carbohydrates, so the food that contains more fat should release more energy when it is burned.*

INVESTIGATE Further

CHALLENGE Students will need to keep the ashes from their food samples to find how much the mass changed. Students' results will probably vary from the values given on product labels because the equipment used in the classroom is crude, contributing to a high rate of error.

Post-Lab Discussion

- Ask: Why was it important that the same amount of water be used in each test? ***A greater mass of water would heat up more slowly with a given amount of energy.***
- Ask: What energy conversions occurred in this lab? Where was energy transferred to? ***Chemical energy from the food molecules changed to thermal energy (heat), electromagnetic energy (light), and sound energy when the food was burned. Some of the thermal energy was captured by the water. Additional thermal energy was lost to the air and to the equipment.***

1.2 FOCUS

Set Learning Goals

Students will

- Understand how radiation travels from one place to another.
- Explain what makes up the electromagnetic spectrum.
- Know how radiation transfers energy.
- Observe an experiment that shows the best of three ways to collect solar energy.

3-Minute Warm-Up

Display Transparency 4 or copy this exercise on the board.

Match the term with the definition.

conservation of energy

chemical energy

mechanical energy

electromagnetic energy

energy

1. type of energy that comes from the Sun *electromagnetic energy*
2. ability to cause change *energy*
3. energy an object has due to its motion or position *mechanical energy*

3-Minute Warm-Up, p. T4

1.2 MOTIVATE

EXPLORE Radiation

PURPOSE To introduce the concept that radiation is something people experience in their everyday lives

TIP *10 min.* Make sure that students do not place their hands too close to the light bulb.

WHAT DO YOU THINK? *Students see light and feel heat. The heat they feel is greater when the lamp is on.*

Ongoing Assessment

Answer: Energy from the Sun travels to Earth in the form of radiation.

KEY CONCEPT

1.2 Radiation transfers energy.

CALIFORNIA Content Standards

6.3.a Students know energy can be carried from one place to another by heat flow or by waves, including water, light and sound waves, or by moving objects.

6.3.d Students know heat energy is also transferred between objects by radiation (radiation can travel through space).

6.4.b Students know solar energy reaches Earth through radiation, mostly in the form of visible light.

BEFORE, you learned

- Energy causes change
- Energy exists in many forms
- Energy can change from one form to another

NOW, you will learn

- How radiation travels
- About the electromagnetic spectrum
- How radiation transfers energy

VOCABULARY

radiation p. 18
wave p. 19
wavelength p. 20
electromagnetic spectrum p. 21

Can you feel radiation?

PROCEDURE

1. Turn on the lamp and wait for it to become warm. It gives off energy in the form of radiation.
2. Hold one hand a short distance from the bulb. Record your observations.
3. Turn the lamp off. The bulb continues to give off energy. Hold your other hand a short distance from the bulb.

MATERIALS

- lamp

WHAT DO YOU THINK?

- What did you see and feel?
- How did radiation affect each hand?

Radiation travels in waves.

On a bright day, sunlight sparkles on water, the windows of buildings, and cars. You can feel sunlight as warmth on your face. If a cloud comes between your face and the Sun, you feel cooler. But how does sunlight travel through empty space to Earth's surface?

The Sun's energy travels to Earth in the form of radiation. **Radiation** is energy that travels across distances in the form of electromagnetic waves. These waves transmit energy that is partly electric and partly magnetic. Types of radiation include visible light, microwaves, and infrared radiation (IHN-fruh-REHD).

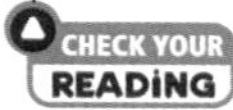

How does energy from the Sun travel to Earth?

RESOURCES FOR DIFFERENTIATED INSTRUCTION

Below Level

UNIT RESOURCE BOOK

- Reading Study Guide A, pp. 24–25
- Decoding Support, p. 48

Advanced

UNIT RESOURCE BOOK

Challenge and Extension, p. 30

English Learners

UNIT RESOURCE BOOK

Spanish Reading Study Guide, pp. 28–29

- Audio Readings in Spanish
- Audio Readings (English)

You have learned that energy can move from one place to another. A **wave** is a disturbance that carries energy from one place to another. Consider what happens when you shake one end of a rope. The rope wiggles up and down or from side to side. This motion, or disturbance, travels in a wave. Energy from the wave travels along the rope. However, the particles that make up the rope do not travel from one end of the rope to the other. A wave transfers energy, but not matter, over long distances.

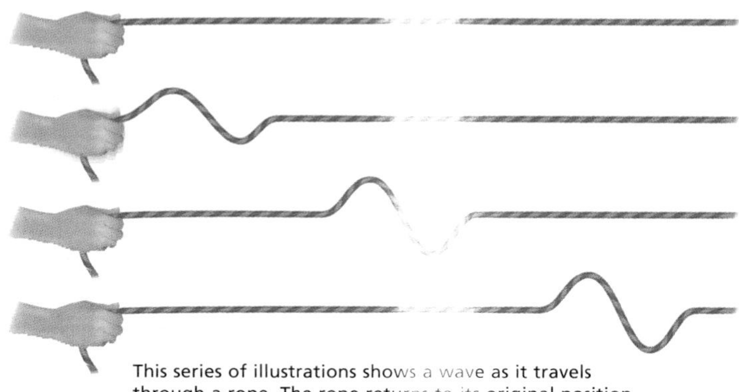

This series of illustrations shows a wave as it travels through a rope. The rope returns to its original position after the energy from the wave has passed through it.

In the rope example, a wave is traveling through matter. However, electromagnetic waves can travel through empty space. If electromagnetic waves could not travel through empty space, then Earth would receive no energy from the Sun.

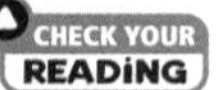

How are electromagnetic waves different from the waves illustrated above?

Energy and Wavelengths

Much of the Sun's energy that reaches Earth is in the form of visible light waves. Your eyes can detect visible light. But there are types of radiation that humans cannot see.

Many types of radiation have less energy than the light you can see. Others have more. For example, infrared radiation has less energy than visible light. Infrared radiation usually warms the materials that absorb it. When you feel heat from a light bulb or from sunlight, you are sensing infrared radiation. Ultraviolet radiation has more energy than visible light. Ultraviolet radiation can cause sunburns.

1.2 INSTRUCT

Teach the Standards

Heat energy and radiation 6.3.d

In this section: Students learn that heat energy can travel between objects by radiation. Ask students to give examples of how heat energy moves between objects by radiation. *On page 18, they learned how heat energy travels by radiation from the Sun to Earth and from a lamp to their hand.*

future opportunities: absorption of solar energy, pp. 48–49; seasons, pp. 51–53 ; water cycle, pp. 60–61; cause of wind, p. 84

Teacher Demo

This demonstration is designed to show that energy can travel as a wave from one point and do work at a distant point. Tie a string between two chairs placed 4 feet apart. Fold a piece of paper so that one quarter of the paper is separate from the rest. Hang the paper over one end of the string near one chair. Hit the other end of the string near the second chair hard with a pencil. The energy will travel through the string, causing an up and down motion that will result in the paper falling off the string.

Ongoing Assessment

Understand how radiation travels from one place to another.

Ask: How does radiation travel from the Sun to Earth? *Radiation travels as electromagnetic waves.*

CHECK YOUR READING *Answer: Waves in the illustration travel through matter (rope); electromagnetic waves travel through empty space.*

DIFFERENTIATE INSTRUCTION

More Reading Support

A What does a wave carry from one place to another? *energy*

B Which kind of wave can travel through empty space? *electromagnetic waves*

English Learners English language learners may need help with the concepts of absorption and reflection. Tell them that *absorption* is rooted in the English word *absorb,* which means "to soak up." A sponge is a good example of something that absorbs. *Reflection* is related to *reflect,* which means "to turn back." A mirror is a good example of something that reflects.

Address Misconceptions

IDENTIFY Ask students to imagine a wave in deep water. Ask: What moves from the beginning to the end of the wave? If students say water (or other matter), they may hold the misconception that matter is transferred in a wave.

CORRECT Have several students stand in a row. Have the first student tap the second on the shoulder, who in turn taps the third student, and so on. Notice that energy is transferred to the end of the row while each student stays in place.

REASSESS Ask: Why doesn't an object bobbing up and down as waves pass move toward the shore? *because waves transfer energy, not matter*

Technology Resources

Visit **ClassZone.com** for background on common student misconceptions.

MISCONCEPTION DATABASE

Teach from Visuals

To help students interpret the "The Electromagnetic Spectrum" visual, ask:

- Where does visible light appear on the spectrum? *between infrared and ultraviolet*
- Which kind of electromagnetic radiation has the shortest wavelength? *gamma rays*
- Which kind of electromagnetic radiation is used to see bones? *x-rays*
- Which kind of electromagnetic radiation is used to carry television broadcasts? *radio waves*

Ongoing Assessment

Explain what makes up the electromagnetic spectrum.

Ask: What determines a wave's type on the electromagnetic spectrum? *its wavelength*

CHECK YOUR READING *Answer: The shorter the wavelength, the more energy an electromagnetic wave has.*

READING VISUALS *Answer: radio waves; radio waves*

Different types of radiation have different wavelengths. A **wavelength** is the distance between one wave crest and the next crest. As shown in the illustration below, a wave crest is the highest point on a wave. A trough is the lowest point on the wave. A wavelength can also be measured from trough to trough. Every type of wave has a wavelength that can be measured.

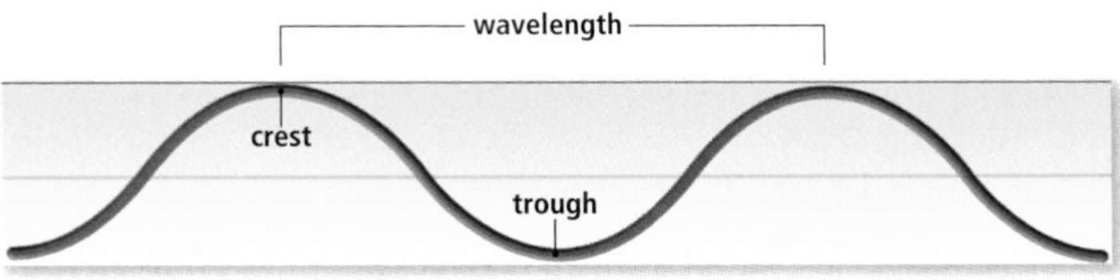

Electromagnetic waves that have longer wavelengths have less energy. For example, infrared radiation has longer wavelengths and less energy than does visible light. Waves with shorter wavelengths have more energy.

CHECK YOUR READING In electromagnetic waves, what is the relationship between wavelength and energy?

The Electromagnetic Spectrum

The different forms of electromagnetic radiation vary in their wavelengths.

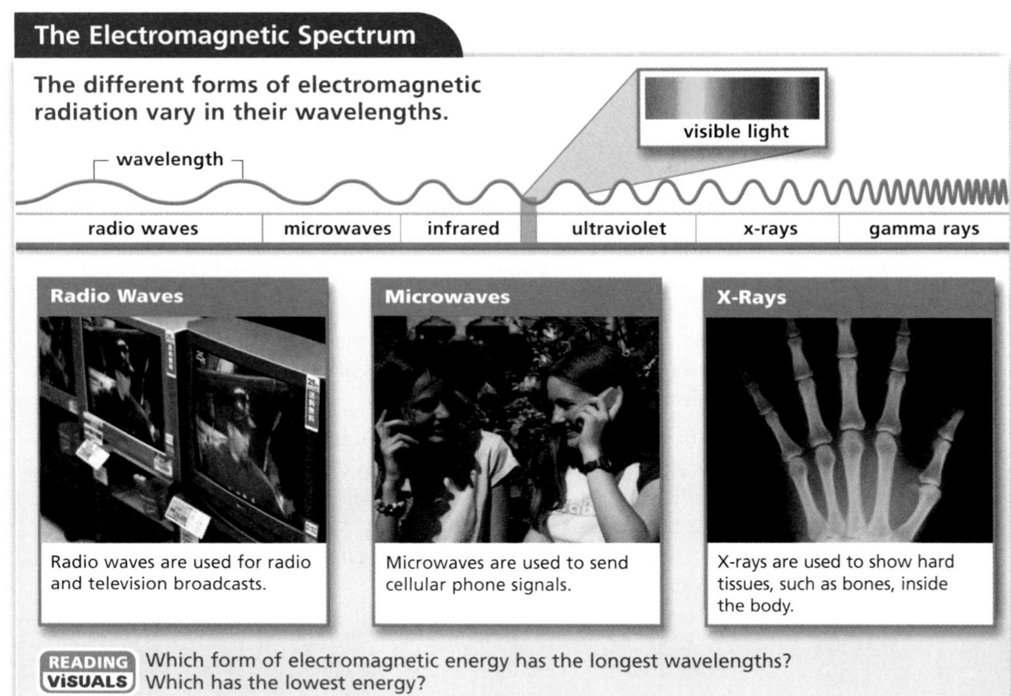

Radio waves are used for radio and television broadcasts.

Microwaves are used to send cellular phone signals.

X-rays are used to show hard tissues, such as bones, inside the body.

READING VISUALS Which form of electromagnetic energy has the longest wavelengths? Which has the lowest energy?

DIFFERENTIATE INSTRUCTION

More Reading Support

C How are wave crests related to wavelength? *Wavelength is the distance between wave crests.*

D What is a wave's crest? *the highest point on a wave*

Below Level Ask each student to get out a clean white sheet of paper. On the paper ask them to draw a picture of one way electromagnetic radiation affects their lives. Examples might include microwaves carrying signals to a cell phone, radio waves carrying radio or television programming, ultraviolet radiation giving students a sunburn at the beach, and x-rays showing a broken bone. Ask students to share the pictures they draw with the class.

Electromagnetic Spectrum

The **electromagnetic spectrum** is the entire range of electromagnetic energy, from radiation that has the shortest wavelengths to radiation that has the longest wavelengths. Visible light is only a small part of the electromagnetic spectrum.

The illustration on page 20 shows the names of each type of electromagnetic energy. On the left-hand side of the illustration are the waves with the longest wavelengths and the lowest energy. Toward the right, the wavelengths become shorter and the energy becomes higher.

People use electromagnetic energy in many ways. Radio waves are used to carry radio signals and television signals. Microwaves are used in microwave ovens to cook food. They are also used to transmit cellular phone signals. X-rays and gamma rays are very high-energy waves that are used in medical technologies. And, of course, people use many kinds of devices that give off visible light.

READING TIP

Spectrum comes from the Latin word *specere*, meaning "to look at." A spectrum is a broad, continuous range of related qualities, ideas, or activities.

Learn more about the electromagnetic spectrum.

Visible Light

The light that comes from the Sun is made up of all colors of visible light blended together. Each color in visible light has its own range of wavelengths. Of the colors of visible light, red light has the longest wavelength and violet light has the shortest wavelength.

You can divide visible light into colors by passing it through a prism, as shown in the photograph at right. Light bends as it passes through the prism. The amount that each color of light bends depends on its wavelength. A rainbow shows the colors of visible light in the order of their wavelengths. A rainbow appears when light bends as it passes through droplets of water in the atmosphere. The droplets of water act like prisms.

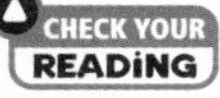

How are the colors of visible light similar? different?

History of Science

In 1901, the first Nobel Prize in Physics was awarded to German scientist Wilhelm Roentgen. In his laboratory, he noticed a new form of radiation coming from an experiment he was conducting using a cathode ray tube. He found that this new radiation could travel farther than cathode rays and even penetrate some samples of wood and rubber. Because of their unknown nature, Roentgen called them x-rays. Roentgen's x-rays were quickly put to medical use. x-rays do not pass through bone, so an image of bones can be made on special paper. These images help doctors identify problems with bones, such as fractures.

Art Connection

Lighting experts in television and in theater mix different colors of lights to make new colors. They start with three colors of light: red, blue, and green. Red and green, for example, are mixed to make yellow; red and blue are added together to make magenta—a purplish red. Mixing red, blue, and green light together creates white light.

For painters, however, the process is very different. Painters start with pigments of magenta, yellow, and cyan—a shade of blue. The different pigments of paint absorb some of the light that strikes them and reflect other parts. You see the light that is reflected. Cyan reflects blue and green light. Yellow reflects red and green light. When cyan and yellow are added together, only green light is reflected. So you see that area of a painting as green. When magenta, yellow, and cyan are mixed together, all the light is absorbed—you see black.

DIFFERENTIATE INSTRUCTION

More Reading Support

E Which waves are used to transmit television signals? *radio waves*

F What does a prism do? *divides visible light into its colors*

Advanced Gamma rays have the shortest wavelengths and the highest energy levels of any form of electromagnetic radiation. Have students who are interested in gamma rays prepare short reports on the unique qualities of this form of radiation and how scientists have harnessed the power of gamma rays to benefit people.

Ongoing Assessment

Explain what makes up the electromagnetic spectrum.

What causes rainbows to appear in the sky? *Water droplets in the sky act as prisms, separating the colors of visible light in the order of their wavelengths.*

Answer: The colors can all be seen by the human eye; they have different wavelengths.

Teach from Visuals

To help students interpret the "Reflection and Absorption" visual, ask:

- Where does solar energy come from? *the Sun*
- What happens to 25 percent of the solar energy that reaches Earth? *It is reflected by the atmosphere and the clouds.*
- What happens to another 20 percent of solar energy as it passes through the atmosphere? *It is absorbed.*
- What happens to most of the solar energy that reaches Earth? *It is absorbed by the land and oceans.*

Real World Example

Although water is actually transparent, large bodies of water, such as deep lakes and oceans, appear blue. This happens for three principal reasons. First, Earth's blue sky reflects off of the water and helps make the water appear blue. Second, the water absorbs more red light than blue, so blue is reflected. Third, water tends to scatter blue light, adding to our blue view of a body of water. The phenomenon takes place only in large bodies of water such as the oceans and the Great Lakes. In a small bowl, you can see through the transparent water to the sides and bottom of the bowl. A shallow pond or stream may appear brown or green rather than blue probably due to sediment in the water.

Ongoing Assessment

Know how radiation transfers energy.

Ask: Which types of electromagnetic energy are mostly absorbed by Earth's atmosphere? *gamma rays, x-rays, ultraviolet, infrared, and microwaves* Which types of electromagnetic energy mostly pass through Earth's atmosphere and reach the surface? *visible light, radio waves*

Earth receives radiation from the Sun.

Earth is extremely small compared with the Sun. It is also far away from the Sun. Therefore, Earth receives only a tiny amount of the energy given off by the Sun. However, the Sun is the major source of energy for processes that occur in Earth's atmosphere and on Earth's surface. You will read more about these processes in Chapter 2.

Electromagnetic energy from the Sun reaches Earth in a little over eight minutes. This energy undergoes no significant change as it travels the 150 million kilometers (93 million miles) through space. However, energy from the Sun goes through many changes as it passes through Earth's atmosphere.

Reflection and Absorption in the Atmosphere

READING TIP

Reflection occurs when something is thrown back or bent back. Absorption occurs when something is taken in or soaked up.

The Sun gives off the full range of energy in the electromagnetic spectrum. Energy from the Sun is called solar energy. All types of electromagnetic energy from the Sun reach the top of Earth's atmosphere. But much of this solar energy does not reach Earth's surface. Some of it is reflected back into space. And some of it is absorbed by the atoms and molecules of the atmosphere.

Almost all of the visible light from the Sun passes through the atmosphere to Earth's surface. However, most of the electromagnetic energy with wavelengths shorter than visible light is absorbed by the atmosphere. A great deal of ultraviolet radiation (UHL-truh-VY-uh-liht), which can cause sunburns and damage plants, is absorbed before it reaches the ground. X-rays and gamma rays are completely absorbed in the atmosphere at heights greater than 100 kilometers (60 miles) above Earth's surface.

Reflection and Absorption

Much of the solar energy that reaches the top of Earth's atmosphere is reflected or absorbed before it reaches Earth's surface.

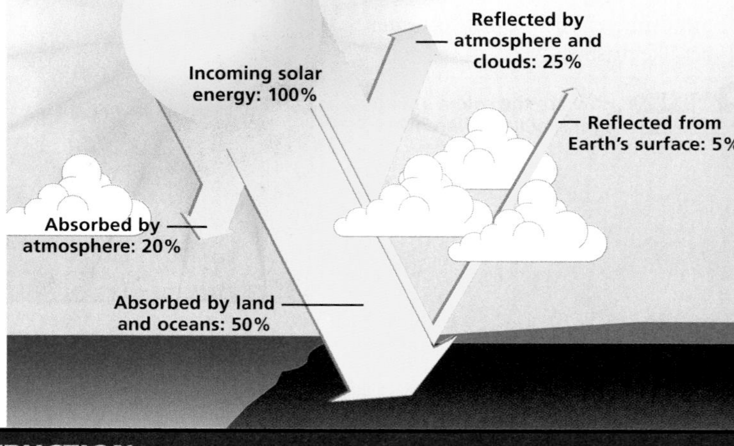

DIFFERENTIATE INSTRUCTION

Advanced Have students consider how products used in the construction of buildings and roadways affect the amount of solar radiation that is reflected or absorbed. Make a list of different types of roofing materials and roadway materials. Roofing materials might include various colors of shingles, wood, metal, and slate. Roadway materials might include cement, blacktop, or brick. Have students determine which materials would be most efficient at reflecting the Sun's radiation, and thus keeping structures cooler.

Challenge and Extension, p. 30

Infrared radiation, microwaves, and radio waves have wavelengths longer than those of visible light. Infrared radiation, which helps keep the planet's surface warm, is mostly absorbed by the atmosphere. Microwaves are mostly absorbed by the atmosphere too. Radio waves are not absorbed. They pass through the atmosphere to Earth's surface, but they have little effect on Earth. The radio waves used to send television and radio signals are generated by devices that people make.

Reflection and Absorption at Earth's Surface

Two main things happen to the solar energy that reaches Earth's surface. Some is reflected, or sent in a new direction. Some is absorbed. When radiation is absorbed, it changes into heat energy. Earth's surface is heated when it absorbs energy from the Sun.

Dark-colored surfaces absorb more solar energy. Therefore, they gain more heat energy. Light-colored surfaces reflect more solar energy, so they gain less heat energy. Consider the clothing you might wear on a sunny summer day. You would feel cooler if you wore light-colored clothes than if you wore similar, dark-colored clothes. The light-colored clothes reflect more solar energy. In the same way, light-colored materials on Earth's surface, such as ice and snow, reflect more solar energy. Dark-colored rocks absorb more solar energy, and they gain more heat energy.

INVESTIGATE Energy Transfer

What improves the collection of solar energy?

PROCEDURE

1. Cover the top of one cup with white plastic, and cover the top of the other cup with black plastic. Secure the plastic with a rubber band.
2. Use the scissors to make a small hole in the center of each cup's plastic lid. Insert a thermometer through each opening.
3. Place the cups in direct sunlight, and record their temperatures every minute for ten minutes.

WHAT DO YOU THINK?

- Which cup showed a greater temperature change? Why do you think this happened?
- Make a line graph of your results to show the change in temperature in each cup.

CHALLENGE Try the experiment again, using aluminum foil instead of white plastic. How do the results differ with the aluminum foil? Why might this be the case?

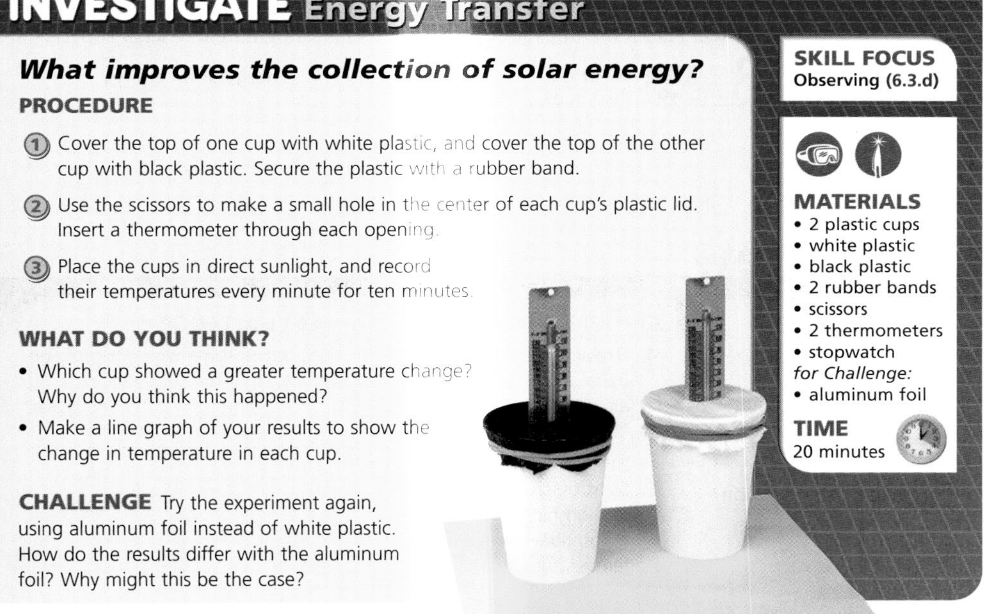

SKILL FOCUS
Observing (6.3.d)

MATERIALS
- 2 plastic cups
- white plastic
- black plastic
- 2 rubber bands
- scissors
- 2 thermometers
- stopwatch

for Challenge:
- aluminum foil

TIME
20 minutes

DIFFERENTIATE INSTRUCTION

More Reading Support

G What heats Earth's surface? *energy from the Sun*

Inclusion Physically challenged students may have difficulty drawing the picture in the below level activity on p. 20. Ask each student to verbally give an example of how electromagnetic radiation has impacted their lives.

INVESTIGATE Energy Transfer

PURPOSE To measure the effect of absorption of solar energy on temperature

TIPS *20 min.* Have one student be responsible for each cup and for reporting to the class the temperature changes.

WHAT DO YOU THINK? *The cup with the black plastic cover showed a greater temperature change. Black objects absorb more solar energy.*

CHALLENGE *The cup with the aluminum foil top will record less of a temperature change than the white cup. Aluminum foil reflects more sunlight than white plastic.*

 Datasheet, Solar Energy, p. 31

Technology Resources

Customize this student lab as needed. Print rubrics to assess student lab reports.

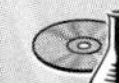 **Lab Generator CD-ROM**

EXPLORE the BIG idea

Revisit "Hot Dog!" on p. 7. Have students explain the role of reflection and absorption in cooking the hot dog.

Real World Examples

Most of the energy we use today to power factories and to light cities comes from fossil fuels such as petroleum, natural gas, and coal. Because fossil fuels will run out one day, scientists are increasingly looking to renewable energy sources such as solar energy to take over. Wind power is another renewable energy source. Turbines on tall towers capture the power of the wind to make electricity. The blades of the turbines look like propellers on airplanes. The rotating blades spin a shaft that turns a generator to produce energy. The larger the blade and the faster the wind, the more energy is produced. In west Texas and in other places in the United States, wind farms with dozens of towers are being set up to generate electricity.

Ongoing Assessment

CHECK YOUR READING *Answer: Solar energy is unlimited and its use doesn't produce harmful waste products, but solar cells are expensive and not very efficient.*

Reinforce the BIG idea

Have students relate the section to the Big Idea.

 Reinforcing Key Concepts, p. 32

1.2 ASSESS & RETEACH

Assess

 Section 1.2 Quiz, p. 6

Reteach

Help students review content of this section by writing two headings on the board: "electromagnetic spectrum—shortest to longest wavelength" and "characteristics." Complete each column with the help of the class.

- *gamma rays—are completely absorbed in the atmosphere*
- *x-rays—used to show hard tissue inside the body; are completely absorbed in the atmosphere*
- *ultraviolet—can cause sunburn and damage plants*
- *visible light—human eyes can detect it; composed of colors having different wavelengths*
- *infrared—warms materials that absorb it; helps heat Earth's surface*
- *microwaves—used to send cellular phone signals*
- *radio waves—used for radio and television broadcasts; passes through Earth's atmosphere to the surface*

Technology Resources

Have students visit **ClassZone.com** for reteaching of Key Concepts.

 CONTENT REVIEW

 CONTENT REVIEW CD-ROM

The Sun as an Energy Resource

Much of the energy used on Earth comes from fossil fuels such as coal, oil, and natural gas. However, the supply of fossil fuels is limited. As a result, people are exploring ways to use other energy sources, including sunlight, to generate electricity. For example, modern solar cells are made of materials that change sunlight into electrical energy. Solar cells are used to provide electrical energy for such things as satellites in orbit around Earth, calculators, and experimental cars.

Solar energy can be used in homes to provide heat and electrical energy.

In addition to changing sunlight into electrical energy, people use the Sun's radiation for heating. The photograph shows a house that uses energy from sunlight. The solar panels on the roof hold solar cells that provide electrical energy, and the large windows help trap the warmth in sunlight.

Energy from the Sun has several advantages compared with fossil fuels. Its supply is not limited, and it does not produce the same harmful waste products that fossil fuels do. But solar cells are not yet commonly used because the materials used to make them are very expensive. Also, solar cells are not very efficient. Large numbers of solar cells produce only a relatively small amount of electrical energy. You will read more in Chapter 13 about using sunlight as an energy source.

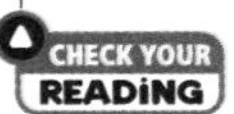 What is an advantage of using solar energy as an energy resource? a disadvantage?

1.2 Review

KEY CONCEPTS

1. How does the Sun's energy travel to Earth? **(6.4.b)**
2. What is the electromagnetic spectrum? **(6.4.b)**
3. What happens to the Sun's energy when it reaches Earth? **(6.3.a)**

CRITICAL THINKING

4. **Draw Conclusions** Would more of the Sun's energy reach a particular part of Earth's surface on a sunny day or on a cloudy day? Explain.
5. **Synthesize** Describe the relationships among energy absorption, heat energy, and temperature.

CHALLENGE

6. **Infer** What would happen on Earth if the Sun's radiation could not travel through space?

ANSWERS

1. as radiation

2. the entire range of electromagnetic energy from radiation with the shortest to the longest wavelengths

3. It is either reflected or absorbed.

4. More of the Sun's energy reaches Earth's surface on a sunny day than a cloudy day. Clouds reflect solar energy.

5. When energy from the Sun is absorbed by an object, the object gains thermal energy. The thermal, or heat, energy raises the temperature of the object.

6. If the Sun's energy could not travel through space, Earth would be a cold, dead planet.

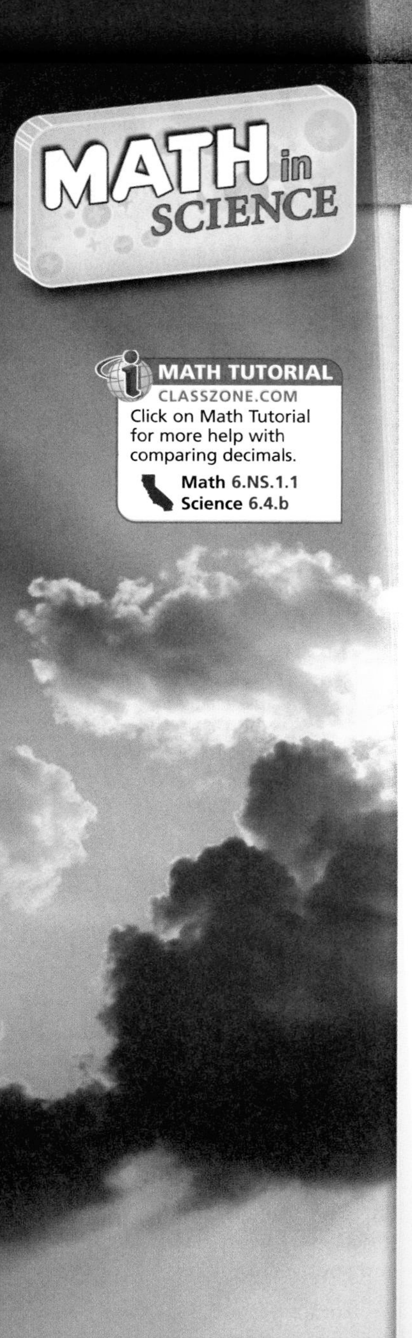

SKILL: COMPARING DECIMALS

Visible Light

Longer wavelengths have less energy. Therefore, red light has less energy than violet light. Wavelengths of visible light are usually measured in nanometers (nm). One nanometer is one-billionth of a meter. To compare wavelengths given in decimals, you can look at their place values.

Steps for comparing decimals

(1) Write the decimals in a column, lining up the decimal points.

(2) If necessary, write zeros to the right of one decimal so that both decimals have the same number of decimal places.

(3) Compare the place values from left to right.

Examples

Example A

Compare the decimals. Which wavelength has less energy?

The hundreds, tens, and ones digits are the same.

Wavelength A: 528.450 nm

Wavelength B: 528.502 nm

The tenths digits are different: 5 > 4.

ANSWER

528.450 nm < 528.502 nm

Wavelength B has less energy.

Example B

Compare two wavelengths from another part of the spectrum. Which has less energy?

The hundreds, tens, and ones digits are the same.

Wavelength A: 712.94 nm

Wavelength B: 712.90 nm

The tenths digits are the same.

The hundredths digits are different: 4 > 0.

ANSWER

712.94 nm > 712.90 nm

Wavelength A has less energy.

Copy each statement and complete it with <, >, or =. Underline the wavelength with less energy.

1. 634.75 nm ___ 634.56 nm
2. 450.5 nm ___ 450.50 nm
3. 752.309 nm ___ 752.311 nm
4. 526.115 nm ___ 526.106 nm
5. 641.75 nm ___ 641.750 nm

Visible Light

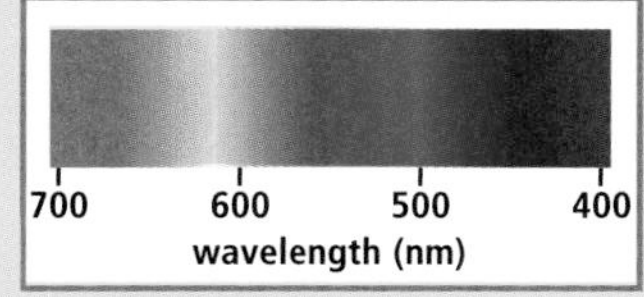

CHALLENGE **Find a value of n that makes the following statement true: 438.0894 nm > n > 438.08925 nm**

ANSWERS

1. 634.75 nm > 634.56 nm
2. 450.5 nm = 450.50 nm
3. 752.309 nm < 752.311 nm
4. 526.115 nm > 526.106 nm
5. 641.75 nm = 641.750 nm

CHALLENGE n = any number from 438.08939 nm to 438.08926 nm

MATH IN SCIENCE

Math Skills Practice for Science

Set Learning Goal

To compare decimals in order to determine which wavelength has less energy

Math Standard

6.NS.1.1 Compare and order positive and negative fractions, decimals, and mixed numbers and place them on a number line.

Present the Science

All parts of the electromagnetic spectrum have wavelengths that can be measured. The wavelengths vary from 3/1000 (0.003) of a nanometer for high-energy gamma rays to 1,000 meters for a radio wave. Visible light falls in the range of 400 to 700 nanometers.

Develop Number Sense Skills

Tell students that a decimal is a way of expressing a numerical value. Every digit to the right of the decimal point indicates a multiple of a negative power of 10. For example, 0.3 represents one-tenth (1/10) of the whole number 3. The decimal 0.03 represents one-hundredth (1/100) of 3, and 0.003 represents one-thousandth (1/1,000) of 3.

DIFFERENTIATION TIP Students with learning disabilities may have an easier time understanding how to compare wavelengths if you start by using whole numbers, for example, 528 versus 543. Then have them practice with numbers that have decimal places to the tenth.

Close

Ask: When comparing wavelengths, how do you determine which has a higher energy level? *Shorter wavelengths indicate higher energy.*

- Math Support, p. 49
- Math Practice, p. 50

Technology Resources

Students can visit **ClassZone.com** for practice in adding measurements.

MATH TUTORIAL

1.3 FOCUS

Set Learning Goals

Students will

- Understand how heat is transferred by conduction.
- Recognize how heat is transferred through the process of convection.
- Infer from an experiment that denser liquids sink.

3-Minute Warm-Up

Display Transparency 5 or copy this exercise on the board:

Answer each question.

1. In what form does radiation travel through empty space? *in waves*
2. List the seven forms of electromagnetic energy that make up the electromagnetic spectrum in order of most to least energy. *gamma rays, x-rays, ultraviolet, visible light, infrared, microwaves, radio waves*
3. Why do people prefer to wear light-colored clothing on a hot day? *Dark clothing absorbs more solar energy, making people hotter.*

3-Minute Warm-Up, p. T5

1.3 MOTIVATE

EXPLORE Conduction

PURPOSE To introduce the concept of conduction to students.

TIP *10 min.* Make sure the water in the large beaker is hot and does not have a chance to cool before you begin the experiment.

WHAT DO YOU THINK? *hot water temperature decreased, and cold water temperature increased; energy flowed from larger beaker to smaller beaker; temperature of the small beaker increased*

KEY CONCEPT

1.3 Heat energy flows from warmer to cooler areas.

CALIFORNIA Content Standards

6.3.c Students know heat flows in solids by conduction (which involves no flow of matter) and in fluids by conduction and by convection (which involves flow of matter).

6.4.d Students know convection currents distribute heat in the atmosphere and oceans.

BEFORE, you learned

- Radiation travels through empty space
- The electromagnetic spectrum includes all the forms of electromagnetic energy
- Radiation transfers energy as heat

NOW, you will learn

- How heat is transferred in matter
- How the process of conduction transfers heat
- How the process of convection transfers heat

VOCABULARY

conduction p. 27
convection p. 28
density p. 28
convection current p. 30

EXPLORE Conduction (6.3.c)

How can you observe a flow of energy?

PROCEDURE

1. Fill the large beaker halfway with hot tap water. Fill the small beaker halfway with cold water. Place a thermometer in each beaker. Record the temperature of the water in each beaker.
2. Without removing the water in either beaker, place the small beaker inside the large beaker. Record the temperature in each beaker every 30 seconds for 2 minutes.

MATERIALS

- 500 mL beaker
- hot tap water
- 200 mL beaker
- cold water
- 2 thermometers
- stopwatch

WHAT DO YOU THINK?

- How did the water temperature in each beaker change?
- In which direction did energy flow? How do you know?

Heat flow is a transfer of energy.

Think about what you might do to keep warm on a cold day. You might sit next to a heater. You might also avoid being near a door that opens to the outside and lets in cold air. Now think about what you might do to keep cool on a hot day. You might wear light clothing and sit in the shade of a tree. In all of these situations, you are trying to control the flow of heat between yourself and your surroundings.

Recall that heat energy moves from a warmer object to a cooler object. You have read about how radiation transfers heat energy. There are two other ways that heat energy is transferred. One is called conduction. The other is called convection.

RESOURCES FOR DIFFERENTIATED INSTRUCTION

Below Level

UNIT RESOURCE BOOK

- Reading Study Guide A, pp. 35–36
- Decoding Support, p. 48

AUDIO CDS

Additional INVESTIGATION, Insulators, pp. 60–68; Teacher Instructions, pp. 274–275

Advanced

UNIT RESOURCE BOOK

Challenge and Extension, p. 41
Challenge Reading, pp. 44–45

English Learners

UNIT RESOURCE BOOK

Spanish Reading Study Guide, pp. 39–40

- Audio Readings in Spanish
- Audio Readings (English)

Heat flow by conduction requires contact.

One way that energy is transferred as heat is through direct contact between objects. **Conduction** is the process that moves energy from one object to another when they are touching. The heat energy moves from one object to another. But there is no flow of matter.

Recall that the atoms and molecules in matter are always moving. The average energy of motion of particles in the warmer object is greater than that of the particles in the cooler object. When particles collide, or bump into each other, some of the energy of motion of faster-moving particles is transferred to slower-moving particles. Therefore, energy is transferred from the warmer object to the cooler object. As long as the objects are touching, conduction continues until the temperatures of the objects are equal.

Conduction can also occur within a single object. In this case, energy is transferred from the warmer part of the object to the cooler part of the object by heat flow. Suppose you put a metal spoon into a cup of hot cocoa. Energy will be conducted from the warm end of the spoon in the cocoa to the cool end until the temperature of the entire spoon is the same.

CHECK YOUR READING How is energy transferred by conduction?

Some materials transfer heat flow by conduction better than others. Materials that transfer energy easily are called conductors. Metals are typically good conductors. You know that when one end of a metal object gets hot, the other end quickly becomes hot as well. Consider a saucepan that has a metal handle. After the pan has been placed on a stove that has been turned on, the handle might become quite hot. You would use something to protect your hand when you held the handle.

Materials that are poor conductors are called insulators. Some examples of insulators are wood and paper. Air is also a poor conductor of heat energy. Many materials that are insulators have a large amount of trapped air inside them. Consider a cup made of plastic foam. It contains many open spaces within it that are filled with trapped air. A plastic foam cup will not easily transfer energy by conduction. As a result, plastic foam is often used to keep cold drinks cold and hot drinks hot.

Think about the handle of the pan mentioned above. Often, the handle is not made of metal, a good conductor. Instead, it is made of a material that is an insulator, such as wood or plastic. Although a wood or plastic handle will get hot when the pan is on a stove, it takes a much longer time for wood or plastic to get hot compared with a metal handle.

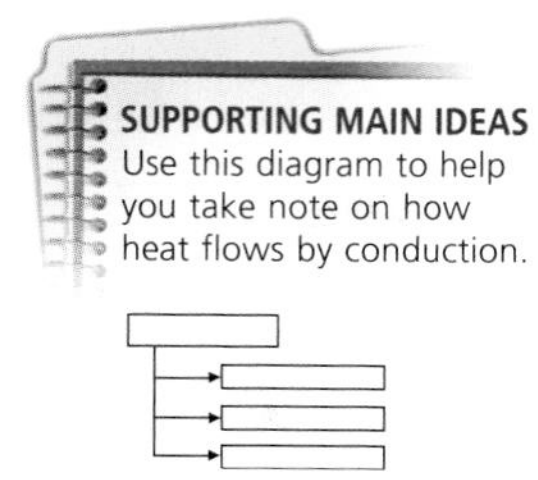

SUPPORTING MAIN IDEAS
Use this diagram to help you take note on how heat flows by conduction.

Conduction transfers energy from the cocoa to the mug and through the gloves to the person's hands.

DIFFERENTIATE INSTRUCTION

More Reading Support

A What happens to the energy of motion of faster-moving particles when they collide with slower-moving particles? *Energy is transferred.*

Advanced Often people associate the term "insulator" with the concept of keeping an object warm or heated. But insulation can also be applied to keeping an object cool. Have students think of insulators that they use the keep objects cool. On a piece of paper, have them draw a diagram of the insulator and label the processes of conduction and insulation as it applies to that product.

 Challenge and Extension, p. 41

Challenge Reading, pp. 44–45

1.3 INSTRUCT

Teach the Standards

Convection 6.3.c

In this section: Explain to students that heat flows from warmer to cooler objects by conduction (which involves no flow of matter) when the objects are touching. Heat flows in fluids by conduction and by convection (which involves flow of matter).

future opportunities: atmospheric convection, p. 59, p. 66, p. 129; mantle convection, pp. 273–274

Address Misconceptions

IDENTIFY Ask students how the flow of energy as heat differs from the flow of a fluid such as water. If students fail to recognize that heat is not a physical form of matter like water, they may hold the misconception that heat is matter.

CORRECT Hold an ice cube in the palm of your hand. Ask students to describe the flow of heat. Point out that energy, not particles of matter, flows from your hand to the ice cube.

REASSESS Ask: What flows from one place to another when an object is heated? *energy*

Technology Resources

Visit **ClassZone.com** for background on common student misconceptions.

 MISCONCEPTION DATABASE

Real World Example

When you go to a football game on a cold day, sit on a wooden bench rather than an aluminum one. When you are seated, heat from your body will flow to the bench. The metal aluminum is a good conductor and will quickly transfer your body heat away from you. Wood, by comparison, is a poor conductor and your place on the bench will warm up and stay warm.

Ongoing Assessment

 *Answer: through direct contact*

Integrate the Sciences

Convection is the process responsible for the movement of much of Earth's internal heat energy. As hot mantle material rises toward the crust, it carries heat energy upward. When it cools, it becomes more dense, and it sinks. As material rises and sinks, it creates convection currents.

Teacher Demo

Fill a glass with cold water. Fill a second glass with hot tap water. Put an equal amount of food coloring into each glass. The food coloring sinks to the bottom in the glass of cold water, but it swirls around to mix in the hot water. In the glass of hot water, surface water is in contact with the cooler air. This water cools and sinks to the bottom, while the hotter water at the bottom rises. The moving water carries the food coloring along with it.

Ongoing Assessment

CHECK YOUR READING *Answer: In convection, atoms and molecules move over much greater distances than in conduction. Convection occurs only in materials that are able to flow.*

Heat flow by convection involves a flow of matter.

Liquid is heated at the bottom of a pan. The hot liquid rises, carrying heat energy with it in the process of convection. Cooler liquid sinks to take the place of the rising liquid.

B Energy can also be transferred through the movement of gases or liquids. **Convection** is the process that transfers energy from place to place by the motion of a gas or liquid. Recall that in conduction, atoms and molecules in objects move over tiny distances and transfer energy by touching other atoms and molecules. The particles themselves do not flow. In convection, the atoms and molecules do move, and they transfer energy over much greater distances. That is why convection occurs only in materials that are able to flow. Materials that are able to flow are called fluids.

You can see convection when you watch a boiling pan of soup on a stove. The stove heats the bottom of the pan, which then heats the soup that is in contact with it by conduction. But then the hot soup rises toward the top of the pan, carrying heat energy with it. It's easy to see small pieces of vegetables or other soup ingredients being carried by the movement of the soup. The movement of hot soup is an example of energy transfer by convection.

How is convection different from conduction?

Density

What causes the hot soup to rise toward the top of the pan? The answer involves density. Before you can continue to explore convection, you need to understand density.

A substance's **density** is a measure of the amount of mass it contains per unit volume. A substance that has a higher density has more mass in a particular volume, or amount of space. Consider a tennis ball and a baseball. They are about the same size—they have a similar volume. But the baseball weighs more than the tennis ball. The baseball has more mass and so is more dense.

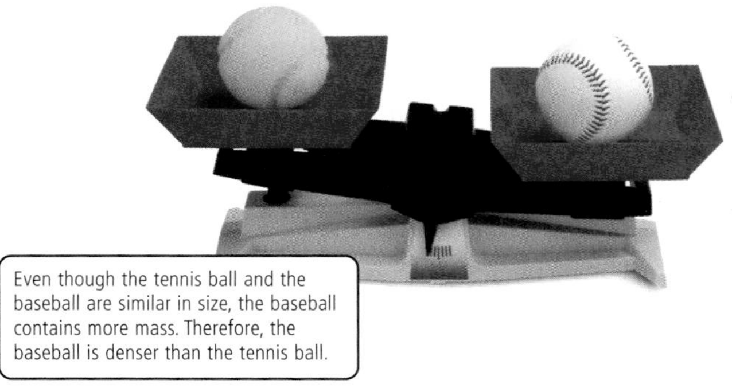

Even though the tennis ball and the baseball are similar in size, the baseball contains more mass. Therefore, the baseball is denser than the tennis ball.

DIFFERENTIATE INSTRUCTION

More Reading Support

B Name the process that transfers energy from place to place by the motion of a gas or liquid. *convection*

English Learners English language learners may have difficulty remembering the difference between the words *conduction* and *convection*. Explain that conduction is the transfer of heat by contact. Heat always travels from the warmer to the colder object. Convection happens only in a gas or liquid. The knowledge that convection occurs only in material that flows is key.

Additional Investigation To reinforce Section 1.3 learning goals, use the following full-period investigation:

Additional INVESTIGATION, Insulators, A, B, & C, pp. 60–68, 274–275

You can use a simple method to compare the densities of a solid and a liquid, or two liquids. You can check to see which one floats on the other. Suppose you drop a small piece of wood and a small piece of rock into a bowl of water. The wood floats because it is less dense than water. The rock sinks because it is more dense than water. Similarly, oil floats on water because oil is less dense than water.

Changes in Density

The density of a substance changes as its temperature changes. The density of a solid object does not change much when the object gets warmer or cooler. Because the atoms and molecules of a solid object are tightly held together, the object's volume cannot change much. But the atoms and molecules of a liquid are more free to move. The density of a liquid can change quite a bit as its temperature changes.

Consider what happens as a liquid changes in temperature. When the liquid becomes warmer, its molecules move faster. The motion makes the molecules collide more, so they stay farther apart. When there is more space between molecules, the liquid is less dense. When the liquid becomes cooler, its molecules move more slowly. The molecules collide less, so they stay closer together. The liquid becomes more dense.

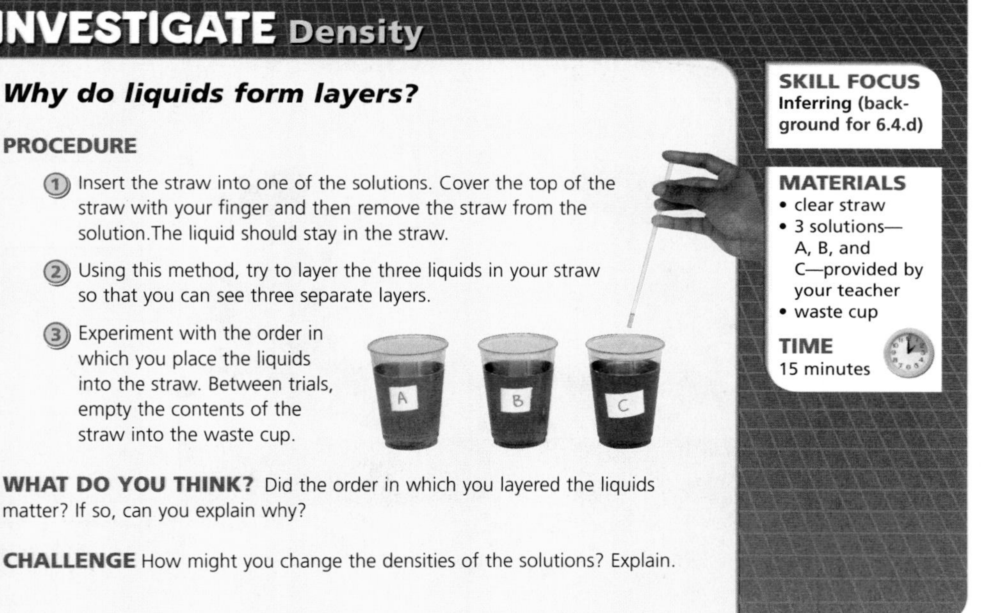

INVESTIGATE Density

Why do liquids form layers?

PROCEDURE

1. Insert the straw into one of the solutions. Cover the top of the straw with your finger and then remove the straw from the solution.The liquid should stay in the straw.
2. Using this method, try to layer the three liquids in your straw so that you can see three separate layers.
3. Experiment with the order in which you place the liquids into the straw. Between trials, empty the contents of the straw into the waste cup.

WHAT DO YOU THINK? Did the order in which you layered the liquids matter? If so, can you explain why?

CHALLENGE How might you change the densities of the solutions? Explain.

SKILL FOCUS
Inferring (background for 6.4.d)

MATERIALS
- clear straw
- 3 solutions—A, B, and C—provided by your teacher
- waste cup

TIME
15 minutes

DIFFERENTIATE INSTRUCTION

More Reading Support

C Why does oil float on water? *because oil is less dense than water*

D What happens to the density of liquid when it becomes cooler? *it becomes more dense*

Below Level Have students sit in groups of three or four. Ask each group to make two drawings. In one drawing, ask group members to show how heat can be transferred from one object to another by conduction. Remind them to clearly show the objects in their drawings. In the second drawing, ask group members to show how convection can transfer heat energy. Have each group show and explain its drawings to the class.

Develop Critical Thinking

APPLY Why do people run hot water on a jar lid when they cannot open the jar? *The heat from the hot water makes the metal of the jar lid become less dense and expand. The seal of the lid becomes less tight, so the lid screws off the jar more easily.*

INVESTIGATE Density

PURPOSE To infer that denser liquids sink and less dense liquids rise

TIPS *15 min.* Make sure the liquids are of different densities. You may find it helpful to have extra straws.

WHAT DO YOU THINK? *Yes. The liquids must be layered from least to most dense. Otherwise, when the straw containing a higher density liquid is placed into a cup with liquid of a lower density, the higher density liquid will sink to the bottom of the cup.*

CHALLENGE *Students might change the densities of a liquid by adding an ingredient to it that will change its mixture and, hence, its density.*

 Datasheet, Explore Density, p. 42

Technology Resources

Customize this student lab as needed. Print rubrics to assess student lab reports.

 **Lab Generator CD-ROM**

Ongoing Assessment

Recognize how heat is transferred through the process of convection.

Ask: Why does a change in temperature affect the density of a solid object less than the density of a liquid? *The atoms and molecules in a solid object are held together more tightly than in a liquid. Therefore, a solid object does not expand or contract as much as a liquid does.*

Teach from Visuals

To help students interpret the "Convection" visual, ask:

- What happens to air as it cools? *It becomes more dense and sinks.*
- What happens to cooler, denser air when it moves under warm air? *It is warmed by conduction from the ground.*

Address Misconceptions

IDENTIFY Ask: In what direction is energy transferred through heat? If students say only upward, they may hold the misconception that heat only rises.

CORRECT Point out that the common phrase "heat rises" is misleading. Have students look at the visual again. Point out that as warm air rises, it carries heat energy upward. However, heat can travel in any direction. Use a radiant heat source to demonstrate this concept. Have students put their hand close to the heat source, but not above it, to observe that heat travels in all directions.

REASSESS Ask students to describe in what direction heat travels outward from a fire. *It travels outward in all directions.*

Technology Resources

Visit **ClassZone.com** for background on common student misconceptions.

MISCONCEPTION DATABASE

Integrate the Sciences

Vultures take advantage of convection. As they soar through the skies in search of food, they use updrafts of warm air to keep aloft. They manipulate their feathers and wings to prevent themselves from sinking when they encounter descending air. Gliding through the air requires significantly less energy than flapping their wings often.

Ongoing Assessment

READING VISUALS *Answers: Air is more dense at 2 and 3, where it is cool; air is less dense at 1, where it is warmer.*

Density and Convection Currents

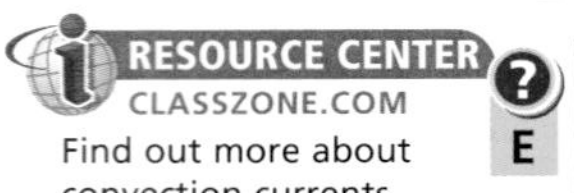

Find out more about convection currents.

E

Differences in density within a liquid or gas can produce the motion of convection. As a gas or liquid becomes warmer and less dense, it tends to rise. As it becomes cooler and more dense, it tends to sink. This motion can form a convection current. A **convection current** is a pattern of movement that occurs when a gas or liquid rises as it becomes warmer in one area and sinks as it becomes cooler in another area. The current flows in a continuous loop.

The illustration below shows a convection current in the atmosphere. During the day, energy from the Sun heats Earth's surface. The warm surface heats the air in contact with it by conduction.

READING TIP

As you read about the cycle that causes a convection current to form, follow the steps in the illustration below. Note that ● = particle of air.

1. As the air is heated, its molecules move farther apart. The warm air becomes less dense, so it rises. As the air rises into the atmosphere, it begins to cool. It will stop rising when it is no longer warmer and less dense than the air above it.
2. As the air continues to cool, its molecules get closer together. The cool air begins to sink when it becomes denser than the warmer air beneath it.
3. Cool, dense air sinks and flows sideways to replace the warm, rising air. When the cooler air becomes warmed by contact with Earth's surface, it will rise too.

Convection

A convection current flows in a continuous loop.

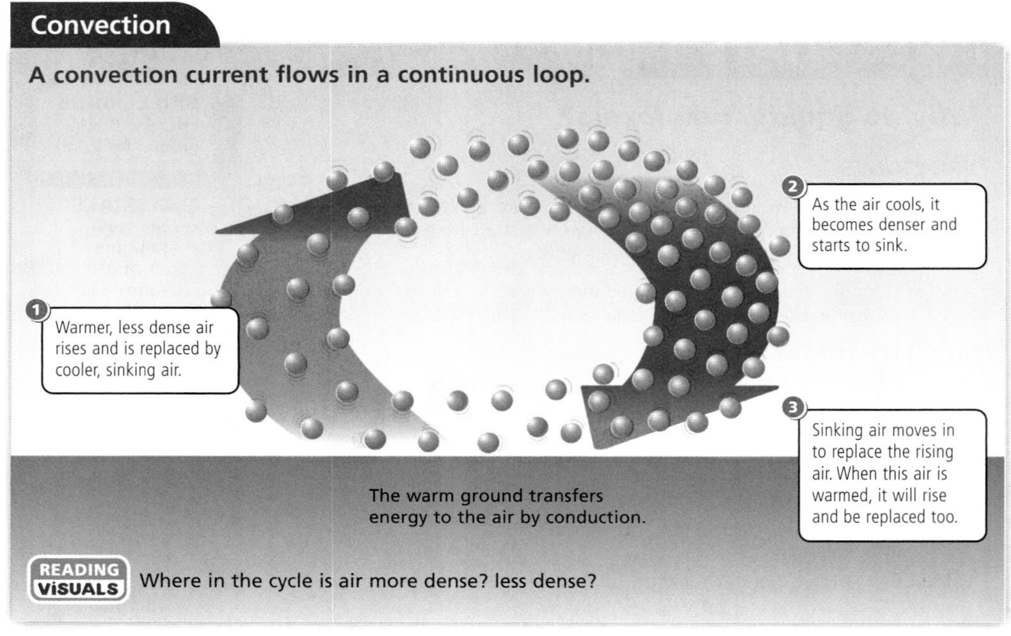

1 Warmer, less dense air rises and is replaced by cooler, sinking air.
2 As the air cools, it becomes denser and starts to sink.
3 Sinking air moves in to replace the rising air. When this air is warmed, it will rise and be replaced too.
The warm ground transfers energy to the air by conduction.

READING VISUALS Where in the cycle is air more dense? less dense?

DIFFERENTIATE INSTRUCTION

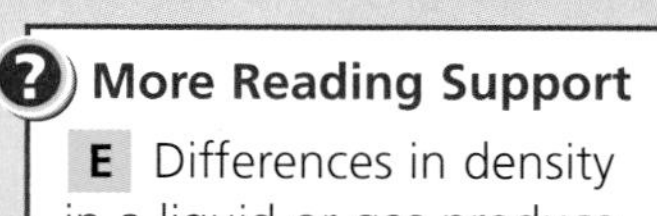

More Reading Support

E Differences in density in a liquid or gas produce what type of motion? *convection*

Below Level Remind students that density is the amount of mass of a substance in a certain volume. Demonstrate volume and density by measuring out a half cup of vegetable oil and a half cup of water. Mix the vegetable oil and water together in a clear jar and have students observe what happens. The vegetable oil is less dense than water, so it floats on top of the water.

Convection currents in liquids are similar to those in the atmosphere. Warm water is less dense than cold water, so warm water tends to rise and cold water tends to sink. Consider what happens in a lake as the seasons change throughout a year.

Lake Turnover

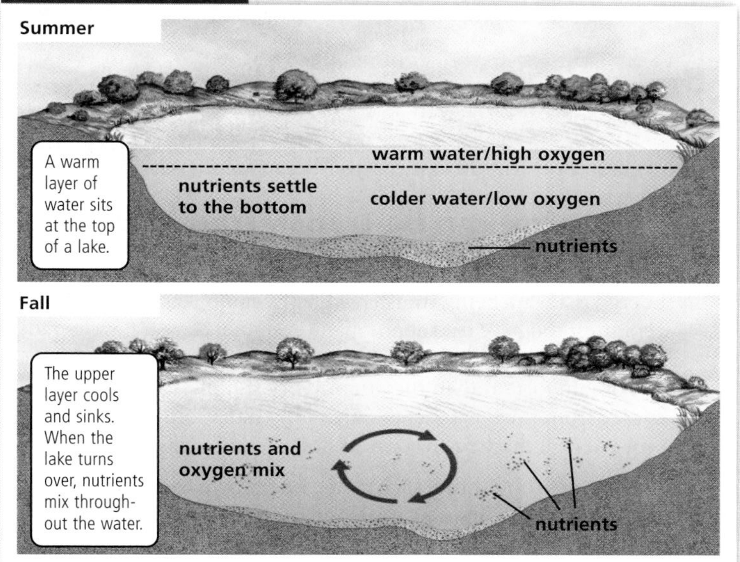
Summer
A warm layer of water sits at the top of a lake.
warm water/high oxygen
nutrients settle to the bottom
colder water/low oxygen
nutrients
Fall
The upper layer cools and sinks. When the lake turns over, nutrients mix throughout the water.
nutrients and oxygen mix
nutrients

In the spring and summer, sunlight can warm a layer of water at the surface of the lake. The layer of warm water is less dense than the layer of cooler water beneath it. The layers of water do not mix easily, and no convection currents form.

The layering of water in the lake affects the organisms that live in it. The layer of warm water is likely to be high in oxygen because it is in contact with the air. Fish may be more plentiful in the upper part of the lake. The layer of cold water is likely to be low in oxygen. But it is likely to be higher in nutrients needed by many of the organisms.

In the fall, the air becomes cooler. The water in contact with the air becomes cooler too. The water loses heat energy to the air above it through conduction. The upper layer of water becomes denser than the water underneath it. As the dense water sinks, warmer water rises to the top of the lake. It too becomes cool and sinks. Convection currents form, and the water of the lake mixes. Oxygen and nutrients become more evenly distributed. Convection stops when the water at the top of the lake is about the same temperature as the air.

Teach from Visuals

To help students interpret the "Lake Turnover" visual, ask:

- Where is the warm water in a lake during the summer? *at the surface*
- Why is the water warmer there in the summer? *Sunlight warms the surface.*
- Why are nutrients found at the bottom of a lake in summer? *The nutrients settle to the bottom. The lack of a convection current during the summer months keeps them at the bottom.*
- What happens to the surface waters of a lake in fall? *They cool and sink.*
- What happens to the nutrients in fall? Why? *The cold surface waters become dense and sink. They start convection currents that mix nutrients throughout the lake water.*

Real World Example

Lake turnover presents challenges to people who fish. During summer, the amount of oxygen in the water is higher near the surface; during winter, oxygen levels are commonly higher at the bottom. Fish must live in the areas where they can access oxygen. Therefore, people can identify the places where fish live and can have success fishing in those places. During and after spring and fall turnover, however, convection currents mix the water in the lake, distributing and replenishing oxygen. As a result, fish can leave their restricted areas and spread throughout the lake and fishing becomes much more challenging.

DIFFERENTIATE INSTRUCTION

More Reading Support

F Why do convection currents not form in lakes during the summer? *The warm water is already at the top of the lake.*

G What cools the waters of a lake during the fall? *air*

Advanced Fluids that become cooler usually grow denser and sink. Water, however, is different. As water cools toward its freezing point (0° Celsius), it exhibits unusual properties. Have interested students research the density of water as it cools. Have them explain what happens to it and why.

Ongoing Assessment

Unerstand how heat is transferred by conduction.

Ask: How is heat in a fireplace transferred by conduction? *The hot coals fall through the grate, make contact with the stone floor of the fireplace, and warm the stone.*

Reinforce the BIG idea

Have students relate the section to the Big Idea.

 Reinforcing Key Concepts, p. 43

1.3 ASSESS & RETEACH

Assess

 Section 1.3 Quiz, p. 7

Reteach

Write the headings "conduction", "convection", and "radiation" on the board. Write students' answers about what they learned in the chapter under each heading. Then point out examples of heat transfer in the classroom. Call upon students to identify these as examples of radiation, conduction, convection, or a combination.

Technology Resources

Have students visit **ClassZone.com** for reteaching of Key Concepts.

 CONTENT REVIEW

 CONTENT REVIEW CD-ROM

The fire warms its surroundings in three ways. It gives off infrared radiation. It warms the air around it by conduction. The warmed air helps heat the room by convection.

Heat energy can be transferred in different ways at the same time.

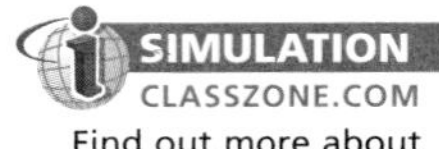

SIMULATION CLASSZONE.COM Find out more about convection currents.

Energy is always being transferred between objects at different temperatures. You have read about many examples of heat flow by radiation, conduction, and convection. In some processes, one type of heat flow is more important than the others. For example, the only way that energy from the Sun reaches Earth is by radiation. However, in many processes, all three forms of heat flow are important.

Consider how a fire, such as the one shown in the photograph, heats its surroundings. As the wood burns, it gives off energy in the form of radiation. Some of this energy is light energy, and some of it is infrared energy. When objects absorb this radiation, they become warmer. Heat from the fire is also transferred by conduction. The hot coals that fall through the grate warm the stone they are in contact with. The fire also warms the air around it by conduction. This warmed air then moves through the room and heats it by convection.

1.3 Review

KEY CONCEPTS

1. What are three ways in which energy can be transferred as heat? Give an example of each. (6.3.c, 6.3.d)
2. How is heat transferred by conduction? (6.3.c)
3. Explain how density is involved in convection. (6.4.d)

CRITICAL THINKING

4. **Analyze** A wool sweater traps air against your body. Is wool a good conductor? Explain.
5. **Synthesize** If you pour out some of the water in a bucket, does the density of the remaining water change? Explain.

CHALLENGE

6. **Infer** Explain why it is incorrect to say that insulation "keeps out the cold."

ANSWERS

1. radiation (solar energy traveling to Earth), conduction (metal spoon in hot cocoa), convection (air moving in a cycle)

2. In conduction, heat is transferred by direct contact between objects.

3. Density drives convection. Warm gases or fluids become less dense and rise; cold ones become more dense and sink.

4. No. Wool does not conduct heat very quickly from your body to surroundings. Wool is an insulator; it traps air against your body.

5. No. The density of a substance changes as its temperature changes. Pouring out some of the water in the bucket will not change the temperature of the water.

6. It is incorrect, because energy flows from a warmer object to a colder one, not vice versa. Insulation slows the transfer of heat energy from an object.

CHEF

Cooking and Heat

6.3.c Students know heat flows in solids by conduction (which involves no flow of matter) and in fluids by conduction and by convection (which involves flow of matter).

A chef makes many decisions about cooking a meal based on heat and temperature. The appropriate temperature and cooking method must be used. A chef must calculate the cooking time of each part of the meal so that everything is finished at the same time. A chef also needs to understand how heat moves through food. For example, if an oven temperature is too hot, meat can be overcooked on the outside and undercooked on the inside.

Bread vs. Meat

Chefs have to understand how heat energy is transferred to different foods. For example, the fluffy texture of bread comes from pockets of gas that separate its fibers. The gas is a poor conductor of energy. Therefore, more energy and a longer cooking time are needed to cook bread than to cook an equal amount of meat.

What Temperature?

Eggs cook very differently under different temperatures. For example, temperature is important when baking meringue, which is made of egg whites and sugar. A Key lime pie topped with meringue is baked at 400°F to make a meringue that is soft. However, meringue baked at 275°F makes light and crisp dessert shells.

Roasting and Heat

The shape of the food being roasted is just as important as what is being roasted. Heat moves more quickly through food with a thin shape than it will through food with a thicker shape.

EXPLORE

1. **COMPARE** Using a cookbook, find the oven temperatures for baking biscuits, potatoes, and beef. Could you successfully cook a roast and biscuits in the oven at the same time?
2. **CHALLENGE** Crack open three eggs. Lightly beat one egg in each of three separate bowls. Follow the steps below.
   1. Heat about two cups of water to 75°C in a small pan.
   2. Pour one of the eggs into the water in the pan.
   3. Observe the egg and record your observations.
   4. Repeat steps 1–3 twice, once with boiling water and then with room-temperature water.

   Describe the differences that you observed among the three eggs. What may account for these differences?

EXPLORE

1. ***COMPARE*** *Yes, by changing the length of time they are in the oven, or by putting them in the oven at different times, you can successfully cook a roast and biscuits in the oven at the same time.*
2. ***CHALLENGE*** *The egg in room-temperature water does not visibly change. In boiling water, it stays in one piece and turns white right away. In 75°C water, it spreads out and slowly turns slightly white. The water temperature determines what happens to the eggs.*

SCIENCE ON THE JOB
Relevance of Science to Nonscience Jobs

Set Learning Goal
To understand why chefs need knowledge of heat and temperature

Present the Science
Many foods, such as beef, chicken, pork, and eggs, can contain microorganisms—such as bacteria—that cause food poisoning. Cooking foods until they reach a certain temperature kills these bacteria. Meat thermometers and other thermometers help ensure that foods reach the correct temperature. In addition, refrigerating leftovers and keeping foods cold help slow the growth of bacteria. Heat and temperature are also important to a chef because part of the job involves the presentation and appeal of food. The structure of protein changes when exposed to high temperatures, so a chef has to know how the texture of foods containing a large amount of protein will change during and after cooking.

Discussion Questions
- Ask: What can cause meat to be overcooked on the outside and undercooked on the inside? *an oven temperature that is too hot*
- Ask: How does the shape of a roast affect how fast it cooks? *Heat moves more quickly through a thin roast than a thick roast.*

Close
Ask: How do chefs use their knowledge of heat and temperature? *to choose the right temperature and cooking method; to finish cooking every part of the meal at the right time; to understand how heat moves through food*

BACK TO

the BIG idea

Tell students to consider the ways in which energy is present in their homes. How do waves and heat flow transfer energy in your home? *Answer: Students may say that radiation from a fireplace or a heater helps heat their homes in winter. Conduction and convection play a part in getting heat from a furnace or radiator to rooms in their homes. Radiation from the Sun may warm their homes to an uncomfortable level on a hot summer day, creating the need for air conditioning—which involves conduction and convection. Energy in the form of microwaves heats or cooks food items in a microwave.*

KEY CONCEPTS SUMMARY

SECTION 1.1

Ask: Which form of energy comes to Earth from the Sun, and how does it move to Earth? *Electromagnetic energy; travels through space*

Ask: What kind of energy does the Sun's energy become after it is transferred from plants to animals and then people? *chemical energy*

SECTION 1.2

Ask: How are waves at opposite ends of the electromagnetic spectrum different? *Wavelengths are different lengths; waves with shorter wavelengths have more energy.*

Ask: What could you determine by measuring the distance between a wave's troughs? *the wavelength*

SECTION 1.3

Ask: What is essential to make conduction work? *Objects have to be in direct contact and have different temperatures.*

Ask: Why does warm air rise in the atmosphere and cold air does not? *As molecules in warm air collide, they spread farther apart, causing the air to become less dense and rise. The molecules in cold air move slower and stay closer together than molecules in warm air.*

Review Concepts

- Big Idea Flow Chart, p. T1
- Chapter Outline, pp. T7–8

1 Chapter Review

the BIG idea

Waves and heat flow transfer energy.

KEY CONCEPTS SUMMARY

1 Change occurs as energy is transferred.

- Energy is the ability to cause a change.
- Different forms of energy produce changes in different ways.
- All living things require energy.
- Work transfers energy.

Energy from sunlight is transferred to plants and then to animals.

VOCABULARY
energy p. 9
heat energy p. 10
temperature p. 10
heat flow p. 11
conservation of energy p. 14
work p. 15

2 Radiation transfers energy.

Radiation is energy that travels in the form of electromagnetic waves. A wavelength is the distance between one wave crest or trough and the next.

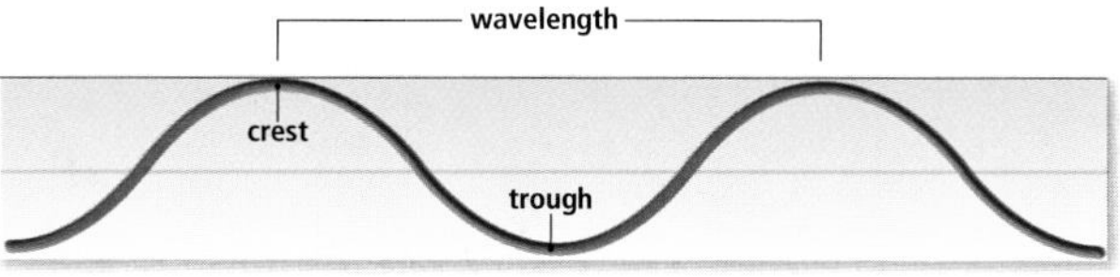

VOCABULARY
radiation p. 18
wave p. 19
wavelength p. 20
electromagnetic spectrum p. 21

3 Heat energy flows from warmer to cooler areas.

Conduction transfers energy by direct contact. Energy from the cocoa is transferred to the mug, to the gloves, and then to the person's hands.

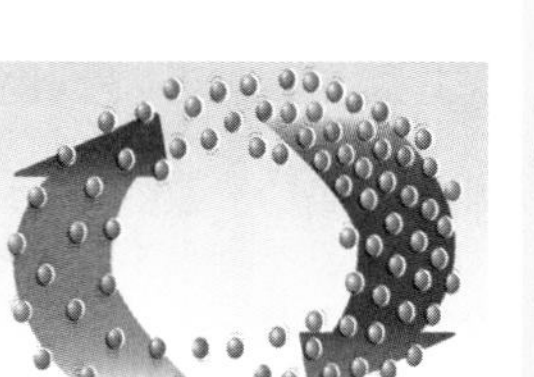

Convection transfers energy by the motion of a gas or liquid. The warm ground transfers energy to the air. Less dense air rises, and denser air sinks.

VOCABULARY
conduction p. 27
convection p. 28
density p. 28
convection current p. 30

34 Unit 1: The Earth System

Technology Resources

Have students visit **ClassZone.com** or use the CD-ROM for a cumulative review of concepts.

CONTENT REVIEW

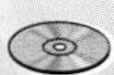
CONTENT REVIEW CD-ROM

Engage students in a whole-class interactive review of Key Concepts. Edit content as you wish.

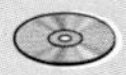
POWER PRESENTATIONS

Reviewing Vocabulary

Copy and complete the chart below. If the right column is blank, give a brief description or definition. If the left column is blank, give the correct term.

Term	Description
1. temperature	
2.	the ability to cause change
3. heat energy	
4.	a disturbance that carries energy from one place to another
5. conduction	
6.	law stating energy can change form but is never created or destroyed
7.	the use of force to move an object some distance
8. radiation	
9.	a measure of the amount of mass a substance contains
10. convection current	
11.	the distance between one wave crest and the next
12.	the range of all types of electromagnetic energy
13. convection	

Reviewing Key Concepts

Multiple Choice *Choose the letter of the best answer.*

14. When energy changes from one form to another, what is usually produced?
- **a.** chemical energy
- **b.** sound energy
- **c.** heat energy
- **d.** mechanical energy

15. Energy from the Sun travels to Earth as (6.3.d)
- **a.** radiation
- **b.** sound energy
- **c.** conduction
- **d.** mechanical energy

16. Which type of energy is stored in food?
- **a.** sound
- **b.** mechanical
- **c.** chemical
- **d.** electromagnetic

17. Which type of energy includes visible light, x-rays, and microwaves? (6.4.b)
- **a.** sound
- **b.** mechanical
- **c.** chemical
- **d.** electromagnetic

Short Answer *Write a short answer to each question.*

18. What is the difference between heat and temperature?

19. Explain why energy cannot travel by conduction through empty space. (6.3.c)

20. What are the parts of a wave? Copy the drawing below onto your paper, and label each part.

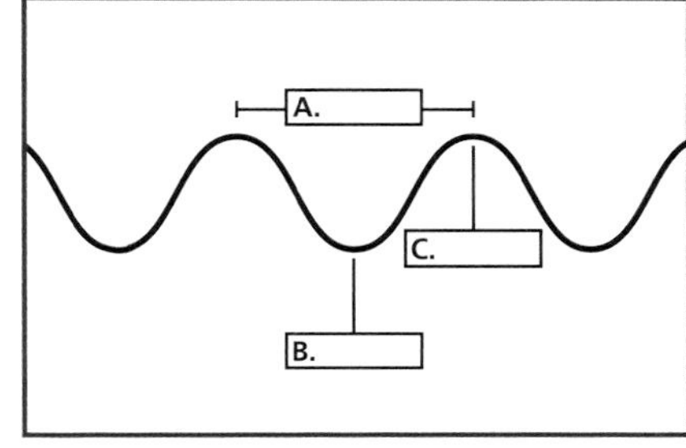

ASSESSMENT RESOURCES

ASSESSMENT BOOK
- Chapter Test A, pp. 8–11
- Chapter Test B, pp. 12–15
- Chapter Test C, pp. 16–19
- Alternative Assessment, pp. 20–21

STANDARDS REVIEW AND PRACTICE, pp. 23–30, 33–34, 37–38, 59–60

Technology Resources

Edit test items and answer choices.

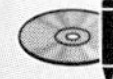 **Test Generator CD-ROM**

Visit **ClassZone.com** to extend test practice.

 **Test Practice**

Reviewing Vocabulary

1. *a measure of the average amount of the energy of motion of the particles in an object*
2. *energy*
3. *total energy of the motion of particles in an object*
4. *wave*
5. *process that moves energy from one object to another when they are touching*
6. *law of conservation of energy*
7. *work*
8. *energy that travels across distances in the form of electromagnetic waves*
9. *density*
10. *pattern of movement that occurs when a gas or liquid rises as it becomes warmer in one area and sinks as it becomes cooler in another area*
11. *wavelength*
12. *electromagnetic spectrum*
13. *process that transfers energy from place to place through the motion of a gas or a liquid*

Reviewing Key Concepts

14. *c*
15. *a*
16. *c*
17. *d*
18. *Heat is the total energy of the motion of particles in an object. Temperature is the average energy of the motion of particles in an object.*
19. *Energy cannot travel through empty space by conduction because conduction requires direct contact between objects.*
20. *A. wavelength; B. trough; C. crest*

Thinking Critically

21. convection

22. conduction

23. conduction

24. The stove warms the liquid in the bottom of the pot—lessening its density—and it rises; colder, denser liquid in the top of the pot sinks.

25. Both forms change to heat energy when absorbed. The Sun is its own energy source, but the stove requires another form of energy to make it work.

26. transfer of energy by radiation from the Sun; convection of hot air

27. conduction: requires contact; both: transfer heat; convection: occurs in moving gases or liquids

28. Sketch should show a prism or water drops in the atmosphere separating white light.

29. Plants change electromagnetic energy from the Sun to chemical energy. Plants store this energy. When animals eat plants, the animals take in the energy and store it in their muscles.

30. Answers will vary.

31. Both capture the Sun's energy. Plants rely on photosynthesis to capture and change solar energy into chemical energy. Solar cells convert the Sun's energy into electricity.

32. A light color would reflect solar energy and keep the house cooler.

the BIG idea

33. After having read the chapter, students may now note forms of energy that are not obvious in the picture, such as the chemical energy stored by the people and the flowers and the heat and sound energy emitted as the cyclists pedal.

34. Energy can change form but can never be created or destroyed. Students may say that they were surprised that energy cannot be destroyed but only changes form.

UNIT PROJECTS

Give students the appropriate Unit Project worksheets from the URB for their projects. Both directions and rubrics can be used as a guide.

R Unit Projects, pp. 5–10

Thinking Critically

The illustration below shows heat energy being transferred as a pot is heated on a stove. Use the illustration to answer the next five questions.

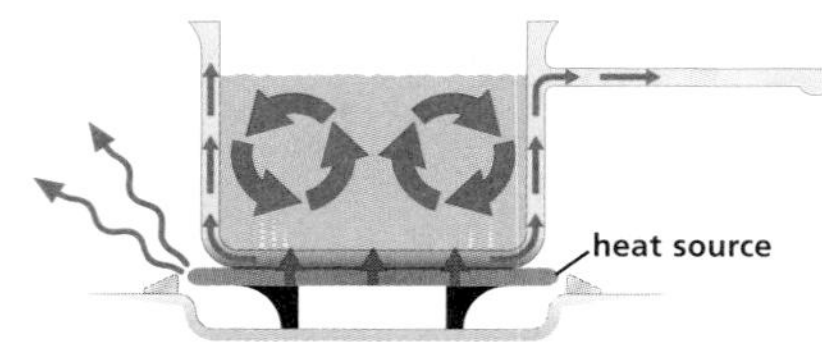

21. OBSERVE What process do the thick arrows in the liquid show? (6.3.c)

22. OBSERVE What process do the thin arrows along the sides of the pot show? (6.3.c)

23. APPLY By what process is heat energy being transferred from the stove to the pot? (6.3.c)

24. APPLY Use your understanding of density to explain the motion of the liquid inside the pot. (6.3.c)

25. COMPARE AND CONTRAST How is the radiation from the hot stove similar to radiation from the Sun? (6.3.d)

26. DRAW CONCLUSIONS Suppose you are outdoors on a hot day and you move into the shade of a tree. Which form of energy transfer are you avoiding? Which type of energy transfer might still cause you to feel hot? Explain. (6.3.d, 6.4.d)

27. COMPARE AND CONTRAST Draw a Venn diagram to compare and contrast conduction and convection. (6.3.c)

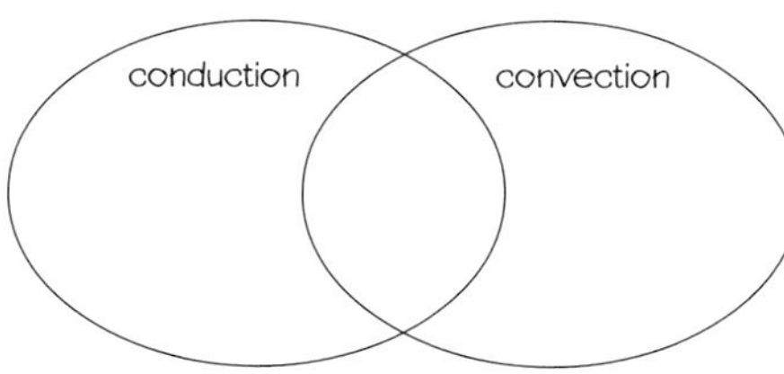

28. COMMUNICATE Draw a sketch that shows how visible light can be separated into different colors. (6.4.b)

29. SYNTHESIZE Explain how the energy stored in wood, corn, and the muscles of an animal all came originally from the Sun. (6.4.a)

30. COMMUNICATE Describe a process in which energy changes forms at least twice. Draw and label a diagram that shows these energy changes.

31. SYNTHESIZE How are plants and solar cells similar? How are the ways in which they capture sunlight and change it into other forms of energy different? Explain.

32. INFER Suppose you live in a hot climate. How would it help to make the roof of your home a light color?

the BIG idea

33. APPLY Look again at the photograph on pages 6 and 7 and consider the opening question. How might your answer have changed after reading the chapter?

34. COMMUNICATE Explain the law of conservation of energy in your own words. What, if anything, about the law of conservation of energy surprised you?

UNIT PROJECTS

If you are doing a unit project, make a folder for your project. Include in your folder a list of the resources you will need, the date on which the project is due, and a schedule to track your progress. Begin gathering data.

MONITOR AND RETEACH

If students have trouble applying the concepts in items 21–31, have them take a second look at the following images in section 3 of the chapter: mug on page 27, heated pan on page 28, and the convection diagram on page 30. Review how conduction works with the mug, the process of convection in the pan, and the processes involved in a convection current in the diagram on page 30.

Students may benefit from summarizing one or more sections of the chapter.

 Summarizing the Chapter, pp. 69–70

Standards-Based Assessment

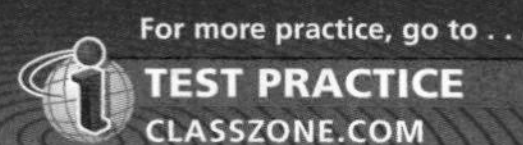

Interpreting Diagrams

The diagrams below illustrate the process that occurs in sea and land breezes.

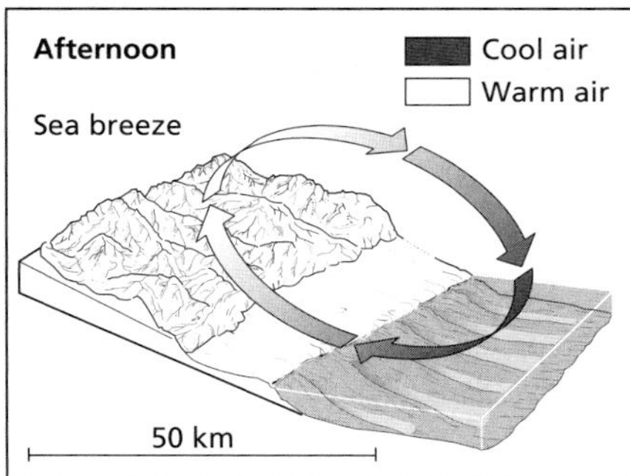

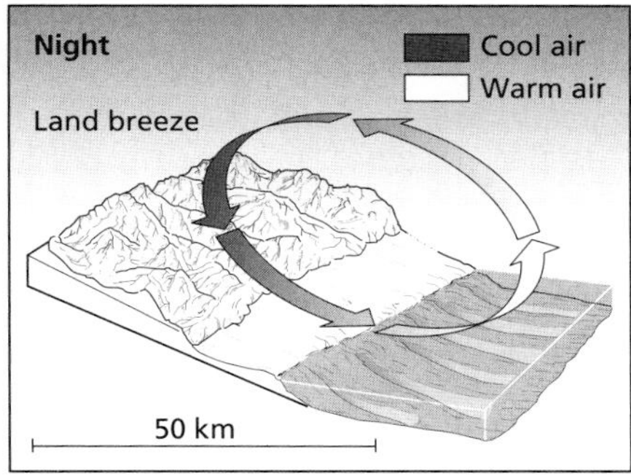

Use the diagrams to answer the next five questions.

1. What is a major difference between the two diagrams?
   a. They show conditions in different areas.
   b. They show conditions during different times of day.
   c. They show conditions that transfer different types of energy.
   d. They show conditions in summer and winter.

2. What happens as the surface of the land becomes warmer?
   a. Its energy decreases.
   b. Its particles move faster.
   c. Its density increases.
   d. Its rate of convection increases.

3. What process transfers energy from the warm ground to the air in contact with it?
   a. convection
   b. condensation
   c. evaporation
   d. conduction

4. Cooler air moves in to replace warmer, rising air during convection because the cooler air
   a. is more dense
   b. has more energy
   c. is less dense
   d. has less energy

5. About how far over water does this land breeze extend?
   a. 1 kilometer
   b. 10 kilometers
   c. 25 kilometers
   d. 50 kilometers

Extended Response

Answer the two questions below in detail.

6. If a puddle of water is frozen, do particles in the ice have any heat energy? Explain.

7. Suppose you place two spoons—one of metal and one of wood—into a cup filled with hot water. The bowl end of the spoon is inside the cup and the handle is sticking up into the air. On each handle, you place a bead, held to the spoon by a dab of margarine. From which spoon will the bead fall first, and why?

REFLECTING ON THE CHAPTER

Have students answer the following questions in their **Science Notebook:**

1. How did what you learned about energy and how it is transferred affect the way you view the world in which you live?
2. What might you do differently based on what you learned in the chapter about energy and its transfer?
3. How did your Unit Project add to what you learned in this chapter about energy and its transfer?

California Content Standards

6.3.c Students know heat flows in solids by conduction (which involves no flow of matter) and in fluids by conduction and by convection (which involves flow of matter).

Analyzing a Diagram

1. b *3. d* *5. b*
2. b *4. a*

Extended Response

6. RUBRIC

4 points for a response that answers the question and correctly explains the concept of heat energy

Sample: Yes, the particles in the ice have heat energy. Matter always has some heat energy, even at low temperatures. Even in a solid such as ice, atoms and molecules are always moving back and forth over tiny distances. The total energy of this motion is the ice's heat energy.

3 points correctly answers the question and mostly explains the concept
2 points correctly answers the question and partly explains the concept
1 point correctly answers the question but does not explain the concept

7. RUBRIC

4 points for a response that answers the question and explains the concept of conduction

The bead will fall first from the metal spoon. Conduction moves heat energy from a warmer part of an object to a cooler part. Metal is a better conductor than wood. Conduction will warm the handle end of the metal and cause the margarine to melt.

3 points correctly answers the question and mostly explains the concept
2 points correctly answers the question and partly explains the concept
1 point correctly answers the question but does not explain the concept

CHAPTER 2 Energy in the Earth System

Earth Science UNIFYING PRINCIPLES

PRINCIPLE 1
Heat energy inside Earth and radiation from the Sun provide energy for Earth's processes.

PRINCIPLE 2
Physical forces, such as gravity, affect the movement of all matter on Earth and throughout the universe.

PRINCIPLE 3
Matter and energy move among Earth's rocks and soil, atmosphere, waters, and living things.

PRINCIPLE 4
Earth has changed over time and continues to change.

Unit: The Earth System BIG IDEAS

CHAPTER 1
Energy and Change
Waves and heat flow transfer energy.

CHAPTER 2
Energy in the Earth System
The Sun is the major source of energy for Earth's atmosphere and surface.

CHAPTER 3
Weather Patterns
Some features of weather have predictable patterns.

CHAPTER 4
Weather Fronts and Storms
The interaction of air masses causes changes in weather.

CHAPTER 2 KEY CONCEPTS

SECTION 1

The Earth system has four major parts.
1. The parts of the Earth system are connected.
2. All four parts of the Earth system shape the planet's surface.

SECTION 2

The Sun provides energy to the Earth system.
1. Earth receives energy from the Sun.
2. Energy from the Sun heats Earth's surface unevenly.
3. Uneven heating is a cause of the seasons.

SECTION 3

Energy is transferred within the Earth system.
1. Little of Earth's internal heat reaches the surface.
2. Energy from the Sun moves through the Earth system.
3. Solar energy drives weather and climate.

The Big Idea Flow Chart is available on p. T9 in the **TRANSPARENCY BOOK.**

Previewing Content

SECTION

The Earth system has four major parts. pp. 41–47

1. The parts of the Earth system are connected.
A **system** is an organized combination of parts that work together to form a whole. Earth is essentially a closed system in which energy enters and leaves but matter, with a few exceptions, does not. Earth has four interconnected parts that are open systems in which both matter and energy can leave and enter. Each part affects the others.

- **atmosphere:** the gaseous "envelope" surrounding Earth and supporting life on the surface (78 percent nitrogen, 21 percent oxygen)
- **hydrosphere:** water in all its forms: gaseous (water vapor), solid (ice and snow), and liquid (rain, streams, oceans, and so on).
- **biosphere:** all living organisms in the Earth system and their environments
- **geosphere:** the rocks, soil, mountains, continents, ocean basins, and other physical features of Earth (except for water)

Note: A **cycle** is a series of events or actions that repeats over and over. Chapter 6 explains the rock cycle and further explains the different layers of Earth's geosphere.

2. All four parts of the Earth system shape the planet's surface.
The atmosphere, hydrosphere, geosphere, and biosphere continuously reshape Earth's surface. Modern technology enables scientists to record, assess, and in some cases predict these changes. Plants, animals, and humans—all parts of the biosphere—can also dramatically change Earth's surface.

SECTION

The Sun provides energy to the Earth system. pp. 48–57

1. Earth receives energy from the Sun.
Most energy at Earth's surface comes from the Sun. Some of this energy takes the form of visible light. Visible light is a type of solar radiation. Radiation is energy that moves across distances in the form of electromagnetic waves. On average, about 30 percent of incoming solar energy is reflected by clouds, the atmosphere, and Earth's surface. Therefore, about 70 percent of solar radiation is absorbed and becomes different forms of energy.

2. Energy from the Sun heats Earth's surface unevenly.
Because of Earth's shape, the Sun heats Earth's surface unevenly. The curved surface causes sunlight to strike the Earth at different angles. At the equator, sunlight strikes the surface at a perpendicular angle. This results in higher temperatures near the equator, because this is where the Sun's energy is most concentrated. At the poles, sunlight strikes Earth's surface at much lower angles; therefore, lower temperatures occur in areas closer to the poles because they receive sunlight that is more spread out and less concentrated.

3. Uneven heating is a cause of the seasons.
The tilt of Earth's **axis** creates annual temperature patterns that we refer to as seasons. Earth's tilted axis causes different amounts of solar energy to strike Earth's surface at different times during the year. The northern and southern hemispheres experience spring, summer, fall, and winter, at opposite times. For example, spring and summer occur in the Northern Hemisphere when Earth is tilted toward the Sun. At the same time, the Southern Hemisphere experiences fall and winter because it is tilted away from the Sun. This is why summer days are longer than winter days. Also, day length influences temperatures during each season. Longer days result in higher surface temperatures as the Sun heats Earth's surface for a longer period of time.

Common Misconceptions

MISCONCEPTION DATABASE
CLASSZONE.COM Background on student misconceptions

EARTH'S MANTLE Students may think that Earth's mantle is entirely liquid. The mantle, the thickest of Earth's layers, is primarily solid but has liquid properties due to the high temperatures in it.

This misconception is addressed on p. 44.

EARTH'S CRUST Many students may think that Earth's crust is very thick. In fact, this outermost layer of the geosphere is thin in comparison with the rest of Earth's rocky layers—the crust is only 5–70 kilometers thick.

This misconception is addressed on p. 45.

Previewing Content

SECTION

Energy is transferred within the Earth system. pp. 58–67

1. **Little of Earth's internal heat reaches the surface.** Immense temperatures are generated within Earth, but because the rock making up Earth's outer layers does not easily conduct heat, little of this heat reaches the surface. Instead, almost all of the heat energy that reaches Earth's surface comes from the Sun.

2. **Energy from the Sun moves through the Earth system.** Energy moves by radiation, conduction, and convection. Earth's surface, heated by the Sun, radiates energy that is absorbed by certain atmospheric gases, which then warm the air. Conduction is the transfer of energy from one substance to another through direct contact. Convection is the transfer of energy from place to place by the motion of heated gas or liquid. Use the diagram below when discussing the transfer of energy.

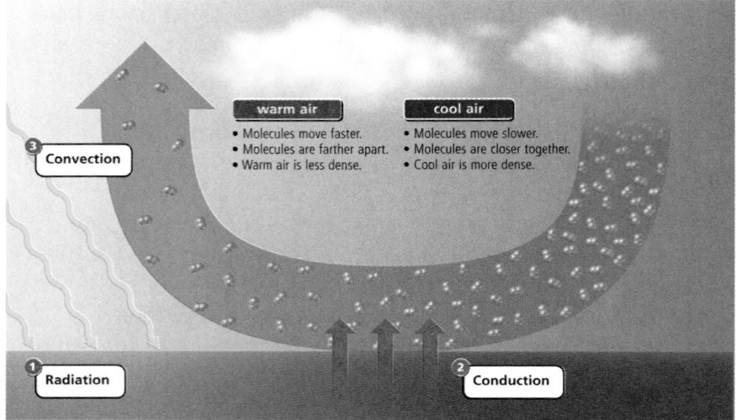
warm air
• Molecules move faster.
• Molecules are farther apart.
• Warm air is less dense.
cool air
• Molecules move slower.
• Molecules are closer together.
• Cool air is more dense.
3 Convection
1 Radiation
2 Conduction

Water on Earth is continuously moving from one place to another. It also changes forms. This continuous movement is known as the **water cycle**. The water cycle involves three processes. Evaporation is the change of water from liquid to vapor. Condensation is the change of water vapor in the atmosphere to liquid. Precipitation is the water or ice that falls from clouds after condensation has taken place.

Energy is also distributed through the Earth's system by winds and ocean currents. Global winds circulate heat around the planet in the atmosphere, while **ocean currents** distribute heat through the ocean. Winds and currents can exchange heat energy.

3. **Solar energy drives weather and climate.** Climate is distinct from weather. **Weather** denotes conditions from moment to moment, and **climate** denotes characteristic weather patterns occurring over time.

Some of the geographical factors that affect climate include
- latitude—the distance north or south of the equator
- presence or absence of large bodies of water
- ocean currents, which transfer energy between regions of the planet
- elevation—the height of land above sea level

Common Misconceptions

CONTENT OF CLOUDS Students may think that clouds are made up of water vapor because they are in the atmosphere and students know that the atmosphere contains water vapor. In actuality, clouds are made up of many tiny droplets of liquid water that are too small and light to be pulled down to Earth by gravity.

 This misconception is addressed on p. 60.

MISCONCEPTION DATABASE
CLASSZONE.COM Background on student misconceptions

Previewing Labs

Lab Generator CD-ROM
Edit these Pupil Edition labs and generate alternative labs.

EXPLORE the BIG idea

How Does Heating Affect Air? p. 39 Students observe the effects of heat on air using hot and cold water and a balloon.	**TIME** 10 minutes **MATERIALS** balloon, small bottle, 2 bowls, ice water, hot tap water
How Fast Does It Chill? p. 39 Students observe the rate of temperature change in different materials.	**TIME** 10 minutes **MATERIALS** outdoor thermometer, paper cup, freezer, soil
SECTION 1 **INVESTIGATE** The Geosphere's Layers, p. 45 Students model the geosphere's layers by using an apple. **ALTERNATIVE:** Teacher Demonstration, URB p. 274	**TIME** 15 minutes **MATERIALS** apple slice
SECTION 2 **INVESTIGATE** Solar Energy, p. 51 Students compare the effect of light angles on heating using thermometers placed at different angles to a light source. **ALTERNATIVE:** Teacher Modeling, URB p. 274	**TIME** 20 minutes **MATERIALS** tape, 2 black paper squares, 2 thermometers, one cardboard tube from a paper towel roll, sunny windowsill or lamp
CHAPTER INVESTIGATION Modeling Solar Energy, pp. 56–57 Students model the Sun's movement over the Earth on the first day of summer at their location and observe how the angle at which the sunlight strikes their location determines the amount of solar energy that location receives. **ALTERNATIVE:** Teacher Demonstration, URB pp. 274–275	**TIME** 40 minutes **MATERIALS** graph paper, flashlight, meter stick, protractor
SECTION 3 **INVESTIGATE** Heating and Cooling Rates, p. 65 Students compare rates of heating and cooling of soil and water by varying temperature and conditions. **ALTERNATIVE:** Teacher Modeling, URB pp. 274–275	**TIME** 25 minutes **MATERIALS** 2 cups, ruler, soil, water at room temperature, 2 thermometers, sunlight or lamp, gravel

R **Additional INVESTIGATION,** Observing Convection, A, B, & C, pp. 120–128; Teacher Instructions, pp. 274–275

Previewing Chapter Resources

INTEGRATED TECHNOLOGY | LABS AND ACTIVITIES

CHAPTER 2
Energy in the Earth System

INTEGRATED TECHNOLOGY

CLASSZONE.COM
- eEdition Plus
- EasyPlanner Plus
- Misconception Database
- Content Review
- Test Practice
- Resource Centers
- Visualizations
- Math Tutorial

SCILINKS.ORG

SCILINKS

CD-ROMS
- eEdition
- EasyPlanner
- Power Presentations
- Content Review
- Lab Generator
- Test Generator

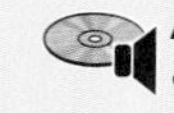

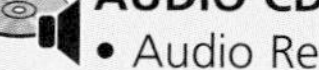

AUDIO CDS
- Audio Readings
- Audio Readings in Spanish

LABS AND ACTIVITIES

EXPLORE the Big Idea, p. 39
- How Does Heating Affect Air?
- How Fast Does It Chill?

UNIT RESOURCE BOOK
Unit Projects, pp. 5–10

Lab Generator CD-ROM
Generate customized labs.

SECTION

1 The Earth system has four major parts.
pp. 41–47

Lesson Plan, pp. 71–72

RESOURCE CENTER, The Earth System

TRANSPARENCY BOOK
- Big Idea Flow Chart, p. T9
- Daily Vocabulary Scaffolding, p. T10
- Note-Taking Model, p. T11
- 3-Minute Warm-Up, p. T12

- INVESTIGATE The Geosphere's Layers, p. 45
- California Close-Up, p. 47

UNIT RESOURCE BOOK
Datasheet, The Geosphere's Layers, p. 80

SECTION

2 The Sun provides energy to the Earth system.
pp. 48–57

Lesson Plan, pp. 82–83

- **RESOURCE CENTER,** Solar Energy
- **VISUALIZATION,** Seasons

TRANSPARENCY BOOK
- Daily Vocabulary Scaffolding, p. T10
- 3-Minute Warm-Up, p. T12
- "Tilt of Earth's Axis and the Seasons" Visual, p. T14

- INVESTIGATE Solar Energy, p. 51
- CHAPTER INVESTIGATION, Modeling Solar Energy, pp. 56–57

UNIT RESOURCE BOOK
- Datasheet, Solar Energy, p. 91
- CHAPTER INVESTIGATION, Modeling Solar Energy, A, B, & C, pp. 111–119

SECTION

3 Energy is transferred within the Earth system.
pp. 58–67

Lesson Plan, pp. 93–94

- **VISUALIZATION,** Radiation, Conduction, and Convection
- **RESOURCE CENTER,** Ocean Currents
- **VISUALIZATION,** Greenhouse Effect
- **MATH TUTORIAL**

TRANSPARENCY BOOK
- Big Idea Flow Chart, p. T9
- Daily Vocabulary Scaffolding, p. T10
- 3-Minute Warm-Up, p. T13
- Chapter Outline, pp. T15–T16

- INVESTIGATE Heating and Cooling Rates, p. 65
- Math in Science, p. 67

UNIT RESOURCE BOOK
- Datasheet, Heating and Cooling Rates, p. 102
- Math Support and Practice, pp. 109–110
- Additional INVESTIGATION, Observing Convection, A, B, & C, pp. 120–128

KEY TO ICONS

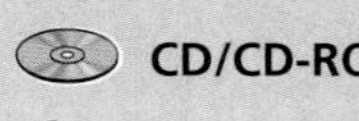 CD/CD-ROM

INTERNET

Pupil Edition

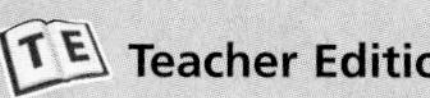 Teacher Edition

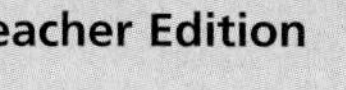 UNIT RESOURCE BOOK

 TRANSPARENCY BOOK

ASSESSMENT BOOK

 STANDARDS REVIEW AND PRACTICE

SCIENCE TOOLKIT

READING AND REINFORCEMENT

 **Modified Lesson Plans for English Learners,** pp. 8–10

- Frame Game, B26–27
- Outline, C43
- Daily Vocabulary Scaffolding, H1–8

 **UNIT RESOURCE BOOK**

- Vocabulary Practice, pp. 106–107
- Decoding Support, p. 108
- Summarizing the Chapter, pp. 129–130

 **Audio Readings CD**
Listen to Pupil Edition.

 **Audio Readings in Spanish CD**
Listen to Pupil Edition in Spanish.

ASSESSMENT

- Chapter Review, pp. 69–70
- Standards-Based Assessment, p. 71

 **ASSESSMENT BOOK**

- Diagnostic Test, pp. 22–23
- Chapter Test, A, B, & C, pp. 27–38
- Alternative Assessment, pp. 39–40

STANDARDS REVIEW AND PRACTICE,
pp. 3–4, 13–14, 21–24, 27–38, 57–58, 65–66

 **McDougal Littell Assessment System**

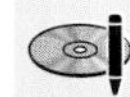 **Test Generator CD-ROM**
Generate customized and Spanish tests.

STANDARDS

California Content Standards
6.1.b, 6.1.g, 6.2.d, 6.3, 6.3.a, 6.3.c, 6.3.d, 6.4.a, 6.4.b, 6.4.c, 6.4.d, 6.4.e, 6.7.a, 6.7.d, 6.7.e

See p. 38 for the standards.

 **UNIT RESOURCE BOOK**

- Reading Study Guide, A & B, pp. 73–76
- Spanish Reading Study Guide, pp. 77–78
- Challenge and Extension, p. 79
- Reinforcing Key Concepts, p. 81

Ongoing Assessment, pp. 43–46

 Section 2.1 Review, p. 46

ASSESSMENT BOOK
Section 2.1 Quiz, p. 24

California Content Standards
6.1.b, 6.1.g, 6.2.d

UNIT RESOURCE BOOK

- Reading Study Guide, A & B, pp. 84–87
- Spanish Reading Study Guide, pp. 88–89
- Challenge and Extension, p. 90
- Reinforcing Key Concepts, p. 92

Ongoing Assessment, pp. 48–51, 53–54

 Section 2.2 Review, p. 55

 **ASSESSMENT BOOK**
Section 2.2 Quiz, p. 25

California Content Standards
6.3.d, 6.4.a, 6.4.b, 6.4.d, 6.7.a, 6.7.d, 6.7.e

 **UNIT RESOURCE BOOK**

- Reading Study Guides, A & B, pp. 95–98
- Spanish Reading Study Guide, pp. 99–100
- Challenge and Extension, p. 101
- Reinforcing Key Concepts, p. 103
- Challenge Reading, pp. 104–105

Ongoing Assessment, pp. 59, 61–64, 66

 Section 2.3 Review, p. 66

 **ASSESSMENT BOOK**
Section 2.3 Quiz, p. 26

California Content Standards
6.3, 6.3.d, 6.4.a, 6.4.c, 6.4.d, 6.4.e

Previewing Resources for Differentiated Instruction

CHAPTER INVESTIGATION

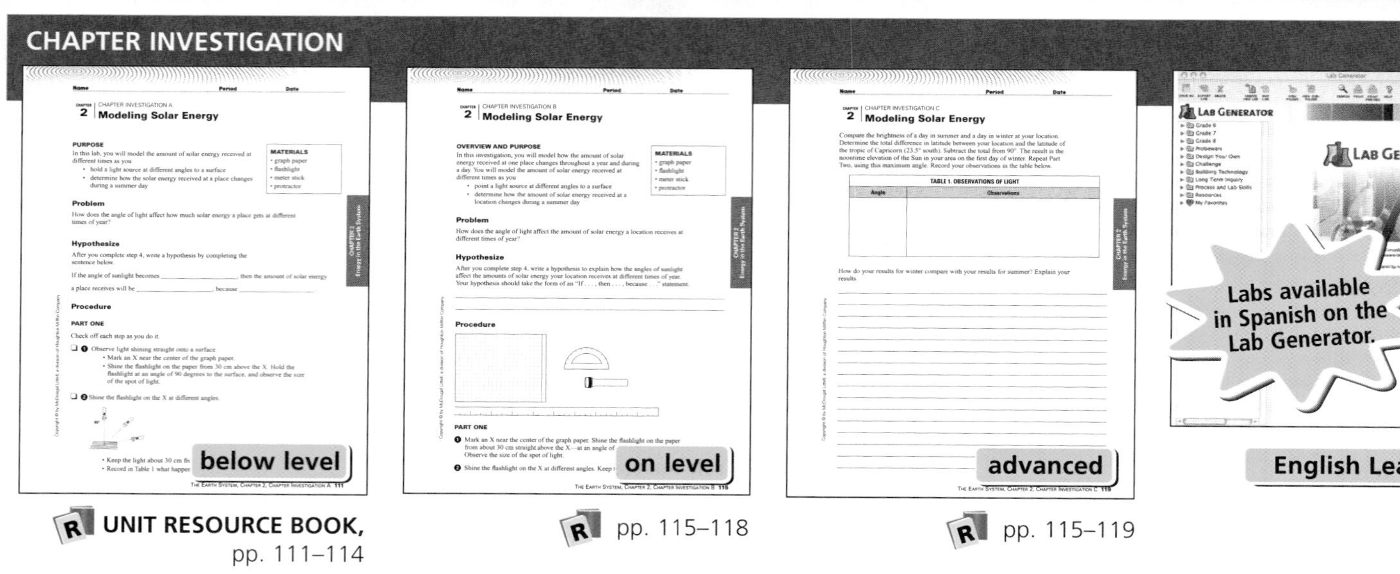

UNIT RESOURCE BOOK, pp. 111–114

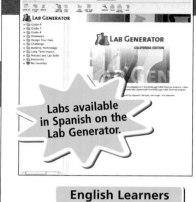

pp. 115–118

pp. 115–119

READING STUDY GUIDE

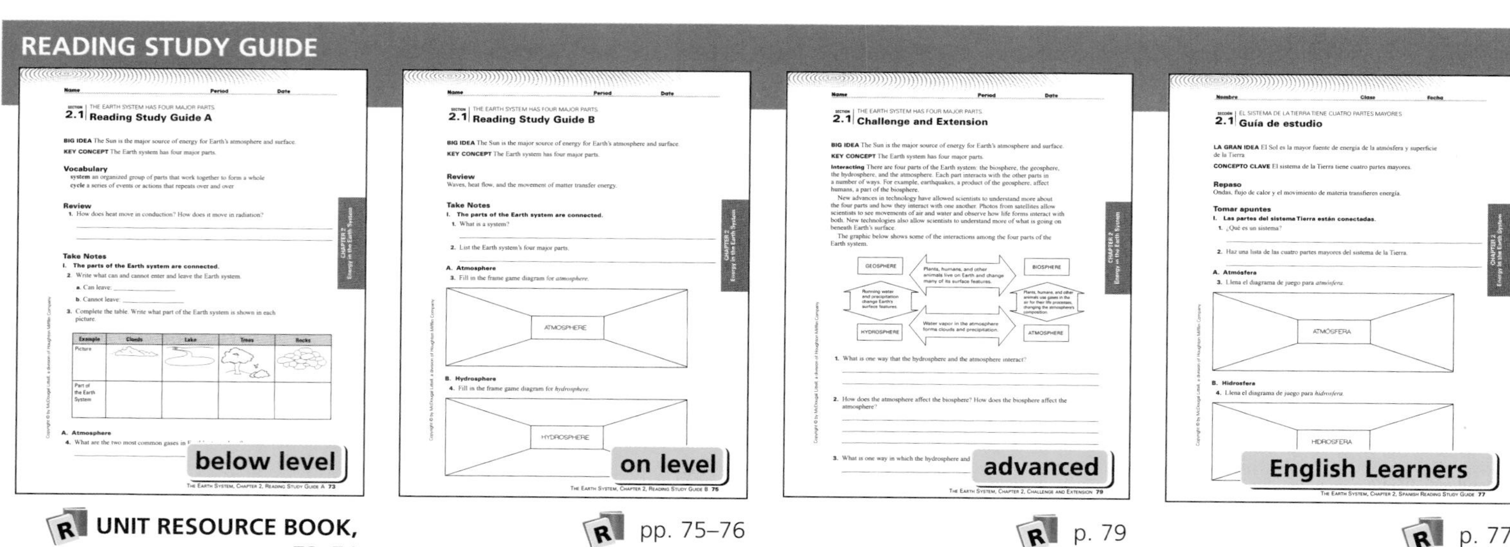

UNIT RESOURCE BOOK, pp. 73–74

pp. 75–76

p. 79

p. 77

CHAPTER TEST

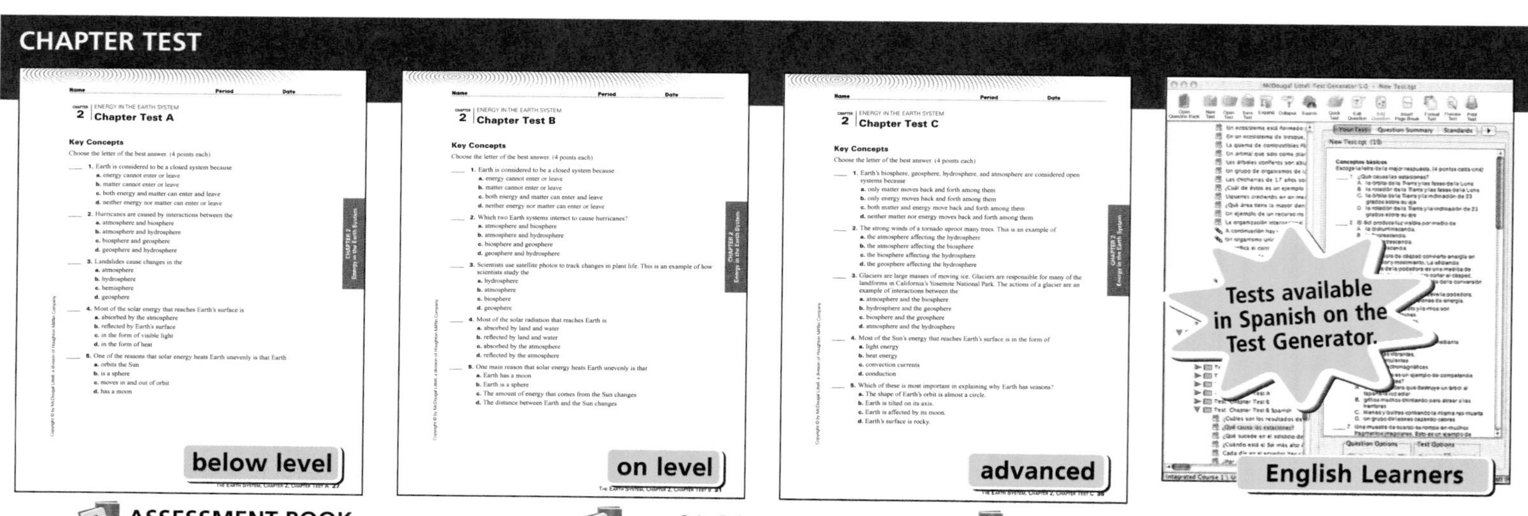

ASSESSMENT BOOK, pp. 27–30

pp. 31–34

pp. 35–38

TECHNOLOGY

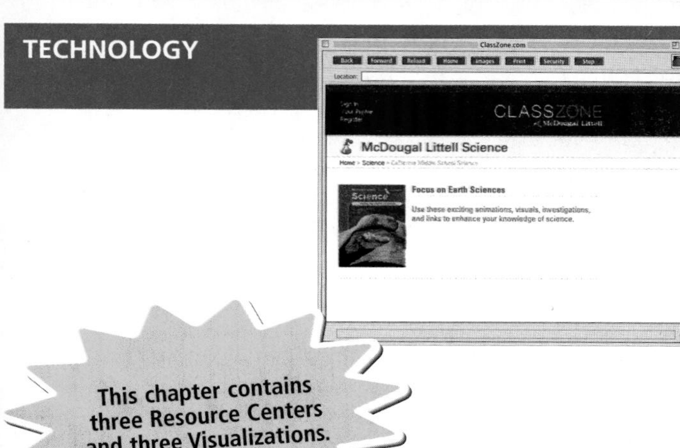

This chapter contains three Resource Centers and three Visualizations.

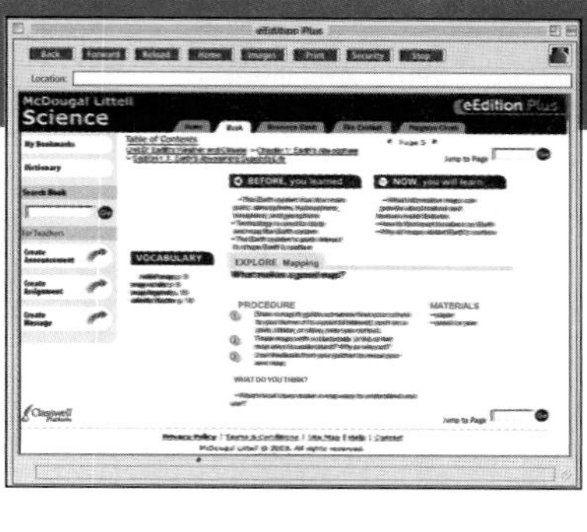

VISUAL CONTENT

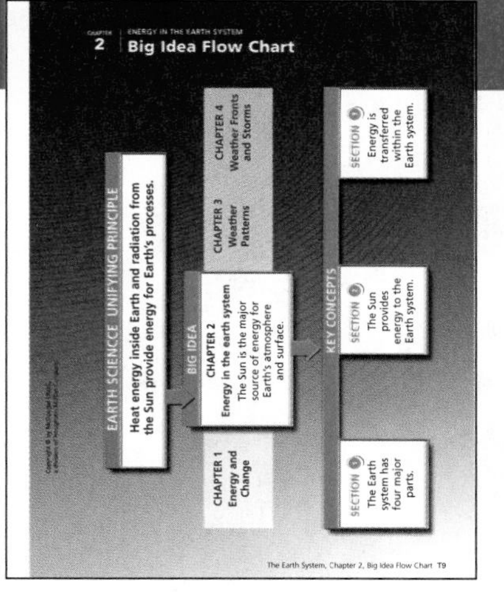

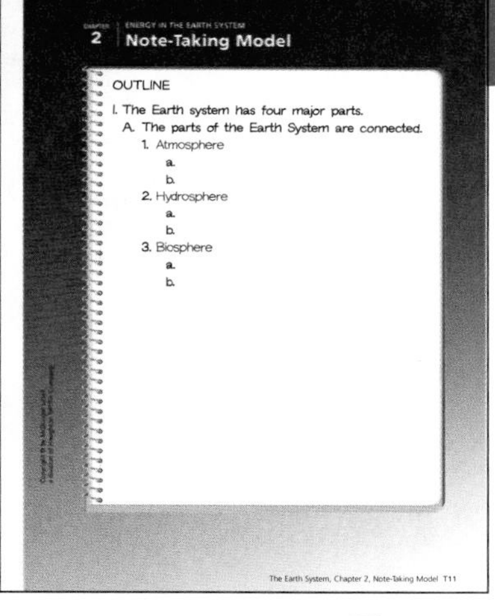

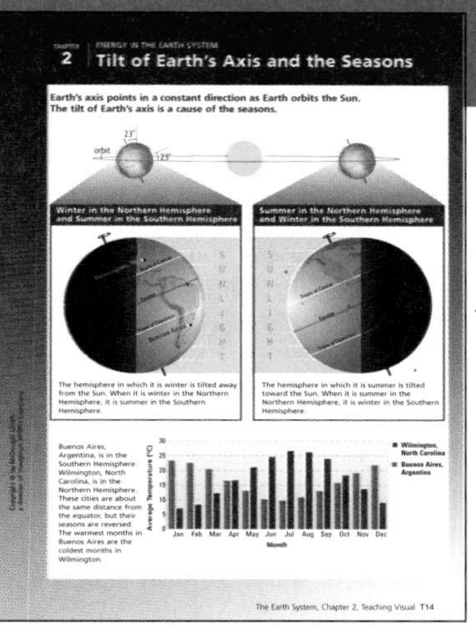

TRANSPARENCY BOOK, p. T9

p. T11

p. T14

MORE SUPPORT

Reinforcing Key Concepts for each section

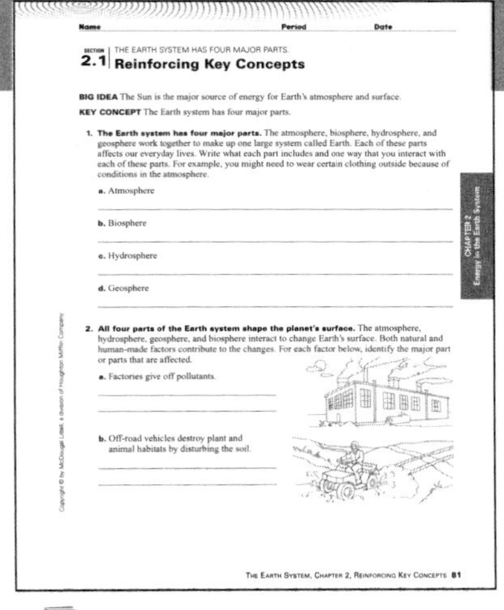

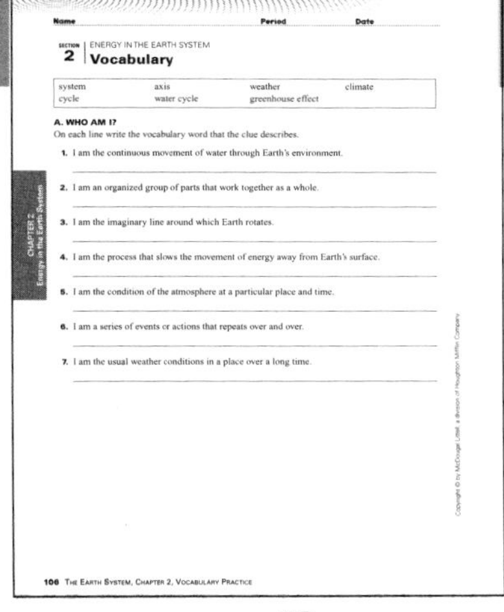

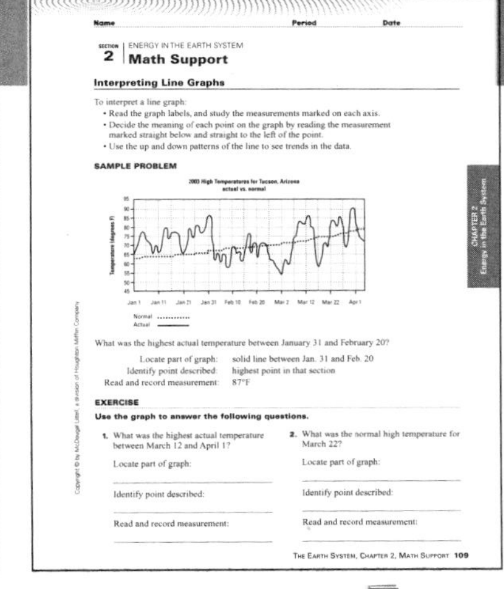

UNIT RESOURCE BOOK, p. 81

pp. 106–107

p. 109

CHAPTER 2

Energy in the Earth System

INTRODUCE

the BIG idea

Have students look at the photograph of the hang glider and discuss how the questions in the box link to the Big Idea. Ask:

- Which part of the Earth system is the hang glider moving through?
- What other parts of the Earth system are visible in the photograph?
- How might energy from the Sun play a role in helping the hang glider stay in the air?

California Content Standards

6.1.b Students know Earth is composed of several layers: a cold, brittle lithosphere; a hot, convecting mantle; and a dense, metallic core.

6.2.d Students know earthquakes, volcanic eruptions, landslides, and floods change human and wildlife habitats.

6.3.a Students know energy can be carried from one place to another by heat flow or by waves, including water, light and sound waves, or by moving objects.

6.3.c Students know heat flows in solids by conduction (which involves no flow of matter) and in fluids by conduction and by convection (which involves flow of matter).

6.3.d Students know heat energy is also transferred between objects by radiation (radiation can travel through space).

6.4.a Students know the sun is the major source of energy for phenomena on Earth's surface; it powers winds, ocean currents, and the water cycle.

6.4.b Students know solar energy reaches Earth through radiation, mostly in the form of visible light.

6.4.c Students know heat from Earth's interior reaches the surface primarily through convection.

6.4.d Students know convection currents distribute heat in the atmosphere and oceans.

6.7.a Develop a hypothesis.

6.7.e Recognize whether evidence is consistent with a proposed explanation.

CHAPTER

Energy in the Earth System

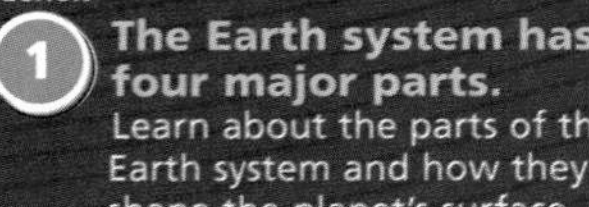

The Sun is the major source of energy for Earth's atmosphere and surface.

Key Concepts

SECTION 1
The Earth system has four major parts.
Learn about the parts of the Earth system and how they shape the planet's surface.

SECTION 2
The Sun provides energy to the Earth system.
Learn how uneven heating of Earth by the Sun is one cause of the seasons.

SECTION 3
Energy is transferred within the Earth system.
Learn how solar energy powers the water cycle and affects weather and climate.

California ClassZone

CLASSZONE.COM

Chapter 2 online resources: Content Review, three Visualizations, three Resource Centers, Math Tutorial, Test Practice

INTERNET PREVIEW

CLASSZONE.COM For student use with the following pages:

Review and Practice
- Content Review, pp. 40, 68
- Math Tutorial: Interpreting Line Graphs, p. 67
- Test Practice, p. 71

Activities and Resources
- Resources: Earth System, p. 44; Solar Energy, p. 49; Ocean Currents, p. 62
- Visualization: Seasons, p. 51; Radiation, Conduction, and Convection, p. 59; Greenhouse Effect, p. 64

What Is Climate?
Code: MDL012

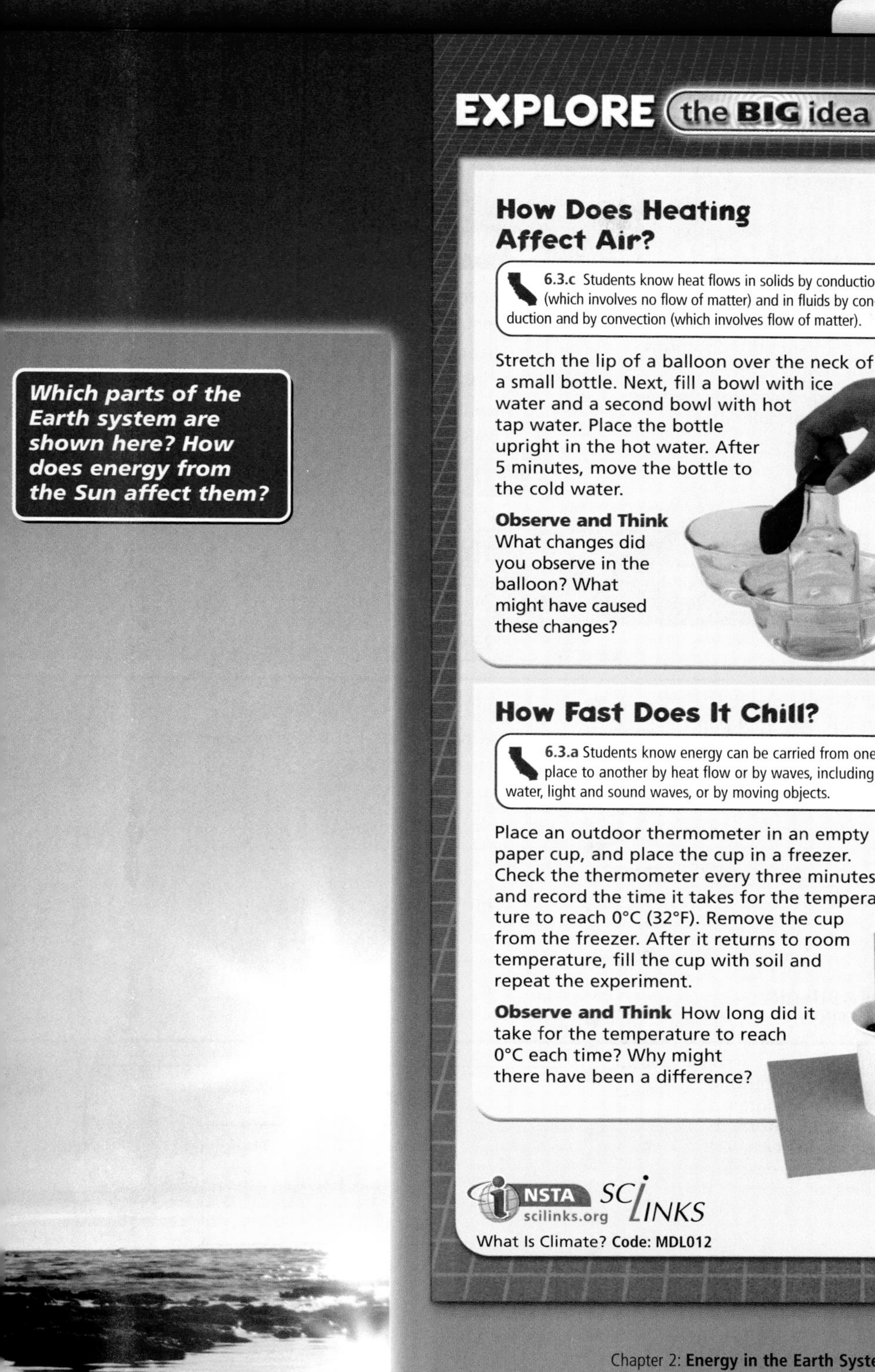

Which parts of the Earth system are shown here? How does energy from the Sun affect them?
EXPLORE the BIG idea
How Does Heating Affect Air?
6.3.c Students know heat flows in solids by conduction (which involves no flow of matter) and in fluids by conduction and by convection (which involves flow of matter).
Stretch the lip of a balloon over the neck of a small bottle. Next, fill a bowl with ice water and a second bowl with hot tap water. Place the bottle upright in the hot water. After 5 minutes, move the bottle to the cold water.
Observe and Think What changes did you observe in the balloon? What might have caused these changes?
How Fast Does It Chill?
6.3.a Students know energy can be carried from one place to another by heat flow or by waves, including water, light and sound waves, or by moving objects.
Place an outdoor thermometer in an empty paper cup, and place the cup in a freezer. Check the thermometer every three minutes and record the time it takes for the temperature to reach 0°C (32°F). Remove the cup from the freezer. After it returns to room temperature, fill the cup with soil and repeat the experiment.
Observe and Think How long did it take for the temperature to reach 0°C each time? Why might there have been a difference?
NSTA scilinks.org SCILINKS
What Is Climate? Code: MDL012
Chapter 2: Energy in the Earth System 39

EXPLORE the BIG idea

These inquiry-based activities are appropriate for use at home or as a supplement to classroom instruction.

How Does Heating Affect Air?

PURPOSE To introduce students to the concept that temperature changes affect air, by having them observe how air in a bottle makes a balloon expand and contract.

TIP *10 min*. Hold the bottle while it is in the water so that it does not tip over.

Answer: In hot water, the balloon expands slightly; in cold water, it deflates. The air in the bottle expanded when heated and contracted when cooled.

REVISIT after p. 59.

How Fast Does It Chill?

PURPOSE To introduce students to the way in which different mediums conduct and retain heat.

TIP *10 min*. Students can fill their cups with houseplant potting soil.

Answer: The thermometer in the empty cup reached 0°C quickly; the thermometer in soil took longer to reach 0°C. Air chills faster than soil does, so the thermometer in soil takes longer to reach 0°C than a thermometer in an empty cup.

REVISIT after p. 65.

TEACHING WITH TECHNOLOGY

Computer Graphing Program Have students use a computer graphing program to construct a line graph of their data from "Investigate Solar Energy," p. 51, and "Investigate Heating and Cooling Rates," p. 65.

CBL and Probeware If students have probeware, they may want to use a temperature probe for the investigations on pp. 51 and 65.

PREPARE

CONCEPT REVIEW

Activate Prior Knowledge

- Place a cup of hot tea on your desk.
- Ask students to identify a form of energy present in the hot cup of tea.
- Remind students that energy flows from warmer areas to cooler areas. Have them infer where heat energy from the cup of tea might move to. *into the air*

TAKING NOTES

Outline

Have students discuss the relationship among outline ideas. Suggest that students use their outlines when studying the chapter.

Vocabulary Strategy

Ask students to think about how they learn best. Do visuals help them understand concepts better than blocks of text? If so, students might want to use plenty of drawings in their frame game diagrams.

Vocabulary and Note-Taking Resources

- Vocabulary Practice, pp. 106–107
- Decoding Support, p. 108

- Daily Vocabulary Scaffolding, p. T10
- Note-Taking Model, p. T11

- Frame Game, B26–27
- Outline, C43
- Daily Vocabulary Scaffolding, H1–8

CHAPTER 2

Getting Ready to Learn

CONCEPT REVIEW

- Energy is the ability to cause change.
- There are different forms of energy.
- Energy flows from warmer areas to cooler areas.

VOCABULARY REVIEW

energy p. 9
temperature p. 10
heat energy p. 10
radiation p. 18
conduction p. 27
convection p. 28

Review concepts and vocabulary.

TAKING NOTES

OUTLINE

As you read, copy the headings onto your paper in the form of an outline. Then add notes in your own words that summarize what you read.

VOCABULARY STRATEGY

Write each new vocabulary term in the center of a **frame game** diagram. Decide what information to frame the term with. Use examples, descriptions, pictures, or sentences that use the term in context.

See the Note-Taking Handbook on pages R45–R51.

SCIENCE NOTEBOOK

I. The Earth system has four major parts.
  A. The parts of the Earth system are connected.
    1. Atmosphere
      a.
      b.
    2. Hydrosphere
      a.
      b.
    3. Biosphere
      a.
      b.

	organized group of parts	
terrarium	SYSTEM	Earth
	parts work together	

CHECK READINESS

Administer the Diagnostic Test to determine students' readiness for new science content and their mastery of requisite math skills.

 Diagnostic Test, pp. 22–23

Technology Resources

Students needing content and math skills should visit **ClassZone.com.**

- CONTENT REVIEW
- MATH TUTORIAL

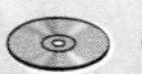 CONTENT REVIEW CD-ROM

KEY CONCEPT

The Earth system has four major parts.

CALIFORNIA Content Standards

6.1.b Students know Earth is composed of several layers: a cold, brittle lithosphere; a hot, convecting mantle; and a dense, metallic core.

6.2.d Students know earthquakes, volcanic eruptions, landslides, and floods change human and wildlife habitats.

BEFORE, you learned
- Waves, heat flow, and the movement of matter transfer energy
- Radiation can travel through matter and empty space
- Conduction transfers heat between objects in contact

NOW, you will learn
- About the parts of the Earth system
- How the parts of the Earth system interact
- How the parts of the Earth system shape the planet's surface

VOCABULARY

system p. 41
cycle p. 44

THINK ABOUT

How do these parts work together?

Look closely at this terrarium. Notice that the bowl and its cover form a boundary between the terrarium and the outside world. What might happen to the entire terrarium if any part were taken away? What might happen if you placed the terrarium in a dark closet?

The parts of the Earth system are connected.

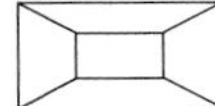

VOCABULARY
Remember to make a frame game diagram for each vocabulary term.

A terrarium is a simple example of a **system**—an organized group of parts that work together to form a whole. To understand a system, you need to see how all its parts work together. This is true for a small terrarium, and it is true for planet Earth.

Both a terrarium and Earth are closed systems. They are closed because matter, such as soil or water, cannot enter or leave. However, energy can flow into or out of the systems. Light and heat can pass through the glass of the terrarium. In the same way, sunlight and heat enter and leave the Earth system through the atmosphere.

The Earth system is made up of four connected parts. These parts are the atmosphere (Earth's air), the hydrosphere (Earth's waters), the biosphere (Earth's living things), and the geosphere (Earth's interior and its rocks and sediments). Each of these parts is an open system because both matter and energy move into and out of it. The four open systems work together to form one large, closed system called Earth.

RESOURCES FOR DIFFERENTIATED INSTRUCTION

Below Level
UNIT RESOURCE BOOK
- Reading Study Guide A, pp. 73–74
- Decoding Support, p. 108

AUDIO CDS

Advanced
UNIT RESOURCE BOOK
Challenge and Extension, p. 79

English Learners
UNIT RESOURCE BOOK
Spanish Reading Study Guide, pp. 77–78

AUDIO CDS
- Audio Readings in Spanish
- Audio Readings (English)

2.1 FOCUS

Set Learning Goals

Students will
- Identify the parts of the Earth system.
- Explain how the parts of the Earth system interact.
- Explain how the parts of the Earth system shape the planet's surface.
- Model the geosphere's layers in an experiment.

3-Minute Warm-Up

Display Transparency 12 or copy this exercise on the board:

Answer *yes* or *no* to each question, and explain the reason for your answer.

1. Are all the planets in our solar system like Earth? ***No, Earth is unique; it supports many different life forms.***
2. Do the oceans cover more of Earth than the continents do? ***Yes. Water covers nearly three-quarters of Earth's surface.***
3. Is Earth's atmosphere made up of just one gas? ***No. Earth's atmosphere is a mixture of gases.***

3-Minute Warm-Up, p. T12

2.1 MOTIVATE

THINK ABOUT

PURPOSE To have students think about how parts of a system affect one another

DISCUSS Remind students that the glass bowl is part of the terrarium. Have students attempt to isolate the most vital components in the terrarium's system. *plants, stones, water, bowl*

If air, water, or soil were taken away, the plants would die. Without plants, there would be less oxygen, since photosynthesis would not occur—the terrarium would have no living things to support. Placing the terrarium in a dark closet would take away sunlight and cause the plants to die.

2.1 INSTRUCT

Teach the Standards

Transfer of energy 6.3.a

In this section: Students build on what they know about the transfer of energy between the different parts of Earth's system, such as when energy in Earth's crust (geosphere) transfers energy into Earth's oceans (hydrosphere), as in the case of an underwater earthquake that triggers a tsunami.

- **previously taught:** incoming solar radiation, pp. 22–23; convection in the atmosphere, p. 30; convection in lakes, p. 31
- **future opportunities:** seismic waves, pp. 309–311; earthquake magnitude, pp. 317–318; tsunamis, pp. 318–319

Language Arts Connection

Have students think of related words that contain the same Greek prefixes and suffixes as those used in each of the four parts of the Earth system. ***hydrology, geology, biology*** Tell students an atmometer is an instrument that measures rates of evaporation.

Develop Critical Thinking

CLASSIFY Have students classify each item below in its proper sphere.

- ocean floor ***geosphere***
- hurricane ***atmosphere***
- bird ***biosphere***
- mountain glacier ***hydrosphere***

Teach from Visuals

Remind students that they can get a preview of chapter content by studying the visuals—photographs, maps, or diagrams—and reading captions.

To help students interpret the "Parts of the Earth System" visual on pages 42–43, ask:

- What landforms do you recognize in this image of Earth? ***Students should recognize the North American continent and the northern part of South America. They may identify Florida, Cuba, the Gulf Coast, and Mexico; Greenland is also visible.***
- What does each of the four inset photographs show? ***one of the Earth system's four major parts***
- What theme is shared by the photographs? ***human exploration of the Earth system through the use of technology***

READING TIP

The names of the Earth system's four parts contain Greek prefixes. *Atmo-* refers to vapor or gas. *Hydro-* refers to water. *Bio-* refers to life, and *geo-* refers to earth.

Atmosphere

The atmosphere (AT-muh-SFEER) is the mixture of gases and particles that surrounds and protects the surface of Earth. Nitrogen makes up about 78 percent of the gases. Oxygen makes up nearly 21 percent. The atmosphere also contains carbon dioxide, water vapor, and other gases.

A

Understanding the atmosphere can help people in their everyday lives. This is because weather, which occurs in the lower atmosphere, affects many things around us. Scientists collect data about what is happening in the atmosphere. The data show that the atmosphere interacts with the other parts of the Earth system to form weather patterns. The more scientists learn about these patterns, the better they can predict local weather.

Hydrosphere

B

The hydrosphere (HY-druh-SFEER) is made up of all the water on Earth in the air, the ocean, lakes, glaciers, rivers and streams, and underground. Water covers nearly three-fourths of Earth's surface. Ocean water is salt water. Only about 3 percent of the hydrosphere is fresh water. About 80 percent of the fresh water is frozen in glaciers and polar ice caps.

Parts of the Earth System

Atmosphere

Over 400 cones make this weather balloon more stable as it gathers data about the atmosphere.

Hydrosphere

This scuba diver uses special equipment to study a kelp forest off the coast of California.

DIFFERENTIATE INSTRUCTION

More Reading Support

A Why is it helpful to understand the atmosphere? ***to predict weather***

B What percentage of Earth's fresh water is frozen? ***about 80 percent***

English Learners Help English learners remember the differences between these similar-sounding terms: *atmosphere, hydrosphere, biosphere,* and *geosphere*. Suggest they separate each term into two parts by writing the prefix and *-sphere* on an index card. Under the Greek prefix, have them write the English meaning ***(Example: hydro- means water)***. They can refer to these cards during lessons.

English learners may not have prior knowledge of terrariums (p. 41) or polar ice caps (p. 42).

Scientists use deep-sea vehicles, special buoys, and satellite images to study the ocean. They have discovered that the ocean contains many currents. Currents at the surface of the ocean are set in motion by winds blowing over the water. Surface currents affect weather patterns. An example of this is when a warm-water current brings heat to nearby land. A current can also carry nutrients long distances. It can provide resources to fish and other ocean organisms.

OUTLINE
As you read, remember to take notes in outline form.

I. Main idea
  A. Supporting idea
    1. Detail
    2. Detail
  B. Supporting idea

How does the hydrosphere affect the atmosphere?

Biosphere

The biosphere (BY-uh-SFEER) includes all life on Earth—in the air, on the land, and in the waters. Most animals need oxygen from the atmosphere and water from the hydrosphere. Plants need nutrients from the soil or the geosphere, water from the hydrosphere, and carbon dioxide and oxygen from the atmosphere.

Scientists have learned a lot about how the biosphere interacts with the other parts of the Earth system. For example, large forests act as Earth's "lungs." Trees absorb carbon dioxide and release oxygen into the atmosphere. When dead trees decay, they return nutrients to the soil.

Name one way the biosphere and the atmosphere act together.

Biosphere

These platforms, built in treetops, are used to observe forest plants and animals.

Geosphere

In mines dug deep underground, scientists can explore Earth's minerals and rocks.

Integrate the Sciences

Make a connection with life science by discussing the fact that the environment of the ocean depths is inhospitable to human life. The incredible pressures in the deep ocean are the biggest obstacle to undersea exploration. Conventional scuba equipment restricts divers to depths of less than 50 meters. Divers must also be careful to limit the duration of their dives and to surface gradually. Failure to do so can result in a painful and sometimes fatal condition known as the bends. Replacing nitrogen with helium in compressed air can allow divers to extend the duration of their dives by limiting the amount of nitrogen absorbed into their blood.

Real World Example

The great depths of the oceans can be explored with the aid of research submersibles. The National Oceanic and Atmospheric Administration (NOAA) runs an undersea laboratory and uses a variety of submersible vehicles that can, in the case of the famous *Alvin*, carry people as deep as 4500 meters. Two types of uncrewed submersibles are also used for sea exploration. ROVs (remotely operated vehicles) operate while attached to ships; AUVs (autonomous underwater vehicles) operate independently, following a programmed set of instructions.

Ongoing Assessment

Identify the parts of the Earth system.

Ask: What are the four parts of the Earths' system? *atmosphere, hydrosphere, biosphere, geosphere*

CHECK YOUR READING *Answer: Warm and cold ocean currents interact with wind patterns to influence Earth's weather.*

CHECK YOUR READING *Answer: Trees exchange gases with the atmosphere, taking in carbon dioxide and giving off oxygen.*

DIFFERENTIATE INSTRUCTION

More Reading Support

C What is the biosphere? *all forms of life on Earth*

D Do plants absorb or release carbon dioxide? *absorb*

Advanced Have students hypothesize how oceans originated on our planet. Ask: How did Earth come to be a water planet? *Volcanic action released steam, which then condensed into liquid water. Some scientists also think that icy comets melted when they struck Earth, which added water to the planet.*

 Challenge and Extension, p. 79

Address Misconceptions

IDENTIFY Ask: Is Earth's mantle solid or liquid? If students say it is liquid, they may hold the misconception that Earth's mantle is entirely liquid because of its liquidlike properties and because it contains pockets of magma.

CORRECT Tell students that Earth's mantle, the thickest of Earth's layers, is primarily solid, but it does have liquid properties due to its high temperatures. Use hot asphalt used to make roads as an example. When the asphalt is very hot, it can be poured and spread around. When it cools, it is a rigid solid. Rock in the mantle is hot enough to flow slowly. In places it melts into magma.

REASSESS What represents Earth's mantle? *hot asphalt*

Technology Resources

Visit **ClassZone.com** for background on common student misconceptions.

MISCONCEPTION DATABASE

Ongoing Assessment

Explain how the parts of the Earth system interact.

Ask: Which parts of the Earth system could be affected by an earthquake under the ocean that causes a tsunami? *geosphere, hydrosphere, biosphere*

CHECK YOUR READING *Answer: Volcanoes throw gases and dust into the atmosphere.*

Find out more about the Earth system.

Geosphere

The geosphere (JEE-uh-SFEER) includes all the features on Earth's surface—the continents, islands, and sea floor. It also includes everything below the surface. As the diagram shows, the geosphere is made up of several layers: crust, mantle, outer core, and inner core. The lithosphere is made up of the crust and the uppermost mantle. You will read more about the lithosphere in Chapter 8.

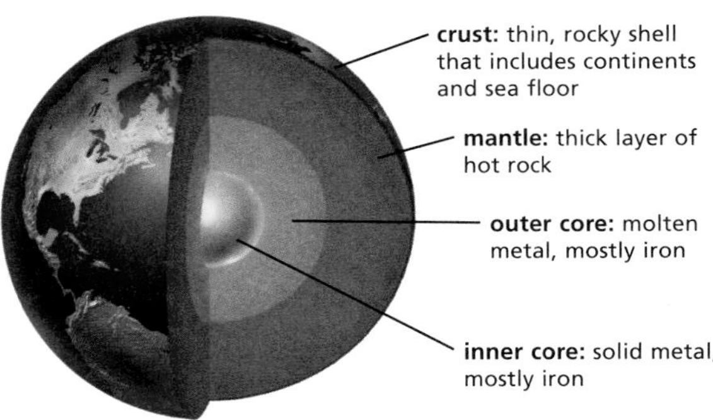

Earth is constantly changing. Some changes, such as the pushing up of mountain ranges, happen over millions of years. Other changes are sudden. An example is when a volcano erupts, sends gases into the air, and covers nearby land with lava. Some changes happen in a repeating pattern, or cycle. A **cycle** is a series of events or actions that repeats over and over. For example, rocks are slowly forming, changing, breaking apart, and re-forming in a set of processes called the rock cycle.

Give an example of matter moving from the geosphere to the atmosphere.

Earth's surface has many landforms, such as these rock formations in Joshua Tree National Park in California.

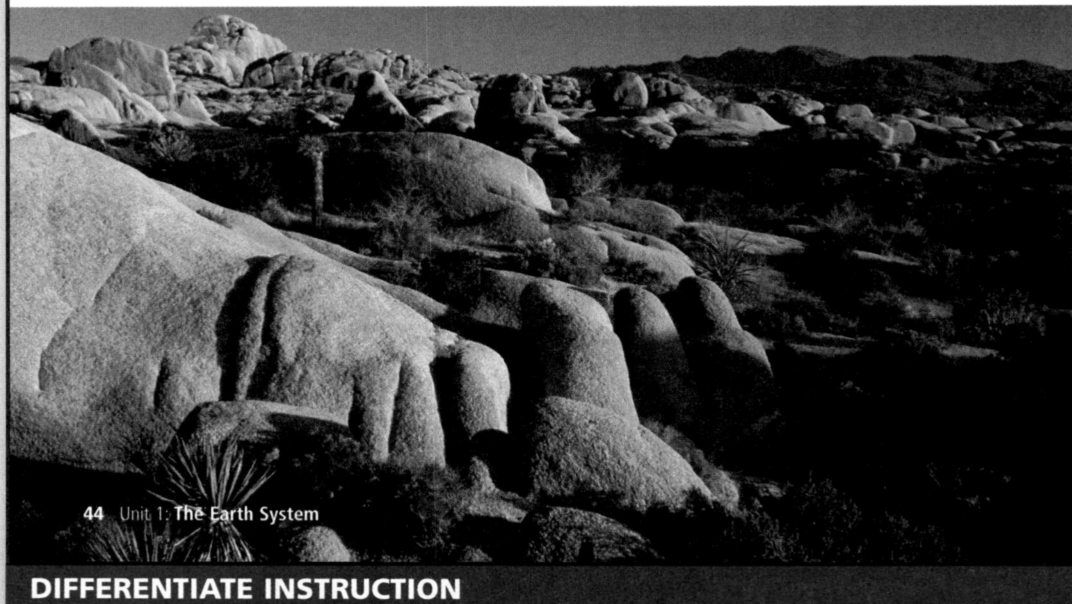

DIFFERENTIATE INSTRUCTION

More Reading Support

E What is the geosphere? *all of the features on Earth's surface—the continents, islands, and sea floor—and everything below the surface*

Below Level To help students remember the details of each "sphere," have them fill in this chart with important facts.

Sphere	Characteristics
Atmosphere	gases and particles that surround Earth, mostly nitrogen
Hydrosphere	all water on and under the Earth, 75 percent of Earth's surface
Biosphere	all living things in air, on land, in water
Geosphere	all surface and below-the-surface features on Earth

INVESTIGATE The Geosphere's Layers

How can you model the geosphere's layers?

PROCEDURE

1. You will be using a piece of apple that your teacher has cut to model the layers of the geosphere. Note: Never eat food in the science classroom.
2. Hold the apple slice and observe it carefully. Compare it with the diagram of the geosphere's layers on page 44.
3. Draw a diagram of the apple and label it with the names of the layers of the geosphere.

WHAT DO YOU THINK?

- What are the four parts of the apple slice?
- What major layer of the geosphere does each part of the apple resemble?

CHALLENGE What other object do you think would make a good model of the geosphere's layers? What model could you build or make yourself?

SKILL FOCUS
Modeling (6.1.b)

MATERIALS
apple slice

TIME
15 minutes

All four parts of the Earth system shape the planet's surface.

Earth's surface is worn away, built up, and reshaped every day. The atmosphere, the hydrosphere, the biosphere, and the geosphere all shape the surface. Here are some of the ways the four parts affect the surface.

Atmosphere and Hydrosphere Not even the hardest rock can stand up to wind and water over time. Over millions of years, rain, wind, and flowing water carve huge formations. You can see an example of this in the photograph of Joshua Tree National Park on page 44.

Geosphere Landmasses pushing together have set off earthquakes and formed volcanoes and mountain ranges around the world.

Biosphere Plants, animals, and human beings have also changed Earth's surface. For example, earthworms help make soil richer. And throughout human history, people have dammed rivers and cleared forests for farmland.

You are part of this process too. Every time you walk or ride a bike across open land, you are changing Earth's surface. Your feet or the bike's tires dig into the ground. This can wear away plants and expose soil to sunlight, wind, and water. If you take the same route every day, over time you will wear a path in the land.

READING TIP

The word *landmass* is a compound word made up of the words *land* and *mass*. It means "a large area of land."

INVESTIGATE
The Geosphere's Layers

PURPOSE To model and identify the geosphere's layers

TIPS *15 min.* Have students review Earth's layers before attempting to compare them with the layers of the apple.

WHAT DO YOU THINK? *outer skin = crust; layer next to the skin = mantle; inner ring and layer = outer core; core and seed = inner cores.*

CHALLENGE *a multicolored clay ball, a round pear, a hard-boiled egg; plastic-foam balls cut in half and painted.*

 Datasheet, The Geosphere's Layers, p. 80

Technology Resources

Customize this student lab as needed or look for an alternative. Print rubrics to assess student lab reports.

 **Lab Generator CD-ROM**

Address Misconceptions

IDENTIFY Ask: Is Earth's crust thick or thin? If students say it is thick, they may not realize that Earth's crust is relatively thin.

CORRECT Refer to the illustration on p. 44. Explain that the red-orange colors represent Earth's interior layers. The crust is represented by just a thin line around the interior.

REASSESS Ask: How thick is Earth's crust compared to other layers? *It is much thinner than the other layers.*

Technology Resources

Visit **ClassZone.com** for background on common student misconceptions.

 **MISCONCEPTION DATABASE**

Ongoing Assessment

Explain how the parts of the Earth system shape the planet's surface.

Ask: What is one example of how the biosphere can shape Earth's surface? *Possible answer: humans damming rivers and clearing forests for farmland*

DIFFERENTIATE INSTRUCTION

More Reading Support

F What impact do you have on the surface? *wearing away plants and soil while riding a bike or walking, which exposes the land to the Sun, wind, and water*

Alternative Assessment Students may present the results of their investigations orally or draw diagrams that compare the apple's layers with Earth's layers. Ask them to list on their diagrams the apple's shortcomings as a model of Earth.

Ongoing Assessment

Answer: Wind and moving water wear away rocky surfaces; landmasses pushing together cause earthquakes and form volcanoes and other mountains; plants, animals, and people wear away or change Earth's surface.

Reinforce the BIG idea

Have students relate the section to the Big Idea.

Reinforcing Key Concepts, p. 81

2.1 ASSESS & RETEACH

Assess

Section 2.1 Quiz, p. 24

Reteach

Draw a cutaway diagram on the board, similar to that on p. 44 but without indications of the boundaries between layers. Ask for volunteers to add the following information to the diagram:

- Locations of the atmosphere, hydrosphere, biosphere, and geosphere
- Compositions of the four spheres
- Boundaries and names of the geosphere's layers
- Composition or nature of each geosphere layer

Technology Resources

Visit **ClassZone.com** for student practice with chapter concepts.

CONTENT REVIEW

CONTENT REVIEW CD-ROM

Landslide in California

Atmosphere and Hydrosphere Heavy winter rains soak the ground until it cannot absorb any more water.

Geosphere With nothing to hold the water-soaked ground, it slides downhill, leaving a deep trench.

Biosphere Homes built on hillsides replace plants whose roots help hold the soil in place.

The photograph above shows a good example of how the four parts of the Earth system can suddenly change Earth's surface. A landslide like this one can happen in a matter of minutes. Sometimes a steep slope may collapse after heavy rains. The slope can become a river of mud that can move or even bury many buildings. The landslide shown above took place in Laguna Beach, California, in 2005.

The four parts of the Earth system continue to shape the surface with every passing year. Scientists study these changes to help them understand the planet's related systems.

Give three examples of how the parts of the Earth system shape the planet's surface.

2.1 Review

KEY CONCEPTS

1. Give your own example of a system and describe its parts.
2. Name the four parts of the Earth system. List one feature from each of the four parts.
3. Give two examples of your own of how Earth systems interact to shape Earth's surface. (6.2.d)

CRITICAL THINKING

4. **Apply** Suppose you see that plants are dying in the class terrarium. What might be missing from its system?
5. **Infer** You visit a state park and see a thin rock wall with a hole, like a window, worn through it. Which of the four parts of the Earth system might have made the hole? Explain.

CHALLENGE

6. **Predict** Imagine that a volcano erupts in a forested area. There is also a small town a few miles away from the base of the volcano. Describe one way that this event would affect the biosphere or the geosphere.

ANSWERS

1. Possible answer: the digestive system—esophagus, stomach, small intestine, large intestine

2. atmosphere: surrounds and protects Earth; hydrosphere: covers nearly three-quarters of Earth's surface; biosphere: includes all life on Earth; geosphere: made of several layers

3. Storms in the atmosphere can cause landslides; animals can wear paths in Earth's surface.

4. water, air, or soil nutrients

5. hydrosphere (rain) or hydrosphere and atmosphere (rain and wind)

6. Lava from the volcano would alter the shape of the geosphere. Heat from the eruption could start fires that would destroy plants and animal habitats (biosphere).

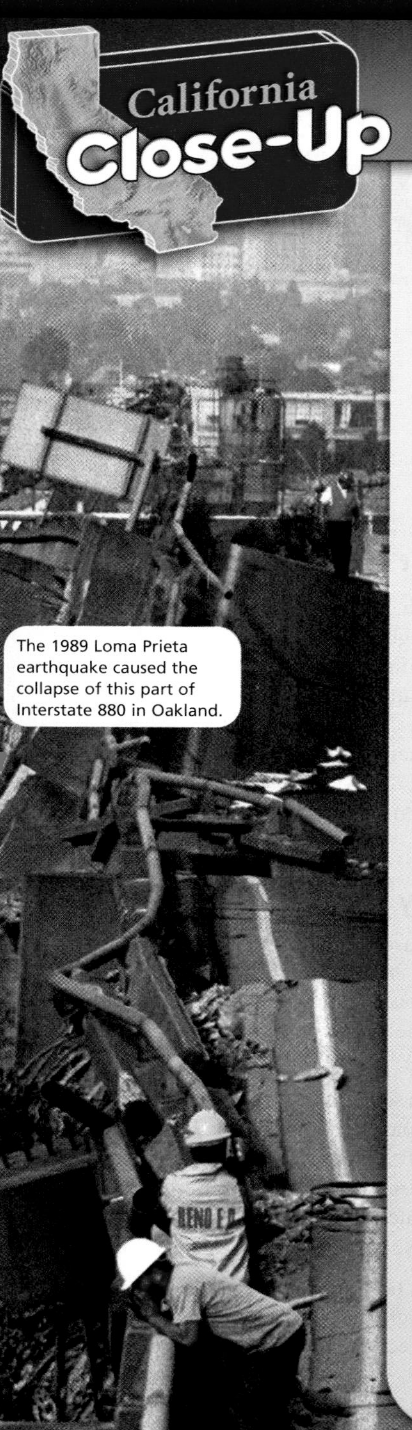

The 1989 Loma Prieta earthquake caused the collapse of this part of Interstate 880 in Oakland.

EARTHQUAKE ENERGY

An Earth-Moving Force

6.1.g Students know how to determine the epicenter of an earthquake and know that the **effects of an earthquake** on any region vary, depending on the size of the earthquake, the distance of the region from the epicenter, the local geology, and the type of construction in the region.

You've probably seen evidence of the damage done by a big earthquake in a movie or maybe even in real life. The earthquake that shook Northridge, California, in 1994 was so strong that it caused some freeway bridges and buildings to collapse.

Earthquakes aren't rare events. Thousands of earthquakes occur around the world each day. However, the shaking of the ground is usually so minor that only the most sensitive instruments can detect it.

It All Adds Up

Hundreds of small earthquakes occur in California in a typical week. Over several years, the small earthquakes may release as much energy as one large earthquake. But if it's the same amount of energy, why are the effects so different?

Many years of frequent, small earthquakes produced the offset in this roadside curb and gutter in Hayward.

Stress Release

An earthquake occurs when underground rocks slip against each other. If the rocks slide easily, many small slips occur. Waves called seismic waves carry the energy outward. However, small waves lose much of their energy to the rocks they move through before the waves reach the surface. Little energy is left to cause damage. But if the rocks get stuck, energy builds up until the rocks give way suddenly. The larger slip produces larger waves that shake the surface with more energy and do more damage.

Small earthquakes release underground energy a little at a time. Think of what happens if you drop a bottle of soda. If you open it quickly, the liquid bubbles and sprays out. But if you turn the cap just a little, you release the energy slowly. Small earthquakes allow energy to be released slowly, causing less damage than energy released all at once.

WRITING ABOUT SCIENCE

Think of another example where energy can be released. It can be in small amounts over a long period of time or in large amounts in a short period of time. Your example might come from nature or everyday life. Describe the example and its effects.

WRITING ABOUT SCIENCE

Writing Applications 6.2.2 This assignment will give students practice writing descriptive expository compositions. Suggest that partners read each other's descriptions and evaluate them in terms of creativity and purpose.

The best descriptions will

- state a thesis or purpose.
- follow an organizational pattern appropriate for a descriptive composition.

CALIFORNIA CLOSE-UP
Science in action in California

Set Learning Goal

To understand the frequency at which earthquakes occur, as well as why some earthquakes do very little damage while others do a great deal of damage.

Present the Science

All earthquakes begin beneath Earth's surface at a point known as the focus; the point on Earth's surface directly above the focus is called the epicenter.

As a quake hits, energy from the earthquake's focus moves outward in all directions in the form of seismic waves. Like all waves, seismic waves carry energy—not matter—from place to place. Earthquakes produce three types of seismic waves: primary waves, secondary waves, and surface waves. Surface waves—the slowest moving of the three wave types—generally cause the most damage when an earthquake hits.

Discussion Questions

Have students share their knowledge and experience with earthquakes.

- Ask: Have you ever experienced a large earthquake? *answers will vary*
- Ask: What types of things happened during the earthquake? *Possible answers: Buildings and other structures shook back and forth, windows shattered, and cracks may have appeared in roads or sidewalks.*
- Ask: Why are earthquakes more common in California than they are in other areas of the world? *Tectonic plates are moving past one another in California.*

Close

Ask: How could you model how seismic waves in the ground carry energy outward? *Possible answer: by throwing a rock into a pond and watching the waves ripple outward*

2.2 FOCUS

Set Learning Goals

Students will

- Identify how Earth receives energy from the Sun.
- Explain why Earth is heated unevenly by the Sun.
- Explain why Earth has seasons.
- Measure through experimentation how the angle of light affects heating.

3-Minute Warm-Up

Display Transparency 12 or copy this exercise on the board:

Fill in the blank with the correct word.

1. An organized group of parts that work together to form a whole is a _____. *system*
2. A _____ is a series of events that repeats over and over. *cycle*
3. Plants, animals, and human beings make up Earth's ________. *biosphere*

3-Minute Warm-Up, p. T12

2.2 MOTIVATE

THINK ABOUT

PURPOSE To have students think about all of the things affected by the Sun

DISCUSS Ask students where energy from sunlight goes. Generate a list of their answers on the board, and compare them to the answers below. ***Some solar energy is used by plants during photosynthesis. Solar energy can make water evaporate, make the wind blow, cause colors to fade, and provide solar cells with the energy to produce electricity.***

Ongoing Assessment

CHECK YOUR READING *Answer: Some is absorbed and some is reflected.*

KEY CONCEPT

2.2 The Sun provides energy to the Earth system.

CALIFORNIA Content Standards

6.3.d Students know heat energy is also transferred between objects by radiation (radiation can travel through space).

6.4.a Students know the sun is the major source of energy for phenomena on Earth's surface; it powers winds, ocean currents, and the water cycle.

6.4.b Students know solar energy reaches Earth through radiation, mostly in the form of visible light.

BEFORE, you learned

- The Earth system has four main parts: atmosphere, hydrosphere, biosphere, and geosphere
- The parts of the Earth system continually interact with each other
- The Earth system's parts interact to shape Earth's surface

NOW, you will learn

- How Earth receives energy from the Sun
- Why Earth is heated unevenly by the Sun
- Why Earth has seasons

VOCABULARY

axis p. 52

THINK ABOUT

Can you feel sunlight?

If you have been on a hot beach, you have felt energy from sunlight. Perhaps you felt sunlight warming your skin or hot sand underneath your feet. It is easy to notice the energy of sunlight when it makes the ground or your skin warm. Where else does the energy from sunlight go?

OUTLINE
Remember to include this heading in your outline of this section.

I. Main idea
  A. Supporting idea
    1. Detail
    2. Detail
  B. Supporting idea

Earth receives energy from the Sun.

As you read in Chapter 1, almost all the energy around you comes from the Sun. That means food energy, fires, and even the warmth of your own body can be traced back to energy from the Sun. A lot of this energy reaches Earth in a form you can see—visible light.

Recall that some of the solar radiation that reaches Earth is reflected, or sent in a new direction. You see most of the objects around you by reflected light. The sand in the picture above looks light in color because it reflects much of the sunlight that hits it. Earth's surface also absorbs some of the sunlight that reaches it. The substance that absorbs the light energy from the Sun is heated by the energy. The sand can become warm or even hot as it absorbs some of the sunlight that hits it.

Color makes a difference in how much energy an object will absorb and how much it will reflect. Light-colored objects, such as the white shirts in the picture above, reflect more light than dark objects. The dark shirts absorb more light.

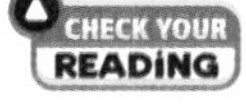

CHECK YOUR READING What happens to the sunlight that reaches Earth's surface?

RESOURCES FOR DIFFERENTIATED INSTRUCTION

Below Level

UNIT RESOURCE BOOK

- Reading Study Guide A, pp. 84–85
- Decoding Support, p. 108

AUDIO CDS

Advanced

UNIT RESOURCE BOOK

Challenge and Extension, p. 90

English Learners

UNIT RESOURCE BOOK

Spanish Reading Study Guide, pp. 88–89

AUDIO CDS

- Audio Readings in Spanish
- Audio Readings (English)

Reflected Solar Energy

Some surfaces reflect more sunlight than others. Lighter surfaces and objects reflect more light. For example, clouds, snow, and light-colored buildings reflect a lot of solar radiation. Dust particles and gases in the atmosphere reflect some sunlight. About 25 percent of the Sun's energy is reflected by clouds and particles in the atmosphere. Another 5 percent of solar energy is reflected by Earth's surface. The energy from the Sun that is reflected goes back into outer space.

Find out more about solar energy.

Absorbed Solar Energy

If 30 percent of the solar energy that reaches Earth is sent back out into space, what happens to the other 70 percent? It is absorbed by Earth's atmosphere and surface. Darker objects or surfaces absorb more sunlight. About 20 percent of the solar energy is absorbed by clouds, particles, and gases in the atmosphere. This energy heats the atmosphere.

About 50 percent of the Sun's energy is absorbed by Earth's surface, as shown in the graph below. Landforms, living things, and the ocean absorb most of this energy. Energy that is absorbed by Earth's atmosphere and surface is later released and is lost to outer space. The amount of energy being absorbed by the Earth system is balanced by the amount of energy being lost. If these amounts were not balanced, Earth's average surface temperature would change over time.

Reflected and Absorbed Energy

This photograph of Lake Tahoe, California, shows that more sunlight is reflected from clouds, snow, and water than from trees, grass, and dark-colored rocks.

Incoming Solar Energy

30% reflected

Reflected Energy	
by atmosphere	25%
by surface	5%
Absorbed Energy	
by atmosphere	20%
by surface	50%

70% absorbed

READING VISUALS How much of the Sun's energy is absorbed by Earth's atmosphere and surface?

DIFFERENTIATE INSTRUCTION

More Reading Support

A Where does reflected energy from the Sun go? *back into outer space*

B Which kind of objects absorb more sunlight, darker objects or lighter objects? *darker objects*

English Learners To help English learners both understand the concepts in this chapter as well as build vocabulary, ask them to prepare a two-column chart with the headings "Lighter Objects" and "Darker Objects." Then ask them to list all the objects in the room that might absorb less sunlight (objects that are white or lighter in color) and objects that might absorb more sunlight (objects that are black or darker in color). Students can present their lists to the class and record additional suggestions.

2.2 INSTRUCT

Teach the Standards

Solar energy 6.4.b

In this section: Help students understand that the Sun is the major source of energy for Earth. Remind students that the Sun provides warmth and light to Earth, and that its affect on temperature is a cause of seasons.

- **previously taught:** visible light, p. 21; sunlight as an energy resource, p. 24
- **future opportunities:** sunlight and wind, p. 84; sunlight and the water cycle, p. 93; solar cells, p. 475

Teach from Visuals

To help students interpret the graph of reflected and absorbed energy on page 49, ask:

- Which reflects more of the Sun's energy, Earth's atmosphere or Earth's surface? *Earth's atmosphere*
- Which absorbs more of the Sun's energy, Earth's atmosphere or Earth's surface? *Earth's surface*
- Compare an area covered in snow to an area that is mostly dark rock and soil. Which area will reflect more sunlight back into outer space? Why? *The area covered in snow will reflect more sunlight; lighter surfaces reflect more sunlight than darker surfaces.*

Develop Critical Thinking

ANALYZE Ask students to reread the second paragraph under "Absorbed Solar Energy." Remind students that the amount of energy being absorbed by Earth's system is balanced by the amount of energy being lost. Ask: If this balance of absorbed and reflected energy by the Earth system did not exist, how would that affect Earth's average surface temperature? *If the Earth system absorbed more energy than it lost, then its average surface temperature would gradually increase. If Earth's system lost more energy than it absorbed, its average surface temperature would decrease gradually.*

Ongoing Assessment

Identify how Earth receives energy from the Sun.

Ask: What happens to energy from the Sun that reaches Earth? *It is absorbed or it is reflected back into outer space.*

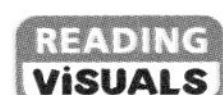

Answer: 70 percent

Integrate the Sciences

The arctic tundra, an Earth biome encircling the North Pole, is made up of large stretches of land across Alaska, Canada, and Siberia. Despite the extreme cold temperatures, a low level of precipitation in the arctic tundra produces a desertlike climate. However, even in this harsh environment, plant and animal life can be found.

Tundra plants have various adaptations to help them survive. Most grow close to the ground and grouped together to protect themselves from cold arctic winds. Many have small leaf structures that prevent them from losing an excessive amount of moisture. For many birds and mammals, the arctic tundra is only a summer home. However, some permanent residents include musk oxen, reindeer, arctic hares, arctic wolves, and brown bears.

Teach from Visuals

To help students interpret the visual of uneven heating, ask:

- Which area on Earth is warmer, the equator or the north and south poles? *the equator*
- Which area probably contains more plants and animals? Why? *the equator, because most plants and animals need light and warmth to survive*
- Is most sunlight that hits areas near the north and south poles reflected or absorbed? Why? *reflected; The poles are covered in light-colored ice and snow, which reflect sunlight back into outer space.*

Ongoing Assessment

Explain why Earth is heated unevenly by the Sun.

Ask: What causes the Sun to heat Earth's surface unevenly? *the curved surface of Earth*

Answer: near the equator

Answer: Areas where sunlight hits Earth's surface at a higher angle receive more solar energy; areas where sunlight hits Earth's surface at a lower angle receive less solar energy.

Energy from the Sun heats Earth's surface unevenly.

READING TIP

A perpendicular angle is a 90° angle. A 90° angle is also called a right angle. A higher angle is closer to 90° than a lower angle is.

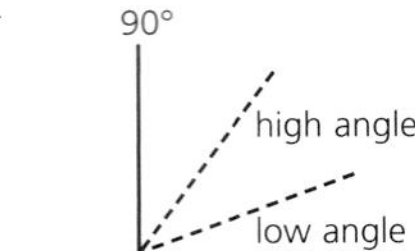

Not all parts of Earth receive equal amounts of the Sun's energy. Light from the Sun hits Earth's curved surface at different angles. Sunlight hits Earth's surface at an angle that is close to perpendicular at the equator, as shown in the diagram below. Near the north and south poles, sunlight hits the surface at a much lower angle. The parts of the surface that receive sunlight at a lower angle receive less solar energy. It's like shining a flashlight on a building. Where the light from the flashlight hits the building straight on, or at a 90° angle, the light is brighter. If you shine the flashlight higher up on the building, the light hits the building at a lower angle. The light beam that hits at an angle spreads out over a larger area. A spread-out beam does not light up the surface as brightly. The same thing happens on Earth's surface because of its curved shape.

The areas on Earth's surface that receive sunlight at high angles heat up more. These areas receive more solar energy. For the same reason, you can get a sunburn faster at noon, when the Sun is highest in the sky.

Where does sunlight hit Earth at the highest angle?

Uneven Heating

Earth's surface receives more heat from the Sun in areas where sunlight hits the surface at high angles.

SUNLIGHT

Equator

Sunlight is more spread out at the poles because it strikes at a lower angle.

Sunlight is concentrated near the equator because it strikes the surface at a high angle.

Sunlight near the poles is spread out.

Sunlight near the equator is concentrated.

READING VISUALS How does the angle of sunlight affect the heating of Earth's surface?

DIFFERENTIATE INSTRUCTION

C Why do you get a sunburn fastest at noon? *because the Sun is highest in the sky and its angle is at the highest point, causing the Earth's surface to heat up more*

Advanced Albedo refers to how much radiation a surface reflects compared with how much it receives. A surface with a high albedo reflects most of the radiation it receives. Ask: Does snow have a high or low albedo? How do you know? *It has a high albedo because it is light colored and therefore reflects most of the sunlight shining on it.*

Challenge and Extension, p. 90

INVESTIGATE Solar Energy

How does the angle of light affect heating?

SKILL FOCUS
Comparing (6.3.d)

PROCEDURE

1. Tape a black square over the bulb of each thermometer. Then tape the thermometers to the cardboard tube as shown.
2. Place the setup on a sunny windowsill or under a lamp. One square should face the light at a 90° angle. Record the temperatures.
3. Wait 10 minutes. Record the temperatures again.

MATERIALS
- tape
- 2 black paper squares
- 2 thermometers
- 1 cardboard tube from a paper towel roll
- sunny windowsill or lamp

TIME
20 minutes

WHAT DO YOU THINK?
- How did the temperature readings change?
- How did the angle of light affect the amount of heat absorbed?

CHALLENGE How could you use the angle of light to model how the amount of solar radiation that hits Earth's surface changes with distance from the equator?

Uneven heating is a cause of the seasons.

The unequal heating of Earth's surface by the Sun is one cause of the seasons. The four seasons are spring, summer, fall, and winter. The range of temperatures and the weather patterns are different in most places during each season. There are fewer seasonal changes near the equator. The temperature stays about the same all year. Near the poles, seasonal changes are much greater. In the winter, temperatures are much lower than during the summer. These temperature changes are caused by differences in the amount of solar energy received throughout the year.

VISUALIZATION CLASSZONE.COM
See a visualization of why there are seasons.

As you have read, it is warmer in areas where sunlight hits Earth's surface at high angles. Also, it is warmer during the summer, because the amount of solar energy received is greater. What causes the amount of solar energy received from the Sun to change at different times of the year? The total amount of energy that Earth receives from the Sun does not change throughout the year. However, the areas where the most solar energy strikes Earth's surface do change. Because the amount of solar energy received by an area changes during the year, average daily temperatures also change.

What changes mark the seasons?

INVESTIGATE Solar Energy

PURPOSE To introduce the concept that the angle of light affects the heating of an object

TIPS *15 min.* Explain that the purpose of the black squares is to absorb radiation on a flat surface.

WHAT DO YOU THINK? *Answers will vary, but the square directly facing the light should be warmer. More heat is absorbed when the light strikes a surface at a high angle.*

CHALLENGE *Sample answer: The reading from the square directly facing the light source represents higher temperatures at the equator, and the reading from the square that is tilted away from the light source represents lower temperatures at the poles.*

Datasheet, Solar Energy, p. 91

Technology Resources

Customize this student lab as needed or look for an alternative. Print rubrics to assess student lab reports.

Lab Generator CD-ROM

Teaching with Technology

If students have a computer, have them use a computer graphing program to construct a line graph of their data. If students have probeware, have them use the temperature probe to record a second set of data.

Ongoing Assessment

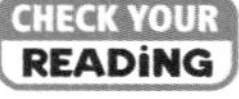

Answer: changes in temperature and different weather patterns

DIFFERENTIATE INSTRUCTION

More Reading Support

D What is one cause of seasons? *unequal heating of Earth's surface by the Sun*

Below Level Ask below level students to use a globe to locate approximately where they live on Earth. Ask them to determine whether they are closer to the Earth's equator or to the North Pole. If indicated on the globe, students may also try to determine the latitude for their location.

Teach Difficult Concepts

Some students may have a hard time understanding the effects of sunlight's various angles. Point out that the angle of sunlight changes throughout the day as well as throughout the seasons. In the early morning, sunlight strikes the ground at a slant and does not seem very warm. In all cases, the angle of light affects temperature. You can do the following demonstration to help students to better understand angles of sunlight.

Teacher Demo

Tie a dozen pencils into a loose bundle so they can slide. Tell students that the bundle represents sunlight. Hold the pencils vertically on a sheet of paper to model concentrated sunlight striking Earth's surface. Ask: Where would the Sun be in this model? *high in the sky* What season might it be? *summer* Next, hold the bundle at an angle while keeping all pencil tips on the paper. Ask: Where would the Sun be in this model? *low in the sky* What time of day might it be? *sunset* What season would most likely have this angle of sunlight at noon? *winter*

Develop Critical Thinking

INFER Suppose Earth's axis did not tilt. Ask: How would a lack of tilt in Earth's axis affect the seasons in the northern and southern hemispheres? *Possible answer: If Earth's axis did not tilt, then no seasonal changes would exist.*

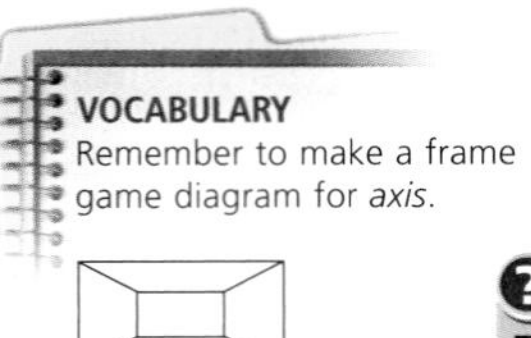

VOCABULARY
Remember to make a frame game diagram for *axis*.

Tilt of Earth's Axis

As you know, Earth rotates, or turns. The rotation causes day and night. At any time, half of Earth is facing the Sun. On the part of Earth facing the Sun, it is daylight. On the half of Earth facing away from the Sun, it is night. Earth rotates around its axis. Earth's **axis** is an imaginary line running through the center of the planet. As you can see in the illustrations on page 53, Earth's axis is not perpendicular to the plane of its orbit around the Sun. Instead, it is tilted at an angle of about 23 degrees. E

This tilt of the axis causes different amounts of solar energy to hit Earth at different times of the year. As Earth revolves around the Sun, different areas of the planet are tilted toward the Sun. This results in sunlight hitting Earth's surface at different angles at different times of the year. This tilt of Earth's axis is a cause of the seasons. The part of Earth that is tilted toward the Sun receives more solar energy than the part tilted away from the Sun.

When the Northern Hemisphere is tilted toward the Sun, it is summer there. At the same time, it is winter in the Southern Hemisphere. This is because the Southern Hemisphere is tilted away from the Sun. In the same way, when it is summer in the Southern Hemisphere, it is winter in the Northern Hemisphere.

Tropic of Cancer

In June the Northern Hemisphere is tilted toward the Sun. As a result, the Sun appears to be higher in the sky. The first day of summer in the Northern Hemisphere is June 21. This day is also the first day of winter in the Southern Hemisphere. At noon on June 21, solar energy strikes Earth's surface at right angles along an imaginary line in the Northern Hemisphere called the tropic of Cancer. You can find the tropic of Cancer in the illustrations on page 53. At all times other than June 21, the perpendicular rays of the Sun hit Earth south of the tropic of Cancer.

Tropic of Capricorn

In December the Northern Hemisphere is tilted away from the Sun. As a result, the Sun appears to be lower in the sky. The first day of winter in the Northern Hemisphere is December 21. This is also the first day of summer in the Southern Hemisphere. At noon on December 21, solar energy strikes Earth's surface at right angles along an imaginary line in the Southern Hemisphere called the tropic of Capricorn. At all other times, the perpendicular rays of the Sun hit Earth north of the tropic of Capricorn.

DIFFERENTIATE INSTRUCTION

More Reading Support

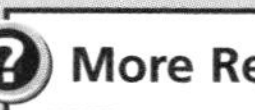

E At what angle is Earth's axis tilted relative to the plane of its orbit? *about 23 degrees*

Alternative Assessment Have students make a sketch of the relative positions of Earth and the Sun in either summer or winter. The sketch should show the tilt of the Earth's axis and the positions of the tropics of Cancer and Capricorn. Have students exchange sketches and identify the season shown in another's sketch.

Tilt of Earth's Axis and the Seasons

Earth's axis points in a constant direction as Earth orbits the Sun. The tilt of Earth's axis is a cause of the seasons.

Winter in the Northern Hemisphere and Summer in the Southern Hemisphere

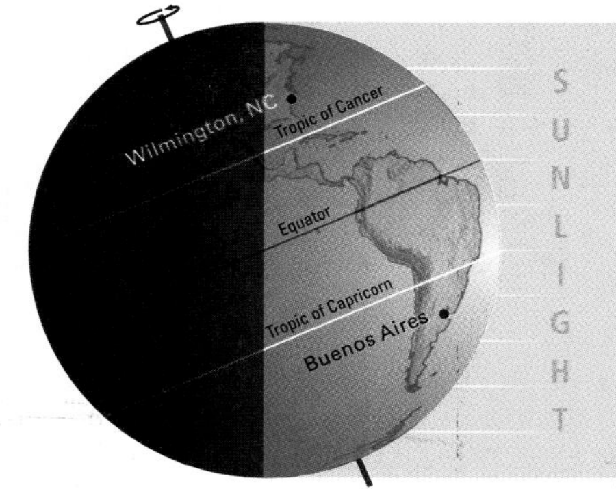

The hemisphere in which it is winter is tilted away from the Sun. When it is winter in the Northern Hemisphere, it is summer in the Southern Hemisphere.

Summer in the Northern Hemisphere and Winter in the Southern Hemisphere

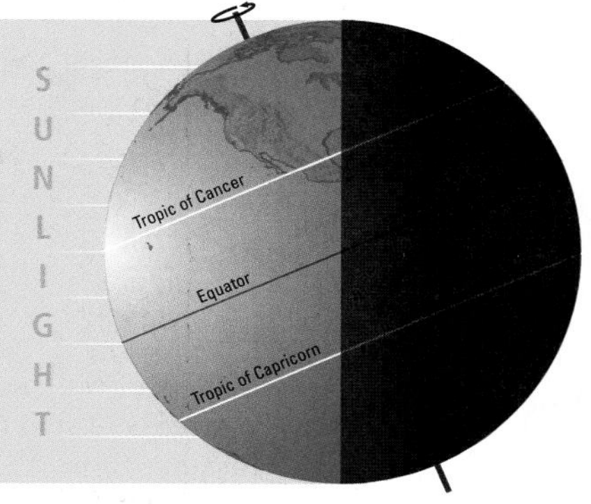

The hemisphere in which it is summer is tilted toward the Sun. When it is summer in the Northern Hemisphere, it is winter in the Southern Hemisphere.

Buenos Aires, Argentina, is in the Southern Hemisphere. Wilmington, North Carolina, is in the Northern Hemisphere. These cities are about the same distance from the equator, but their seasons are reversed. The warmest months in Buenos Aires are the coldest months in Wilmington.

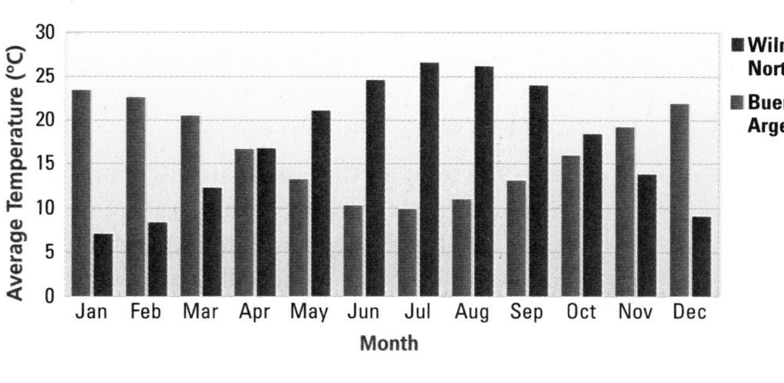

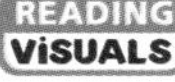

How does the tilt of Earth's axis cause temperatures to be higher in the Northern Hemisphere during July and lower during January?

DIFFERENTIATE INSTRUCTION

Alternative Assessment Have students work in pairs. Instruct each pair of students to research the average temperature for June and December for a city in California. Then, as a class, make a list on the board of the different cities and their average temperatures. Give reasons for any major temperature differences noticed in certain cities. Students can use encyclopedias, atlases, or the Internet to research a city.

Teach from Visuals

To help students understand the "Tilt of Earth's Axis and the Seasons" visual on pages 52–53, ask:

- When it is winter in the Northern Hemisphere, what season is it in the Southern Hemisphere? *summer*

To help students interpret the temperature graph, ask:

- During which month are temperatures in Buenos Aires, Argentina, and Wilmington, North Carolina, relatively the same? *April*
- Which city has higher average temperatures during its summer? *Wilmington*

This visual is also available as T14 in the Transparency Book.

Develop Critical Thinking

Ask students to explain why Wilmington might be warmer than Buenos Aires during the summer, even though the two cities are about the same distance from the equator. *Sample answer: Other factors besides distance from the equator may affect seasonal temperatures in Wilmington, such as land formations, elevation above sea level, proximity to water, or ocean currents.*

Ongoing Assessment

Explain why Earth has seasons.

Ask: What are two causes of seasons? *unequal heating of Earth's surface by the Sun and the tilt of Earth's axis*

Temperatures in the Northern Hemisphere are higher in July because that half of Earth is tilted toward the Sun and therefore receives more direct sunlight. In January the Northern Hemisphere is tilted away from the Sun, so temperatures are lower.

Teach from Visuals

Point out that the map is a flat representation of part of the curved surface on the globe. To help students relate the map to the globe, have them match latitudes represented on the right side of the map with latitudes on the globe.

To help students interpret the "Latitude and Temperature" visual on page 54, ask:

- How are the degree measurements on the land part of the map different from the degree measurements on the far right and left sides of the map? *Degree measurements on the land part are temperature measurements in degrees Celsius. Degree measurements on the far right and left sides of the map (over water) are measurements of latitude.*
- In addition to degrees Celsius, in what unit is air temperature sometimes measured? *degrees Fahrenheit, or °F*

Develop Geometry Skills

Explain to students that the globe is a sphere, or a circle in three dimensions.

Ask students to observe the image of the globe on this page. Point out that a line running between the poles would meet the equator at a right angle, which is 90°. The angle would cover one quarter of the globe's circumference.

Have students determine mathematically how many degrees are in the total sphere. *(90° x 4 = 360°)*

Summarize that a circle or sphere has 360 total degrees, that each half has 180 degrees, and each quarter has 90 degrees.

Ongoing Assessment

CHECK YOUR READING *Answer: Temperatures generally decrease as latitude increases.*

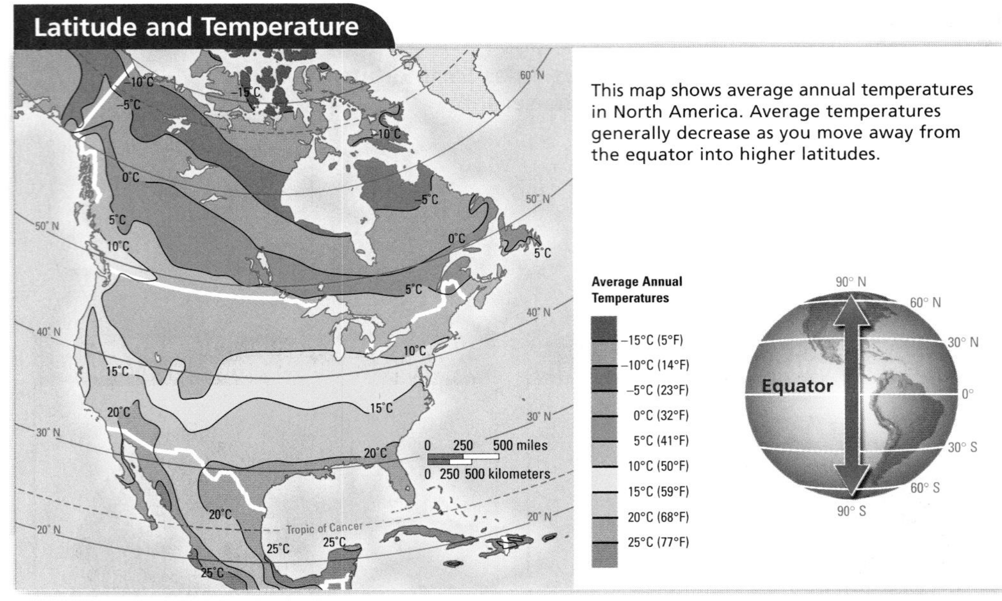

This map shows average annual temperatures in North America. Average temperatures generally decrease as you move away from the equator into higher latitudes.

Latitude

READING TIP Notice on the globe in the illustration that latitude numbers get higher as you move away from the equator.

F You have read that the amount of solar radiation received at Earth's surface is related to distance from the equator. One way to measure distance from the equator is latitude. Latitude is the distance in degrees north or south of the equator. The equator is at 0 degrees latitude. Each degree equals 1/360 of the distance around the planet. You will read more about latitude in Chapter 5.

Because of the unequal heating caused by Earth's curved shape, temperatures usually go down as you move away from the equator toward either the North Pole or the South Pole. As you can see in the map above, these temperature changes do not follow lines of latitude. Factors other than latitude affect average annual temperatures.

G The temperature of an area depends in part on its height above sea level. In the atmosphere, temperature normally goes down as height goes up. Therefore, the temperatures high on a mountain are usually cooler than those in the valley below. Also, the temperature of an area depends in part on how close it is to a large lake or the ocean. Water heats and cools more slowly than land. Large bodies of water cause areas along a coast to be cooler in summer and warmer in winter than land at the same latitude in the middle of a continent.

What is the connection between latitude and temperature?

DIFFERENTIATE INSTRUCTION

More Reading Support

F What is used to measure distance in degrees north or south of the equator? *latitude*

G Which heats and cools more slowly, water or land? *water*

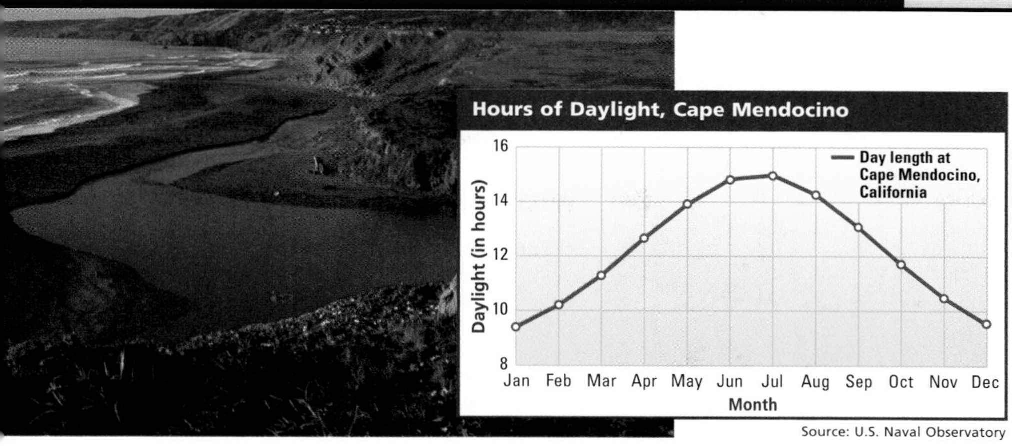

Source: U.S. Naval Observatory

Hours of Daylight

The temperatures in the different seasons are also affected by the length of the days. For example, at Cape Mendocino, California, the summer sunlight heats the ground for about 15 hours per day on June 21. But, on December 21, the day is only about 9 hours long. In the winter, solar energy does not heat Earth's surface as much as in the summer. The greater the hours of daylight, the more the Sun's energy heats Earth's surface. Therefore, another reason it is warmer in the summer is that the days are longer.

The closer you are to the poles, the more the day length varies. Near the poles, there is sunlight for 18 hours or more during the summer. At the north and south poles, the Sun does not set at all for six months of the year. And during the winter at the poles, there is no sunlight. The winter at the poles is cold and dark. Close to the equator, the lengths of the day and night are almost equal all year round. Areas near the equator have about 12 hours of daylight all year. That's one reason why the seasons near the equator do not have large changes in temperature.

2.2 Review

KEY CONCEPTS

1. What two things happen to the solar radiation that reaches Earth? (6.3.d)
2. What part of Earth's surface receives the most solar energy? Explain. (6.3.d)
3. What causes the amount of solar energy received in a particular area to change throughout the year? (6.3.d)

CRITICAL THINKING

4. **Apply** On June 21 are there more hours of daylight in San Francisco or at the equator? Explain.
5. **Infer** If Earth's axis were not tilted, how would the seasons be affected?

CHALLENGE

6. **Predict** Which would likely be hotter in the Northern Hemisphere, a cloudy day in July or a sunny day in July? Explain.

ANSWERS

1. It is reflected or absorbed.

2. the area near the equator, because that is where sunlight hits Earth at the highest angle

3. the tilt of Earth's axis

4. There are more hours of daylight in San Francisco on June 21. In the summer, the days grow longer the closer you are to the poles; in areas closer to the equator, the length of the day and night are almost equal all year.

5. If Earth's axis were not tilted, there would be no seasonal changes.

6. A sunny day in July would be warmer. On a cloudy day, the clouds would reflect most of the sunlight back into outer space.

Teach from Visuals

To help students interpret the "Hours of Daylight" visual, ask:

- During which months are the days less than 10 hours long in Cape Mendocino, California? *December and January*
- During which months are the days about 14 hours or longer? *May through August*
- If a similar graph were prepared for a city near the equator, how do you think it would differ from the one pictured here? Why? *The curve would look more like a straight line. Near the equator, the hours of daylight do not fluctuate much throughout the year.*

Reinforce the BIG idea

Have students relate the section to the Big Idea.

 Reinforcing Key Concepts, p. 92

2.2 ASSESS & RETEACH

Assess

 Section 2.2 Quiz, p. 25

Reteach

Attach a world map to the board. Write a random date on the board beside the map. Ask for student volunteers to participate in this activity. Blindfold volunteers and spin them in a circle, so that they lose orientation. Then ask each volunteer to touch a spot on the world map. Remove the blindfolds. Based on what they have learned about seasons and the tilt of the Earth's axis, have each volunteer describe the season, temperature, and weather for the part of Earth that they chose. *Student responses will vary depending on what area of the map they select and the date that you choose.*

Technology Resources

Have students visit **ClassZone.com** for reteaching of Key Concepts.

 **CONTENT REVIEW**

 **CONTENT REVIEW CD-ROM**

CHAPTER INVESTIGATION

Focus

PURPOSE To model the amount of solar energy received at different times

OVERVIEW Students will observe different angles of light on graph paper. Students use their observations to conclude:

- angles of sunlight affect the amount of solar energy a location receives throughout the year.
- changing angles of sunlight affect the amount of solar energy a location receives throughout a day.

Lab Preparation

- Make sure all students know how to use a protractor before beginning the lab. Review its use, if necessary.
- Have students read through the investigation and prepare their data tables. (Make sure they leave space before their data tables for notes from Part One.) Or you may wish to copy and distribute datasheets and rubrics.

UNIT RESOURCE BOOK, pp. 111–119

SCIENCE TOOLKIT, F14

Lab Management

In Part One, students may move the flashlight through a range of angles in order to determine what happens to the light.

In Part Two, choose a location different from the one students will use in the lab. On the board, guide students through the mathematical steps they need to take in steps 5–7. In step 8, if students have trouble moving the flashlight to the maximum angle they calculated in step 7, have one student create the angle by holding a pencil in the air at the correct angle. The maximum angle should be reached only briefly at the center of the arc. Students can use their protractor to help find both positions.

CHAPTER INVESTIGATION

Modeling Solar Energy

OVERVIEW AND PURPOSE In this investigation you will model how the amount of solar energy received at one place changes throughout a year and during a day. You will model the amount of solar energy received at different times as you

- point a light source at different angles to a surface
- determine how the amount of energy received at a location changes during a summer day

Problem

How does the angle of light affect the amount of solar energy a location receives at different times of year?

Hypothesize

After performing step 4, write a hypothesis to explain how the angle of sunlight affects the amount of solar energy your location receives. Your hypothesis should take the form of an "If . . . , then . . . , because . . ." statement.

MATERIALS
- graph paper
- flashlight
- meter stick
- protractor

6.3.d, 6.4.b, 6.7.a, 6.7.e

Procedure

PART ONE

1. Mark an X near the center of the graph paper. Shine the flashlight onto the paper from about 30 cm straight above the X—at an angle of 90° to the surface. Estimate the length of the spot of light.

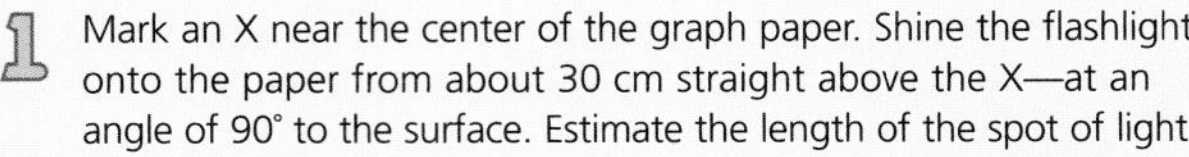

2. Shine the flashlight onto the X at different angles. Measure and record the angles. Keep the flashlight at the same distance. Record the estimated length of the spot of light at the angles.

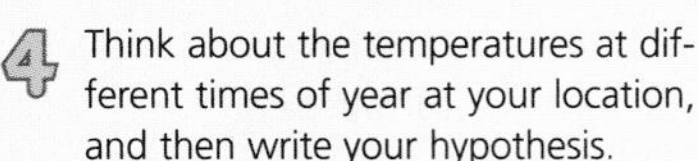

3. Repeat step 2, but observe just one square near the X. Write down what happens to the brightness of the light as you change the angle. The brightness shows how much energy the area receives from the flashlight.

4. Think about the temperatures at different times of year at your location, and then write your hypothesis.

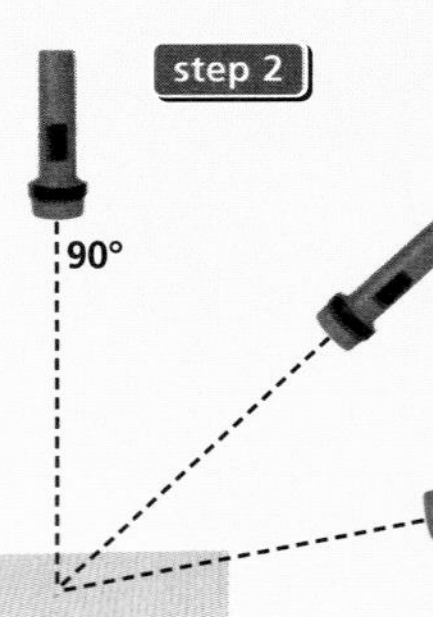

INVESTIGATION RESOURCES

CHAPTER INVESTIGATION, Modeling Solar Energy
- Level A, pp. 111–114
- Level B, pp. 115–118
- Level C, p. 119

Advanced students should complete Levels B & C.

Writing a Lab Report, D12–13

Technology Resources

Customize this student lab as needed or look for an alternative. Print rubrics to assess student lab reports.

Lab Generator CD-ROM

Content Standard
6.4.b Students know solar energy reaches Earth through radiation, mostly in the form of visible light.

Investigation Standard
6.7.a Develop a hypothesis.

PART TWO

5 Find from your teacher the latitude of your location. You will use this information to calculate the Sun's noontime elevation at your location on June 21, the first day of summer.

6 Subtract the latitude of the tropic of Cancer, which is at 23.5° north, from your latitude.

7 Subtract the number you calculated in step 6 from 90°. Your result is the Sun's noontime elevation in degrees above the horizon in your location on the first day of summer.

8 Point the light at the X on the graph paper. Move the flashlight in an arc from one side of the graph paper to the other. The maximum angle of the flashlight above the paper should be the angle you calculated in step 7. The movement of the flashlight represents the apparent movement of the Sun across the sky.

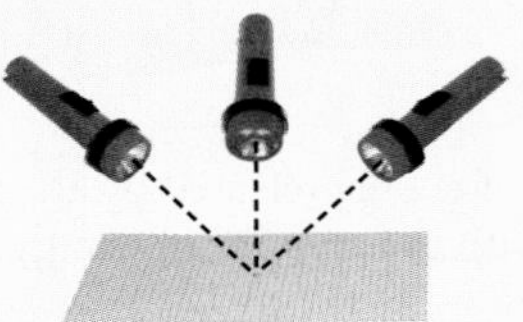

9 Observe how the brightness of the light near the X changes as you move the flashlight through the arc.

Observe and Analyze

Write It Up

1. **RECORD** Draw the setup of your materials in each part of the investigation. Organize your notes.
2. **ANALYZE** Describe how the angle of the flashlight in step 2 affected the spot of light. Which angle concentrated the light into the smallest area?
3. **EVALUATE** In Part Two, what part of the flashlight arc represented sunrise? noon? sunset?
4. **COMPARE** Compare the brightness of light your area receives during a day at noon and at sunset.

Conclude

Write It Up

1. **EVALUATE** Why do areas closer to the equator receive more solar energy?
2. **APPLY** Why are you more likely to get a sunburn at noon than at sunrise?
3. **INTERPRET** Do your results support your hypothesis? Explain why or why not.

INVESTIGATE Further

CHALLENGE Compare the brightness of a day in summer and a day in winter at your location. Determine the total difference in latitude between your location and the latitude of the tropic of Capricorn (23.5° south). Subtract the total from 90°. The result is the noontime elevation of the Sun in your area on the first day of winter. Repeat Part Two using this maximum angle.

Modeling Solar Energy

Problem How does the angle of light affect the amount of solar energy a location receives at different times of year?

Hypothesize

Observe and Analyze

Table 1. Angle of Light and Brightness

Angle of Light (°)	Length of Spot (cm)	Brightness
15		
30		
45		

Observe and Analyze

SAMPLE DATA Length of Spot: 15, 20 cm; 30, 15 cm; 45, 10 cm. Brightness: 15, dim; 30, medium; 45, bright.

1. Drawing should include information in the photographs.

2. The spot was largest at low angles. It was concentrated into the smallest area at a 90° angle.

3. Sunrise and sunset are represented when the flashlight is at the beginning and end of the arc. Noon is represented when the flashlight reaches the maximum angle calculated in step 7.

4. Students should observe that the light in their area is brighter at noon and less bright at sunset.

Conclude

1. *Areas closer to the equator receive more solar energy because sunlight hits those areas at higher angles.*
2. *You are more likely to get a sunburn at noon because the sunlight hitting your skin at a high angle is more concentrated than later in the day, when the angle of light is lower.*
3. *Sample answer: Data supported the hypothesis that slanted light results in less concentrated solar energy (and cooler weather) in winter because the energy from sunlight is more spread out.*

INVESTIGATE Further

CHALLENGE Answers will vary depending upon the latitude of the student's location. However, students should observe that brightness at noon on a winter day at their location is less than on a summer day because of the lower angle of sunlight.

Post-Lab Discussion

Help students see the meaning of the angles they measured. The zero line of the protractor should have been parallel to the surface so that students measured the angle from the horizon up to the position of the "Sun."

Based on the data collected from their labs, ask students how their results would differ by changing their location to the Southern Hemisphere, and subtracting their new location from the latitude of the tropic of Capricorn to find the Sun's noontime elevation on June 21. *The Sun would be low in the sky because June 21 is the first day of winter in the Southern Hemisphere.*

2.3 FOCUS

Set Learning Goals

Students will

- Demonstrate how heat is transferred over Earth's surface.
- Explain how solar energy powers the water cycle.
- Explain how solar energy affects weather and climate.
- Compare through experimentation the heating and cooling rates of soil and water.

3-Minute Warm-Up

Display Transparency 13 or copy this exercise on the board:

Fill in each blank with the correct word.

1. Darker objects on Earth's surface _____ more sunlight than lighter objects. *absorb*
2. The tropic of Cancer is found in the _______ Hemisphere. *Northern*
3. _____ is the distance in degrees north or south of the equator. *Latitude*

3-Minute Warm-Up, p. T13

2.3 MOTIVATE

THINK ABOUT

PURPOSE To compare the amount of internal heat generated by a volcano beneath Earth's surface with the amount of energy transferred daily to Earth's surface by the Sun

DISCUSS Tell students that Earth's surface receives energy from two main sources: Earth's interior and the Sun. However, because of the composition of Earth's surface, much more energy reaches Earth's surface from the Sun. Tell students that they will learn why in this section.

KEY CONCEPT

2.3 Energy is transferred within the Earth system.

CALIFORNIA Content Standards

6.4.a Students know the sun is the major source of energy for phenomena on Earth's surface; it powers winds, ocean currents, and the water cycle.

6.4.c Students know heat from Earth's interior reaches the surface primarily through convection.

6.4.d Students know convection currents distribute heat in the atmosphere and oceans.

BEFORE, you learned

- Earth receives energy from the Sun as radiation
- The curve of Earth's surface causes it to be heated unequally
- One cause of the seasons is the unequal heating of Earth's surface

NOW, you will learn

- How heat is transferred over Earth's surface
- How solar energy powers the water cycle
- How solar energy affects weather and climate

VOCABULARY

water cycle p. 60
weather p. 62
ocean current p. 62
greenhouse effect p. 63
climate p. 65

THINK ABOUT

Where does most of Earth's energy come from?

Look at the photograph of an erupting volcano. Where is the energy that fuels the volcano coming from? A huge amount of energy is released from Earth's interior by an erupting volcano. How does the amount of energy released by an eruption from Earth's interior compare with the amount of energy that comes to Earth from the Sun every day?

OUTLINE
Remember to take notes in the form of an outline as you read.

I. Main idea
  A. Supporting idea
    1. Detail
    2. Detail
  B. Supporting idea

Little of Earth's internal heat reaches the surface.

Almost all of the energy that reaches Earth's surface comes from the Sun. Earth's interior is very hot. But very little of the heat in Earth's interior reaches the surface. Convection currents carry some heat from inside Earth toward the surface. You will read more about this in Chapter 8. But the rock that makes up Earth's outer layers does not conduct heat easily. Therefore, only a small amount of heat is carried from Earth's interior to the atmosphere. You can see signs of Earth's internal heat in a few places. Volcanoes, hot springs, and geysers are places where Earth's internal heat reaches the surface. The amount of energy released by an erupting volcano is huge. But that amount is tiny compared with the amount of energy Earth receives from the Sun.

RESOURCES FOR DIFFERENTIATED INSTRUCTION

Below Level

UNIT RESOURCE BOOK

- Reading Study Guide A, pp. 95–96
- Decoding Support, p. 108

AUDIO CDS

Advanced

UNIT RESOURCE BOOK

- Challenge and Extension, p. 101
- Challenge Reading, pp. 104–105

English Learners

UNIT RESOURCE BOOK

Spanish Reading Study Guide, pp. 99–100

AUDIO CDS

- Audio Readings in Spanish
- Audio Readings (English)

Additional INVESTIGATION,
Observing Convection, A, B, & C, pp. 120–128;
Teacher Instructions, pp. 274–275

58 Unit 1: The Earth System

Energy from the Sun moves through the Earth system.

As you read in Chapter 1, energy from the Sun reaches Earth through radiation. Life on Earth depends on solar radiation. Plants change sunlight to stored energy. Humans and other animals that eat plants use this stored energy. Therefore, the Sun provides both plants and animals with the energy they need to live.

See radiation, conduction, and convection in action.

When solar radiation is absorbed by the atmosphere or by Earth's surface, it changes into heat energy. Recall that heat energy can be transferred in three ways—radiation, conduction, and convection.

The illustration below shows each of these processes. Solar radiation heats Earth's surface. Energy is carried by conduction from Earth's surface to the air molecules touching it. The warm air then carries energy upward by convection.

The Sun provides energy for many processes that take place at Earth's surface. It causes winds to blow and currents to move across the surface of the ocean. Energy from the Sun also causes water to move in a cycle between the atmosphere and Earth's surface.

CHECK YOUR READING What questions do you have about how energy from the Sun moves through the four parts of the Earth system?

Transfer of Energy

Radiation, conduction, and convection move energy from place to place.

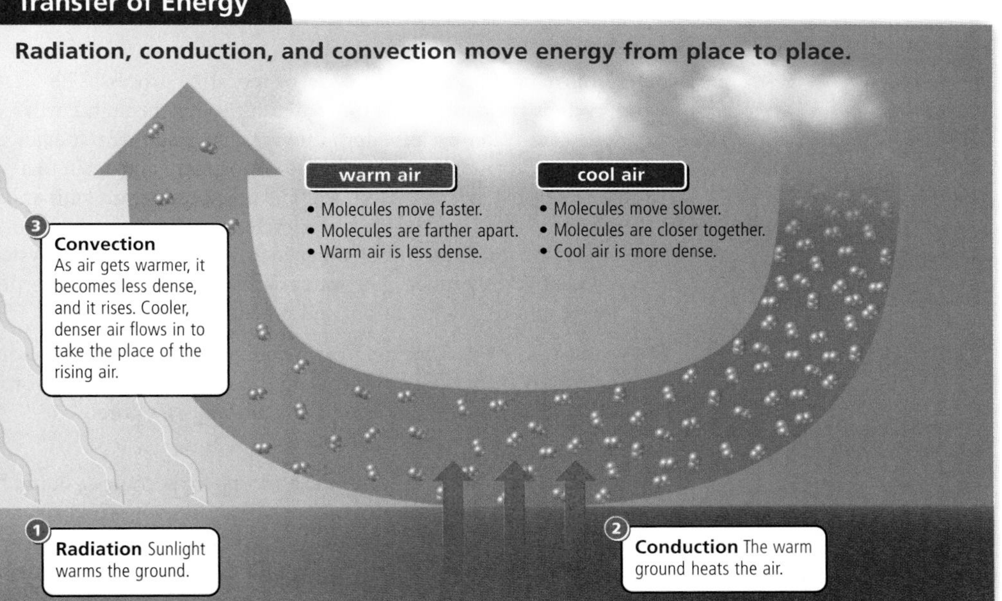

warm air
• Molecules move faster.
• Molecules are farther apart.
• Warm air is less dense.
cool air
• Molecules move slower.
• Molecules are closer together.
• Cool air is more dense.
3 Convection As air gets warmer, it becomes less dense, and it rises. Cooler, denser air flows in to take the place of the rising air.
1 Radiation Sunlight warms the ground.
2 Conduction The warm ground heats the air.

2.3 INSTRUCT

Teach the Standards

Water cycle 6.4.a

In this section: Remind students that the Sun's energy powers phenomena, including the water cycle, that help support plant and animal life on Earth.

- **previously taught:** hydrosphere, pp. 42–43, 45
- **future opportunities:** evaporation and condensation, p. 92; types of precipitation, p. 104

EXPLORE the BIG idea

Revisit: "How Does Heating Affect Air?" on p. 39. Have students explain the reason for what they observed.

Teach Difficult Concepts

Give students an everyday example to help them distinguish between radiation, conduction, and convection. For example, tell them to picture an electric stove with a pot of water on top. The burner of the stove radiates energy. Energy is also transferred by conduction to the bottom of the pot and to the water. The water begins to move, transferring energy by convection. The following demonstration will help reinforce these processes.

Teach from Visuals

To help students interpret the "Transfer of Energy" visual, ask:

- What does the illustration indicate about molecules in cool air? *They are closer together.*
- What does the illustration indicate about molecules in warm air? *They are farther apart.*
- Why does the warmer air rise? *it is less dense than cooler air*

Ongoing Assessment

Student questions will vary.

DIFFERENTIATE INSTRUCTION

More Reading Support

A What are the three ways that heat energy can be transferred? *radiation, conduction, and convection*

English Learners English learners may need help understanding the academic vocabulary in this section, including the word *transferred. Transfer* can be used as a noun or a verb. *Transferred* is a verb. Have students write the definition of *transferred* in their notebooks, along with a sample sentence.

Advanced To reinforce section 2.3 learning goals, use the following full-period investigation:

Additional INVESTIGATION, Observing Convection, A, B, & C, pp. 120–128, 274–275 (Advanced students should complete levels B and C.)

Teach from Visuals

To help students interpret the visual showing the water cycle, ask:

- What three processes are shown to occur during the water cycle? *evaporation, condensation, precipitation*
- What happens to water that falls to the ground from clouds? *It flows along the ground; collects in puddles, ponds, lakes, rivers, and oceans; and sinks into the ground.*

Address Misconceptions

IDENTIFY Ask: What are clouds composed of? If students say "water vapor," they may hold the misconception that clouds are made up of gases.

CORRECT Have students breathe onto the palms of their hands. Explain that their breath contains water vapor. Breathe onto a mirror. Tell students that the droplets on the mirror are caused by the condensation of the water vapor in your breath. Explain that water droplets in clouds are like the droplets on the mirror. Explain that when a cloud's temperature is below freezing, the water droplets become ice crystals.

REASSESS Ask: Is it true that clouds are made up of gases? Explain your answer. *No, clouds consist of water droplets or, when below freezing, ice crystals.*

Technology Resources

Visit **ClassZone.com** for background on common student misconceptions.

MISCONCEPTION DATABASE

The Water Cycle

Water on Earth moves in a repeating cycle.

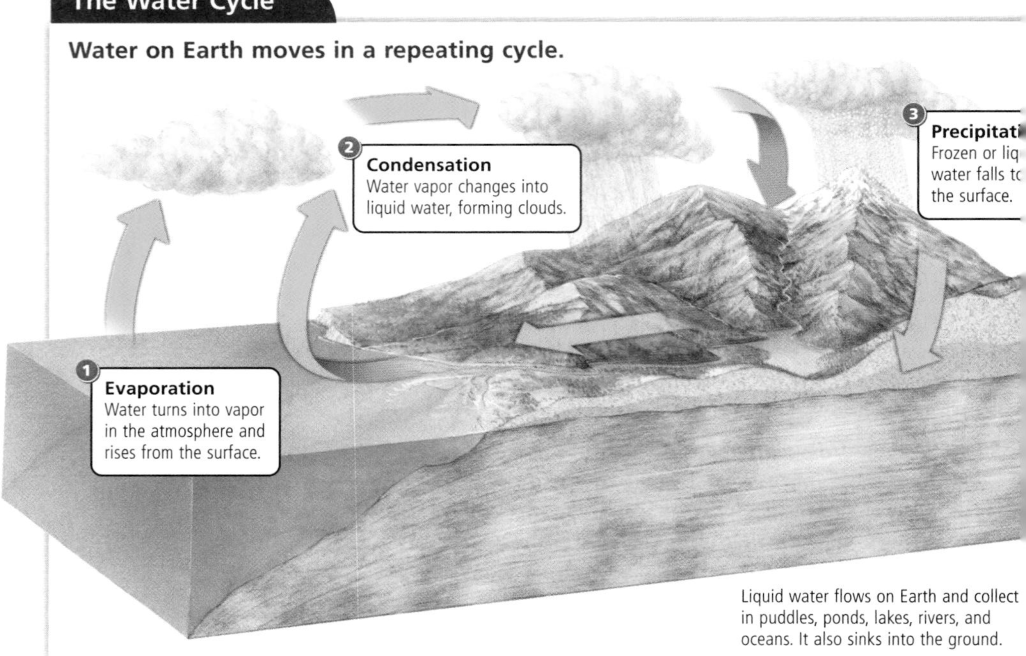

1 Evaporation
Water turns into vapor in the atmosphere and rises from the surface.
2 Condensation
Water vapor changes into liquid water, forming clouds.
3 Precipitati
Frozen or liq
water falls t
the surface.
Liquid water flows on Earth and collect
in puddles, ponds, lakes, rivers, and
oceans. It also sinks into the ground.

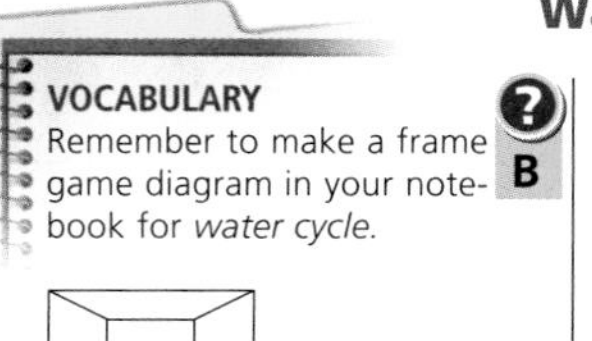
VOCABULARY
Remember to make a frame game diagram in your notebook for *water cycle.*

Water Cycle

B Water's movement on Earth is a cycle, or repeating process. The **water cycle** is the continuous movement of water through Earth's systems. In the water cycle, water is always changing form. It change from a liquid on land to a vapor in the atmosphere and again to a liquid or solid that falls to the surface. The flow of water on land and underground is also part of the water cycle. As water moves in the water cycle, the total amount of water in any part of the Earth syster does not change very much. The water cycle includes three major prc esses: evaporation, condensation, and precipitation.

C ❶ **Evaporation** Water changes from a liquid to vapor by evaporation. Heat energy from the Sun warms up the surface of the ocean or another body of water. Some of the liquid water evaporates. It becomes water vapor, an invisible gas.

❷ **Condensation** Water vapor in the atmosphere becomes a liquid b condensation. Condensation takes place as air cools. Cold air can hold less water vapor than warm air. As a result, some of the vapor condenses. This means that it turns into droplets of liquid water. These droplets form clouds.

DIFFERENTIATE INSTRUCTION

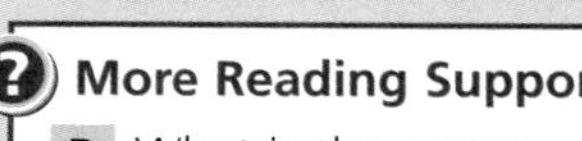
More Reading Support

B What is the water cycle? *the continuous movement of water through Earth's systems*

C What is the opposite of condensation? *evaporation*

Advanced Biosphere 2 is a totally enclosed environment that mimics Earth's environment. Invite students to research the way the water cycle in Biosphere 2 works. Have them create sketches or charts to compare the water cycle in Biosphere 2 with Earth's water cycle.

3 Precipitation Water or ice that falls from clouds is precipitation. Inside a cloud, water droplets or bits of ice bump together and join to become larger. They finally become heavy enough to fall as precipitation, such as rain or snow. The water from precipitation sinks into the soil or flows into streams and rivers.

Plants also play a role in the water cycle. They pull water up from the ground through their roots. Then they release much of it into the air through their leaves. How does the water move when it is released into the atmosphere? Water moves through the lower atmosphere by convection currents. Warm, moist air rises. When the water vapor in the air cools, it condenses to form clouds. Water falls back to the surface as rain or snow.

Heat energy is absorbed when water evaporates. This energy changes the liquid water to water vapor. When water condenses, heat energy is released. In this way, the water cycle moves both water and heat energy through the atmosphere.

CHECK YOUR READING How does water enter the atmosphere?

This photograph shows Yosemite National Park in winter. How does it show each part of the water cycle in action?

Real World Example

Rain, hail, sleet, snow, freezing rain, and fog are all part of the water cycle.

Ongoing Assessment

Explain how solar energy powers the water cycle.

Ask: How does energy from the Sun power the water cycle? *The Sun causes water to evaporate and become water vapor, which rises into the atmosphere. As air cools, this water vapor forms into water droplets through condensation, which then returns water to Earth as precipitation.*

CHECK YOUR READING *Answer: Energy from the Sun causes water to evaporate and rise into the atmosphere as water vapor.*

DIFFERENTIATE INSTRUCTION

More Reading Support

D How do plants play a role in the water cycle? *They pull water up from the ground through their roots; they release water into the air through their leaves.*

Below Level Read the definitions of *evaporation, condensation,* and *precipitation* aloud to students. Ask them to draw a picture of the water cycle, and have them include arrows to show how water moves. Ask them to label the arrows "evaporation," "condensation,"and "precipitation." Then have them look at the diagram on page 60 and revise their drawings if necessary.

Teach from Visuals

To help students interpret the "Global Surface Currents" visual, ask:

- What color are the arrows for surface currents? *red and blue*
- What color represents warm water currents? *red*
- What temperature is the Gulf Stream current? *warm*

Ongoing Assessment

Demonstrate how heat is transferred over Earth's surface.

Ask: What are some ways in which heat is transferred over Earth's surface? *convection currents, global winds, ocean currents*

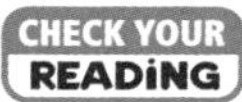
CHECK YOUR READING *Answer: a mass of moving water*

READING VISUALS *Answer: the Gulf Stream current and the North Atlantic current*

RESOURCE CENTER CLASSZONE.COM

Learn more about ocean currents.

CALIFORNIA Focus

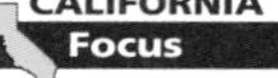

The California Current carries cool water south from the Gulf of Alaska. Because the current flows close to the coastline of northern California, this region has cooler coastal waters than southern California.

Winds and Ocean Currents

E

Weather is the condition of the atmosphere at a certain time and place. On a TV news program, forecasters predict what the weather will be like over the next few days. Wind direction and wind speed are important in forecasting the weather. Wind is air that is moving parallel to the ground. Global winds blow steadily from a certain direction over large distances. Earth's major wind patterns carry heat energy through the atmosphere by convection. You will read more about winds in Chapter 3.

F

Global winds circulate heat around Earth in the atmosphere. Heat energy also flows around Earth in the ocean. An **ocean current** is a mass of moving water. Many different currents move water through the oceans. As ocean currents move water, they carry heat around the globe. Convection is the main process by which currents transfer heat around the planet.

CHECK YOUR READING What is an ocean current?

Global Surface Currents

Surface currents are caused by winds. Currents move warm water away from the equator and cool water away from the poles.

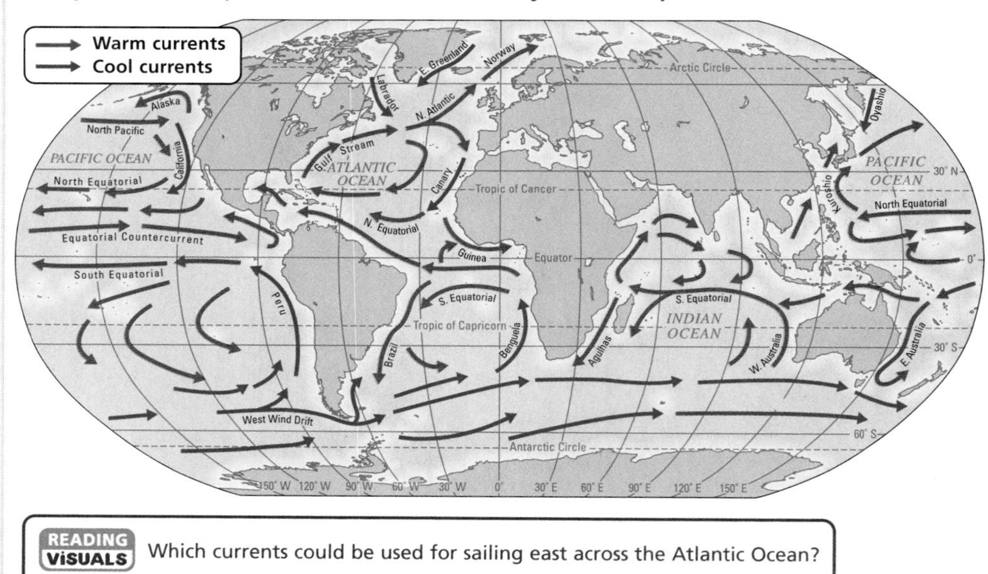

READING VISUALS Which currents could be used for sailing east across the Atlantic Ocean?

DIFFERENTIATE INSTRUCTION

More Reading Support

E What is weather? *the condition of the atmosphere at a certain time and place*

F What do ocean currents distribute around the globe? *heat energy*

Inclusion Some students may have difficulty reading and analyzing the Global Surface Currents map. To help students better understand the patterns and locations of ocean currents across the globe, provide them with a copy of a world map. Using red markers to represent warm currents and blue markers to represent cool currents, have students try to duplicate the location and direction of the ocean currents illustrated on the map on page 62.

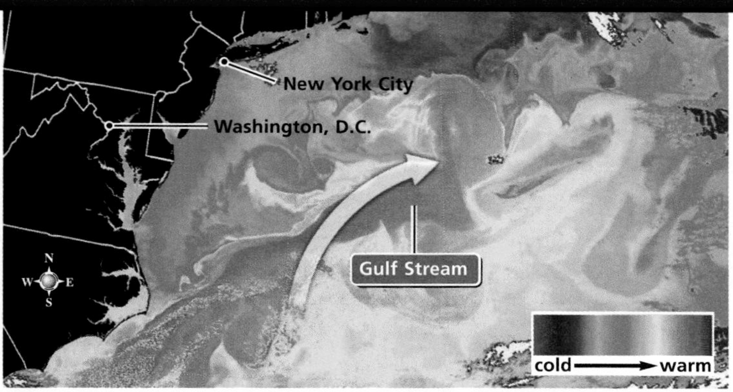

This satellite image uses false colors to show the Gulf Stream, a surface current that flows along the eastern coast of the United States. The colors show the temperature of the water.

The uneven heating of Earth's surface causes winds to blow. As winds blow over the ocean surface, they cause surface currents to flow. The currents usually reach only about 100 to 200 meters (300–500 ft) down into the ocean, but they cover large areas. The map on page 62 shows major ocean currents.

Earth's rotation causes surface currents to flow into giant clockwise patterns in the Northern Hemisphere. In the Southern Hemisphere, currents flow counterclockwise. The shapes of the continents also affect the paths of surface currents.

Surface currents carry warm water away from the equator and cool water away from the poles. In this way, surface currents help make temperatures on Earth more even. Global winds and ocean currents keep areas near the equator from getting hotter and hotter. They also spread some of the energy from the Sun around the planet.

The ocean and the atmosphere also act together to affect weather. Wind causes surface water to move. At the same time, the water changes the temperature of the air above it. Areas that are affected by warm ocean currents have warmer climates. Look at the Gulf Stream, shown above. It carries warm water toward northern Europe. The climate in that area is milder because of the Gulf Stream.

What causes ocean surface currents?

Greenhouse Effect

A coat helps keep you warm by slowing the movement of heat away from your body. In a similar way, certain gases in the atmosphere slow the movement of heat energy away from Earth's surface. This process is known as the **greenhouse effect.** The gases absorb and give off infrared radiation. This process slows the loss of energy from the atmosphere to outer space. You cannot see infrared radiation, but you can feel it as heat. The greenhouse effect got its name because both a greenhouse and Earth's atmosphere act to trap heat, even though they do it in different ways.

History of Science

As Earth rotates, the ocean surface currents curl due to the Coriolis effect. This same effect is seen in global wind patterns, which also curve as Earth spins beneath them. The Coriolis effect is named after French mathematician and scientist Gaspard-Gustave de Coriolis (1792–1843), who discussed the physics behind this phenomenon in his 1835 paper "On the Equations of Relative Motion of System of Bodies." It wasn't until the beginning of the 20th century, however, that the term *Coriolis force* was coined to describe this effect. Oddly enough, Coriolis' writings did not deal with Earth's rotation, but simply the transfer of energy in rotating systems.

Ongoing Assessment

Answer: wind

DIFFERENTIATE INSTRUCTION

More Reading Support

G What is the greenhouse effect? *a process by which certain gases in Earth's atmosphere slow the movement of heat energy away from Earth's surface*

Teach from Visuals

To help students interpret the visual of the greenhouse effect, ask:

- Which image of the visual illustrates Earth as it really is? *the second image*
- What are the greenhouse gases doing in the second image of the visual? *The greenhouse gases are absorbing some infrared radiation and releasing some. Earth's surface is warmer.*
- What would happen if Earth's atmosphere did not contain greenhouse gases, as illustrated in the first image? *Infrared radiation reradiated from Earth's surface would be lost into outer space. The Earth's temperature would drop and the planet would become too cold to support most forms of life.*

Integrate the Sciences

Because ultraviolet radiation, visible light, and infrared radiation have both electric and magnetic properties, they are known as electromagnetic radiation. These and other forms of energy are part of the electromagnetic spectrum, which you learned about in Chapter 1. Visible light is seen as ranges of red, orange, yellow, green, blue, and violet light, with red light having the least energy per wave. The full electromagnetic spectrum, in order of increasing energy per wave, includes radio waves, microwaves, infrared radiation, visible light (red through violet), ultraviolet radiation, x-rays, and gamma rays.

Ongoing Assessment

CHECK YOUR READING *Greenhouse gases absorb some radiation given off by Earth's surface and keeps Earth's surface temperature around 15°C (59°F).*

The Greenhouse Effect

Greenhouse gas molecules absorb and emit infrared radiation.

Atmosphere Without Greenhouse Gases

Radiation from Earth's surface is lost directly to space.
Average Temperature: –18°C

Atmosphere with Greenhouse Gases

Radiation from the surface is lost more slowly. Earth's surface is warmer.
Average Temperature: 15°C

sunlight **infrared radiation**

The atmosphere is much thinner than shown here.

Greenhouse gases include carbon dioxide, methane, and water vapor. Greenhouse gases do not form a single layer. They are mixed together with nitrogen, oxygen, and other gases in the air.

See how the greenhouse effect works.

Radiation from the Sun, including visible light, warms Earth's surface. The surface absorbs some energy. The surface also releases some of the energy back into the atmosphere as infrared radiation. If the atmosphere had no greenhouse gases, the infrared radiation would be lost to outer space. Earth's average surface temperature would be only about –18°C (0°F). Water would freeze, and it would be too cold for most life forms on Earth to survive.

Greenhouse gases absorb some of the infrared radiation given off by Earth's surface. The gases then give off this energy as infrared radiation. Some of the energy is absorbed again by the surface, while some of the energy goes out into space. The greenhouse effect keeps Earth's average surface temperature around 15°C (59°F). Human activities add more greenhouse gases to the atmosphere. Earth is getting warmer. Many people are concerned that these extra gases are adding to this warmth. Even a small increase in average temperature could affect climates around the planet.

CHECK YOUR READING How do greenhouse gases affect Earth's atmosphere?

DIFFERENTIATE INSTRUCTION

More Reading Support

H What are some examples of greenhouse gases? *carbon dioxide, methane, water vapor*

I What is Earth's average surface temperature? *15°C (59°F)*

Advanced Have students briefly research the ozone layer. Th have students work together to make a large data table displayin the differences between the ozone layer and the greenhouse effect. The table should have two rows labeled "the ozone layer" and "greenhouse effect" and columns for gases involved, radiation involved, and layer of the atmosphere involved.

R Challenge and Extension, p. 101

Have students who are interested in learning about how sunscre blocks harmful radiation read the following article.

R Challenge Reading, pp. 104–105

Solar energy drives weather and climate.

Weather conditions can change daily or even hourly. But the climate of an area changes over much longer periods. **Climate** describes the weather conditions in a place over a long time. Scientists often focus on patterns of precipitation and temperature when they classify climates. Four factors affect these patterns: latitude, distance from large bodies of water, ocean currents, and land elevation. You read about each of these factors earlier in this chapter.

Latitude Latitude affects temperature because solar radiation heats Earth's surface unevenly. It is usually warmer closer to the equator and cooler toward the poles.

Distance from Water Land heats up and cools off faster than water. The ocean and large lakes slow down heating and cooling of the air. For this reason, areas along coasts usually have milder temperatures than areas far inland. Large bodies of water also affect precipitation.

Ocean Currents Ocean currents carry energy from one part of the ocean to another. In general, warm-water currents carry warmth toward the poles. Warm-water currents help keep areas along coasts warm. Cold-water currents cool these areas. Moving heat from warm areas to cooler areas helps even out extremes in Earth's surface temperatures.

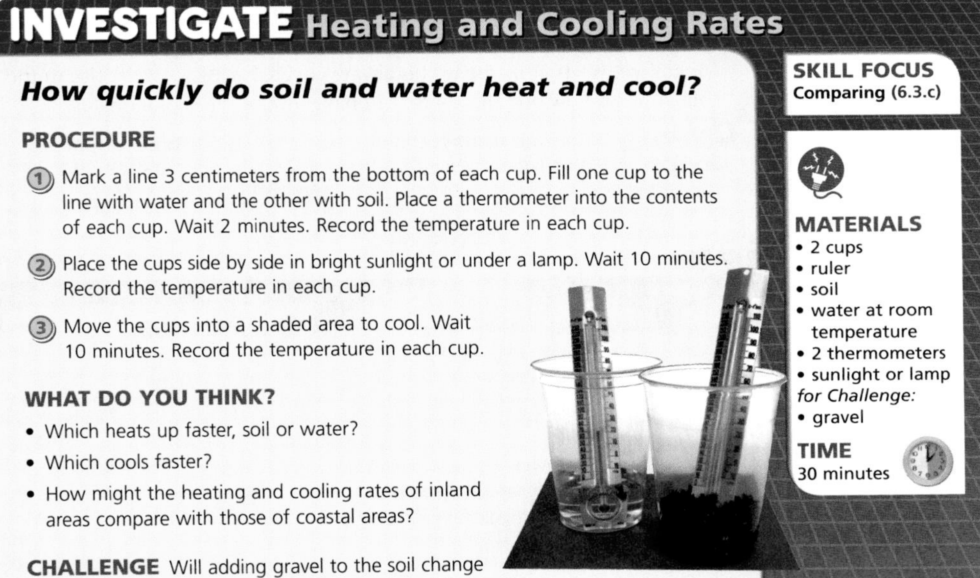

INVESTIGATE Heating and Cooling Rates

How quickly do soil and water heat and cool?

SKILL FOCUS
Comparing (6.3.c)

PROCEDURE

1. Mark a line 3 centimeters from the bottom of each cup. Fill one cup to the line with water and the other with soil. Place a thermometer into the contents of each cup. Wait 2 minutes. Record the temperature in each cup.
2. Place the cups side by side in bright sunlight or under a lamp. Wait 10 minutes. Record the temperature in each cup.
3. Move the cups into a shaded area to cool. Wait 10 minutes. Record the temperature in each cup.

WHAT DO YOU THINK?

- Which heats up faster, soil or water?
- Which cools faster?
- How might the heating and cooling rates of inland areas compare with those of coastal areas?

CHALLENGE Will adding gravel to the soil change your results? Repeat the activity to test your prediction.

MATERIALS
- 2 cups
- ruler
- soil
- water at room temperature
- 2 thermometers
- sunlight or lamp

for Challenge:
- gravel

TIME
30 minutes

EXPLORE the BIG idea

Revisit "How Fast Does It Chill?" on p. 39. Have students explain the reason for what they observed.

INVESTIGATE Heating and Cooling Rates

PURPOSE To compare the heating and cooling rates of soil and water

TIPS *25 min.* Suggest the following:

- To obtain water at room temperature, mix cold and hot water from the tap, testing temperature continually with your fingers.
- If you are using a lamp, be careful not to let water touch the light bulb.

WHAT DO YOU THINK? *Soil heats up faster. Soil cools faster. Inland areas heat up and cool faster than coastal areas because the ocean influences the temperatures of coastal areas.*

CHALLENGE *Compared to the cup with just soil, the cup with soil and gravel took longer to heat up and longer to cool down.*

 Datasheet, Heating and Cooling Rates, p. 102

Technology Resources

Customize this student lab as needed. Print rubrics to assess student lab reports.

 **Lab Generator CD-ROM**

Teaching with Technology

If students have a computer, have them use a computer graphing program to construct a line graph of their data. If students have probeware, have them use the temperature probe to record a second set of data.

DIFFERENTIATE INSTRUCTION

More Reading Support

J What is climate? *the characteristic weather conditions in a place over a long period of time*

Below Level Remind students that climate and weather are complex topics, and many factors must be considered. Point out that they have already learned that latitude affects climate, and on page 66, they will learn that altitude affects it also. Prompt students to make a chart entitled "Factors that Affect Climate." Have them list and describe each factor as they read about it.

Ongoing Assessment

Explain how solar energy affects weather and climate.

Ask: In what ways does energy from the Sun affect climate? *Sample answer: Solar radiation heats Earth's surface unevenly, causing areas closer to the equator to have a warmer climate, while areas closer to the North Pole or South Pole generally have colder climates.*

Answer: latitude, distance from large bodies of water, ocean currents, land elevation

Reinforce the BIG idea

Have students relate the section to the Big Idea.

 Reinforcing Key Concepts, p. 103

2.3 ASSESS & RETEACH

Assess

 Section 2.3 Quiz, p. 26

Reteach

Have students make an outline of Section 2.3 summarizing the main ideas and supporting details. Explain to them that the section's main ideas are blue heads—the first one being "Little of Earth's internal heat reaches the surface." Make sure students support the three main ideas with supporting details. Tell students to look at topic sentences of paragraphs and at titles of visuals to help identify supporting details, which may include vocabulary terms and other specific information.

Technology Resources

Visit **ClassZone.com** for student practice with chapter concepts.

 CONTENT REVIEW

 CONTENT REVIEW CD-ROM

Mountain Climates

Because altitude changes sharply on a mountain, different climates can exist within a small area.

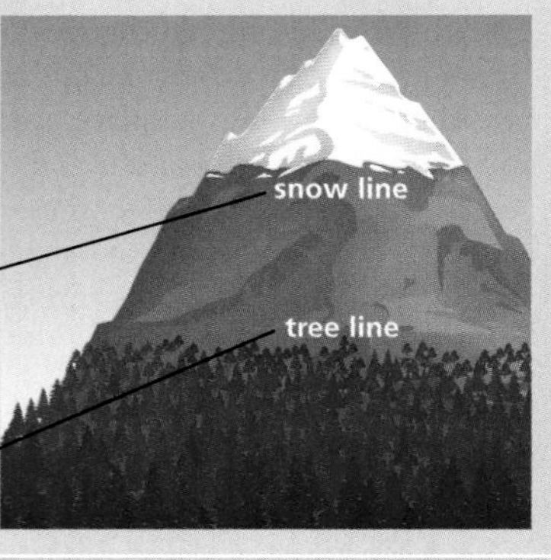

snow line
tree line
Even at the equator, a mountain peak can be covered with snow and ice.
Temperatures are too cold above this elevation for trees to grow.

Land Elevation Recall that elevation is the height of land above sea level. Elevation affects temperature. If you rode a cable car up a mountain, the temperature would decrease by about 6.5°C (11.7°F) for every kilometer you rose in elevation. Why does it get colder as you move higher up? The lowest layer of the atmosphere is warmed mainly by conduction from Earth's surface and by convection currents. As convection lifts the warmed air to higher altitudes, the air cools.

The effect of elevation on temperature can cause an area near the equator to be cold. One example is Mount Stanley, a tall mountain near the border of Uganda and the Democratic Republic of the Congo in Africa. Mount Stanley lies a short distance from the equator. However, it has ice sheets at its top and is always covered with snow. Notice in the illustration how one mountain can have several types of climates.

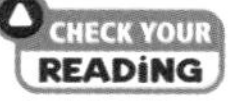 What four factors influence temperature and precipitation patterns?

2.3 Review

KEY CONCEPTS

1. Describe the three processes that transfer energy over Earth's surface. **(6.3)**
2. Explain the three processes that make up the water cycle. **(6.4.a)**
3. How do ocean currents carry heat around the globe? **(6.4.d)**

CRITICAL THINKING

4. **Predict** How could a region's climate change if a cold-water ocean current stopped flowing past it?
5. **Infer** What would happen to Earth's climates if all ocean currents and global winds stopped?

CHALLENGE

6. **Draw Conclusions** What effect would an increase in greenhouse gases in the atmosphere have on Earth's overall temperature?

ANSWERS

1. Sunlight warms Earth's surface through radiation; energy is transferred from the surface to air molecules through conduction; warm air carries energy upward by convection.

2. Water turns into vapor through evaporation; water vapor in the atmosphere becomes liquid through condensation; water falls from clouds by precipitation.

3. by moving warm water away from the equator

4. It would probably become warmer.

5. If all ocean currents and global winds stopped, heat would no longer be distributed throughout the Earth system, causing some climates to become hotter and others colder.

6. If the greenhouse gases in Earth's atmosphere increased, global temperatures would rise.

SKILL: INTERPRETING LINE GRAPHS

Carbon Dioxide Levels

Since the 1950s, carbon dioxide levels have been measured in air samples collected at the Mauna Loa Observatory in Hawaii. Carbon dioxide is an important greenhouse gas. The graphs below show the carbon dioxide data plotted in two different ways. In the graph on the left, the scale showing carbon dioxide levels starts at 0 parts per million (ppm) and goes up to 400 ppm. The graph on the right offers a close-up view of the same data. The vertical scale on the right-hand graph is broken to focus on the values from 310 ppm to 380 ppm.

MATH TUTORIAL
CLASSZONE.COM
Click on Math Tutorial for more help with interpreting line graphs.

Math 6.MS.1.1

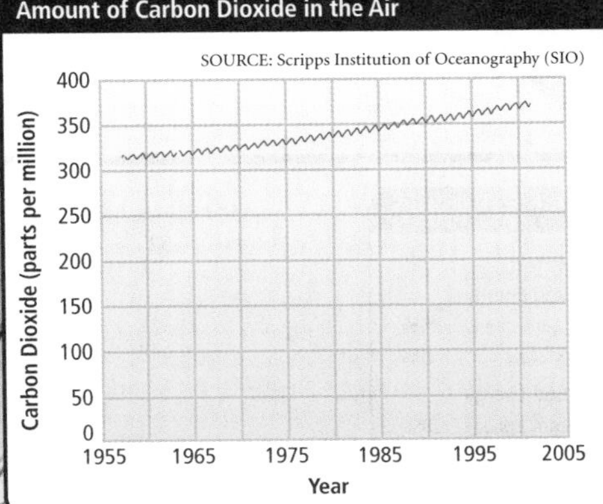

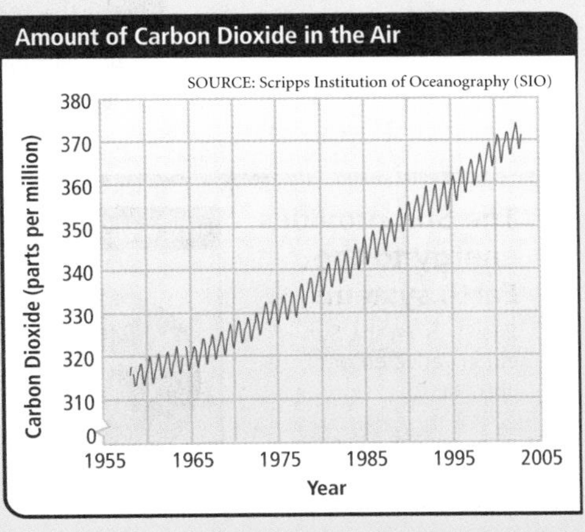

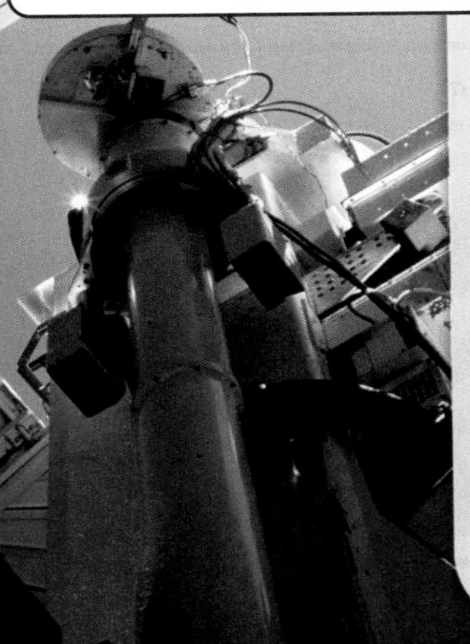

Use the graphs to answer the following questions.

1. What was the carbon dioxide level at the beginning of 1995?
2. The data show a 17 percent increase in the carbon dioxide level in the air from 1958 through 2001. Which graph shows this increase more clearly? Why?
3. In both graphs, the line that shows carbon dioxide levels is jagged, because carbon dioxide levels rise and fall regularly as the seasons change. In some years, the seasonal rise and fall is greater than in other years. Which graph emphasizes these variations more? Why?

CHALLENGE The carbon dioxide level in the air in the Northern Hemisphere starts falling in May or June each year and continues to fall through October. What do you think causes this change to occur? Hint: Consider the relationship between plants and carbon dioxide.

ANSWERS

1. 360 parts per million

2. left graph; The unbroken scale on the y-axis starts at 0.

3. right graph; It has a shorter y-axis scale, which causes the line to rise and fall more steeply with the seasons each year.

CHALLENGE *In the Northern Hemisphere, the CO_2 level falls in springtime, when plants that were dormant during the winter begin photosynthesis again, drawing CO_2 from the atmosphere.*

MATH IN SCIENCE
Math Skills Practice for Science

Set Learning Goal
To interpret data of carbon dioxide levels plotted on a line graph

Math Standard

6.MR.2.4 Use a variety of methods, such as words, numbers, symbols, charts, graphs, tables, diagrams, and models, to explain mathematical reasoning.

Present the Science
Carbon dioxide (CO_2) is one of a number of substances—mostly gases—in the atmosphere. It is measured in parts per million (ppm).

Develop Computation Skills
Make sure students understand that plotting data on a line graph requires two axes, the *x*-axis (horizontal, bottom) and the *y*-axis (vertical, left side). In these graphs, the data show change over time.

Emphasize that the two graphs present exactly the same data but in different views. The graph on the right truncates the *y*-axis to display only the range of CO_2 concentration that is covered by the data in the given 50-year range. Explain that the breaks in the line at several points in the 1950s and 1960s are due to the fact that data is unavailable for several months during these periods.

Close
Ask: How would a line graph showing global warming and the line graphs on this page be similar? *The data plotted would show a line rising from left to right.*

- Math Support, p. 109
- Math Practice, p. 110

Technology Resources

Students can visit **ClassZone.com** for practice in adding measurements.

MATH TUTORIAL

BACK TO

the BIG idea

How is the transfer of the Sun's energy apparent in all four parts of Earth's system? *Earth's geosphere is heated by radiation. Earth's atmosphere receives heat energy from Earth's surface by conduction, and then heat energy is carried through the atmosphere by convection. Some gases in the atmosphere absorb solar radiation directly. Plants, which are part of Earth's biosphere, use the Sun's energy for photosynthesis. The Sun's energy causes evaporation in Earth's hydrosphere, and water vapor eventually condenses which leads to condensation in Earth's atmosphere. Precipitation returns water to Earth's geosphere.*

KEY CONCEPTS SUMMARY

SECTION 2.1

Ask: Give two examples that illustrate how different parts of the Earth system work together. *water evaporates from a lake (hydrosphere and atmosphere); an animal decomposes and returns nutrients to the soil (biosphere and geosphere)*

SECTION 2.2

Ask: What parts of the Earth system tend to reflect the Sun's energy? What parts tend to absorb it? *The atmosphere reflects a bit more of the Sun's energy than it absorbs; Earth's surface (geosphere and hydrosphere) absorbs much more than it reflects.*

SECTION 2.3

Ask: What type of heat transfer occurs when air is heated from below? *convection*

Ask: What happens when the level of greenhouse gases increases? *Earth's temperature rises.*

Review Concepts

- Big Idea Flow Chart, p. T9
- Chapter Outline, pp. T15–T16

2 Chapter Review

the BIG idea

The Sun is the major source of energy for Earth's atmosphere and surface.

KEY CONCEPTS SUMMARY

The Earth system has four major parts.

The atmosphere, hydrosphere, biosphere, and geosphere work together to form one large Earth system.

VOCABULARY
system p. 41
cycle p. 44

The Sun provides energy to the Earth system.

Energy from the Sun is either reflected or absorbed.

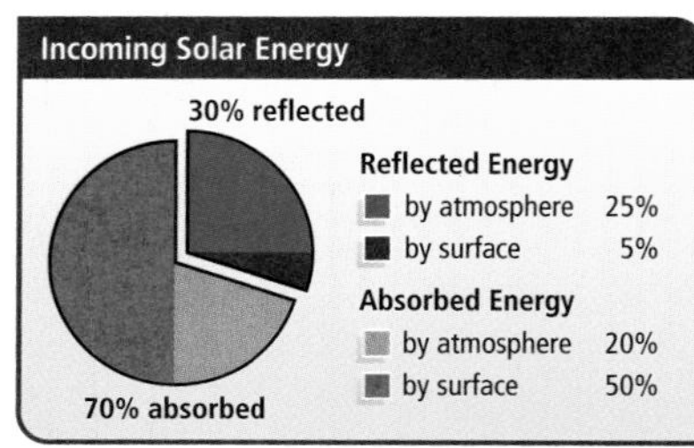

VOCABULARY
axis p. 52

Energy is transferred within the Earth system.

Radiation, conduction, and convection move energy from place to place.

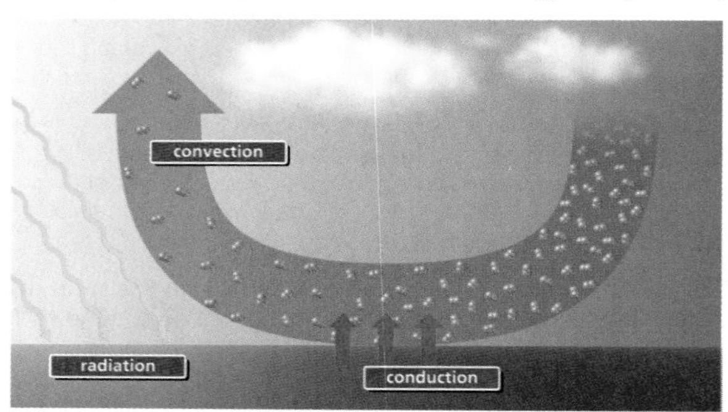

VOCABULARY
water cycle p. 60
weather p. 62
ocean current p. 62
greenhouse effect p. 63
climate p. 65

68 Unit 1: **The Earth System**

Technology Resources

Have students visit **ClassZone.com** or use the CD-ROM for a cumulative review of concepts.

CONTENT REVIEW

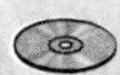

CONTENT REVIEW CD-ROM

Engage students in a whole-class interactive review of Key Concepts. Edit content as you wish.

POWER PRESENTATIONS

Reviewing Vocabulary

Draw a word triangle for each of the vocabulary terms listed below. Define the term, use it in a sentence, and draw a picture to help you remember the term. A sample is shown below.

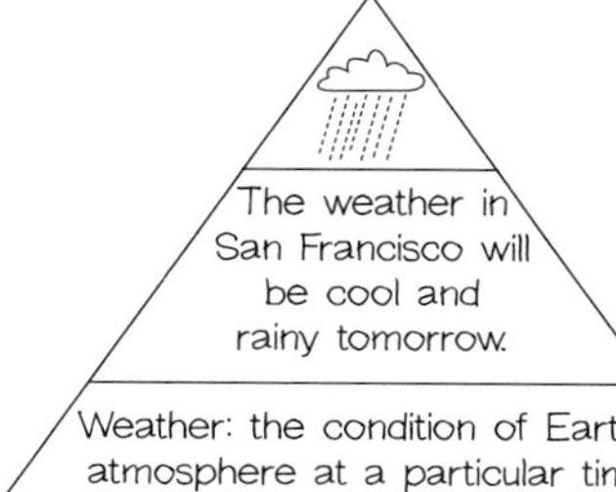

The weather in San Francisco will be cool and rainy tomorrow.
Weather: the condition of Earth's atmosphere at a particular time and place

1. system
2. cycle
3. axis
4. water cycle
5. greenhouse effect

Reviewing Key Concepts

Multiple Choice *Choose the letter of the best answer.*

6. Which process forms clouds?
   - **a.** evaporation
   - **b.** precipitation
   - **c.** condensation
   - **d.** runoff
7. Continents, islands, mountains, and the ocean floor form part of the
   - **a.** biosphere
   - **b.** atmosphere
   - **c.** hydrosphere
   - **d.** geosphere
8. Compared with weather patterns, climate patterns are more
   - **a.** long-term
   - **b.** severe
   - **c.** short-term
   - **d.** local
9. Most of the heat energy at Earth's surface comes from (6.4.a)
   - **a.** Earth's interior
   - **b.** volcanic eruptions
   - **c.** the Sun
   - **d.** oil and gas
10. What area of Earth's surface receives more solar energy? (6.3.d)
    - **a.** North Pole
    - **b.** South Pole
    - **c.** Northern Hemisphere
    - **d.** equator
11. What causes different amounts of solar energy to strike Earth's surface at different times of the year? (6.3.d)
    - **a.** the tilt of Earth's axis
    - **b.** the distance between the Sun and Earth
    - **c.** the revolution of the Sun around Earth
    - **d.** the curve of Earth's surface
12. What is the main process by which ocean currents transfer heat energy around Earth? (6.4.d)
    - **a.** conduction
    - **b.** convection
    - **c.** precipitation
    - **d.** radiation
13. What keeps Earth's surface warm?
    - **a.** conduction
    - **b.** the water cycle
    - **c.** convection
    - **d.** the greenhouse effect

Short Answer *Write a short answer to each question.*

14. Give an example of a feature from each of the four parts of the Earth system.
15. Describe how the northern and southern hemispheres are tilted with respect to the Sun in December. What season is it in each hemisphere?
16. What three processes transfer heat over Earth's surface? (6.3)
17. Describe how water moves through the atmosphere in the water cycle. (6.4.a)

ASSESSMENT RESOURCES

ASSESSMENT BOOK
- Chapter Test A, pp. 27–30
- Chapter Test B, pp. 31–34
- Chapter Test C, pp. 35–38
- Alternative Assessment, pp. 39–40

STANDARDS REVIEW AND PRACTICE, pp. 3–4, 13–14, 21–24, 27–38, 57–58, 65–66

Technology Resources

Edit test items and answer choices.

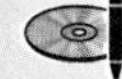

Test Generator CD-ROM

Visit **ClassZone.com** to extend test practice.

Test Practice

Reviewing Vocabulary

Check drawings for accuracy.

1. *organized group of parts that work together to form a whole; There are four parts to the Earth system: the atmosphere, the biosphere, the hydrosphere, and the geosphere.*
2. *continually repeating process; Spring, summer, fall, and winter are the four periods in Earth's seasonal cycle.*
3. *imaginary line running through the center of a planet; Earth's axis is tilted at an angle of about 23 degrees.*
4. *continuous movement of water through Earth's systems; The water cycle includes three major processes: evaporation, condensation, and precipitation.*
5. *process by which certain gases in Earth's atmosphere slow the movement of energy away from Earth's surface; Without the greenhouse effect, it would be too cold on Earth for most life forms to survive.*

Reviewing Key Concepts

6. c	*9. c*	*12. b*
7. d	*10. d*	*13. d*
8. a	*11. a*	

14. *Sample answers: atmosphere: gases; hydrosphere: Pacific Ocean; biosphere: trees; geosphere: mountains*
15. *In December, the Northern Hemisphere is tilted away from the Sun and the Southern Hemisphere is tilted toward the Sun; this causes it to be winter in the Northern Hemisphere and summer in the Southern Hemisphere.*
16. *The three processes that transfer heat over Earth's surface are radiation, conduction, and convection.*
17. *Heat from the Sun causes liquid water to evaporate, becoming invisible water vapor. As air cools, this water vapor condenses into water droplets, forming visible clouds. When the droplets are heavy enough, they fall back to the surface as precipitation, such as rain or snow.*

Thinking Critically

18. the water cycle
19. precipitation; the arrow pointing from the cloud down to Earth
20. evaporation; absorbs heat energy
21. Plants pull up water from the ground and release much of it into the air through their leaves.
22. The water cycle provides a renewable source of fresh water.
23. Radiation from the Sun provides the energy that plants and animals need to live.
24. Because of the high elevation, the climate would be cold.
25. Answers will vary.
26. biosphere; atmosphere; hydrosphere; geosphere; atmosphere
27. Earth would be too cold to support life.
28. a dark-colored area of bare soil; Dark-colored objects absorb sunlight.
29. global winds, ocean currents, and movement of water through the water cycle
30. Fewer greenhouse gases would cause more of the Sun's energy to be lost to space.
31. Temperatures decrease as you move away from the equator.
32. Answers will vary.

the BIG idea

33. Energy from the Sun causes evaporation. Water vapor in the air condenses into water droplets. Droplets that are heavy enough fall as precipitation.
34. hydrosphere: ocean, atmosphere: sky, geosphere: rocks, biosphere: person; Solar energy warms the rocks, which transfer heat energy to the air, wind causes ocean waves, and the person's eyes detect visible light.

UNIT PROJECTS

Collect schedules, materials lists, and questions. Be sure dates and materials are obtainable, and questions are focused.

 Unit Projects, pp. 5–10

Thinking Critically

Use the diagram to answer the next five questions.

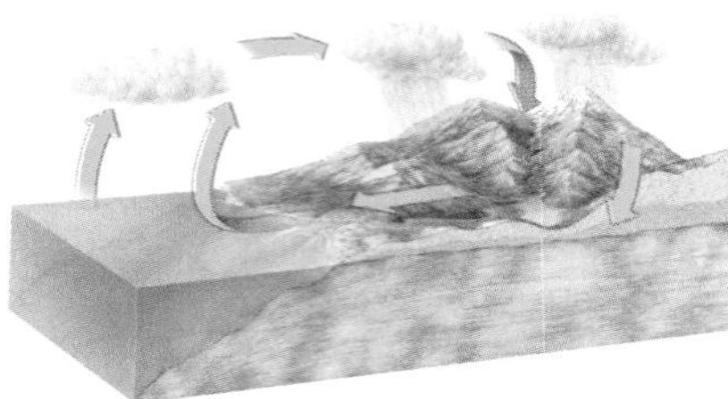

18. **CLASSIFY** What series of processes is shown in the diagram above? (6.4.a)
19. **OBSERVE** What process results in rain and snow falling on Earth's surface? Which arrow in the diagram represents this process? (6.4.a)
20. **INFER** What process results in water vapor becoming part of the atmosphere? Does this process absorb or release heat energy? (6.4.a)
21. **DRAW CONCLUSIONS** How are plants involved in this cycle? (6.4.a)
22. **EXPLAIN** Explain why this cycle is important to humans, plants, and animals. (6.4.a)

23. **APPLY** Why is the transfer of energy by radiation important to life on Earth? (6.4.b)
24. **PREDICT** What would you expect the climate at the top of a tall mountain located at the equator to be like?
25. **SYNTHESIZE** Give an example of how the four parts of the Earth system interact.
26. **CLASSIFY** Classify the following according to which part of the Earth system each belongs: a horse, a cloud, a glacier, a rock, water vapor.
27. **DRAW CONCLUSIONS** What would happen if all of the solar energy that reached Earth was reflected by the atmosphere? (6.3.d)
28. **ANALYZE** Which would be heated more by the Sun—a white, snow-covered area or a dark-colored area of bare soil? Explain. (6.3.d)
29. **SYNTHESIZE** What features of the Earth system distribute heat around the planet? (6.4.d)
30. **INFER** What would happen if the amounts of carbon dioxide, methane, and water vapor in the atmosphere decreased greatly? Explain.
31. **COMMUNICATE** Describe how temperature patterns change as distance from the equator increases.
32. **EVALUATE** Describe a place that has what you consider to be a perfect climate. Explain how the following factors affect the temperature of that place:
    - latitude
    - elevation
    - distance from large bodies of water
    - ocean currents

the BIG idea

33. **SYNTHESIZE** Explain how energy from the Sun is related to rain and other types of precipitation. (6.4.a)
34. **APPLY** Look again at the photograph on pages 38–39. Give an example from the photograph of each part of the Earth system. Then give an example of how energy affects that part. (6.4.a)

UNIT PROJECTS

If you need to create graphs or other visuals for your project, be sure you have grid paper, poster board, markers, and other supplies.

MONITOR AND RETEACH

If students have trouble applying the concepts in items 18–22, divide the class into three groups: assign the first group evaporation, the second group condensation, and the third group precipitation. Have groups review the text relevant to their topic on pages 60–61 and the diagram on page 60. Then, as a class, ask each group to describe in their own words the process they studied. As students discuss, make a flow diagram on the board.

Students may benefit from summarizing one or more sections of the chapter.

 Summarizing the Chapter, pp. 129–130

Standards-Based Assessment

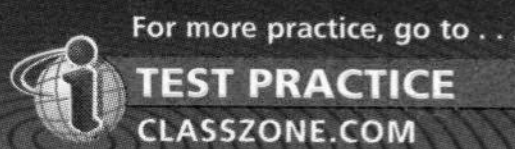

Analyzing a Diagram

This diagram shows the four major parts of the Earth system. Use it to answer the questions below.

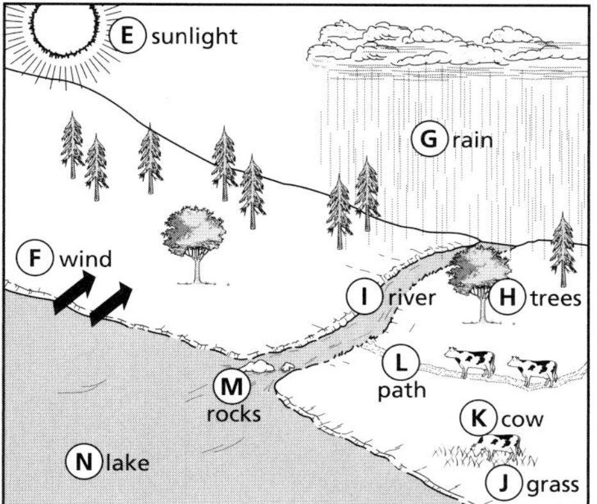

1. Where is the main source of energy for the Earth system?
   a. E **c.** G
   b. F **d.** L
2. Where is the biosphere shaping the geosphere?
   a. E **c.** L
   b. F **d.** M
3. Where is matter moving from one part of the hydrosphere to another?
   a. I to N **c.** J to H
   b. G to H **d.** N to M
4. Which items belong to the geosphere?
   a. F and G **c.** I and N
   b. H and J **d.** M and L
5. Which process is occurring at M, where water is running over the rocks?
   a. The geosphere is shaping the atmosphere.
   b. The atmosphere is shaping the biosphere.
   c. The hydrosphere is shaping the geosphere.
   d. The biosphere is shaping the geosphere.
6. Where is matter moving from the atmosphere to the biosphere?
   a. E to F **c.** G to H
   b. F to M **d.** I to G
7. At K, the cow is eating grass. What kind of movement in the Earth system does this represent?
   a. from the atmosphere to the hydrosphere
   b. from the hydrosphere to the biosphere
   c. between two parts of the geosphere
   d. between two parts of the biosphere
8. Which is an example of how the hydrosphere is supported by the geosphere?
   a. I, because the river receives the rain
   b. H, because the trees are rooted in the ground
   c. M, because the river drains into the lake
   d. N, because the lake is contained by a basin

Extended Response

Answer the two questions below in detail. Include some of the terms shown in the word box. In your answers, underline each term you use.

geosphere	surface	system
atmosphere	hydrosphere	biosphere

9. Rain falls and soaks into the soil. Plants and animals use some of the water. More of the water drains into a river, and then enters the ocean. Describe this process as movements among the major parts of the Earth system.

10. Describe an example of how people can shape the surface of the geosphere.

REFLECTING ON THE CHAPTER

Have students answer the following questions in their **Science Notebook:**

1. Which fact or facts in this chapter surprised you the most?
2. How do the concepts in this chapter relate to your life?
3. As you begin thinking about your Unit Project, what concept or concepts in this chapter have influenced your thinking?

California Content Standards

6.4.a Students know the sun is the major source of energy for phenomena on Earth's surface; it powers winds, ocean currents, and the water cycle.

Analyzing a Diagram

1. a	*3. a*	*5. c*	*7. d*
2. c	*4. d*	*6. c*	*8. d*

Extended Response

9. RUBRIC

4 points for a response that correctly answers the question and uses the following terms accurately:

- geosphere
- atmosphere
- hydrosphere
- biosphere

Sample answer: Rain falls through the atmosphere (air) and soaks into the surface of the geosphere (soil). Some of the water is used by the biosphere (plants and animals). Some of the water drains into other parts of the hydrosphere (bodies of water).

3 points for a response that uses three terms accurately
2 points for a response that uses two terms accurately
1 point for a response that uses one term accurately

10. RUBRIC

4 points for a response that correctly answers the question and uses the following terms accurately:

- geosphere
- surface

Sample answer: People can shape the surface of the geosphere by using a backhoe to remove dirt on a lot to flatten the land. Afterwards, a construction crew can build a house on that spot.

3 points for a response that correctly answers the question and uses the term geosphere accurately
2 points for a response that correctly answers the question but doesn't use either of the terms
1 point for a response that uses the term *geosphere* accurately but doesn't answer the question satisfactorily

FOCUS

Set Learning Goals

Students will

- Observe how scientists created new theories of temperature and heat by building on earlier observations.
- Learn the characteristics of temperature and heat and how they are measured.
- Write a procedure for an experiment to test a specific method of calculating temperature.

California Content Standards

6.3.a Students know energy can be carried from one place to another by heat flow or by waves, including water, light and sound waves, or by moving objects.

6.3.c Students know heat flows in solids by conduction (which involves no flow of matter) and in fluids by conduction and by convection (which involves flow of matter).

6.3.d Students know heat energy is also transferred between objects by radiation (radiation can travel through space).

6.7.d Communicate the steps and results from an investigation in written reports and oral presentations.

INSTRUCT

Point out to students that the top half of the timeline shows major events in the scientific study of temperature and heat and the years in which they occurred. The bottom half addresses the developments in technology based on the scientific discoveries in the top half. The gap between 320 B.C. and A.D. 1600 represents a block of time that has been omitted.

Teach from Visuals

350 B.C. To help students better understand the ancient Greek theory of matter, have them review the diagram of the basic qualities of matter. Ask students to create a table of the four basic substances and their characteristics to illustrate which substances were thought to have which two qualities.

TIMELINES in Science

6.3.a, 6.3.c, 6.3.d, 6.7.d

ABOUT TEMPERATURE AND HEAT

Most likely, the first fires early people saw were caused by lightning. Eventually, people realized that fire provided warmth and light, and they learned how to make it themselves. During the Stone Age 25,000 years ago, people used firewood to cook food as well as to warm and light their shelters. Wood was the first fuel.

This timeline shows a few of the many steps on the path toward understanding temperature and heat. Notice how the observations and ideas of previous thinkers sparked new theories by later scientists. The boxes below the timeline show how technology has led to new insights and to applications related to temperature and heat.

445 B.C.

Four Basic Substances Named

Greek philosopher Empedocles says that everything on Earth is made of some combination of four basic substances: earth, air, fire, and water. Different types of matter have different qualities depending on how they combine these substances.

350 B.C.

Aristotle Expands Theory of Matter

Greek philosopher Aristotle names four basic qualities of matter: dryness, wetness, hotness, and coldness. Each of the four basic substances has two of these qualities.

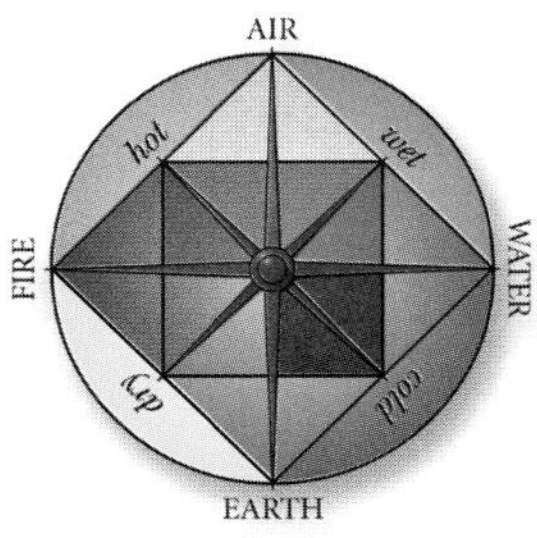

EVENTS

480 B.C. | 440 B.C. | 400 B.C. | 360 B.C. | 320 B.C.

APPLICATIONS AND TECHNOLOGY

People have been trying to understand and control heat since early times.

DIFFERENTIATE INSTRUCTION

Below Level For students who may have difficulty understanding how information is organized on a timeline, point out the dates on the center line. Explain how the dates become more recent when read from left to right. Show them the lines connecting the event boxes to the specific dates on the timeline. Discuss how timelines are a good way to show the order in which events happened.

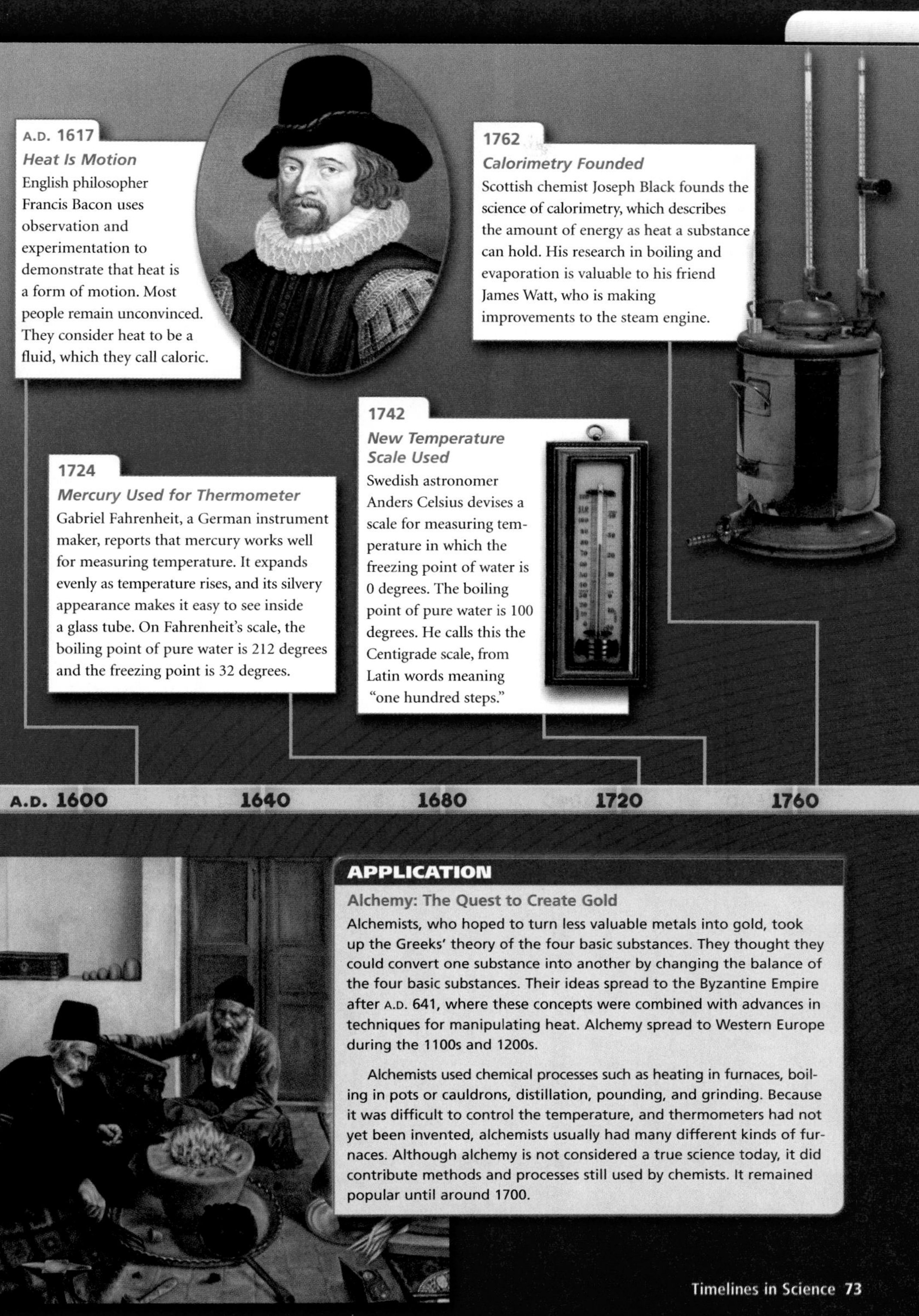

A.D. 1617
Heat Is Motion
English philosopher Francis Bacon uses observation and experimentation to demonstrate that heat is a form of motion. Most people remain unconvinced. They consider heat to be a fluid, which they call caloric.
1762
Calorimetry Founded
Scottish chemist Joseph Black founds the science of calorimetry, which describes the amount of energy as heat a substance can hold. His research in boiling and evaporation is valuable to his friend James Watt, who is making improvements to the steam engine.
1742
New Temperature Scale Used
Swedish astronomer Anders Celsius devises a scale for measuring temperature in which the freezing point of water is 0 degrees. The boiling point of pure water is 100 degrees. He calls this the Centigrade scale, from Latin words meaning "one hundred steps."
1724
Mercury Used for Thermometer
Gabriel Fahrenheit, a German instrument maker, reports that mercury works well for measuring temperature. It expands evenly as temperature rises, and its silvery appearance makes it easy to see inside a glass tube. On Fahrenheit's scale, the boiling point of pure water is 212 degrees and the freezing point is 32 degrees.
A.D. 1600
1640
1680
1720
1760
APPLICATION
Alchemy: The Quest to Create Gold
Alchemists, who hoped to turn less valuable metals into gold, took up the Greeks' theory of the four basic substances. They thought they could convert one substance into another by changing the balance of the four basic substances. Their ideas spread to the Byzantine Empire after A.D. 641, where these concepts were combined with advances in techniques for manipulating heat. Alchemy spread to Western Europe during the 1100s and 1200s.
Alchemists used chemical processes such as heating in furnaces, boiling in pots or cauldrons, distillation, pounding, and grinding. Because it was difficult to control the temperature, and thermometers had not yet been invented, alchemists usually had many different kinds of furnaces. Although alchemy is not considered a true science today, it did contribute methods and processes still used by chemists. It remained popular until around 1700.
Timelines in Science 73

Scientific Process

1724 Gabriel Fahrenheit improved on existing technology to measure temperature through his observations and investigations. He found that mercury was more accurate in measuring temperature than the alcohol thermometers of the time. Fahrenheit then developed the mercury thermometer, which we still use today.

Sharing Results

1762 Chemist Joseph Black experimented with the amount of heat a substance can hold. His results helped James Watt, who was working on improvements to the steam engine. Ask students what research Black was conducting that was critical to Watt's work. *boiling and evaporation*

Mathematics Connection

1742 The Celsius scale is the metric scale for measuring temperature. Most countries use the Celsius scale for everyday temperature measurement. Scientists also use this scale for their experiments. In the United States, the Fahrenheit scale is used to measure temperature. To convert a Celsius temperature to a Fahrenheit temperature, multiply the Celsius temperature by 9/5 and then add 32 to the result. Write the formula °F = 9/5(°C) + 32 on the board. Ask students to convert 35°C to Fahrenheit. *95°F*

Application

ALCHEMY While alchemy is no longer considered a true science, for some time it was a major source of chemical knowledge. Because alchemists experimented with turning metals such as lead into gold, they gained wide knowledge about chemical substances. The alchemist's workshop became the forerunner of the modern chemistry laboratory. Alchemists used tools such as funnels, beakers, and balances. Although alchemists failed to produce gold from other materials, their experimentation was successful in other ways. Ask students what impact alchemy had on science and technology. *Alchemy created many chemical processes and tools that are still used by chemists today.*

DIFFERENTIATE INSTRUCTION

Advanced Have students use the temperature conversion formula shown in the Mathematics Connection on this page to convert Fahrenheit to Celsius. Ask students what the formula for the conversion is. *°C = 5/9 (°F − 32)* Then ask students to convert 98.6°F to Celsius. *37°C*

Scientific Process

Refer students to Francis Bacon's observations on page 73. Despite his experiments, people still believed that heat is fluid rather than a form of motion. Thompson's observations about friction and heat provided evidence that contradicted the leading hypothesis of the time. With evidence against the fluid theory of heat mounting, scientists began to consider seriously other ideas about the nature of heat.

Technology

VACUUM FLASK The reflective silver coating that a vacuum flask, or thermos, uses to keep fluids hot is the same type of technology that NASA used on the Mars rover. To keep heat from escaping out of the rover body and cold air from entering during landing, the outside of the rover's body was painted gold. This coating helps reduce energy that is spread outward from the rover's body. It also prevents the body from emitting heat energy into its cold surroundings.

Integrate the Sciences

One way in which clouds are formed is by convection, that is, when warm air rises. The Sun's heat causes Earth's water (from lakes, oceans, and rivers) to evaporate into the air. When that air is heated, it becomes less dense than the surrounding air. As a result, it rises. As the moist air continues to rise, it expands and becomes cooler. The water vapor in the air condenses and forms clouds.

Application

USING THERMAL ENERGY FROM PONDS The idea of using ponds with a salt gradient to collect and store thermal energy was developed after natural examples of such ponds were discovered. The energy from these ponds can be used for applications such as purifying water and producing electricity. Ask students what some of the benefits of using solar-energy ponds might be. ***provides clean, cost-effective electricity***

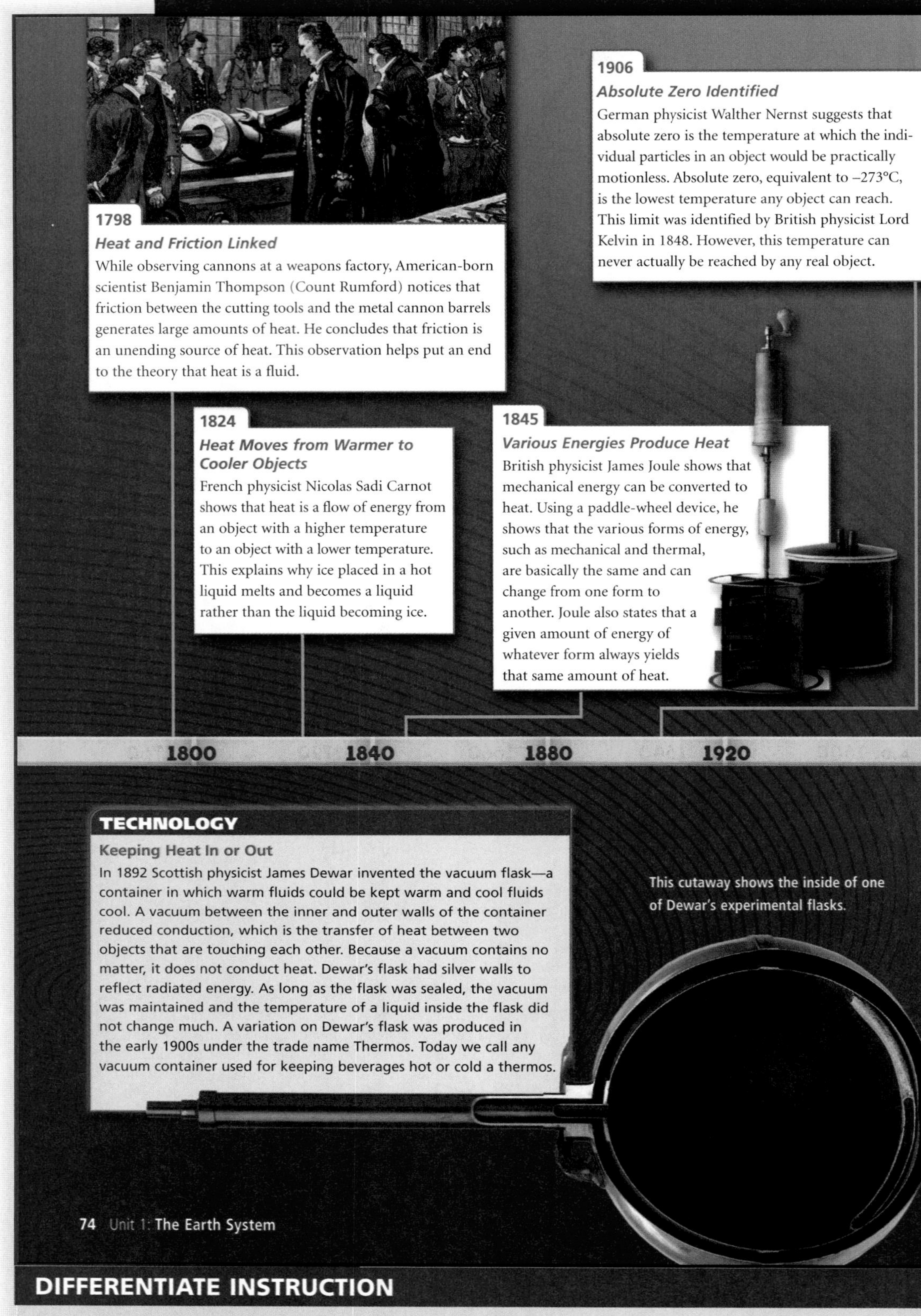

1798
Heat and Friction Linked
While observing cannons at a weapons factory, American-born scientist Benjamin Thompson (Count Rumford) notices that friction between the cutting tools and the metal cannon barrels generates large amounts of heat. He concludes that friction is an unending source of heat. This observation helps put an end to the theory that heat is a fluid.
1906
Absolute Zero Identified
German physicist Walther Nernst suggests that absolute zero is the temperature at which the individual particles in an object would be practically motionless. Absolute zero, equivalent to –273°C, is the lowest temperature any object can reach. This limit was identified by British physicist Lord Kelvin in 1848. However, this temperature can never actually be reached by any real object.
1824
Heat Moves from Warmer to Cooler Objects
French physicist Nicolas Sadi Carnot shows that heat is a flow of energy from an object with a higher temperature to an object with a lower temperature. This explains why ice placed in a hot liquid melts and becomes a liquid rather than the liquid becoming ice.
1845
Various Energies Produce Heat
British physicist James Joule shows that mechanical energy can be converted to heat. Using a paddle-wheel device, he shows that the various forms of energy, such as mechanical and thermal, are basically the same and can change from one form to another. Joule also states that a given amount of energy of whatever form always yields that same amount of heat.
1800
1840
1880
1920
TECHNOLOGY
Keeping Heat In or Out
In 1892 Scottish physicist James Dewar invented the vacuum flask—a container in which warm fluids could be kept warm and cool fluids cool. A vacuum between the inner and outer walls of the container reduced conduction, which is the transfer of heat between two objects that are touching each other. Because a vacuum contains no matter, it does not conduct heat. Dewar's flask had silver walls to reflect radiated energy. As long as the flask was sealed, the vacuum was maintained and the temperature of a liquid inside the flask did not change much. A variation on Dewar's flask was produced in the early 1900s under the trade name Thermos. Today we call any vacuum container used for keeping beverages hot or cold a thermos.
74 Unit 1: The Earth System

This cutaway shows the inside of one of Dewar's experimental flasks.

DIFFERENTIATE INSTRUCTION

Below Level **1798** Have students rub their hands together to demonstrate how friction produces heat.

2003
Wasps Stay Cool
Scientists in Israel have found evidence that some wasps have an internal air-conditioning system. Like a refrigerator, the wasp uses energy to stay cooler than the air around it. The energy may come from several sources, such as the energy generated by an electric current produced when the wasp's shell is exposed to sunlight. This ability to stay cool allows wasps to hunt for food even on very hot days.

RESOURCE CENTER
CLASSZONE.COM
Learn about current temperature and heat research.

1960 2000

APPLICATION

Using Thermal Energy from Ponds

Ponds can be used to store solar energy. The goal is to turn the solar energy into energy people can use. Salt must be added to the ponds, however, so that the water at the bottom is denser than the water at the top. This prevents thermal energy stored on the bottom from moving up to the surface, where it would be lost to the air through evaporation. A net on the surface helps prevent wind from mixing the water layers.

SPOTLIGHT on DAVID CROSTHWAIT

David Crosthwait (1898–1976) was a leader in the United States in the field of heat transfer. He received 39 U.S. patents for his inventions related to heating, ventilating, and air-conditioning. He was an expert on methods of heating and cooling with water.

In the 1920s and 1930s, huge skyscrapers were being built. Crosthwait was hired to design the heating system for Radio City Music Hall in New York City's Rockefeller Center.

Crosthwait's inventions improved heating systems in large buildings. His innovations include an improved boiler, a new thermostat control, and a new vacuum pump. Crosthwait's influence lives on, as steam is still used to heat and cool many skyscrapers in the United States.

ACTIVITIES

Design a Procedure

Many people claim that it is possible to determine the temperature by listening to the chirping of crickets. Crickets are sensitive to changes in air temperature and chirp more quickly when the temperature rises. To calculate the temperature in degrees Celsius, count the number of chirps in 7 seconds and add 5.

Write a procedure for an experiment that would test this claim. What factors would you consider testing? What range of temperatures would you test?

Writing About Science

Alchemy has fascinated people for centuries. Research its influence on both the technology and procedures of modern chemistry. Write a short report.

DIFFERENTIATE INSTRUCTION

Advanced Encourage students to trace the development of ideas from the ancient Greeks to the present. Students might create a visual or model that represents each new idea as building on the previous idea.

Spotlight on

David Crosthwait was born in Nashville and grew up in Kansas City, Missouri. Point out to students that in the 1900s, it was relatively uncommon for an African American to receive acclaim for work in the sciences. Interested students may want to read more about Crosthwait's work and the obstacles he overcame.

Crosthwait used science to create practical technology. Students probably know that dry-cleaning establishments use steam to remove stains and wrinkles. Steam is also used by hospitals to sterilize surgical instruments. But most steam is used for heating and cooling buildings. Today in New York City, not only Rockefeller Center is heated and cooled by steam, but also the Metropolitan Museum of Art and the United Nations.

ACTIVITIES

Design a Procedure

Refer students to the steps of the scientific process as they write their procedure for the experiment. Remind them to include in their procedure ways to record findings clearly.

Writing About Science

Suggest that students look up the history of alchemy on the Internet or in the library. Some might focus on contributions of a specific culture, such as Egyptian, Chinese, Indian, or Islamic alchemists.

Technology Resources

Students can visit **ClassZone.com** for information about temperature and heat.

CHAPTER

Weather Patterns

Earth Science
UNIFYING PRINCIPLES

PRINCIPLE 1
Heat energy inside Earth and radiation from the Sun provide energy for Earth's processes.

PRINCIPLE 2
Physical forces, such as gravity, affect the movement of all matter on Earth and throughout the universe.

PRINCIPLE 3
Matter and energy move among Earth's rocks and soil, atmosphere, waters, and living things.

PRINCIPLE 4
Earth has changed over time and continues to change.

Unit:
The
Earth System
BIG IDEAS

CHAPTER 1
Energy and Change
Waves and heat flow transfer energy.

CHAPTER 2
Energy in the Earth System
The Sun is the major source of energy for Earth's atmosphere and surface.

CHAPTER 3
Weather Patterns
Some features of weather have predictable patterns.

CHAPTER 4
Weather Fronts and Storms
The interaction of air masses causes changes in weather.

CHAPTER 3
KEY CONCEPTS

SECTION 1

Air pressure varies in the atmosphere.
1. Air exerts pressure.
2. Air pressure is related to altitude and density.

SECTION 2

The atmosphere has wind patterns.
1. Uneven heating causes air to move.
2. Earth's rotation affects wind direction.
3. Bands of calm air separate global wind belts.
4. Jet streams flow high above Earth's surface.
5. Patterns of heating and cooling cause local winds and monsoons.

SECTION 3

Most clouds form as air rises and cools.
1. Temperature affects water in the air.
2. Water vapor condenses and forms clouds.

SECTION 4

Water falls to Earth's surface as precipitation.
1. Precipitation forms from water droplets or ice crystals.
2. Precipitation can carry pollution.

The Big Idea Flow Chart is available on p. T17 in the **TRANSPARENCY BOOK.**

Previewing Content

SECTION

Air pressure varies in the atmosphere. pp. 79–82

1. Air exerts pressure.
Gravity causes air molecules to be pulled toward Earth's surface. Air molecules bounce off objects and exert a force on these objects. **Air pressure** is defined as the force of molecules pushing on an area. Because air molecules move in all directions, air pressure pushes in all directions.

2. Air pressure is related to altitude and density.
Air pressure varies, depending upon the weight of the overlying atmosphere. Air pressure decreases with altitude because the higher an area is located, the less air there is pushing down on it. Density also decreases with altitude; the air molecules in air at sea level are denser than air molecules in air over a mountain because the higher air pressure at sea level pushes them closer together. Just as air pressure affects the density of air, density affects air pressure. Air pressure is usually higher in dense air than in thin air because dense air has more molecules bouncing around in it.

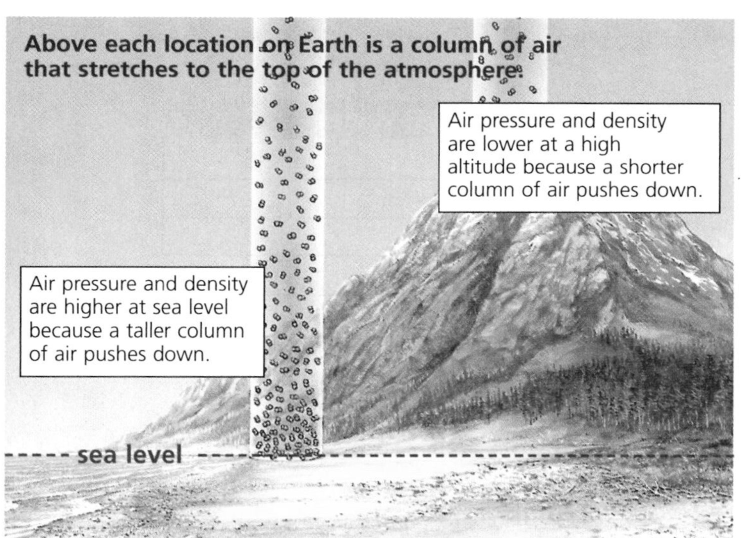

Above each location on Earth is a column of air that stretches to the top of the atmosphere.
Air pressure and density are lower at a high altitude because a shorter column of air pushes down.
Air pressure and density are higher at sea level because a taller column of air pushes down.
sea level

SECTION

The atmosphere has wind patterns. pp. 83–91

1. Uneven heating causes air to move.
The uneven heating of Earth's surface causes air pressure to differ from place to place at the same altitude. These pressure differences cause air to move horizontally as **wind.** Winds that travel for thousands of kilometers in steady patterns are called **global winds.**

2. Earth's rotation affects wind direction.
Earth rotates from west to east. This rotation changes the direction of objects moving over Earth's surface—a phenomenon known as the **Coriolis effect.** In the Northern Hemisphere, the Coriolis effect deflects winds to the right in the direction of motion. Winds in the Southern Hemisphere are deflected to the left.

3. Bands of calm air separate global wind belts.
Global winds are caused by the uneven heating of Earth's curved surface. Because of the Coriolis effect, winds do not flow directly from the high pressure over the poles to the low pressure at the equator. Instead, each hemisphere has three belts of global winds: the trade winds, the westerlies, and the easterlies. These wind belts are separated by calm regions of high or low pressure: the doldrums (sometimes called the intertropical convergence zone), the horse latitudes, the subpolar lows, and the polar highs.

4. Jet streams flow high above Earth's surface.
The uneven heating of Earth's surface also causes jet streams. **Jet streams** travel for thousands of kilometers, usually in the upper troposphere. These long-distance winds move at great speeds, always from west to east, around the globe. Two main jet streams—a polar jet stream and a subtropical jet stream—are usually found in each hemisphere.

5. Patterns of heating and cooling cause local winds and monsoons.
Some winds change in regular patterns. For example, the different heating and cooling rates of land and water can cause winds to change direction daily (sea and land breezes) or seasonally (**monsoons**).

Common Misconceptions

MISCONCEPTION DATABASE
CLASSZONE.COM Background on student misconceptions

AIR PRESSURE Students may think that air pressure pushes only downward. The air pressure at sea level is about 14.7 pounds per square inch. If air pressure were exerted only downward, you would feel 14.7 pounds of downward pressure on every square inch of your hand. You don't feel this pressure because air is pushing in all directions.

 This misconception is addressed on p. 80.

CORIOLIS EFFECT Students may think that the Coriolis effect causes water to swirl in a particular direction down a drain. In reality, the Coriolis effect influences movements only across large distances, such as the movements of global winds and ocean currents.

 This misconception is addressed on p. 86.

Previewing Content

SECTION

Most clouds form as air rises and cools. pp. 92–101

1. Temperature affects water in the air.
Differences in temperature fuel the water cycle, wherein water is constantly recycled between Earth's surface and atmosphere. The water cycle is made up of three processes: evaporation, condensation, and precipitation.

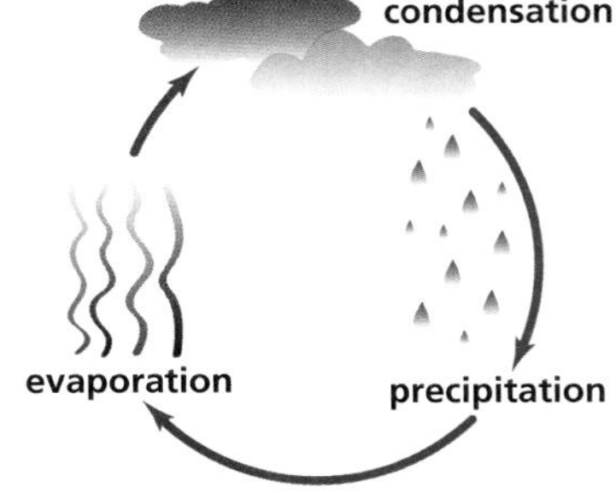

- **Evaporation** is the process by which liquid water changes into a gas.
- **Condensation** is the process by which a gas, such as water vapor, changes into a liquid.
- **Precipitation** is any type of liquid or solid water that falls to Earth's surface. You can copy the visual above to use when teaching the water cycle.

2. Water vapor condenses and forms clouds.
Clouds are made of condensed water vapor. They can form when warm air rises, expands, and cools. Water vapor in the air then condenses around tiny solid particles. Clouds are classified according to their altitudes, the ways they form, and their general characteristics. The main types of clouds are

- cirrus, or wispy clouds
- cumulus, or puffy clouds
- stratus, or layered clouds

There are many subtypes of clouds; their names are often combinations of Latin word parts that suggest their appearance.

Fog is another type of cloud. It rests on the ground or a body of water.

SECTION

Water falls to Earth's surface as precipitation. pp. 102–107

1. Precipitation forms from water droplets or ice crystals.
Precipitation of any kind originates from a cloud. About a million cloud droplets combine together to form a single raindrop. Precipitation can also form when below-freezing temperatures inside a cloud cause water vapor to change into ice crystals. Air temperature determines which type of precipitation falls to Earth's surface. Types of precipitation include: rain and drizzle, **freezing rain, sleet,** snow, and **hail.**

2. Precipitation can carry pollution.
Factories, power plants, and vehicles release sulfur dioxide and nitrogen oxides into the air. These gases combine with moisture in the air to produce sulfuric and nitric acids. The acids then mix with cloud droplets and fall to Earth as acid rain. **Acid rain** is precipitation that has become more acidic than normal because of pollution. Normal rain is made slightly acidic by the presence of dissolved CO_2. The table below compares the pH of acid rain in the United States with that of other substances. A neutral pH value is 7. The lower the pH value, the more acidic the substance is.

pH Values	
lemon	2.2–2.5
tomato	4.2
acid rain	5.5–4.2
rain	5.6
pure water	7.0
seawater	7.8–8.2

Common Misconceptions

MISCONCEPTION DATABASE
CLASSZONE.COM Background on student misconceptions

WEIGHT OF HUMID AIR Students may think that on humid days the air feels heavy because of its water vapor content. However, water vapor weighs less than dry air—the molecular weight of water is 18, and the average molecular weight of dry air is 29. Therefore, the more humid a quantity of air is, the less it weighs.

This misconception is addressed on p. 94.

Previewing Labs

Lab Generator CD-ROM
Edit these Pupil Edition labs and generate alternative labs.

EXPLORE the BIG idea

How Does Air Motion Affect Balloons? p. 77 Students observe air movement.	**TIME** 10 minutes **MATERIALS** 2 balloons, string, pencil
Internet Activity: Wind, p. 77 Students are introduced to wind patterns.	**TIME** 20 minutes **MATERIALS** computer with Internet access

SECTION 1

EXPLORE Air Pressure, p. 79 Students observe an effect of a change in air pressure.	**TIME** 10 minutes **MATERIALS** peeled hard-boiled egg, glass bottle, 2 wooden matches
INVESTIGATE Air Pressure, p. 81 Students collect data to measure changes in air pressure. **ALTERNATIVE:** Reading Activity, URB p. 274	**TIME** 15 minutes **MATERIALS** round balloon, metal can, rubber band, tape, thin straw, ruler, scissors

SECTION 2

EXPLORE Solar Energy, p. 83 Students use a flashlight to see how light varies in intensity across a curved surface.	**TIME** 10 minutes **MATERIALS** globe, flashlight, ruler
INVESTIGATE Coriolis Effect, p. 85 Students model how Earth's rotation affects winds. **ALTERNATIVE:** Reading Activity, URB p. 274	**TIME** 10 minutes **MATERIALS** round balloon, felt-tip pen

SECTION 3

EXPLORE Condensation, p. 92 Students observe condensation on a mirror.	**TIME** 5 minutes **MATERIALS** hand mirror
INVESTIGATE Condensation, p. 95 Students observe cloud formation inside a plastic bottle. **ALTERNATIVE:** Teacher Demonstration, URB p. 274	**TIME** 10 minutes **MATERIALS** clear 1-liter plastic bottle with cap, water at room temperature, tablespoon, matches
CHAPTER INVESTIGATION **Relative Humidity,** pp. 100–101 Students construct a psychrometer and use it to measure relative humidity. **ALTERNATIVE:** Teacher Modeling, URB p. 274 R Relative Humidity Chart, p. 183	**TIME** 40 minutes **MATERIALS** 2 thermometers, cotton or felt cloth, 3 rubber bands, plastic bowl, water at room temperature, scissors, pint milk carton, ruler, Relative Humidity Chart

SECTION 4

INVESTIGATE Precipitation, p. 103 Students analyze precipitation data from California. **ALTERNATIVE:** Direct Instruction, URB p. 275 R California Precipitation Map, p. 173	**TIME** 15 minutes **MATERIALS** California Precipitation Map

R **Additional INVESTIGATION,** Estimating Wind Speed, A, B, & C, pp. 193–201; Teacher Instructions, pp. 274–276

Previewing Chapter Resources

CHAPTER 3 Weather Patterns

INTEGRATED TECHNOLOGY

CLASSZONE.COM
- eEdition Plus
- EasyPlanner Plus
- Misconception Database
- Content Review
- Test Practice
- Visualization
- Resource Centers
- Internet Activity: Wind
- Math Tutorial

SCILINKS.ORG

SCILINKS

CD-ROMS
- eEdition
- EasyPlanner
- Power Presentations
- Content Review
- Lab Generator
- Test Generator

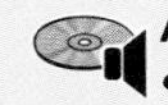

AUDIO CDS
- Audio Readings
- Audio Readings in Spanish

LABS AND ACTIVITIES

EXPLORE the Big Idea, p. 77
- How Does Air Motion Affect Balloons?
- Internet Activity: Wind

UNIT RESOURCE BOOK
Unit Projects, pp. 5–10

Lab Generator CD-ROM
Generate customized labs.

SECTION

1 Air pressure varies in the atmosphere.
pp. 79–82

Lesson Plan, pp. 131–132

RESOURCE CENTER, Air Pressure

TRANSPARENCY BOOK
- Big Idea Flow Chart, p. T17
- Daily Vocabulary Scaffolding, p. T18
- Note-Taking Model, p. T19
- 3-Minute Warm-Up, p. T20

- EXPLORE Air Pressure, p. 79
- INVESTIGATE Air Pressure, p. 81

UNIT RESOURCE BOOK
Datasheet, Air Pressure, p. 140

SECTION

2 The atmosphere has wind patterns.
pp. 83–91

Lesson Plan, pp. 142–143

- **RESOURCE CENTER,** Global Winds
- **VISUALIZATION,** Coriolis Effect
- **MATH TUTORIAL**

TRANSPARENCY BOOK
- Daily Vocabulary Scaffolding, p. T18
- 3-Minute Warm-Up, p. T20
- "Global Winds" Visual, p. T22

- EXPLORE Solar Energy, p. 83
- INVESTIGATE Coriolis Effect, p. 85
- Math in Science, p. 91

UNIT RESOURCE BOOK
- Datasheet, Coriolis Effect, p. 151
- Additional INVESTIGATION, Estimating Wind Speed, A, B, & C, pp. 193–201
- Math Support and Practice, pp. 181–182

SECTION

3 Most clouds form as air rises and cools.
pp. 92–101

Lesson Plan, pp. 153–154

RESOURCE CENTER, Clouds

TRANSPARENCY BOOK
- Daily Vocabulary Scaffolding, p. T18
- 3-Minute Warm-Up, p. T21

- EXPLORE Condensation, p. 92
- INVESTIGATE Condensation, p. 95
- CHAPTER INVESTIGATION, Relative Humidity, pp. 100–101

UNIT RESOURCE BOOK
- Datasheet, Condensation, p. 162
- CHAPTER INVESTIGATION, Relative Humidity, A, B, & C, pp. 184–192
- Relative Humidity Chart, p. 183

SECTION

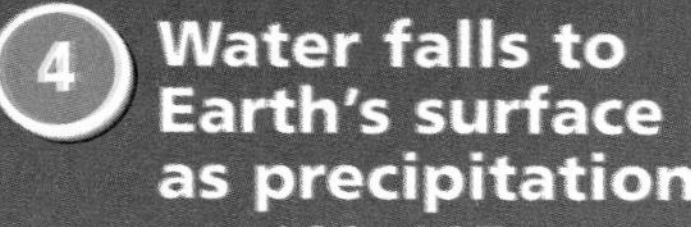

4 Water falls to Earth's surface as precipitation.
pp. 102–107

Lesson Plan, pp. 164–165

RESOURCE CENTER, Lightning

TRANSPARENCY BOOK
- Big Idea Flow Chart, p. T17
- Daily Vocabulary Scaffolding, p. T18
- 3-Minute Warm-Up, p. T21
- Chapter Outline, pp. T23–T24

- INVESTIGATE Precipitation, p. 103
- Extreme Science, p. 107

UNIT RESOURCE BOOK
- California Precipitation Map, p. 173
- Datasheet, Precipitation, p. 174

KEY TO ICONS

CD/CD-ROM · Teacher Edition · TRANSPARENCY BOOK · STANDARDS REVIEW AND PRACTICE
INTERNET · Pupil Edition · UNIT RESOURCE BOOK · ASSESSMENT BOOK · SCIENCE TOOLKIT

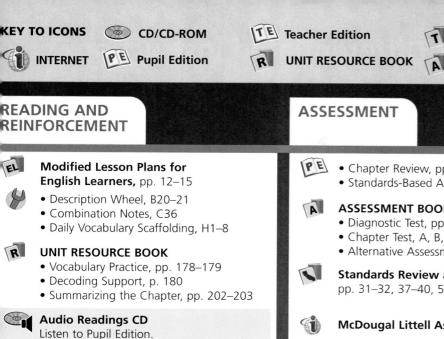

READING AND REINFORCEMENT	ASSESSMENT	STANDARDS
Modified Lesson Plans for English Learners, pp. 12–15 • Description Wheel, B20–21 • Combination Notes, C36 • Daily Vocabulary Scaffolding, H1–8 **UNIT RESOURCE BOOK** • Vocabulary Practice, pp. 178–179 • Decoding Support, p. 180 • Summarizing the Chapter, pp. 202–203 **Audio Readings CD** Listen to Pupil Edition. **Audio Readings in Spanish CD** Listen to Pupil Edition in Spanish.	• Chapter Review, pp. 109–110 • Standards-Based Assessment, p. 111 **ASSESSMENT BOOK** • Diagnostic Test, pp. 41–42 • Chapter Test, A, B, & C, pp. 47–58 • Alternative Assessment, pp. 59–60 **Standards Review and Practice,** pp. 31–32, 37–40, 57–60, 63–66 **McDougal Littell Assessment System** **Test Generator CD-ROM** Generate customized and Spanish tests.	California Content Standards 6.4.a, 6.4.d, 6.4.e, 6.7.a, 6.7.b, 6.7.d, 6.7.e See p. 76 for the standards.
UNIT RESOURCE BOOK • Reading Study Guides, A & B, pp. 133–136 • Spanish Reading Study Guide, pp. 137–138 • Challenge and Extension, p. 139 • Reinforcing Key Concepts, p. 141	Ongoing Assessment, pp. 79, 81–82 Section 3.1 Review, p. 82 **ASSESSMENT BOOK** Section 3.1 Quiz, p. 43	California Content Standards 6.4.e
UNIT RESOURCE BOOK • Reading Study Guides, A & B, pp. 144–147 • Spanish Reading Study Guide, pp. 148–149 • Challenge and Extension, p. 150 • Reinforcing Key Concepts, p. 152	Ongoing Assessment, pp. 83–85, 87–90 Section 3.2 Review, p. 90 **ASSESSMENT BOOK** Section 3.2 Quiz, p. 44	California Content Standards 6.4.a, 6.4.d, 6.4.e
UNIT RESOURCE BOOK • Reading Study Guides, A & B, pp. 155–158 • Spanish Reading Study Guide, pp. 159–160 • Challenge and Extension, p. 161 • Reinforcing Key Concepts, p. 163	Ongoing Assessment, pp. 93, 95–99 Section 3.3 Review, p. 99 **ASSESSMENT BOOK** Section 3.3 Quiz, p. 45	California Content Standards 6.4.a, 6.4.e, 6.7.a, 6.7.b, 6.7.d, 6.7.e
UNIT RESOURCE BOOK • Reading Study Guides, A & B, pp. 166–169 • Spanish Reading Study Guide, pp. 170–171 • Challenge and Extension, p. 172 • Reinforcing Key Concepts, p. 175 • Challenge Reading, pp. 176–177	 Ongoing Assessment, pp. 103–106  Section 3.4 Review, p. 106  **ASSESSMENT BOOK** Section 3.4 Quiz, p. 46	California Content Standards 6.4.a, 6.4.e

Previewing Resources for Differentiated Instruction

CHAPTER INVESTIGATION

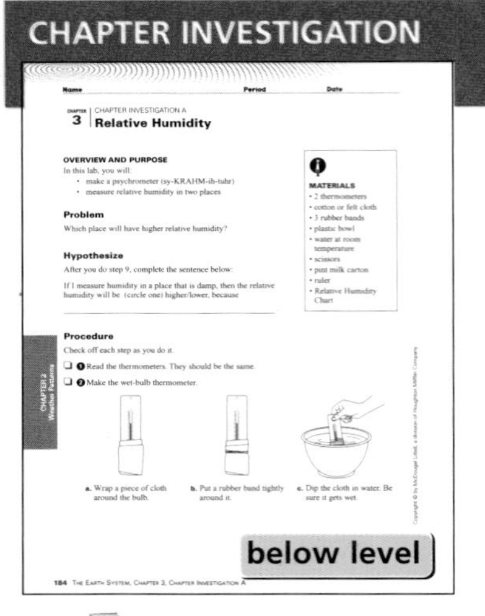

Chapter 3 | Chapter Investigation A

Relative Humidity

below level

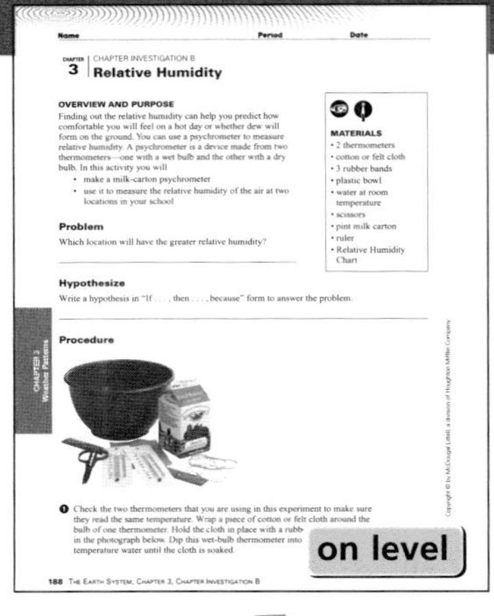

Chapter 3 | Chapter Investigation B

Relative Humidity

on level

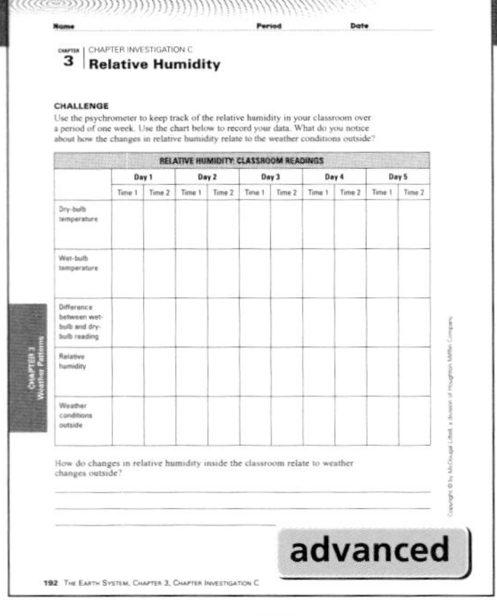

Chapter 3 | Chapter Investigation C

Relative Humidity

advanced

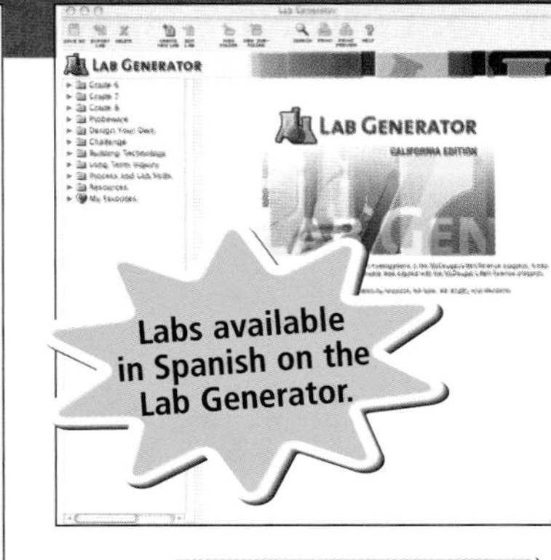

Lab Generator
Labs available in Spanish on the Lab Generator.

English Learners

UNIT RESOURCE BOOK, pp. 184–187

pp. 188–191

pp. 188–192

READING STUDY GUIDE

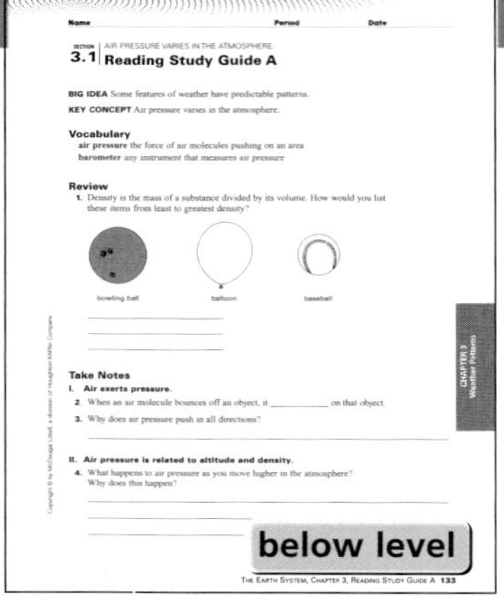

Section 3.1 | Air Pressure Varies in the Atmosphere

Reading Study Guide A

below level

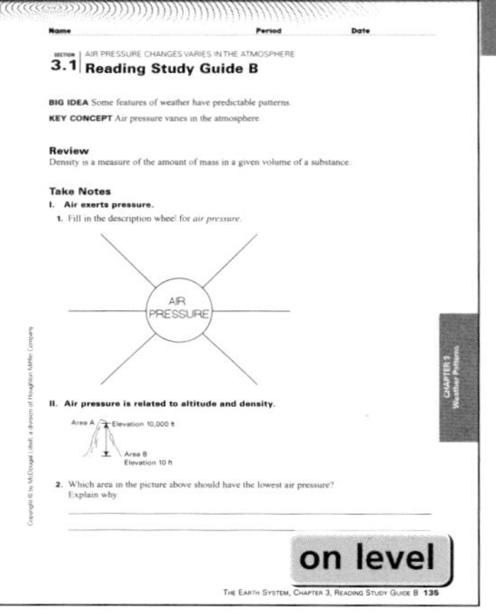

Section 3.1 | Air Pressure Changes Varies in the Atmosphere

Reading Study Guide B

on level

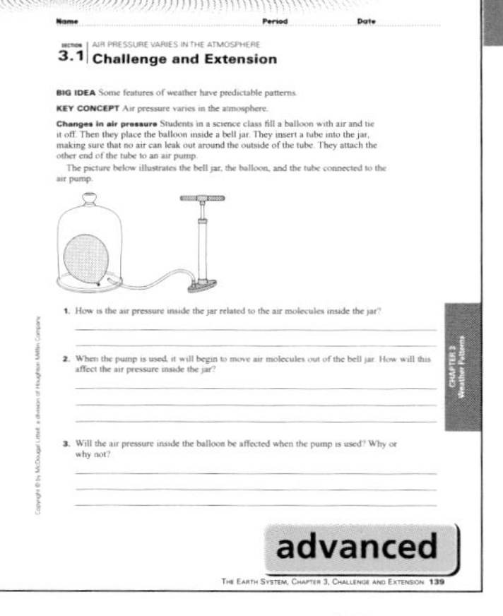

Section 3.1 | Air Pressure Varies in the Atmosphere

Challenge and Extension

advanced

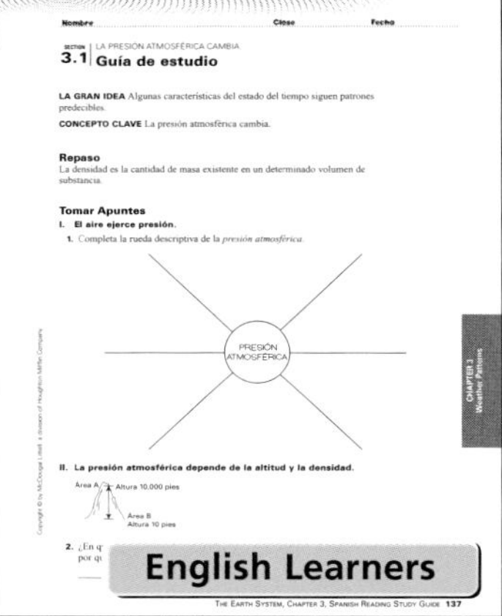

Sección 3.1 | La presión atmosférica cambia

Guía de estudio

English Learners

UNIT RESOURCE BOOK, pp. 133–134

pp. 135–136

p. 139

p. 137

CHAPTER TEST

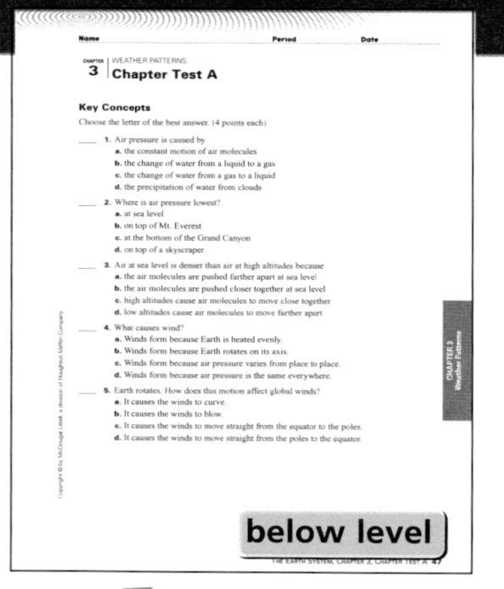

Chapter 3 | Weather Patterns

Chapter Test A

below level

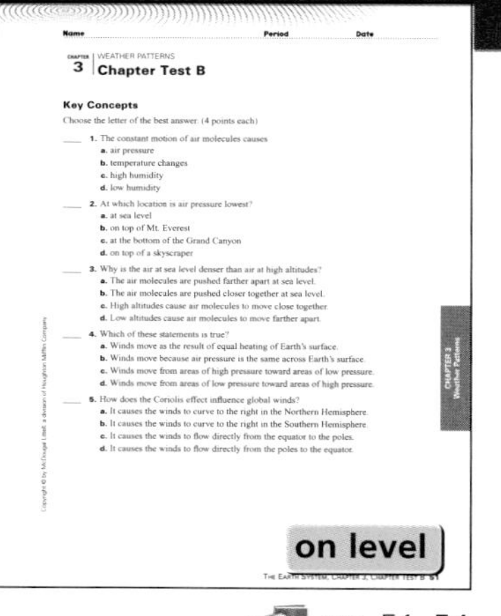

Chapter 3 | Weather Patterns

Chapter Test B

on level

Chapter 3 | Weather Patterns

Chapter Test C

advanced

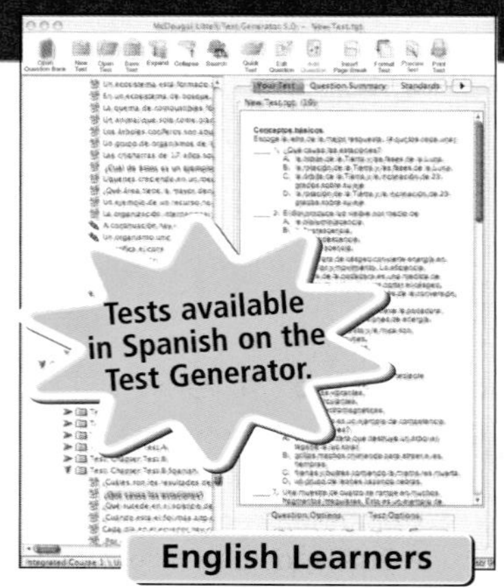

Tests available in Spanish on the Test Generator.

English Learners

ASSESSMENT BOOK, pp. 47–50

pp. 51–54

pp. 55–58

TECHNOLOGY

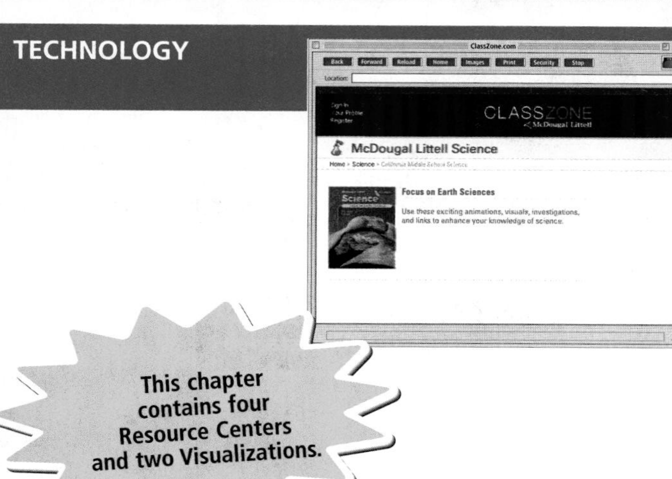

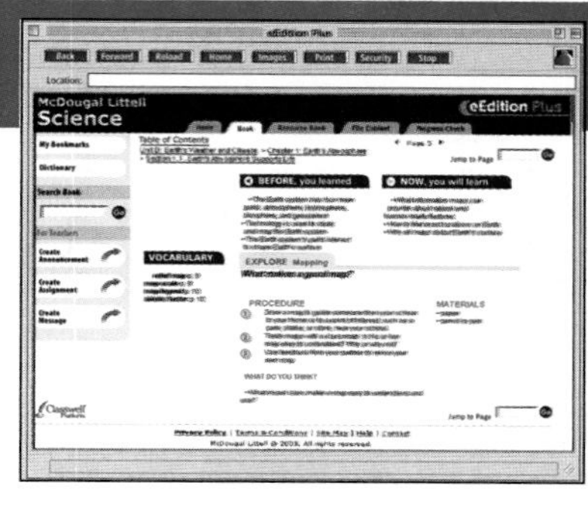

CLASSZONE.COM

CD/CD-ROMS

CLASSZONE.COM

VISUAL CONTENT

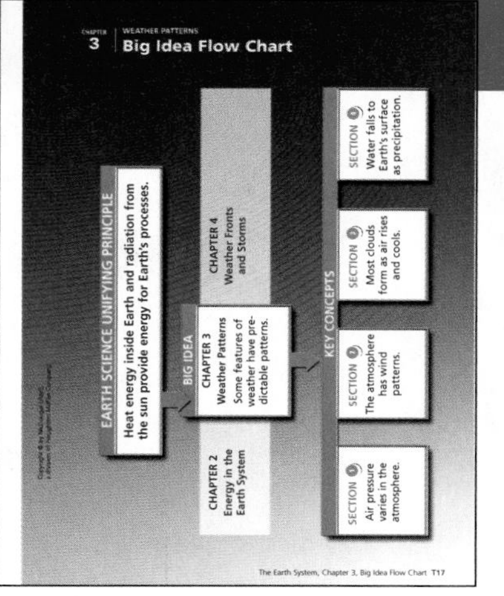

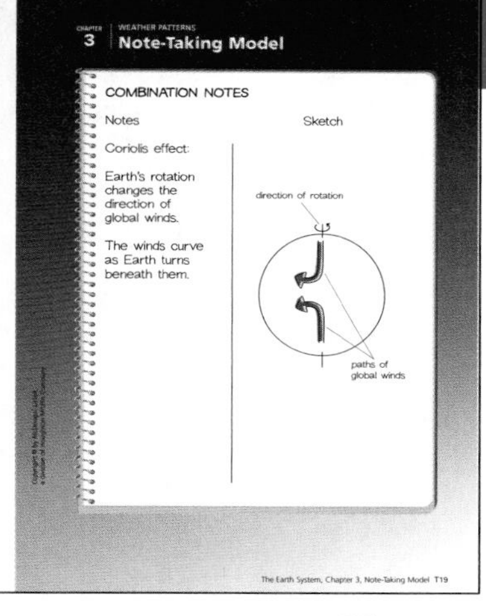

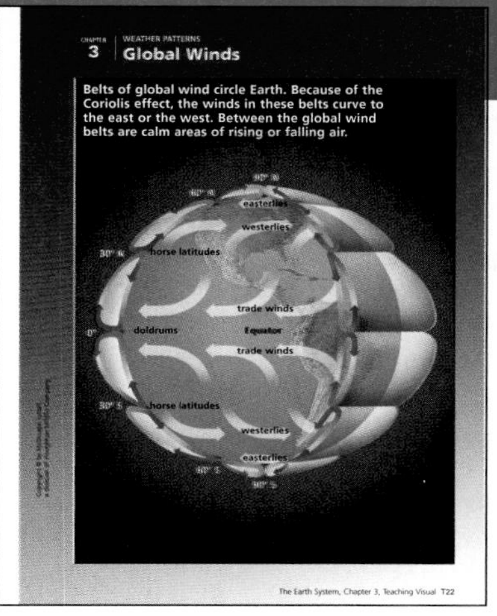

TRANSPARENCY BOOK, p. T17

p. T19

p. T22

MORE SUPPORT

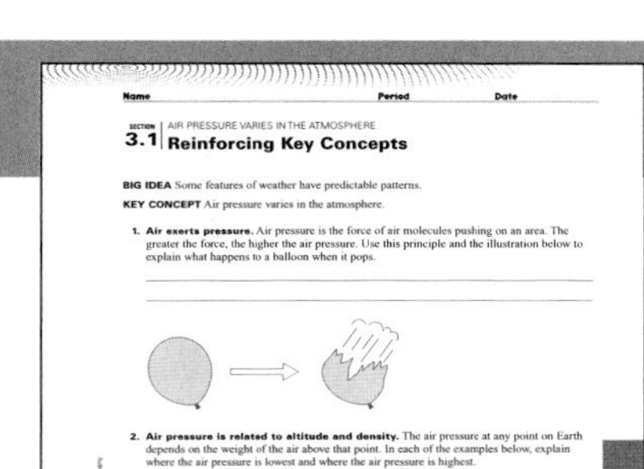

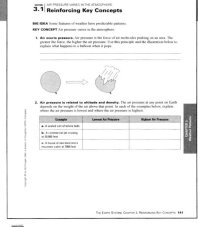

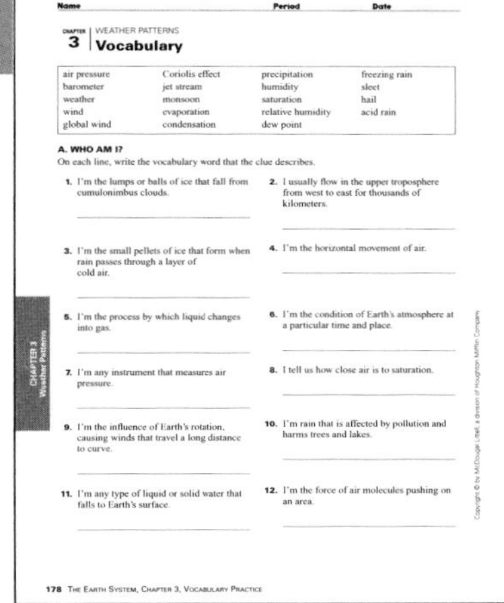

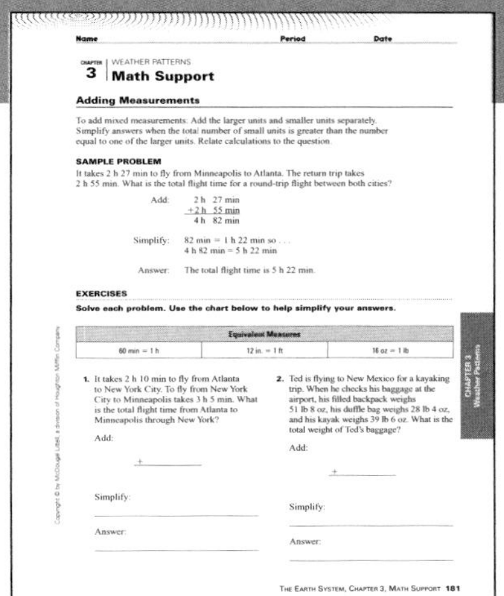

UNIT RESOURCE BOOK, p. 141

pp. 178–179

p. 181

CHAPTER

Weather Patterns

INTRODUCE

the BIG idea

Have students look at the photograph of the lightning and storm clouds in the distance. Discuss how the question in the box links to the Big Idea. For further discussion:

- Ask: How would you describe the weather today? Is it wet? dry? cold? warm?
- Describe any clouds in the sky.
- Ask: What relationship do you see between certain types of clouds and specific weather conditions, such as lightning, rain, or warm temperatures?

California Content Standards

6.4.a Students know the sun is the major source of energy for phenomena on Earth's surface; it powers winds, ocean currents, and the water cycle.

6.4.d Students know convection currents distribute heat in the atmosphere and oceans.

6.4.e Students know differences in pressure, heat, air movement, and humidity result in changes of weather.

6.7.a Develop a hypothesis.

6.7.b Select and use appropriate tools and technology (including calculators, computers, balances, spring scales, microscopes, and binoculars) to perform tests, collect data, and display data.

6.7.d Communicate the steps and results from an investigation in written reports and oral presentations.

6.7.e Recognize whether evidence is consistent with a proposed explanation.

CHAPTER

Weather Patterns

the BIG idea

Some features of weather have predictable patterns.

Key Concepts

SECTION 1 **Air pressure varies in the atmosphere.** Learn how air pressure changes and how it is measured.

SECTION 2 **The atmosphere has wind patterns.** Learn how wind develops and about different types of wind.

SECTION 3 **Most clouds form as air rises and cools.** Learn how water changes form in the atmosphere and about different types of clouds.

SECTION 4 **Water falls to Earth's surface as precipitation.** Learn about the different types of precipitation and about acid rain.

California ClassZone

CLASSZONE.COM

Chapter 3 online resources: Content Review, two Visualizations, four Resource Centers, Math Tutorial, Test Practice

What weather conditions do you see in the distance?

INTERNET PREVIEW

CLASSZONE.COM For student use with the following pages:

Review and Practice
- Content Review, pp. 78, 108
- Math Tutorial: Adding Measures of Time, p. 91
- Test Practice, p. 111

Activities and Resources
- Internet Activity: Wind, p. 77
- Resource Centers: Air Pressure, p. 81; Global Winds, p. 86; Clouds, p. 96; Lightning, p. 107
- Visualization: Coriolis Effect, p. 84

Atmospheric Pressure and Winds **Code: MDL010**

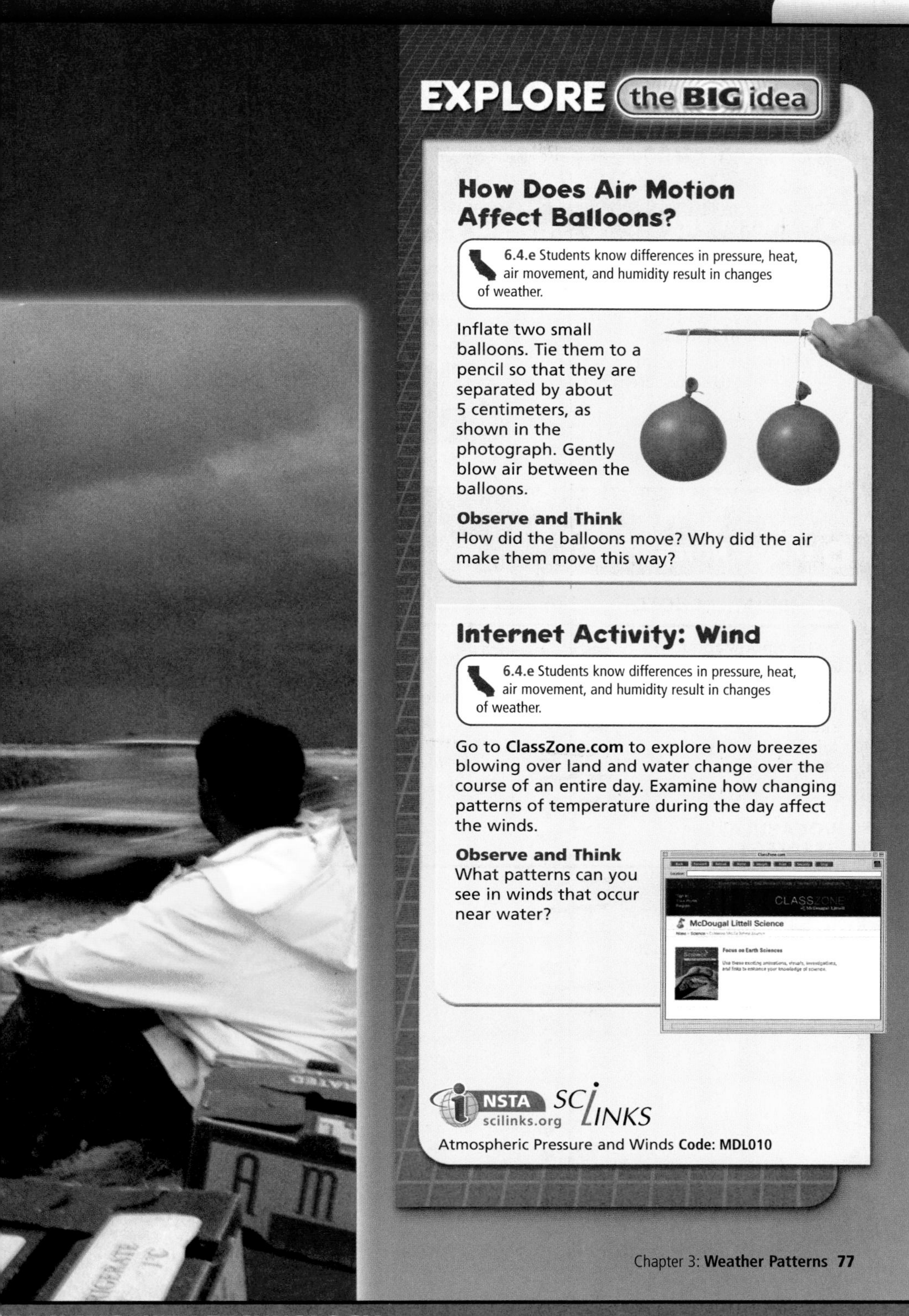

EXPLORE (the BIG idea)

How Does Air Motion Affect Balloons?

6.4.e Students know differences in pressure, heat, air movement, and humidity result in changes of weather.

Inflate two small balloons. Tie them to a pencil so that they are separated by about 5 centimeters, as shown in the photograph. Gently blow air between the balloons.

Observe and Think
How did the balloons move? Why did the air make them move this way?

Internet Activity: Wind

6.4.e Students know differences in pressure, heat, air movement, and humidity result in changes of weather.

Go to **ClassZone.com** to explore how breezes blowing over land and water change over the course of an entire day. Examine how changing patterns of temperature during the day affect the winds.

Observe and Think
What patterns can you see in winds that occur near water?

NSTA scilinks.org SCILINKS
Atmospheric Pressure and Winds **Code: MDL010**

Chapter 3: **Weather Patterns 77**

EXPLORE (the BIG idea)

These inquiry-based activities are appropriate for use at home or as a supplement to classroom instruction.

How Does Air Motion Affect Balloons?

PURPOSE To introduce students to the relationship between air pressure and air movement.

TIP *10 min.* Students should try to make balloons the same size and the same distance from the pencil.

Answer: The balloons moved closer together. The blowing caused the air between the balloons to be different from the air on the other sides of the balloons.

REVISIT after p. 81.

Internet Activity: Wind

PURPOSE To introduce students to local wind patterns.

TIP *20 min.* Students might try predicting whether sea breezes occur during the day or at night.

Sample answer: Winds near water blow inland during the day and out to sea at night.

REVISIT after p. 89.

TEACHING WITH TECHNOLOGY

CBL and Probeware If you have a graphing calculator and a barometer probe, take daily air pressure readings after teaching p. 82. If you have a relative humidity sensor, do the same after students perform the Chapter Investigation on pp. 100–101.

PREPARE

CONCEPT REVIEW

Activate Prior Knowledge

- Ask students to explain what happens to energy from the Sun that reaches Earth.
- Ask students what the relationship is between energy from the Sun and global winds.
- Have students recall how conduction and convection transfer heat energy.

TAKING NOTES

Combination Notes

Combining a sketch with notes will help students to visualize a new concept and connect it with a concrete example. Using a two-column format, students can write their notes in one column and draw a sketch in the other.

Vocabulary Strategy

Description wheels can include as much information as students want to add. They become easy study devices when students look back through their notes.

Vocabulary and Note-Taking Resources

- Vocabulary Practice, pp. 178–179
- Decoding Support, p. 180

- Daily Vocabulary Scaffolding, p. T18
- Note-Taking Model, p. T19

- Description Wheel, B20–21
- Combination Notes, C36
- Daily Vocabulary Scaffolding, H1–8

CHAPTER 3

Getting Ready to Learn

CONCEPT REVIEW

- The Sun supplies the atmosphere's energy.
- Energy moves throughout the Earth system.
- Heat energy flows from warmer to cooler areas.

VOCABULARY REVIEW

convection p. 28
density p. 28
water cycle p. 60
See Glossary for definitions.
altitude, atmosphere

CONTENT REVIEW
CLASSZONE.COM

Review concepts and vocabulary.

TAKING NOTES

COMBINATION NOTES

To take notes about a new concept, first make an informal outline of the information. Then make a sketch of the concept and label it so that you can study it later.

VOCABULARY STRATEGY

Place each vocabulary term at the center of a **description wheel.** Write some words describing it on the spokes.

SCIENCE NOTEBOOK

NOTES

Air pressure
- is the force of air molecules pushing on an area
- pushes in all directions

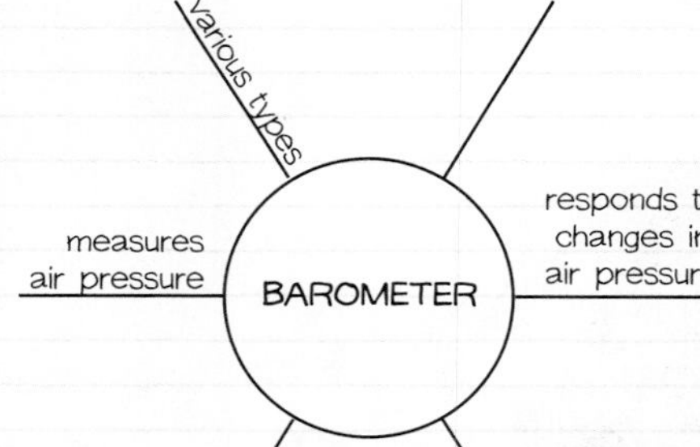

See the Note-Taking Handbook on pages R45–R51.

CHECK READINESS

Administer the Diagnostic Test to determine students' readiness for new science content and their mastery of requisite math skills.

 Diagnostic Test, pp. 41–42

Technology Resources

Students needing content and math skills should visit **ClassZone.com.**

- **CONTENT REVIEW**
- **MATH TUTORIAL**

CONTENT REVIEW CD-ROM

KEY CONCEPT

Air pressure varies in the atmosphere.

CALIFORNIA Content Standard

6.4.e Students know differences in pressure, heat, air movement, and humidity result in changes of weather.

BEFORE, you learned

- Density is the amount of mass in a given volume of a substance
- Air becomes less dense as temperature increases
- Differences in density cause air to rise and sink

NOW, you will learn

- How the movement of air molecules causes air pressure
- How air pressure varies
- How differences in air pressure affect the atmosphere

VOCABULARY

air pressure p. 79
barometer p. 82

EXPLORE Air Pressure (6.4.e)

What does air do to the egg?

PROCEDURE

1. Set a peeled hard-boiled egg in the mouth of a bottle. Make sure that the egg can't slip through.
2. Light the matches. Remove the egg, and drop the matches into the bottle. Quickly replace the egg.
3. Watch carefully, and record your observations.

MATERIALS

- peeled hard-boiled egg
- glass bottle
- 2 wooden matches

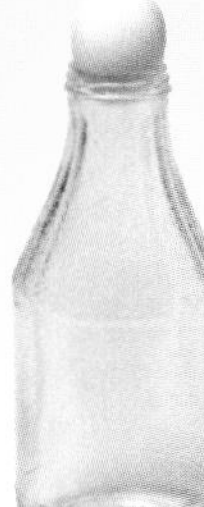

WHAT DO YOU THINK?

- What happened when you placed the egg back on top of the bottle?
- What can your observations tell you about the air in the bottle?

Air exerts pressure.

Air molecules move constantly. As they move, they bounce off each other like rubber balls. They also bounce off every surface they hit. As you read this book, billions of air molecules are bouncing off your body, the book, and everything else around you.

Each time an air molecule bounces off an object, it pushes, or exerts a force, on that object. When billions of air molecules bounce off a surface, the force is spread over the area of that surface. **Air pressure** is the force of air molecules pushing on an area. The greater the force, the higher the air pressure. Because air molecules move in all directions, air pressure pushes in all directions.

VOCABULARY
Add a description wheel for *air pressure* to your notebook.

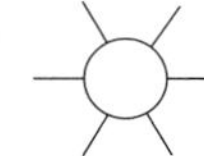

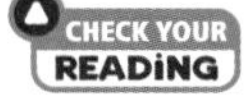

CHECK YOUR READING How does the number of air molecules relate to air pressure?

RESOURCES FOR DIFFERENTIATED INSTRUCTION

Below Level

UNIT RESOURCE BOOK

- Reading Study Guide A, pp. 133–134
- Decoding Support, p. 180

AUDIO CDS

Advanced

UNIT RESOURCE BOOK

Challenge and Extension, p. 139

English Learners

UNIT RESOURCE BOOK

Spanish Reading Study Guide, pp. 137–138

AUDIO CDS

- Audio Readings in Spanish
- Audio Readings (English)

3.1 FOCUS

Set Learning Goals

Students will

- Recognize how the movement of air molecules causes air pressure.
- Describe how air pressure varies.
- Explain how differences in air pressure affect the atmosphere.
- Construct a barometer to measure changes in air pressure.

3-Minute Warm-Up

Display Transparency 20 or copy this exercise on the board:

Match the word with the definition.

density convection molecules

1. process that transfers energy in rising and falling air *convection*
2. the amount of mass in a given volume of substance *density*
3. rising temperatures cause these to move faster in air *molecules*

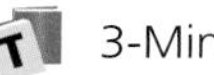

3-Minute Warm-Up, p. T20

3.1 MOTIVATE

EXPLORE Air Pressure

PURPOSE To introduce the concept that air molecules exert force

TIP *10 min.* Ask students to return any remaining matches to your desk immediately after completing the activity.

WHAT DO YOU THINK? *The egg gets pushed into the bottle because the air pressure inside the bottle is lower than the air pressure outside. Students may conclude that the air inside the bottle is somehow different from the outside air.*

Ongoing Assessment

Recognize how the movement of air molecules causes air pressure.

Ask: What do air molecules do when they bounce off an object? *They exert a force on the object.*

Answer: The greater the number of air molecules, the greater the air pressure.

3.1 INSTRUCT

Teach the Standards

Pressure and air movement 6.4.e

In this section: Students learn about the relationship between pressure and air movement. Have students make a flow chart that shows how air moves based on areas of high and low pressure.

- **previously taught:** atmosphere, pp. 41–46; convection, conduction, and radiation, p. 59; weather and climate, pp. 65–66
- **future opportunities:** humidity, pp. 92–99; high- and low-pressure systems, pp. 120–121, 123–127

Address Misconceptions

IDENTIFY Ask: Does air press only in a downward direction? If students answer yes, they may hold the misconception that air pressure acts only in a downward direction.

CORRECT Hold your hand out in a horizontal position. Tell students that air molecules are bouncing off all sides of your hand, not just the top. These air molecules exert pressure in all directions.

REASSESS Ask: How would you describe the movement of air molecules? *They move in all directions.* In which direction does the force act on my hand? *The molecules push in all directions.*

Technology Resources

Visit **ClassZone.com** for background on common student misconceptions.

MISCONCEPTION DATABASE

Teach from Visuals

To help students interpret the visual of air pressure and density at different locations, ask: How does the density of air molecules in the columns change from bottom to top? *Air molecules are more densely packed near the bottom of the columns. There are fewer and fewer air molecules toward the top.*

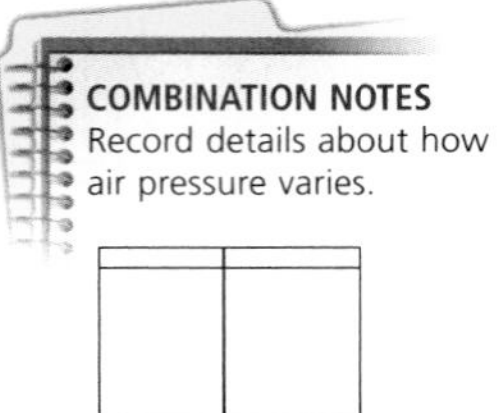

COMBINATION NOTES
Record details about how air pressure varies.

Air pressure is related to altitude and density.

The air pressure at any area on Earth depends on the weight of the air above that area. If you hold out your hand, the force of air pushing down on your hand is greater than the weight of a bowling ball. So why don't you feel the air pushing down on your hand? Remember that air pushes in all directions. The pressure of air pushing down is balanced by the pressure of air pushing up from below.

A Air pressure decreases as you move higher in the atmosphere. Think of a column of air directly over your body. If you stood at sea level, this column would stretch from where you stood to the top of the atmosphere. The air pressure on your body would be equal to the weight of all the air in the column. But if you stood on a mountain, the column of air would be shorter. With less air above you, the pressure would be lower. At an altitude of 5.5 kilometers (3.4 mi), air pressure is about half what it is at sea level.

REMINDER
Density is the amount of mass in a given volume of a substance.

B Air pressure and density are related. Just as air pressure decreases with altitude, so does the density of air. Notice in the illustration that air molecules at sea level are closer together than air molecules over the mountain. Since the pressure is greater at sea level, the air molecules are pushed closer together. Therefore, the air at sea level is denser than air at high altitudes.

Air Pressure and Density

Above each location on Earth is a column of air that stretches to the top of the atmosphere.

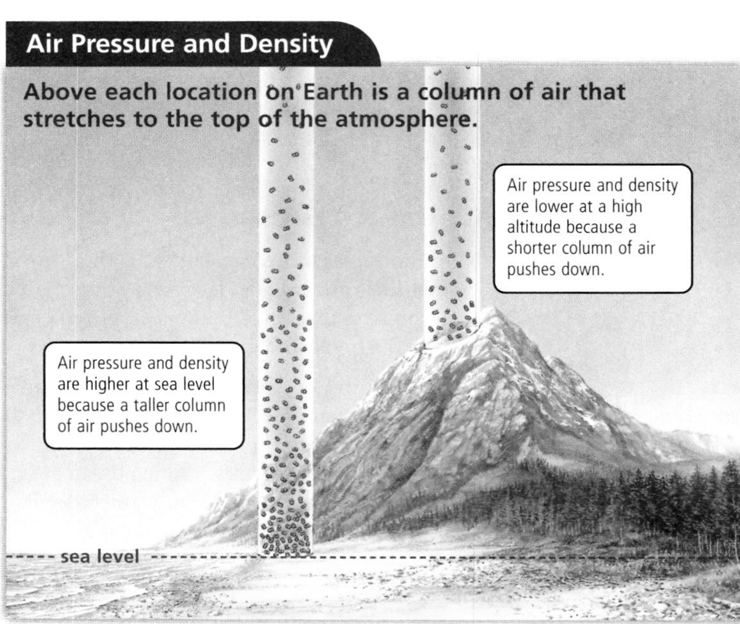

Air pressure and density are lower at a high altitude because a shorter column of air pushes down.
Air pressure and density are higher at sea level because a taller column of air pushes down.
sea level

DIFFERENTIATE INSTRUCTION

More Reading Support

A As altitude increases, air pressure does what? *decreases*

B Air pressure is related to altitude and what else? *density*

English Learners English learners may need help with these terms and concepts: *sea level* on p. 80, *cutting the straw at an angle* on p. 81, and *chamber* on p. 82. They may not have prior knowledge of *can of tennis balls* on p. 81, or *riding an elevator* on p. 82.

Pressure and Air Motion

You've read that air pressure decreases as you move to higher altitudes. Air pressure also often varies in two locations at the same altitude. You can observe how such pressure differences affect air when you open a new can of tennis balls. You may hear a hiss as air rushes into the can. The air inside the sealed can of tennis balls is at a lower pressure than the air outside the can. When you break the seal, air moves from outside the can toward the lower pressure inside it.

RESOURCE CENTER
CLASSZONE.COM
Find out more about air pressure.

Air pressure differences in the atmosphere affect air in a similar way. If the air pressure were the same at all locations, air wouldn't move much. Because of differences in pressure, air starts to move from areas of higher pressure toward areas of lower pressure. The air may move only a short distance, or it may travel many kilometers. You will learn more about how air moves in response to pressure differences in Section 3.2.

CHECK YOUR READING How do differences in air pressure affect the movement of air?

INVESTIGATE Air Pressure

How can you measure changes in air pressure?

PROCEDURE

1. Cut open a balloon along one side until you get close to the end. Stretch the balloon across the open top of the can. Secure it tightly in place with a rubber band.
2. Cut the straw on an angle to make a pointer. Tape the other end of the straw to the center of the balloon.
3. Tape a ruler against a wall or a box so that the end of the pointer almost touches the ruler. Record the position of the pointer against the ruler.
4. Record the position of the pointer at least once a day for the next five days. Look for small changes in its position. For each day, record the air pressure printed in a local newspaper.

WHAT DO YOU THINK?

- In what direction did the pointer move when the air pressure went up? when the air pressure went down?
- Explain how your instrument worked.

CHALLENGE Predict what would happen to the pointer if you repeated this experiment but poked some small holes in the balloon.

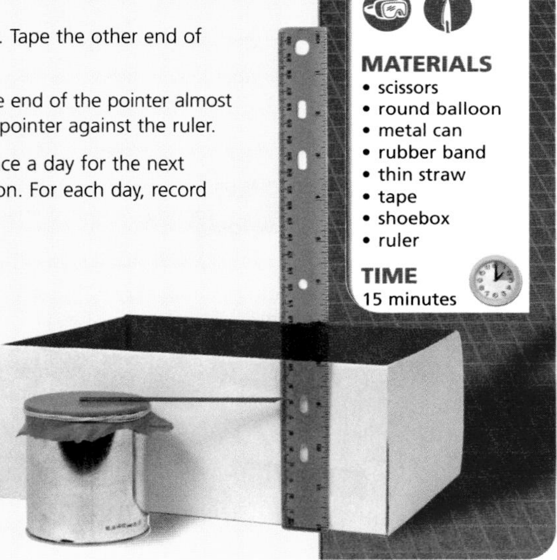

SKILL FOCUS
Collecting data (6.4.e)

MATERIALS
- scissors
- round balloon
- metal can
- rubber band
- thin straw
- tape
- shoebox
- ruler

TIME
15 minutes

DIFFERENTIATE INSTRUCTION

More Reading Support

C Can air pressure be different at places that have the same altitude? *yes*

D Air starts to move from areas of high pressure toward where? *areas of low pressure*

Advanced A mercury barometer indicates changes in air pressure by changes in the height of a column of mercury. An aneroid barometer, like the one shown on p. 82, includes a sealed chamber that expands or contracts with changes in air pressure. Have interested students research and draw sketches of mercury and aneroid barometers.

Challenge and Extension, p. 139

INVESTIGATE Air Pressure

PURPOSE To collect data in order to measure changes in air pressure

TIPS *15 min.*

- Cut straws at an angle before giving them to students.
- Television and the Internet are other potential sources of daily air pressure readings.

WHAT DO YOU THINK? *The pointer went up when the air pressure increased and down when the air pressure decreased. Higher air pressure pushes harder on the balloon and causes the pointer to tilt upward. When the air pressure is lower, there is less force on the balloon and the pointer goes down.*

CHALLENGE *Air would flow into the can, and you would not get accurate readings.*

Datasheet, Air Pressure, p. 140

Technology Resources

Customize this student lab as needed or look for an alternative. Print rubrics to assess student lab reports.

Lab Generator CD-ROM

EXPLORE the BIG idea

Revisit "How Does Air Motion Affect Balloons?" on p. 77. Have students explain their results.

Ongoing Assessment

Describe how air pressure varies.

Ask: How does air pressure at an altitude of 5.5 kilometers compare with air pressure at sea level? *Air pressure at an altitude of 5.5 kilometers is about half of what it would be at sea level.*

CHECK YOUR READING *Answer: Air moves from areas of higher pressure toward areas of lower pressure.*

Ongoing Assessment

Explain how differences in air pressure affect the atmosphere.

Ask: How are differences in air pressure related to the movement of air? *Air moves from areas of higher pressure toward areas of lower pressure.*

READING VISUALS *Answer: the one on the right; because air pressure decreases with altitude*

Reinforce the BIG idea

Have students relate the section to the Big Idea.

 Reinforcing Key Concepts, p. 141

3.1 ASSESS & RETEACH

Assess

 Section 3.1 Quiz, p. 43

Reteach

Help students review this section's concepts by writing the headings "Air Pressure" and "Air Molecules" on the board. Encourage students to state facts about each concept. Remind them that air pressure is the force of air molecules pushing on an area. *Air Pressure: pushes in all directions, decreases as altitude increases, causes air to move when there are pressure differences, can be measured with a barometer. Air Molecules: move constantly, exert pressure, are denser at low altitudes, move from areas of higher pressure toward areas of lower pressure*

Technology Resources

Have students visit **ClassZone.com** for reteaching of Key Concepts.

 CONTENT REVIEW

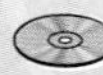 CONTENT REVIEW CD-ROM

How a Barometer Works

High Air Pressure

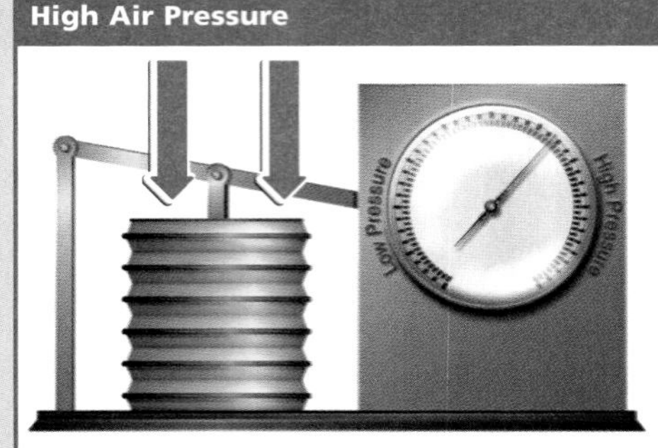

The flexible chamber on the barometer contracts when the air pressure increases.

Low Air Pressure

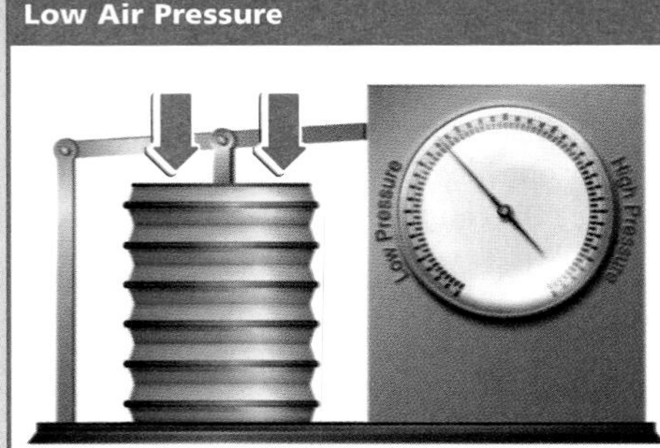

The chamber expands when the air pressure decreases.

READING VISUALS Which of these barometer readings would be the more likely one on a mountain? Explain why.

Barometers and Air Pressure

Air pressure can be measured in different ways. A **barometer** is any instrument that measures air pressure. The illustrations above show a simplified version of a common type of barometer. This type contains a sealed flexible chamber that has little air inside. The chamber contracts when the outside air pressure is high and expands when the air pressure is low. A series of levers or other devices turns the motion of the chamber into something that can be read—the movement of a needle on a dial or a jagged line on a strip of graph paper.

3.1 Review

KEY CONCEPTS

1. How does the movement of air molecules cause pressure? (6.4.e)
2. How does altitude affect air pressure? (6.4.e)
3. How is air density related to air pressure? (6.4.e)

CRITICAL THINKING

4. **Apply** Would you expect the air pressure in a valley that's below sea level to be higher or lower than air pressure at sea level? Explain.
5. **Predict** Two barometers are placed one kilometer apart. One shows higher pressure than the other. What will happen to air between them?

CHALLENGE

6. **Infer** The eardrum is a thin sheet of tissue that separates air in the middle part of your ear from air outside your ear. What could cause your eardrum to make a popping sound as you ride up a tall building in an elevator?

ANSWERS

1. Air molecules move constantly and bounce off surfaces, exerting force or pressure on surfaces.

2. Air pressure decreases as altitude increases.

3. Higher air pressure indicates that air is denser.

4. Air pressure would be higher in the valley because air pressure decreases as altitude increases.

5. Air will start to move from the area of higher pressure toward the area of lower pressure.

6. The higher pressure inside the ear pushes the eardrum outward as the air pressure in the elevator decreases.

KEY CONCEPT

3.2 The atmosphere has wind patterns.

CALIFORNIA Content Standards

6.4.a Students know the sun is the major source of energy for phenomena on Earth's surface; it powers winds, ocean currents, and the water cycle.

6.4.e Students know differences in pressure, heat, air movement, and humidity result in changes of weather.

BEFORE, you learned

- Solar energy heats Earth's surface and atmosphere
- Differences in density cause air to move
- Air pressure differences set air in motion

NOW, you will learn

- About forces that affect wind
- About global winds
- About patterns of heating and cooling

VOCABULARY

wind p. 83
global wind p. 84
Coriolis effect p. 85
jet stream p. 88
monsoon p. 90

EXPLORE Solar Energy (6.4.a)

How does Earth's shape affect solar heating?

PROCEDURE

1. Place a globe on a desk in a darkened room.
2. Point a flashlight at the equator on the globe from a distance of about 15 centimeters. Keep the flashlight level. Observe the lighted area on the globe.
3. Keeping the flashlight level, raise it up and point it at the United States. Observe the lighted area.

MATERIALS

- globe
- flashlight
- ruler

WHAT DO YOU THINK?

- How were the two lighted areas different?
- What might have caused the difference?

Uneven heating causes air to move.

On local news broadcasts, weather forecasters often spend several minutes discussing what the weather will be like over the next few days. Recall that weather is the condition of Earth's atmosphere at a particular time and place. Wind is an important part of weather. You will read about other weather factors later in this chapter.

Wind is air that moves horizontally, or parallel to the ground. Remember that air pressure can differ from place to place at the same altitude. Uneven heating of Earth's surface causes such pressure differences, which set air in motion. Over a short distance, wind moves directly from higher pressure toward lower pressure.

REMINDER Remember that air pressure is the force that air molecules exert on an area.

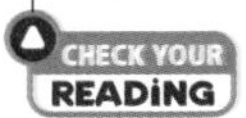

CHECK YOUR READING What is the relationship between air pressure and wind?

3.2 FOCUS

Set Learning Goals

Students will

- Describe the forces that affect wind.
- Describe global winds.
- Explain patterns of heating and cooling.
- Conduct an experiment to model the Coriolis effect.

3-Minute Warm-Up

Display Transparency 20 or copy this exercise on the board:

Are these statements true? If not, correct them.

1. Differences in pressure cause the horizontal movement of air. *true*
2. Air pressure and air density increase with altitude. *Air pressure and air density decrease with altitude.*
3. The Sun supplies most of Earth's energy. *true*

T 3-Minute Warm-Up, p. T20

3.2 MOTIVATE

EXPLORE Solar Energy

PURPOSE To introduce the concept that the intensity of sunlight varies on Earth

TIP *10 min.* Many globes are made of paper and cannot be labeled, but students might cover globes with paper and outline the lighted area on the paper.

WHAT DO YOU THINK? *The light was more concentrated at the equator and more spread out at the United States. The angle at which the light hit these locations was different.*

RESOURCES FOR DIFFERENTIATED INSTRUCTION

Below Level

UNIT RESOURCE BOOK

- Reading Study Guide A, pp. 144–145
- Decoding Support, p. 180

AUDIO CDS

R Additional INVESTIGATION, Estimating Wind Speed, A, B, & C, pp. 193–201; Teacher Instructions, pp. 274–275

Advanced

UNIT RESOURCE BOOK

- Challenge and Extension, p. 150

English Learners

UNIT RESOURCE BOOK

Spanish Reading Study Guide, pp. 148–149

AUDIO CDs

- Audio Readings in Spanish
- Audio Readings (English)

Ongoing Assessment

CHECK YOUR READING *Answer: Differences in air pressure cause winds.*

3.2 INSTRUCT

Teach the Standards

Winds 6.4.a

In this section: Students learn how uneven heating of Earth's surface causes global winds. Ask: Would you expect air to move toward an area of high pressure or away from it? *away*

- **previously taught:** conduction and convection, pp. 27–32; wind and ocean currents, pp. 62–63
- **future opportunities:** cold and warm fronts, pp. 118–119; hurricanes and wind storms, pp. 123–127

Teach from Visuals

To help students interpret the "How Wind Forms" Visual

- Ask: Is the wind moving toward high or low pressure? *low pressure*
- Tell students that in the lower atmosphere, temperature generally decreases as altitude increases. Then ask them to predict what will happen to the rising warm air. *It will cool, become more dense, and sink.*

Teach Difficult Concepts

Students may have a hard time understanding how differences in air pressure relate to wind strength. Remind them that air pressure is a force per unit area and that the effects of a force—in this case, wind—increase as the intensity of the force increases. To help students understand, you might try the demonstration below.

Teacher Demo

Obtain a bicycle pump. Slowly push down on the pump handle, allowing students to feel the resulting "breeze." Pull the handle back up, then push down forcibly, again allowing students to feel the air rush out. Ask: Which force was the strongest? *the second one* Which "wind" was the strongest? *the second one*

Ongoing Assessment

CHECK YOUR READING *Answer: The difference in air pressure between two areas determines the strength of wind.*

View an animation of the Coriolis effect.

How Wind Forms

Wind moves from an area of high pressure toward an area of low pressure.

1. Warmer air rises.
2. Cooler air sinks.

low pressure

high pressure

3. Wind moves across surface.

The illustration above shows a common pattern of air circulation caused by uneven heating of Earth's surface:

1. Sunlight strongly heats an area of ground. The ground heats the air. The warm air rises, and an area of low pressure forms.
2. Sunlight heats an area of ground less strongly. The cooler, denser air sinks slowly, and an area of high pressure forms.
3. Air moves as wind across the surface, from higher toward lower pressure.

When the difference in pressure between two areas is small, the wind may move too slowly to be noticeable. A very large pressure difference can produce wind strong enough to uproot trees.

What factor determines the strength of wind?

The distance winds travel varies. Some winds die out quickly after blowing a few meters. In contrast, **global winds** travel thousands of kilometers in steady patterns. Global winds last for weeks.

Uneven heating between the equator and the north and south poles causes global winds. Notice in the illustration at left how sunlight strikes Earth's curved surface. Near the equator, concentrated sunlight heats the surface to a high temperature. Warm air rises, producing low pressure.

In regions closer to the poles, the sunlight is more spread out. Because less of the Sun's energy reaches these regions, the air above them is cooler and denser. The sinking dense air produces high pressure that sets global winds in motion.

Sunlight is concentrated near the equator because it strikes the surface directly.

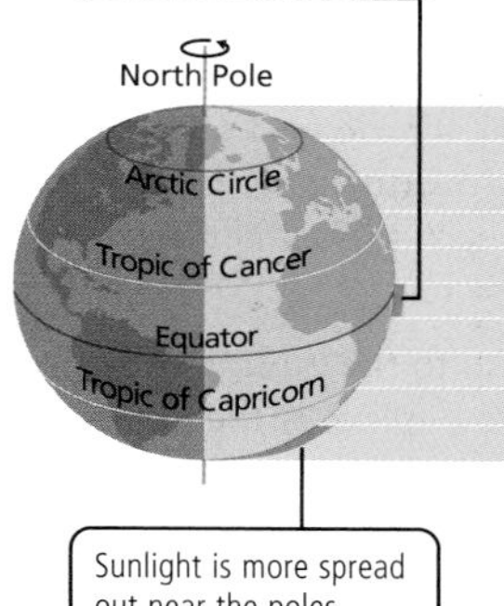

Sunlight is more spread out near the poles because it strikes at a lower angle.

84 Unit 1: The Earth System

DIFFERENTIATE INSTRUCTION

More Reading Support

A The uneven heating of Earth causes what? *air circulation*

B What winds travel thousands of kilometers in steady patterns? *global winds*

English Learners English learners may have difficulty using the words *affect* and *effect* correctly. Explain that *affect* is usually a verb and *effect* is usually a noun. For example, on p. 85 the term *Coriolis effect* contains the noun *effect*. The Investigate on p. 85 contains an example of the verb *affect:* "How did the rotation affect the lines that you drew?"

Earth's rotation affects wind direction.

If Earth did not rotate, global winds would flow directly from the poles to the equator. However, Earth's rotation changes the direction of winds and other objects moving over Earth. The influence of Earth's rotation is called the **Coriolis effect** (KAWR-ee-OH-lihs). Global winds curve as Earth turns beneath them. In the Northern Hemisphere, winds curve to the right of the direction of motion. Winds in the Southern Hemisphere curve to the left. The Coriolis effect is noticeable only for winds that travel long distances.

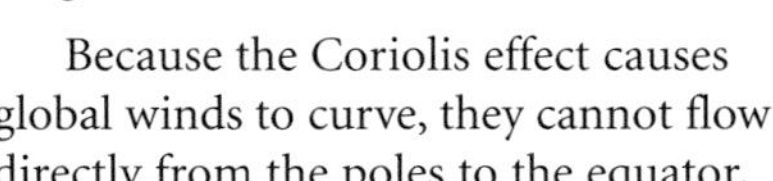

Because the Coriolis effect causes global winds to curve, they cannot flow directly from the poles to the equator. Instead, global winds travel along three routes in each hemisphere. These routes, which circle the world, are called global wind belts.

CHECK YOUR READING In which direction do winds curve in the Northern Hemisphere?

INVESTIGATE Coriolis Effect

How does Earth's rotation affect wind?

PROCEDURE

1. Blow up a balloon and tie it off.
2. Have a classmate slowly rotate the balloon to the right. Draw a line straight down from the top of the balloon to the center as the balloon rotates.
3. Now draw a line from the bottom of the balloon straight up to the center as the balloon rotates.

WHAT DO YOU THINK?

- How did the rotation affect the lines that you drew?
- How does this activity demonstrate the Coriolis effect?

CHALLENGE How might changing the speed at which the balloon is rotated affect your results? Repeat the activity to test your prediction.

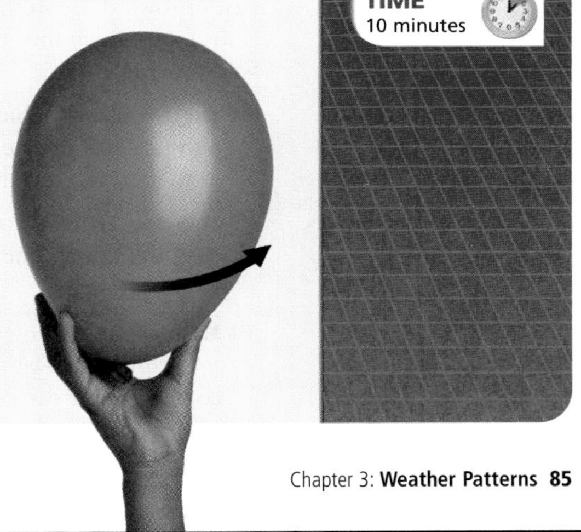

SKILL FOCUS
Modeling (6.4.e)

MATERIALS
- round balloon
- felt-tip pen

TIME
10 minutes

INVESTIGATE Coriolis Effect

PURPOSE To model the Coriolis effect to see how Earth's rotation affects wind

TIPS *10 min.* Divide students into pairs, then suggest the following:

- Use a different-colored marker to draw a circle around the middle of the balloon to represent the equator. Put a dot on both the top and bottom of the balloon to represent the poles.
- When deciding how the rotation affected which way the line curved, do so from the vantage point of an observer standing at the "pole" from which the line starts.

WHAT DO YOU THINK? *The line curved to the right in the first instance and to the left in the second. This activity demonstrates that Earth's rotation affects the direction of objects moving over Earth.*

CHALLENGE *Sample answer: The curves would be sharper.*

Datasheet, Coriolis Effect, p. 151

Technology Resources

Customize this student lab as needed or look for an alternative. Print rubrics to assess student lab reports.

Lab Generator CD-ROM

Ongoing Assessment

Describe the forces that affect wind.

Ask: What force affects wind direction? *Earth's rotation, which causes the Coriolis effect*

CHECK YOUR READING *Answer: to the right*

DIFFERENTIATE INSTRUCTION

More Reading Support

C What causes the Coriolis effect? *Earth's rotation*

D Global winds travel along how many routes in each hemisphere? *three*

Advanced The Coriolis effect influences other objects that move over Earth, including ocean currents. Have interested students research how the Coriolis effect influences ocean currents and how these currents, in turn, influence weather patterns. Students can draw diagrams of the major ocean currents and use captions to summarize their findings.

Address Misconceptions

IDENTIFY Ask: Does water swirl down a drain one way in the Northern Hemisphere and the opposite way in the Southern Hemisphere? If students answer yes, they may hold the misconception that the Coriolis effect causes water to swirl in a particular direction down a drain. In reality, the Coriolis effect influences movements only across large distances, such as the movements of global winds and ocean currents.

CORRECT Refer students to the diagram on page 85. Ask: What do you see in the illustration, besides wind, that might be influenced by the Coriolis effect? *oceans* Tell students that the Coriolis effect influences movements only across large distances. The direction that water swirls down a drain is influenced by irregularities in the shape of the basin. Often, a person can change the direction of the swirling by stirring the water in the opposite direction.

REASSESS Ask: Does the Coriolis effect influence global winds or local breezes? Explain your answer. *It influences global winds, since it affects only things that move for long distances over Earth.* Would you expect the Coriolis effect to influence large oceans or something as small as a water basin? *large oceans*

Technology Resources

Visit **ClassZone.com** for background on common student misconceptions.

MISCONCEPTION DATABASE

History of Science

One of the first models of air circulation was developed in 1735 by English scientist George Hadley. Hadley proposed that winds in each hemisphere circulated in one large cell. He contributed greatly to our understanding of the way air moves, but his model was far too simple to explain global wind patterns.

Bands of calm air separate global wind belts.

Learn more about global winds.

Earth's rotation and the uneven heating of its surface cause a pattern of wind belts separated by calm regions. Each calm region is a zone of either high pressure or low pressure. The illustration on page 87 shows how each wind belt and the calm regions that border it form a giant loop of moving air. These loops are called circulation cells. The section of a cell that flows along Earth's surface is global wind. Notice that the direction of airflow changes from one circulation cell to the next.

Calm Regions

The air usually stays calm in high-pressure and low-pressure zones. Winds are light, and they often change direction.

READING TIP As you read about each region or wind belt, locate it in the diagram on page 87.

E

1. **The doldrums** are a low-pressure zone near the equator. There, warm air rises to the top of the troposphere, which is the atmosphere's lowest layer. Then the air spreads out toward the poles. The rising, moist air produces clouds and heavy rain. During the hottest months, heavy evaporation from warm ocean water in the region fuels tropical storms.
2. **The horse latitudes** are high-pressure zones located about 30° north and 30° south of the equator. Warm air traveling away from the equator cools and sinks in these regions. The weather tends to be clear and dry.

Wind Belts

As dense air sinks to Earth's surface in the horse latitudes and other high-pressure zones, it flows out toward regions of low pressure. This pattern of air movement produces three global wind belts in each hemisphere. Because of the Coriolis effect, the winds curve toward the east or toward the west. Some global winds are named for the directions from which they blow. The westerlies, for example, blow from west to east.

F

3. **The trade winds** blow from the east, moving from the horse latitudes toward the equator. These strong, steady winds die out as they come near the equator.
4. **The westerlies** blow from the west, moving from the horse latitudes toward the poles. They bring storms across much of the United States.
5. **The easterlies** blow from the east, moving from the polar regions toward the mid-latitudes. Stormy weather often occurs when the cold air of the easterlies meets the warmer air of the westerlies.

DIFFERENTIATE INSTRUCTION

More Reading Support

E What low-pressure zone is found near the equator? *doldrums*

F What are the three wind belts? *trade winds, westerlies, and easterlies*

Additional Investigation To reinforce Section 3.2 learning goals, use the following full-period investigation:

Additional INVESTIGATION, Estimating Wind Speed, A, B, & C, pp. 193–201, 274–276 (Advanced students should complete Levels B and C.)

Below Level For students struggling to understand where these zones are, explain that *latitude* refers to a distance in degrees north or south of the equator. Use a globe to show the latitudes of some global wind belts and calm regions.

Global Winds

Belts of global wind circle Earth. Because of the Coriolis effect, the winds in these belts curve to the east or the west. Between the global wind belts are calm areas of rising or falling air.

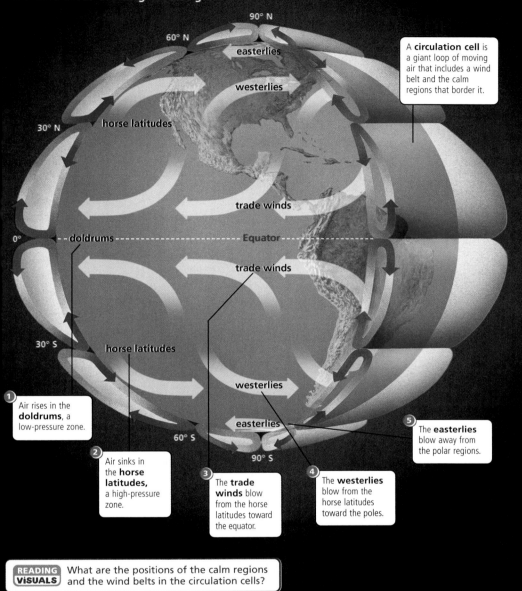

90° N
60° N
easterlies
westerlies
30° N
horse latitudes
trade winds
0°
doldrums
Equator
trade winds
30° S
horse latitudes
westerlies
easterlies
60° S
90° S

A **circulation cell** is a giant loop of moving air that includes a wind belt and the calm regions that border it.

1. Air rises in the **doldrums**, a low-pressure zone.
2. Air sinks in the **horse latitudes,** a high-pressure zone.
3. The **trade winds** blow from the horse latitudes toward the equator.
4. The **westerlies** blow from the horse latitudes toward the poles.
5. The **easterlies** blow away from the polar regions.

READING VISUALS What are the positions of the calm regions and the wind belts in the circulation cells?

DIFFERENTIATE INSTRUCTION

Alternative Assessment Have students use a computer graphics program to make models of global wind patterns. Students should use arrows to indicate wind direction and label each zone. Also, have them include latitudes and areas of high and low pressure. Give students the option of drawing the wind patterns if they are not comfortable with their computer skills.

Teach from Visuals

To help students interpret the global winds visual, ask:

- At what latitudes would you find calm areas of rising or falling air? *at roughly 0°, 30°, 60°, and 90°*
- Where are areas of low pressure and high pressure located? *low pressure: 0° latitude and 60° south and north latitude; high pressure: 30° and 90° south and north latitude*
- How does air move in the circulation cell of the trade winds? *At around 30° latitude, air sinks and moves toward the equator. There, it warms, rises, and moves back toward 30° latitude.*

The visual "Global Winds" is available as T22 in the Transparency Book.

Integrate the Sciences

Friction is a force that resists the motion of surfaces that are in contact with each other. The amount of friction depends in part on the characteristics of the surfaces involved. Land is covered with trees, mountains, buildings, and other features that slow wind down due to friction. Oceans, on the other hand, are much smoother, so that little friction results between the water and winds. For this reason, wind speed over water is usually greater than over land.

Ongoing Assessment

READING VISUALS *Answer: The calm regions are the parts that flow near a neighboring cell. The wind belts are the parts of cells that flow near Earth's surface.*

Teacher Demo

To help students understand how global winds affected early sailors, fashion a model ship from a piece of cork and cloth, or obtain a small plastic ship. Next, fill a long rectangular container with water and place the ship in the right, or east, end of the container. Place a fan near that end, taking care not to let the cord touch the water. Tell students that the fan represents the trade winds and the water represents the Atlantic Ocean—Europe is on the right side, and North America is on the left. Then turn the fan on and allow students to observe how the wind blows the ship across the Atlantic. Ask: What would happen if the people in the ship tried to recross the ocean along the same route? *The ship would be pushed back by the trade winds.*

Develop Critical Thinking

COMPARE AND CONTRAST Have students summarize what they have learned about wind belts. Ask: How do jet streams differ from global wind belts? How are they similar? *Jet streams flow faster and at higher altitudes than global winds. Also, jet streams loop north and south. Like the global wind belts, jet streams are caused by the uneven heating of Earth's surface and flow for thousands of kilometers.*

Ongoing Assessment

Describe global winds.

Ask: From which directions do the three global wind belts and the jet streams flow? *trade winds: east; westerlies: west; easterlies: east; jet streams: west*

Effects of Wind on Travel

Before the invention of steam engines, sailors used to dread traveling through the doldrums and the horse latitudes. There often wasn't enough wind to move their sailing ships. A ship might stall for days or even weeks, wasting precious supplies of food and fresh water.

G

To avoid the calm regions, sailors sought out global wind belts. The trade winds got their name because traders used them to sail from east to west. For centuries, sailors relied on the trade winds to reach North America from Europe. They would return by sailing north to catch the westerlies and ride them across the Atlantic.

Jet streams flow high above Earth's surface.

COMBINATION NOTES Record information about how jet streams flow and their effects on weather and travel.

H

Not all long-distance winds travel along Earth's surface. **Jet streams** are fast-moving winds that circle Earth from west to east at high altitudes. Air often moves in jet streams at speeds greater than 200 kilometers per hour (125 mi/hr). Like global winds, jet streams form because Earth's surface is heated unevenly. Instead of following a straight line, jet streams curve north and south, as shown on the globe below.

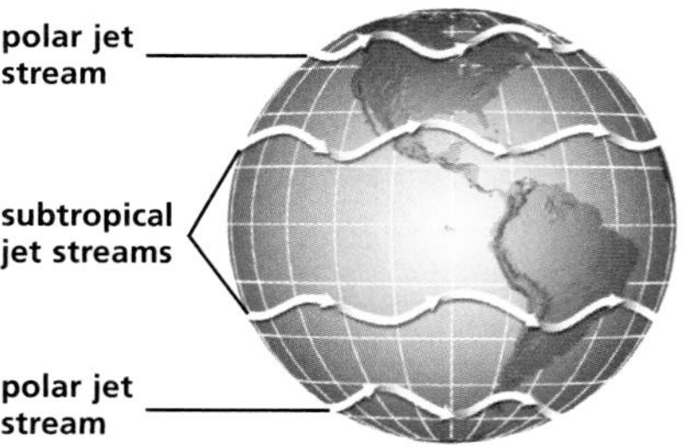

Jet streams flow in a wavy pattern from west to east around the world. They change positions during the year.

Each hemisphere usually has two jet streams, a polar jet stream and a subtropical jet stream. The polar jet streams flow closer to the poles in summer than in winter.

The polar jet stream has a strong influence on weather in North America. It can pull cold air down from Canada into the United States and pull warm air up toward Canada. In addition, strong storms tend to form along its curves. Scientists must know where the jet stream is flowing to make accurate weather predictions.

Jet streams also affect air-travel times. They usually flow 10 to 15 kilometers (6–9 mi) above Earth's surface. Since airplanes often fly at these altitudes, their travel times can be lengthened or shortened by the strong wind of a jet stream.

DIFFERENTIATE INSTRUCTION

More Reading Support

G What wind belt helped sailors reach North America from Europe? *trade winds*

H Where in the atmosphere do jet streams flow? *high altitudes*

Advanced Tell students that the polar jet stream flows faste in the winter than it does in the summer. Ask them to infer why *Wind speed is related to differences in air pressure. Therefore there must be greater differences in air pressure in the upper troposphere in the winter than in the summer.*

Patterns of heating and cooling cause local winds and monsoons.

Have you ever noticed how the wind can change in predictable ways? For example, at the beach on a hot day you will often feel a cool breeze coming off the water. At night a breeze will flow in the opposite direction. The change in the breeze occurs because water and land heat up and cool down at different rates.

CALIFORNIA Focus

Los Angeles often experiences Santa Ana winds, local winds that form as air rushes from high inland plateaus through low areas such as the Santa Ana Canyon. These winds blow toward an area of low pressure over the ocean.

Local Winds

Some winds change daily in a regular pattern. These local winds blow within small areas.

- Sea breezes and land breezes occur near shorelines. During the day, land heats up faster than water. The air over the land rises and expands. Denser ocean air moves into the area of low pressure, producing a sea breeze. As the illustration below shows, this pattern is reversed at night, when land cools faster than water. Warm air rises over the ocean, and cooler air flows in, producing a land breeze.

Sea Breeze
Warmer air rises over land during the day.
Cooler air blows in from water.
Land Breeze
Cooler air blows out from land.
Warmer air rises over water at night.

REMINDER

Red arrows stand for warmer air. Blue arrows stand for cooler air.

- Valley breezes and mountain breezes are caused by a similar process. Mountain slopes heat up and cool faster than the valleys below them. During the day, valley breezes flow up mountains. At night mountain breezes flow down into valleys.

CHECK YOUR READING How do mountains and bodies of water affect patterns of heating and cooling?

Teach from Visuals

To help students interpret the visuals of sea and land breezes, ask:

- Where is the area of low pressure that produces a sea breeze located? *over land*
- Where is the area of low pressure that produces a land breeze located? *over water*
- Why is air warmer over the land during the day and warmer over the water at night? *because land and water absorb and release heat at different rates*

EXPLORE the BIG idea

Revisit "Internet Activity: Wind" on p. 77. Have students describe their observations.

Ongoing Assessment

Explain patterns of heating and cooling.

Ask: If water heated up faster than land, in which direction would wind flow during the day near the coast? *out to sea*

CHECK YOUR READING *Answer: Mountain slopes heat up and cool down faster than the valleys below them, so that winds flow up the slopes during the day and down the slopes during the night. Bodies of water heat up and cool down slower than land, so that winds flow inland during the day and toward the water during the night.*

DIFFERENTIATE INSTRUCTION

More Reading Support

I When do sea breezes occur? *during the day*

J When do mountain breezes occur? *at night*

Advanced Tell students that sea breezes are strongest when there are no clouds in the sky. Ask them to infer why. *Sample answer: With no clouds to block the Sun's energy from warming the land, air above the land is heated more quickly. The heated air rises, and dense ocean air moves into the area of low pressure. This increased rate of heating over land speeds up the movement of air.*

R Challenge and Extension, p. 150

Ongoing Assessment

 *Answer: Winter monsoons originate over land and are cool and dry. Summer monsoons originate over water and are moist; they bring heavy rains.*

Reinforce 

Have students relate the section to the Big Idea.

 Reinforcing Key Concepts, p. 152

3.2 ASSESS & RETEACH

Assess

Section 3.2 Quiz, p. 44

Reteach

Make a transparency of a globe, using the diagram on p. 87 as a guide. Do not put any arrows or labels on the transparency. Place the transparency on an overhead projector. Then, with the help of the class, fill in the diagram with the wind belts, using a different-colored marker for each belt. Students should come up with the pertinent information. If they stall, ask leading questions, such as, In which direction do the trade winds blow? and What low-pressure zone is located near the equator? As an alternative activity, you can make copies of the diagram on p. 87, delete the labels and arrows, and let students fill in the information individually.

Technology Resources

Have students visit **ClassZone.com** for reteaching of Key Concepts.

 CONTENT REVIEW

 CONTENT REVIEW CD-ROM

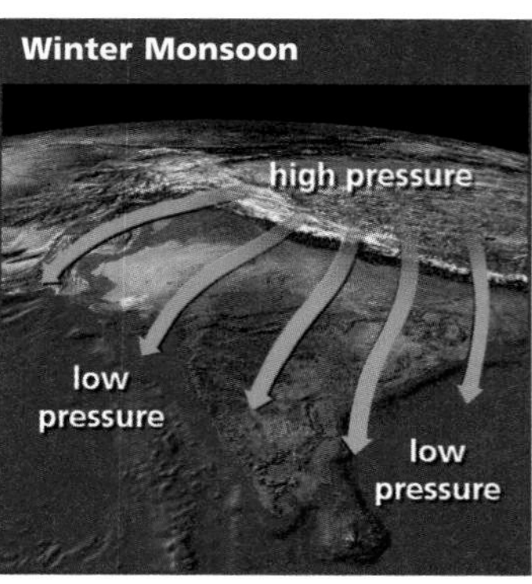

Dry air blows from the high-pressure area over the continent to the low-pressure areas over the ocean.

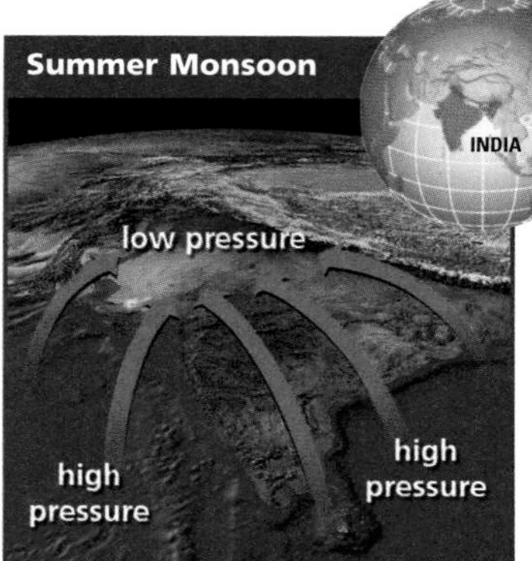

Moist air blows from the high-pressure areas over the ocean to the low-pressure area over the continent.

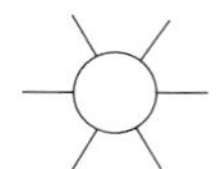

VOCABULARY
Add a description wheel for *monsoon* to your notebook.

Monsoons

Winds that change direction with the seasons are called **monsoons.** Like sea breezes and land breezes, monsoons are caused by the different heating and cooling rates of land and sea. However, monsoons flow longer distances and affect much larger areas.

Winter monsoons occur in regions where the land becomes much cooler than the sea during winter. High pressure builds over the land, and cool, dry wind blows out toward the sea. During summer this pattern reverses as the land becomes much warmer than the sea. Moist wind flows inland, often bringing heavy rains. The most extreme monsoons occur in South Asia and Southeast Asia. Farmers there depend on rain from the summer monsoon to grow crops.

 How do monsoon winds affect rainfall?

3.2 Review

KEY CONCEPTS

1. How does the uneven heating of Earth's surface cause winds to flow? (6.4.a)
2. How does Earth's rotation influence the movement of global winds? (6.4.e)
3. Why do some winds change direction in areas where land is near water? (6.4.e)

CRITICAL THINKING

4. **Compare and Contrast** How are global winds and local winds similar? How are they different?
5. **Analyze** Make a table that shows the causes and effects of local winds and monsoons.

CHALLENGE

6. **Predict** Suppose that a city is located in a valley between the sea and a mountain range. What kind of wind pattern would you predict for this area?

ANSWERS

1. It causes differences in air pressure, which causes air to move.

2. It causes global winds to curve.

3. Land and water heat up and cool down at different rates. These differences cause daily or seasonal changes in air pressure, leading to changes in wind direction.

4. Both winds are caused by the uneven heating of Earth's surface. Global winds flow over longer distances and are affected by the Coriolis effect.

5. Check students' tables for accuracy.

6. During the day, air would blow from the sea into the city and out of the city up the mountain slopes. At night, the pattern would reverse.

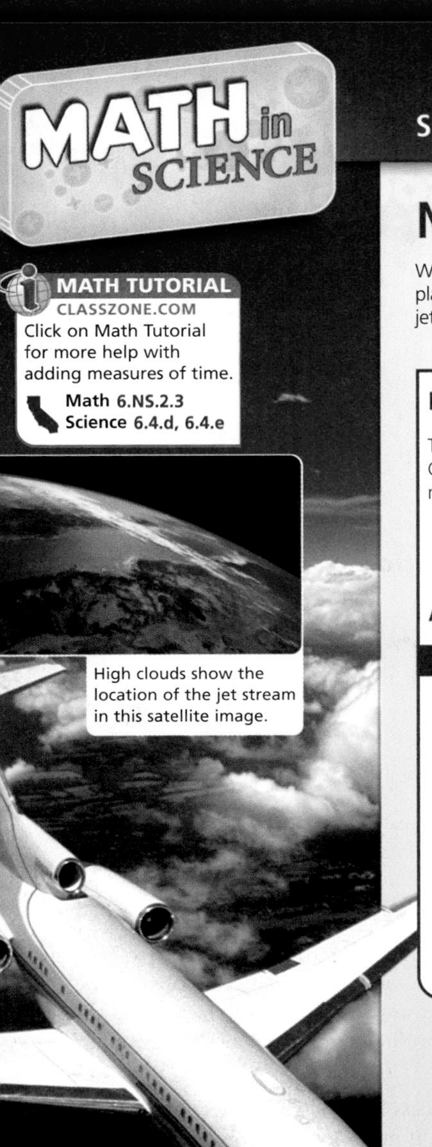

SKILL: ADDING MEASUREMENTS

Navigate the Jet Stream

When an airplane flies in the same direction as a jet stream, the airplane gets a boost in its speed. Pilots can save time if they fly with the jet stream. But flying against the jet stream slows an airplane down.

MATH TUTORIAL
CLASSZONE.COM
Click on Math Tutorial for more help with adding measures of time.

Math 6.NS.2.3
Science 6.4.d, 6.4.e

High clouds show the location of the jet stream in this satellite image.

Example

To determine the total flight time between San Francisco and Chicago, with a stop in Denver, you need to add the hours and minutes separately. Set up the problem like this:

San Francisco to Denver:	2 h	10 min
Denver to Chicago:	1 h	45 min
Total flight time:	3 h	55 min

ANSWER The total flight time is 3 hours 55 minutes.

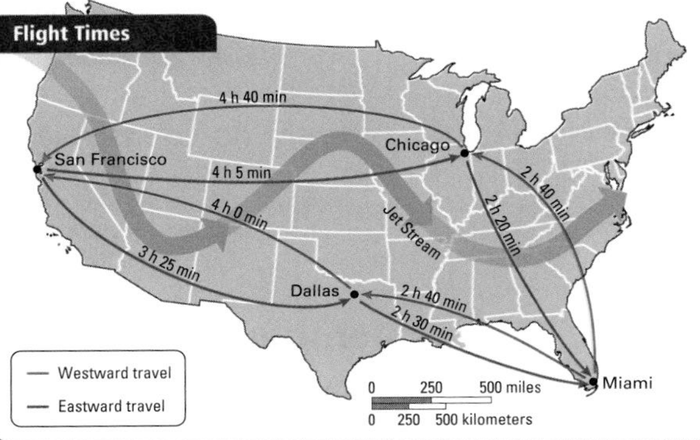

Use the map to answer the following questions.

1. What is the total flight time for an airplane flying from San Francisco to Miami through Chicago?
2. What is the total flight time for an airplane flying from San Francisco to Miami through Dallas?
3. Which route from Miami to San Francisco is faster? What is the time difference between the routes?
4. Compare the flight time from Chicago to San Francisco with the flight time from San Francisco to Chicago.

CHALLENGE Use the map scale to find the approximate distance between San Francisco and Chicago. What is the average air speed of an airplane that flies the route in 4 hours?

ANSWERS

1. 4 h 5 min + 2 h 20 min = 6 h 25 min

2. 3 h 25 min + 2 h 30 min = 5 h 55 min

3. Miami to San Francisco through Dallas is faster than through Chicago.
Through Chicago: 2 h 40 min + 4 h 40 min = 7 h 20 min
Through Dallas: 2 h 40 min + 4 h 0 min = 6 h 40 min
7 h 20 min − 6 h 40 min = 40 min

4. The flight from San Francisco to Chicago is 35 minutes shorter (4 h 40 min − 4 h 5 min = 0 h 35 min).

CHALLENGE *1800 mi ÷ 4 h = 450 mi/h*

MATH IN SCIENCE
Math Skills Practice for Science

Set Learning Goal

To add measurements to determine how flight times are affected by a jet stream

Math Standard

6.NS.2.3 Solve addition, subtraction, multiplication, and division problems, including those arising in concrete situations, that use positive and negative integers and combinations of these operations.

Present the Science

During World War II, U.S. pilots flew at high altitudes to avoid enemy fire. Their flight times were substantially reduced when they flew west to east in certain regions. The Swedish-American meteorologist Carl-Gustaf Rossby discovered belts of fast-moving, high-altitude winds, or jet streams.

Develop Computation Skills

- Remind students that they can divide a number of minutes by 60 to find the number of hours; the remainder is minutes. The number of minutes should never exceed 59.
- For question 3, have students practice expressing numbers of minutes in terms of hours and minutes. Ask: How would you change 95 minutes to hours and minutes? *One hour is 60 minutes. Thus, 95 min = 60 min + 35 min = 1 h 35 min.*

DIFFERENTIATION TIP For students with poor vision, list flight times in large writing on the board.

Close

Ask students to summarize how jet streams affect air travel. Tell them to refer to directions in their answer. *They decrease times for west-to-east flights and increase times for east-to-west flights.*

- Math Support, p. 181
- Math Practice, p. 182

Technology Resources

Students can visit **ClassZone.com** for practice in adding measurements.

MATH TUTORIAL

3.3 FOCUS

Set Learning Goals

Students will

- Explain how water in the atmosphere changes.
- Explain how clouds form.
- Describe types of clouds.
- Observe a model of how clouds form.

3-Minute Warm-Up

Display Transparency 21 or copy this exercise on the board:

Answer each question.

1. Does wind move horizontally or vertically? *horizontally*
2. Does warm air rise or sink? *rise*
3. Does air move from low- to high-pressure areas or from high to low? *high to low*
4. What does the Coriolis effect cause winds to do? *curve*

 3-Minute Warm-Up, p. T21

3.3 MOTIVATE

EXPLORE Condensation

PURPOSE To introduce the concept of condensation

TIP *5 min.* Divide the class into small groups. A clear glass of cool water can serve as a substitute for the hand mirror.

WHAT DO YOU THINK? *Tiny water droplets condensed on the mirror. There was little temperature difference between the air in the room and the air the classmate breathed out. The mirror, however, was cooler than the classmate's breath, which caused water vapor in the breath to condense on the mirror.*

KEY CONCEPT

3.3 Most clouds form as air rises and cools.

CALIFORNIA Content Standards

6.4.a Students know the sun is the major source of energy for phenomena on Earth's surface; it powers winds, ocean currents, and the water cycle.

6.4.e Students know differences in pressure, heat, air movement, and humidity result in changes of weather.

BEFORE, you learned

- Water vapor circulates from Earth to the atmosphere
- Warm air is less dense than cool air and tends to rise

NOW, you will learn

- How water in the atmosphere changes
- How clouds form
- About the types of clouds

VOCABULARY

evaporation p. 92
condensation p. 92
precipitation p. 93
humidity p. 94
saturation p. 94
relative humidity p. 94
dew point p. 94

EXPLORE Condensation (6.4.e)

How does condensation occur?

PROCEDURE

1. Observe the air as a classmate breathes out.
2. Observe a mirror as a classmate breathes onto it.

MATERIALS
hand mirror

WHAT DO YOU THINK?

- What changes did you observe on the mirror?
- Why could you see water on the mirror but not in the air when your classmate breathed out?

Temperature affects water in the air.

Water is always in the atmosphere. You may see water in solid form, such as falling snow. Water may also be present as liquid water droplets. Even if you can't see any water, it is still part of the air as water vapor, an invisible gas. When temperatures change, water changes its form.

- **Evaporation** is the process by which a liquid changes into a gas. For water to evaporate, it needs extra energy.
- **Condensation** is the process by which a gas, such as water vapor, changes into a liquid. Condensation occurs when moist air cools.

The picture on the left shows the processes of evaporation and condensation at work. Water in a teakettle absorbs heat. It gets enough energy to evaporate into water vapor. The invisible water vapor rises and escapes from the kettle. When the vapor hits the cooler air outside the kettle, it cools and condenses into tiny but visible water droplets.

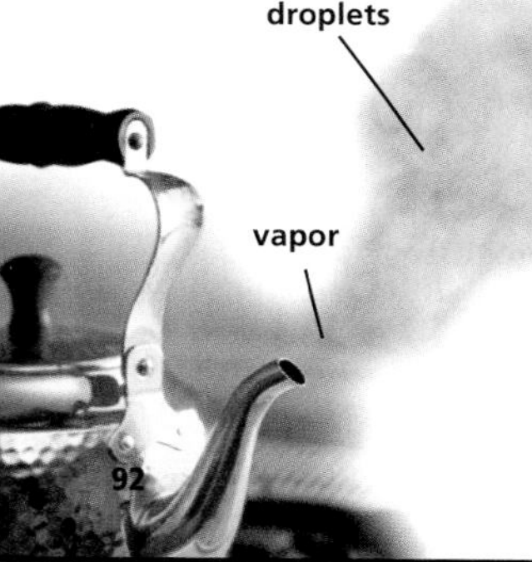

92

RESOURCES FOR DIFFERENTIATED INSTRUCTION

Below Level

UNIT RESOURCE BOOK

- Reading Study Guide A, pp. 155–156
- Decoding Support, p. 180

Advanced

UNIT RESOURCE BOOK

Challenge and Extension, p. 161

English Learners

UNIT RESOURCE BOOK

Spanish Reading Study Guide, pp. 159–160

- Audio Readings in Spanish
- Audio Readings (English)

Water in the Air

Vast amounts of Earth's water are recycled. The oceans hold most of the water. Water is also stored in lakes, rivers, and ice sheets; in plants; and underground. Energy from sunlight causes molecules to evaporate from the surface of a body of water. These molecules become part of the air in the form of water vapor.

As air rises in the atmosphere, it cools. The loss of heat causes water vapor to condense into tiny water droplets or ice crystals. If the droplets or crystals grow and become heavy enough, they fall as rain, snow, sleet, or hail. Any type of liquid or solid water that falls to Earth's surface is called **precipitation.** Earth's water goes through a never-ending cycle of evaporation, condensation, and precipitation.

VOCABULARY Add a description wheel for *precipitation* to your notebook.

Water vapor can also condense on solid surfaces. Have you ever gotten your shoes wet while walking on grass in the early morning? The grass was covered with dew, which is water that has condensed on cool surfaces at night. If the temperature is cold enough, water vapor can change directly into a covering of ice, called frost.

CHECK YOUR READING Summarize the way water moves in the water cycle. For each part of the cycle, specify whether water exists as a gas, liquid, or solid.

Water Cycle

1 Water evaporates from bodies of water.
2 Water vapor condenses to form clouds.
3 Water falls to Earth's surface as precipitation.

DIFFERENTIATE INSTRUCTION

More Reading Support

A What does it mean to say that water is recycled? *that it moves continually between Earth's surface and the atmosphere*

B Rain is a type of what? *precipitation*

English Learners English learners may have difficulty distinguishing between the words *then* and *than*. Explain that *then* is used in reference to time and *than* is used to make comparisons. On p. 95 in the Condensation lab, *then* is used several times in sequences of events. On p. 94, however, *than* is used to make a comparison. "For a while the air gains water vapor because more water evaporates than condenses."

3.3 INSTRUCT

Teach the Standards

Water cycle 6.4.a

In this section: Students learn how energy from the Sun fuels a never-ending cycle of evaporation, condensation, and precipitation known as the water cycle. Have students draw a diagram that follows the path of a rain drop through each stage of the water cycle.

- **previously taught:** energy movement, p. 11; radiation, p. 22; Earth system, pp. 41–44; water cycle, pp. 60–61
- **future opportunities:** hurricanes, pp.123–124; thunderstorms, pp. 128–130; water cycle and ecosystems, p. 385; temperature and water cycle, p. 389; air quality and acid rain, p. 499

Develop Critical Thinking

HYPOTHESIZE Have students form hypotheses about some part of the water cycle. For example, students may hypothesize that water evaporates more quickly from a lake during summer than during winter. Write the hypotheses on the board. If time permits, have the class brainstorm how they could test their ideas.

Ongoing Assessment

Explain how water in the atmosphere changes.

Ask: What are the three processes that water goes through in the water cycle? *Water goes through evaporation, which is the changing of a liquid to a gas; condensation, which is the changing of a gas to a liquid, and precipitation, which is the falling of liquid or solid water to Earth's surface.*

CHECK YOUR READING *Answer: Water evaporates from bodies of liquid water. It then rises as a gas in the atmosphere and condenses into liquid to form clouds. Then it falls back to Earth's surface as liquid or solid precipitation.*

Address Misconceptions

IDENTIFY Ask: What weighs more: humid air or dry air? If students answer humid air, they may hold the misconception that on humid days the air is heavier because of its water vapor content.

CORRECT Tell students that the molecular weight of water is 18. The molecular weight of dry air is, on average, 29. In fact, the more humid a quantity of air is, the less dense and heavy it is.

REASSESS Ask: Which is less dense, humid air or dry air? *humid air* Which would travel faster and farther, a baseball hit in humid air or a baseball hit in dry air? *a baseball hit in humid air*

Technology Resources

Visit **ClassZone.com** for background on common student misconceptions.

MISCONCEPTION DATABASE

Teach Difficult Concepts

Students may have a hard time understanding how temperature affects evaporation and condensation. Remind them that heat causes water molecules in air to move faster. It's difficult for these fast-moving molecules to join together and condense. In contrast, water molecules move slower and closer together as air cools, and the rate of condensation increases.

Humidity and Relative Humidity

C

On a warm summer day, evaporation of moisture from your skin can help you feel comfortable. However, a lot of water vapor in the air can cause less moisture to evaporate from your skin. With less evaporation, the air will seem hotter and damper. **Humidity** is the amount of water vapor in air. Humidity varies from place to place and from time to time.

The illustration shows how humidity increases in a sealed container. As water molecules evaporate into the air, some start to condense and return to the water. For a while the air gains water vapor because more water evaporates than condenses. But eventually the air reaches **saturation,** a condition in which the rates of evaporation and condensation are equal. Any additional water that evaporates is balanced by water that condenses.

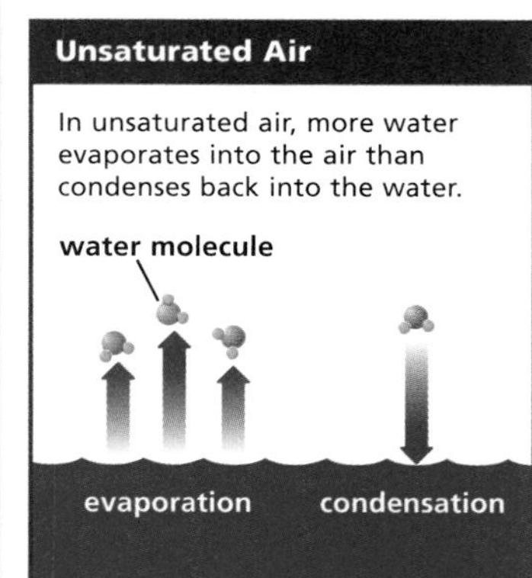

Unsaturated Air
In unsaturated air, more water evaporates into the air than condenses back into the water.
water molecule
evaporation
condensation

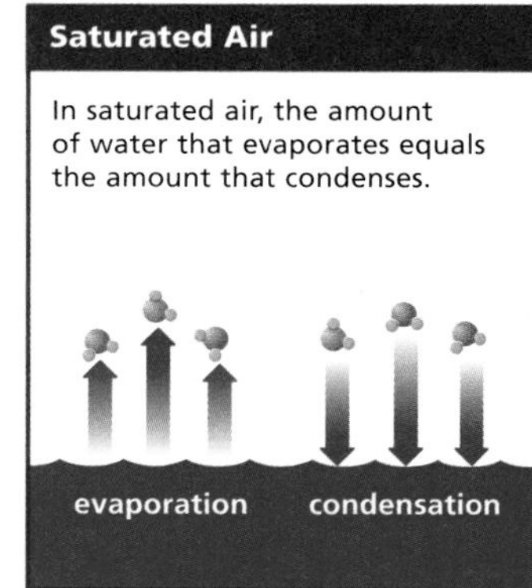

Saturated Air
In saturated air, the amount of water that evaporates equals the amount that condenses.
evaporation
condensation

READING TIP
Relative means "considered in comparison with something else."

The amount of water vapor in air at saturation depends on the temperature of the air. The warmer air is, the more water vapor it takes to saturate it. Scientists use this principle to describe the humidity of air in two different ways: relative humidity and dew point.

Relative humidity compares the amount of water vapor in air with the maximum amount of water vapor that can be present at that temperature. For example, air with 50 percent relative humidity has half the amount of water needed for saturation. If the amount of water vapor in air stays the same, relative humidity will decrease as the air heats up and increase as the air cools.

? D

Dew point is the temperature at which air with a given amount of water vapor will reach saturation. For example, air with a dew point of 26°C (79°F) will become saturated if it cools to 26°C. The higher the dew point of air, the more water vapor the air contains.

94 Unit 1: **The Earth System**

DIFFERENTIATE INSTRUCTION

More Reading Support

C What is humidity? *the amount of water vapor in the air*

D The temperature at which air will reach saturation is called what? *dew point*

Advanced Tell students that heat index describes how warm the air actually feels. Explain to students that at high temperatures, even a low level of relative humidity increases the heat index. Ask students to infer why it is impossible for a temperature of 120°F and a relative humidity level of 90% to exist simultaneously. *Sample answer: Relative humidity increases as air cools down and decreases as air heats up. Therefore, a high air temperature of 120°F would yield a much lower relative humidity level than 90 percent.*

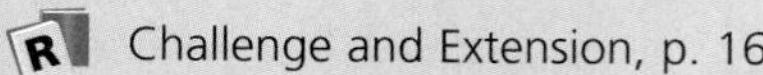
Challenge and Extension, p. 161

Water vapor condenses and forms clouds.

Clouds are made of condensed water vapor. As warm air rises in the atmosphere, it cools. When the air cools to its dew point—the temperature at which air reaches saturation—water vapor condenses into tiny droplets or ice crystals. These droplets and crystals are so light that they either float as clouds on rising air or fall very slowly.

Rising warm air can produce clouds. Water vapor begins to condense when the air cools to its dew point.

Recall how dew condenses on grass. Water vapor condenses on liquid water or on something solid. There are no large solid surfaces in the air. However, the air is filled with tiny particles such as dust, smoke, and salt from the ocean. Water vapor condenses on these particles.

INVESTIGATE Condensation

How does a cloud form?

PROCEDURE

1. Add a spoonful of water to the bottle to increase the humidity inside it.
2. Lay the bottle on its side. Light a match, blow it out, and then stick the match into the bottle for a few seconds to let smoke flow in. Replace the cap.
3. Squeeze the bottle quickly and then release it. Observe what happens when the bottle is allowed to expand.

WHAT DO YOU THINK?

- What happened to the water vapor inside the bottle when you squeezed the bottle and then let it expand?
- How did the smoke affect what happened to the water vapor?

CHALLENGE How would the cloud change if you raised or lowered the temperature inside the bottle?

SKILL FOCUS
Observing (6.4.e)

MATERIALS
- clear 1-liter plastic bottle with cap
- water at room temperature
- tablespoon
- matches

TIME
10 minutes

INVESTIGATE
Condensation

PURPOSE To observe how clouds form

TIPS *10 min.* Suggest the following to students:

- To make it easier to observe changes in the bottle, place the bottle against a dark background.
- Test your prediction for the Challenge question.

WHAT DO YOU THINK? *The water vapor condensed and a cloud formed. Water must condense on something solid—without the smoke particles, the water could not have condensed.*

CHALLENGE *Sample answer: Lowering the temperature would increase the rate of condensation and cause a thicker cloud to form. Raising the temperature would decrease the rate of condensation.*

Datasheet, Condensation, p. 162

Technology Resources

Customize this student lab as needed or look for an alternative. Print rubrics to assess student lab reports.

Lab Generator CD-ROM

Ongoing Assessment

Explain how clouds form.

Ask: What is the first step in cloud formation? *Warm air rises and cools.*

DIFFERENTIATE INSTRUCTION

More Reading Support

E What are clouds made of? *condensed water vapor*

F What do cloud droplets condense on? *tiny solid particles*

Below Level In the Condensation lab above, some students may expect the cloud to look puffy and white—similar to a cumulus cloud. Stress that it takes billions upon billions of water droplets to form the fluffy white clouds we see in the sky.

Teacher Demo

Students may have a hard time understanding how clouds stay in the air. Use the following demonstration to show that it takes only the slightest updraft to keep cloud droplets aloft. Obtain a small, white downy feather. Place the feather in your hand, raise it to about eye level, then blow on it lightly, keeping the feather aloft. Afterwards, tell students that although clouds may appear huge when viewed from Earth's surface, the droplets that make up clouds are extremely small and light—it takes only a slight updraft to keep them, like the feather, aloft.

History of Science

In the early 1800s, two men worked separately to develop classification systems for clouds. The first man, Jean Baptiste Lamarck, published his system in his native language, French. He unwisely opted to have it printed in a journal that included astrological forecasts, and his work was therefore viewed as unscientific. The second man, Luke Howard of England, used Latin, the language of scholars during that time, to name the types of clouds. By using words that were understood in many countries, Howard ensured that his classification would stand the test of time—the cloud classification system used today stems from his original work.

Ongoing Assessment

CHECK YOUR READING *Answer: Clouds formed at high altitudes are made of ice crystals. Clouds formed at low altitudes are made of water droplets (or a mixture of ice crystals and water droplets).*

Observe different types of clouds.

Characteristics of Clouds

If you watch the sky over a period of time, you will probably observe clouds that do not look alike. Clouds have different characteristics because they form under different conditions. The shapes and sizes of clouds are mainly determined by air movement. For example, puffy clouds form in air that rises sharply or moves straight up and down. Flat, smooth clouds covering large areas form in air that rises gradually.

G Location affects the composition of clouds. Since the troposphere gets colder with altitude, clouds that form at high altitudes are made of tiny ice crystals. Closer to Earth's surface, clouds are made of water droplets or a mixture of ice crystals and water droplets.

CHECK YOUR READING How are clouds that form at high altitudes different from clouds that form close to Earth's surface?

COMBINATION NOTES Record information about the three main cloud types.

In the illustration on page 97, notice that some cloud names share word parts. That is because clouds are classified and named according to their altitudes, the ways they form, and their general characteristics. The three main types of clouds are cirrus, cumulus, and stratus. These names come from Latin words that suggest the clouds' appearances.

H

- ***Cirrus*** (SEER-uhs) means "curl of hair." Cirrus clouds appear feathery or wispy.
- ***Cumulus*** (KYOOM-yuh-luhs) means "heap" or "pile." Cumulus-type clouds can grow to be very tall.
- ***Stratus*** (STRAT-uhs) means "spread out." Stratus-type clouds form in flat layers.

Word parts are used to tell more about clouds. For example, names of clouds that produce precipitation contain the word part *nimbo-* or *nimbus.* Names of clouds that form at a medium altitude have the prefix *alto-*.

Cirrus Clouds

Cirrus clouds form in very cold air at high altitudes. Made of ice crystals, they have a wispy or feathery appearance. Strong winds often blow streamers or "tails" off cirrus clouds. These features show the direction of the wind in the upper troposphere. You will usually see cirrus clouds in fair weather. However, they can be a sign that a storm is approaching.

cirrus clouds

DIFFERENTIATE INSTRUCTION

More Reading Support

G Clouds that form at high altitudes are made of what? *ice crystals*

H What does *cirrus* mean? *"curl of hair"*

Advanced Clouds can form when two air masses of different temperatures meet—as the warm air is forced upward, it expands and cools, and water vapor condenses. Clouds can also form when warm air reaches a mountain slope. Have students infer why. *Sample answer: When the warm air reaches the mountain, it is forced to rise. The air then expands and cools, and water vapor condenses.*

Cloud Types

The three main cloud types are cirrus, cumulus, and stratus. These names can be combined with each other and with other word parts to identify more specific cloud types.

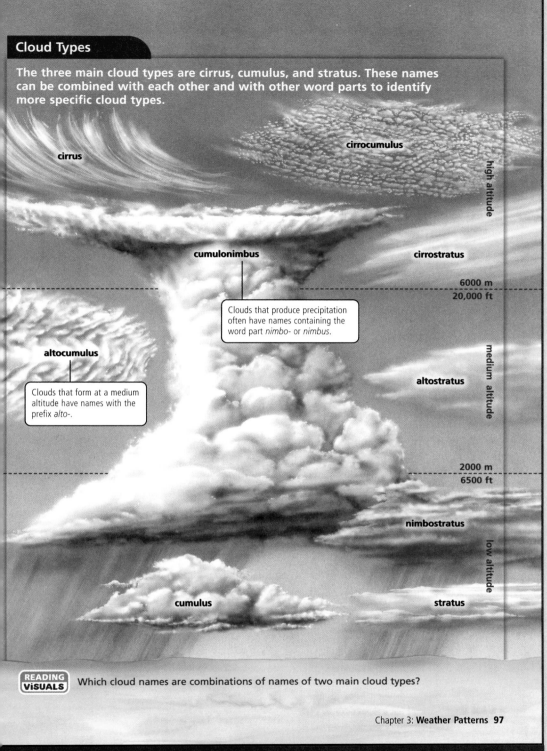

cirrus

cirrocumulus

high altitude

cumulonimbus

cirrostratus

6000 m
20,000 ft

Clouds that produce precipitation often have names containing the word part *nimbo-* or *nimbus*.

altocumulus

Clouds that form at a medium altitude have names with the prefix *alto-*.

altostratus

medium altitude

2000 m
6500 ft

nimbostratus

low altitude

cumulus

stratus

READING VISUALS Which cloud names are combinations of names of two main cloud types?

DIFFERENTIATE INSTRUCTION

Advanced Make copies of the visual and pass them out to students. Have students use a field guide to clouds to sketch and label additional types of clouds on their copies of the visual.

Alternative Assessment Have students use cotton balls to model the different types of clouds. Students can stretch out the cotton balls to make them resemble cirrus or stratus clouds or pile the balls on top of one another to form cumulus clouds. Have them discuss what materials they could use to model tall cumulonimbus clouds.

Teach from Visuals

To help students interpret the cloud types visual:

- Tell students that clouds are classified according to their altitudes: high, medium, and low. However, a cumulonimbus cloud is often classified as a "cloud of vertical development." Ask: On the basis of the visual, why do you think this is so? ***Sample answer: because a cumulonimbus cloud extends from a low altitude to a high altitude***
- Ask: Which cloud's name indicates that it is a medium-altitude, layered cloud? *altostratus*
- Ask: How are cirrocumulus and cirrostratus clouds alike? How are they different? ***Both are high-altitude clouds. The two differ in shape—cirrocumulus clouds are puffy, and cirrostratus clouds are layered.***

Real World Example

Since ancient times, people have looked to the sky to forecast the weather, so that a body of folklore has developed around clouds. Some of this folklore is based more on myth than reality. However, certain cloud types do tend to precede certain types of weather, just as early sky-watchers noted. For example, if the moon appears pale and hazy over a period of several hours, it may be covered by wispy cirrus or cirrostratus clouds. These clouds often precede a warm front and therefore indicate that rain is on the way.

Ongoing Assessment

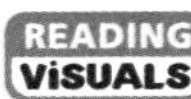

Answer: cirrocumulus and cirrostratus

Develop Critical Thinking

APPLY Ask the following questions to reinforce cloud characteristics:

- What keeps cumulus clouds separate from one another? ***Warm air rises straight up and cooler air sinks along the sides of the clouds.***
- Why are stratus clouds generally smooth and spread out? ***because they form without strong air movement***
- Scientists have many names for clouds, including *stratocumulus.* What can you infer about the location and shape of a stratocumulus cloud? ***Sample answer: Its name contains the prefix*** strato- ***so it is a low-altitude cloud. It is puffy like a cumulus cloud, but spread out in a thick layer like a stratus cloud.***

Ongoing Assessment

CHECK YOUR READING *Answer: They are the tallest clouds, and they produce thunderstorms.*

READING TIP

As you read each description of a main cloud type, look back at the visual on page 97. Notice the different clouds that have the main cloud type as part of their names.

Cumulus Clouds

? I

cumulus clouds

Cumulus clouds are puffy white clouds with darker bases. They look like cotton balls floating in the sky. There are several varieties of cumulus clouds. Usually they appear in the daytime in fair weather, when warm air rises and its water vapor condenses. Cooler air sinks along the sides of the clouds, keeping cumulus clouds separate from one another.

cumulonimbus clouds

If cumulus clouds keep growing taller, they can produce showers. The precipitation usually lasts less than half an hour in an area because the clouds are moving. The tallest clouds are cumulonimbus clouds, or thunderheads. These clouds produce thunderstorms that drop heavy rainfall. A cumulonimbus cloud can tower 18 kilometers (11 mi) above Earth's surface. By comparison, jet planes usually fly at about 10 kilometers (6 mi). Strong high-altitude winds often cause the top of the cloud to jut out sharply.

How are cumulonimbus clouds different from other cumulus clouds?

Stratus Clouds

stratus clouds

Have you ever noticed on some days that the whole sky looks gray? You were looking at stratus clouds. They form in layers when air cools over a large area without rising or when the air is gently lifted. Stratus clouds are smooth because they form without strong air movement.

Some low stratus clouds are so dark that they completely block out the Sun. These clouds produce steady, light precipitation—unlike the brief showers that come from cumulus clouds. Stratus clouds that form at high altitudes are much thinner than low stratus clouds. You can see the Sun and the Moon through them. The ice crystals in high stratus clouds can make it seem as if there's a circle of colored light around the Sun or the Moon.

DIFFERENTIATE INSTRUCTION

More Reading Support

I Cumulus clouds usually form in daytime in what kind of weather? ***fair***

J What type of cloud forms in layers? ***stratus***

Inclusion Physically challenged students may have difficulty drawing sketches or writing answers in their notebooks. Encourage these students to record their answers or observations on audiotape. For example, if an activity calls for students to draw different cloud types, allow physically challenged students to tape their descriptions of the types. If students do not have access to tape recorders, they can give oral descriptions.

This layer of fog covers most of the Golden Gate Bridge. The fog formed as water vapor condensed in the air above cool ocean water.

Fog

Fog is a cloud that rests on the ground or a body of water. Like stratus clouds, fog has a smooth appearance. It usually forms when a surface is colder than the air above it. Water vapor in the air condenses as it cools, forming a thick mist. Fog on land tends to be heaviest at dawn, after the ground has cooled overnight. It clears as the ground is heated up by sunlight.

Fog can look beautiful rolling over hills or partly covering structures such as bridges. However, it often makes transportation dangerous by limiting visibility. In the United States close to 700 people die each year in automobile accidents that occur in dense fog.

3.3 Review

KEY CONCEPTS

1. Describe the three forms in which water is present in the atmosphere. (6.4.a)
2. How does altitude affect the composition of clouds? (6.4.e)
3. How are clouds classified? (6.4.e)

CRITICAL THINKING

4. **Summarize** Describe the main characteristics of cirrus, cumulus, and stratus clouds.
5. **Draw Conclusions** Why might cumulonimbus clouds be more likely to form on sunny days than on days with little sunlight?

CHALLENGE

6. **Apply** Imagine that the sky has turned very cloudy after a hot morning. You notice that the bread in your sandwich is soggy and the towels on the towel rack won't dry. Explain why these things are happening. Use the following terms in your answer: *condensation, evaporation, relative humidity.*

Ongoing Assessment

Describe types of clouds.

Ask: How does fog compare to cirrus, cumulus, and stratus clouds? *Fog is a smooth cloud that rests on the ground or a body of water. It is most like flat, layered stratus clouds, which can form close to Earth's surface. In contrast, wispy cirrus clouds form at high altitudes, and puffy cumulus clouds can grow quite tall.*

Reinforce 

Have students relate the section to the Big Idea.

 Reinforcing Key Concepts, p. 163

3.3 ASSESS & RETEACH

Assess

 Section 3.3 Quiz, p. 45

Reteach

Have pairs of students work cooperatively to test each other on cloud types. Let students develop their own assessment procedures. For example, students may wish to sketch different clouds and have their partners identify them. Other pairs might focus on cloud prefixes and suffixes. Still other pairs might test each other on the weather conditions associated with various cloud types.

Technology Resources

Have students visit **ClassZone.com** for reteaching of Key Concepts.

 **CONTENT REVIEW**

 **CONTENT REVIEW CD-ROM**

ANSWERS

1. Sample answer: solid: snow; liquid: rain; gas: water vapor

2. At high altitudes, clouds are made of ice crystals. At lower altitudes, clouds are made of water droplets or a mixture of droplets and ice crystals.

3. according to altitude and appearance

4. cirrus: made of ice crystals, located at high altitudes; cumulus: puffy and white with darker bases; stratus: form in layers over a large area

5. Sunshine increases the air temperature, making air rise.

6. The clouds have lowered the air temperature, so that the rate of evaporation has decreased and the rate of condensation has increased. Relative humidity is high.

CHAPTER INVESTIGATION

Focus

PURPOSE To construct a psychrometer in order to measure relative humidity

OVERVIEW Students will use thermometers and milk cartons to construct psychrometers. They will take wet-bulb and dry-bulb temperature readings at several locations around the school and use a chart to determine relative humidities. Students will find the following:

- Unless the relative humidity is 100 percent, wet-bulb readings are lower than dry-bulb readings.
- Relative humidity is related to changes in the weather.

Lab Preparation

- Review how to use the Relative Humidity Table before beginning the investigation. Tell students to use a ruler as a guide by placing it below the line for the dry-bulb reading.
- Prior to the investigation, have students read through the investigation and prepare their data tables. Or you may wish to copy and distribute datasheets and rubrics.

 UNIT RESOURCE BOOK, pp. 184–192

 SCIENCE TOOLKIT, F14

Lab Management

Divide students into groups of three or four. Assign different groups to take two readings inside the school, two readings outside, and one reading inside and one reading outside. Then compare results and discuss patterns.

SAFETY Tell students to notify you immediately if a thermometer should break—they should not try to clean up the glass themselves.

INCLUSION Some students may have difficulty with the Relative Humidity Table. Review how to subtract measurements before beginning the investigation.

CHAPTER INVESTIGATION

Relative Humidity

OVERVIEW AND PURPOSE Finding out the relative humidity can help you predict how comfortable you will feel on a hot day or whether dew will form on the ground. You can use a psychrometer to measure relative humidity. A psychrometer is a device made from two thermometers—one with a wet bulb and the other with a dry bulb. In this activity you will

- make a milk-carton psychrometer
- use it to measure the relative humidity of the air at two locations in your school

Problem

Which location will have the greater relative humidity?

Hypothesize

Write a hypothesis in "If . . . , then . . . , because . . ." form to answer the problem.

MATERIALS
- 2 thermometers
- cotton or felt cloth
- 3 rubber bands
- plastic bowl
- water at room temperature
- scissors
- pint milk carton
- ruler
- Relative Humidity Chart

6.4.e, 6.7.a, 6.7.b, 6.7.d, 6.7.e

Procedure

1. Make a table like the one shown on the sample notebook page to record your data.
2. Check the two thermometers that you are using in this experiment to make sure they show the same temperature. Wrap a piece of cotton or felt cloth around the bulb of one thermometer. Hold the cloth in place with a rubber band as shown in the photograph. Dip this wet-bulb thermometer into a bowl of room-temperature water until the cloth is soaked.
3. Use scissors to cut a small hole in one side of the milk carton, 2 centimeters from the bottom of the carton. Place the wet-bulb thermometer on the same side as the hole that you made in the milk carton, and attach it with a rubber band. Push the tail of the cloth through the hole. Attach the dry-bulb thermometer as shown.

step 3

INVESTIGATION RESOURCES

 CHAPTER INVESTIGATION, Relative Humidity
- Relative Humidity Table, p. 183
- Level A, pp. 184–187
- Level B, pp. 188–191
- Level C, p. 192

Advanced students should complete Levels B & C.

 Writing a Lab Report, D12–13

Technology Resources

Customize this student lab as needed or look for an alternative. Print rubrics to assess student lab reports.

 **Lab Generator CD-ROM**

Content Standard
6.4.e Students know differences in pressure, heat, air movement, and humidity result in changes of weather.

Investigation Standard
6.7.b Select and use appropriate tools and technology (including calculators, computers, balances, spring scales, microscopes, and binoculars) to perform tests, collect data, and display data.

4 Fill the carton with water to just below the hole so that the cloth will remain wet. Empty the bowl and place the completed psychrometer inside it.

5 Write "science room" under the heading "Location 1" in your data table. Take your first readings in the science classroom about 10 minutes after you set up your psychrometer. Read the temperatures on the two thermometers in degrees Celsius. Record the temperature readings for the first location in the first column of your table.

6 Choose a second location in your school, and identify it under the heading "Location 2" in the data table. Take a second set of temperature readings with your psychrometer in this location. Record the readings in the second column of your table.

7 Subtract the wet-bulb reading from the dry-bulb reading for each location. Record this information in the third row of your data table.

8 Use the relative humidity table your teacher provides to find each relative humidity (expressed as a percentage). In the left-hand column, find the dry-bulb reading for location 1 that you recorded in step 5. Then find in the top line the number you recorded in step 7 (the difference between the dry-bulb and wet-bulb readings). Record the relative humidity in the last row of your data table. Repeat these steps for location 2.

Observe and Analyze

Write It Up

1. **RECORD OBSERVATIONS** Draw the setup of your psychrometer. Be sure your data table is complete.
2. **IDENTIFY** Identify the variables and constants in this experiment. List them in your **Science Notebook.**
3. **COMPARE** How do the wet-bulb readings compare with the dry-bulb readings?
4. **ANALYZE** If the difference between the temperature readings on the two thermometers is large, is the relative humidity high or low? Explain why.

Conclude

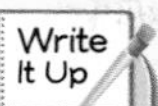

1. **INTERPRET** Answer the question in the problem. Compare your results with your hypothesis.
2. **IDENTIFY LIMITS** Describe any possible errors that you made in following the procedure.
3. **APPLY** How would you account for the differences in relative humidity that you obtained for the two locations in your school?

INVESTIGATE Further

CHALLENGE Use the psychrometer to keep track of the relative humidity in your classroom over a period of one week. Make a new chart to record your data. What do you notice about how the changes in relative humidity relate to the weather conditions outside?

Relative Humidity

Problem Which location will have the greater relative humidity?

Hypothesize

Observe and Analyze

Table 1. Relative Humidity at Two Locations

	Location 1	Location 2
Dry-bulb temperature		
Wet-bulb temperature		
Difference between dry-bulb and wet-bulb readings		
Relative humidity		

Conclude

Observe and Analyze

SAMPLE DATA location 1: dry-bulb temperature 24°C, wet-bulb temperature 21°C, relative humidity 76%; location 2: dry-bulb temperature 22°C, wet-bulb temperature 18°C, relative humidity 68%

1. *Students should provide accurate drawings and complete tables.*
2. *independent variable: location of reading; dependent variable: humidity; constant: psychrometer setup*
3. *Answers will vary, but in general wet-bulb readings should be lower than dry-bulb readings unless the relative humidity is 100 percent.*
4. *It is low, because the difference shows that water is evaporating quickly from the wet bulb.*

Conclude

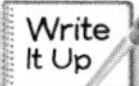

1. *Answers will vary, depending on observations and results in the investigation.*
2. *Sample answer: Temperature readings may have been inaccurate.*
3. *Sample answer: Trees, windows, the heating system, and other factors may affect the humidity recorded at a particular location.*

INVESTIGATE Further

CHALLENGE Sample answer: Relative humidity increases as temperature decreases, and vice versa.

ost-Lab Discussion

sk: Which groups tended to record the greatest differences relative humidity readings? *Answer: groups that took one easurement inside and one measurement outside*

eaching with Technology

ave students use CBL and a relative humidity sensor to take relative umidity readings outside and inside. Make a data table of their findings n the board, and calculate an average for indoor and outdoor readings.

3.4 FOCUS

Set Learning Goals

Students will

- Explain how precipitation forms.
- Describe how precipitation is measured.
- Define acid rain.
- Analyze data to learn how precipitation patterns vary across California.

3-Minute Warm-Up

Display Transparency 21 or copy this exercise on the board:

Match each definition with the correct term.

Definitions

1. liquid or solid water that falls to Earth's surface *b*
2. the amount of water vapor in air compared with the maximum amount that can be present at that temperature *d*
3. the condition of Earth's atmosphere at a particular time and place *a*
4. the process by which a gas changes into a liquid *c*

Terms

a. weather c. condensation
b. precipitation d. relative humidity

 3-Minute Warm-Up, p. T21

3.4 MOTIVATE

THINK ABOUT

PURPOSE To introduce the concept of how water droplets combine to form larger droplets

DEMONSTRATE Sprinkle water droplets on a tilted cookie sheet and have students observe how the droplets combine and eventually flow down the cookie sheet.

Sample answer: Some drops are heavier than others. When they become too heavy to remain suspended, they fall.

KEY CONCEPT

3.4 Water falls to Earth's surface as precipitation.

CALIFORNIA Content Standards

6.4.a Students know the sun is the major source of energy for phenomena on Earth's surface; it powers winds, ocean currents, and the water cycle.

6.4.e Students know differences in pressure, heat, air movement, and humidity result in changes of weather.

BEFORE, you learned

- Water moves between Earth's surface and the atmosphere
- Water vapor condenses into clouds

NOW, you will learn

- How precipitation forms
- How precipitation is measured
- About acid rain

VOCABULARY

freezing rain p. 104
sleet p. 104
hail p. 104
acid rain p. 106

THINK ABOUT

Why does steam from a shower form large drops?

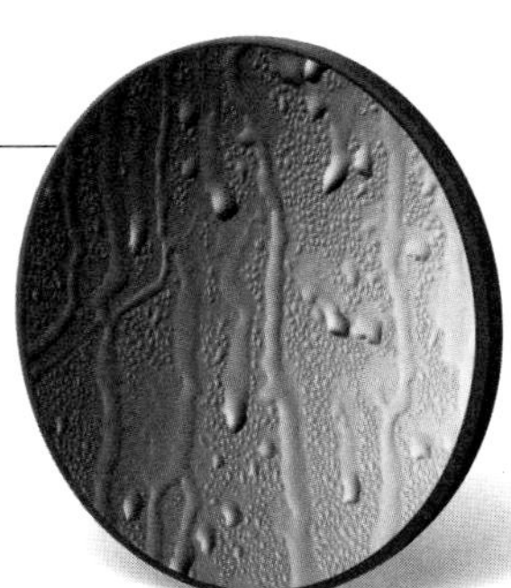

When you run a hot shower, the bathroom fills up with water vapor. The vapor condenses into tiny droplets that make it seem as if you are standing in fog. You may also see larger drops running down cool surfaces, such as a mirror. Why do some drops fall while others remain suspended?

Precipitation forms from water droplets or ice crystals.

All precipitation comes from clouds. For example, rain occurs when water droplets in a cloud fall to the ground. Then why doesn't every cloud produce precipitation? Cloud droplets are much smaller than a typical raindrop. They weigh so little that it takes only a slight upward movement of air to hold them up. In order for rain to fall from a cloud and reach Earth's surface, the cloud droplets must become larger and heavier.

One way that precipitation can form is through the combining of cloud droplets. The tiny droplets of water move up and down in clouds. Some collide with each other and combine, forming slightly bigger droplets. As the droplets continue to combine, they grow larger and larger. Eventually they become heavy enough to fall. It takes about a million droplets to make a single raindrop.

Water droplets combining to form a raindrop

RESOURCES FOR DIFFERENTIATED INSTRUCTION

Below Level

UNIT RESOURCE BOOK

- Reading Study Guide A, pp. 166–167
- Decoding Support, p. 180

 **AUDIO CDS**

Advanced

UNIT RESOURCE BOOK

- Challenge and Extension, p. 172
- Challenge Reading, pp. 176–177

English Learners

UNIT RESOURCE BOOK

Spanish Reading Study Guide, pp. 170–171

 **AUDIO CDS**

- Audio Readings in Spanish
- Audio Readings (English)

Another way that precipitation can form is through the growth of ice crystals. When the temperature inside a cloud is below freezing, water vapor changes into tiny ice crystals. The crystals grow by collecting more water vapor or by colliding and merging with one another. When the crystals become heavy enough, they fall from the cloud. Snow isn't the only type of precipitation that forms this way. Most rain in the United States actually starts out as falling ice crystals. Before the crystals reach the ground, they melt in a layer of warm air.

CHECK YOUR READING How do cloud droplets become large enough to fall as precipitation?

Measuring Precipitation

Scientists use a rain gauge to measure rainfall. A funnel or opening at the top of the gauge allows rain to flow into a cylinder. By measuring the water collected, you can find out how much rain fell in a storm or over a period of time.

READING TIP A gauge (gayj) is an instrument used for measuring or testing.

Snow depth can be measured with a long ruler. Because the amount of water in snow varies, scientists use a special gauge to find out how much water the snow contains. A built-in heater melts the snow so that it can be measured just like rain.

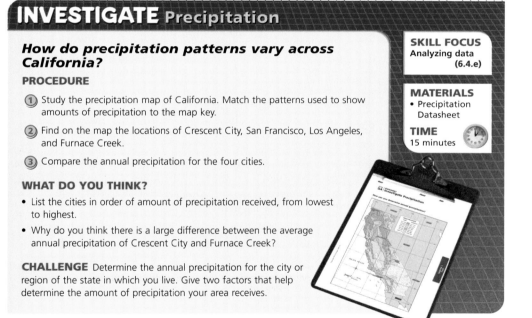

INVESTIGATE Precipitation

How do precipitation patterns vary across California?

SKILL FOCUS Analyzing data (6.4.e)

MATERIALS
- Precipitation Datasheet

TIME 15 minutes

PROCEDURE

1. Study the precipitation map of California. Match the patterns used to show amounts of precipitation to the map key.
2. Find on the map the locations of Crescent City, San Francisco, Los Angeles, and Furnace Creek.
3. Compare the annual precipitation for the four cities.

WHAT DO YOU THINK?

- List the cities in order of amount of precipitation received, from lowest to highest.
- Why do you think there is a large difference between the average annual precipitation of Crescent City and Furnace Creek?

CHALLENGE Determine the annual precipitation for the city or region of the state in which you live. Give two factors that help determine the amount of precipitation your area receives.

3.4 INSTRUCT

Teach the Standards

Changes of Weather 6.4.e

In this section: Students will learn that precipitation forms as water droplets or ice crystals combine in clouds and become heavy enough to fall.

- **previously taught:** water cycle, pp. 60–61; climate, p. 65
- **future opportunities:** weather fronts, pp. 118–119; storms, pp. 123–130

INVESTIGATE Precipitation

PURPOSE To analyze precipitation patterns across California

TIPS *15 min.* Tell students to make sure they understand the symbols on the map before beginning.

WHAT DO YOU THINK? *Furnace Creek, Los Angeles, Sacramento, Crescent City; because Crescent City is close to the ocean and Furnace Creek is far inland.*

CHALLENGE *Student responses will vary depending on location.*

 California Precipitation Map, p. 173

 Datasheet, Precipitation, p. 174

Technology Resources

Customize this student lab as needed or look for an alternative. Print rubrics to assess student lab reports.

 **Lab Generator CD-ROM**

Ongoing Assessment

Explain how precipitation forms.

Ask: How does precipitation form from ice crystals? *Water vapor in clouds changes into ice crystals, which grow until they become heavy enough to fall.*

CHECK YOUR READING *Answer: by combining with one another*

DIFFERENTIATE INSTRUCTION

More Reading Support

A Most rain in the United States starts out as what? *ice crystals*

B How do scientists measure rainfall? *with rain gauges*

English Learners Have students write the definitions for *freezing rain, sleet, hail,* and *acid rain* in their Science Word Dictionaries. Some English learners may be unfamiliar with the concept of steam in a shower (p. 102). Also, be sure that students do not confuse the words *lightning* and *lighting* (p. 107).

Real World Example

Weather forecasters were not always the professionals we see on television today. During the 1940s and 1950s, weather was not considered real news and was presented more like entertainment. One of the first weather announcers was an animated sheep called Wooly Lamb. Later, cartoonists, musicians, and beauty contestants presented the weather, sometimes singing and dancing their way through the forecasts.

Integrate the Sciences

Raindrops can join together and grow in size as long as the surface tension—the force that holds them together—is greater than the frictional drag of the air they fall through. When a raindrop reaches a size of about 5 mm, however, frictional drag becomes greater than surface tension, and the raindrop breaks up into smaller drops.

Ongoing Assessment

Describe how precipitation is measured.

Ask: How is snow measured? *with rulers and with gauges that have built-in heaters*

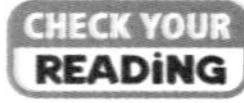

Answer: freezing rain, sleet, and snow

When you watch weather reports on television, you often see storm systems passing across a weather map. Some of these images are made with Doppler radar. The radar shows which areas are getting precipitation and how fast it is falling. Forecasters use this information to estimate the total amount of precipitation an area will receive.

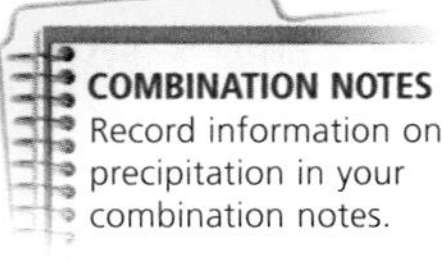

COMBINATION NOTES Record information on precipitation in your combination notes.

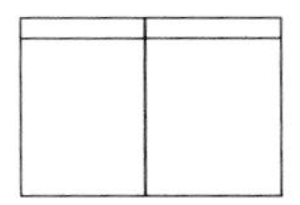

Types of Precipitation

Precipitation reaches Earth's surface in various forms. Some precipitation freezes or melts as it falls through the atmosphere.

1. **Rain and Drizzle** Rain is the most common type of precipitation. Raindrops form from liquid cloud droplets or from ice crystals that melt as they fall. A light rain with very small drops is called drizzle. Drizzle usually comes from stratus clouds, which don't have enough air movement to build up larger raindrops.
2. **Freezing Rain** Raindrops may freeze when they hit the ground or other surfaces in cold weather. **Freezing rain** covers surfaces with a coating of ice. During an ice storm, roads become slippery and dangerous. The weight of ice can also bring down trees and power lines.
3. **Sleet** When rain passes through a layer of cold air, it can freeze before hitting the ground. The small pellets of ice that form are called **sleet.**
4. **Snow** As ice crystals grow and merge in clouds, they become snowflakes. Snowflakes come in many different shapes and sizes. Usually they have six sides or branches. When snow falls through moist air that is near freezing, the flakes tend to join together in clumps. When snow falls through colder and drier air, snowflakes don't join together, and the snow is powdery.

Most snowflakes have six branches or sides.

D

5. **Hail** Surprisingly, the largest type of frozen precipitation often arrives in warm weather. Lumps or balls of ice that fall from cumulonimbus clouds are called **hail.** During a thunderstorm, violent air currents hurl ice pellets around the cloud. These pellets grow as water droplets freeze onto them at high elevations. Some start to fall and then are pushed back up again. They may repeat this process several times, adding a layer of ice each time. Eventually they fall to the ground.

Large hailstones can damage property and injure people and animals. The biggest hailstone ever found in the United States weighed 1.7 pounds and was about as wide as a compact disc.

Which forms of precipitation undergo a change after they leave a cloud?

DIFFERENTIATE INSTRUCTION

More Reading Support

C What is a light rain with very small drops called? *drizzle*

D Hail falls from what type of clouds? *cumulonimbus*

Below Level Use simple demonstrations to help students visualize different types of precipitation. For example, a spray bottle with an adjustable nozzle can be used to model the difference between rain and drizzle. Use the same bottle to spray water on an ice pack to model freezing rain.

Advanced Have students who are interested in learning about the smell caused by rain read the following article:

Challenge Reading, pp. 176–177

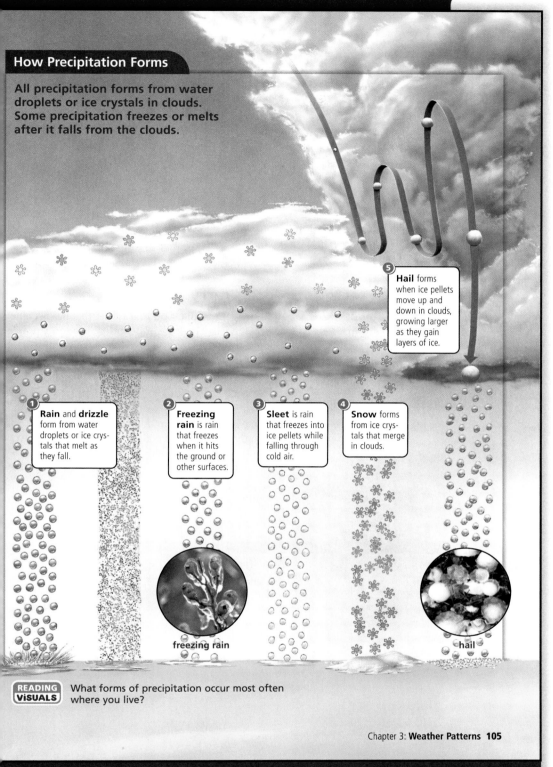

How Precipitation Forms

All precipitation forms from water droplets or ice crystals in clouds. Some precipitation freezes or melts after it falls from the clouds.

5 **Hail** forms when ice pellets move up and down in clouds, growing larger as they gain layers of ice.

READING VISUALS What forms of precipitation occur most often where you live?

DIFFERENTIATE INSTRUCTION

Alternative Assessment Have students make booklets showing the different types of precipitation. Students can cut out photographs from magazines, download images from the Internet, or draw pictures themselves. Encourage interested students to take their own photographs for the booklets. Students should label all pictures and include captions explaining how the precipitation forms and any changes it may undergo as it falls to Earth's surface.

Advanced

R Challenge and Extension, p. 172

Teach from Visuals

To help students interpret the visual on precipitation formation:

- Have them compare and contrast freezing rain and sleet. *Both fall from clouds as raindrops. Freezing rain freezes once it hits the ground or cold surfaces. Sleet freezes as it falls through cold air.*
- Ask: Which type of precipitation always forms from ice crystals? *Snow is the only type that always forms from ice crystals.*
- Ask: Which types of precipitation are the most similar? Explain your answer. *Sample answer: Rain and drizzle are the most similar because they both form from water droplets or from ice crystals that melt as they fall. The only real difference is in the size of the drops—in a drizzle, the drops are generally smaller than raindrops.*

Develop Critical Thinking

INFER To help students better understand precipitation, ask the following questions:

- What is the major factor in determining which type of precipitation falls to Earth's surface? *air temperature*
- What does the fact that most rain starts out as falling ice crystals tell you about temperatures in clouds? *Sample answer: Temperatures in clouds are generally colder than temperatures closer to Earth's surface.*

Ongoing Assessment

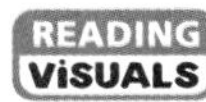

Answers will vary, depending on the climate of the area.

Ongoing Assessment

Define acid rain.

Ask: What is acid rain? *rain that is more acidic than normal because of pollution*

Answer: Sulfur dioxide and nitrogen oxides enter the air as pollution and combine with water vapor to form acids. The acids mix with cloud droplets or ice crystals that fall as precipitation.

Reinforce the BIG idea

Have students relate the section to the Big Idea.

 Reinforcing Key Concepts, p. 175

3.4 ASSESS & RETEACH

Assess

 Section 3.4 Quiz, p. 46

Reteach

To be sure students understand the relationship between cloud types and precipitation, give them the following scenario: You're watching a weather forecast on television. The forecaster says that hail is falling to the north of your area and a light drizzle is falling to the south. Infer which types of clouds are to the north and south of your area. *Hail falls from cumulonimbus clouds, so these types of clouds are to the north. Drizzle usually falls from stratus clouds, so these types of clouds are to the south.*

Technology Resources

Have students visit **ClassZone.com** for reteaching of Key Concepts.

 CONTENT REVIEW

 CONTENT REVIEW CD-ROM

These trees have few needles because acid rain has damaged the trees.

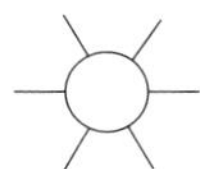

VOCABULARY
Add a description wheel for *acid rain* to your notebook.

Precipitation can carry pollution.

Rainwater is naturally a little acidic. **Acid rain** is rain that has become much more acidic than normal because of pollution. Factories, power plants, automobiles, and some natural sources release sulfur dioxide and nitrogen oxides into the air. These gases can combine with water vapor to form sulfuric acid and nitric acid. The acids mix with cloud droplets or ice crystals that eventually fall to Earth's surface as precipitation.

Because wind can blow air pollution hundreds of kilometers, acid rain may fall far from the source of the pollution. Acid rain harms trees and raises the acidity of lakes, making it difficult for fish to live in them. Acid rain also damages the surfaces of buildings and sculptures.

 How does acid rain form? Your answer should mention water vapor.

3.4 Review

KEY CONCEPTS

1. What are the two ways that rain can form? **(6.4.a)**
2. How are rain and snow measured? **(6.4.e)**
3. What human activities cause acid rain? **(6.4.e)**

CRITICAL THINKING

4. **Compare and Contrast** How are sleet and freezing rain similar? How are they different?
5. **Draw Conclusions** When a large hailstone is cut open, four layers can be seen. What conclusions can you draw about the formation of the hailstone?

CHALLENGE

6. **Predict** Temperatures in a cloud and on the ground are below freezing. A warmer layer of air lies between the cloud and the ground. What type of precipitation do you predict will occur? Explain.

ANSWERS

1. from water droplets that fall from clouds or from ice crystals that melt as they fall through warm air

2. Rain is measured with a rain gauge. Snow depth can be measured with a ruler, and snow's water content is measured with a heated rain gauge.

3. transportation, manufacturing, and power generation

4. Both are types of frozen precipitation. Sleet freezes as it falls through the air. Freezing rain remains liquid until it falls on a cold surface.

5. The hailstone moved up and down within a cloud at least four times, gaining new layers.

6. Freezing rain; ice crystals from the cold cloud will melt as they fall through the layer of warm air and will refreeze upon contact with the cold ground.

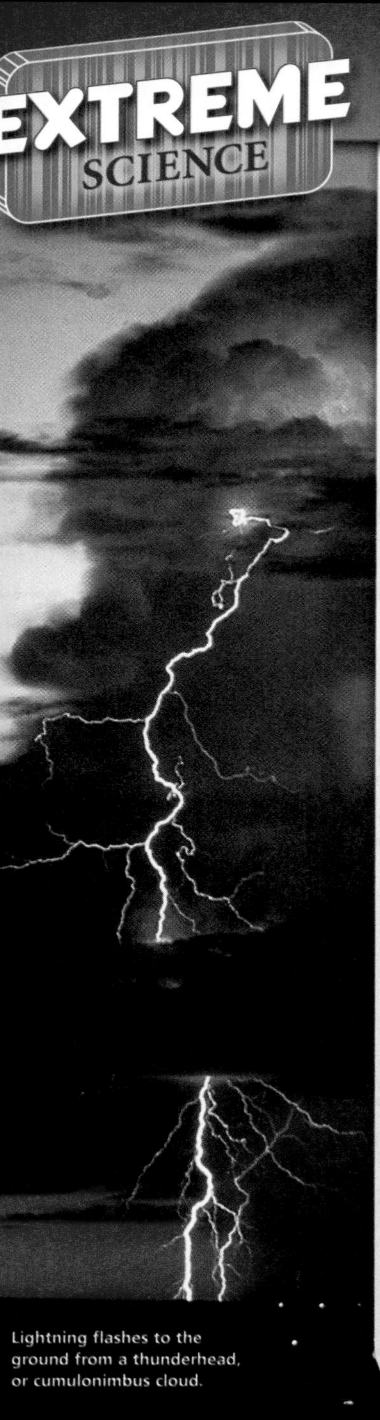

Lightning flashes to the ground from a thunderhead, or cumulonimbus cloud.

ELEMENTS OF WEATHER

Caught Inside a Thunderhead

6.4.e Students know differences in pressure, heat, air movement, and humidity result in changes of weather.

In 1959, engine failure forced Lieutenant Colonel William Rankin to eject from his plane at a high altitude. When his parachute opened, he thought he was out of danger. However, he soon realized that he was caught inside a cumulonimbus cloud during a fierce thunderstorm.

As Rankin hung by his parachute, violent convection currents inside the cloud tossed him "up, down, sideways, clockwise." The rain was so heavy that he feared he would drown in midair. Lightning flashed all around him. Rankin finally landed after 40 minutes. He had many injuries, including bruises from hailstones. Fortunately, none of the storm's lightning had struck him.

Where Lightning Strikes

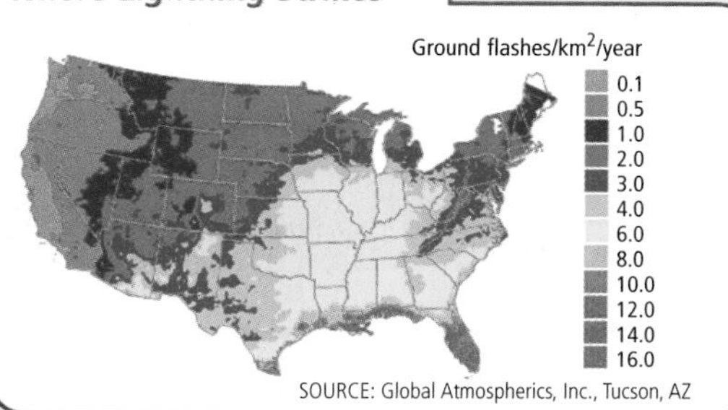

SOURCE: Global Atmospherics, Inc., Tucson, AZ

Water, Wind, Hail, and Lightning

- A cumulonimbus cloud, or thunderhead, can rise to over 18 kilometers above Earth's surface. Convection currents transfer energy in the form of heat from Earth's surface to the storm.
- A cumulonimbus cloud may contain 500,000 tons of water.
- Thunderstorm clouds cause 8 million lightning flashes each day.

EXPLORE

1. **ANALYZE** Find where you live on the map. Use the color key to figure out how often lightning strikes each square kilometer in your area.
2. **CHALLENGE** Use information from the Resource Center to propose an explanation for the pattern of lightning frequencies shown on the map.

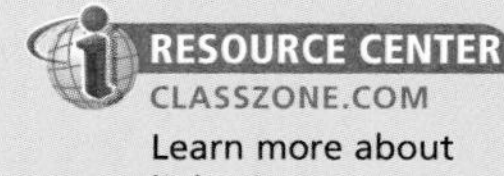

Learn more about lightning.

107

EXPLORE

1. ***ANALYZE*** *Answers will vary, depending on students' location.*
2. ***CHALLENGE*** *It takes the right combination of weather conditions for thunderstorms to develop. For example, some areas are too cold or too dry.*

EXTREME SCIENCE
Fun and Motivating Science

Set Learning Goal

To recognize patterns of lightning frequency

Present the Science

On average, lightning strikes about 100 times per second. In the United States it occurs most frequently in the Southeast, where the weather is dominated by maritime tropical air masses. Lightning is one of the most devastating natural hazards—the National Weather Service estimates that 7500 forest fires are caused by lightning each year. In addition, lightning accounts for 200 deaths annually in the United States alone. Property damage adds up to hundreds of millions of dollars yearly.

Discussion Questions

Discuss some of the hazards associated with thunderstorms, such as high winds, hail, fires, and floods. Help students to see that they can reduce their risk of injury by following certain safety guidelines.

Ask: What should you do if you see a thunderstorm approaching? *seek shelter immediately*

Ask: What should you do if you are caught outdoors in a thunderstorm and no shelter is available? *stay away from trees, fences, and other objects that lightning is likely to strike*

Close

Ask: Which area gets the most lightning? *Florida* Which area gets the least? *West Coast*

Technology Resources

Students can visit **ClassZone.com** to find out more about lightning strikes in their area.

 **RESOURCE CENTER**

BACK TO

the BIG idea

Have students look back at the photograph on pp. 76–77. Ask them to use the photograph to summarize what they've learned about clouds and to predict what weather conditions will result. *Answer: The clouds in the distance appear tall and dark. They are probably cumulonimbus clouds, which are a type of cumulus cloud. They usually form during the day in fair weather, when warm air rises and condenses. Cumulonimbus clouds can be 18 km high and produce thunderstorms with heavy rainfall.*

KEY CONCEPTS SUMMARY

SECTION 3.1
Ask: Do the air molecules at the bottom of the column represent denser or thinner air? *denser*

SECTION 3.2
Ask: What has caused the area on the left to have higher pressure than the area on the right? *uneven heating of Earth's surface*

Ask: What is probably happening to the air in the area of low pressure? *It is rising and expanding.*

SECTION 3.3
Ask: What must be present in the air for cloud droplets to form? *tiny particles of solids, such as dust or smoke*

Ask: What type of cloud is shown in the illustration? *cumulus*

SECTION 3.4
Ask: What happens to a water droplet when it becomes too heavy for air to hold up? *It falls as precipitation.*

Ask: What other types of precipitation form from ice crystals? *drizzle, freezing rain, sleet, hail*

Review Concepts

- Big Idea Flow Chart, p. T17
- Chapter Outline, pp. T23–T24

3 Chapter Review

the BIG idea

Some features of weather have predictable patterns.

KEY CONCEPTS SUMMARY

1 Air pressure varies in the atmosphere.

Air pressure is the force of air molecules pushing on an area. Air pressure decreases as you move higher in the atmosphere. Air pressure can also differ in two locations at the same altitude.

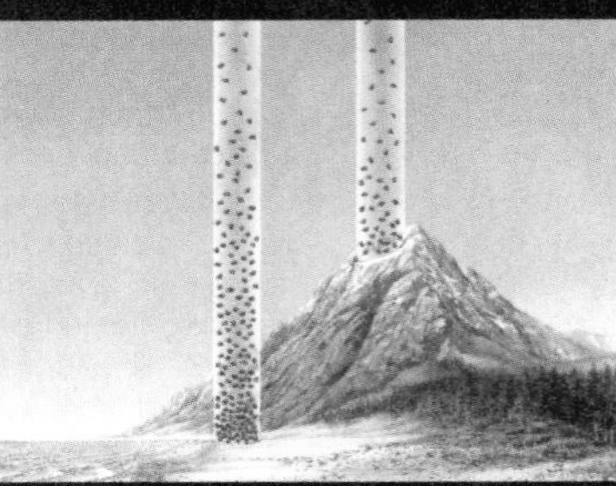

VOCABULARY
air pressure p. 79
barometer p. 82

2 The atmosphere has wind patterns.

Wind blows from areas of high pressure toward areas of low pressure. Earth's rotation causes long-distance winds to curve.

VOCABULARY
wind p. 83
global wind p. 84
Coriolis effect p. 85
jet stream p. 88
monsoon p. 90

3 Most clouds form as air rises and cools.

Clouds are made of tiny water droplets or ice crystals that condense from water vapor in rising air.

VOCABULARY
evaporation p. 92
condensation p. 92
precipitation p. 93
humidity p. 94
saturation p. 94
relative humidity p. 94
dew point p. 94

4 Water falls to Earth's surface as precipitation.

Water droplets in clouds merge to form raindrops.

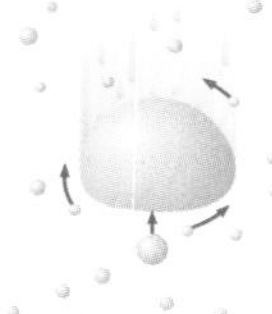

Ice crystals in clouds can form snow, rain, and other types of precipitation.

VOCABULARY
freezing rain p. 104
sleet p. 104
hail p. 104
acid rain p. 106

108 Unit 1: **The Earth System**

Technology Resources

Have students visit **ClassZone.com** or use the CD-ROM for a cumulative review of concepts.

CONTENT REVIEW

CONTENT REVIEW CD-ROM

Engage students in a whole-class interactive review of Key Concepts. Edit content as you wish.

POWER PRESENTATIONS

Reviewing Vocabulary

Write a definition of each term. Use the meaning of the underlined root to help you.

Word	Root Meaning	Definition
EXAMPLE air pressure	to apply force	the force of air molecules pushing on an area
1. barometer	weight	
2. saturation	to fill	
3. global wind	sphere	
4. monsoon	season	
5. evaporation	steam	
6. condensation	thick	
7. humidity	moist	
8. precipitation	thrown down	

Reviewing Key Concepts

Multiple Choice *Choose the letter of the best answer.*

9. The movement of air molecules causes (6.4.e)
- **a.** air density
- **b.** air pressure
- **c.** humidity
- **d.** relative humidity

10. Winds curve as they move across Earth's surface because of (6.4.e)
- **a.** the Coriolis effect
- **b.** air pressure
- **c.** humidity
- **d.** relative humidity

11. Jet streams generally flow toward the (6.4.e)
- **a.** north
- **b.** south
- **c.** east
- **d.** west

12. Condensation increases with greater (6.4.e)
- **a.** relative humidity
- **b.** air temperature
- **c.** air pressure
- **d.** wind speed

13. Any type of liquid or solid water that falls to Earth's surface is called (6.4.a)
- **a.** precipitation
- **b.** dew
- **c.** a monsoon
- **d.** humidity

14. What are low-altitude clouds composed of? (6.4.e)
- **a.** snowflakes
- **b.** raindrops
- **c.** water droplets
- **d.** water vapor

15. Clouds made of ice crystals form under conditions of (6.4.e)
- **a.** strong winds
- **b.** high altitude
- **c.** low humidity
- **d.** high pressure

16. Which type of cloud is most likely to bring thunderstorms? (6.4.e)
- **a.** stratus
- **b.** altostratus
- **c.** cumulonimbus
- **d.** cirrus

17. Over short distances wind blows toward areas of (6.4.e)
- **a.** high pressure
- **b.** high density
- **c.** low temperature
- **d.** low pressure

18. The doldrums and the horse latitudes are both regions of (6.4.e)
- **a.** high air pressure
- **b.** light winds
- **c.** heavy rains
- **d.** low temperatures

19. As altitude increases, air pressure usually (6.4.e)
- **a.** decreases
- **b.** increases
- **c.** varies more
- **d.** varies less

Short Answer *Write a short answer to each question.*

20. What causes land breezes to flow at night? (6.4.e)

21. Why does hair take longer to dry after a shower on days with high relative humidity? (6.4.e)

22. How does air pressure affect air density? (6.4.e)

23. Why are dust and other particles necessary for precipitation? (6.4.a)

24. How did global wind belts and calm regions affect transportation in the past? (6.4.e)

ASSESSMENT RESOURCES

ASSESSMENT BOOK
- Chapter Test A, pp. 47–50
- Chapter Test B, pp. 51–54
- Chapter Test C, pp. 55–58
- Alternative Assessment, pp. 59–60

STANDARDS REVIEW AND PRACTICE
pp. 31–32, 37–40, 57–60, 63–66

Technology Resources

Edit test items and answer choices.

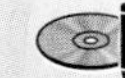

Test Generator CD-ROM

Visit **ClassZone.com** to extend test practice.

Test Practice

Reviewing Vocabulary

1. *an instrument that measures air pressure*
2. *a condition in which the evaporation of water into the air is balanced by the condensation of water*
3. *winds that travel thousands of kilometers in steady patterns*
4. *winds that change direction with the seasons*
5. *the process by which a liquid changes to a gas*
6. *the process by which a gas changes into a liquid*
7. *the amount of water vapor in the air*
8. *liquid or solid water that falls to Earth's surface*

Reviewing Key Concepts

9. *b*
10. *a*
11. *c*
12. *a*
13. *a*
14. *c*
15. *b*
16. *c*
17. *d*
18. *b*
19. *a*
20. *Land cools off faster than the sea, and air flows toward the resulting low-pressure area over the water.*
21. *The humid air is close to saturation, so evaporation is slow.*
22. *Density increases as air pressure increases, because higher pressure pushes air molecules closer together.*
23. *Such particles are solids but are light enough to stay in the atmosphere for long periods. Water vapor will only condense on something solid.*
24. *Sailors used to seek out global wind belts to speed their sailing ships. They also avoided zones of high and low pressure because the winds there were often too light to move ships.*

Thinking Critically

25. The sunlight warms the air and the soil in the terrarium and gives energy to plants.

26. The diagram should indicate water evaporating from the soil, condensing on the glass, and sliding or falling down.

27. Air is warmer inside the terrarium than outside it.

28. Sample answer: a week or two

29. Ice would cool the bottom of the terrarium, so water would condense on the ground. This might cause fog to form.

30. The terrarium would probably dry out as water vapor escaped through the hole.

31. Both are caused by the different heating and cooling rates of land and water. Monsoons are seasonal, whereas sea breezes occur daily.

32. The air will become less dense because air expands as it rises.

33. First, sulfur dioxide and nitrogen oxides could have been released into the air. Winds flowing eastward could have moved the gases over the forest. The gases could have combined with water vapor in clouds to form acids that eventually fell as acid rain.

34. sleet

35. freezing rain

36. rain

37. snow

38. hail

the BIG idea

39. Answers should reflect information learned in the chapter.

40. Responses should indicate how energy from the Sun produces the basic elements of weather.

UNIT PROJECTS

Check to make sure students are working on their projects. Check schedules and work in progress.

 Unit Projects, pp. 5–10

Thinking Critically

The soil in this terrarium was soaked with water two weeks ago. Then the box was sealed so that no moisture could escape. Use the diagram to answer the next six questions.

25. IDENTIFY EFFECTS How does sunlight affect conditions inside the terrarium? (6.4.a)

26. ANALYZE Draw a diagram of the water cycle inside the terrarium. (6.4.a)

27. INFER What do the water drops on the glass indicate about the temperatures inside and outside the terrarium? (6.4.a)

28. PREDICT Explain how long you think the plants will live without being watered.

29. PREDICT What would happen if you placed the terrarium on top of a block of ice? (6.4.a)

30. HYPOTHESIZE How would conditions inside the terrarium change if there were a hole in one side of it? (6.4.a)

31. COMPARE AND CONTRAST How are sea breezes and monsoon winds alike, and how are they different? (6.4.e)

32. PREDICT A cumulus cloud is growing taller. What will happen to the density of the air beneath it? Explain. (6.4.e)

33. INFER Imagine that a group of factories and power plants lies 200 kilometers to the west of a forest where trees are dying. Describe three steps in a process that could be causing the trees to die.

IDENTIFY EFFECTS Write the type of precipitation that would form under each set of conditions. (6.4.e)

Conditions	Precipitation
34. above-freezing air inside a cloud and freezing air beneath it	
35. above-freezing air beneath a cloud and freezing temperatures on the ground	
36. below-freezing air inside a cloud and above-freezing temperatures in the air beneath it and on the ground	
37. below-freezing air inside a cloud and beneath it	
38. ice pellets hurled around by air currents inside a cloud	

the BIG idea

39. APPLY Look again at the photograph on pages 76–77. Now that you have finished the chapter, how would you change your response to the question on the photograph? (6.4.e)

40. WRITE Write one or more paragraphs explaining how energy from the Sun influences the weather. In your discussion, include at least three of the following topics: (6.4.a)

- global wind belts
- high- and low-pressure areas
- local winds
- monsoons
- the water cycle
- cloud formation

UNIT PROJECTS

If you need to do an experiment for your unit project, gather the materials. Be sure to allow enough time to observe results before the project is due.

MONITOR AND RETEACH

If students have trouble applying the concepts in items 25–33, review each step of the water cycle. Students should refer to the diagram on p. 93, then make a three-part sketch of the water cycle.
Part 1 should show how water evaporates from bodies of water.
Part 2 should show how water vapor condenses to form clouds.
Part 3 should show water falling to Earth as precipitation.
Students may benefit from summarizing one or more sections of the chapter.

 Summarizing the Chapter, pp. 202–203

Standards-Based Assessment

For more practice, go to . . .
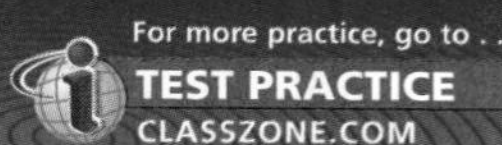

Analyzing a Diagram

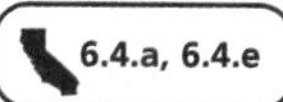

This diagram shows the water cycle. Use it to answer the questions below.

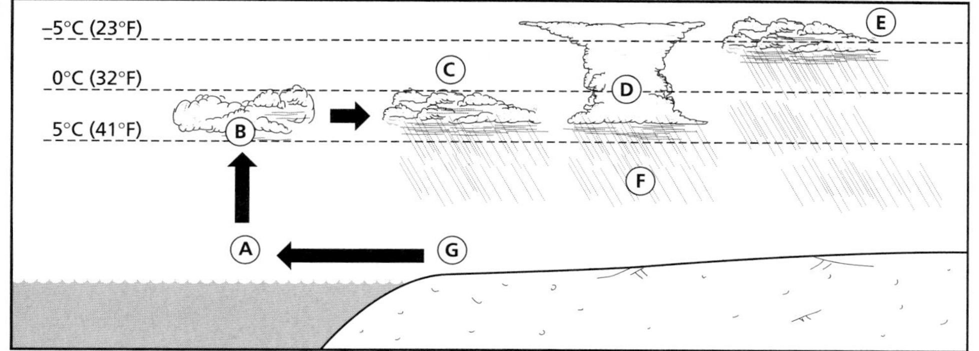

1. Where is evaporation occurring?
- **a.** A
- **b.** D
- **c.** F
- **d.** G

2. Where is condensation occurring?
- **a.** A
- **b.** B
- **c.** F
- **d.** G

3. Where is precipitation shown?
- **a.** A
- **b.** C
- **c.** E
- **d.** F

4. Where is hail most likely to form?
- **a.** C
- **b.** D
- **c.** E
- **d.** F

5. From which cloud will precipitation fall as snow and then turn to rain?
- **a.** B
- **b.** C
- **c.** D
- **d.** E

6. Which is the best estimate for the temperature in B?
- **a.** 8°C (46°F)
- **b.** 3°C (37°F)
- **c.** –3°C (27°F)
- **d.** –8°C (17°F)

7. What does the arrow pointing up between A and B indicate?
- **a.** the movement of moisture
- **b.** the direction of the wind
- **c.** a low pressure area
- **d.** a reflection off the water

Extended Response

Answer the two questions below in detail. Include some of the terms shown in the word box. In your answers underline each term you use.

low air pressure	cool air	west
high air pressure	warm air	east
Coriolis effect		

8. Whenever Richard rides in an airplane, he feels a pop inside his ears. Explain what is happening in the air to produce the pop in Richard's ears.

9. Winds tend to blow from west to east across the United States. If Earth spun in the other direction, how might the winds across the United States be different?

REFLECTING ON THE CHAPTER

Have students answer the following questions in their **Science Notebook:**

1. Which topics in this chapter would you like to learn more about?
2. How do the concepts in this chapter relate to your life?
3. How should you revise your plan for experimenting if your Unit Project is not working to your expectations?

California Content Standards

6.4.a Students know the sun is the major source of energy for phenomena on Earth's surface; it powers winds, ocean currents, and the water cycle.

6.4.e Students know differences in pressure, heat, air movement, and humidity result in changes of weather.

Analyzing a Diagram

1. a *2. b* *3. d* *4. b* *5. d* *6. b* *7. a*

Extended Response

8. RUBRIC

4 points for a response that correctly answers the question and uses the following terms accurately:

- low air pressure
- high air pressure

Sample: As Richard rides up in the airplane, the air pressure decreases as his altitude increases. The air inside his ear is still at a high air pressure, so it tries to move toward the area of low air pressure outside his ear.

3 points correctly answers the question and uses one term accurately

2 points correctly answers the question, but does not use the terms

9. RUBRIC

4 points for a response that correctly answers the question and uses the following terms accurately:

- east
- west
- Coriolis effect

Sample: The Coriolis effect would still cause the global winds to curve, but the wind belt over the United States would probably move from east to west instead.

3 points correctly answers the question and uses the term *Coriolis effect* accurately

2 points correctly uses the term *Coriolis effect*

1 point indicates that the global winds curve

CHAPTER

Weather Fronts and Storms

Earth Science UNIFYING PRINCIPLES

PRINCIPLE 1
Heat energy inside Earth and radiation from the Sun provide energy for Earth's processes.

PRINCIPLE 2
Physical forces, such as gravity, affect the movement of all matter on Earth and throughout the universe.

PRINCIPLE 3
Matter and energy move among Earth's rocks and soil, atmosphere, waters, and living things.

PRINCIPLE 4
Earth has changed over time and continues to change.

Unit: The Earth System BIG IDEAS

CHAPTER 1
Energy and Change
Waves and heat flow transfer energy.

CHAPTER 2
Energy in the Earth System
The Sun is the major source of energy for Earth's atmosphere and surface.

CHAPTER 3
Weather Patterns
Some features of weather have predictable patterns.

CHAPTER 4
Weather Fronts and Storms
The interaction of air masses causes changes in weather.

CHAPTER 4 KEY CONCEPTS

SECTION 1

Weather changes as air masses move.

1. Air masses are large bodies of air.
2. Weather changes where air masses meet.

SECTION 2

Low-pressure systems can become storms.

1. Hurricanes form over warm ocean water.
2. Winter storms produce snow and ice.

SECTION 3

Vertical air motion can cause severe storms.

1. Thunderstorms form from rising moist air.
2. Tornadoes form in severe thunderstorms.

SECTION 4

Weather forecasters use advanced technologies.

1. Weather data come from many sources.
2. Weather data can be displayed on maps.
3. Forecasters use computer models to predict weather.

The Big Idea Flow Chart is available on p. T25 in the **TRANSPARENCY BOOK.**

Previewing Content

SECTION

Weather changes as air masses move. pp. 115–122

1. Air masses are large bodies of air.

An **air mass** is a large volume of air in which temperature and humidity are nearly the same at different locations at the same altitude. (Air gets colder as you move up.)
Air masses are named for two characteristics of the regions where they form:

- continental (dry) or maritime (moist)
- polar (cold) or tropical (warm)

As global winds move air masses, they may change air masses' characteristics slowly. Thus, a maritime polar air mass that moves over land may become less moist.

2. Weather changes where air masses meet.

A **front** is the boundary between air masses. Three types of fronts are: cold fronts, warm fronts, and stationary fronts. Each front can produce a different type of weather. In cold fronts, warm air is pushed steeply up by cold air. Brief, heavy storms may form. In warm fronts, warm air rises gently over cold air. Prolonged periods of steady rain or snow may occur. In a stationary front, neither air mass advances. Clouds may form along the front. A fourth type of front, an occluded front, occurs when one front overtakes another. An example is shown below. Occluded fronts are common in low-pressure systems.

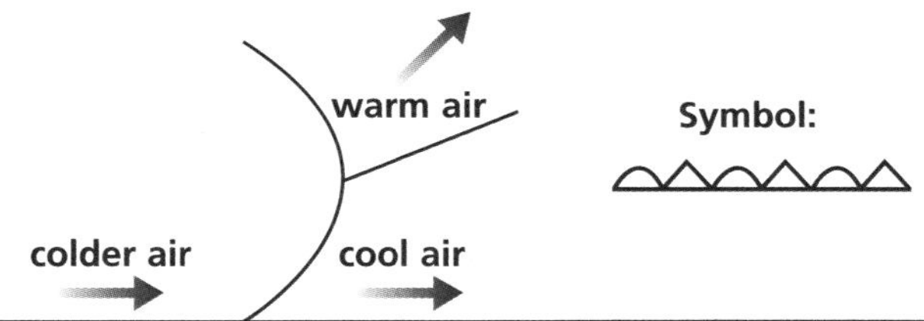

An occluded front occurs when one front overtakes another. The air in between is pushed upward.

Regions of high and low air pressure give rise to systems of weather. A **high-pressure system** is shown by isobars (lines on a map that connect places that have the same air pressure) that form closed loops around a local high, or center of high pressure. High-pressure systems often bring fair weather. A **low-pressure system** is shown by isobars that form closed loops around a local low. Such a low often forms where air masses meet, and it may develop into a stormy system that includes several fronts.

SECTION

Low-pressure systems can become storms. pp. 123–127

1. Hurricanes form over warm ocean water.

A **hurricane** begins as a tropical depression, or low-pressure system over warm tropical water. The depression is called a **tropical storm** when wind speeds reach 65 km/h and a hurricane when wind speeds reach 120 km/h. Warm ocean water provides the energy needed for hurricane formation. When hurricanes reach land or cooler water, they lose energy and eventually die out. The effects of hurricanes include:

- **storm surges,** or huge masses of water pushed inland by a hurricane
- heavy rains and floods
- wind damage
- tornadoes

2. Winter storms produce snow and ice.

Winter storms form when two air masses collide, producing a strong low-pressure system. Different types of winter storms include blizzards, lake-effect snow, and ice storms. **Blizzards** are blinding snowstorms with winds of at least 56 km/h and low temperatures. Lake-effect snow forms when cold air gains moisture and warmth as it passes over large bodies of water; when the air reaches land, it cools again and releases its moisture as snow. Ice storms develop when the air is warmer than the surface. When cold rain reaches the colder ground, it freezes.

Common Misconceptions

MISCONCEPTION DATABASE
CLASSZONE.COM Background on student misconceptions

PRESSURE SYSTEMS Students may hold the misconception that high-pressure centers are associated with warm temperatures and low-pressure centers are associated with cold temperatures. In fact, both types of centers may cause warm and cold temperatures. For example, cold waves are long periods of below-normal temperatures caused by strong high-pressure systems.

This misconception is addressed on p. 120.

Previewing Content

SECTION

Vertical air motion can cause severe storms. pp. 128–133

1. Thunderstorms form from rising moist air.
Lightning is the spark of electricity that causes a bright flash of light during a storm. The air around the lightning is heated and cooled quickly, producing a sound wave known as thunder. A **thunderstorm** is a storm with lightning and thunder. Thunderstorms form in the following way:

Step 1 Warm, humid air is forced upward. As condensation occurs and energy is released, a cumulonimbus cloud forms.

Step 2 Ice particles near the top of the cloud begin to fall, producing strong downdrafts next to the updrafts. Winds and heavy rain or hail accompany this severe stage of the storm.

Step 3 The downdrafts spread out and block the updrafts. The storm dies out.

The effects of thunderstorms include flash floods, strong winds, hail, and lightning. Use the visual below when discussing lightning.

Lightning occurs when opposite electrically-charged particles between a cloud and the ground meet.

2. Tornadoes form in severe thunderstorms.
Under some conditions, the up-and-down air motion of a thunderstorm may produce a **tornado.** A tornado is a violently rotating column of air between a cloud and the ground. Most tornadoes occur in North America in the spring, when wind conditions are just right to form these violent storms. Tornadoes can tear off roofs and damage trees. The strongest tornadoes can lift cars or demolish buildings.

SECTION

Weather forecasters use advanced technologies. pp. 134–141

1. Weather data comes from many sources.
A **meteorologist** is a scientist who studies the weather. Meteorologists may develop weather forecasts by using data from radar stations, satellites, and instrument packages in ground stations, weather buoys, airplanes, and ships.

2. Weather data can be displayed on maps.
The gathered weather data are combined, summarized, and displayed on maps for ease of use. Surface weather maps usually show highs, lows, fronts, and other current or predicted features. Air pressure is often depicted by **isobars,** lines that connect places that have the same air pressure. Satellite images include both visible-light and infrared images. Visible-light images show clouds in sunlight; infrared images show clouds by day or night and also show cloud heights. Maps can also show patterns of temperature and other information.

3. Forecasters use computer models to predict weather.
Anyone can make simple forecasts based on observations and a knowledge of weather patterns. Meteorologists rely on data gathered from other sources and computer models to analyze weather data and make forecasts. Computers can create maps of weather data. Meteorologists analyze the various forecasts and use their own expertise to make a weather prediction. Short-term forecasts—up to three days in advance—are more reliable than long-term forecasts, especially near stormy systems, where atmospheric conditions change quickly.

Common Misconceptions

LIGHTNING Students may hold the misconception that lightning never strikes twice in the same place. In reality, lightning tends to strike the highest features in a given location. Sometimes these features are repeatedly hit.

This misconception is addressed on p. 129.

MISCONCEPTION DATABASE
CLASSZONE.COM Background on student misconceptions

Previewing Labs

Lab Generator CD-ROM
Edit these Pupil Edition labs and generate alternative labs.

EXPLORE the BIG idea

How Does Cold Air Move? p. 113 Students are introduced to the movement of air masses.	**TIME** 10 minutes **MATERIALS** refrigerator
How Does Weather Move? p. 113 Students are introduced to the effect fronts have on weather.	**TIME** 15 minutes **MATERIALS** newspaper weather maps (spanning three consecutive days)

SECTION 1

EXPLORE Air Masses, p. 115 To help students recognize the effect of a surface on temperature and humidity.	**TIME** 15 minutes **MATERIALS** 3 bowls, ice, warm water, 3 shoeboxes, plastic wrap
INVESTIGATE Air Masses, p. 117 Students infer how differences in density affect colliding air masses. **ALTERNATIVE:** Teacher Demonstration, URB p. 276	**TIME** 25 minutes **MATERIALS** 500-mL beaker, stiff cardboard, scissors, 2 cups, small beaker, salt, water, food coloring

SECTION 2

EXPLORE Hurricanes, p. 123 Students observe how friction affects a spinning top and relate the information to hurricane strength.	**TIME** 10 minutes **MATERIALS** sheet of paper, top
INVESTIGATE Ice, p. 126 Students observe how salt affects ice to infer why it is put on icy roads. **ALTERNATIVE:** Reading Activity, URB p. 276	**TIME** 10 minutes **MATERIALS** 2 ice cubes, 2 cups, table salt

SECTION 3

INVESTIGATE Updrafts, p. 130 Students observe the motion of heated water to infer how updrafts form. **ALTERNATIVE:** Teacher Demonstration, URB p. 276	**TIME** 20 minutes **MATERIALS** 4 cardboard squares, 5 foam cups, clear container, cool tap water, food coloring, eye dropper, hot tap water

SECTION 4

EXPLORE Weather Maps, p. 134 Students interpret symbols on a weather map and relate a weather forecast to actual weather conditions.	**TIME** 10 minutes **MATERIALS** newspaper weather map
CHAPTER INVESTIGATION **Design a Weather Center,** pp. 140–141 Students observe, measure, and record weather conditions, then analyze the data. **ALTERNATIVE:** Reading Activity, URB p. 276	**TIME** 40 minutes **MATERIALS** thermometer, magnetic compass, other weather instruments such as wind vane and psychrometer, graph paper

Additional INVESTIGATION, Hurricane Hugo, A, B, & C, pp. 263–271; Teacher Instructions, p. 276

Previewing Chapter Resources

	INTEGRATED TECHNOLOGY	LABS AND ACTIVITIES

CHAPTER 4 Weather Fronts and Storms

INTEGRATED TECHNOLOGY

 **CLASSZONE.COM**
- eEdition Plus
- EasyPlanner Plus
- Misconception Database
- Content Review
- Test Practice
- Visualizations
- Resource Centers
- Math Tutorial

 **SCILINKS.ORG**

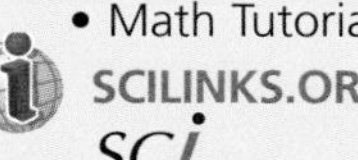

 **CD-ROMS**
- eEdition
- EasyPlanner
- Power Presentations
- Content Review
- Lab Generator
- Test Generator

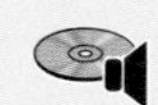 **AUDIO CDS**
- Audio Readings
- Audio Readings in Spanish

LABS AND ACTIVITIES

 EXPLORE the Big Idea, p. 113
- How Does Cold Air Move?
- How Does Weather Move?

 **UNIT RESOURCE BOOK**
Unit Projects, pp. 5–10

 **Lab Generator CD-ROM**
Generate customized labs.

SECTION 1 Weather changes as air masses move. pp. 115–122

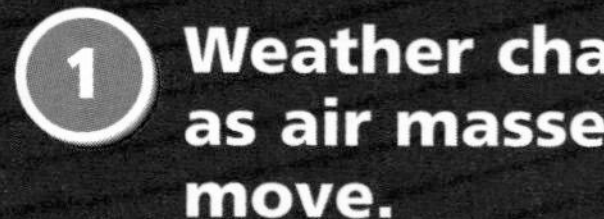

 Lesson Plan, pp. 204–205

- **VISUALIZATION,** Warm and Cold Fronts
- **MATH TUTORIAL**

 **TRANSPARENCY BOOK**
- Big Idea Flow Chart, p. T25
- Daily Vocabulary Scaffolding, p. T26
- Note-Taking Model, p. T27
- 3-Minute Warm-Up, p. T28
- "Fronts and Weather" Visual, p. T30

- EXPLORE Air Masses, p. 115
- INVESTIGATE Air Masses, p. 117
- Math in Science, p. 122

 **UNIT RESOURCE BOOK**
- Datasheet, Air Masses, p. 213
- Math Support, p. 252
- Math Practice, p. 253

SECTION 2 Low-pressure systems can become storms. pp. 123–127

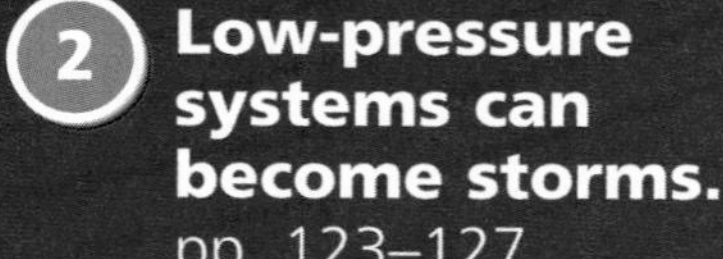

 Lesson Plan, pp. 215–216

 **VISUALIZATION,** Progress of a Hurricane

 **TRANSPARENCY BOOK**
- Daily Vocabulary Scaffolding, p. T26
- 3-Minute Warm-Up, p. T28

- EXPLORE Hurricanes, p. 123
- INVESTIGATE Ice, p. 126

 **UNIT RESOURCE BOOK**
- Datasheet, Ice, p. 224
- Additional INVESTIGATION, Hurricane Hugo, A, B, & C, pp. 263–271

SECTION 3 Vertical air motion can cause severe storms. pp. 128–133

 Lesson Plan, pp. 226–227

 **TRANSPARENCY BOOK**
- Daily Vocabulary Scaffolding, p. T26
- 3-Minute Warm-Up, p. T29

- INVESTIGATE Updrafts, p. 130
- Think Science, p. 133

 **UNIT RESOURCE BOOK**
Datasheet, Updrafts, p. 235

SECTION 4 Weather forecasters use advanced technologies. pp. 134–141

 Lesson Plan, pp. 237–238

 **RESOURCE CENTER,** Weather Forecasting

 **TRANSPARENCY BOOK**
- Big Idea Flow Chart, p. T25
- Daily Vocabulary Scaffolding, p. T26
- 3-Minute Warm-Up, p. T29
- Chapter Outline, pp. T31–T32

- EXPLORE Weather Maps, p. 134
- CHAPTER INVESTIGATION, Design a Weather Center, pp. 140–141

 **UNIT RESOURCE BOOK**
CHAPTER INVESTIGATION, Design a Weather Center, A, B, & C, pp. 254–262

KEY TO ICONS: CD/CD-ROM · Teacher Edition · TRANSPARENCY BOOK · STANDARDS REVIEW AND PRACTICE · INTERNET · Pupil Edition · UNIT RESOURCE BOOK · ASSESSMENT BOOK · SCIENCE TOOLKIT

READING AND REINFORCEMENT	ASSESSMENT	STANDARDS
Modified Lesson Plans for English Learners, pp. 15–18 • Choose Your Own Strategy, C35–44 • Main Idea Web, C38–39 • Daily Vocabulary Scaffolding, H1–8 **UNIT RESOURCE BOOK** • Vocabulary Practice, pp. 249–250 • Decoding Support, p. 251 • Summarizing the Chapter, pp. 272–273 **Audio Readings CD** Listen to Pupil Edition. **Audio Readings in Spanish CD** Listen to Pupil Edition in Spanish.	• Chapter Review, pp. 143–144 • Standards-Based Assessment, p. 145 **ASSESSMENT BOOK** • Diagnostic Test, pp. 61–62 • Chapter Test, A, B, & C, pp. 67–78 • Alternative Assessment, pp. 79–80 **STANDARDS REVIEW AND PRACTICE,** pp. 23–24, 37–40, 59–60, 65–66 **McDougal Littell Assessment System** **Test Generator CD-ROM** Generate customized and Spanish tests.	California Content Standards 6.3.a, 6.4.d, 6.4.e, 6.7.b, 6.7.c See p. 112 for the standards.
UNIT RESOURCE BOOK • Reading Study Guide, A & B, pp. 206–209 • Spanish Reading Study Guide, pp. 210–211 • Challenge and Extension, p. 212 • Reinforcing Key Concepts, p. 214	Ongoing Assessment, pp. 115–121 Section 4.1 Review, p. 121 **ASSESSMENT BOOK** Section 4.1 Quiz, p. 63	California Content Standards 6.4.e
UNIT RESOURCE BOOK • Reading Study Guide, A & B, pp. 217–220 • Spanish Reading Study Guide, pp. 221–222 • Challenge and Extension, p. 223 • Reinforcing Key Concepts, p. 225 • Challenge Reading, pp. 247–248	Ongoing Assessment, pp. 124–127 Section 4.2 Review, p. 127 **ASSESSMENT BOOK** Section 4.2 Quiz, p. 64	California Content Standards 6.3.a, 6.4.e
UNIT RESOURCE BOOK • Reading Study Guide, A & B, pp. 228–231 • Spanish Reading Study Guide, pp. 232–233 • Challenge and Extension, p. 234 • Reinforcing Key Concepts, p. 236	Ongoing Assessment, pp. 128–132 Section 4.3 Review, p. 132 **ASSESSMENT BOOK** Section 4.3 Quiz, p. 65	California Content Standards 6.2.d, 6.4.d, 6.4.e
UNIT RESOURCE BOOK • Reading Study Guide, A & B, pp. 239–242 • Spanish Reading Study Guide, pp. 243–244 • Challenge and Extension, p. 245 • Reinforcing Key Concepts, p. 246	Ongoing Assessment, pp. 134–139 Section 4.4 Review, p. 139 **ASSESSMENT BOOK** Section 4.4 Quiz, p. 66	California Content Standards 6.4.e, 6.7.b, 6.7.c

Previewing Resources for Differentiated Instruction

CHAPTER INVESTIGATION

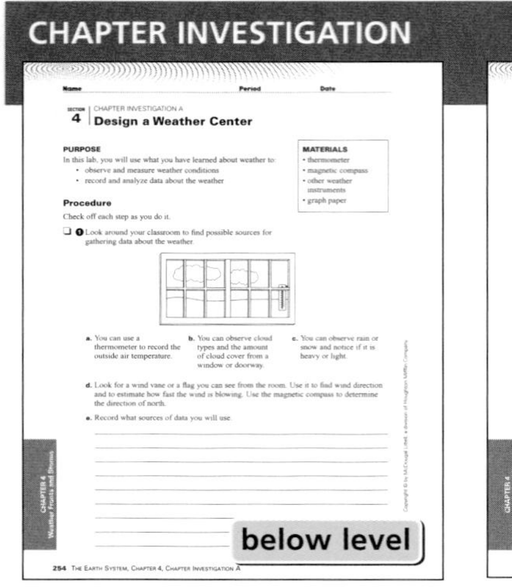

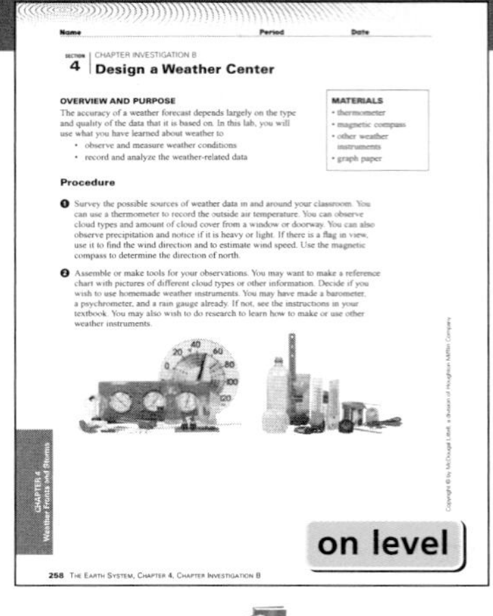

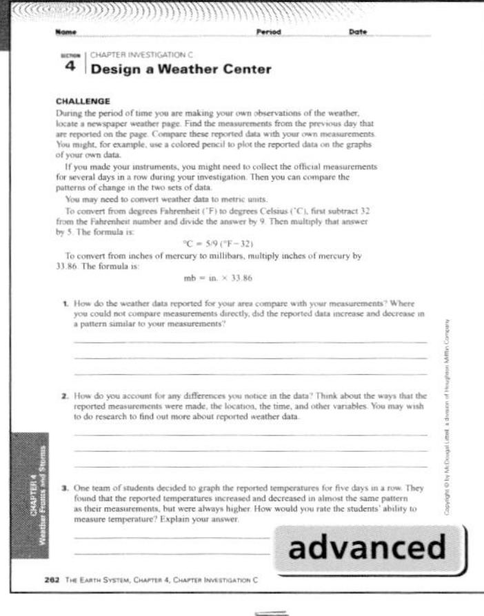

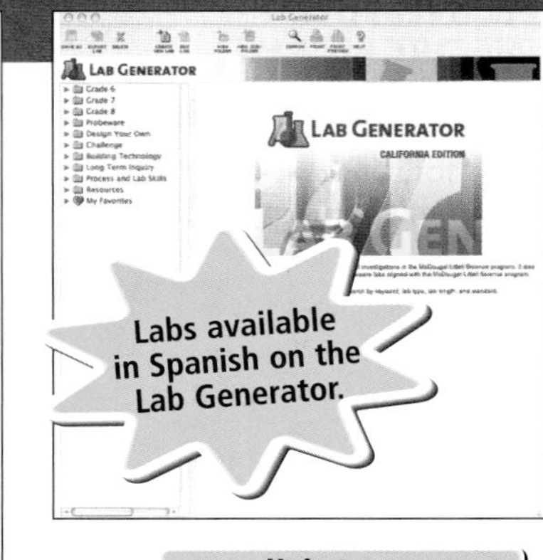

UNIT RESOURCE BOOK, pp. 254–257

pp. 258–261

pp. 258–262

READING STUDY GUIDE

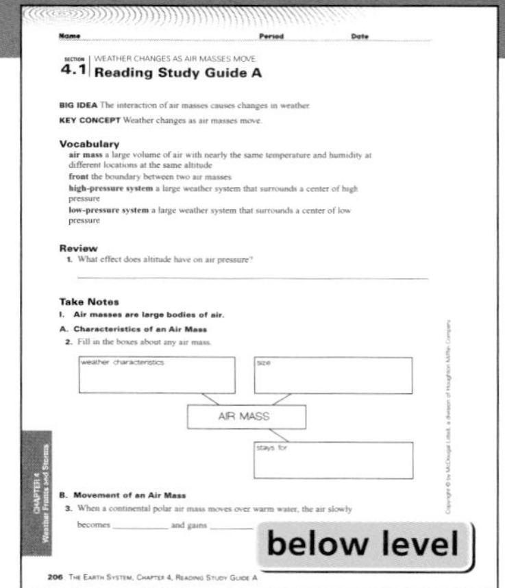

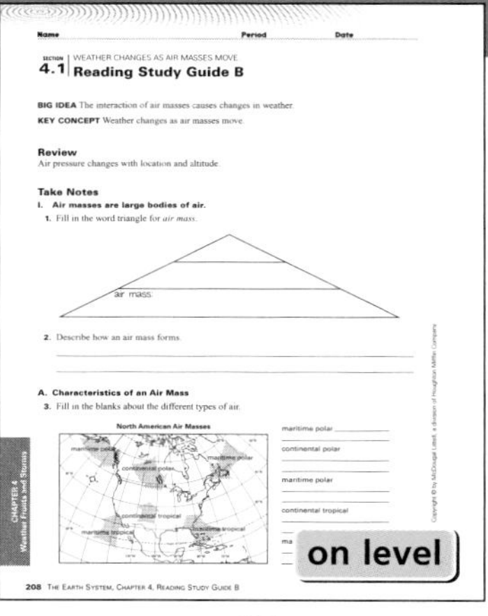

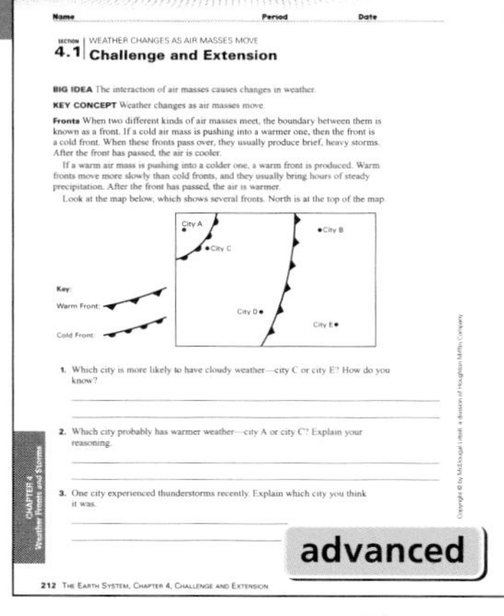

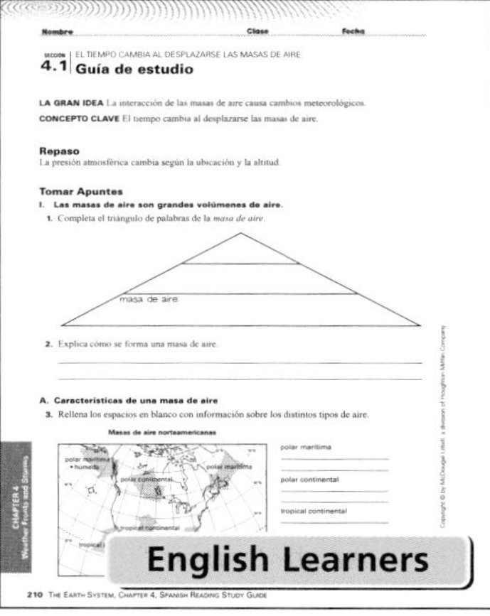

UNIT RESOURCE BOOK, pp. 206–207

pp. 208–209

p. 212

p. 210

CHAPTER TEST

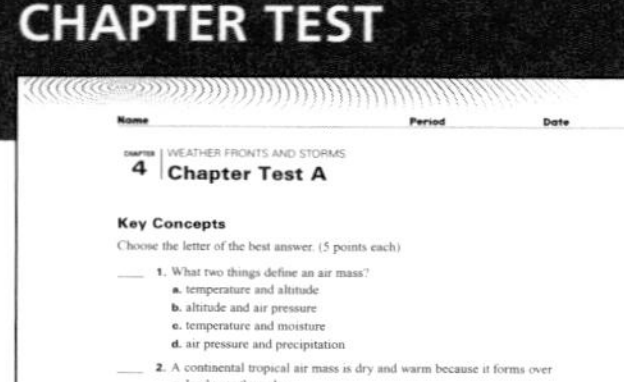

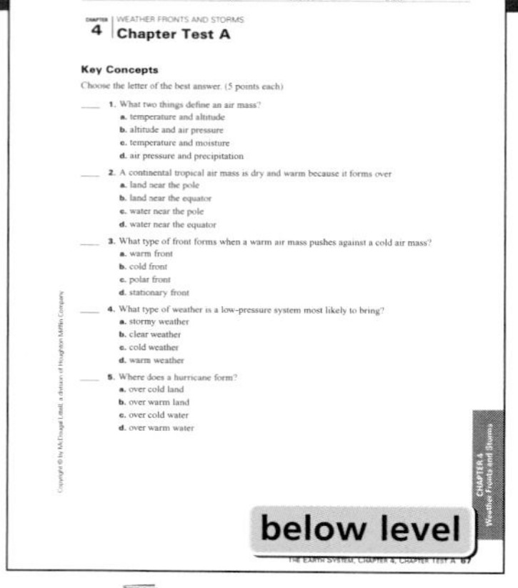

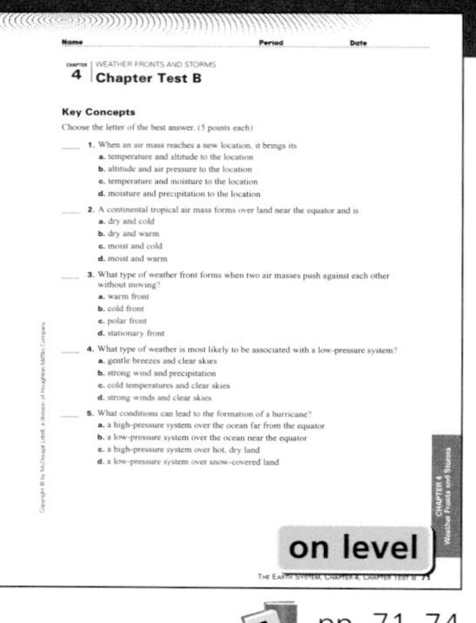

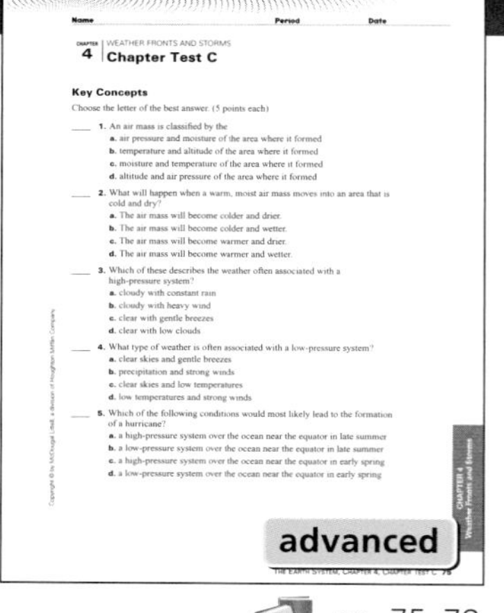

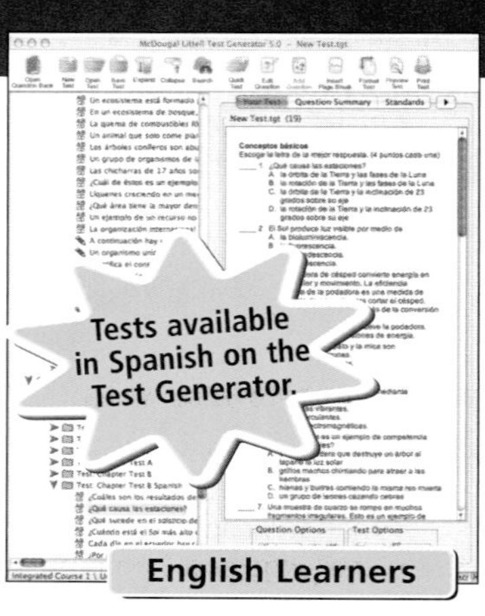

ASSESSMENT BOOK, pp. 67–70

pp. 71–74

pp. 75–78

TECHNOLOGY

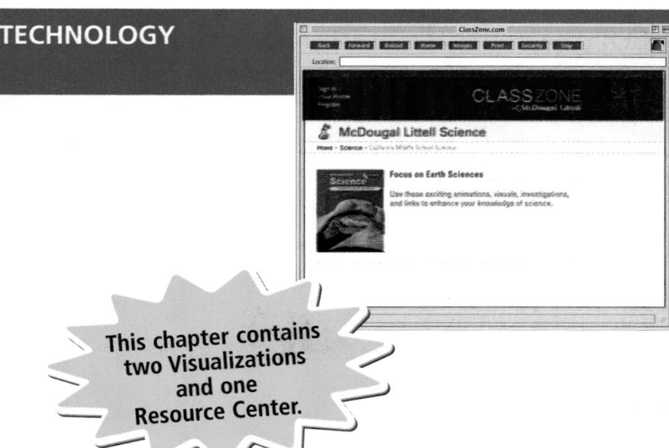

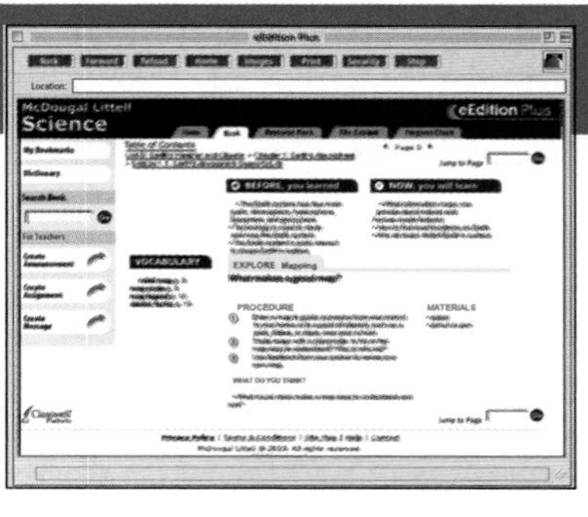

VISUAL CONTENT

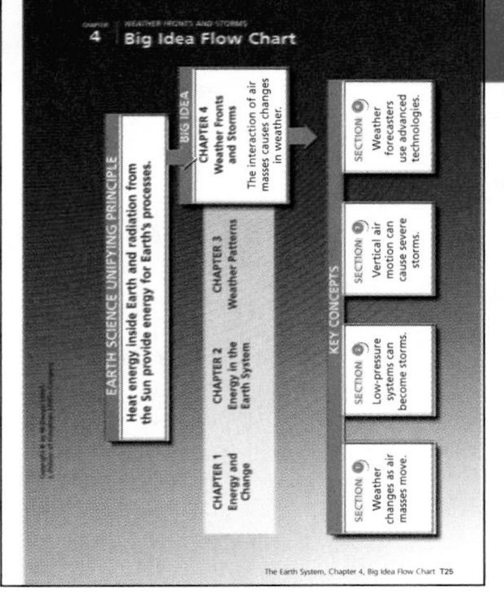

TRANSPARENCY BOOK, p. T25

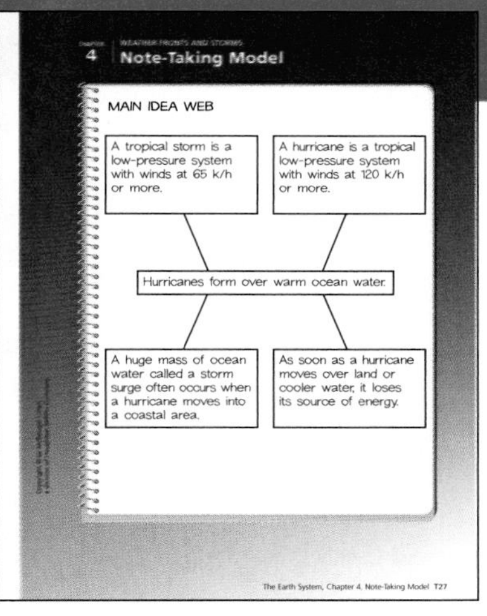

4 Note-Taking Model
MAIN IDEA WEB
A tropical storm is a low-pressure system with winds at 65 k/h or more.
A hurricane is a tropical low-pressure system with winds at 120 k/h or more.
Hurricanes form over warm ocean water.
A huge mass of ocean water called a storm surge often occurs when a hurricane moves into a coastal area.
As soon as a hurricane moves over land or cooler water, it loses its source of energy.

p. T27

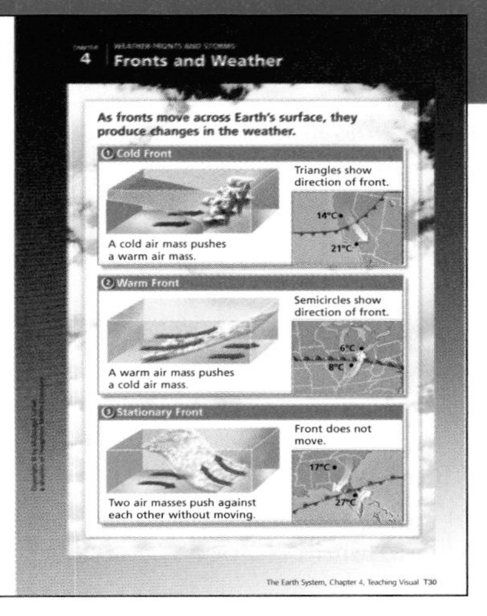

4 Fronts and Weather
As fronts move across Earth's surface, they produce changes in the weather.
Cold Front
Triangles show direction of front.
A cold air mass pushes a warm air mass.
Warm Front
Semicircles show direction of front.
A warm air mass pushes a cold air mass.
Stationary Front
Front does not move.
Two air masses push against each other without moving.

p. T30

MORE SUPPORT

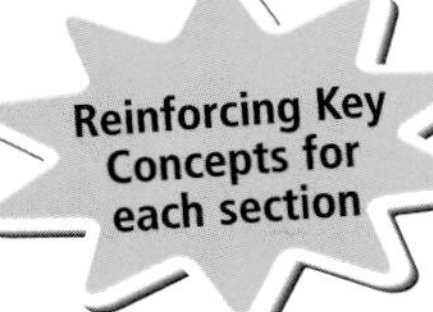

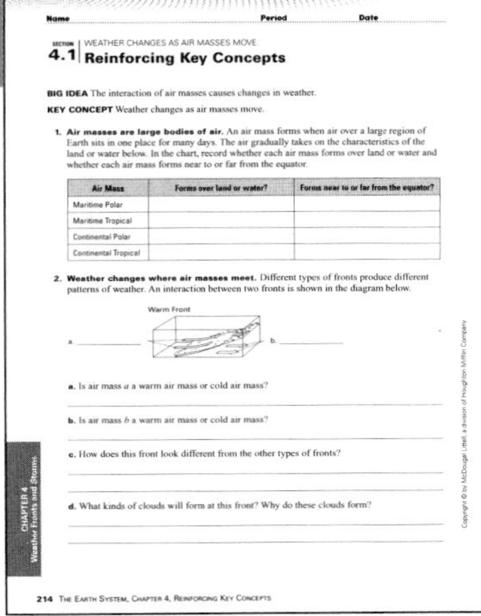

UNIT RESOURCE BOOK, p. 214

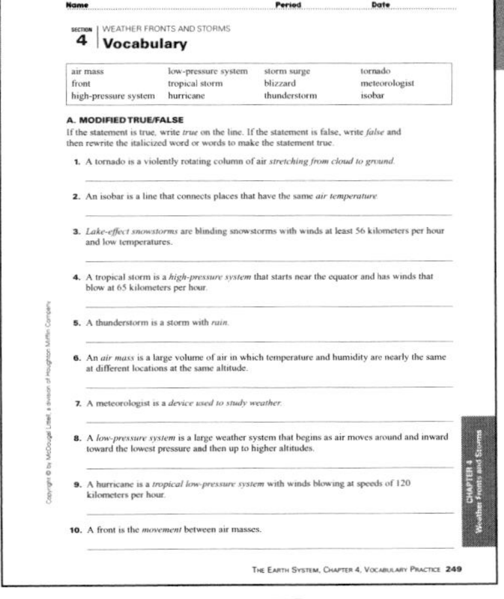

pp. 249–250

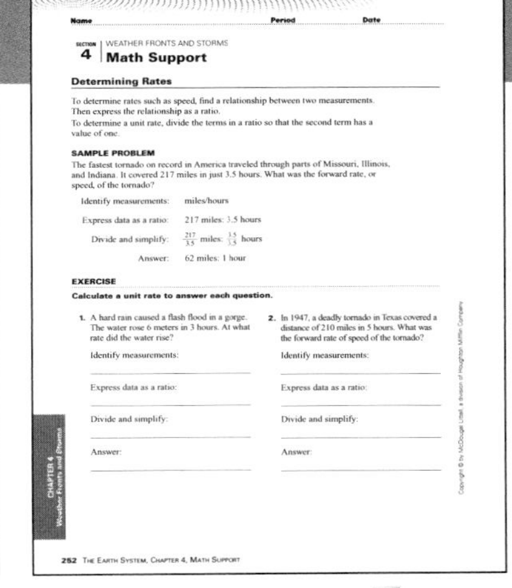

p. 252

CHAPTER

Weather Fronts and Storms

INTRODUCE

the BIG idea

Have students look at the photograph of the storm and discuss how the question in the box links to the Big Idea:

- What happens during a storm?
- How can weather move a house?
- How do you think weather forecasters know when a storm is coming?

California Content Standards

6.3.a Students know energy can be carried from one place to another by heat flow or by waves, including water, light and sound waves, or by moving objects.

6.4.d Students know convection currents distribute heat in the atmosphere and oceans.

6.4.e Students know differences in pressure, heat, air movement, and humidity result in changes of weather.

6.7.b Select and use appropriate tools and technology (including calculators, computers, balances, spring scales, microscopes, and binoculars) to perform tests, collect data, and display data.

6.7.e Recognize whether evidence is consistent with a proposed explanation.

CHAPTER

Weather Fronts and Storms

the BIG idea

The interaction of air masses causes changes in weather.

Key Concepts

SECTION 1

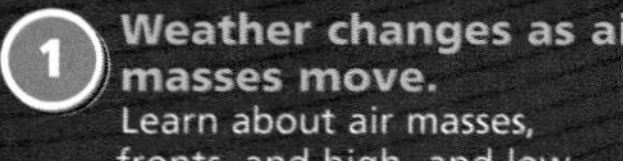

Weather changes as air masses move.
Learn about air masses, fronts, and high- and low-pressure systems.

SECTION 2

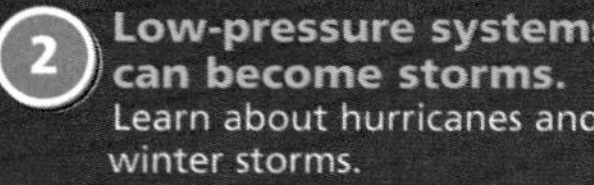

Low-pressure systems can become storms.
Learn about hurricanes and winter storms.

SECTION 3

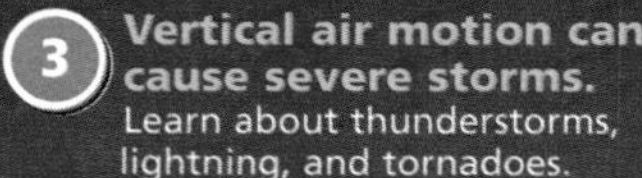

Vertical air motion can cause severe storms.
Learn about thunderstorms, lightning, and tornadoes.

SECTION 4

Weather forecasters use advanced technologies.
Learn about different types of weather data and how forecasters predict weather.

California ClassZone

CLASSZONE.COM

Chapter 4 online resources: Content Review, two Visualizations, one Resource Center, Math Tutorial, Test Practice

What types of weather can move a house?

INTERNET PREVIEW

CLASSZONE.COM For student use with the following pages:

Review and Practice
- Content Review, pp. 114, 142
- Math Tutorial: Rates as Ratios, p. 122
- Test Practice, p. 145

Activities and Resources
- Visualizations: Warm and Cold Fronts, p. 118; Progress of a Hurricane, p. 124
- Resource Center: Weather Forecasting, p. 135

Severe Weather
Code: MDL011

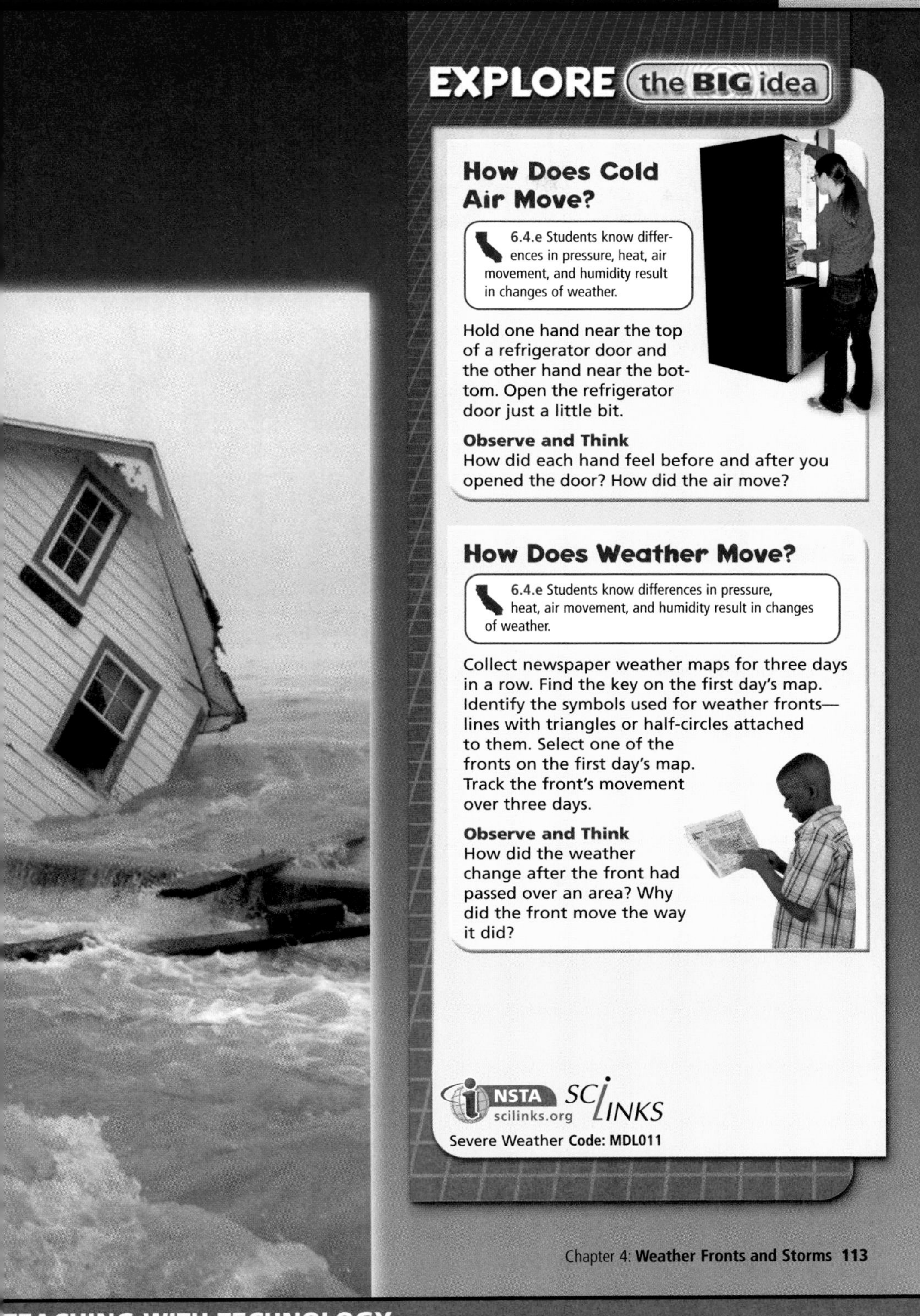

EXPLORE the BIG idea

How Does Cold Air Move?

6.4.e Students know differences in pressure, heat, air movement, and humidity result in changes of weather.

Hold one hand near the top of a refrigerator door and the other hand near the bottom. Open the refrigerator door just a little bit.

Observe and Think
How did each hand feel before and after you opened the door? How did the air move?

How Does Weather Move?

6.4.e Students know differences in pressure, heat, air movement, and humidity result in changes of weather.

Collect newspaper weather maps for three days in a row. Find the key on the first day's map. Identify the symbols used for weather fronts—lines with triangles or half-circles attached to them. Select one of the fronts on the first day's map. Track the front's movement over three days.

Observe and Think
How did the weather change after the front had passed over an area? Why did the front move the way it did?

NSTA scilinks.org SCILINKS
Severe Weather **Code: MDL011**

Chapter 4: **Weather Fronts and Storms** **113**

EXPLORE the BIG idea

These inquiry-based activities are appropriate for use at home or as a supplement to classroom instruction.

How Does Cold Air Move?

PURPOSE To introduce students to the concept of air masses. Students will feel cold air move downward after the refrigerator door is opened.

TIP *10 min.* Tell students to pay attention to temperature differences and air movement.

Answer: top: little change; bottom: cold; cold air moved down and out

REVISIT after p. 117.

How Does Weather Move?

PURPOSE To introduce students to the concept of weather fronts. Students will track the movement of a front over three days.

TIP *10 min.* Have students choose a front near a city that has its temperature listed.

Answer: Fronts tend to move eastward. Fronts moving north will bring warm weather, and fronts moving south will bring cold weather.

REVISIT after p. 119.

TEACHING WITH TECHNOLOGY

Animated Maps Have students access online weather maps that show weather patterns through animations.

CBL and Probeware If students have probeware, they can use a temperature probe for the Chapter Investigation on pp. 140–141. Depending on what other weather instrument they choose, they may be able to use additional probeware as well.

PREPARE

CONCEPT REVIEW

Activate Prior Knowledge

- Ask students to describe cloud formation in terms of air density and temperature—that is, clouds form as warm, less dense air rises, expands, and cools.
- Ask students to explain what would happen to sinking air. Would the water vapor in the air condense or evaporate? Would clouds form?

TAKING NOTES

Main Idea Web

Tell students to write the blue heading in the center and draw a box around it. As they read, they should look for topic sentences that convey important details related to the main idea. Highlighted words and red headings are also important terms and details. Students should write the related details around the main idea, draw boxes around them, and then connect them to the main idea.

Choose Your Own Strategy

Having students choose their own note-taking strategies will allow them to use the strategies that personally fit them best. It is also a good review of the strategies already presented, such as frame games, description wheels, and magnet words.

Vocabulary and Note-Taking Resources

- Vocabulary Practice, pp. 249–250
- Decoding Support, p. 251

- Daily Vocabulary Scaffolding, p. T26
- Note-Taking Model, p. T27

- Choose Your Own Strategy, B20–B21, B24–B27
- Main Idea Web, C38–C39
- Daily Vocabulary Scaffolding, H1–H8

CHAPTER 4

Getting Ready to Learn

CONCEPT REVIEW

- Temperature affects air density.
- Pressure differences make air move.
- Uneven heating of Earth's surface produces winds.
- Clouds form as air rises, expands, and cools.

VOCABULARY REVIEW

convection p. 28
evaporation p. 92
condensation p. 92
relative humidity p. 94

Review concepts and vocabulary.

TAKING NOTES

MAIN IDEA WEB

Write each new blue heading—a main idea—in a box. Then put notes with important terms and details into boxes around the main idea.

CHOOSE YOUR OWN STRATEGY

Take notes about new vocabulary terms using one or more of the strategies from earlier chapters—**Magnet Word, Frame Game,** or **Description Wheel**. Feel free to mix and match the strategies, or use an entirely different vocabulary strategy.

See the Note-Taking Handbook on pages R45–R51.

SCIENCE NOTEBOOK

Air masses are large bodies of air.
Marine air masses form over water.
Continental air masses form over land.
Tropical air masses are warm.
Polar air masses are cold.

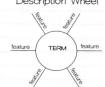

Description Wheel

TERM — feature, feature, feature, feature, feature, feature

Magnet Word

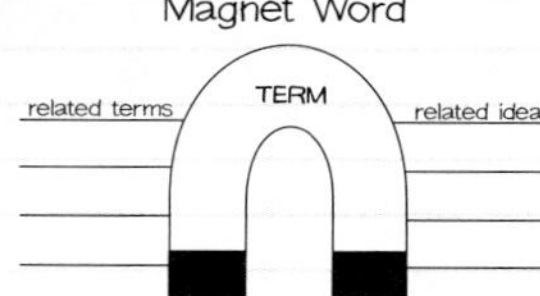

Frame Game

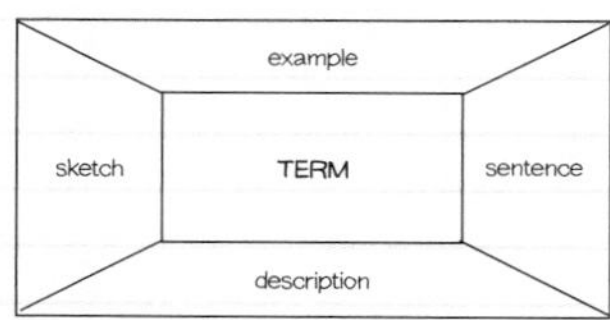

CHECK READINESS

Administer the Diagnostic Test to determine students' readiness for new science content and their mastery of requisite math skills.

 Diagnostic Test, pp. 61–62

Technology Resources

Students needing content and math skills should visit **ClassZone.com.**

- **CONTENT REVIEW**
- **MATH TUTORIAL**

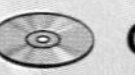 **CONTENT REVIEW CD-ROM**

KEY CONCEPT

Weather changes as air masses move.

CALIFORNIA Content Standard

6.4.e Students know differences in pressure, heat, air movement, and humidity result in changes of weather.

BEFORE, you learned

- Air pressure changes with location and altitude
- Water vapor in the atmosphere condenses when air rises

NOW, you will learn

- What air masses are
- What happens when air masses meet
- How pressure systems affect the weather

VOCABULARY

EXPLORE Air Masses (6.4.e)

How does an air mass form?

PROCEDURE

1. Put ice into one bowl and warm water into a second bowl. Leave the third bowl empty.
2. Place each bowl in a different box and cover the box with plastic wrap. Wait a few minutes.
3. Put your hand into each box in turn.

MATERIALS

- 3 bowls
- ice
- warm water
- 3 shoeboxes
- plastic wrap

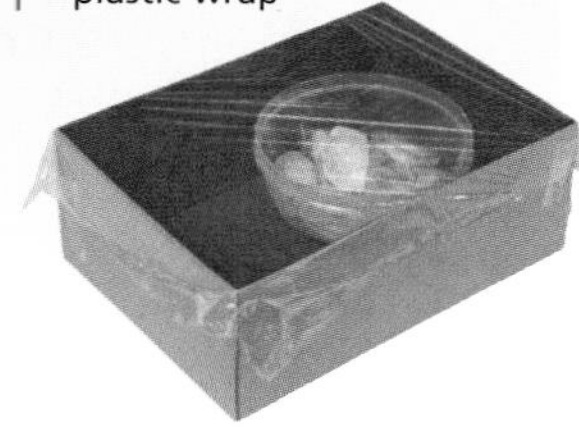

WHAT DO YOU THINK?

- How would you describe the air in each box?
- Which box's air feels the most humid? Why?

Air masses are large bodies of air.

VOCABULARY Add *air mass* to your notebook, using the vocabulary strategy of your choice.

You have probably experienced the effects of air masses—one day is hot and humid, and the next day is cool and pleasant. The weather changes when a new air mass moves into your area. An **air mass** is a large volume of air in which temperature and humidity are nearly the same in different locations at the same altitude. An air mass can cover many thousands of square kilometers.

An air mass forms when the air over a large region of Earth sits in one place for many days. The air gradually takes on the characteristics of the land or water below it. Where Earth's surface is cold, the air becomes cold. Where Earth's surface is wet, the air becomes moist. As an air mass moves, it brings its temperature and moisture to new locations.

CHECK YOUR READING Explain how the weather can change with the arrival of a new air mass. Your answer should include two ways that weather changes.

RESOURCES FOR DIFFERENTIATED INSTRUCTION

Below Level

UNIT RESOURCE BOOK

- Reading Study Guide A, pp. 206–207
- Decoding Support, p. 251

AUDIO CDS

Advanced

UNIT RESOURCE BOOK

Challenge and Extension, p. 212

English Learners

UNIT RESOURCE BOOK

Spanish Reading Study Guide, pp. 210–211

AUDIO CDS

- Audio Readings in Spanish
- Audio Readings (English)

4.1 FOCUS

Set Learning Goals

Students will

- Describe air masses.
- Explain what happens when air masses meet.
- Determine how two types of pressure systems affect the weather.
- Infer from an experiment how density affects colliding air masses.

3-Minute Warm-Up

Display Transparency 28 or copy this exercise on the board:

Are these statements true? If not, correct them.

1. Air pressure pushes only in a downward direction. *Air pressure pushes in all directions.*
2. The Coriolis effect influences air motion across Earth's surface. *True*
3. The changing of a gas to a liquid is evaporation. *The changing of a gas to a liquid is condensation.*

3-Minute Warm-Up, p. T28

4.1 MOTIVATE

EXPLORE Air Masses

PURPOSE To help students recognize the effect of a surface on temperature and humidity

TIP *15 min.* Leave the plastic wrap loose at a corner so it can be easily lifted.

WHAT DO YOU THINK? *box with ice: cool; box with warm water: warm and moist; box with empty bowl: dry and at room temperature. The box with warm water was most humid because the air was likely saturated.*

Ongoing Assessment

CHECK YOUR READING *Sample answer: It could become cooler and drier over cold land.*

4.1 INSTRUCT

Teach the Standards

Weather and air masses 6.4.e

In this section: Remind students that an air mass is a large volume of air in which temperature and humidity are similar at the same altitude. Ask students to name the three types of fronts, and explain how pressure and the movement of air along fronts affect weather.

previously taught: weather, pp. 62–63; wind, pp. 83–84

future opportunities: low-pressure systems, pp. 123–127

Teach from Visuals

To help students interpret the "North American Air Masses" visual, ask:

- What do the arrows show? *the place where an air mass forms and the direction in which it might move*
- Dry, warm air is typical of which air mass? *continental tropical*
- What type of air mass would likely bring wet, cold weather? *maritime polar*
- What types of air masses affect your location most often? *Sample answer for a student in California: maritime tropical*

Real World Example

For the sake of convenience, meterologists often use letters or symbols to designate weather phenomena. For example, the lowercase letters *c* and *m* represent continental and maritime air masses, respectively. Capital letters, such as *T* (tropical) and *P* (polar), indicate the source of an air mass. Thus, a martime tropical air mass would be abbreviated as mT.

Ongoing Assessment

Describe air masses.

Ask: How does a maritime tropical air mass compare with a continental tropical air mass? *The maritime tropical air mass is moist and warm. The continental tropical air mass is dry and warm.*

Answer: over land

North American Air Masses

maritime polar • moist • cool
continental polar • dry • cool
maritime polar • moist • cool
continental tropical • dry • warm
maritime tropical • moist • warm
maritime tropical • moist • warm
Arctic Circle
Tropic of Cancer
0 500 1000 miles
0 500 1000 kilometers

READING VISUALS Look at the moisture of air masses from different locations. Where do dry air masses start out?

Characteristics of an Air Mass

Some regions of Earth's surface, such as those shown in the map above, produce air masses again and again. The characteristics of an air mass depend on the region where it forms. A hot desert produces dry, hot air masses, while cool ocean waters produce moist, cool air masses. Scientists classify air masses into categories according to the characteristics of regions. Each category name is made of two words—one for moisture, one for temperature.

The first word of an air mass's category name tells whether the air mass formed over water or dry land. It describes the moisture of the air mass.

- **Continental** air masses form over land. Air becomes dry as it loses its moisture to the dry land below it.
- **Maritime** (MAR-ih-TYM) air masses form over water. Air becomes moist as it gains water vapor from the water below it.

READING TIP The word *maritime* has the same root as the word *marine*. Both come from the Latin word *mare*, which means "sea."

? A

The second word of a category name tells whether an air mass formed close to the equator. It describes the air mass's temperature.

- **Tropical** air masses form near the equator. Air becomes warm as it gains energy from the warm land or water.
- **Polar** air masses form far from the equator. Air becomes cool as it loses energy to the cold land or water.

? B

116 Unit 1: The Earth System

DIFFERENTIATE INSTRUCTION

More Reading Support

A Where do maritime air masses form? *over water*

B What two words identify the temperature of air masses? tropical *and* polar

English Learners English learners may need help with the concepts of *continental, maritime, tropical,* and *polar.* Explain that *continental* refers to land, as in the word *continent,* and that *maritime* refers to the ocean, as in the word *marine.* Use a globe to show students tropical and polar regions.

The combination of words gives the characteristics of the air mass. A maritime tropical air mass is moist and warm, while a continental polar air mass is dry and cold.

What can you tell from each word of an air mass's name?

Movement of an Air Mass

Air masses can travel away from the regions where they form. They move with the global pattern of winds. In most of the United States, air masses generally move from west to east. They may move along with the jet stream in more complex and changing patterns.

When an air mass moves to a new region, it carries along its characteristic moisture and temperature. As the air moves over Earth's surface, the characteristics of the surface begin to change the air mass. For example, if a continental polar air mass moves over warm water, the air near the surface will become warmer and gain moisture. These changes begin where the air touches the surface. It may take days or weeks for the changes to spread upward through the entire air mass. An air mass that moves quickly may not change much. If it moves quickly enough, a continental polar air mass can move cold air from northern Canada all the way to the southern United States.

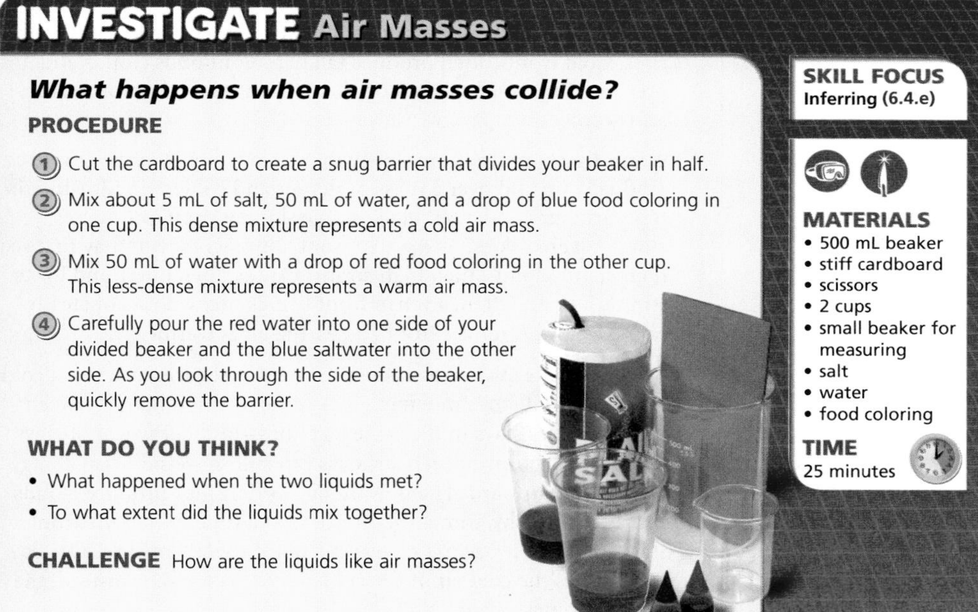

INVESTIGATE Air Masses

What happens when air masses collide?

PROCEDURE

1. Cut the cardboard to create a snug barrier that divides your beaker in half.
2. Mix about 5 mL of salt, 50 mL of water, and a drop of blue food coloring in one cup. This dense mixture represents a cold air mass.
3. Mix 50 mL of water with a drop of red food coloring in the other cup. This less-dense mixture represents a warm air mass.
4. Carefully pour the red water into one side of your divided beaker and the blue saltwater into the other side. As you look through the side of the beaker, quickly remove the barrier.

WHAT DO YOU THINK?

- What happened when the two liquids met?
- To what extent did the liquids mix together?

CHALLENGE How are the liquids like air masses?

SKILL FOCUS
Inferring (6.4.e)

MATERIALS
- 500 mL beaker
- stiff cardboard
- scissors
- 2 cups
- small beaker for measuring
- salt
- water
- food coloring

TIME
25 minutes

INVESTIGATE Air Masses

PURPOSE Infer how density affects colliding air masses

TIPS *25 min.* Mix the water ahead of time. Then suggest the following:

- Cut the cardboard slightly larger than the container; gently mash the edges as you push it into the container.
- Make sure the bottom of the cardboard is snug against the container. If the container has a curved bottom, dampen the bottom of the cardboard so that it will mold to the container's shape.
- Repeat the experiment several times to be sure of your results.

WHAT DO YOU THINK? *The dense, blue liquid moved under the less dense, red liquid. They didn't mix very much.*

CHALLENGE *Air masses also move without mixing much.*

Datasheet, Air Masses, p. 213

Technology Resources

Customize this student lab as needed or look for an alternative. Print rubrics to assess student lab reports.

Lab Generator CD-ROM

EXPLORE the BIG idea

Revisit "How Does Cold Air Move?" on p. 113. Have students explain the reasons for their observations.

Ongoing Assessment

CHECK YOUR READING *Answer: first word indicates moisture, second word indicates temperature*

DIFFERENTIATE INSTRUCTION

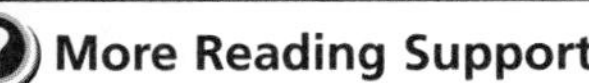

More Reading Support

C In which direction do air masses move across most of the United States? *from west to east*

Advanced Have students revise the experiment above to test what would happen if the liquids had the same density. Tell them to write a hypothesis before conducting the test. A hypothesis might be, "If the liquids had the same density, then they would mix together, because only the differences in density cause one to rise above the other." Students should then explain their procedure. For example, they can place equal amounts of salt in each cup of water to give the liquids the same density.

Challenge and Extension, p. 212

Teach Difficult Concepts

Students may have difficulty understanding how water in the atmosphere and temperature affect one another. If dry air loses energy, the temperature drops. If humid air loses energy, water vapor condenses and releases energy, so the temperature drops less. Energy that might cause a change in temperature instead causes a change in the state of water, so the temperature change is more moderate. As a result, moist air masses tend to have more moderate temperatures than dry air masses. A continental air mass might be hot or cold, whereas a maritime air mass that originated at a similar latitude will be merely warm or cool.

History of Science

The term "front" was first used by Norwegian scientists during World War I. At that time, many meteorologists were conducting research on the interactions of air masses. The clash of opposing air masses was considered analogous to clashing armies on the battlefront.

Ongoing Assessment

Explain what happens when air masses meet.

Ask: What happens when cold, dense air pushes warmer air? *A cold front forms as the cold, dense air moves forward, pushing the warmer air up.* What kind of weather would you expect? *Clouds and brief, heavy storms are likely.*

Answer: The temperature would decrease.

Weather changes where air masses meet.

When a new air mass moves over your area, you can expect the weather to change. Perhaps you have heard a weather forecaster talk about fronts. A **front** is a boundary between air masses. The weather near a front can differ from the weather inside the rest of an air mass. As one air mass pushes another, some of the air at the boundary will be pushed upward. Clouds can form in this rising air. The weather often becomes cloudy or stormy as a front passes. Afterward, you experience the temperature and humidity of the air mass that has moved in.

Fronts and Weather

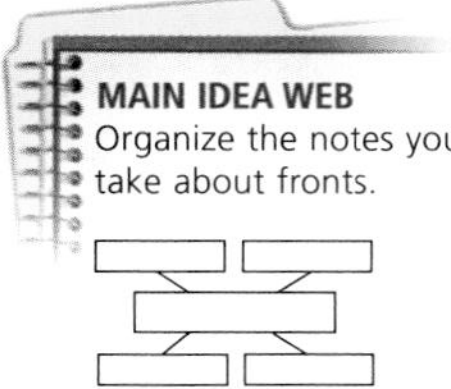

MAIN IDEA WEB
Organize the notes you take about fronts.

Different types of fronts produce different patterns of weather. When a cold, dense air mass pushes warmer air, it produces a cold front. When a warm air mass pushes colder air, it produces a warm front. These names tell you which way the temperature will change but not how much it will change. A cold front can turn a heat wave into normal summer weather or turn cold winter air into very cold weather.

How would the weather change if a cold front moved into your area today?

1. **Cold fronts** can move into regions quickly. As you can see on page 119, a cold front is steeper than the other types of fronts. As a mass of cold, dense air moves forward, warmer air ahead of it is pushed upward. Water vapor in the warm air condenses as the air rises. Cold fronts often produce tall cumulonimbus clouds and precipitation. Brief, heavy storms are likely. After the storms, the air is cooler and often very clear.

2. **Warm fronts** move more slowly than cold fronts. Warm air moves gradually up and over a mass of denser and colder air. Moisture in the warm air condenses all along the sloping front, producing cloud-covered skies. As a warm front approaches, you may first see high cirrus clouds, then high stratus clouds, then lower and lower stratus clouds. Often, a warm front brings many hours of steady rain or snow. After the front passes, the air is warmer.

3. **Stationary fronts** occur when air masses first meet or when a cold or warm front stops moving. For a while, the boundary between the air masses stays in the same location—in other words, it stays stationary. The air in each air mass can still move sideways along the front or upward. The upward air motion may produce clouds that cover the sky, sometimes for days at a time. When the front starts moving, it becomes a warm front if the warm air advances and pushes the cold air. If the cold air moves forward instead, the front becomes a cold front.

VISUALIZATION
CLASSZONE.COM
See how the air moves in warm fronts and cold fronts.

DIFFERENTIATE INSTRUCTION

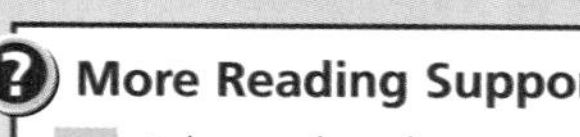

More Reading Support

D A boundary between air masses is called what? *front*

E What are three types of fronts? *cold, warm, and stationary*

Advanced Have students look at a weather Web site to determine what the fourth type of front is (occluded front). Occluded fronts often form when a rapidly moving cold front overtakes the slower-moving cool air mass in a warm front. The warm air is then "wedged" between two cooler air masses and is forced upward. Have students explain the symbol for an occluded front. *The symbol is a cold and warm front merged, with both fronts pointing in the same direction.*

Fronts and Weather

As fronts move across Earth's surface, they produce changes in the weather.

① Cold Front

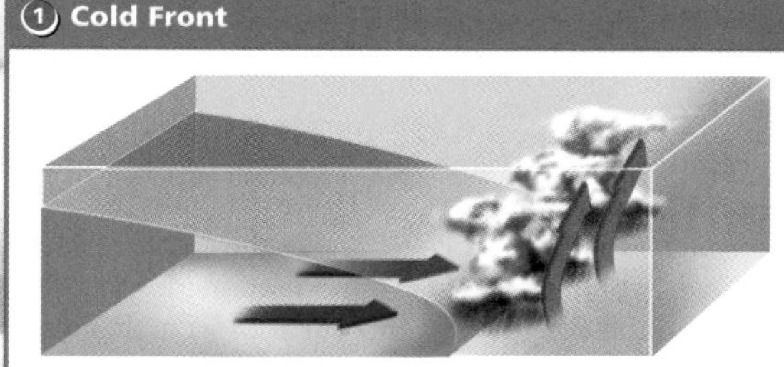

Triangles show the direction that a cold front moves.

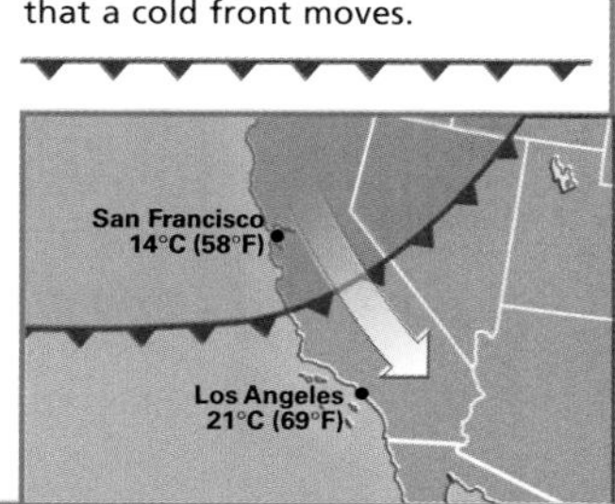

A **cold front** forms when a cold air mass pushes a warm air mass and forces the warm air to rise. As the warm air rises, its moisture condenses and forms tall clouds.

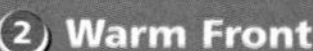

② Warm Front

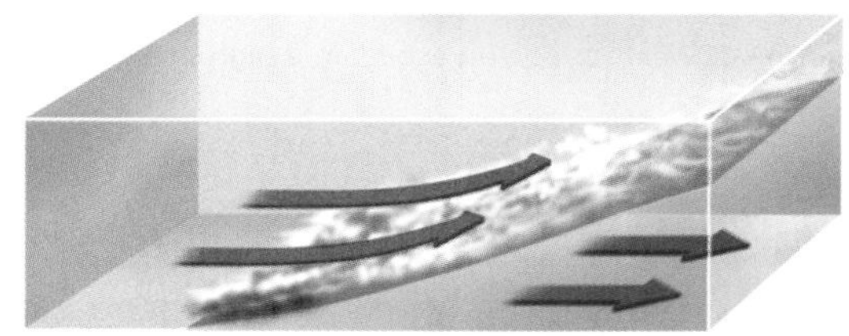

Semicircles show the direction that a warm front moves.

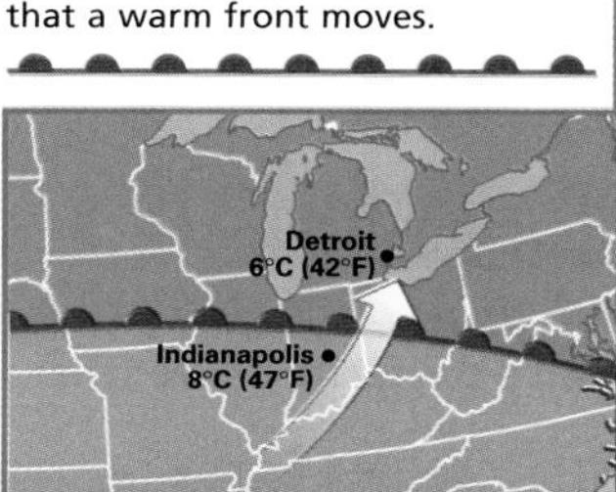

A **warm front** forms when a warm air mass pushes a cold air mass. The warm air rises slowly over the cold air and its moisture condenses into flat clouds.

③ Stationary Front

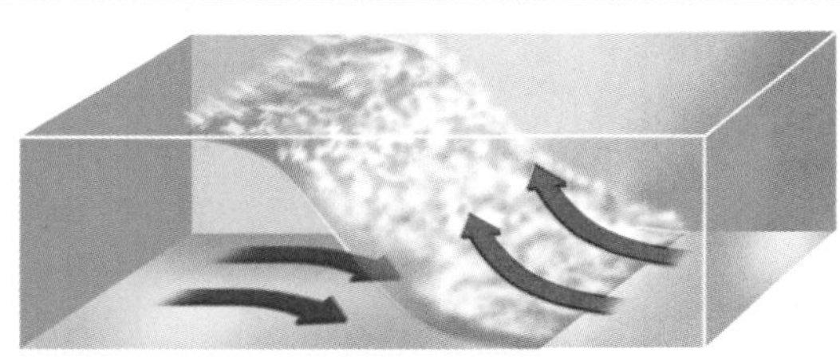

Alternating triangles and semicircles show a stationary front.

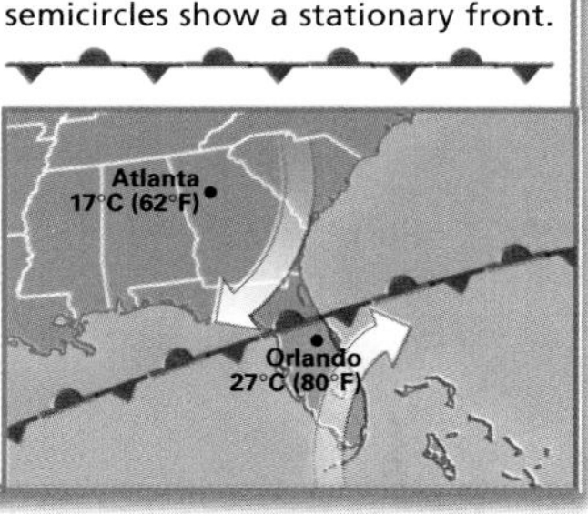

A **stationary front** occurs when two air masses push against each other without moving. A stationary front becomes a warm or cold front when one air mass advances.

READING VISUALS PREDICT **Which city will the cold front affect next?**

Teach from Visuals

Make sure students understand that the front symbols (triangles, semicircles) point outward in the direction in which the front is moving.

To help students interpret the "Fronts and Weather" visual, ask:

- How do the symbols for cold fronts and warm fronts differ? *They differ by shape—a cold front symbol is a line with triangles; a warm front symbol is a line with with semicircles.*
- Which city will soon experience a cold front? *Los Angeles* Which will experience a warm front? *Detroit*
- Compare the "slope" of rising air in a cold front and a warm front. *In a cold front, warm air rises steeply over cold air. In a warm front, warm air rises in a gentle slope over cold air.*

The visual "Fronts and Weather" is available as T30 in the Transparency Book.

Develop Critical Thinking

INFER Ask: Why do you think the symbol for a stationary front is a combination of triangles and semicircles? *A stationary front is the boundary between two different air masses. It may become either a warm or a cold front once it starts moving. The symbol for a stationary front is a combination of the symbols for cold and warm fronts.*

EXPLORE the BIG idea

Revisit "How Does Weather Move?" on p. 113. Have students explain the reasons for their observations.

Ongoing Assessment

READING VISUALS *Answer: Los Angeles*

IFFERENTIATE INSTRUCTION

elow Level Use analogies to help students distinguish between ne three types of fronts. For example, tell students to think of the tringles that represent a cold front as icicles. They can visualize the emicircles that represent a warm front as water droplets. A stationary ont is the boundary between two different air masses, so its symbol is combination of "icicles" and "water droplets." Encourage students to ink of other ways to distinguish between the front symbols. For xample, blue is often associated with cold temperatures and red is ften associated with warm temperatures.

Teach Difficult Concepts

Students may be confused by the terms *center* and *system*. Explain that *center* refers to the highest or lowest pressure in a region. *System* refers to both the center and the air surrounding the center. In a well-organized pressure system, air moves all the way around the high or low center.

Address Misconceptions

IDENTIFY Ask: If a high-pressure system moved over us, what would happen to the weather? If students say that it would be warmer or colder, ask whether all high-pressure systems bring warmer (or colder) weather. If students think they do, they may hold the misconception that high pressure involves a particular temperature.

CORRECT If students think that high pressure means warm temperatures, describe or give examples of the clear, cold weather of a cold wave. If students think that high pressure means cold temperatures, describe or give examples of the cloudless, rainless days that can occur during a heat wave. Both can be caused by high-pressure systems.

REASSESS Ask students to describe the weather at the high in the visual. *The sky is clear; the temperature is not known.*

Technology Resources

Visit **ClassZone.com** for background on common student misconceptions.

MISCONCEPTION DATABASE

Ongoing Assessment

Explain what happens when air masses meet.

Ask how two air masses can produce a low-pressure system. *A low-pressure center forms between the air masses and the fronts become part of the system.*

CHECK YOUR READING *Answer: fair (clear) and calm*

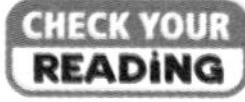
Answer: It looks similar to convection (pp. 30 and 59), or global wind cells (p. 87), and local winds (p. 89).

High-Pressure Systems

F

You may have seen the letters H and L on a weather map. These letters mark high-pressure centers and low-pressure centers, often simply called highs and lows. Each center is the location of the highest or lowest pressure in a region. The pressure differences cause air to move in ways that may make a high or low become the center of a whole system of weather.

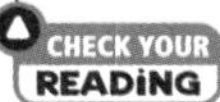
A *system* includes different parts that work together.

At a high-pressure center, air sinks slowly down. As the air nears the ground, it spreads out toward areas of lower pressure. In the Northern Hemisphere, the Coriolis effect makes the air turn clockwise as it moves outward. A **high-pressure system** is formed when air moves all the way around a high-pressure center. Most high-pressure systems are large and change slowly. When a high-pressure system stays in one location for a long time, an air mass may form. The air—and resulting air mass—can be warm or cold, moist or dry.

A high-pressure system generally brings clear skies and calm air or gentle breezes. This is because as air sinks to lower altitudes, it warms up a little bit. Water droplets evaporate, so clouds often disappear.

CHECK YOUR READING What type of weather do you expect in a high-pressure system?

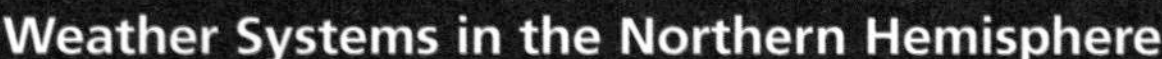
Weather Systems in the Northern Hemisphere

High-pressure systems and low-pressure systems produce patterns of weather across Earth's surface.

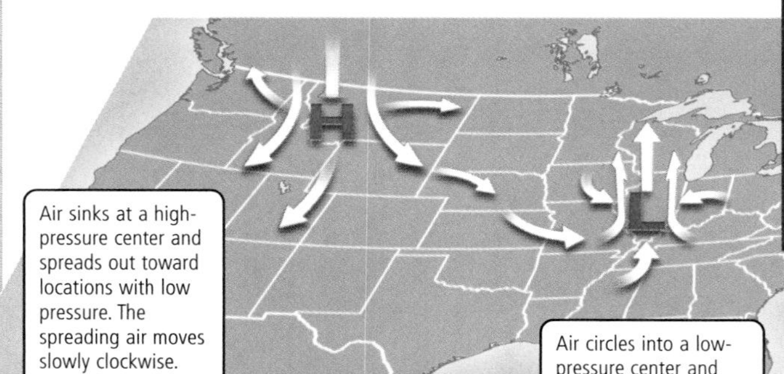

H
L
Air sinks at a high-pressure center and spreads out toward locations with low pressure. The spreading air moves slowly clockwise.
Air circles into a low-pressure center and moves upward. The motion is counterclockwise and can be quick.

A spiral of clouds often shows the location of a low-pressure system.

READING VISUALS With your finger, trace the motion of air, starting above the high. Where have you seen similar patterns in earlier chapters?

DIFFERENTIATE INSTRUCTION

More Reading Support

F What do the letters H and L stand for on a weather map? *high- and low-pressure centers*

Advanced Ask students what they have learned about the Coriolis effect in relation to the movement of air in high-pressure systems. Ask them to infer how air moves around a high-pressure system in the Southern Hemisphere. *in a counterclockwise direction*

Low-Pressure Systems

A small area of low pressure can also develop into a larger system. A **low-pressure system** is a large weather system that surrounds a center of low pressure. It begins as air moves around and inward toward the lowest pressure and then up to higher altitudes. The upward motion of the air lowers the air pressure further, and so the air moves faster. The pattern of motion strengthens into a low-pressure weather system. The rising air produces stormy weather. In the Northern Hemisphere, the air in a low-pressure system circles in a counterclockwise direction.

A low-pressure system can develop wherever there is a center of low pressure. One place this often happens is along a boundary between a warm air mass and a cold air mass. The diagram shows an example of this process.

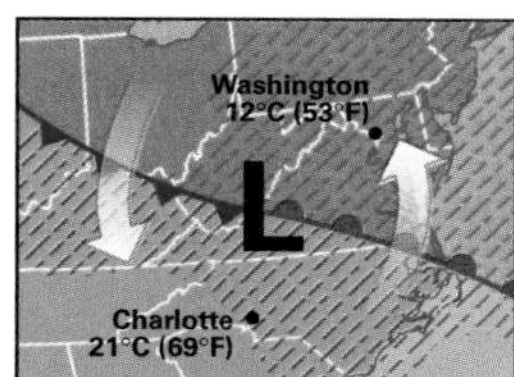

- Part of the boundary between the air masses moves south and becomes a cold front.
- Part of the boundary moves north and becomes a warm front.
- A center of low pressure forms where the ends of the two fronts meet.

The low-pressure center and fronts become parts of a whole system of weather. Rising air at the fronts and at the low can cause very stormy weather.

The diagram on page 120 shows how air moves between pressure centers. Air moves down, out, and around a high-pressure center. Then it swirls around and into a low-pressure center and moves upward. Highs and lows affect each other as they move across the surface. Large weather systems generally move with the pattern of global winds—west to east over most of North America. But, within a weather system, winds can blow in different directions.

4.1 Review

KEY CONCEPTS

1. What are the two characteristics of an air mass that you need to know in order to classify it? (6.4.e)
2. What happens when a warmer air mass pushes a cooler air mass? (6.4.e)
3. What type of weather system brings calm, clear weather? (6.4.e)

CRITICAL THINKING

4. **Compare and Contrast** Explain how air moves differently in low- and high-pressure systems.
5. **Apply** If the weather becomes stormy for a short time and then becomes colder, which type of front has passed?

CHALLENGE

6. **Synthesize** You check a barometer and observe that the air pressure has been dropping all day. Is tonight's weather more likely to be calm or stormy?

ANSWERS

1. temperature and moisture

2. A warm front forms. The warm air rises slowly over the cold air, and its moisture condenses into clouds.

3. a high-pressure system

4. Air sinks into a high-pressure center and spreads out in a clockwise direction. Air spirals around a low-pressure center and moves in a counterclockwise direction.

5. a cold front

6. It is likely to be stormy because decreasing pressure indicates that a low-pressure system or front is approaching; both are associated with clouds and, possibly, storms.

Ongoing Assessment

Determine how pressure systems affect the weather.

Ask: What type of weather is often associated with low-pressure systems? *stormy weather*

Teach from Visuals

To help students interpret the weather system maps on p. 120, ask:

- What do the arrows show? *They show how air moves around and between high- and low-pressure centers.*
- Locate the *H* and *L* on the inset map. What is different about these areas? *L is surrounded by a spiral of clouds; H is clear.*

Reinforce the BIG idea

Have students relate the section to the Big Idea.

 Reinforcing Key Concepts, p. 214

4.1 ASSESS & RETEACH

Assess

 Section 4.1 Quiz, p. 63

Reteach

Display a map of the United States that has all states labeled. Then place students in pairs and provide each pair with a newspaper weather map. Choose states that have fronts going through them and assign a different state to each pair. Have students identify the type of front and the high- or low-pressure system that are influencing the weather in their assigned state.

Technology Resources

Have students visit **ClassZone.com** for reteaching of Key Concepts.

 CONTENT REVIEW

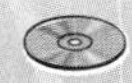 CONTENT REVIEW CD-ROM

MATH IN SCIENCE

Math Skills Practice for Science

Set Learning Goal

To determine rates to measure the speed of a moving cold front

Math Standards

6.NS.1.2 Interpret and use ratios in different contexts (e.g., batting averages, miles per hour) to show the relative sizes of two quantities, using appropriate notations (*a/b*, *a* to *b*, *a:b*).

6.AF.2.2 Demonstrate an understanding that *rate* is a measure of one quantity per unit value of another quantity.

Present the Science

Fronts move and change as air masses move. Cold fronts tend to move faster than warm fronts.

Develop Algebra Skills

Tell students that a ratio is a way of comparing numbers. A ratio can also be written as *500 km : one day* or as *500 km to one day.* Also, remind students that the mean is simply the average of the rates. To calculate the mean, add the rates together, then divide by the total number of rates.

DIFFERENTIATION TIP Students with learning disabilities may have an easier time estimating the front's movement if they use a pencil and the edge of a sheet of paper to mark off the distances traveled. They can compare the marked-off distances to the scale.

Close

Ask: Does the front appear to be speeding up or slowing down? Explain. ***It appears to be slowing down because the front's movement between Friday and Saturday is less than the front's movement on previous days.***

- Math Support, p. 252
- Math Practice, p. 253

Technology Resources

Students can visit **ClassZone.com** for practice with rates as ratios.

MATH TUTORIAL

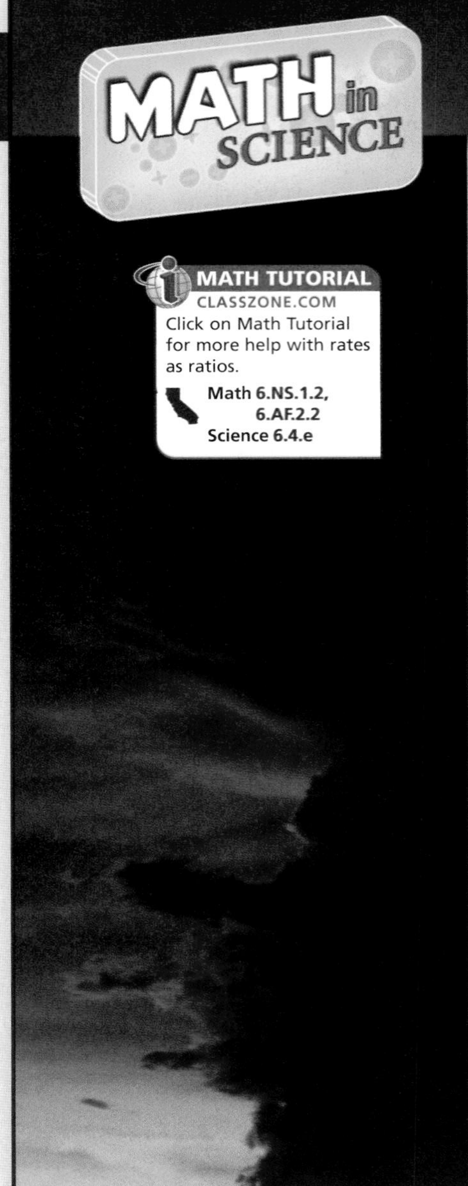

MATH TUTORIAL
CLASSZONE.COM
Click on Math Tutorial for more help with rates as ratios.

Math 6.NS.1.2, 6.AF.2.2
Science 6.4.e

SKILL: DETERMINING RATES

Movement of a Front

Scientists measure the speeds of weather fronts to forecast weather conditions. The speed at which a front moves is an example of a rate. A rate can be written as a ratio. For example, the rate of a front that moves a distance of 500 kilometers in 1 day can be written as follows:

500 kilometers : 1 day

The map below shows the movement of a cold front over four consecutive days. Use the map scale to determine the distance that the front moves on each day.

Cold Front Movement

Answer the following questions.

1. What was the front's rate of movement between Wednesday and Thursday? Express your answer as a ratio.

   ? : 1 day

2. What was the front's rate of movement between Friday and Saturday? Express your answer as a ratio.
3. What was the mean rate of the front's movement from Wednesday to Saturday? Remember, *mean* means "average." Express your answer as a ratio.

CHALLENGE Use the rate from Wednesday to Saturday to estimate the day on which the front must have moved through San Francisco.

122 Unit 1: The Earth System

ANSWERS

1. 750 km : 1 day
2. 600 km : 1 day
3. 700 km : 1 day

$$750 + 750 + 600 = 2100 \qquad \frac{2100}{3} = 700$$

Students' measurements may vary by 50 km or so.

CHALLENGE *On Wednesday, the front was about 1400 km from San Francisco. It is moving at a rate of roughly 700 km per day. It would have passed San Francisco on Monday.*

KEY CONCEPT

Low-pressure systems can become storms.

CALIFORNIA Content Standard

6.4.e Students know differences in pressure, heat, air movement, and humidity result in changes of weather.

BEFORE, you learned

- Moving air masses cause changes in weather
- A low-pressure system brings stormy weather

NOW, you will learn

- How hurricanes develop
- About the dangers of hurricanes
- About different types of winter storms

VOCABULARY

tropical storm p. 123
hurricane p. 123
storm surge p. 125
blizzard p. 126

EXPLORE Hurricanes (6.4.e)

What things make hurricanes lose strength?

PROCEDURE

1. Crumple a piece of paper, then flatten it out. Crumple and flatten it out again.
2. Spin the top on the flattened paper. Count the seconds until it stops spinning.
3. Spin the top on a smooth surface. Count the seconds until it stops spinning.

WHAT DO YOU THINK?
How does the texture of the surface affect the rate at which the top loses energy?

MATERIALS
- sheet of paper
- top

MAIN IDEA WEB
Remember to make notes about hurricanes.

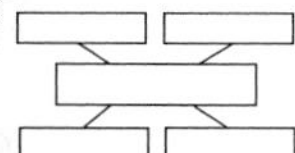

Hurricanes form over warm ocean water.

Near the equator, warm ocean water provides the energy that can turn a low-pressure center into a violent storm. As water evaporates from the ocean, energy moves from the ocean water into the air. This energy makes warm air rise faster. Tall clouds and strong winds develop. As winds blow across the water from different directions into the low, the Coriolis effect bends their paths into a spiral. The winds blow faster and faster around the low, which becomes the center of a storm system.

A **tropical storm** is a low-pressure system that starts near the equator and has winds that blow at 65 kilometers per hour (40 mi/h) or more. A **hurricane** (HUR-ih-KAYN) is a tropical low-pressure system with winds blowing at speeds of 120 kilometers per hour (74 mi/h) or more—strong enough to uproot trees. Hurricanes are called typhoons or cyclones when they form over the Indian Ocean or the western Pacific Ocean.

RESOURCES FOR DIFFERENTIATED INSTRUCTION

Below Level

UNIT RESOURCE BOOK
- Reading Study Guide A, pp. 217–218
- Decoding Support, p. 251

AUDIO CDS

Additional INVESTIGATION, Hurricane Hugo, A, B, & C, pp. 263–271; Teacher Instructions, pp. 276

Advanced

UNIT RESOURCE BOOK
- Challenge and Extension, p. 223
- Challenge Reading, pp. 247–248

English Learners

UNIT RESOURCE BOOK
Spanish Reading Study Guide, pp. 221–222

AUDIO CDS
- Audio Readings in Spanish
- Audio Readings (English)

4.2 FOCUS

Set Learning Goals

Students will
- Explain how hurricanes develop.
- Recognize the dangers from hurricanes.
- Compare the different types of winter storms.
- Observe an experiment that shows why salt is put on icy roads.

3-Minute Warm-Up

Display Transparency 28 or copy this exercise on the board:

Draw a diagram to show how air moves around a low-pressure system. Label the low-pressure center and use arrows to show the direction of air movement.

 3-Minute Warm-Up, p. T28

4.2 MOTIVATE

EXPLORE Hurricanes

PURPOSE To help students understand one factor that affects hurricane strength

TIP *10 min.* Have students work in pairs. While one student observes the spinning top, his or her partner can keep track of the time using a stopwatch or clock, or by counting seconds.

WHAT DO YOU THINK? *The top loses energy faster on a rough surface. It spins longer on a smooth surface.*

Teach Difficult Concepts

Ask students whether they have heard the term *cyclone.* This term has several meanings. Students may have heard it used informally to mean "tornado." Meteorologists use the term to refer to a low-pressure system, whether or not that system has hurricane-force winds. It is also used to refer to a hurricane in the western Pacific Ocean.

4.2 INSTRUCT

Teach the Standards

Hurricanes and winter storms 6.4.e

In this section: Students learn how low-pressure systems are involved in creating hurricanes and severe winter storms. Ask students to recall from memory a hurricane or winter storm that they experienced or heard about in the news. Ask them to recall some of the effects of either type of storm.

- **previously taught:** weather, pp. 62–63; wind, pp. 83–84; weather and air masses, 118–121
- **future opportunities:** tornadoes, p. 131

History of Science

In 1971 engineer Herbert Saffir and meteorologist Dr. Robert Simpson jointly developed a classification system for hurricanes. The Saffir-Simpson hurricane scale ranks hurricanes from 1 to 5, with 5 being the most powerful. Factors such as wind speed, lowest pressure reading, and damage potential contribute to the rankings. A category 1 hurricane causes minimal damage. A category 3 hurricane causes floods and structural damage to small buildings and mobile homes. A category 5 hurricane is considered catastrophic. Only three category 5 hurricanes have struck the United States, the last being Hurricane Andrew in 1992.

Ongoing Assessment

Explain how hurricanes develop.

Ask: How does a low-pressure system develop into a hurricane? *Sample answer: Water evaporates over a warm ocean, moving energy from the ocean to the air. The warm, moist air rises quickly. Tall clouds and strong winds form. The winds blow faster and faster in a spiral around the low-pressure center.*

CHECK YOUR READING *Answer: warm ocean water*

Formation of Hurricanes

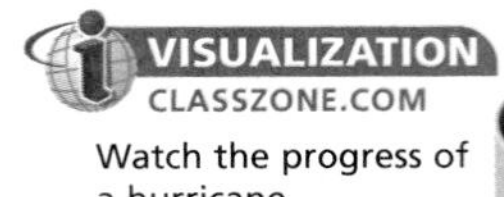

Watch the progress of a hurricane.

In the eastern United States, hurricanes most often strike between August and October. Energy from warm water is necessary for a low-pressure center to build into a tropical storm and then into a hurricane. The ocean water where these storms develop only gets warm enough—26°C (80°F) or more—near the end of summer.

Tropical storms and hurricanes generally move westward with the trade winds. Near land, however, they will often move north, south, or even back eastward. As long as a storm stays above warm water, it can grow bigger and more powerful. As soon as a hurricane moves over land or over cooler water, it loses its source of energy. The winds lose strength and the storm dies out. If a hurricane moves over land, the rough surface of the land reduces the winds even more.

A tropical storm may gain energy and become a hurricane. When the hurricane shown below moved north, the storm lost energy and was called a tropical storm again as its winds slowed.

What is the source of a hurricane's energy?

Structure of a Hurricane

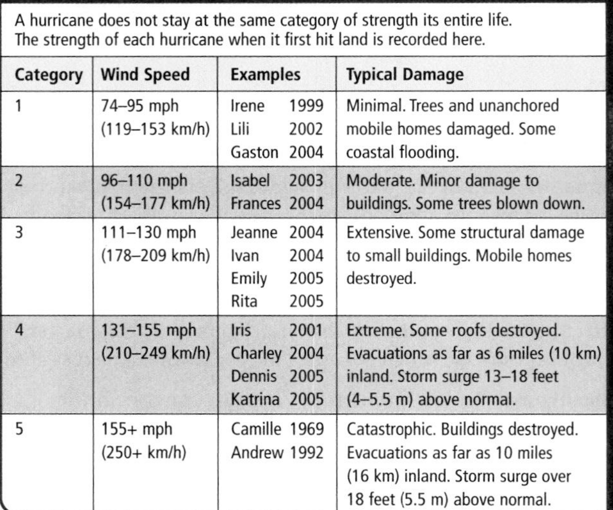

Saffir-Simpson Hurricane Scale

A hurricane does not stay at the same category of strength its entire life. The strength of each hurricane when it first hit land is recorded here.

Category	Wind Speed	Examples	Typical Damage
1	74–95 mph (119–153 km/h)	Irene 1999 Lili 2002 Gaston 2004	Minimal. Trees and unanchored mobile homes damaged. Some coastal flooding.
2	96–110 mph (154–177 km/h)	Isabel 2003 Frances 2004	Moderate. Minor damage to buildings. Some trees blown down.
3	111–130 mph (178–209 km/h)	Jeanne 2004 Ivan 2004 Emily 2005 Rita 2005	Extensive. Some structural damage to small buildings. Mobile homes destroyed.
4	131–155 mph (210–249 km/h)	Iris 2001 Charley 2004 Dennis 2005 Katrina 2005	Extreme. Some roofs destroyed. Evacuations as far as 6 miles (10 km) inland. Storm surge 13–18 feet (4–5.5 m) above normal.
5	155+ mph (250+ km/h)	Camille 1969 Andrew 1992	Catastrophic. Buildings destroyed. Evacuations as far as 10 miles (16 km) inland. Storm surge over 18 feet (5.5 m) above normal.

Eye: The small center of a hurricane is clear and calm because air is moving downward.
Bands of thunderstorms give the hurricane a spiral shape.
Eye wall: Just outside the eye, the air swirls upward very quickly. It is like a wall of stormy weather.

DIFFERENTIATE INSTRUCTION

More Reading Support

A When do most hurricanes strike in the United States? *August–October*

B A hurricane begins to lose energy when it moves over what? *land or cooler water*

Additional Investigation To reinforce Section 4.2 learning goals, use the following full-period investigation:

Additional INVESTIGATION, Hurricane Hugo, A, B, & C, pp. 263–271, 276 (Advanced students should complete Levels B and C.)

At the center of a hurricane is a small area of clear weather, 20–50 kilometers (10–30 mi) in diameter, called the eye. The storm's center is calm because air moves downward there. Just around the eye, the air moves very quickly around and upward, forming a tall ring of cumulonimbus clouds called the eye wall. This ring produces very heavy rains and tremendous winds. Farther from the center, bands of heavy clouds and rain spiral inward toward the eye.

SAFETY TIPS

HURRICANES

- Before a storm, prepare a plan to leave the area. Gather emergency supplies.
- Listen to weather reports for storm updates.
- Secure loose objects outside, and cover windows.
- If ordered to evacuate, leave immediately.
- During a storm, stay indoors and away from windows.
- After a storm, be aware of power lines, hanging branches, and flooded areas.

Effects of Hurricanes

A hurricane can pound a coast with huge waves and sweep the land with strong winds and heavy rains. Hurricane winds can lift cars, uproot trees, and tear the roofs off buildings. Hurricanes may also produce tornadoes that cause even more damage. Heavy rains from hurricanes may make rivers overflow their banks and flood nearby areas. When a hurricane moves into a coastal area, it often pushes a huge mass of ocean water known as a **storm surge.** In a storm surge, the sea level rises several meters, backing up rivers and flooding the shore. A storm surge can be destructive and deadly. Large waves add to the destruction. A hurricane may affect an area for a few hours or a few days, but the flooding and damage may take weeks, months, or years to clean up.

CHECK YOUR READING What are the effects of hurricanes? Make a list for your answer.

The National Hurricane Center helps people know when to prepare for a hurricane. The center puts out a tropical-storm or hurricane watch when a storm is likely to strike within 36 hours. People are sometimes evacuated, or moved away for safety, from areas where they may be in danger. As the danger gets closer—24 hours or less—the center issues a tropical-storm or hurricane warning. The warning stays in effect until the danger has passed.

This photograph shows New Orleans, Louisiana, after it was hit by Hurricane Katrina in August 2005. The hurricane's storm surge flooded part of the city and also weakened several levees, or earthen dams. Most of the flooding happened after levees broke and allowed water from a nearby lake to pour into the city.

DIFFERENTIATE INSTRUCTION

More Reading Support

C What is the calm center of a hurricane called? *the eye*

D A huge mass of ocean water, pushed inland by a hurricane, is called what? *storm surge*

Advanced Students can plot the paths of current or past tropical storms and hurricanes on a map of the Atlantic or Pacific Ocean. They can use symbols or colors to represent different stages of the storms. Ask students to consider the sizes of the storms as well as the locations of their centers.

- Challenge and Extension, p. 223
- Challenge Reading, pp. 247–248

Real World Example

The 1983 hurricane that devastated Long Island and southern New England made a 12-day journey across the Atlantic before slamming into the coast. Neither the U.S. Weather Bureau nor the general public knew the storm was coming. Today, people know when a hurricane is approaching. In 2003 the National Weather Service began providing hurricane forecasts five days in advance of a storm's arrival. This allows time for people and resources to be moved to safety.

Teacher Demo

Do the following demonstration to help students visualize the relationship between storm surges and floods. Lay a piece of plastic on the floor near a wall. Cut off one short end of a shoebox and place the shoebox on the plastic so that its uncut end is flush against the wall. Put packing peanuts in the box. Tell students that the filled shoebox represents a flowing river. Then pour some more packing peanuts on the plastic in front of the shoebox and, using the cut-off piece of cardboard or your hands, shove the packing peanuts toward the shoebox so that the first pile of packing peanuts is forced back and spill out. Ask: What did the second pile of packing peanuts represent? *a storm surge* What happened to the "river" in this model? *It overflowed its banks.*

Ongoing Assessment

Recognize the dangers from hurricanes.

Ask: What should you do if a hurricane is approaching your area? *Prepare, listen to weather reports, and evacuate if advised. If you remain in your town, stay indoors and away from windows.*

CHECK YOUR READING *Answer: storm surge, strong winds, heavy rains, tornadoes, floods, huge waves*

INVESTIGATE Ice

PURPOSE Observe how salt affects ice to infer why it is put on icy roads.

TIPS *10 min.* Place students in small groups, then suggest the following:

- Use about a teaspoon of salt on one ice cube.
- Place a thin, but complete, layer of salt on the ice.

WHAT DO YOU THINK? *The salted ice melted faster. People put salt on roads to help the ice melt faster so that it will be safer to drive.*

CHALLENGE *Sample answer: Sand and cinders increase traction. In addition, cinders are dark and thus absorb sunlight, which in turn makes the ice melt faster. Students can repeat this experiment using sand or cinders on an ice cube rather than salt. Be sure students test only one variable at a time.*

 Datasheet, Ice, p. 224

Technology Resources

Customize this student lab as needed or look for an alternative. Print rubrics to assess student lab reports.

 **Lab Generator CD-ROM**

Teaching with Technology

Have students check the National Weather Service's Web site for current storm watches and storm warnings for the United States.

Ongoing Assessment

Compare the different types of winter storms.

Ask: What causes most winter storms? *weather systems that form when two air masses collide*

Winter storms produce snow and ice.

CALIFORNIA Focus
Fresh water is scarce in southern California. However, along the northern coast, excess rain and snowmelt cause flooding of rivers during the winter.

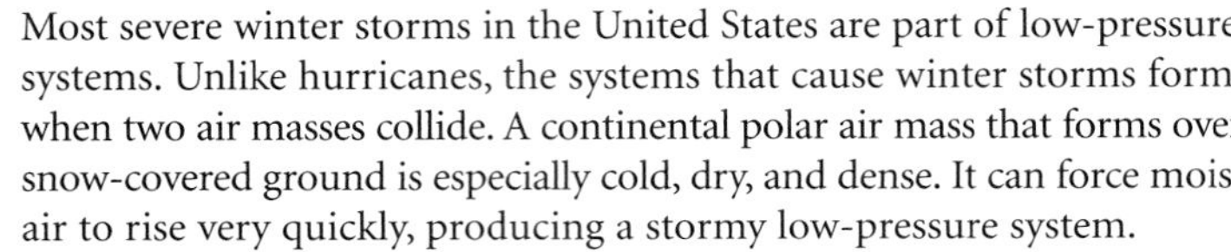

Most severe winter storms in the United States are part of low-pressure systems. Unlike hurricanes, the systems that cause winter storms form when two air masses collide. A continental polar air mass that forms over snow-covered ground is especially cold, dry, and dense. It can force moist air to rise very quickly, producing a stormy low-pressure system.

The National Weather Service (NWS) alerts people to dangerous weather. The NWS issues a winter storm watch up to 48 hours before a storm is expected. A winter storm warning means that dangerous conditions are already present or will affect an area shortly.

VOCABULARY
Remember to add *blizzard* to your notebook, using the vocabulary strategy of your choice.

Blizzards Strong winds can blow so much snow into the air at once that it becomes difficult to see and dangerous to travel. **Blizzards** are blinding snowstorms with winds of at least 56 kilometers per hour (35 mi/h) and low temperatures—usually below –7°C (20°F). Blizzards occur in many parts of the northern and central United States. Wind and snow can knock down trees and power lines. Without heat, buildings can become very cold, and water in pipes may freeze. Schools, hospitals, and businesses may have to close. Deep, heavy snow on top of a building may cause the roof to cave in.

Lake-Effect Snowstorms Some of the heaviest snows fall in the areas just east and south of the Great Lakes. Cold air from the northwest gains moisture and warmth as it passes over the Great Lakes. Over cold land, the air cools again and releases the moisture as snow. The lake effect can cover areas downwind of the Great Lakes with clouds and snow even when the rest of the region has clear weather.

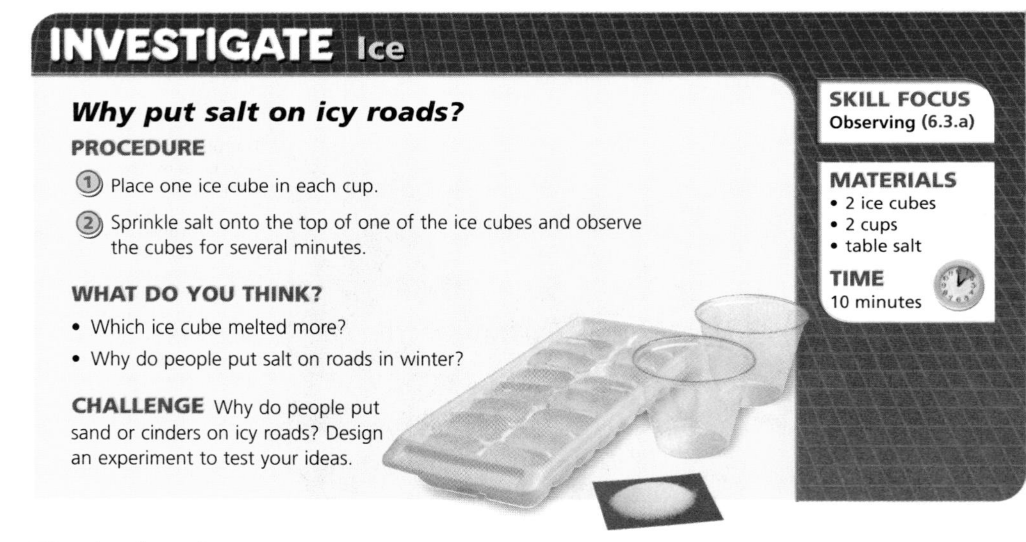

INVESTIGATE Ice

Why put salt on icy roads?

PROCEDURE

1. Place one ice cube in each cup.
2. Sprinkle salt onto the top of one of the ice cubes and observe the cubes for several minutes.

WHAT DO YOU THINK?

- Which ice cube melted more?
- Why do people put salt on roads in winter?

CHALLENGE Why do people put sand or cinders on icy roads? Design an experiment to test your ideas.

SKILL FOCUS
Observing (6.3.a)

MATERIALS
- 2 ice cubes
- 2 cups
- table salt

TIME
10 minutes

DIFFERENTIATE INSTRUCTION

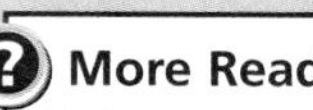

More Reading Support

E What type of weather system may include severe winter storms? *a low-pressure system*

F Where do lake-effect snowstorms occur? *near the Great Lakes*

Below Level When discussing lake-effect snow, display a large map of the Great Lakes area. Read the student text aloud, using the map to point out how cold air from the northwest sweeps over the lakes. Show where the heaviest snows can be expected. *just east and south of the lakes*

English Learners English learners may need help with the use of *lake effect* as both a noun and an adjective (in *lake-effect snow*). Also, identifying the Great Lakes on a map or globe may supply needed background knowledge.

SAFETY TIPS

WINTER STORMS

- Before a storm, prepare emergency kits for home and car.
- Listen to weather reports for updates.
- If caught in a storm, find or make a shelter and try to stay dry.
- If you are in a car or truck, make sure the exhaust pipe is clear and open a window a little bit.
- Use a colored cloth, fire, or light to help rescuers find you.
- Exercise a little to keep warm and keep blood flowing to your fingers and toes.
- If at home, stay inside even if there is no heat or power. Wear layers of clothing.

Ice Storms When rain falls onto freezing-cold ground, conditions can become dangerous. The cold rain freezes as it touches the ground and other surfaces. This freezing rain covers everything with heavy, smooth ice. The ice-covered roads become slippery and dangerous. Drivers may find it hard to steer and to stop their cars. Branches or even whole trees may break from the weight of ice. Falling branches can block roads, tear down power and telephone lines, and cause other damage. Damage from ice storms can sometimes shut down entire cities.

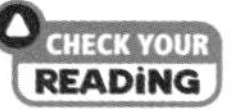
CHECK YOUR READING What type of precipitation occurs in each type of winter storm?

4.2 Review

KEY CONCEPTS

1. Where and when do hurricanes form? (6.4.e)
2. What are two ways that hurricanes can cause floods? (6.4.e)
3. List three of the possible dangers from winter storms. (6.4.e)

CRITICAL THINKING

4. **Compare and Contrast** What are the differences between the eye and the eye wall of a hurricane?
5. **Compare** What do hurricanes and winter storms have in common?

CHALLENGE

6. **Apply** If the wind is blowing from the west and the conditions are right for lake-effect snow, will the snow fall to the north, south, east, or west of a lake? Drawing a diagram may help you work out an answer.

ANSWERS

1. Hurricanes form over warm ocean water near the equator. They typically form in late summer from August to October.

2. Heavy rains can cause rivers to overflow their banks. Storm surges can flood coastal areas.

3. Sample answer: slippery roads, fallen power lines, caved-in buildings

4. Air in the eye is moving downward and is calm. Air in the stormy eye wall is swirling rapidly upward.

5. Both are low-pressure systems associated with stormy weather.

6. The snow will fall to the east of the lake.

Ongoing Assessment

CHECK YOUR READING *Answer: blizzards: heavy snow; lake-effect snow: snow; ice storms: freezing rain*

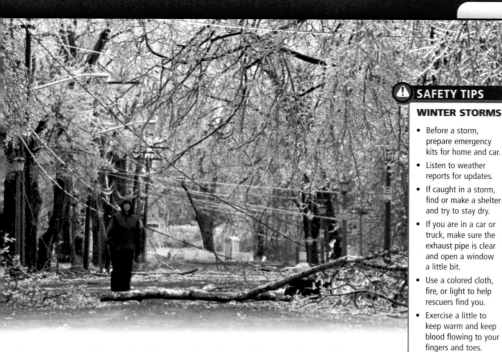

Reinforce the BIG idea

Have students relate the section to the Big Idea.

 Reinforcing Key Concepts, p. 225

4.2 ASSESS & RETEACH

Assess

A Section 4.2 Quiz, p. 64

Reteach

Place students in small groups and have them develop an emergency plan for their town in the event of severe weather. Students can play the role of local officials. They should consider the effects of a type of storm likely to affect their area and should decide how to protect and assist residents, protect public property, and restore services after the storm. Encourage students to be creative. They can write press releases or conduct a press conference, describing the storm and what actions will be taken when a powerful storm strikes.

Technology Resources

Have students visit **ClassZone.com** for reteaching of Key Concepts.

 **CONTENT REVIEW**

 **CONTENT REVIEW CD-ROM**

4.3 FOCUS

Set Learning Goals

Students will
- Explain how thunderstorms develop.
- Describe the effects of thunderstorms.
- Describe tornadoes and their effects.
- Infer through experimentation how updrafts form.

3-Minute Warm-Up

Display Transparency 29 or copy this exercise on the board.

What type of clouds often form at a cold front? Draw a diagram to show how this happens. *Cumulonimbus clouds form along cold fronts. Diagrams should resemble the first visual on p. 119 and depict a cross-section view of a cold front pushing warm, humid air upward into a cumulonimbus cloud.*

 3-Minute Warm-Up, p. T29

4.3 MOTIVATE

THINK ABOUT

PURPOSE To understand and identify the source of energy that fuels thunderstorms

DISCUSS Ask: How are the sources of energy that cause warm air to rise and thunderstorms to form similar?

Ongoing Assessment

CHECK YOUR READING *Answer: Thunder is an effect of lightning.*

KEY CONCEPT

4.3 Vertical air motion can cause severe storms.

CALIFORNIA Content Standards

6.4.d Students know convection currents distribute heat in the atmosphere and oceans.

6.4.e Students know differences in pressure, heat, air movement, and humidity result in changes of weather.

BEFORE, you learned
- Fronts produce changes in weather
- Rising moist air can produce clouds and precipitation

NOW, you will learn
- How thunderstorms develop
- About the effects of thunderstorms
- About tornadoes and their effects

VOCABULARY

thunderstorm p. 128
tornado p. 131

THINK ABOUT

Where do thunderstorms get their energy?

Thunderstorms form as warm, moist air rises quickly in strong convection currents. As water vapor in the rising air condenses, it releases energy in the form of heat. This energy provides fuel for the thunderstorm. What is the source of energy that causes currents of warm air to rise in the first place?

Thunderstorms form from rising moist air.

If you have ever shuffled your shoes on a carpet, you may have felt a small shock when you touched a doorknob. Electrical charges collected on your body and then jumped to the doorknob in a spark of electricity.

In a similar way, electrical charges build up near the tops and bottoms of clouds as pellets of ice move up and down through the clouds. Suddenly, a charge sparks from one part of a cloud to another or between a cloud and the ground. The spark of electricity, called lightning, causes a bright flash of light. The air around the lightning is briefly heated to a temperature hotter than the surface of the Sun. This fast heating produces a sharp wave of air that travels away from the lightning. When the wave reaches you, you hear it as a crack of thunder. A **thunderstorm** is a storm with lightning and thunder.

VOCABULARY Add the term *thunderstorm* to your notebook. Use the vocabulary strategy of your choice.

CHECK YOUR READING Is thunder a cause or an effect of lightning?

RESOURCES FOR DIFFERENTIATED INSTRUCTION

Below Level

UNIT RESOURCE BOOK
- Reading Study Guide A, pp. 228–229
- Decoding Support, p. 251

AUDIO CDS

Advanced

UNIT RESOURCE BOOK
Challenge and Extension, p. 234

English Learners

UNIT RESOURCE BOOK
Spanish Reading Study Guide, pp. 232–233

AUDIO CDS
- Audio Readings in Spanish
- Audio Readings (English)

Formation of Thunderstorms

Thunderstorms get their energy from humid air. When warm, humid air near the ground moves vertically into cooler air above, the rising air, or updraft, can build a thunderstorm quickly.

B

1. Rising humid air forms a cumulus cloud. The water vapor releases energy when it condenses into cloud droplets. This energy increases the air motion. The cloud continues building up into the tall cumulonimbus cloud of a thunderstorm.
2. Ice particles form in the low temperatures near the top of the cloud. As the ice particles grow large, they begin to fall and pull cold air down with them. This strong downdraft brings heavy rain or hail—the most severe stage of a thunderstorm.
3. The downdraft can spread out and block more warm air from moving upward into the cloud. The storm slows down and ends.

Thunderstorms can form at a cold front or within an air mass. At a cold front, air can be forced upward quickly. Within an air mass, uneven heating can produce convection and thunderstorms. In some regions, the conditions that produce thunderstorms occur almost daily during part of the year. In Florida, for example, the wet land and air warm up during a long summer day. Then, as you see in the diagram, cool sea breezes blow in from both coasts of the peninsula at once. The two sea breezes together push the warm, humid air over the land upward quickly. Thunderstorms form in the rising air.

In contrast, the summer air along the coast of California is usually too dry to produce thunderstorms. The air over the land heats up, and a sea breeze forms, but there is not enough moisture in the rising warm air to form clouds and precipitation.

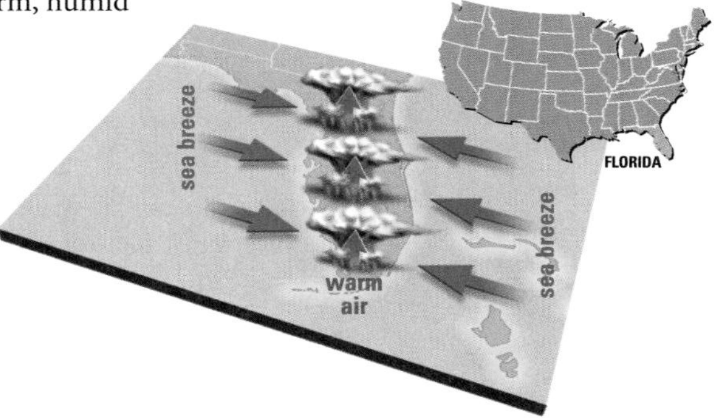

DIFFERENTIATE INSTRUCTION

More Reading Support

A Where do thunderstorms get their energy from? *humid air*

B What air motion produces thunderstorms? *rising air*

English Learners English learners may need help with the following uses of terms: "*crack* of thunder" on p. 128 (not like *a crack in a wall*); "winds *once* knocked down" on p. 130 (as in "at a time in the past," not to be confused with something that happens "one time"); the use of *may* and *might* on p. 132 to indicate examples or typical results.

4.3 INSTRUCT

Teach the Standards

Tornadoes 6.4.e

In this section: Students learn how humid air provides the energy needed to create severe thunderstorms and tornadoes. Ask students to describe in their own words how thunderstorms form.

previously taught: weather, pp. 62–63; wind, pp. 83–84; weather and air masses, 118–121; low-pressure systems, pp. 123–127

Teach from Visuals

To help students interpret the visual on thunderstorm formation, ask:

- Which diagram shows the most severe stage of a thunderstorm? *diagram 2*
- Compare the first two stages. Why does the cloud become tall? *air movesupward*

Address Misconceptions

IDENTIFY Ask: If a building is struck by lightning, is it safe from lightning in the future? If students answer "yes," they may hold the misconception that lightning never strikes the same place twice.

CORRECT Tell students that lightning tends to strike the highest features in a given location, such as lone trees or flagpoles.

REASSESS Ask: If these tall features aren't destroyed by lightning, will they be struck again? Why? *They will be struck again. If they are not destroyed, they will still be the highest features in a given location.*

Technology Resources

Visit **ClassZone.com** for background on common student misconceptions.

MISCONCEPTION DATABASE

Ongoing Assessment

Explain how thunderstorms develop.

Ask students to describe the three stages of thunderstorm development. *Stage 1: rising air forms a cumulonimbus cloud; stage 2: falling ice particles form downdrafts and heavy precipitation; stage 3: downdrafts spread out, updrafts stop, and the storm dies out.*

INVESTIGATE Updrafts

PURPOSE Observe the motion of heated water to infer how updrafts form.

TIP *20 min.* Use the 5th cup to hold 2 drops of food coloring. Make sure students are careful adding the coloring.

WHAT DO YOU THINK? *The water above the cup of hot water was heated, became less dense, and moved upward. Just as the heated water rose, heated air in a thunderstorm rises.*

CHALLENGE *Sample answer: Observe the motion of leaves, dust, or smoke in the air.*

 Datasheet, Updrafts, p. 235

Technology Resources

Customize this student lab as needed or look for an alternative. Print rubrics to assess student lab reports.

 **Lab Generator CD-ROM**

Ongoing Assessment

Describe the effects of thunderstorms.

Ask: How can rain from thunderstorms be dangerous and cause damage? *Heavy rain can cause floods, which can wash away people and objects.*

CHECK YOUR READING *Answer: The dangerous effects of thunderstorms include flash floods, winds, hail, and lightning. Students will vary on which effects they find surprising.*

INVESTIGATE Updrafts

How do updrafts form?

PROCEDURE

1. Set up the cardboard, the cups, the container, and the cool water as shown in the photograph. Wait for the water to become still.
2. Use the eyedropper to place 2–3 drops of coloring at the bottom of the water.
3. Slide a cup of hot water (about 70°C) beneath the food coloring.

WHAT DO YOU THINK?
In what ways was the motion of the water like the air in a thunderstorm?

CHALLENGE How could you observe updrafts in air?

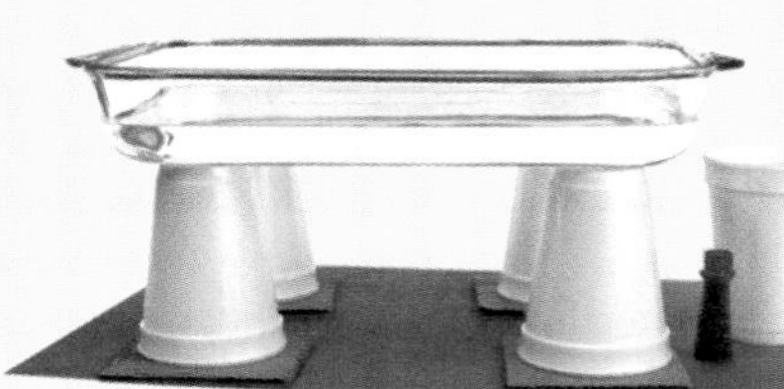

SKILL FOCUS
Inferring (6.4.d)

MATERIALS
- 4 cardboard squares
- 5 foam cups
- clear container
- cool water
- food coloring
- eyedropper
- hot tap water

TIME
20 minutes

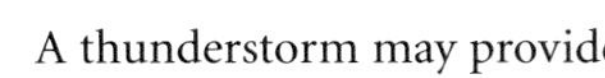

Effects of Thunderstorms

A thunderstorm may provide cool rain at the end of a hot, dry spell. The rain can provide water for crops and restore lakes and streams. However, thunderstorms are often dangerous.

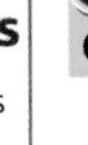 C

Flash floods can be strong enough to wash away people, cars, and even houses. One thunderstorm can produce millions of liters of rain. If a thunderstorm dumps all its rain in one place, or if a series of thunderstorms dump rain onto the same area, the water can cover the ground or make rivers overflow their banks.

Winds from a thunderstorm can be very strong. They can blow in bursts that exceed 270 kilometers per hour (170 mi/hr). Thunderstorm winds once knocked down a stretch of forest in Canada that was about 16 kilometers (10 mi) wide and 80 kilometers (50 mi) long. Thunderstorms can also produce sudden, dangerous bursts of air that move downward and spread out.

Hail causes nearly $1 billion in damage to property and crops in the United States every year. Hail can wipe out entire fields of a valuable crop in a few minutes. Large hailstones can damage roofs and kill livestock.

Lightning can kill or seriously injure any person it hits. It can damage power lines and other equipment. Lightning can also spark dangerous forest fires.

CHECK YOUR READING In what ways are thunderstorms dangerous? Did any surprise you?

SAFETY TIPS

 D

THUNDERSTORMS

- Stay alert when storms are predicted or dark, tall clouds are visible.
- If you hear thunder, seek shelter immediately and stay there for 30 minutes after the last thunder ends.
- Avoid bodies of water, lone trees, flagpoles, and metal objects.
- Stay away from the telephone, electrical appliances, and pipes.
- If flash floods are expected, move away from low ground.
- Do not try to cross flowing water, even if it looks shallow.

DIFFERENTIATE INSTRUCTION

More Reading Support

C Does a flash flood happen quickly or slowly? *quickly*

D What should you do when you hear thunder? *seek shelter immediately*

Tornadoes form in severe thunderstorms.

Under some conditions, the up-and-down air motion that produces tall clouds, lightning, and hail may produce a tornado. A **tornado** is a violently rotating column of air stretching from a cloud to the ground. A tornado moves along the ground in a winding path underneath the cloud. The column may even rise off the ground and then come down in a different place.

READING TIP

A spinning column of air is not called a tornado unless it touches the ground. If it touches water instead, it is called a waterspout.

You cannot see air moving. A tornado may become visible when water droplets appear below the cloud in the center of the rotating column. A tornado may lift dust and debris from the ground, so the bottom of the column becomes visible, as you see in the photographs below. Water droplets and debris may make a tornado look like an upright column or a twisted rope.

CHECK YOUR READING What makes a tornado become visible?

More tornadoes occur in North America than anywhere else in the world. Warm, humid air masses move north from the Gulf of Mexico to the central plains of the United States. There, the warm air masses often meet cold, dense air and form thunderstorms. In the spring, the winds in this region often produce the conditions that form tornadoes. A thunderstorm may form a series of tornadoes or even a group of tornadoes all at once.

Tornado Formation

As a tornado forms, a funnel cloud seems to stretch down from the cloud above.

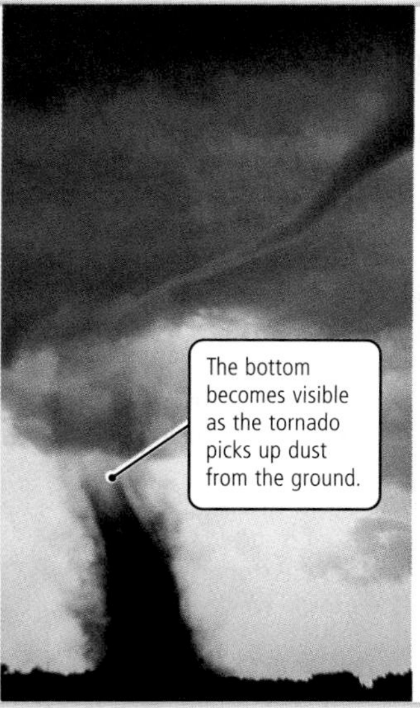

The bottom becomes visible as the tornado picks up dust from the ground.

The tornado moves along the ground before it dies out.

Real World Example

The National Skywarn Program is a network of trained severe storm spotters. Organized by the National Weather Service (NWS), the network is made up of amateur weather enthusiasts, who keep a watch on the sky and immediately report dangerous conditions to their nearest NWS office. The network is particularly useful for tornadoes, which can develop so quickly that even the most advanced technology can't predict when and where they'll strike. In such cases, a reliable eyewitness report may save the lives of hundreds of people in the path of the twister.

Teach from Visuals

Help students notice the less visible parts of the tornado by having them trace the tornado's column in each photograph with their finger. The column curves slightly to the left as the funnel extends down to the slight disturbance on the ground in the first photograph, to the left and then down to the dark bottom in the second photograph; and almost straight down the center in the third photograph.

Ongoing Assessment

CHECK YOUR READING *Answer: water droplets in the center of the rotating column and dust and debris from ground*

DIFFERENTIATE INSTRUCTION

More Reading Support

E What type of storm may produce a tornado? *a thunderstorm*

F Where do tornadoes most often occur? *in North America*

Advanced Have interested students develop a storm-safety plan for the class. They might examine existing procedures, review safety advice from the Federal Emergency Management Agency, and look at tips and survivor stories on the National Weather Service's Web site.

R Challenge and Extension, p. 234

Ongoing Assessment

Describe tornadoes and their effects.

Ask: One percent of tornadoes are very violent—what kind of damage can they do? *Answer: They can lift or completely demolish sturdy buildings.*

Reinforce 

Have students relate the section to the Big Idea.

 Reinforcing Key Concepts, p. 236

4.3 ASSESS & RETEACH

Assess

 Section 4.3 Quiz, p. 65

Reteach

Tell students to imagine they work for the National Skywarn Program. It is their job to notify the National Weather Service when dangerous conditions develop. Tell them you will describe several weather conditions, and they can choose one of three options in response: Continue normal activities, closely monitor the weather, notify the NWS immediately.

Then give students the following scenarios:

- A cold front is approaching. *Monitor the weather closely.*
- A funnel cloud is spotted. *Notify the NWS immediately.*
- A high-pressure system has developed. *Continue normal activities.*

Technology Resources

Have students visit **ClassZone.com** for reteaching of Key Concepts.

 CONTENT REVIEW

 CONTENT REVIEW CD-ROM

SAFETY TIPS

TORNADOES

- Listen for tornado warnings when severe weather is predicted.
- If you are in a car or mobile home, get out and go into a sturdy building or a ditch or depression.
- Go to the basement if possible.
- Avoid windows and open areas.
- Protect your head and neck.

Effects of Tornadoes

The powerful winds of a tornado can cause damage as the bottom of the tornado moves along the ground. Tornado winds can also pick up and slam dirt and small objects into buildings or anything else in the tornado's path.

The most common tornadoes are small and last only a few minutes. Their winds may be strong enough to break branches off trees, damage chimneys, and tear highway billboards. A typical path along the ground may be 100 meters (300 ft) wide and 1.5 kilometers (1 mi) long.

Larger tornadoes are less common but have stronger winds and last longer. About 20 percent of tornadoes are strong enough to knock over large trees, lift cars off the ground, and tear the roofs off houses. Very few—about 1 percent of all tornadoes—are violent enough to lift or completely demolish sturdy buildings. These huge tornadoes may last more than two hours. You can find more details about tornadoes in the Appendix.

Paths of Tornadoes

A tornado moves along with its thunderstorm. It travels at the same pace and weaves a path that is impossible to predict. A tornado may appear suddenly and then disappear before anyone has time to report it. However, the conditions that form tornadoes may persist, so citizens' reports are still useful. The National Weather Service issues a tornado watch when the weather conditions might produce tornadoes. A tornado warning is issued when a tornado has been detected.

4.3 Review

KEY CONCEPTS

1. What conditions produce thunderstorms? (6.4.d)
2. How can rain from thunderstorms become dangerous? (6.4.e)
3. How do tornadoes cause damage? (6.4.e)

CRITICAL THINKING

4. **Compare** What do hail and tornadoes have in common? **Hint:** Think about how each forms.
5. **Synthesize** Which type of front is most likely to produce thunderstorms and tornadoes? Explain why.

CHALLENGE

6. **Compare and Contrast** If you saw the photograph above in a newspaper, what details would tell you that the damage was due to a tornado and not a hurricane?

132 Unit 1: **The Earth System**

ANSWERS

1. Warm, humid air near the ground moves into cooler air above and rises quickly.

2. If one thunderstorm dumps all of its rain in one place, or if a series of thunderstorms dump rain over one area, floods can develop.

3. Winds can break branches off trees, damage chimneys, and tear roofs off houses.

4. Both start from the up-and-down motion in a storm.

5. The warm air at a cold front rises quickly, so it is likely to produce thunderstorms and tornadoes.

6. Some of the houses in the photograph are untouched. There's a small path of destruction, which is indicative of a tornado.

SKILL: EVALUATING HYPOTHESES

What Type of Weather Buried This Truck?

6.7.e Recognize whether evidence is consistent with a proposed explanation.

This picture was taken soon after a weather event partly buried this truck in Britannia Beach, British Columbia.

Observations and Inferences

One observer made this analysis.

a. The truck, the tree, and two fences in the background were partly buried by sand and stones.
b. No stones are visible inside the truck.
c. The rounded stones must have come from an ocean or river.
d. The tree near the truck has green leaves. The wind must have been too weak to tear off the leaves.
e. The area is near the Pacific Ocean. It is far from the equator. There is a very large island between the location and the open ocean.

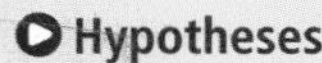

BRITISH COLUMBIA
Vancouver Island
Britannia Beach

A waterway leads south and west from Britannia Beach to a bay, around an island, to the Pacific Ocean.

Hypotheses

The observer made the following hypotheses.

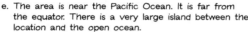

a. A storm surge carried sand and stones from the Pacific Ocean. The material covered a large area. The truck floated, so it was not filled with material.
b. A tornado picked up the truck with other material. It dumped everything together, and the material partly buried the truck, fences, and tree.
c. Thunderstorms produced a flash flood that carried sand and stones from a riverbed to this area. The flood receded and left material that covered the area.
d. The truck was parked on a pile of snow during a blizzard. When the snow melted, the area under the truck collapsed and the truck sank into the ground.

Evaluate Each Hypothesis

Review each hypothesis and think about whether the observations support it. Some facts may rule out some hypotheses. Some facts may neither support nor weaken some hypotheses.

CHALLENGE How could you model one or more of the hypotheses with a toy truck, sand, and a basin of water?

ANSWERS

HYPOTHESIS a *Not reasonable. The large island would have likely lessened the surge.*

HYPOTHESIS b *Not reasonable. The truck would have stones on top as well as inside if all the debris was dumped together.*

HYPOTHESIS c *Reasonable. No observations contradict this hypothesis.*

HYPOTHESIS d *Not reasonable. The leaves on the trees indicate that it is not winter. Plus, a truck is not heavy enough to sink into stone-covered ground.*

CHALLENGE *Sample answer: To model a flash flood you could observe how the sand settles around the truck to see whether your hypothesis is supported.*

THINK SCIENCE
Scientific Methods of Thinking

Set Learning Goal

To evaluate hypotheses by checking them against observations and inferences

Present the Science

The Canadian city of Britannia Beach, British Columbia, is located by Howe Sound, a wide channel of water on the west coast that connects to the Pacific Ocean. Britannia Beach is close to the city of Vancouver.

The flash flood that buried this truck is the type that strikes low lying areas near a water channel, stream, or river. This flood of water can uproot trees, tear down buildings, and pull down bridges and dams.

Guide the Activity

- Remind students that an inference is a conclusion based on observations. Ask them to give an example of an inference on the part of the observer. *Example: The wind must have been too weak to tear off the leaves.*
- Encourage students to use the visuals to make their own observations and inferences.
- Suggest that students review the different types of weather to see what information applies to this event. For example, a hurricane would probably lose energy as it moved over the cool water far from the equator.
- Students might make a table to compare each observation and inference to each hypothesis.

COOPERATIVE LEARNING STRATEGY
Have students work in groups of four to analyze the hypotheses. Afterwards, each student in the group should provide a brief explanation of why the group either accepted or rejected a particular hypothesis.

Close

Ask: Which hypothesis did you find least convincing? Why? *The first, because the island would block a storm surge.*

4.4 FOCUS

Set Learning Goals

Students will

- Explain the different ways weather data is collected.
- Explain how different types of weather data are displayed.
- Describe how meteorologists forecast the weather.

3-Minute Warm-Up

Display Transparency 29 or copy this exercise on the board:

Fill in the blank with the correct word.

1. The boundary between two air masses is called a _______. *front*
2. Stormy weather is often associated with _______ pressure systems. *low-*
3. Calm, clear weather is usually associated with _______ pressure systems. *high-*

3-Minute Warm-Up, p. T29

4.4 MOTIVATE

EXPLORE Weather Maps

PURPOSE To interpret symbols on a weather map and relate a weather forecast to actual weather conditions

TIP *10 min.* Large-circulation newspapers generally have the most detailed weather maps. You can also print out weather maps from the Internet, using the Web sites of local television stations or the National Weather Service.

WHAT DO YOU THINK? *Warm fronts, cold fronts, high- and low-pressure systems. Short-term weather forecasts should be comparable to actual weather conditions.*

Ongoing Assessment

CHECK YOUR READING *Answer: weather conditions in the region around you and forecasts*

KEY CONCEPT

4.4 Weather forecasters use advanced technologies.

CALIFORNIA Content Standard

6.4.e Students know differences in pressure, heat, air movement, and humidity result in changes of weather.

BEFORE, you learned

- Weather changes when air masses move
- High-pressure systems bring fair weather
- Fronts and low-pressure systems bring stormy weather

NOW, you will learn

- How weather data are collected
- How weather data are displayed
- How meteorologists forecast the weather

VOCABULARY

meteorologist p. 134
isobar p. 137

EXPLORE Weather Maps (6.4.e)

What does a weather map show?

PROCEDURE

1. Look at the weather outside. Write down the conditions you observe.
2. Use the map to check the weather conditions for your region.

WHAT DO YOU THINK?

- What symbols on the map do you recognize?
- How does the information on the weather map compare with the weather you observed outside?

MATERIALS

newspaper weather map

Weather data come from many sources.

Looking at the weather outside in the morning can help you decide what to wear. Different things give you clues to the current weather. If you see plants swaying from side to side, you might infer that it is windy. If you see a gray sky and wet, shiny streets, you might decide to wear a raincoat.

You might also check a weather report to get more information. A weather report can show conditions in your area and also in the region around you. You can look for weather nearby that might move into your area during the day. More detailed predictions of how the weather will move and change may be included in a weather report by a meteorologist. A **meteorologist** (MEE-tee-uh-RAHL-uh-jihst) is a scientist who studies weather.

VOCABULARY
Remember to add *meteorologist* to your notebook, using the vocabulary strategy of your choice.

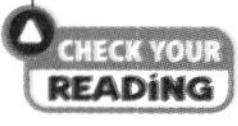
CHECK YOUR READING What information can a weather report show?

RESOURCES FOR DIFFERENTIATED INSTRUCTION

Below Level

UNIT RESOURCE BOOK

- Reading Study Guide A, pp. 239–240
- Decoding Support, p. 251

AUDIO CDS

Advanced

UNIT RESOURCE BOOK

Challenge and Extension, p. 245

English Learners

UNIT RESOURCE BOOK

Spanish Reading Study Guide, pp. 243–244

AUDIO CDS

- Audio Readings in Spanish
- Audio Readings (English)

In order to predict the weather, meteorologists look at past and current conditions. They use many forms of technology to gather data. The illustration below shows how weather information is gathered. For example, radar stations and satellites use advanced technologies to gather data for large areas at a time.

RESOURCE CENTER
CLASSZONE.COM
Learn more about weather forecasting and your local weather.

Instruments within the atmosphere can make measurements of local weather conditions. Newer instruments can make measurements often and automatically and then report the results almost instantly. Instruments are placed in many ground stations on land and weather buoys at sea. Instruments can also be carried by balloons, ships, and planes. These instruments report a series of measurements along a path within the atmosphere.

Collection of Weather Data

Instruments that gather weather data use many technologies and can be found in many places.

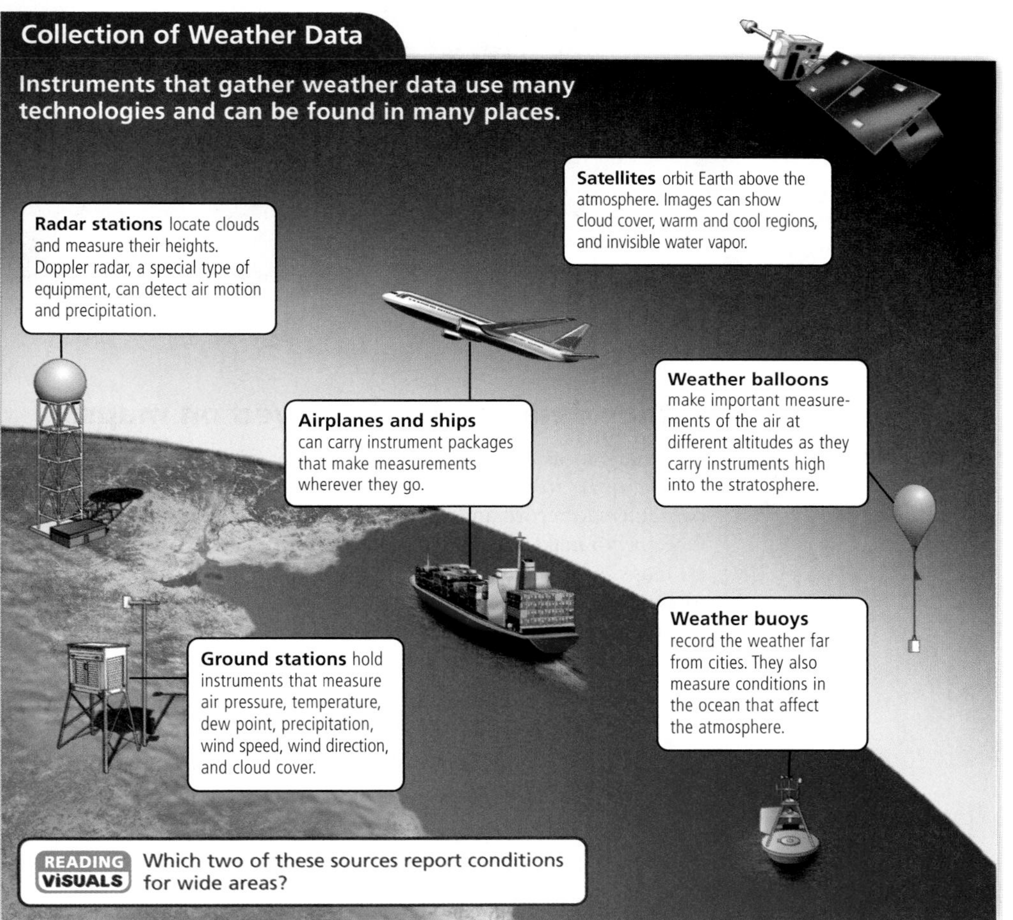

Satellites orbit Earth above the atmosphere. Images can show cloud cover, warm and cool regions, and invisible water vapor.
Radar stations locate clouds and measure their heights. Doppler radar, a special type of equipment, can detect air motion and precipitation.
Airplanes and ships can carry instrument packages that make measurements wherever they go.
Weather balloons make important measurements of the air at different altitudes as they carry instruments high into the stratosphere.
Ground stations hold instruments that measure air pressure, temperature, dew point, precipitation, wind speed, wind direction, and cloud cover.
Weather buoys record the weather far from cities. They also measure conditions in the ocean that affect the atmosphere.

READING VISUALS Which two of these sources report conditions for wide areas?

4.4 INSTRUCT

Teach the Standards

Weather-predicting technology, 6.4.e

In this section: Explain that meteorologists use different types of technology—as well as knowledge of pressure, heat, air movement, and humidity—to predict changes in weather.

previously taught: weather, pp. 62–63; wind, pp. 83–84; weather and air masses, 118–121; low-pressure systems, pp. 123–127

Develop Critical Thinking

APPLY Have students apply what they read about weather instruments in earlier chapters. Ask them to describe which type of instruments might be found in a ground station, and what these instruments measure. *Sample answer: thermometers to measure temperature, barometers to measure air pressure, and rain gauges to measure precipitation*

Integrate the Sciences

Doppler radar uses the Doppler effect, which is a change in the frequency of sound or electromagnetic waves due to the movement of the source or observer. In meteorology, radio waves are "bounced off" rain drops; the waves are picked up by receivers, and computers then calculate the distance and speed of a storm. In astronomy, the Doppler effect is used to analyze the motion of galaxies.

Teach from Visuals

To help students interpret the visual of weather data instruments, ask:

- Which instrument would you use to find the height of clouds? *radar*
- Which instrument could give you information on ocean conditions? *weather buoys*

Ongoing Assessment

Explain the different ways weather data is collected.

Ask: What types of weather data are collected by satellites? *information about cloud cover, warm and cool regions, and water vapor*

DIFFERENTIATE INSTRUCTION

READING VISUALS *Answer: radar stations, satellites*

More Reading Support

A Meteorologists look at past conditions to do what? *predict weather*

B Which instruments get data for large areas? *radar stations, satellites*

Teach from Visuals

To help students interpret the "Information on a Weather Map" visual, ask:

- What type of pressure system is located off the east coast? *low-pressure system*
- Notice the front associated with this system—is it the same throughout? *No; the very northern part of the front is stationary while the remainder is a cold front.*
- Study the Station Symbol. How much of the circle is filled to show cloud cover? *all of it* If cloud cover were 50%, what fraction of the circle would be filled? *one-half*

Mathematics Connection

Tell students that the cloud-cover part of a station symbol is a modified circle graph. Fractions of 0, 1/4, 1/2, and 3/4 are shown in the usual way. A fraction that is 1/8 more than one of these has a small bar added to the appropriate symbol. The bar makes the symbol easier to read when it is small. Provide students with some symbols that have different amounts of cloud cover. Then have students calculate the decimal fraction that corresponds to each symbol. Have them provide the exact fraction (such as 0.375 for a cloud cover of 3/8) and then round to one decimal place to approximate the cloud cover (0.4 in this case).

Symbols and decimal equivalents are in the Appendix.

Ongoing Assessment

Explain how different types of weather data are displayed.

Ask students to explain how precipitation is displayed on a weather map. *Different colors indicate amounts of precipitation.*

CHECK YOUR READING *Answer: Information is shown by symbols and colored areas on maps.*

Information on a Weather Map

Meteorologists use maps to display a lot of weather information at once.

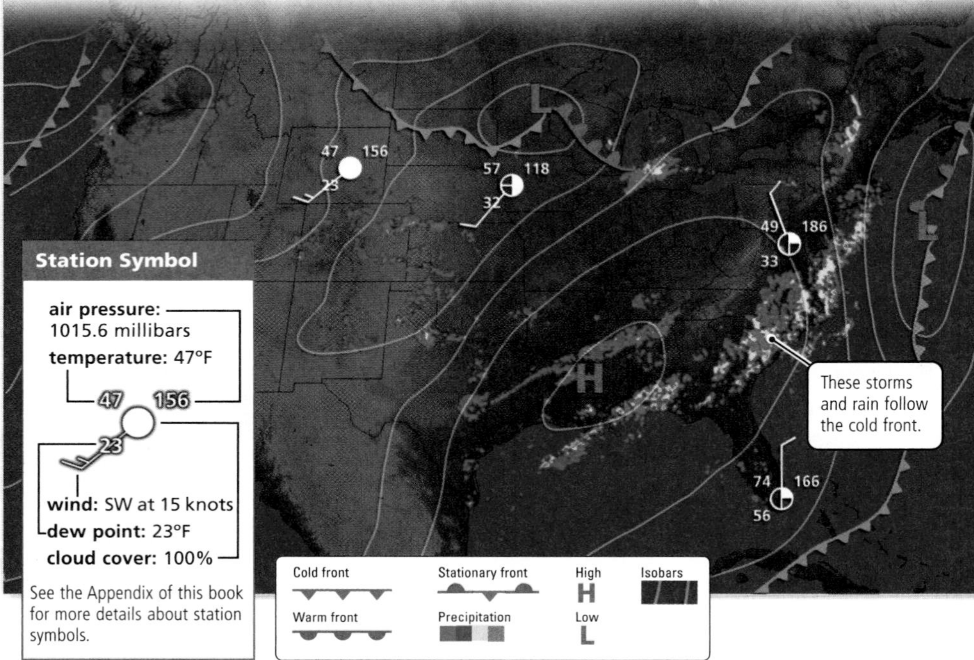

Weather data can be displayed on maps.

MAIN IDEA WEB
Add notes about weather data to your notebook.

C

Automatic measurements from many sources constantly pour in to the National Oceanic and Atmospheric Administration. Scientists use computers to record and use the enormous amount of data gathered. One way to make the information easier to understand is to show it on maps. A single map can show many different types of data together to give a more complete picture of the weather. The map above combines information from ground stations with Doppler radar measurements of precipitation.

- Precipitation is shown as patches of blue, green, yellow, and red. The colors indicate the amounts of rain or other precipitation.
- Station symbols on the map show data from ground stations. Only a few stations are shown.
- Symbols showing fronts and pressure patterns are added to the map to make the overall weather patterns easier to see.

CHECK YOUR READING How is information from Doppler radar shown?

DIFFERENTIATE INSTRUCTION

More Reading Support

C What organization gathers weather data from many sources? *National Oceanic and Atmospheric Administration*

Below Level Have students search the National Weather Service Web site or newspapers for examples of different weather maps and images. Have them orally describe the data on the maps.

Computer programs are used to combine information from many ground stations. The resulting calculations give the highs, lows, and fronts that are marked on the map. The cold front near the East Coast has triangles to show that the front is moving eastward. This cold front produced the heavy rain that is visible in the Doppler radar data.

Air Pressure on Weather Maps

The map below shows conditions from the same date as the map on page 136. Thin lines represent air pressure. An **isobar** (EYE-suh-BAHR) is a line that connects places that have the same air pressure. Each isobar represents a different air pressure value. All the isobars together, combined with the symbols for highs and lows, show the patterns of air pressure that produce weather systems.

READING TIP
Iso- means "equal," and *bar* means "pressure."

Each isobar is labeled with the air pressure for that whole line in units called millibars (MIHL-uh-BAHRZ). A lower number means a lower air pressure. As you read earlier, differences in pressure cause air to move. Meteorologists use isobars to understand air motion.

Sometimes air-pressure measurements are listed in inches of mercury. This unit comes from an old type of barometer that measures how high the air pressure pushes a column of mercury, a liquid metal. Computer-controlled instruments are used more often today, but the measurements may be converted to inches of mercury.

Understanding Isobars

Isobars show pressure patterns, which determine winds.

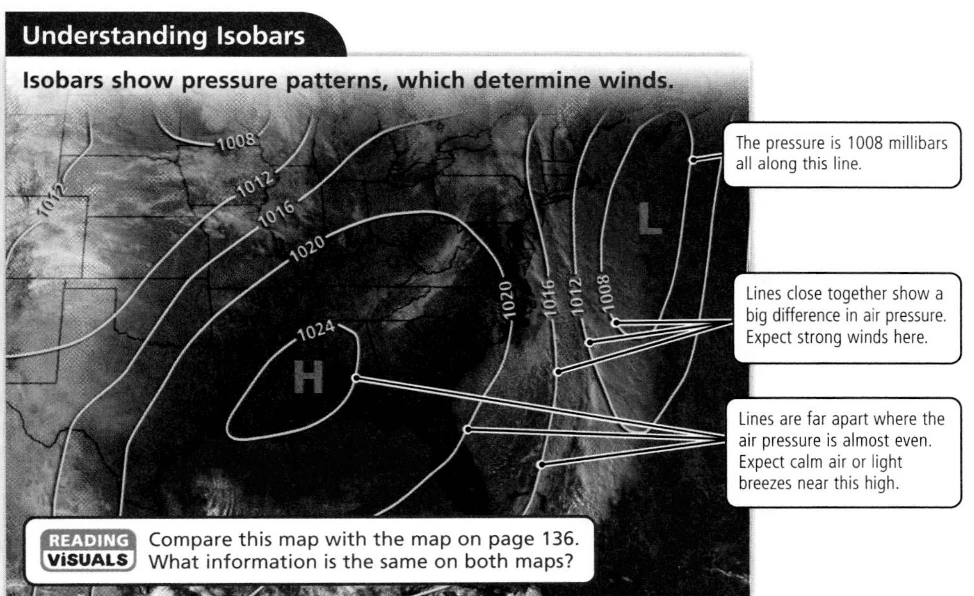

1008
1012
1016
1020
1024
1012
H
L
1020
1016
1012
1008
The pressure is 1008 millibars all along this line.
Lines close together show a big difference in air pressure. Expect strong winds here.
Lines are far apart where the air pressure is almost even. Expect calm air or light breezes near this high.

READING VISUALS Compare this map with the map on page 136. What information is the same on both maps?

Teach Difficult Concepts

To help students better understand isobars, tell them that the prefix *iso-* comes from the Greek word *isos*, which means equal. Explain that scientists often use lines that connect points of equal values on maps. Isotherms, for example, are lines that connect points of equal temperature. Use the following demonstration to help students relate the information to similar maps.

Teacher Demo

Show students a topographic map. Ask: What do contour lines show? *points of equal elevation* Next, draw three closed contour lines on the board to make a topographic map of a hill. Label the largest, outside circle 240 km. Label the middle circle 260 km. Label the innermost circle 280 km. Inside the innermost circle, write the elevation 300 km. Ask: If this were a map that showed isobars, would it represent a high- or low-pressure system? Explain. *It would represent a high-pressure system because the numbers get progressively larger.*

Teach from Visuals

To help students interpret the visual, point out that isobars are closed. Closed isobars generally are found in well-developed pressure systems. Ask: Which center appears to be developing into a well-organized system? *the low center*

Teaching with Technology

Have students view annotated maps to see weather changes.

Ongoing Assessment

READING VISUALS *Answer: H, L, isobars*

DIFFERENTIATE INSTRUCTION

More Reading Support

D Which type of weather measurement is shown by isobars on a map? *air pressure*

Advanced Have students compile information to make a station symbol that demonstrates local weather at a particular time. Once outside, they can approximate cloud cover and use a barometer and thermometer to find air pressure and temperature. Help them use a compass to determine wind direction. You can supplement this activity and fill in the holes (such as wind speed and dew point) by checking a weather map from a local newspaper, or by having students look for local weather information on the Internet.

R Challenge and Extension, p. 245

Real World Example

Weather maps often contain information that students may not associate with the condition of the atmosphere at a particular time and place, such as the amount of pollution or pollen. The links in the resource center referred to on p. 135 include a wide range of weather maps to explore with students.

Ongoing Assessment

READING VISUALS *Sample answer: Northeast: temperature—49°F, partly cloudy*

CHECK YOUR READING *Answer: Computers can create maps quickly and can combine many types of data to develop forecasts.*

Satellite Images

Visible Light

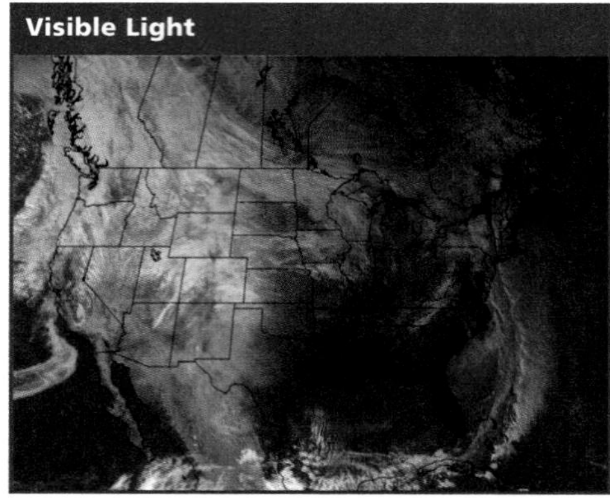

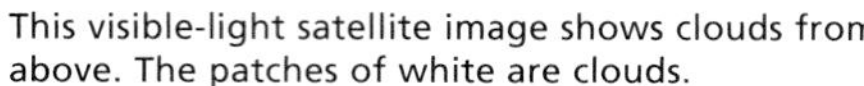

This visible-light satellite image shows clouds from above. The patches of white are clouds.

Infrared Radiation

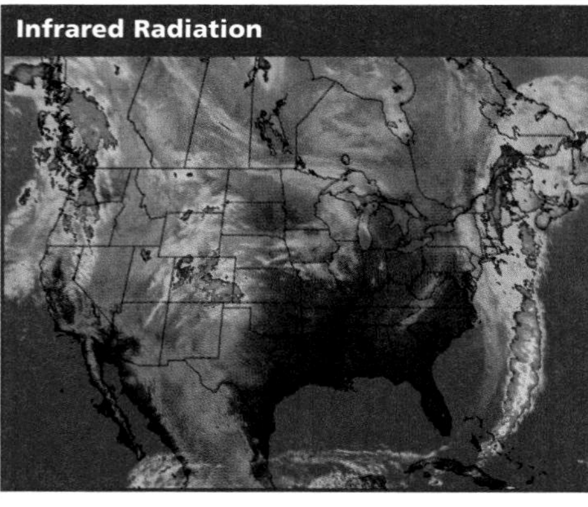

This infrared satellite image also shows clouds, but uses colors to show where there are tall clouds.

READING VISUALS Find a location on these maps and the map on page 136. What were the weather conditions?

Satellite Images and Special Maps

Satellites take different types of images from space. Some images record the visible light that reflects off clouds and Earth's surface. Clouds and snow-covered land look white in sunlight. Unfortunately, visible-light images do not show much at night.

The colors on this map represent different ranges of temperature (°F).

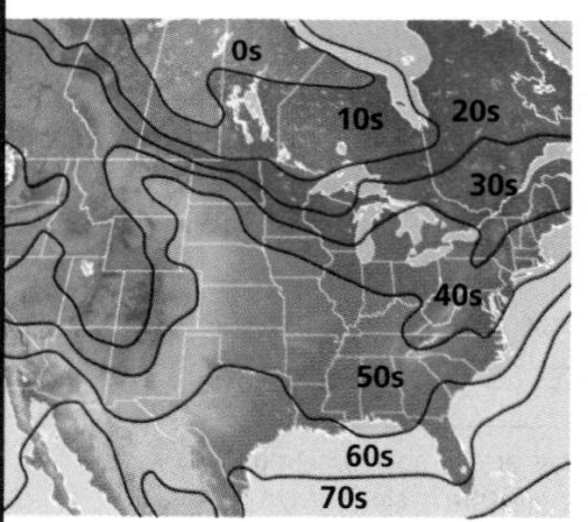

E Another type of image shows infrared radiation given off by the warm surface and cooler clouds. These infrared images can show cloud patterns even at night because objects with different temperatures show up differently. Air temperatures change with altitude, so infrared images also show which clouds are low and which are high or tall. You can see in the maps above how visible and infrared satellite images show similar clouds but different details. Outlines of the states have been added to make the images easier to understand.

Data from ground stations and other sources can be used to make other types of maps. The map at left shows the pattern of temperatures on the same date as the images above and the map on page 136. Other maps may show winds or amounts of pollution. A map can be made to show any type of measurement or weather prediction. Different types of maps are often used together to give a more complete picture of the current weather.

CHECK YOUR READING Why would a weather report show more than one map?

DIFFERENTIATE INSTRUCTION

More Reading Support

E Which type of image shows cloud patterns at night? *infrared image*

Alternative Assessment Have students find different types of maps, using newspapers, television, or the Internet as resources. Then have them make charts listing all the maps found and what each one demonstrates. Have students write a brief paragraph comparing and contrasting the different maps. What are the benefits and limitations of each? Which one displays the most information?

Forecasters use computer models to predict weather.

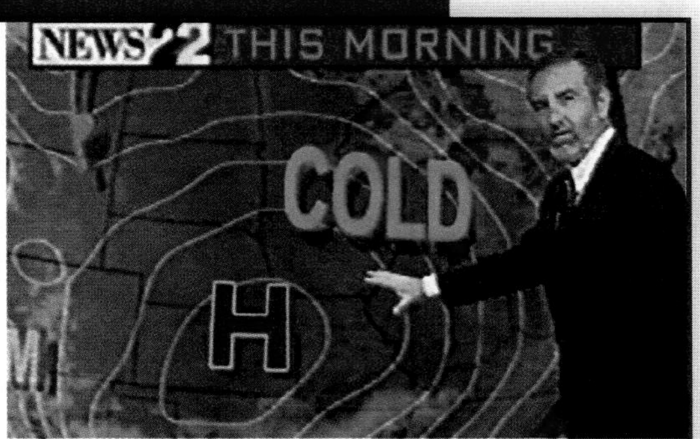

Forecasters use maps and satellite images to communicate weather conditions and predictions.

Instruments can measure only the current weather conditions. Most people want to know what the weather will be like in the future.

Forecasters can make some predictions from their own observations. If they see cirrus clouds above and high stratus clouds to the west, they might infer that a warm front is approaching. They would predict weather typical for a warm front—more clouds, then rain, and eventually warmer weather. If they also have information from other places, the forecasters might be able to tell where the warm front is already and how fast it is moving. They might be able to predict how soon it will arrive and even how warm the weather will be after the front passes.

Computers have become an important tool for forecasting weather. When weather stations send in data, computers can create maps right away. Computer models combine many types of data to forecast what might happen next. Different computer models give different types of forecasts. Scientists study the computer forecasts, then apply their knowledge and experience to make weather predictions.

Forecasting the weather is complicated. As a result, some forecasts are more dependable than others. The farther in advance a forecast is made, the more time there is for small differences between the predicted and the actual weather to add up. For this reason, short-range forecasts—up to three days in advance—are the most accurate. Forecasts of fast-changing weather, such as severe storms, are less accurate far in advance. It is best to watch for new predictions close to the time the storm is forecast.

4.4 Review

KEY CONCEPTS

1. List three of the sources of weather data.
2. What does a map with isobars show? (6.4.e)
3. How do meteorologists use computers?

CRITICAL THINKING

4. **Draw Conclusions** Why do meteorologists not combine all their weather information into one map?
5. **Analyze** How is the information from radar and satellites different from the information from ground stations?

CHALLENGE

6. **Apply** Suppose you are planning an afternoon picnic a week in advance. Fair weather is forecast for that day, but a storm is expected that night. What will you do? Explain your reasoning.

ANSWERS

1. Accept any three of the following: satellites, radar stations, instruments on weather balloons and ships, and ground stations

2. patterns of pressure

3. to collect, organize, and display data, and to predict weather

4. There is too much information to display on one map—it would be very difficult to read and interpret the map.

5. Radar and satellites gather data for large areas at a time; ground stations report conditions for one specific place.

6. Have a rain date or sheltered space. Stormy weather can change quickly.

Ongoing Assessment

Describe how meteorologists forecast the weather.

Ask: How do observations help meteorologists forecast the weather? *Meteorologists might observe clouds or weather conditions to infer that a front is approaching or use observations that have been collected and displayed on maps.*

Reinforce the BIG idea

Have students relate the section to the Big Idea.

 Reinforcing Key Concepts, p. 246

4.4 ASSESS & RETEACH

Assess

 Section 4.4 Quiz, p. 66

Reteach

Divide students into pairs. Photocopy a weather map from a national news source and distribute a copy to each group. Try to use a map that has a lot of information on it. If possible, use one with station symbols. Ask students what information the map tells them. Make a list of their responses on the board. Call their attention to features they may have missed or misinterpreted.

Technology Resources

Have students visit **ClassZone.com** for reteaching of Key Concepts.

 **CONTENT REVIEW**

 **CONTENT REVIEW CD-ROM**

CHAPTER INVESTIGATION

Focus

PURPOSE Students observe, measure, and record weather conditions, then analyze the data.

OVERVIEW Students will use their senses and homemade or commercial instruments to observe and measure weather conditions over a period of time. They will graph numerical data and search for trends. Students will find that:

- weather is complicated
- some types of data, such as cloud cover and precipitation, are strongly related
- some observations, such as the types of clouds or the changes in air pressure, may be used to make reasonable one-day forecasts

Lab Preparation

- You may want to set up a weather station outside.
- Discuss the characteristics of a good observation chart.
- Prior to the investigation, have students read through the investigation and prepare their data tables. Or you may wish to copy and distribute datasheets and rubrics.

UNIT RESOURCE BOOK, pp. 254–262

SCIENCE TOOLKIT, F13

Lab Management

- Have students work together in small groups. Each group might construct a different instrument. The class as a whole can then share data.
- Tell students to choose their observation sites carefully. For example, wind vanes should be used in open areas.

SAFETY Tell students to notify you immediately if a thermometer should break.

INCLUSION Mount a thermometer with large numbers outside the window so that students with visual and physical impairments can easily read it.

CHAPTER INVESTIGATION

Design a Weather Center

OVERVIEW AND PURPOSE The accuracy of a weather forecast depends largely on the type and quality of the data that it is based on. In this lab, you will use what you have learned about weather to

- observe and measure weather conditions
- record and analyze the weather-related data

MATERIALS
- thermometer
- magnetic compass
- other weather instruments
- graph paper

6.4.e, 6.7.b

Procedure

1. Survey the possible sources of weather data in and around your classroom. You can use a thermometer to record the outside air temperature. You can observe cloud types and the amount of cloud cover from a window or doorway. You can also observe precipitation and notice if it is heavy or light. If there is a flag in view, use it to find the wind direction and to estimate wind speed.

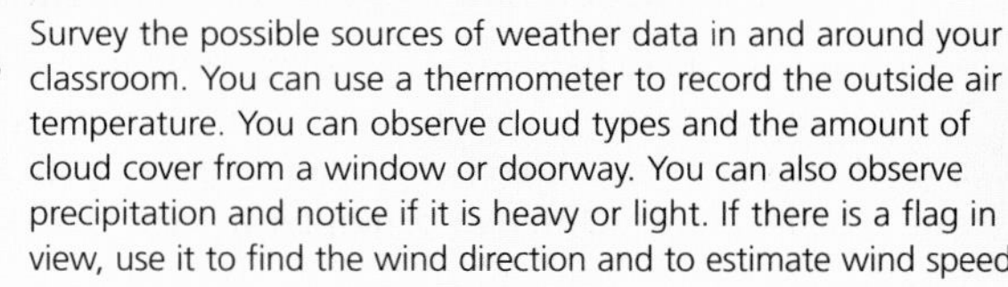

2. Assemble or make tools for your observations. You may want to make a reference chart with pictures of different cloud types or other information. Decide if you wish to use homemade weather instruments. You may have made a barometer, and a psychrometer already. If not, see the instructions on pages 81 and 100. You may also wish to do research to learn how to make or use other weather instruments, such as a rain gauge.

3. Make an initial set of observations. Write down the date and time in your **Science Notebook.** Record the readings from the thermometer and other instruments.

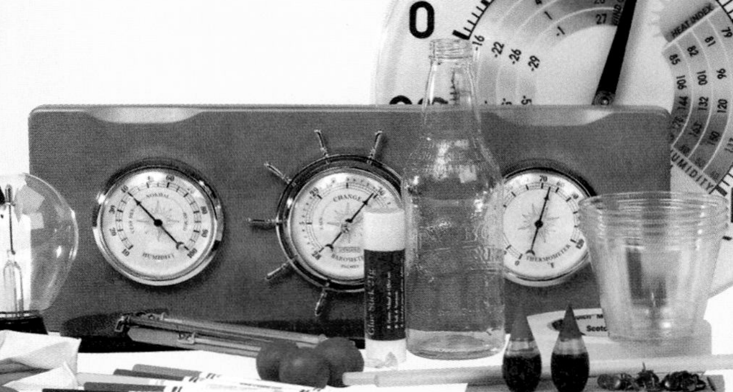

140 Unit 1: The Earth System

INVESTIGATION RESOURCES

CHAPTER INVESTIGATION, Design a Weather Center
- Level A, pp. 254–257
- Level B, pp. 258–261
- Level C, p. 262

Advanced students should complete Levels B & C.

Writing a Lab Report, D12–D13

Technology Resources

Customize this student lab as needed or look for an alternative. Print rubrics to assess student lab reports.

Lab Generator CD-ROM

Content Standard
6.4.e Students know differences in pressure, heat, air movement, and humidity result in changes of weather.

Investigation Standard
6.7.b Select and use appropriate tools and technology (including calculators, computers, balances, spring scales, microscopes, and binoculars) to perform tests, collect data, and display data.

4 Decide how to record your observations of the clouds, the wind, and any precipitation. Organize your notes to make it easy for you to record later observations in a consistent way.

5 Create a chart with a row for each type of observation you are making. You might darken fractions of circles to record amounts of cloud cover, as in the station symbols on page 136. Make sure each row has a heading and enough room for numbers, words, or sketches. Include a row for notes that do not belong in the data rows.

6 Record your observations every day at the same time. Try to make the observations exactly the same way each time. If you have to redraw your chart, copy the information carefully.

Observe and Analyze (Write It Up)

1. **GRAPH** Graph the data you collected that represent measurable quantities. Use graphs that are appropriate to your data. Often a simple line graph will work. Choose an appropriate scale and interval based on the range of your data. Make the *x*-axis of each graph the same so that you can compare the different types of data easily.
2. **COMPARE AND CONTRAST** Look at your graphs for patterns in your data. Some aspects of weather change at the same time because they are related to each other. Did one type of change occur before a different type of change? If so, this pattern may help you predict weather.

Conclude (Write It Up)

1. **INTERPRET** Did a front pass through your area during the period you observed? What observations helped you answer this question?
2. **EVALUATE** Why was it necessary to observe at the same time each day?
3. **APPLY** If you predicted that each day's weather would be repeated the next day, how often would you be right?

INVESTIGATE Further

CHALLENGE Locate a newspaper weather page for the period during which you were making your weather observations. How do the weather data reported for your area compare with your measurements? How do you account for any differences you notice in the data?

Design a Weather Center

Table 1. Daily Weather Chart

Date/time of observations			
Temperature (°C)			
Cloud types			
Cloud coverage	○	○	○
Precipitation (cm) and notes			
Wind direction			
Other notes			

Observe and Analyze

SAMPLE DATA Day 1: temperature: 18°C, cloud type: stratus, cloud coverage: 100%, precipitation: 3.6 cm, wind direction: northwest

1. *Graphs should generally not be bar graphs. They should accurately reflect gathered data. Students may want to make at least three graphs, plotting the days on the x-axes. A variable such as temperature, air pressure, and amount of precipitation should be plotted on each y-axis.*
2. *Sample answer: Decreases in air pressure and cloud formation occurred together.*

Conclude

1. *Sample answer: A cold front passed through the area. Clouds formed, rain fell, and temperatures dropped following the passage of the front.*
2. *Sample answer: The data would not be comparable if some readings were taken at night and others were taken during the day.*
3. *Answers will depend on students' location. Some areas have variable weather; others have fairly consistent weather over long periods of time.*

INVESTIGATE Further

CHALLENGE Weather data should be comparable to student measurements. Differences may be due to local variations in weather conditions or differences in instruments and measurement techniques.

Post-Lab Discussion

- Have several volunteers share their graphs with the class. Discuss the similarities and differences among the observations. Ask students to hypothesize why these similarities and/or differences exist.
- Ask: After observing your results, what would you want to study further? If you could do a follow-up experiment, what would it be? What different weather instruments would you use?

BACK TO

the BIG idea

Refer students back to the visual on p. 116. Help them relate the interactions of air masses to weather changes. Ask: How might these types of air masses produce a cold front in Maine? *A polar air mass from the north might push into a tropical air mass.* How might a winter storm system be produced? *The meeting of a continental polar air mass and one of the warm air masses might produce a low and fronts, as shown on p. 121.*

KEY CONCEPTS SUMMARY

SECTION 4.1

Ask: What type of front is shown in the visual? *cold front* What other types of fronts did you learn about? *warm fronts and stationary fronts*

Ask: In which direction does air move around a low-pressure system? *counter-clockwise*

SECTION 4.2

Ask: Would you expect a hurricane to develop during winter? Why or why not? *No; in winter, ocean water is not warm enough to provide the energy to form a hurricane.*

SECTION 4.3

Ask: What are some dangers of thunderstorms and tornadoes? *thunderstorms: flash floods, strong winds, hail, lightning; tornadoes: damaging winds, flying objects*

SECTION 4.4

Ask: What are some sources of weather data? *ground and radar stations, satellite*

Ask: How are these sources related to the map? *They provide the data used to produce maps.*

Review Concepts

- Big Idea Flow Chart, p. T25
- Chapter Outline, pp. T31–32

4 Chapter Review

the BIG idea

The interaction of air masses causes changes in weather.

CONTENT REVIEW CLASSZONE.COM

KEY CONCEPTS SUMMARY

Weather changes as air masses move.

Air masses meet and produce **fronts,** which can bring lowered pressure and stormy weather. Fronts can be cold, warm, or stationary.

VOCABULARY
air mass p. 115
front p. 118
high-pressure system p. 120
low-pressure system p. 121

Low-pressure systems can become storms.

Hurricanes and winter storms develop from low-pressure systems.

Hurricanes form over warm ocean water.

VOCABULARY
tropical storm p. 123
hurricane p. 123
storm surge p. 125
blizzard p. 126

Vertical air motion can cause severe storms.

Rising moist air can produce **thunderstorms.** The up-and-down motion of air in a thunderstorm can produce a **tornado.**

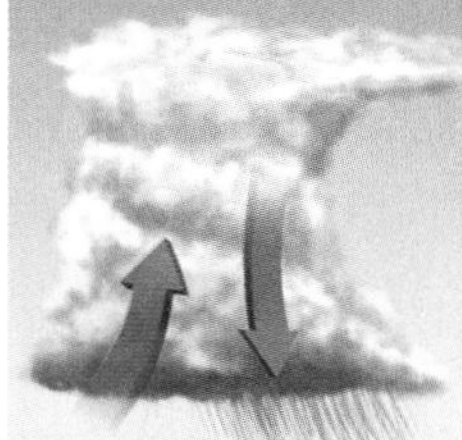

VOCABULARY
thunderstorm p. 128
tornado p. 131

Weather forecasters use advanced technologies.

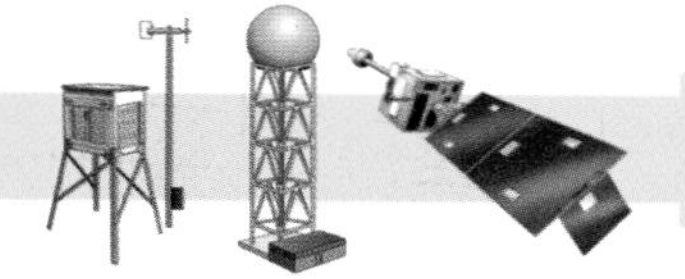

Weather information comes from many sources.

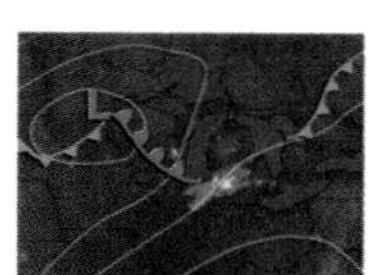

Meteorologists use weather data and computer models to forecast weather.

VOCABULARY
meteorologist p. 134
isobar p. 137

Technology Resources

Have students visit **ClassZone.com** or use the CD-ROM for a cumulative review of concepts.

CONTENT REVIEW

CONTENT REVIEW CD-ROM

Engage students in a whole-class interactive review of Key Concepts. Edit content as you wish.

POWER PRESENTATIONS

Reviewing Vocabulary

Describe each term below, using the related term as part of the description.

Term	Related Term	Description
EXAMPLE hurricane	low-pressure system	a low-pressure system in the tropics with winds at least 120 km/h
1. front	air mass	
2. low-pressure system	low-pressure center	
3. storm surge	hurricane	
4. tropical storm	low-pressure system	
5. air mass	humidity	
6. thunderstorm	convection	
7. tornado	thunderstorm	
8. blizzard	low-pressure system	

Reviewing Key Concepts

Multiple Choice *Choose the letter of the best answer.*

9. What qualities are nearly the same at different locations in a single air mass? (6.4.e)
a. temperature and pressure
b. temperature and humidity
c. air pressure and wind speed
d. air pressure and humidity

10. Which is the name for an air mass that forms over the ocean near the equator? (6.4.e)
a. maritime tropical **c.** continental tropical
b. maritime polar **d.** continental polar

11. A meteorologist is a scientist who
a. predicts meteor showers
b. studies maps
c. studies the weather
d. changes the weather

12. An isobar shows locations with the same (6.4.e)
a. temperature **c.** air pressure
b. rainfall **d.** wind speed

13. Which is produced when a warm air mass pushes a colder air mass? (6.4.e)
a. a stationary front **c.** a warm front
b. a cold front **d.** a thunderstorm

14. Which can be measured in inches of mercury?
a. air pressure **c.** hail
b. temperature **d.** lightning

15. Which source provides measurements for just one location?
a. ground station **c.** weather balloon
b. radar station **d.** satellite

16. Compared with warm fronts, cold fronts are (6.4.e)
a. faster moving **c.** more cloudy
b. less dense **d.** less steep

17. Which statement is usually true of high-pressure systems in North America? (6.4.e)
a. They bring fair weather.
b. They change quickly.
c. The air in them is cold and dense.
d. The air in them moves counterclockwise.

18. Thunderstorms often begin with the rising of (6.4.d)
a. cool, dry air **c.** warm, dry air
b. cool, humid air **d.** warm, humid air

19. What is the relationship between lightning and thunder? (6.4.e)
a. They have separate causes.
b. They have the same cause.
c. Lightning causes thunder.
d. Thunder causes lightning.

Short Answer *Write a short answer to each question.*

20. Why are hurricanes in the eastern United States more likely in autumn than in spring? (6.4.e)

21. What causes lake-effect snow? (6.4.e)

22. In what four ways can thunderstorms be dangerous? (6.2.d)

ASSESSMENT RESOURCES

ASSESSMENT BOOK
- Chapter Test A, pp. 67–70
- Chapter Test B, pp. 71–74
- Chapter Test C, pp. 75–78
- Alternative Assessment, pp. 79–80

STANDARDS REVIEW AND PRACTICE, pp. 23–24, 37–40, 59–60, 65–66

Technology Resources

Edit test items and answer choices.

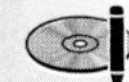

Test Generator CD-ROM

Visit **ClassZone.com** to extend test practice.

Test Practice

Reviewing Vocabulary

1. a boundary between air masses
2. a weather system that surrounds a low-pressure center
3. a huge mass of water pushed by a hurricane
4. a low-pressure system in the tropics with winds of at least 65 km/h
5. a large volume of air characterized by a particular humidity and temperature
6. a storm with lightning and thunder (often produced by convection)
7. a rotating column of air between a thunderstorm cloud and the ground
8. a blinding snowstorm associated with a low-pressure system

Reviewing Key Concepts

9. b
10. a
11. c
12. c
13. c
14. a
15. a
16. a
17. a
18. d
19. c
20. Ocean water is too cold in the spring to provide the energy needed for hurricane formation.
21. Cold air gains warmth and moisture as it passes over the Great Lakes. When it reaches land, it cools again and releases the moisture as snow.
22. They can cause flash floods that wash away houses. The winds of thunderstorms can damage trees and roofs. The hail from thunderstorms can damage crops. Lightning can cause fires and loss of life.

Thinking Critically

23. *continental polar—dry (no clouds or rain at fronts) and cold (from north)*
24. *They make it stormy.*
25. *Washington D.C.; It is in the path of a front.*
26. *Oklahoma City is behind the front, in the colder air mass. Little Rock is in the warmer air mass.*
27. *It will get colder as the front passes.*
28. *No, winter weather in the north and moderate temperatures in the south suggest winter.*
29. *Answers depend on local conditions.*
30. *Diagrams should indicate that both visible light images and infrared images show cloud cover. Visible light works in daytime only. Infrared works at night and also shows cloud height.*
31. *brief, heavy precipitation*
32. *cloudy, followed by rain or snow*
33. *clouds and thunderstorms*
34. *cloudy and rain*
35. *fair weather*
36. *possible tornado*
37. *possible tropical storm or hurricane*
38. *freezing rain or ice storm*
39. *The air moves down; weather is usually fair.*
40. *A hurricane is most dangerous because its effects include storm surges, floods, high winds, tornadoes, and thunderstorms.*

the BIG idea

41. *It looks as though a storm surge is occurring. Storm surges are caused by hurricanes.*
42. *Diagrams might show: high-pressure system replaced by a low-pressure system; collision of warm and cold air; rising of warm, humid air; raindrop formation*

UNIT PROJECTS

Have students present their projects. Use rubrics to evaluate their work.

 Unit Projects, pp. 5–10

Thinking Critically

Use this weather map to answer the next six questions. The numbers under each city name are the highest and the lowest temperature for the day in degrees Fahrenheit.

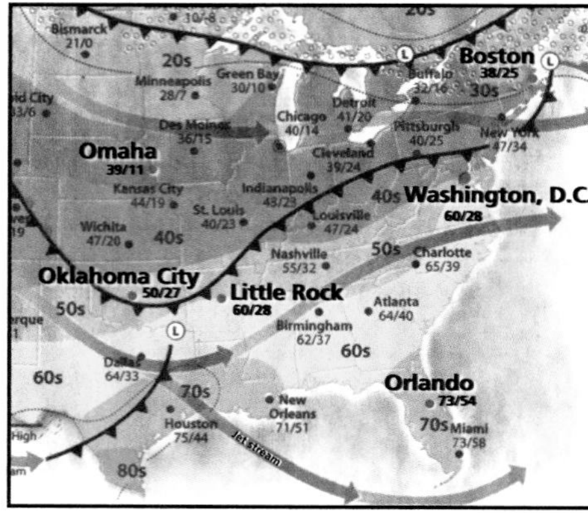

23. **INFER** Name and describe the air mass that has moved south to Omaha from Canada. (6.4.e)
24. **IDENTIFY EFFECTS** How are two low-pressure systems affecting the weather near Boston? (6.4.e)
25. **PREDICT** Explain whether Washington, D.C., or Orlando is more likely to have a big change in weather in the next two days. (6.4.e)
26. **COMPARE AND CONTRAST** Explain the difference in temperature between Oklahoma City and Little Rock. (6.4.e)
27. **PREDICT** How will the weather in Little Rock change in the next day or two? (6.4.e)
28. **APPLY** Does this map indicate that it is hurricane season? Explain your reasoning. (6.4.e)
29. **CONNECT** Describe today's weather and explain what fronts and pressure systems might be influencing it. (6.4.e)
30. **COMPARE AND CONTRAST** Use a Venn diagram to compare images from visible light and infrared radiation. (6.4.e)

PREDICT *For each set of conditions listed in the chart, write a weather prediction.* (6.4.e)

Conditions	Prediction
31. A cold front is moving into an area that has warm, moist air.	
32. A warm front is moving into an area that has cold, dense air.	
33. A cool sea breeze is blowing inland, causing warm, humid air to rise.	
34. Air pressure is falling and the temperature is rising.	
35. Air pressure is increasing and the temperature is steady.	
36. A thunderstorm is developing spinning winds at its center.	
37. A low-pressure center is over the Atlantic Ocean where the water temperature is above 27°C (81°F).	
38. Cold air is pushing warm air where the air is 2°C (36°F) and the ground is -3°C (27°F).	

39. **COMPARE** How is the air motion in the eye of a hurricane similar to the air motion at a high-pressure center? (6.4.e)
40. **EVALUATE** Which type of storm is most dangerous? Explain your reasoning. (6.4.e)

the BIG idea

41. **APPLY** Look again at the photograph on pages 112–113. Now that you have finished the chapter, how would you change your response to the question on the photograph? (6.4.e)
42. **SEQUENCE** Draw a storyboard with at least four sketches to show how cool, sunny weather might change into warm, rainy weather. (6.4.e)

UNIT PROJECTS

Evaluate all of the data, results, and information from your project folder. Prepare to present your project to the class. Be ready to answer questions posed by your classmates about your results.

MONITOR AND RETEACH

If students have trouble applying the concepts in items 23–28, draw the symbols for highs, lows, and fronts on the board. Have students identify each symbol and describe associated weather conditions. Break down the formation of a cold front into three steps. **Step 1** should show how cold air pushes warm air steeply upward. **Step 2** should show that as the warm air rises, its moisture condenses and forms tall clouds. **Step 3** should show heavy raindrops falling.
Students may benefit from summarizing sections of the chapter.

 Summarizing the Chapter, pp. 272–273

Standards-Based Assessment

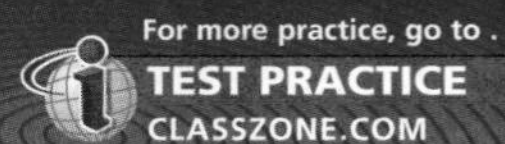

Analyzing a Map

Use this weather map to answer the questions below.

6.4.d, 6.4.e

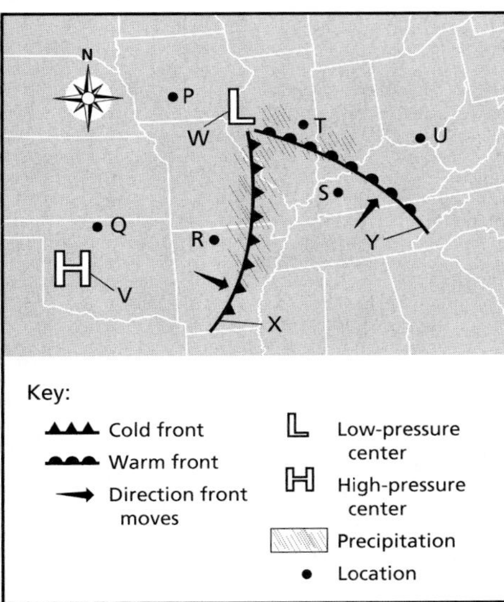

1. Which letter labels a cold front?
   a. Q **b.** U **c.** X **d.** Y

2. Which word best describes the general movement of the fronts?
   a. to the north **b.** to the east **c.** clockwise **d.** counterclockwise

3. A warm front occurs where warm air moves into colder air. Which of these locations is probably warmest?
   a. R **b.** S **c.** T **d.** U

4. Temperatures usually change quickly near a front and more slowly away from a front. The temperature at Q is 10°C (50°F). The temperature at S is 20°C (68°F). Which is the best estimate for the temperature at R?
   a. 6°C (43°F) **b.** 11°C (52°F) **c.** 20°C (68°F) **d.** 24°C (75°F)

5. If the fronts continue to move as shown, which location will get warmer soon?
   a. Q **b.** R **c.** S **d.** T

6. Low pressure often brings stormy weather, and high pressure often brings fair weather. Which of these locations is most likely to have clear skies?
   a. Q **b.** R **c.** S **d.** U

Extended Response

Use the map above to answer the two questions below in detail. Include some of the terms shown in the word box. Underline each term you use in your answers.

cold front	humid	west
warm front	east	prevailing winds

7. Along which front on the weather map above would you expect to find cumulonimbus clouds? Explain why.

8. The weather system shown on the map above is in the continental United States. In which direction do you expect it to move? Explain why.

REFLECTING ON THE CHAPTER

Have students answer the following questions in their **Science Notebook:**

1. Would you like to be a meteorologist? Why or why not?
2. Do you think scientists should work to control the weather, or is it better to let nature take its course? Please give reasons for your response.
3. What new things have you learned about weather while working on your Unit Project?

California Content Standards

6.4.d Students know convection currents distribute heat in the atmosphere and oceans.

6.4.e Students know differences in pressure, heat, air movement, and humidity result in changes of weather.

Analyzing a Map

1. c *3. b* *5. d*
2. d *4. b* *6. a*

Extended Response

7. RUBRIC
4 points for a response that correctly answers the question and uses the following terms accurately:
- cold front
- cumulonimbus clouds
- humid

Sample: the cold front; Cold fronts push warm air up. Water vapor in the warm, humid air condenses as the air rises. This produces cumulonimbus clouds and then storms.
3 points for a response that correctly answers the question and uses two terms accurately
2 points for a response that correctly answers the question and uses one term accurately
1 point for a response that correctly answers the question, but doesn't use the terms

8. RUBRIC
4 points for a response that correctly answers the question and uses the following terms accurately:
- prevailing winds
- west
- east

Sample: west to east; Weather systems are moved by the global pattern of prevailing winds, which move west to east. Sometimes the jet stream interferes with these wind patterns and causes systems to change directions.
3 points for a response that uses two terms accurately
2 points for a response that correctly answers the question and uses one term accurately
1 point for a response that correctly answers the question, but doesn't use the terms

UNIT 2

Earth's Surface

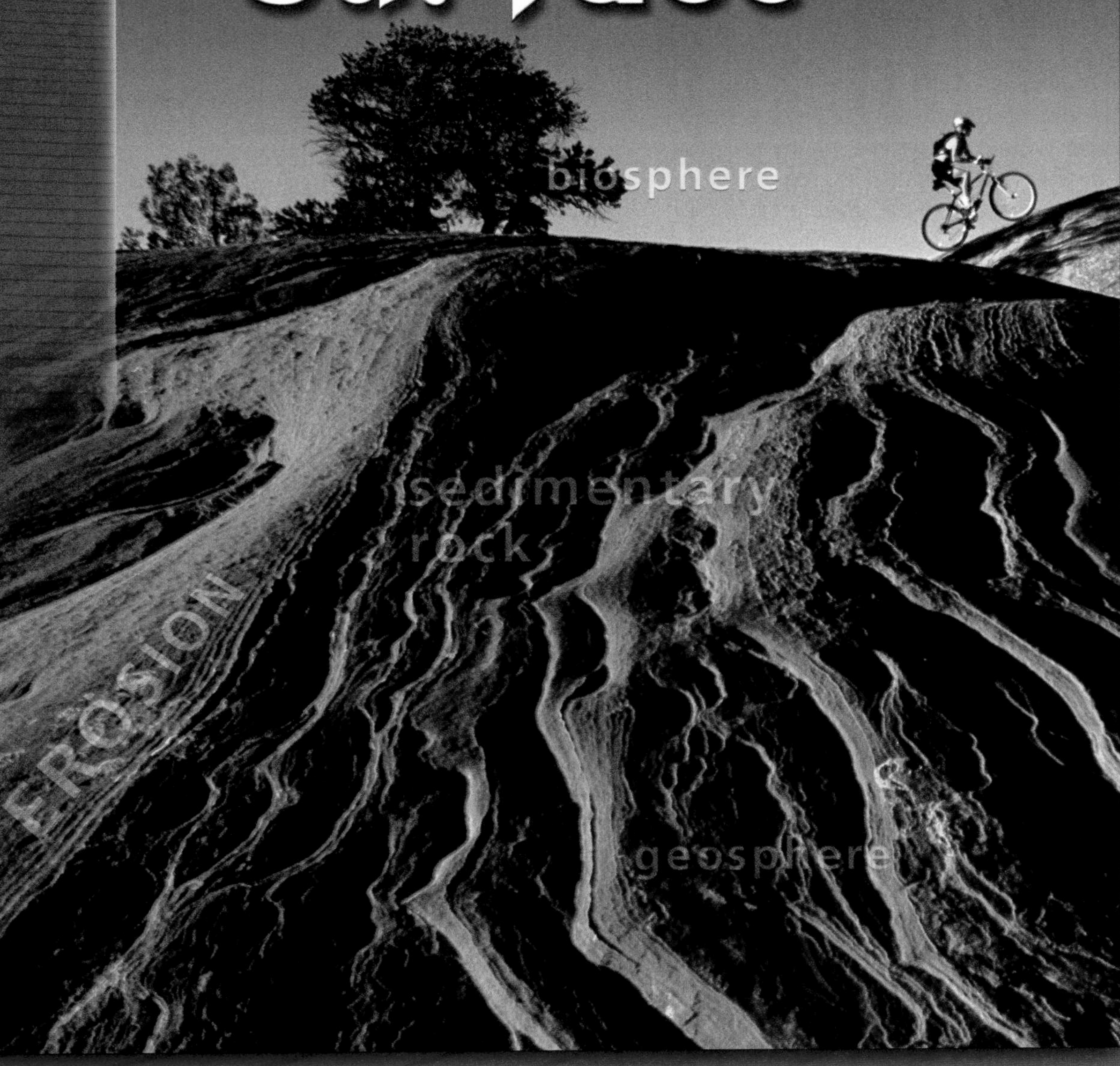

Contents Overview

Unit 2 Scientific Background

Below is an in-depth look at some subtopics of the concepts presented in this unit.

VIEWS OF EARTH TODAY: Mapping Coastal Topography

Coastal areas are especially prone to erosion by water and wind, and they can change dramatically within a short period of time as a result of hurricanes and other major storms. In order to monitor changes in the shorelines of the United States, government agencies, private institutions, and businesses are making use of remote sensing technologies that provide accurate, high-resolution topographic data on coastal areas. Two types of remote sensors that are used for this purpose are IfSar and LIDAR.

IfSAR, or InSAR, stands for Interferometric Synthetic Aperture Radar. It consists of a sensor that is mounted to the bottom of an aircraft and transmits radar pulsars to the ground. By measuring the time it takes for the radar signals to return, the elevations of targeted areas can be determined. IfSAR is used in conjunction with Global Positioning System (GPS) and other technology to pinpoint locations. The data can then be processed to produce highly detailed topographic maps and images.

LIDAR stands for Light Detection and Ranging. It also consists of an aircraft-mounted sensor. However, LIDAR sends out laser pulses rather than radar pulses. Like IfSAR, LIDAR determines surface elevations by measuring the time it takes for signals to return, and it is used in conjunction with GPS. In partnership with other government agencies, NASA began collecting LIDAR data along U.S. beaches in 1996 using its Airborne Topographic Mapper.

Coastal Management Uses Government officials use the maps and images obtained through remote sensing as aids in managing coastal areas. The topographic information helps with such coastal management tasks as:

- monitoring changes in shorelines and beach volume over time
- identifying the amount of erosion caused by hurricanes and other storms
- assessing the effectiveness of beach stabilization and erosion-control projects
- quantifying dune movement and elevation loss
- analyzing flood risk
- determining construction setback lines for beaches
- planning urban development
- determining the extent of wetlands and other wildlife habitats
- predicting landslides

MINERALS AND ROCKS: Geologic Cycles

One of the basic principles of geology is that matter and energy cycle through the various components of the Earth system—the atmosphere, hydrosphere, lithosphere, and biosphere—over time. Although the various geologic cycles, such as the hydrologic cycle, the rock cycle, and biogeochemical cycles, are often studied separately, they are all interconnected. In fact, the various cycles are sometimes considered parts of one overall geologic cycle.

All the multitude of natural processes, including evaporation, precipitation, groundwater flow, flooding, weathering, erosion, deposition, earthquakes, and volcanic eruptions, contribute to the various geologic cycles in which matter and energy move through the different spheres of the Earth system. The main sources of energy for geologic cycles are the Sun (solar energy), Earth's interior (geothermal energy), and gravity (gravitational energy).

The Hydrologic Cycle, or water cycle, involves the cycling of water through the oceans, glaciers and ice sheets, lakes and streams, groundwater, the atmosphere, the lithosphere, and living things. The main processes in the hydrologic cycle are evaporation, condensation, and precipitation.

The Rock Cycle involves the cycling of elements through the three types of rock: igneous, sedimentary, and metamorphic. The processes of weathering, erosion, deposition, and plate tectonic activity play major roles in the rock cycle.

Biogeochemical Cycles, such as the carbon cycle and the nitrogen cycle, involve the cycling of elements necessary for life through all the components of the Earth system. Carbon, for example, moves through the oceans as a dissolved ion, through the atmosphere as in the form of carbon dioxide gas, through the lithosphere as part of carbonate minerals and rocks, and through the biosphere as a component of organic compounds in living things. The carbon cycle involves such biological processes as photosynthesis, respiration, and decomposition.

Biogeochemical cycles involve the six elements that are considered necessary for life: carbon, hydrogen, oxygen, nitrogen, sulfur, and phosphorus. These six elements are basic components of all cells. They combine in different ways to form carbohydrates, lipids, proteins, and nucleic acids.

EROSION AND DEPOSITION: Differential Erosion

Different rocks and even different parts of one rock may weather at different rates, a process called *differential erosion* or *differential weathering.* These differences in erosion rates produce a wide variety of landforms and unusual rock formations.

Factors Affecting Erosion Rates The resistance of rock to weathering depends on a number of factors. One of the most important factors is the exact mineral composition of the rock. Among the common silicate minerals, the ones that crystallize at lower temperatures are more resistant to weathering. These minerals include mica and quartz. Non-silicate minerals, such as the carbonates, oxides, and sulfides, erode more quickly than most silicate minerals. In general, harder minerals erode less readily than softer ones.

Another factor that influences erosion rates is the presence or absence of *joints* (cracks) in the rock. Joints expose more surface area to the action of water and so increase a rock's susceptibility to weathering.

Igneous and Metamorphic Rocks In general, igneous and metamorphic rocks are more resistant to weathering than are sedimentary rocks. But within each rock group, some rocks are more resistant than others. Among igneous rocks, granite is more resistant to chemical weathering than basalt is. Granite contains quartz, a mineral that is highly stable, whereas basalt does not.

Among the metamorphic rocks, gneiss is more erosion-resistant than schist and slate. The softness of marble, another metamorphic rock, makes it less resistant to erosion.

Sedimentary Rocks Among the sedimentary rocks, shale erodes most readily. The erosion rate of limestone varies with the climate because limestone is resistant to physical weathering but not to chemical weathering. In dry climates, limestone resists erosion. In humid climates, however, it erodes quickly because water easily dissolves carbonate. Quartz sandstone, another sedimentary rock, is highly resistant to weathering because the mineral quartz is so resistant.

Landforms Resulting from Differential Erosion In an area with two or more types of rock that differ in resistance to erosion, the most resistant rock will form hills, ridges, cliffs, or mountains, while the least resistant rock will be removed to form valleys or canyons. Igneous and metamorphic rocks, because of their comparative resistance to erosion, form many mountains. The peaks of the Sierra Nevada in eastern California, for example, consist of granite that has been uplifted and exposed by the erosion of less resistant surrounding rock. In Canyonlands National Park in Utah, the differential erosion of several types of sedimentary rock has produced cliffs and slopes. The cliffs consist of resistant sandstone and limestone, while the slopes formed from shale, which erodes easily.

Many unusual rock formations also result from differential erosion. At Devils Tower in Wyoming, soft sedimentary rock eroded away to leave a column of hard igneous rock that rises up more than 1,000 feet. At Bryce Canyon National Park in Utah, many of the tall rock spires called hoodoos are covered by dolomite, an erosion-resistant sedimentary rock that protects the more easily eroded limestone underneath. In many other areas of the West, differential erosion has contributed to the formation of such rock formations as pillars, pinnacles, arches, and bridges.

VIDEO SUMMARY

SCIENTIFIC AMERICAN FRONTIERS

"The Wild West: All That Glitters," a segment of the *Scientific American Frontiers* series that aired on PBS stations, presents one scientist's determined 15-year effort to prove a surprising hypothesis. Although most of the world's diamonds come from Russia, Australia, and southern Africa, prospector Chuck Fipke was certain that he could find diamonds in Canada. Fipke knew that diamonds form where Earth's crust is thick enough to create the pressure needed to squeeze carbon into diamond crystals. Once formed, these crystals reach the surface of Earth's crust only through chimneys of molten rock called kimberlite pipes. Fipke targeted northwestern Canada because he saw the same thick crust there. Finding the kimberlite pipes was not easy, though. Fipke finally came up with a second hypothesis: Glaciers had scraped off the tops of the pipes and carried the materials downhill. By moving his search site back toward where the glaciers had started, he was at last rewarded by the discovery of kimberlite pipes and top-quality diamonds.

California Content Standards

6.3.d Students know heat energy is also transferred between objects by radiation (radiation can travel through space).

6.4.b Students know solar energy reaches Earth through radiation, mostly in the form of visible light.

FRONTIERS in Science

REMOTE SENSING

Technology high above Earth's surface is giving scientists a whole new look at our planet. This image is of Jasper Ridge, near Palo Alto, California.

California Content Standards

6.3.d Students know heat energy is also transferred between objects by radiation (radiation can travel through space).

6.4.b Students know solar energy reaches Earth through radiation, mostly in the form of visible light.

SCIENTIFIC AMERICAN FRONTIERS

View the video segment "All That Glitters" to learn how explorers use remote sensing and other methods to find valuable materials.

148 Unit 2: Earth's Surface

ADDITIONAL RESOURCES

Technology Resources

 **Scientific American Frontiers Video:** *All That Glitters:* 11-minute video segment that introduces the unit.

 **ClassZone.com**
CAREER LINK, Mineralogist

Guide student viewing and comprehension of the video:

 Video Teaching Guide, pp. 1–2; Video Viewing Guide, p. 3; Video Wrap-Up, p. 4

Scientific American Frontiers Video Guide, pp. 21–24

Unit projects procedures and rubrics:

 Unit Projects, pp. 5–10

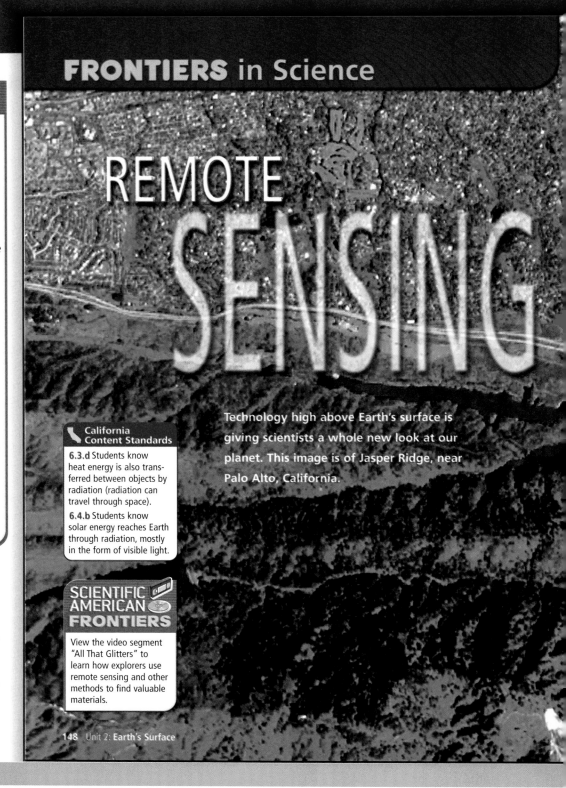

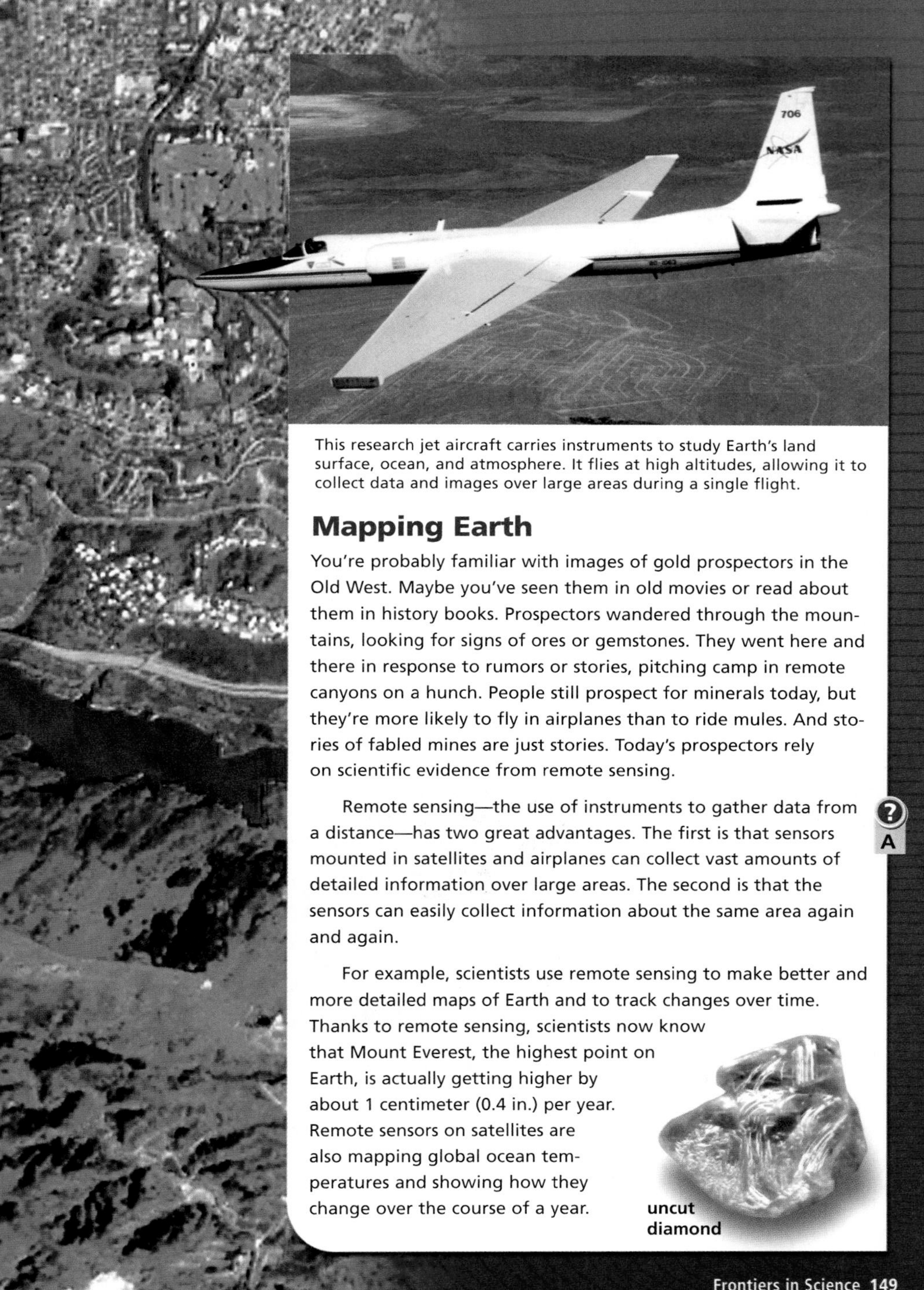

This research jet aircraft carries instruments to study Earth's land surface, ocean, and atmosphere. It flies at high altitudes, allowing it to collect data and images over large areas during a single flight.

Mapping Earth

You're probably familiar with images of gold prospectors in the Old West. Maybe you've seen them in old movies or read about them in history books. Prospectors wandered through the mountains, looking for signs of ores or gemstones. They went here and there in response to rumors or stories, pitching camp in remote canyons on a hunch. People still prospect for minerals today, but they're more likely to fly in airplanes than to ride mules. And stories of fabled mines are just stories. Today's prospectors rely on scientific evidence from remote sensing.

Remote sensing—the use of instruments to gather data from a distance—has two great advantages. The first is that sensors mounted in satellites and airplanes can collect vast amounts of detailed information over large areas. The second is that the sensors can easily collect information about the same area again and again. ? A

For example, scientists use remote sensing to make better and more detailed maps of Earth and to track changes over time. Thanks to remote sensing, scientists now know that Mount Everest, the highest point on Earth, is actually getting higher by about 1 centimeter (0.4 in.) per year. Remote sensors on satellites are also mapping global ocean temperatures and showing how they change over the course of a year.

uncut diamond

FOCUS

Set Learning Goals

Students will

- Analyze how remote sensing is used to locate minerals.
- Discuss additional applications of remote sensing.
- Complete a unit project relating to map-reading, mineral formation, or glacial erosion.

Tell students that remote sensing is pushing the frontiers of science by giving scientists previously unattainable views of Earth. Ask them to predict how images of Earth taken high above its surface might be used to find minerals underground. Have them revise their predictions after viewing the "The Wild West: All That Glitters" video.

INSTRUCT

Technology Design

Ask students to identify the technological advantages of remote sensing over other types of data-gathering techniques. *Remote sensing takes much less time to cover large areas and to gather data repeatedly than does traveling on the ground to collect data, especially in rugged areas.*

Teach from Visuals

Have students identify features that are visible in the photograph. Ask: Could you see all these features if you were standing on the ground? Explain. *Features such as hills and trees might interfere with your view.*

Asking a Question

Because of remote sensing, scientists know that Mt. Everest is still growing. Have students develop questions related to this fact. *Sample answer: Why is Mt. Everest still growing? How big will it get?*

DIFFERENTIATE INSTRUCTION

More Reading Support

A What is remote sensing? *using instruments to gather data from a distance*

Advanced Ask students to infer why scientists map and track changes in global ocean temperatures. *Changes in ocean temperatures may indicate climatic changes. Temperature changes could affect marine ecosystems, such as coral reefs.*

Integrate the Sciences

Remote-sensing instruments detect electromagnetic radiation, which includes radio waves, microwaves, infrared radiation, visible light, ultraviolet radiation, x-rays, and gamma rays. Electromagnetic waves are classified by wavelength—radio waves are the longest; gamma waves are the shortest.

Tell students that wavelength refers to the distance between similar points on successive waves. For example, wavelength is the distance between the crests, or highest points, of two waves.

Scientific Process

Ask students to identify the scientific processes described on this page. *collecting data, analyzing data*

Determining What Is Known

Ask: Why did some prospectors infer there might be diamonds in northern Canada? *The region is geologically similar to the world's major diamond-producing areas.*

Detecting Minerals from Above

One of the many uses of remote sensing is to find new sources of valuable minerals, such as diamonds. To detect minerals from airplanes or satellites, remote sensors make use of the energy in sunlight. Sunlight reaches Earth as radiation, which travels in the form of waves. All objects absorb some types of radiation and reflect others. The particular wavelengths absorbed or reflected depend upon the materials that make up the objects. Each kind of material has a unique "fingerprint" of the wavelengths it absorbs and the wavelengths it reflects.

B

Energy from the Sun reflects at different wavelengths from materials at Earth's surface. Instruments on the jet analyze the reflected energy and map the surface.

When sunlight strikes Earth's surface, some of it is reflected back into the sky. Some of the radiation is absorbed by rocks and other objects and then emitted, or given off, in a different form. Remote sensors in airplanes and satellites collect the reflected and emitted radiation and analyze it to determine which types of rocks and minerals lie on the surface. The remote sensing systems collect so much data that computer processing and analysis are difficult and expensive. Still, the data are usually clear enough to show the types of minerals located in the regions scanned. However, minerals that are buried cannot be detected by remote sensing from aircraft or satellites. The sensors receive only energy from or near the surface.

C

SCIENTIFIC AMERICAN FRONTIERS

View the "All that Glitters" segment of your *Scientific American Frontiers* video to see how finding certain common minerals can indicate the presence of a valuable mineral like diamond.

IN THIS SCENE FROM THE VIDEO **a mineral prospector searches for diamonds in a cylinder of rock drilled from beneath Earth's surface.**

SEARCHING FOR DIAMONDS People used to think that North America did not have many diamonds. However, northern Canada is geologically similar to the world's major diamond-producing areas: southern Africa, Russia, and Australia. A few diamond prospectors kept searching, using remote sensing and other techniques. The prospectors looked for more common minerals that form under the same conditions as diamonds. They made maps showing where these minerals were most plentiful and used the maps to search for diamond-rich rock. Once the prospectors realized that the glaciers of the last ice age had moved the minerals, they looked for and found diamonds farther northward. Canada is now a big producer of diamonds.

DIFFERENTIATE INSTRUCTION

More Reading Support

B Energy from the Sun travels in what form? *waves*

C How does light reach sensors? *It reflects from Earth's surface.*

Below Level Show students satellite images taken with remote-sensing instruments. Such images can be downloaded from government Web sites, including NASA and NOAA. Try to obtain images that include color-coded keys. The colors correspond to different wavelengths.

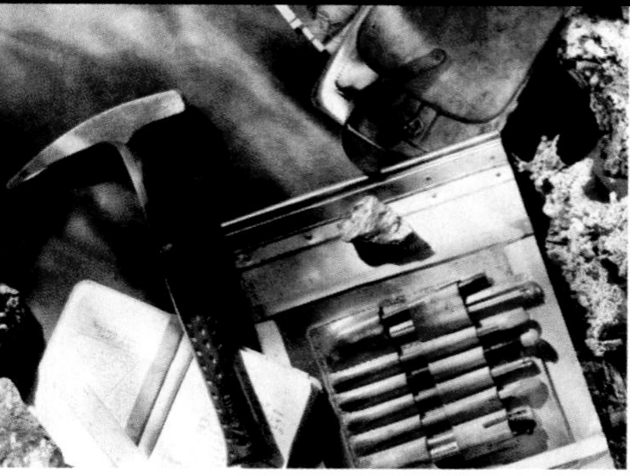

Remote sensing can show the presence of minerals that occur with diamonds, but people must still use older methods to collect samples for further analysis.

Prospecting for Diamonds

One of the major regions of mineral exploration in which remote sensing is used is in the Northwest Territories of Canada, where the first diamond mine began operating in 1998. The Canada Centre for Remote Sensing has helped develop sensing equipment that can fit easily onto light airplanes and computer equipment to analyze results quickly. The sensing equipment is used to detect certain types of minerals that are often found along with diamonds.

Using remote sensing to locate minerals associated with diamonds or valuable ores is only a beginning. The data cannot show how far the minerals or ores extend underground. Prospectors must still explore the area and take samples. However, remote sensing gives mineral prospectors an excellent idea of where to start looking.

UNANSWERED Questions

As scientists use remote sensing to study Earth's land surface, ocean, and atmosphere, they work to answer new questions.

- Can remote sensing be used to locate sources of iron, platinum, or gold in areas that are difficult to explore on foot?
- How do changes in water temperature at the ocean surface affect long-range weather patterns and the health of ocean organisms?
- How do different types of clouds affect the amount of sunlight reaching Earth's surface and the average temperature of the surface?

UNIT PROJECTS

As you study this unit, work alone or with a group on one of the projects listed below.

Hiker's Guide Video (6.7.f)

Like prospectors, wilderness hikers must be able to read maps that show the shape of the land. Prepare a video to teach hikers how to choose hiking and camping areas by reading maps.

- Obtain a topographic map of a wilderness area in a national or state park.
- Write a script outlining what you will teach and how you will videotape it.
- Present your video and display the maps you used.

Diamond Mine Model (6.1.b)

Diamonds can be carried toward Earth's surface by kimberlite pipes. Show how diamonds are mined from kimberlite.

- Build a model of a diamond-mine tunnel that passes through kimberlite.
- Present your model to your class. Explain the relationship between kimberlite and diamonds.

Glacier Photo Essay (6.2.a)

Make a photo essay showing how glaciers reshape Earth's surface as they move and melt.

- Find images of areas that are or have been affected by glaciers. Write captions for them.
- Present the images as a photo essay on a poster or in a portfolio.

Learn more about careers in mineralogy.

UNANSWERED Questions

Have students read the questions and think of some of their own. Remind them that scientists always end up with more questions—that inquiry is the driving force of science.

- With the class, generate on the board a list of new questions.
- Students can add to the list after they watch the *Scientific American Frontiers* Video.
- Students can use the list as a springboard for choosing their Unit Projects.

UNIT PROJECTS

Encourage students to pick the project that most appeals to them. Point out that each is long-term and will take several weeks to complete. You might group or pair students to work on projects and in some cases guide student choice. Some of the projects have student choice built into them. Each project has two worksheet pages, including a rubric. Use the pages to guide students through criteria, process, and schedule.

Unit Projects, pp. 5–10

REVISIT concepts introduced in this article:

Chapter 5
- Technology is used to map Earth, pp. 170–174

Chapter 6
- Minerals are all around us, pp. 183–188
- Geologic maps show Earth's surface features, pp. 206–212

Chapter 7
- Glaciers carve land and move sediments, pp. 245–250

DIFFERENTIATE INSTRUCTION

More Reading Support

D When searching for minerals, what can't the data from remote sensing show? *how far the minerals extend underground*

Differentiate Unit Projects Projects are appropriate for varying abilities. Allow students to choose the ones that interest them most and let them vary their product. Encourage below-level students to give visual or oral presentations or to record audio presentations about their topic. You might suggest that they try "Glacier Photo Essay." Encourage advanced students to complete "Hiker's Guide Video."

CHAPTER

Views of Earth Today

Earth Science UNIFYING PRINCIPLES

PRINCIPLE 1
Heat energy inside Earth and radiation from the Sun provide energy for Earth's processes.

PRINCIPLE 2
Physical forces, such as gravity, affect the movement of all matter on Earth and throughout the universe.

PRINCIPLE 3
Matter and energy move among Earth's rocks and soil, atmosphere, waters, and living things.

PRINCIPLE 4
Earth has changed over time and continues to change.

Unit: Earth's Surface BIG IDEAS

CHAPTER 5
Views of Earth Today
Modern technology has changed the way we view and map Earth.

CHAPTER 6
Minerals and Rocks
Minerals and rocks are basic building blocks of Earth.

CHAPTER 7
Erosion and Deposition
Water, wind, and ice shape Earth's surface.

CHAPTER 5 KEY CONCEPTS

SECTION 1

Maps and globes are models of Earth.

1. Maps show natural and human-made features.
2. Latitude and longitude show locations on Earth.
3. Map projections distort the view of Earth's surface.

SECTION 2

Topographic maps show the shape of the land.

1. Topographic maps use contour lines to show features.
2. Contour lines follow certain rules.

SECTION 3

Technology is used to map Earth.

1. Remote sensing provides detailed images of Earth.
2. Geographic information systems display data in layers.

The Big Idea Flow Chart is available on p. T33 in the **TRANSPARENCY BOOK.**

Previewing Content

SECTION

Maps and globes are models of Earth. pp. 155–163

1. Maps show natural and human-made features.
A map is a model of Earth on a flat surface. A globe represents Earth as if viewed from outer space.

- A **relief map** shows the elevations of land features, such as mountains, plains, and plateaus.
- A **map scale** relates distances on a map to actual distances on Earth's surface.
- A **map legend,** also called a key, explains the meaning of each symbol used on a map.

2. Latitude and longitude show locations on Earth.
A grid of imaginary lines over Earth helps pinpoint locations. **Latitude** lines circle the world parallel to the equator; they are also called parallels. **Longitude** lines, or meridians, run north-south between Earth's poles.

- The **equator** is the latitude line dividing Earth into northern and southern hemispheres.
- The **prime meridian** divides Earth into western and eastern hemispheres.

The Global Positioning System relies on satellite communications and electronic and computer technologies. By using a GPS receiver, a person can find not only the latitude and longitude of a place but its elevation as well.

3. Map projections distort the view of Earth's surface.
A globe is the most accurate way to represent Earth's surface. Mapmakers use different **projections** to make two-dimensional representations of the surface. Each kind of projection distorts the surface in some way.

- A cylindrical, or Mercator, projection distorts landmasses near the poles but shows true directions in straight lines (helpful for navigation).
- In a conic projection, shapes and distances are undistorted only along a particular parallel (useful for mapping large areas in the mid-latitudes).
- A planar projection can be used to plot the shortest distance between two points, but it distorts shapes away from the center point (useful for flight navigation).

SECTION

Topographic maps show the shape of the land. pp. 164–169

1. Topographic maps use contour lines to show features.
Topography is the shape of the land. Topographic maps show the surface features of particular areas, including natural features such as mountains, valleys, and bodies of water, as well as human-made features such as airports, bridges, and roads. They can be used to determine:

- **elevation:** how high a point is above sea level
- **slope:** the steepness of a landform
- **relief:** the difference in elevation between the high and low points of an area

Contour lines on a topographic map are lines that show the elevations of land above or below sea level; all points connected by a contour line have the same elevation.

2. Contour lines follow certain rules.
These rules can be used to interpret topographic maps:

- Contour lines never cross, because each line represents a specific elevation.
- Circles show the highest and lowest points.
- On a given map, the contour interval is always the same. The closer the contour lines, the steeper the slope; the more space between the lines, the more gradual the slope.
- Index contour lines are the darker, bolder, lines on a map, often marked with numbers that label elevations.

A **contour interval** is the difference in elevation between one contour line and the next.

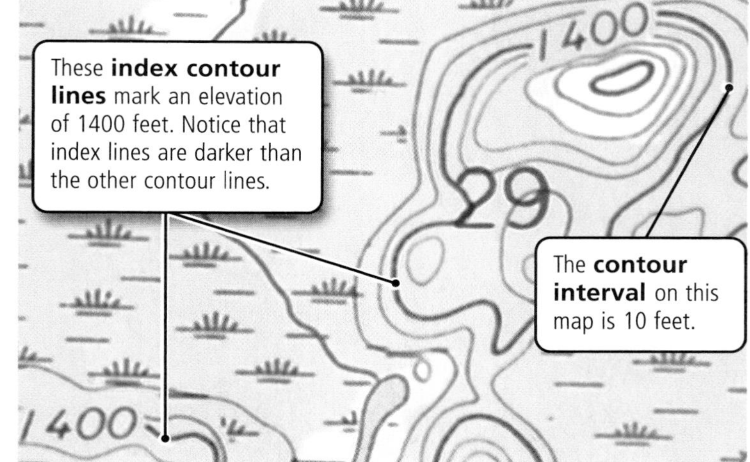

1400
29
1400
These **index contour lines** mark an elevation of 1400 feet. Notice that index lines are darker than the other contour lines.
The **contour interval** on this map is 10 feet.

Common Misconceptions

MISCONCEPTION DATABASE
CLASSZONE.COM Background on student misconceptions

MAP DISTORTION Many students viewing maps think that what they see are accurate images of Earth's landmasses and bodies of water. In fact, all map projections distort the shapes of Earth's landmasses and oceans.

This misconception is addressed on p. 160.

Previewing Content

SECTION

Technology is used to map Earth.

pp. 170–175

1. **Remote sensing provides detailed images of Earth.** Satellites use sensors to detect different types of energy from Earth's surface. They relay the data to computers on Earth, which process the data to create images.
   - A **sensor** is any mechanical or electrical device that receives and responds to a signal, such as light.
   - **False-color images** highlight particular information or features on a map or image.

   Orbiting satellites used in mapmaking are equipped with sensors that constantly record data from Earth's surface. These instruments measure the invisible electromagnetic waves that every object emits. Because the waves are unique to particular types of objects, computers can identify objects through data analysis. The computers convert the data collected into a code, then to pixels, or electronic dots, which are used to form images.

2. **Geographic information systems display data in layers.** GIS combine data from satellite images, statistical surveys, and land surveys to make maps. A GIS map is a composite of several layers. Each layer is dedicated to a specific feature showing, for example, terrain, population, or roadways. The computer systems are used to assemble, store, manipulate, and display data about specific locations.

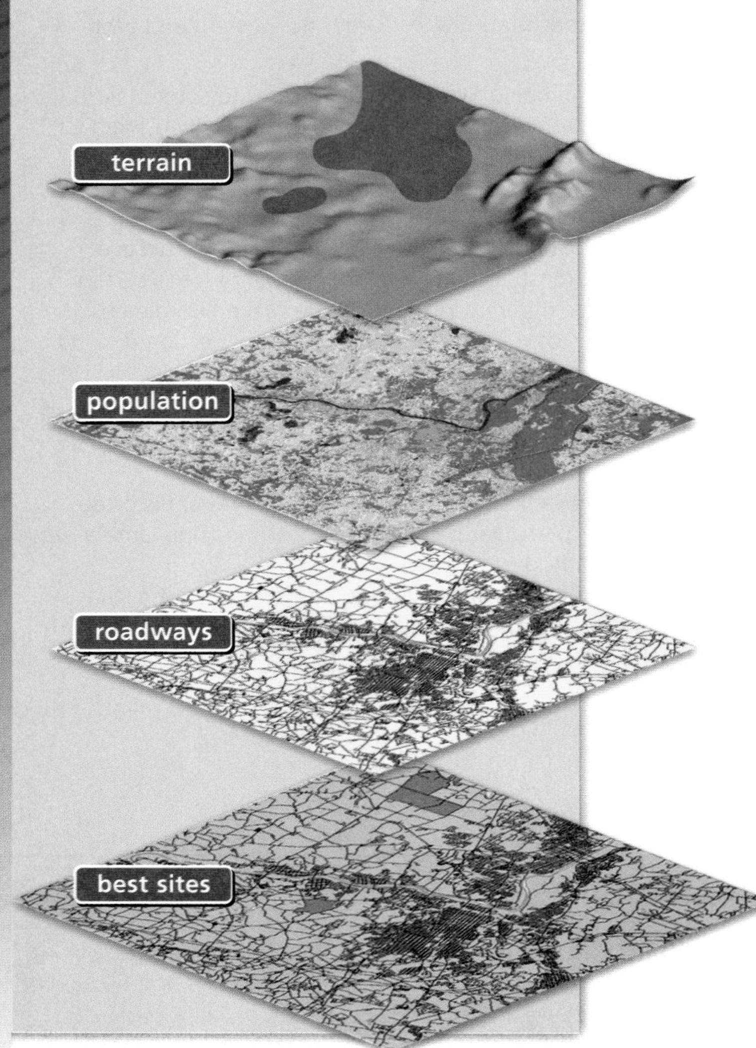

Previewing Labs

Lab Generator CD-ROM
Edit these Pupil Edition labs and generate alternative labs.

EXPLORE the BIG idea

Earth's Changing Surface, p. 153 Students search their surroundings for evidence of erosional forces.	**TIME** 20 minutes **MATERIALS** paper or notebook to record observations
Internet Activity: Mapping, p. 153 Students use the Internet to learn about three-dimensional mapping of Earth from space.	**TIME** 20 minutes **MATERIALS** computer with Internet access

SECTION 

EXPLORE Mapping, p. 155 Students draw a map and then evaluate a classmate's to see what makes a good map.	**TIME** 25 minutes **MATERIALS** paper, pencil or pen
INVESTIGATE California's Natural Resources, p. 159 Students analyze a map of California to determine locations of natural resources and lines of latitude and longitude that are closest to where students live. **ALTERNATIVE:** Direct Instruction, p. 211–212 R California Nature Resources Map, pp. 20–21	**TIME** 15 minutes **MATERIALS** California Natural Resources Map

SECTION 

EXPLORE Topographic Maps, p. 164 Students use their own knuckles to explore the concept of topography.	**TIME** 10 minutes **MATERIALS** washable colored pen
CHAPTER INVESTIGATION Investigate Topographic Maps, pp. 168–169 Students build three-dimensional terrain models out of clay and then produce topographic maps to show slope, elevation, and relief of their models. **ALTERNATIVE:** Reading Activity, p. 211–212	**TIME** 40 minutes **MATERIALS** half-gallon cardboard juice container, scissors, 8 sticks of modeling clay, transparency or sheet protector, 10 cm cellophane tape, ruler, 4–6 cups of water, food coloring, box of spaghetti, erasable marker pen

R **Additional INVESTIGATION,** Make a Map by Triangulation, A, B, & C, pp. 59–67; Teacher Instructions, pp. 211–212

Previewing Chapter Resources

	INTEGRATED TECHNOLOGY	LABS AND ACTIVITIES
CHAPTER 5 **Views of Earth Today**	 CLASSZONE.COM • eEdition Plus • EasyPlanner Plus • Misconception Database • Content Review • Visualization • Resource Centers • Simulation • Test Practice • Internet Activity: Mapping • Math Tutorial  **CD-ROMS** • eEdition • EasyPlanner • Power Presentations • Content Review • Lab Generator • Test Generator  **AUDIO CDS** • Audio Readings • Audio Readings in Spanish SCILINKS.ORG 	 EXPLORE the Big Idea, p. 153 • Earth's Changing Surface • Internet Activity: Mapping  **UNIT RESOURCE BOOK** • Family Letter, p. vii • Spanish Family Letter, p. viii • Unit Projects, pp. 5–10  **Lab Generator CD-ROM** Generate customized labs.
SECTION 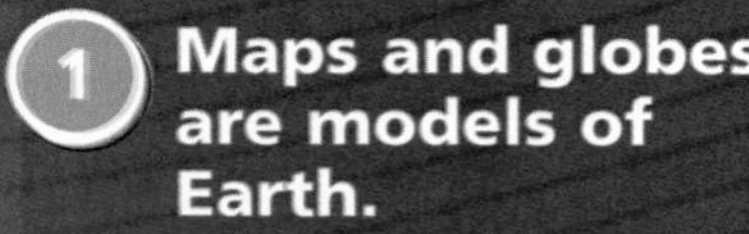 1 **Maps and globes are models of Earth.** pp. 155–163  Lesson Plan, pp. 11–12	 • **VISUALIZATION,** Latitude and Longitude • **RESOURCE CENTER,** Map Projections • **MATH TUTORIAL**  **TRANSPARENCY BOOK** • Big Idea Flow Chart, p. T33 • Daily Vocabulary Scaffolding, p. T34 • Note-Taking Model, p. T35 • 3-Minute Warm-Up, p. T36 • "Latitude and Longitude" Visual, p. T38	 • EXPLORE Mapping, p. 155 • INVESTIGATE California's Natural Resources, p. 159 • Math in Science, p. 163  **UNIT RESOURCE BOOK** • Datasheet, California's Natural Resources, pp. 20–21 • Math Support & Practice, pp. 48–49 • Additional INVESTIGATION, Make a Map by Triangulation, A, B, & C, pp. 59–67
 SECTION 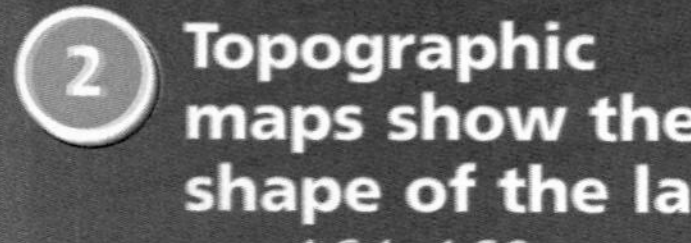 2 **Topographic maps show the shape of the land.** pp. 164–169  Lesson Plan, pp. 23–24	 **SIMULATION,** Topographic Maps and Surface Features  **TRANSPARENCY BOOK** • Daily Vocabulary Scaffolding, p. T34 • 3-Minute Warm-Up, p. T36	 • EXPLORE Topographic Maps, p. 164 • CHAPTER INVESTIGATION, Investigate Topographic Maps, pp. 168–169  **UNIT RESOURCE BOOK** CHAPTER INVESTIGATION, Investigate Topographic Maps, A, B, & C, pp. 50–58
SECTION  3 **Technology is used to map Earth.** pp. 170–175  Lesson Plan, pp. 33–34	 **RESOURCE CENTER,** GIS  **TRANSPARENCY BOOK** • Big Idea Flow Chart, p. T33 • Daily Vocabulary Scaffolding, p. T34 • 3-Minute Warm-Up, p. T37 • Chapter Outline, pp. T39–40	 California Close-Up, p. 175

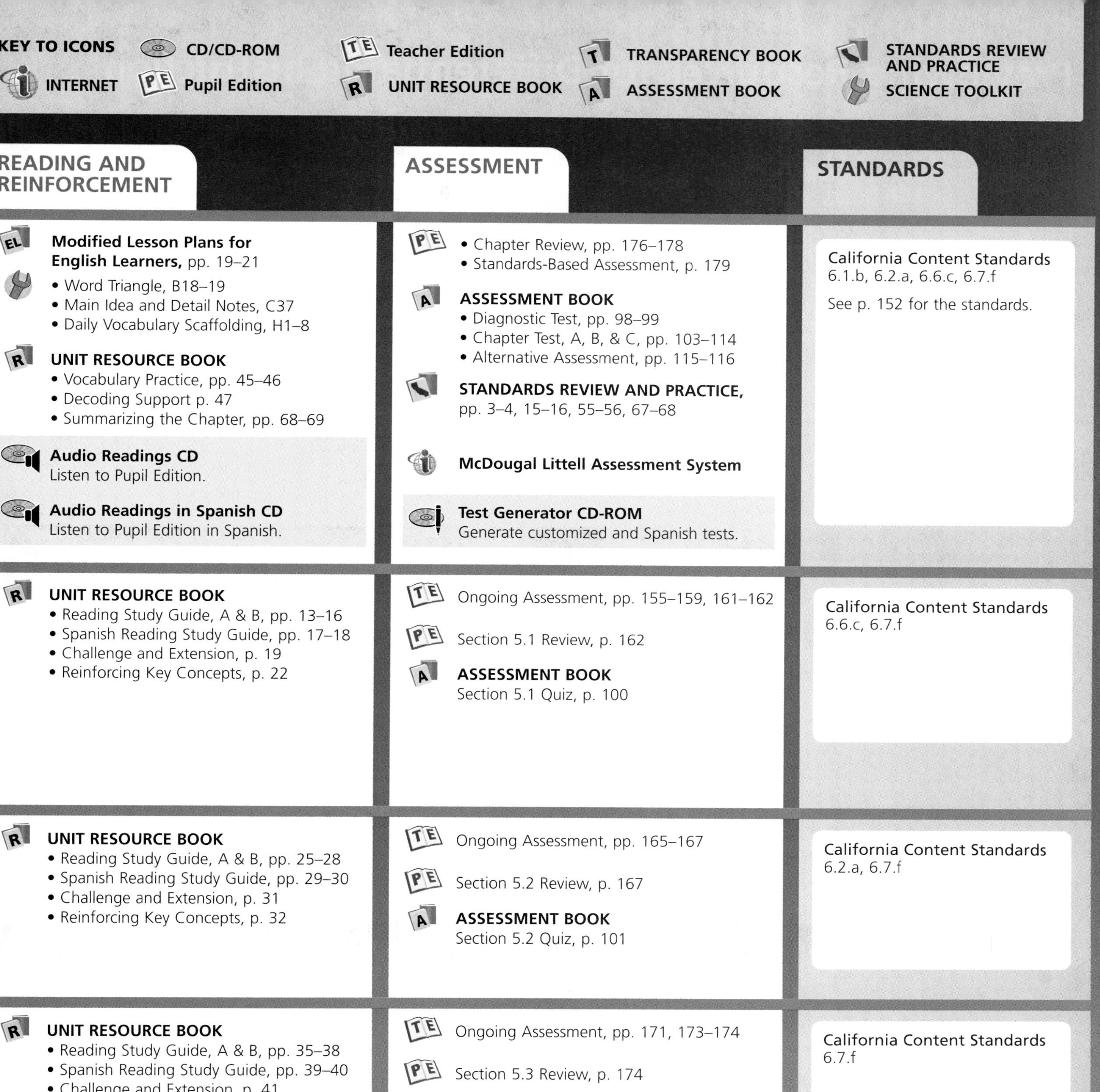

KEY TO ICONS
CD/CD-ROM
Teacher Edition
TRANSPARENCY BOOK
STANDARDS REVIEW AND PRACTICE
INTERNET
Pupil Edition
UNIT RESOURCE BOOK
ASSESSMENT BOOK
SCIENCE TOOLKIT

READING AND REINFORCEMENT	ASSESSMENT	STANDARDS
Modified Lesson Plans for English Learners, pp. 19–21 • Word Triangle, B18–19 • Main Idea and Detail Notes, C37 • Daily Vocabulary Scaffolding, H1–8 **UNIT RESOURCE BOOK** • Vocabulary Practice, pp. 45–46 • Decoding Support p. 47 • Summarizing the Chapter, pp. 68–69 **Audio Readings CD** Listen to Pupil Edition. **Audio Readings in Spanish CD** Listen to Pupil Edition in Spanish.	• Chapter Review, pp. 176–178 • Standards-Based Assessment, p. 179 **ASSESSMENT BOOK** • Diagnostic Test, pp. 98–99 • Chapter Test, A, B, & C, pp. 103–114 • Alternative Assessment, pp. 115–116 **STANDARDS REVIEW AND PRACTICE,** pp. 3–4, 15–16, 55–56, 67–68 **McDougal Littell Assessment System** **Test Generator CD-ROM** Generate customized and Spanish tests.	California Content Standards 6.1.b, 6.2.a, 6.6.c, 6.7.f See p. 152 for the standards.
UNIT RESOURCE BOOK • Reading Study Guide, A & B, pp. 13–16 • Spanish Reading Study Guide, pp. 17–18 • Challenge and Extension, p. 19 • Reinforcing Key Concepts, p. 22	Ongoing Assessment, pp. 155–159, 161–162 Section 5.1 Review, p. 162 **ASSESSMENT BOOK** Section 5.1 Quiz, p. 100	California Content Standards 6.6.c, 6.7.f
UNIT RESOURCE BOOK • Reading Study Guide, A & B, pp. 25–28 • Spanish Reading Study Guide, pp. 29–30 • Challenge and Extension, p. 31 • Reinforcing Key Concepts, p. 32	Ongoing Assessment, pp. 165–167 Section 5.2 Review, p. 167 **ASSESSMENT BOOK** Section 5.2 Quiz, p. 101	California Content Standards 6.2.a, 6.7.f
UNIT RESOURCE BOOK • Reading Study Guide, A & B, pp. 35–38 • Spanish Reading Study Guide, pp. 39–40 • Challenge and Extension, p. 41 • Reinforcing Key Concepts, p. 42 • Challenge Reading, pp. 43–44	Ongoing Assessment, pp. 171, 173–174 Section 5.3 Review, p. 174 **ASSESSMENT BOOK** Section 5.3 Quiz, p. 102	California Content Standards 6.7.f

Previewing Resources for Differentiated Instruction

CHAPTER INVESTIGATION

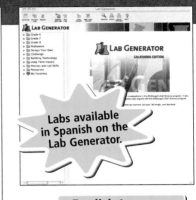

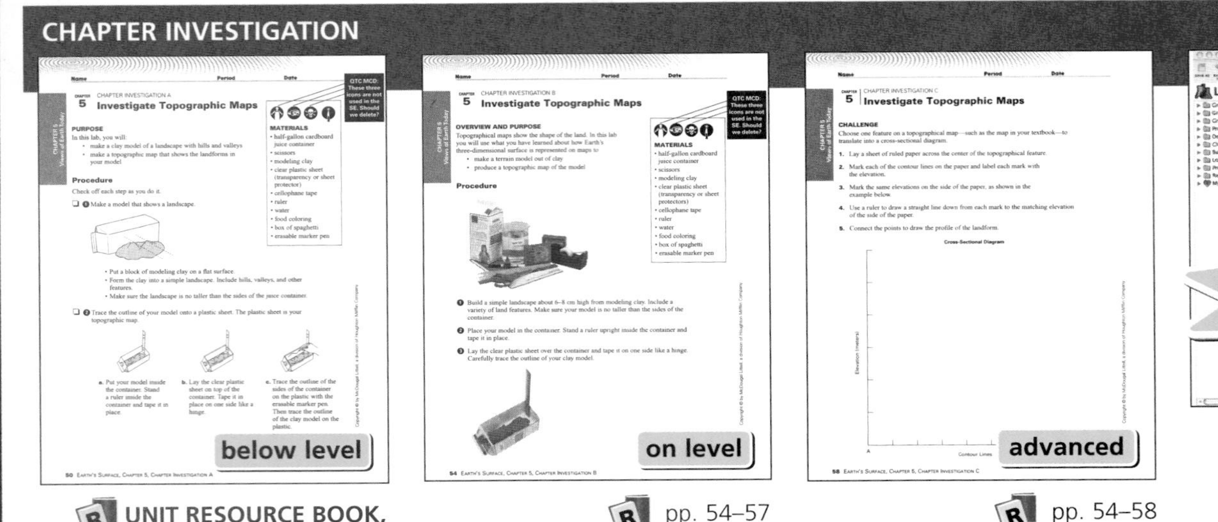

Labs available in Spanish on the Lab Generator.

English Learners

UNIT RESOURCE BOOK, pp. 50–53

pp. 54–57

pp. 54–58

READING STUDY GUIDE

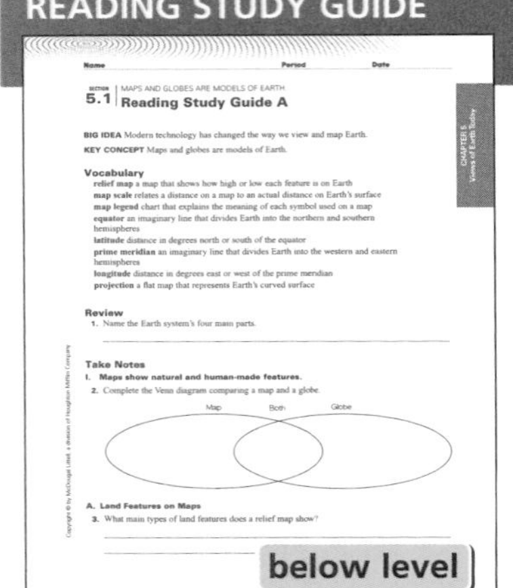

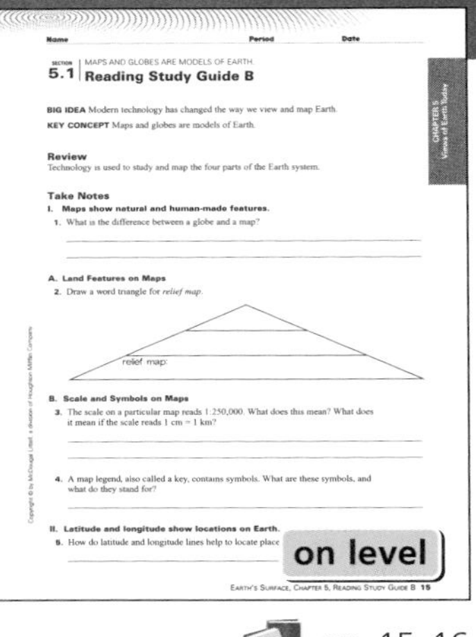

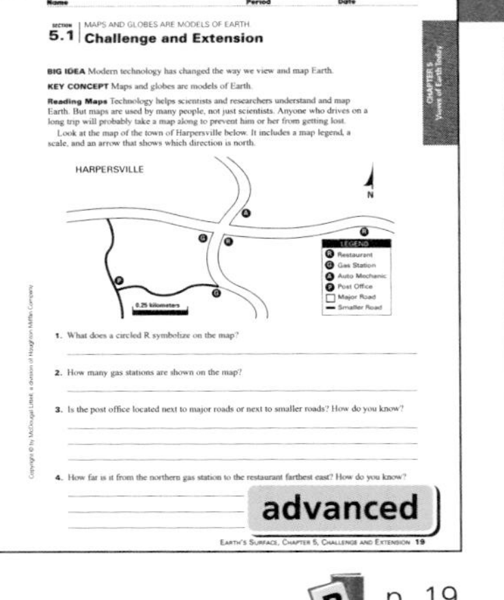

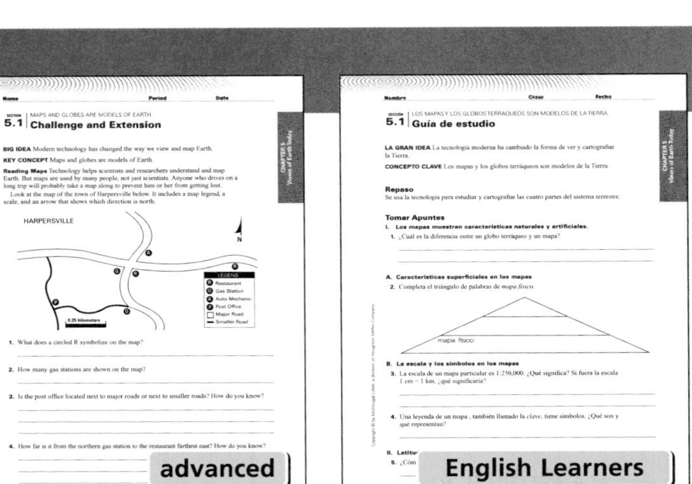

UNIT RESOURCE BOOK, pp. 13–14

pp. 15–16

p. 19

p. 17

CHAPTER TEST

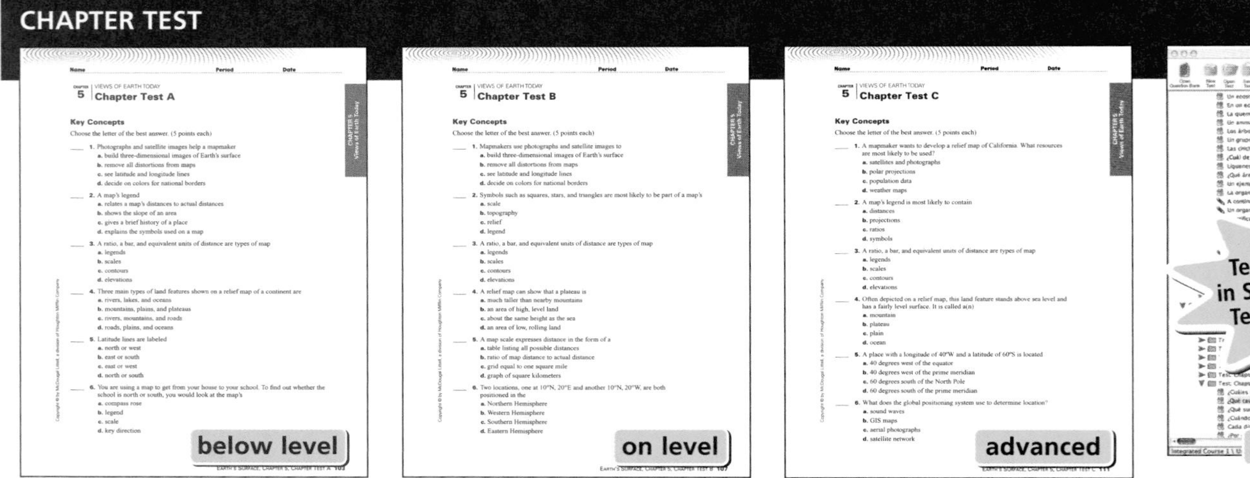

Tests available in Spanish on the Test Generator.

English Learners

ASSESSMENT BOOK, pp. 103–106

pp. 107–110

pp. 111–114

TECHNOLOGY

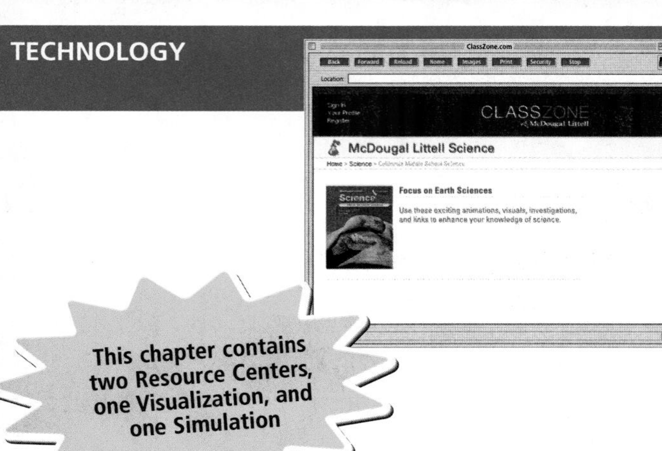

This chapter contains two Resource Centers, one Visualization, and one Simulation

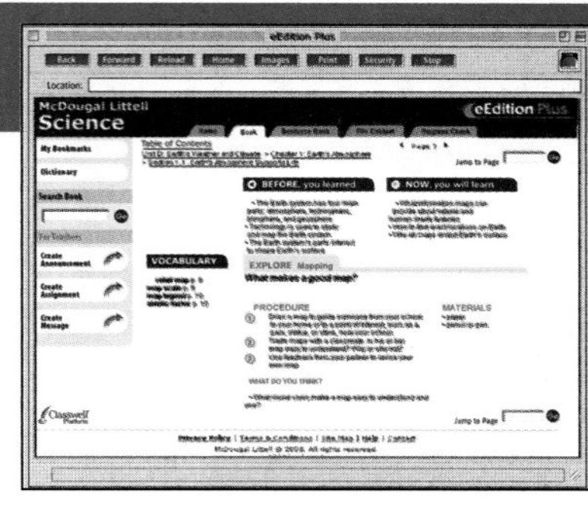

VISUAL CONTENT

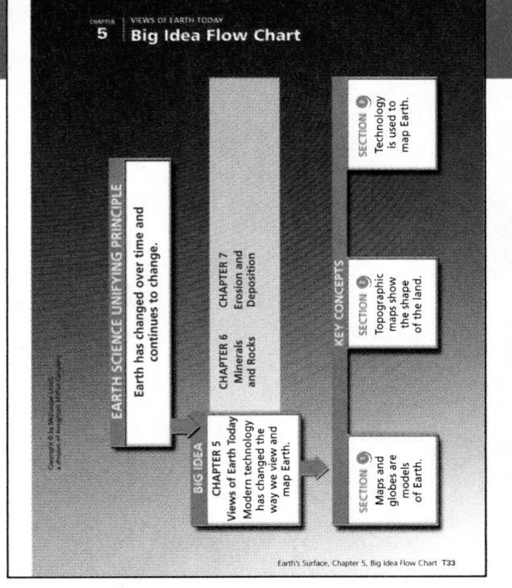

TRANSPARENCY BOOK, p. T33

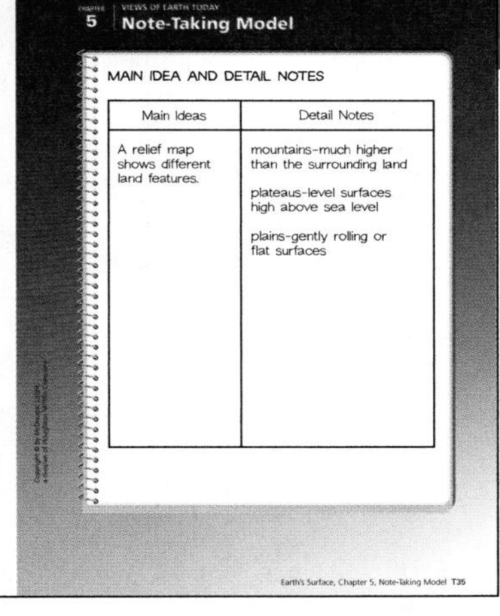

p. T35

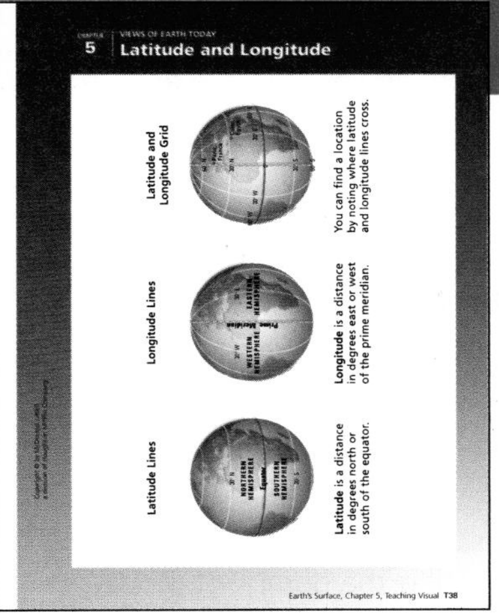

p. T38

MORE SUPPORT

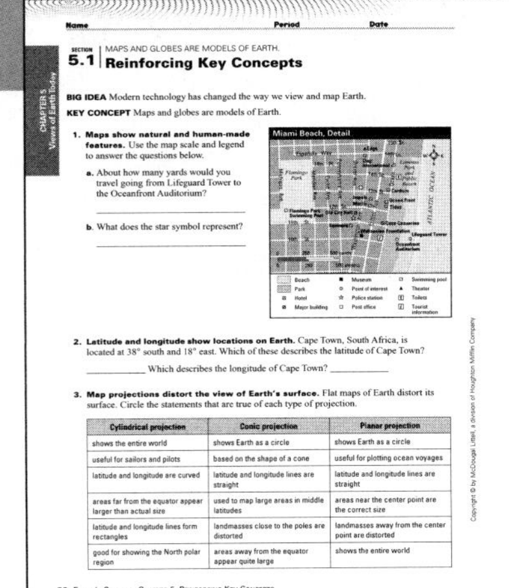

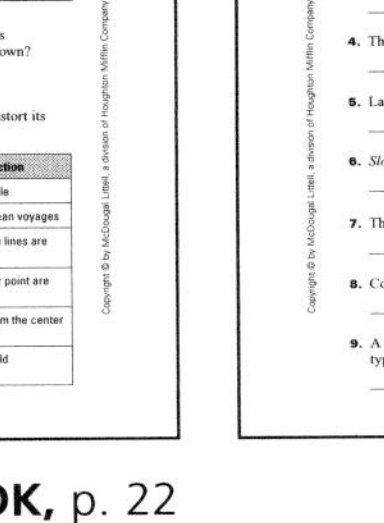

UNIT RESOURCE BOOK, p. 22

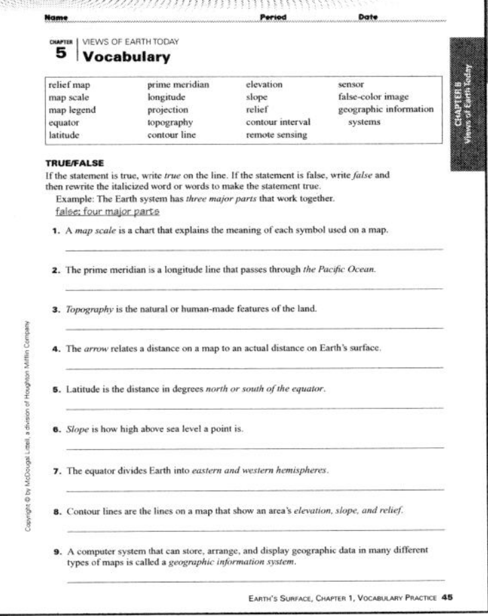

pp. 45–46

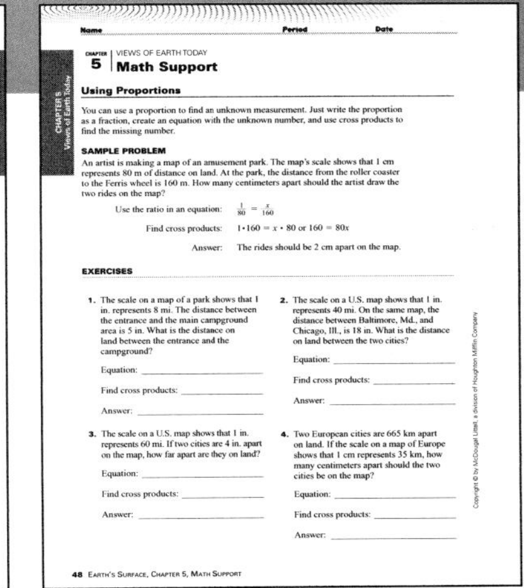

p. 48

CHAPTER 5 Views of Earth Today

INTRODUCE

the BIG idea

Have students look at the satellite photographs and describe what they see. Have them discuss how the question in the box relates to the Big Idea. Ask:

- How is it possible to take such images of Earth?
- Do you remember the first time you saw a photograph of Earth taken from outer space? How did that particular view of our planet affect you?
- How do you suppose ancient people came up with their images of Earth?

California Content Standards

6.1.b Students know Earth is composed of several layers: a cold, brittle lithosphere; a hot, convecting mantle; and a dense, metallic core.

6.2.a Students know water running downhill is the dominant process in shaping the landscape, including California's landscape.

6.6.c Students know the natural origin of the materials used to make common objects.

6.7.f Read a topographic map and a geologic map for evidence provided on the maps and construct and interpret a simple scale map.

CHAPTER 5 Views of Earth Today

the BIG idea

Modern technology has changed the way we view and map Earth.

Key Concepts

SECTION 1 **Maps and globes are models of Earth.** Learn how to locate any place on Earth and how Earth's sphere is portrayed on flat maps.

SECTION 2 **Topographic maps show the shape of the land.** Learn about representing the features of Earth's surface on flat maps.

SECTION 3 **Technology is used to map Earth.** Learn how satellites and computers are used to provide more detailed maps of Earth.

California ClassZone

CLASSZONE.COM

Chapter 5 online resources: Content Review, Simulation, Visualization, three Resource Centers, Math Tutorial, Test Practice

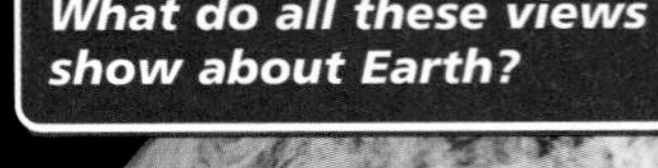

What do all these views show about Earth?

Swirling clouds over North and South America: NASA Terra satellite data

152 Unit 2: **Earth's Surface**

INTERNET PREVIEW

CLASSZONE.COM For student use with the following pages:

Review and Practice
- Content Review, pp. 154, 176
- Math Tutorial: Solving Proportions, p. 163
- Test Practice, p. 179

Activities and Resources
- Internet Activity: Mapping, p. 153
- Visualization: Latitude and Longitude, p. 158; Resource Centers: Map Projections, p. 162; GIS, p. 173; Simulation: Topographic Maps, p. 167

NSTA
scilinks.org
SCiLINKS

Topographic Maps
Code: MDL071

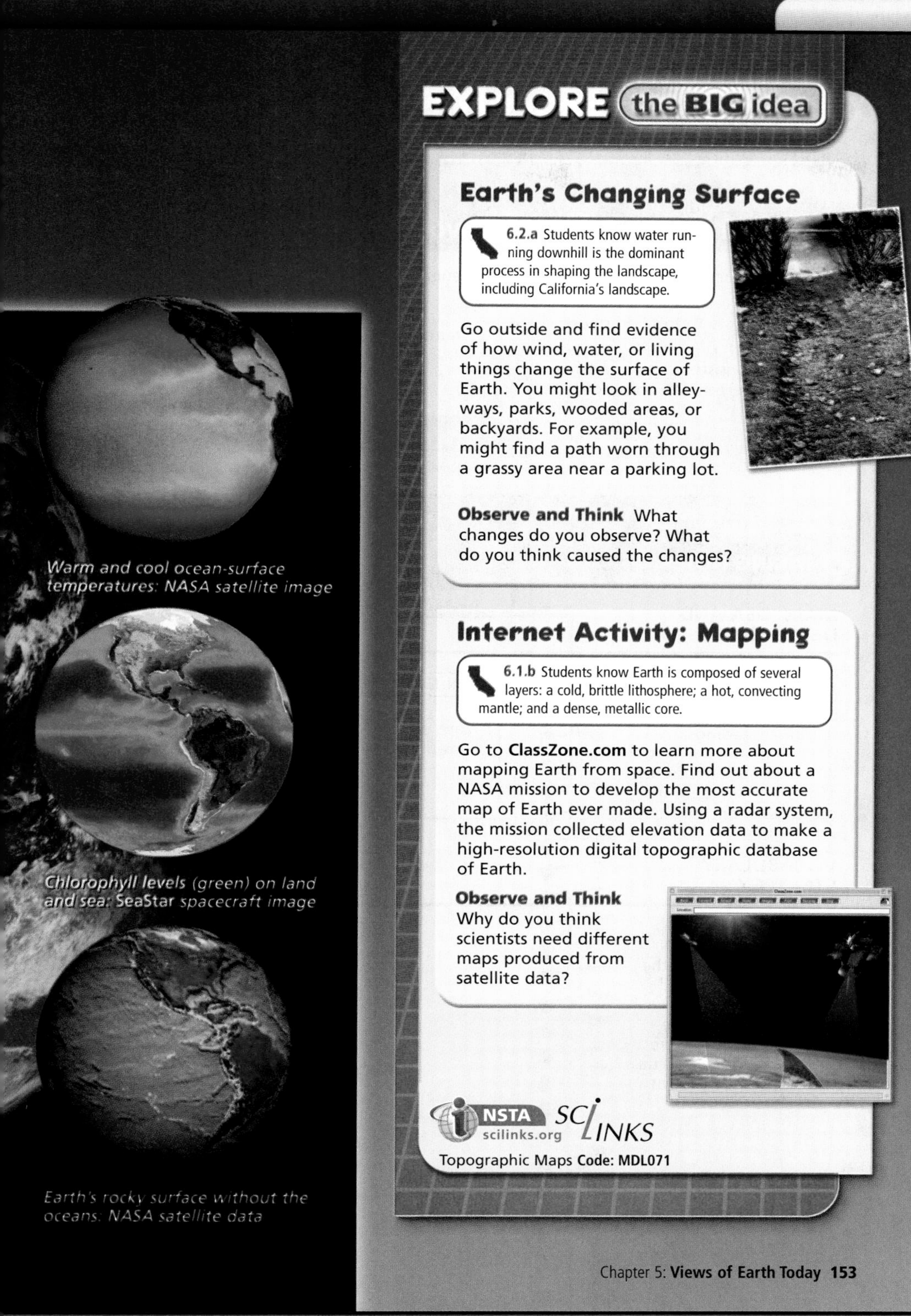

EXPLORE the BIG idea

Earth's Changing Surface

6.2.a Students know water running downhill is the dominant process in shaping the landscape, including California's landscape.

Go outside and find evidence of how wind, water, or living things change the surface of Earth. You might look in alleyways, parks, wooded areas, or backyards. For example, you might find a path worn through a grassy area near a parking lot.

Observe and Think What changes do you observe? What do you think caused the changes?

Internet Activity: Mapping

6.1.b Students know Earth is composed of several layers: a cold, brittle lithosphere; a hot, convecting mantle; and a dense, metallic core.

Go to **ClassZone.com** to learn more about mapping Earth from space. Find out about a NASA mission to develop the most accurate map of Earth ever made. Using a radar system, the mission collected elevation data to make a high-resolution digital topographic database of Earth.

Observe and Think Why do you think scientists need different maps produced from satellite data?

NSTA scilinks.org SCILINKS

Topographic Maps **Code: MDL071**

Warm and cool ocean-surface temperatures: NASA satellite image

Chlorophyll levels (green) on land and sea: SeaStar spacecraft image

Earth's rocky surface without the oceans: NASA satellite data

Chapter 5: **Views of Earth Today** **153**

EXPLORE the BIG idea

These inquiry-based activities are appropriate for use at home or as a supplement to classroom instruction.

Earth's Changing Surface

PURPOSE To introduce students to the erosional forces around them

TIP *20 min.* If an outside activity is not feasible, students can conduct their investigations from a window.

Answer: Student observations may include evidence such as cracks in walls, ruts worn in alleys, and slope erosion. Students should reason that animal activity, including that of insects and people, and the forces of wind, water, and/or freezing, caused such changes.

REVISIT after p. 164.

Internet Activity: Mapping

PURPOSE To introduce students to the latest technology used in the three-dimensional mapping of Earth

TIP *20 min.* Ask students to predict the technologies required to map Earth.

Answer: Students may say that scientists need to study different parts of Earth or to study how Earth is changing.

REVISIT after p. 174.

EACHING WITH TECHNOLOGY

PS If you have access to hand-held GPS units, you may wish to end students to opposite ends of the school and have them compare ne readings. The Global Positioning System and related devices are ntroduced on p. 160.

PREPARE

CONCEPT REVIEW

Activate Prior Knowledge

- If possible, display a pumpkin to demonstrate Earth's oblate shape.
- Ask students to discuss how two seemingly separate items—for example, a furniture factory and a rain forest—can be interconnected. *Wood to make furniture might come from a rain forest.*

TAKING NOTES

Main Idea and Detail Notes

By using graphic organizers to sort out main ideas and make connections between supporting details, students become active readers with improved comprehension.

Vocabulary Strategy

The word triangle functions as a pyramid of meaning. When students define a word, construct a meaningful context for it, and illustrate it, that word becomes part of their vocabulary.

Vocabulary and Note-Taking Resources

- Vocabulary Practice, pp. 45–46
- Decoding Support, p. 47

- Daily Vocabulary Scaffolding, p. T34
- Note-Taking Model, p. T35

- Word Triangle, B18–19
- Main Idea and Detail Notes, C37
- Daily Vocabulary Scaffolding, H1–8

CHAPTER 5

Getting Ready to Learn

CONCEPT REVIEW

- Many processes shape Earth's surface.
- The crust is Earth's outermost layer.
- Earth consists of many parts that interact with one another.

VOCABULARY REVIEW

energy p. 9

See Glossary for definitions.

matter, planet, satellite

Review concepts and vocabulary.

TAKING NOTES

MAIN IDEA AND DETAIL NOTES

Make a two-column chart. Write the main ideas, such as those in the blue headings, in the column on the left. Write details about each of those main ideas in the column on the right.

VOCABULARY STRATEGY

Draw a **word triangle** diagram for each new vocabulary term. On the bottom line write and define the term. Above that, write a sentence that uses the term correctly. At the top, draw a picture to show what the term looks like.

See the Note-Taking Handbook on pages R45–R51.

SCIENCE NOTEBOOK

MAIN IDEAS	DETAIL NOTES
1. Maps show natural and human-made features.	1. Relief maps show how high or low land features are. 1. Road and city maps include a map scale.

Northern Hemisphere
Earth
equator
Southern Hemisphere

California is located north of the equator, in the Northern Hemisphere.

equator: imaginary line that divides Earth into northern and southern hemispheres

CHECK READINESS

Administer the Diagnostic Test to determine students' readiness for new science content and their mastery of requisite math skills.

 Diagnostic Test, pp. 98–99

Technology Resources

Students needing content and math skills should visit **ClassZone.com.**

- **CONTENT REVIEW**
- **MATH TUTORIAL**

CONTENT REVIEW CD-ROM

KEY CONCEPT

Maps and globes are models of Earth.

CALIFORNIA Content Standard

6.7.f Read a topographic map and a geologic map for evidence provided on the maps and construct and interpret a simple scale map.

BEFORE, you learned

- The Earth system's parts interact to shape Earth's surface
- Earth's crust has many different features

NOW, you will learn

- What information maps can provide about natural and human-made features
- How to find exact locations on Earth
- Why all maps distort Earth's surface

VOCABULARY

relief map p. 156
map scale p. 157
map legend p. 157
equator p. 158
latitude p. 158
prime meridian p. 159
longitude p. 159
projection p. 160

EXPLORE Mapping (6.7.f)

What makes a good map?

PROCEDURE

1. Draw a map to guide someone from your school to your home or to a point of interest, such as a park, statue, or store, near your school.
2. Trade maps with a classmate. Is his or her map easy to understand? Why or why not?
3. Use feedback from your partner to revise your own map.

MATERIALS

- paper
- pencil or pen

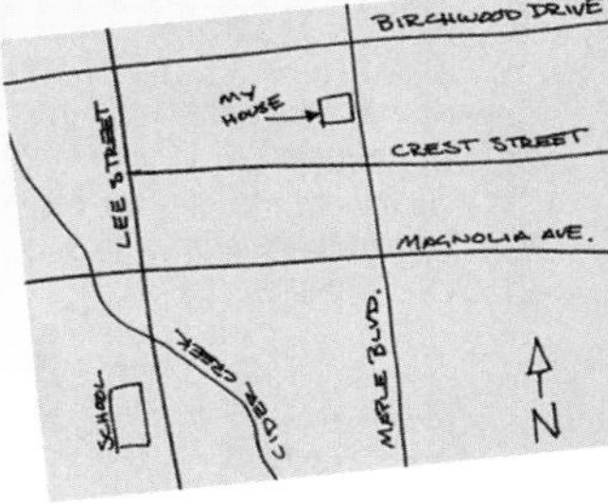

WHAT DO YOU THINK?
What visual clues make a map easy to understand and use?

Maps show natural and human-made features.

Have you ever drawn a map to help someone get to your home? If so, your map is actually a rough model of your neighborhood. It shows important streets and landmarks. Any map you use is a flat model of Earth's surface, showing Earth's features as seen from above.

In contrast, a globe shows Earth in three dimensions. A globe is a sphere that shows the relative sizes and shapes of Earth's land and water features.

In this section you will learn how maps and globes provide different types of information about Earth's surface. They can show everything from city streets to land features to the entire world.

CHECK YOUR READING How are maps and globes alike? How are they different?

RESOURCES FOR DIFFERENTIATED INSTRUCTION

Below Level

UNIT RESOURCE BOOK
- Reading Study Guide A, pp. 13–14
- Decoding Support, p. 47

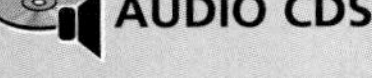

AUDIO CDS

Advanced

UNIT RESOURCE BOOK
Challenge and Extension, p. 19

English Learners

UNIT RESOURCE BOOK
Spanish Reading Study Guide, pp. 17–18

AUDIO CDS

- Audio Readings in Spanish
- Audio Readings (English)

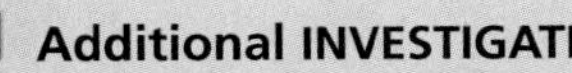

Additional INVESTIGATION, Make a Map by Triangulation, A, B, & C, pp. 59–67; Teacher Instructions, pp. 211–212

5.1 FOCUS

Set Learning Goals

Students will

- Describe the types of information maps can provide about natural and human-made features.
- Explain how to find exact locations on Earth.
- Explain why all maps distort Earth's surface.
- Analyze data from a map of California's natural resources to learn about latitude and longitude.

3-Minute Warm-Up

Display Transparency 36 or copy this exercise on the board:

Remember that the Earth system has four main parts that interact. Identify the parts involved in the following scenarios.

1. Wind blows a sailboat across a lake. *atmosphere/hydrosphere*
2. A bear digs under a log to search for food. *biosphere/geosphere*
3. People wear a path through a forest, and rain further erodes the path. *biosphere/hydrosphere/geosphere*

3-Minute Warm-Up, p. T36

5.1 MOTIVATE

EXPLORE Mapping

PURPOSE To introduce students to the concept of maps as easy-to-use tools

TIP *25 min.* Encourage students to use well-known landmarks.

WHAT DO YOU THINK? *street names, landmarks, and compass directions*

Ongoing Assessment

CHECK YOUR READING *Answer: Both are models of Earth that show various features. Maps show Earth's features as if viewed from above. Globes show Earth as if seen from outer space.*

5.1 INSTRUCT

Teach the Standards

Map scale 6.7.f

In this section: Make sure students understand that a map scale relates distances on a map to actual distances on Earth's surface. Explain the three types of map scales: ratio, bar scale, and equivalent-units scale.

- **previously taught:** weather maps, pp. 134–139
- **future opportunities:** topographic maps, pp. 164–169

Teach from Visuals

To help students read the relief map, ask:

- How does the map show relief? *Different colors indicate different elevations, and shading gives a three-dimensional appearance to the landscape.*
- How can you tell which mountain ranges are highest? *High mountain ranges appear as large ripples, with the darkest shadows.*

Teach Difficult Concepts

Emphasize the term *three-dimensional* when describing the landscape view offered by relief maps.

Real World Example

Accurate relief maps are important for ensuring aviation safety, assessing risks of natural hazards, and creating sustainable urban development. A mission flown by the space shuttle *Endeavour* increased map accuracy for many parts of the world. The 2000 Shuttle Radar Topography Mission produced three-dimensional measurements for more than 80 percent of Earth's land area. Every 15 minutes, the shuttle scanned an area the size of Alaska.

Ongoing Assessment

CHECK YOUR READING *Answer: Unlike a mountain, a plateau is fairly level; unlike a plain, a plateau is usually high above sea level.*

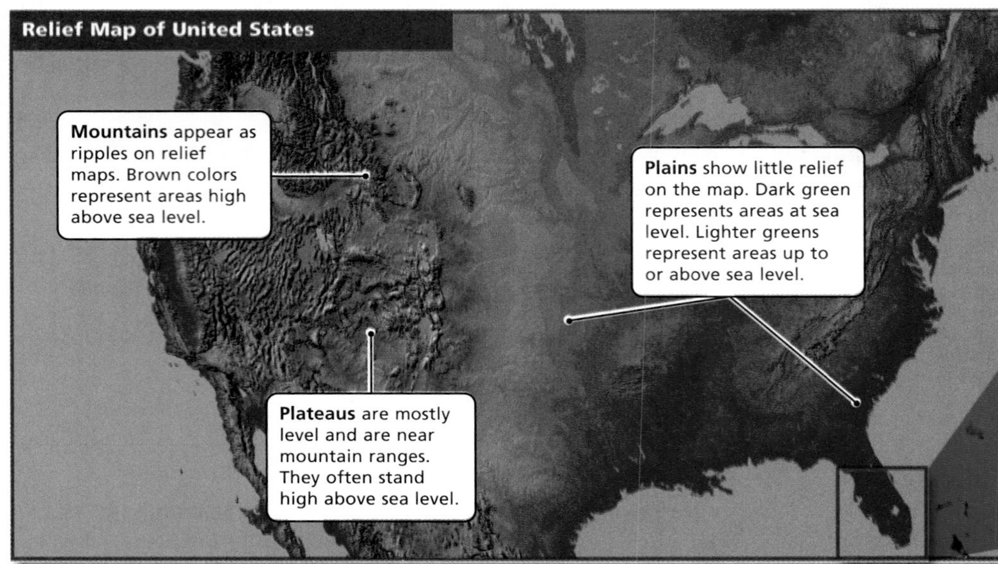

Relief Map of United States
Mountains appear as ripples on relief maps. Brown colors represent areas high above sea level.
Plains show little relief on the map. Dark green represents areas at sea level. Lighter greens represent areas up to or above sea level.
Plateaus are mostly level and are near mountain ranges. They often stand high above sea level.

VOCABULARY
Add a word triangle diagram for *relief map* to your notebook.

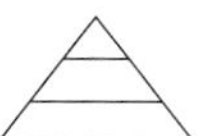

Land Features on Maps

A

When scientists or travelers want to know about the landscape of an area, they often use a relief map. A **relief map,** such as the one above, shows how high or low each feature is on Earth. A mapmaker uses photographs or satellite images to build a three-dimensional view of Earth's surface. A relief map shows three main types of land features: mountains, plains, and plateaus.

Mountains stand higher than the land around them. A mountain's base may cover several square kilometers. A group of mountains is called a mountain range. Mountain ranges connected in a long chain form a mountain belt. The Rocky Mountains in the United States are part of a huge mountain belt. It includes the Canadian Rockies and the Andes Mountains in South America.

Plateaus have fairly level surfaces but stand high above sea level. Plateaus are often found near large mountain ranges. In the United States, the Colorado Plateau is about 3350 meters (11,000 ft) above sea level. This plateau includes parts of Arizona, Colorado, New Mexico, and Utah.

Plains are gently rolling or flat features. The United States has two types of plains. Coastal plains lie near the eastern and southeastern shores, and interior plains lie in the center of the nation. The interior Great Plains cover the middle third of the United States.

CHECK YOUR READING How is a plateau different from either a mountain or a plain?

DIFFERENTIATE INSTRUCTION

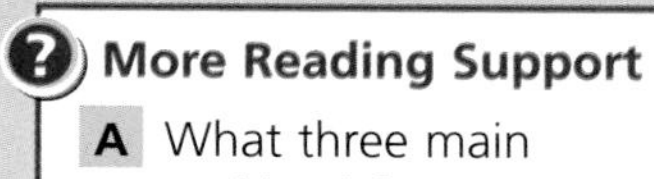

More Reading Support

A What three main types of land features does a relief map show? *mountains, plains, and plateaus*

English Learners English learners may lack background knowledge of *sea level* on p. 156 and *cross products* on p.163. Allow English learners to use their home countries as points of reference when learning to use maps. They might study street maps of major cities in their countries or use a globe to find their countries' latitudes and longitudes.

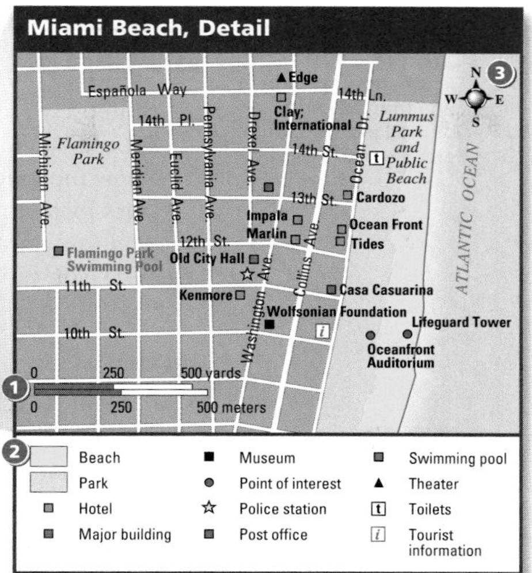

Scale and Symbols on Maps

The maps most people use are road and city maps like the ones above. These maps provide information about both human-made features and natural features. To use these maps, you need to know how to read a map scale and a map legend, or key.

1. A **map scale** relates distances on a map to actual distances on Earth's surface. Notice that on the map of southern Florida above, the scale is in kilometers and miles. On the Miami Beach map, the scale is in meters and yards. The smaller the area a map shows, the more detail it includes.

   The scale can be given as a ratio, a bar, or equivalent units of distance. For example, a ratio of 1:25,000 means that 1 centimeter on the map represents 25,000 centimeters (0.25 kilometer) on Earth.

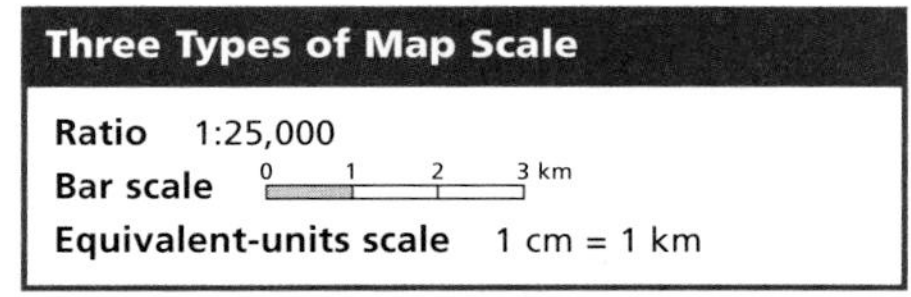
Three Types of Map Scale

Ratio 1:25,000
Bar scale 0 1 2 3 km
Equivalent-units scale 1 cm = 1 km

2. A **map legend,** also called a key, is a chart that explains the meaning of each symbol used on a map. Symbols can stand for highways, parks, and other features. The legend on the Miami Beach map shows major points of interest for tourists.

3. A map usually includes a compass rose to show which directions are north, south, east, and west. Usually, north on a map points to the top of the page.

READING TIP
As used here, *legend* does not refer to a story. It is based on the Latin word *legenda,* which means "to be read."

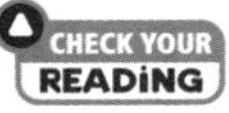
CHECK YOUR READING What information do map scales and map legends provide?

Teach from Visuals

To help students interpret the maps of southern Florida and Miami Beach, ask:

- How are the two maps related? *The first shows the southern part of Florida; the second enlarges one city in southern Florida—Miami Beach—to show more detail.*
- How are the two maps similar? *Both are oriented with north at the top, as indicated by the direction arrows.*
- How do you know where on the first map the second map is located? *A shaded region extends from the city's location on the first map to the second map.*

Develop Critical Thinking

APPLY Have students apply their knowledge of maps to plan a car trip from Orlando to Miami. Ask them to name the parts of the map on which they would find the following information:

- types of roads they will follow *legend*
- direction(s) they will travel *compass rose*
- the distance they must drive *scale*
- cities and towns they will pass through *labels on the map*

Ongoing Assessment

Describe the types of information maps can provide about natural and human-made features.

Ask: What are two types of information about natural features and human-made features that maps provide? *natural—locations, elevations, shapes, and relief; human-made—sizes and locations of cities and roads*

CHECK YOUR READING *Answer: A scale relates distances on a map to actual distances on Earth's surface. A legend explains the meaning of each symbol used on a map.*

DIFFERENTIATE INSTRUCTION

More Reading Support

B Why do maps have scales? *to show how distances on the map are related to actual distances on Earth*

Advanced Briefly describe the characteristics of deltas, canyons, and valleys. Then have students search reference sources and the Internet to find relief maps that show these features. Ask them to identify as many deltas, valleys, and canyons as they can and then to describe how the three-dimensional quality of the relief maps allowed them to recognize the features.

R Challenge and Extension, p. 19

History of Science

The latitude/longitude system of locating places on Earth was probably first developed around 150 A.D. by Claudius Ptolemy, a Greek astronomer and geographer. Ptolemy lived and worked in Alexandria, Egypt, which at that time was a crossroads for travelers. Ptolemy developed a grid of meridians (longitude lines) and parallels (latitude lines) to establish coordinates for as many as 8,000 places mentioned by the travelers he encountered.

Teach from Visuals

To help students interpret the "Latitude and Longitude" visual, ask:

- Is the equator a latitude line or a longitude line? *latitude line*
- What are the latitude and the longitude of the place where the equator and the prime meridian cross? *0°, 0°*
- Which set of lines divides Earth in a way similar to the division of an orange into segments? *longitude lines*

This visual is also available as T38 in the Transparency Book.

Teach Difficult Concepts

Students may become confused about the east-west latitude lines that indicate angular distances north and south on the globe and the north-south meridians that indicate angular distances east and west on the globe. Copy the diagram "Latitude and Longitude" on the board, using one color for latitude lines and a different color for longitude lines. Then write the coordinates of various locations, using the corresponding colors for the latitude and longitude measurements. Point out that latitude lines go to 90°, whereas longitude lines go to 180°.

Ongoing Assessment

Answer: Cairo: 30° N, 30° E; Paris: 50° N; 2° E

Explore how latitude and longitude help you find locations on Earth's surface.

Latitude and longitude show locations on Earth.

Suppose you were lucky enough to find dinosaur bones in the desert. Would you know how to find that exact spot again? You would if you knew the longitude and latitude of the place. Latitude and longitude lines form an imaginary grid over the entire surface of Earth. This grid provides everyone with the same tools. Using latitude and longitude, you can locate any place on the planet.

Latitude

READING TIP
Hemi- is a Greek prefix meaning "half."

Latitude is based on an imaginary line that circles Earth halfway between the north and south poles. This line is called the **equator.** The equator divides Earth into northern and southern hemispheres. A hemisphere is one half of a sphere.

Latitude is a distance in degrees north or south of the equator, which is 0°. A degree is 1/360 of the distance around a full circle. If you start at one point on the equator and travel all the way around the world back to that point, you have traveled 360 degrees.

The illustration below shows that latitude lines are parallel to the equator. These lines are evenly spaced between the equator and the poles. Latitude lines show distance north or south of the equator.

Latitude and Longitude

The **equator** divides Earth into northern and southern hemispheres.

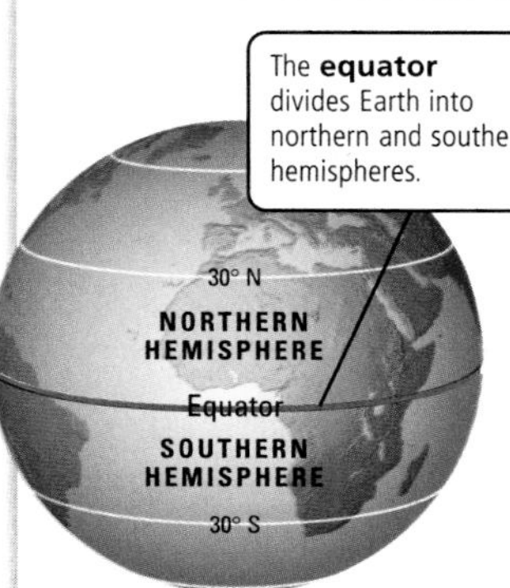

Latitude is a distance in degrees north or south of the equator.

The **prime meridian** divides Earth into eastern and western hemispheres.

30° W
WESTERN HEMISPHERE
Prime Meridian
30° E
EASTERN HEMISPHERE

Longitude is a distance in degrees east or west of the prime meridian.

60° N
Paris, France
30° N
Cairo, Egypt
60° W
30° W
0°
30° E
60° E
30° S
60° S

You can find a location by noting where latitude and longitude lines cross.

READING VISUALS What are the approximate latitudes and longitudes of Cairo, Egypt, and Paris, France?

DIFFERENTIATE INSTRUCTION

C What is the equator? *an imaginary line dividing Earth into two hemispheres*

D What is latitude? *distance in degrees north or south of the equator*

Below Level The game Battleship® can help students gain a sense of latitude and longitude. One player calls out a coordinate set that consists of a letter from the vertical axis and a number from the horizontal axis. If one of the other player's ships is at those coordinates, then the ship is hit. The game is available at toy stores, or it can be reproduced by having students draw their "ships" on graphs with numbers on the *x*-axes and letters on the *y*-axes.

A label of north or south shows whether a location is in the northern or southern hemisphere. For instance, the North Pole is 90° north, or 90° N, while the South Pole is 90° south, or 90° S. However, latitude is only half of what you need to locate any spot on Earth. You also need to know its longitude.

Longitude

Longitude is based on an imaginary line that stretches from the North Pole through Greenwich, England, to the South Pole. This line is called the **prime meridian.** Any place up to 180° west of the prime meridian is in the Western Hemisphere. Any place up to 180° east of the prime meridian is in the Eastern Hemisphere.

Longitude is a distance in degrees east or west of the prime meridian, which is 0°. Beginning at the prime meridian, longitude lines are numbered 0° to 180° west and 0° to 180° east.

Longitude lines are labeled east or west to indicate whether a location is in the eastern or western hemisphere. For example, the longitude of Santa Cruz, California, is about 122° west, or 122° W. The city of Hamburg, Germany, is about 10° east, or 10° E. If you understand latitude and longitude, you can find any spot on Earth's surface.

READING TIP

There is an easy way to remember the difference between latitude and longitude. Think of longitude lines as the "long" lines that go from pole to pole.

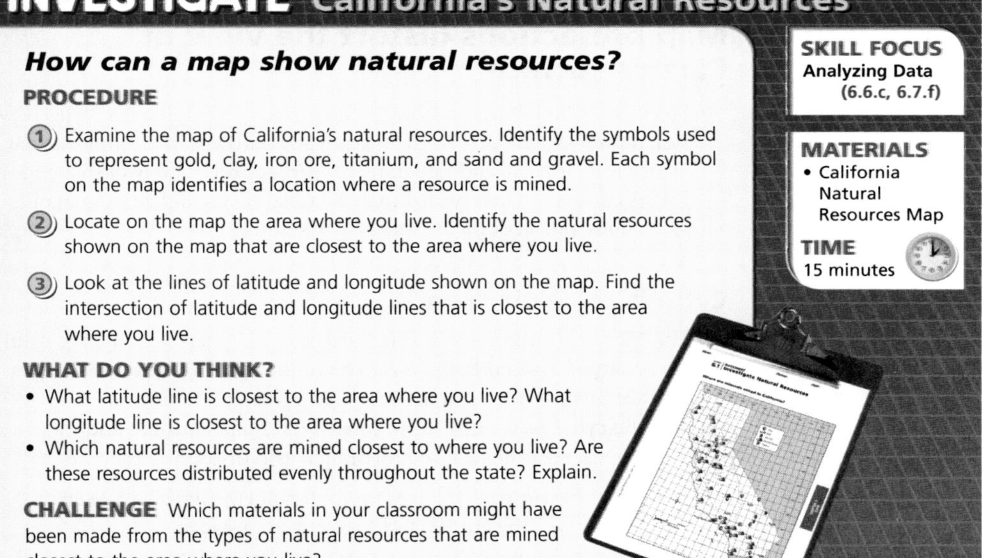

INVESTIGATE California's Natural Resources

How can a map show natural resources?

PROCEDURE

1. Examine the map of California's natural resources. Identify the symbols used to represent gold, clay, iron ore, titanium, and sand and gravel. Each symbol on the map identifies a location where a resource is mined.
2. Locate on the map the area where you live. Identify the natural resources shown on the map that are closest to the area where you live.
3. Look at the lines of latitude and longitude shown on the map. Find the intersection of latitude and longitude lines that is closest to the area where you live.

WHAT DO YOU THINK?

- What latitude line is closest to the area where you live? What longitude line is closest to the area where you live?
- Which natural resources are mined closest to where you live? Are these resources distributed evenly throughout the state? Explain.

CHALLENGE Which materials in your classroom might have been made from the types of natural resources that are mined closest to the area where you live?

SKILL FOCUS
Analyzing Data (6.6.c, 6.7.f)

MATERIALS
- California Natural Resources Map

TIME
15 minutes

History of Science

Finding longitude at sea was a long-standing challenge. Determining longitude requires knowing time differences; measuring it by the positions of the Sun or stars, as was done for latitude, was impossible. In the 1700s, reliable clocks were invented. The clocks allowed mariners to compare local times with the time at Greenwich on the prime meridian, and thus enabled them to calculate exact longitudes.

INVESTIGATE California's Natural Resources

PURPOSE To analyze data about California's natural resources and learn about latitude and longitude

TIP *15 min.* Discuss the map's scale so students appreciate the true distances between places shown on the map.

WHAT DO YOU THINK? *Answers will vary but may include that clay and sand and gravel are mined throughout much of the state but that iron is mined in few areas.*

CHALLENGE *Answers will vary but may include clay in ceramics or gold in computer electronics.*

 Datasheet, California's Natural Resources, pp. 20–21

Technology Resources

Customize this student lab as needed or look for an alternative. Print rubrics to assess student lab reports.

 **Lab Generator CD-ROM**

DIFFERENTIATE INSTRUCTION

More Reading Support

E What is the prime meridian? *an imaginary line that runs from the North Pole through Greenwich, England, to the South Pole*

Inclusion Project and enlarge the map onto a screen so that visually impaired students can more easily find where they live and participate in the lab.

Ongoing Assessment

Explain how to find exact locations on Earth.

Ask: How are latitude and longitude used to find exact locations on Earth? *They allow people to plot locations as sets of coordinates.*

Teaching with Technology

If you have access to hand-held GPS units, send students to opposite ends of the schoolyard or block and have them record degrees, minutes, and seconds of latitude and longitude. Compare students' data as part of a classroom discussion about GPS technology.

Real World Example

GPS measurements are accurate to within 10 to 20 meters for nonmilitary users, but this was not always the case. The U.S. government intentionally decreased the accuracy of non-military GPS signals for purposes of military security. Until 2000, these signals, altered under a program called "selective availability," were accurate only to within 100 meters.

Address Misconceptions

IDENTIFY Hold up a flat map of the world and ask: Does this accurately show the shapes and sizes of the continents and oceans? If students answer yes, they may hold the misconception that map projections are accurate images of Earth's landmasses and oceans.

CORRECT Hold a globe next to the map and ask students to point out differences in the shapes of extreme northern landmasses (such as Greenland). Ask them to consider why they look different.

REASSESS Ask: Is a globe or a map a better representation of the size and shape of Earth? Why? *A globe, because it is shaped like Earth and shows Earth's curved surface.*

Technology Resources

Visit **ClassZone.com** for background on common student misconceptions.

MISCONCEPTION DATABASE

CHECK YOUR READING *Answer: A network of 24 satellites circling Earth sends signals to ground receivers. A computer inside a GPS receiver uses the signals to calculate the user's exact latitude, longitude, and elevation.*

Global Positioning System

The Global Positioning System (GPS) is a network of satellites. They are used to find the latitude, longitude, and elevation, or height above sea level, of any site. Twenty-four GPS satellites circle Earth and send signals that are picked up by receivers on the surface. At least three satellites need to be above the horizon for GPS to work. A computer inside a receiver uses the satellite signals to calculate the user's exact location—latitude, longitude, and elevation. GPS is an accurate, easy method for finding location.

Never be lost again. This hiker t GPS unit to find out his current longitude. He then locates these map to pinpoint his exact locatic

GPS devices are used by many people, including pilots, sailors, hikers, and mapmakers. Some cars now have GPS receivers and digital road maps stored in their computers. A driver types in an address, and the car's computer finds the best way to get there. F

CHECK YOUR READING Explain how GPS can help someone find his or her exact location.

Map projections distort the view of Earth's surface.

The most accurate way to show Earth's surface is on a globe. A globe, however, cannot show much detail. It is also awkward to carry. People use flat maps for their detail and ease of use. A **projection** is a way of showing Earth's curved surface on a flat map. Mapmakers use different types of projections, but all of them distort Earth's surface.

Cylindrical Projection

READING TIP
The Mercator (muhr-KAY-tuhr) map projection was developed by Flemish mapmaker Gerhardus Mercator in 1568.

The Mercator projection shows Earth as if the map were a large cylinder wrapped around the planet. The outlines of the landmasses and seas are then drawn onto the map. As shown in the diagram on page 161, the cylinder is unrolled to form a flat map. Latitude and longitude appear as straight lines, forming a grid of rectangles.

The Mercator projection is useful for navigating at sea or in the air. It shows the entire world, except for areas near the poles, on one map. People can plot a course by drawing straight lines.

DIFFERENTIATE INSTRUCTION

More Reading Support

F How is the Mercator projection useful? *It shows almost the entire world on one map and allows navigators to plot courses by drawing straight lines between points.*

Additional Investigation To reinforce Section 5.1 learning goals, use the following full-period investigation:

Additional INVESTIGATION, Make a Map by Triangulation A, B, & C, pp. 59–67, 211–212
(Advanced students should complete Levels B and C.)

Below Level Have students create a chart to differentiate between characteristics of latitude and longitude.

The problem with Mercator maps is that areas far away from the equator appear much larger than they really are. On the map below, Greenland looks bigger than South America. In reality, South America is about eight times larger than Greenland.

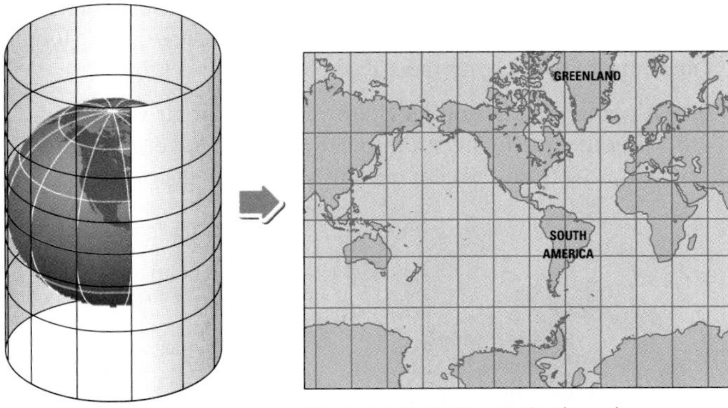

Mercator projection Latitude and longitude lines form a grid of rectangles. Areas away from the equator are distorted.

Conic Projections

Conic projections are based on the shape of a cone. The diagram below shows how a cone of paper might be wrapped around the globe. The paper touches the surface only at the middle latitudes, halfway between the equator and the North Pole.

When the cone is flattened out, the latitude lines are curved slightly. The curved lines represent the curved surface of Earth. This allows the map to show the true sizes and shapes of some landmasses.

Conic projections are most useful for mapping large areas in the middle latitudes, such as the United States. However, landmasses near the equator or near the north or south pole will be distorted.

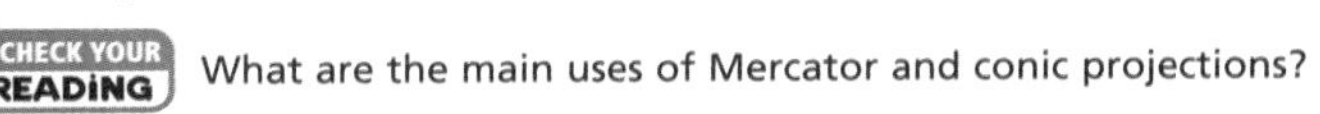

CHECK YOUR READING What are the main uses of Mercator and conic projections?

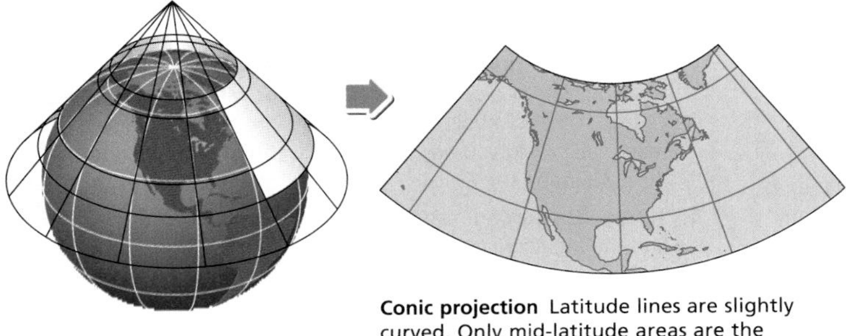

Conic projection Latitude lines are slightly curved. Only mid-latitude areas are the correct size and shape.

DIFFERENTIATE INSTRUCTION

More Reading Support

G What regions are conic projections most useful for mapping? *regions in the middle latitudes, roughly halfway between the equator and the poles*

Advanced Encourage students to draw pictures of the continental United States as they imagine it might look in a conic projection, a Mercator projection, and a planar projection. Later, show them maps of each type. Discuss with students any differences between their conceptions and the appearance of the United States on each of the actual maps.

Teach Difficult Concepts

Some students will have difficulty understanding map projections and the differences among various types. Emphasize that each projection is most accurate for a different region of the globe. To help students understand, you might try the following demonstration.

Teacher Demo

Use construction paper to model a Mercator projection. Wrap a globe in the paper so that it touches the globe at the equator and forms a cylinder. Show the view looking down on the North Pole. Explain that where the paper touches, the distortion is least, and where the paper is most distant from the globe—near the poles—the most distortion occurs. On the globe, longitude lines meet at the poles. In the projection, the longitude lines are spread out until they are parallel, so that the land becomes "stretched out of shape."

Develop Critical Thinking

EVALUATE Ask students which type of map projection each of the following people would be likely to use:

- an airline pilot calculating the fastest route from Los Angeles to Sydney, Australia *Mercator*
- a ship captain plotting a course from New York to London *Mercator*
- a mapmaker drawing the state of Iowa *conic*

Ongoing Assessment

Explain why all maps distort Earth's surface.

Ask: Why does a map always distort features of Earth's surface? *because Earth is a sphere and representing it on a flat map involves stretching one area or another out of shape*

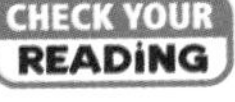

CHECK YOUR READING *Answer: Mercator: navigation; conic: mapping areas in the middle latitudes accurately*

Ongoing Assessment

 *Answer: north and south polar regions*

Reinforce the BIG idea

Have students relate the section to the Big Idea.

 Reinforcing Key Concepts, p. 22

5.1 ASSESS & RETEACH

Assess

 Section 5.1 Quiz, p. 100

Reteach

Display a map of a state, region, or community, and ask students to identify the features that make it useful. List their answers on the board. Ask:

- Does the map show land features? If so, what features?
- What type of scale does it have?
- Where can you find the meanings of the symbols used on the map?
- Does the map indicate latitudes and longitudes? If so, what units are used?
- What type of projection may have been used to produce this map? Why?

Ask students to pull out the maps they made in the activity on page 155. Discuss any improvements they might make to their maps.

Technology Resources

Have students visit **ClassZone.com** for reteaching of Key Concepts.

 CONTENT REVIEW

 CONTENT REVIEW CD-ROM

RESOURCE CENTER CLASSZONE.COM

Find out more about map projections and how they are used.

Planar Projections

Planar projections were developed to help people find the shortest distance between two points. They are drawn as if a circle of paper were laid on a point on Earth's surface. As you look at the diagram below, notice how the shape of the sphere is transferred to the flat map. When a planar map represents the polar region, the longitude lines meet at the center like the spokes of a wheel.

A planar map is good for plotting ocean or air voyages and for showing the north and south polar regions. However, landmasses farther away from the center point are greatly distorted.

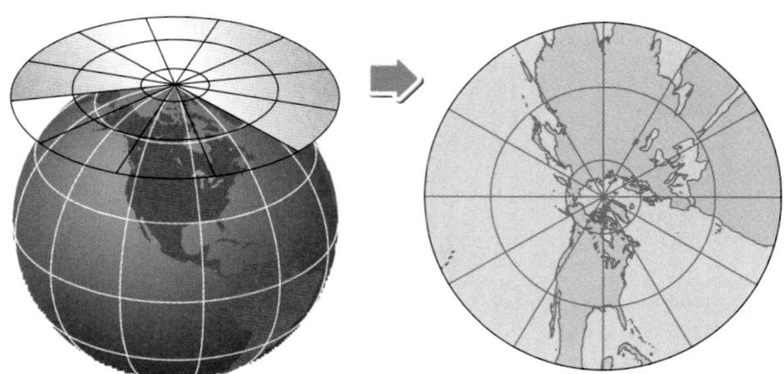

Planar projection Only areas near the center point are the correct size and shape.

The Mercator, conic, and planar projections are all attempts to solve the problem of representing a curved surface on a flat map. Each projection can show certain areas of the world accurately but distorts other areas.

 What areas does the planar projection show accurately?

5.1 Review

KEY CONCEPTS

1. What natural and human-made features can maps show? Give two examples of each. (6.7.f)
2. Explain how latitude and longitude can help you locate any place on Earth. (6.7.f)
3. Why do all flat maps distort Earth's surface? (6.7.f)

CRITICAL THINKING

4. **Provide Examples** Imagine that your family is on a long car trip. What symbols on a road map would you pay the most attention to? Explain.
5. **Apply** Use a world map to find the approximate latitudes and longitudes of Moscow, Russia; Tokyo, Japan; Denver, Colorado; and La Paz, Bolivia.

CHALLENGE

6. **Apply** Working with a partner or with a small group, select the shortest airline route from Chicago to London, using a globe and a Mercator map. **Hint:** Notice that as you go farther north on the globe, the longitude lines become closer together.

ANSWERS

1. natural: mountains, rivers; human-made: bridges, roads

2. The exact location of any place can be expressed as a number of degrees north or south of the equator (latitude) and a number of degrees east or west of the prime meridian (longitude).

3. Earth is a sphere. It is impossible to portray a curved surface as flat without some distortion.

4. Students should mention direction arrows and symbols for highways, food, fuel, and lodging.

5. Moscow: 56° N, 38° E
Tokyo: 36° N, 140° E
Denver: 40° N, 105° W
La Paz: 17° S, 68° W

6. The shortest airline route will be an arctic route across the Atlantic Ocean.

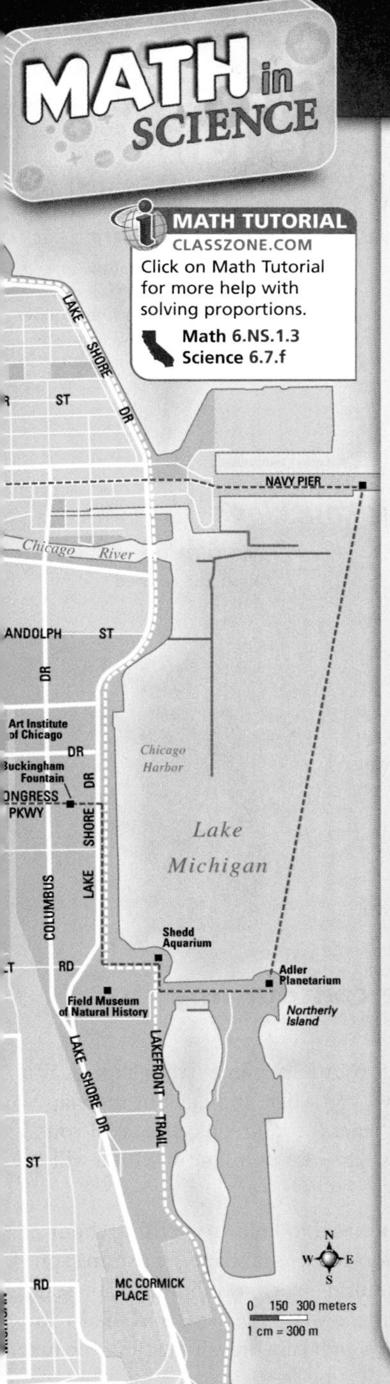

SKILL: USING PROPORTIONS

How Far Is It?

Buckingham Fountain

A science class is visiting Chicago and is using the map on the left to walk to the lakefront museums. Remember, a map scale shows how distances on the map compare to actual distances on the ground.

Example

In this case, the map scale indicates that 1 centimeter on the map represents 300 meters on the ground. The map scale shows this as equivalent units. By using these units to write a proportion, you can use cross products to determine actual distances.

What distance does 3 cm on the map represent? Set up the problem like this:

$$\frac{1 \text{ cm}}{300 \text{ m}} = \frac{3 \text{ cm}}{x}$$

(1) $1 \text{ cm} \cdot x = 3 \text{ cm} \cdot 300 \text{ m}$

(2) $x = 3 \cdot 300 \text{ m}$

(3) $x = 900 \text{ m}$

ANSWER 3 centimeters on the map represents 900 meters on the ground.

Use cross products and a metric ruler to answer the following questions.

1. The science class divides into two groups. Each group starts at Buckingham Fountain. How far, in meters, will one group walk to get to the Adler Planetarium if they follow the red dotted line?
2. How far, in meters, will the other group walk to get to the end of Navy Pier if they follow the blue dotted line?
3. The group that walked to Adler decides to take a boat to join the other group at Navy Pier. How far, in meters, is their boat ride along the red dotted line?

CHALLENGE **What is the total distance, in kilometers, that the two groups traveled? Set up the problem as a proportion. Hint: There are 1000 meters in a kilometer.**

ANSWERS

1. 2100 m *2. 4200 m* *3. 2700 m*

CHALLENGE *2100 m + 2700 m + 4200 m = 9000 m*

$$\frac{1 \text{ km}}{1000 \text{ m}} = \frac{X}{9000 \text{ m}}$$

$$X \cdot 1000 \text{ m} = 1 \text{ km} \cdot 9000 \text{ m}$$

$$X = \frac{1 \text{ km} \cdot 9000 \text{ m}}{1000 \text{ m}}$$

$$X = 9 \text{ km}$$

MATH IN SCIENCE

Math Skills Practice for Science

Set Learning Goal

To use a map scale to determine the actual distance on Earth represented by a distance on a map

Math Standard

6.NS.1.3 Use proportions to solve problems (e.g., determine the value of *N* if 4/7 = *N*/21, find the length of a side of a polygon similar to a known polygon). Use cross-multiplication as a method for solving such problems, understanding it as the multiplication of both sides of an equation by a multiplicative inverse.

Present the Science

Point out to students that this map represents a relatively small area and that many maps will show larger areas. Ask them to predict how the scales of these other maps will differ from the one shown here.

Develop Algebra Skills

Remind students that the goal of using cross products is to isolate the variable on one side of the equation. Review the applicable algebra rules, and show several examples of the use of cross products.

Close

Ask students to imagine situations in which it would be appropriate to use large-scale and small-scale maps. *Large-scale maps: navigating city streets or hiking in a small nature reserve; Small-scale maps: on an interstate driving trip or a cross-country flight* Ask which type they are most familiar with using. *Answers will vary. Many students have probably used road maps, the scales of which depend on the size of their states.*

- Math Support, p. 48
- Math Practice, p. 49

Technology Resources

Students can visit **ClassZone.com** for practice using properties.

 **MATH TUTORIAL**

5.2 FOCUS

Set Learning Goals

Students will

- Explain how contour lines show elevation, slope, and relief.
- Explain the rules contour lines follow.
- Describe the common symbols used on topographic maps.

3-Minute Warm-Up

Display Transparency 36 or copy this exercise on the board:

Match each definition with the correct term.

Definitions

1. distance in degrees from equator *b*
2. relates distance on a map to actual distance on Earth's surface *a*
3. distance in degrees from prime meridian *c*

Terms

a. map scale
b. latitude
c. longitude
d. projection

 3-Minute Warm-Up, p. T36

5.2 MOTIVATE

EXPLORE Topographic Maps

PURPOSE To introduce the concept that contour lines connect points of equal elevation

TIP *10 min.* Students should look at their knuckles from the side and from the top to see how the circles change.

WHAT DO YOU THINK? *Knuckles rise like a mountain range when fist is clenched; flatten out like a plain when hand is open flat; circles represent a way to draw the shape of knuckles.*

EXPLORE the BIG idea

Revisit "Earth's Changing Surface" on p. 153. Have students use terms from the chapter to explain changes to Earth's surface that they report.

KEY CONCEPT

5.2 Topographic maps show the shape of the land.

CALIFORNIA Content Standard

6.7.f Read a topographic map and a geologic map for evidence provided on the maps and construct and interpret a simple scale map.

BEFORE, you learned

- Different maps provide information about natural and human-made features
- Latitude and longitude are used to find places on Earth
- All flat maps distort Earth's surface

NOW, you will learn

- How contour lines show elevation, slope, and relief
- What rules contour lines follow
- What common symbols are used on topographic maps

VOCABULARY

topography p. 164
contour line p. 165
elevation p. 165
slope p. 165
relief p. 165
contour interval p. 166

EXPLORE Topographic Maps (6.7.f)

How can you map your knuckles?

PROCEDURE

1. Hold your fist closed, knuckles up, as shown in the photo.
2. Draw circles around the first knuckle. Make sure the circles are the same distance from each other.
3. Flatten out your hand. Observe what happens. Write down your observations.

MATERIAL

washable colored pen

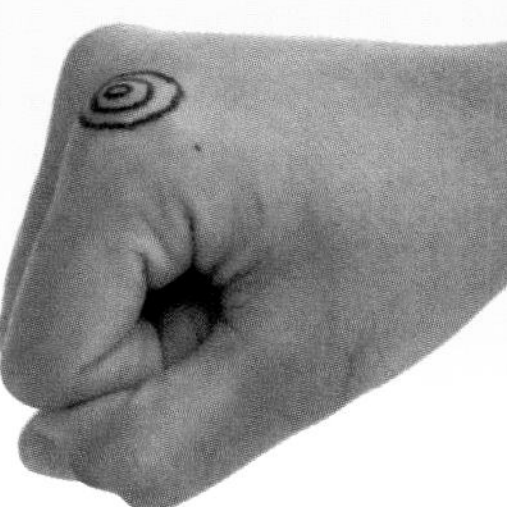

WHAT DO YOU THINK?

- How does the height of your knuckles change when you clench your fist, then flatten out your hand?
- What do you think the circles represent?

Topographic maps use contour lines to show features.

VOCABULARY
Add a word triangle diagram for *topography* to your notebook.

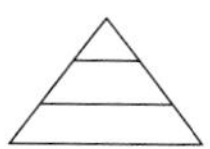

Imagine you are on vacation with your family in a national park. You have a simple trail map that shows you where to hike. But the map does not tell you anything about what the land looks like. Will you have to cross any rivers or valleys? How far uphill or downhill will you have to hike?

To answer these questions, you need to know something about the topography of the area. **Topography** is the shape, or features, of the land. These features can be natural—such as mountains, plateaus, and plains. They can be human-made—such as dams and roads. To show the topography of an area, mapmakers draw a topographic map.

RESOURCES FOR DIFFERENTIATED INSTRUCTION

Below Level

UNIT RESOURCE BOOK

- Reading Study Guide A, pp. 25–26
- Decoding Support, p. 47

 **AUDIO CDS**

Advanced

UNIT RESOURCE BOOK

Challenge and Extension, p. 31

English Learners

UNIT RESOURCE BOOK

Spanish Reading Study Guide, pp. 29–30

 **AUDIO CDS**

- Audio Readings in Spanish
- Audio Readings (English)

A topographic map is a flat map that uses lines to show Earth's surface features. Distance and elevation are given in feet or meters. Take a look at the topographic map of Mount Hood on this page. The wiggly lines on the map are called **contour lines.** They show an area's elevation, slope, and relief.

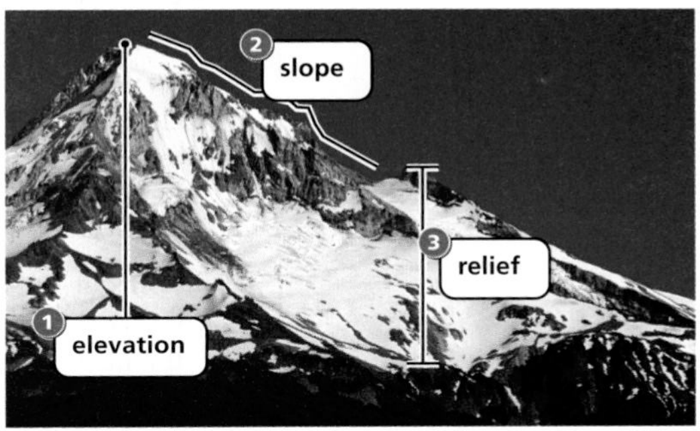

slope
relief
elevation

1. The **elevation** of a place is how high above sea level it is. An area can range from a few meters to several thousand meters above sea level. The numbers on the contour lines show the elevations of different points in the Mount Hood area.
2. The **slope** of a landform or area is how steep it is. The more gradual the slope, the farther apart the contour lines on the map. The steeper the slope, the closer together the contour lines.
3. The **relief** of an area is the difference between its high and low points. For example, subtracting the lowest elevation on the map from the highest gives you a measure of the area's relief.

CHECK YOUR READING What is the difference between elevation and slope?

Mount Hood Topographic Map

A topographic map shows the land as if you were above the land looking down on it.

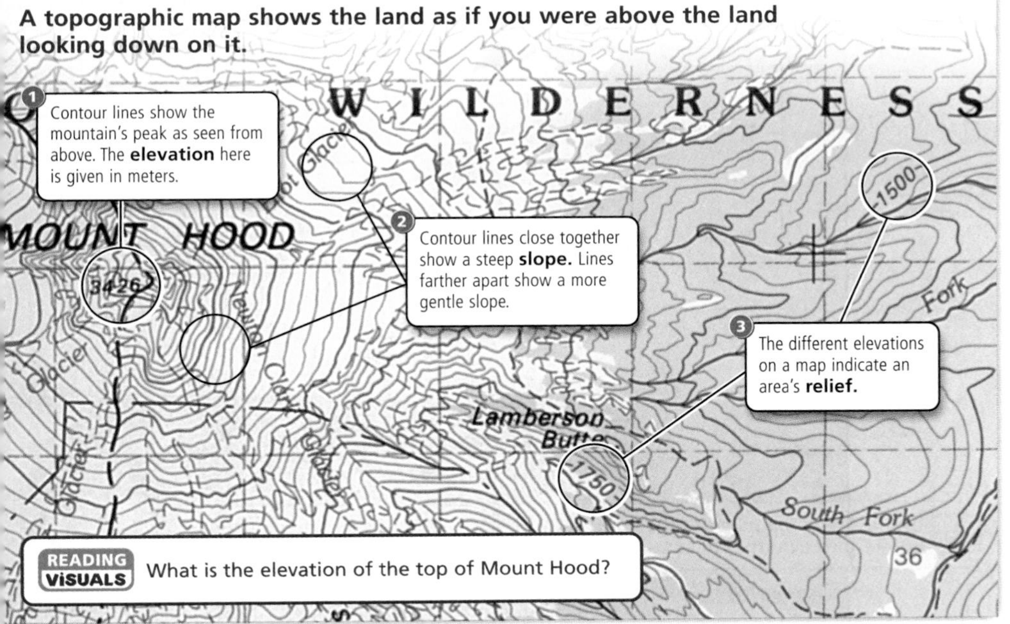

WILDERNESS
MOUNT HOOD
Contour lines show the mountain's peak as seen from above. The elevation here is given in meters.
3426
Contour lines close together show a steep slope. Lines farther apart show a more gentle slope.
The different elevations on a map indicate an area's relief.
1500
Lamberson Butte
1750
South Fork
Fork
36

READING VISUALS What is the elevation of the top of Mount Hood?

5.2 INSTRUCT

Teach the Standards

Topographic maps 6.7.f

In this section: Explain that a topographic map is a flat map that represents Earth's surface features with contour lines, which show elevation, slope, and relief.

- **previously taught:** using maps, pp. 155–157
- **future opportunities:** remote sensing, pp. 170–171; GIS, pp. 173–174; geologic maps, 206–212

Teach Difficult Concepts

Help students visualize how contour lines indicate steepness. Set a spring toy vertically to show its "contour lines" stacked on top of one another. While holding the bottom firmly in place, push the top to one side and have students view it from above. They should see the "contour lines" spread out as the slope becomes gentler. Stretch one end of the spring into a gradual slope, and stack the other end into a steeper slope. This will show both close and spread-apart contour lines.

Teach from Visuals

To help students interpret the topographic map of Mount Hood, ask:

- How do the contour lines indicate the location of Mount Hood's peak? *The peak is within the smallest circle in the series of closed circles.*
- Where on the map are the slopes most gradual? *The contour lines are farthest apart near the map's right edge, indicating gentler slopes.*

Ongoing Assessment

Explain how contour lines show elevation, slope, and relief.

Ask: How do you find the relief of an area on a topographical map? *Subtract the lowest elevation of the area from its highest elevation.*

CHECK YOUR READING *Answer: Elevation is height above sea level, whereas slope is the steepness of the land.*

 *Answer: 3426 meters*

DIFFERENTIATE INSTRUCTION

More Reading Support

A What is a topographic map? *a flat map in which lines are used to show Earth's surface features*

B What do contour lines show? *elevation, slope, and relief*

English Learners Have English learners verbally explain the differences between *elevation, slope,* and *relief.* Point out that on p. 165, the words *gradual* and *gentle* are used in different places to describe slope. Help English learners understand what these words mean in this context and that they are synonyms.

History of Science

In 1879, Congress assigned the task of mapping the country to the U.S. Geological Survey. The USGS published its first topographic map that same year. In the 1940s, the USGS began producing maps from aerial photographs, using a technique known as photogrammetry. Today a series of more than 54,000 connected maps cover the lower 48 states and Hawaii. Each map shows an area, or quadrangle, measuring 7.5 minutes of latitude by 7.5 minutes of longitude. The 2700 maps of Alaska each cover a quadrangle of 15 minutes of latitude and longitude.

Teach from Visuals

To help students interpret the topographic map of Ely, ask:

- What is the highest elevation labeled on the map? *A peak in the middle of the map is labeled at 1427 ft.*
- What is the elevation between the index contour lines on this map? *50 ft.*

Develop Critical Thinking

INFER Discuss contour intervals with students. They have read that contour intervals can vary from map to map. Ask students the following question:

How would the contour interval of a topographic map of the Mount Everest region differ from that of a topographic map of Kansas? *The Mount Everest area has greater relief; therefore, the map would have a larger contour interval than would the Kansas map.*

Ongoing Assessment

Explain the rules contour lines follow.

Ask: What rules apply to contour lines? *Contour lines never cross. They form closed circles around high and low points and are spaced at equal intervals of elevation. Some are darkened and may have labels indicating elevations.*

READING VISUALS *Answer: Highest point is within the fifth contour line above the index contour line labeled 1400 ft.*
5 × 10 = 50 ft, 1400 + 50 = 1450 ft

Contour lines follow certain rules.

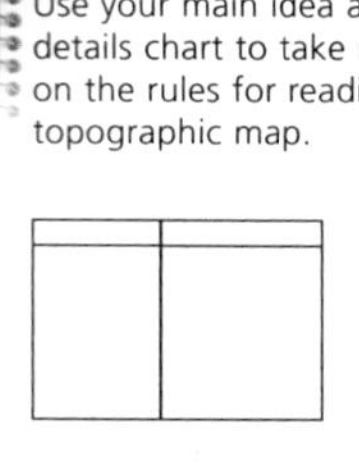

MAIN IDEA AND DETAILS Use your main idea and details chart to take notes on the rules for reading a topographic map.

Contour lines on topographic maps can help you picture landforms in your mind. Think of the following statements as rules for reading topographic maps:

- **Lines never cross.** Contour lines never cross, because each line shows an exact elevation.
- **Circles show highest and lowest points.** Contour lines form closed circles around mountaintops and hilltops. They also form circles around depressions, or sunken areas in the ground. Sometimes, the elevation of a mountain or hill is written in meters or feet in the middle of the circle.
-  C **Contour interval is always the same on a map.** The **contour interval** is the difference in elevation from one contour line to the next. For example, the contour interval on the map below is 10 feet. This means that the change in elevation between contour lines is always 10 feet. The contour interval can differ from map to map, but it is always the same on one map.

Ely, Minnesota, Topographic Map

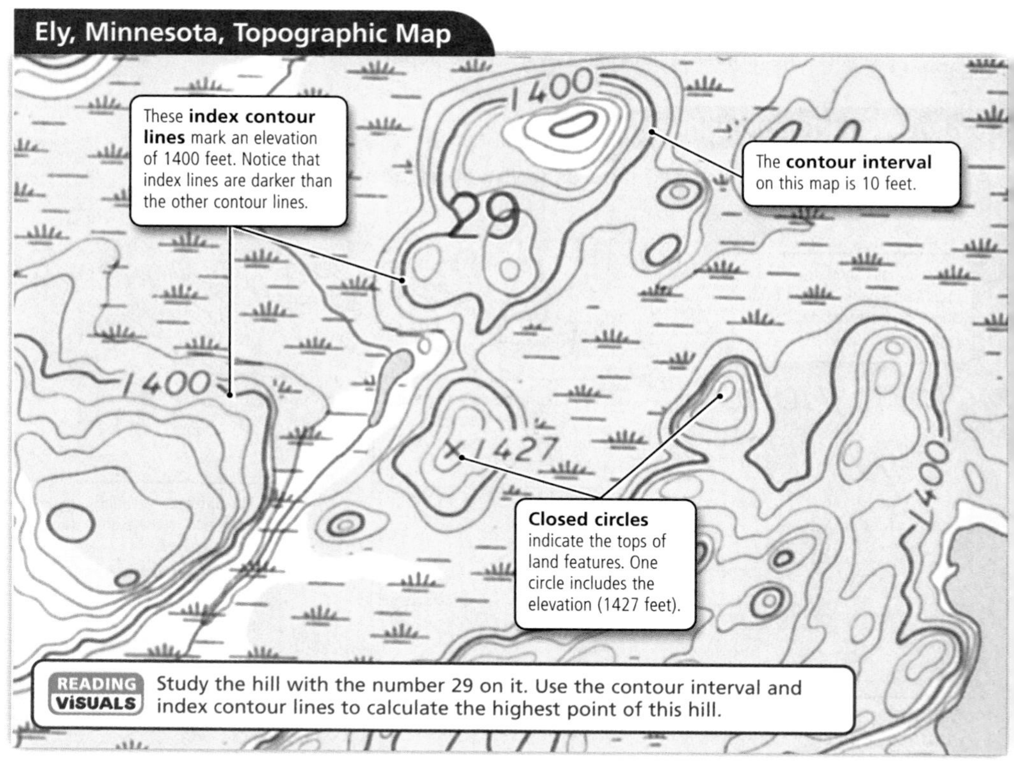

READING VISUALS Study the hill with the number 29 on it. Use the contour interval and index contour lines to calculate the highest point of this hill.

DIFFERENTIATE INSTRUCTION

 **More Reading Support**

C What is a contour interval? *It is the change in elevation from one contour line to the next.*

Advanced To challenge students, ask: How might each of these people use a topographic map in their work: an air rescue pilot, a river captain, a professional mountain climber, and a cross-country ski guide. *Pilot: to search terrain and know where to land; river captain: to pilot his boat safely along a river channel; climber: to plan a route up a mountain; guide: to choose a route that matches the abilities of the people he or she leads.*

 Challenge and Extension, p. 31

- **Index contour lines mark elevations.** The darker contour lines on a map are called index contour lines. Numbers that show elevations are often written on these lines. To calculate higher or lower elevations, simply count the number of lines above or below an index line. Then multiply that number by the contour interval. Look at the Ely map, where one index line marks 1400 feet. To find the elevation of a point three lines up from this index line, you would multiply 10 feet (the contour interval) by 3. Add the result, 30, to 1400. The point's elevation is 1430 feet.

What information do index contour lines provide?

CALIFORNIA Focus

The highest elevation in California is Mt. Whitney, which rises 4419 meters (14,497 ft) above sea level. The lowest elevation in California is in Death Valley, at a spot that is 86 meters (282 ft) below sea level.

Besides contour lines, topographic maps also contain symbols for natural and human-made features. Below are some common map symbols that the United States Geological Survey (USGS) uses on its topographic maps.

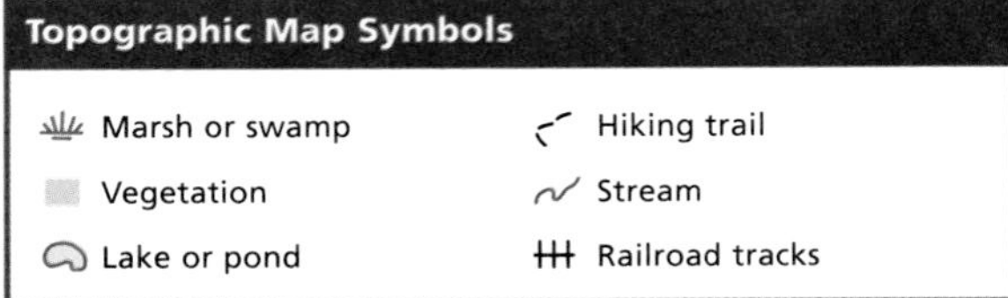

Topographic Map Symbols
Marsh or swamp
Vegetation
Lake or pond
Hiking trail
Stream
Railroad tracks

Discover the relationship between topographic maps and surface features.

The USGS provides topographic maps for nearly every part of the United States. These maps cover urban, rural, and wilderness areas. Hikers and campers are not the only ones who use topographic maps. Engineers, archaeologists, forest rangers, biologists, and others depend on them as well.

5.2 Review

KEY CONCEPTS

1. How do contour lines show elevation, slope, and relief? (6.7.f)
2. Why do contour lines never cross on a topographic map? (6.7.f)
3. How would you show the top of a hill, an area of vegetation, or a hiking trail on a topographic map? (6.7.f)

CRITICAL THINKING

4. **Apply** For an area with gently sloping hills and little relief, would you draw contour lines close together or far apart? Explain why.
5. **Compare and Contrast** How would a road map and a topographic map of the same area differ? What information would each provide?

CHALLENGE

6. **Synthesize** Work with a group to make a topographic map of the area around your school. First decide how big an area you will include. Then choose a contour interval, a map scale, and symbols for buildings, sports fields, and other features. Let other students test the map's accuracy.

ANSWERS

1. The numbers on the contour lines show elevation. The distance between contour lines shows slope. The differences between high and low places show relief.

2. Each one represents a specific elevation. Closed circles represent high and low points; contour intervals are always the same for any given map.

3. with a closed circle; green shading; or a broken black line

4. far apart; the changes in elevation are gradual.

5. road: would show the highway network, bodies of water, and cities; topographic: would show how the landscape looks and how high or low the land is

6. Students should include contour interval, index contour lines, elevation figures, compass rose, legend, and scale.

Ongoing Assessment

Describe the common symbols used on topographic maps.

Describe some symbols used on topographic maps. *railroad track: a line crossed by short perpendicular lines; marsh: a stylized tuft of marsh grass; lake or pond: an area outlined in blue; stream: a blue line; hiking trail: a broken black line.*

Answer: Many are labeled with specific elevations.

Reinforce the BIG idea

Have students relate the section to the Big Idea.

 Reinforcing Key Concepts, p. 32

Assess

 Section 5.2 Quiz, p. 101

Reteach

Provide students with a topographic map of a wilderness area in a mountain region. Ask them to plan a cross-country hike from one significant feature shown on the map to another, some distance away. Have each student trace a route in pencil on the printout and then describe the route and the reason it was chosen. Ask for volunteers to present their routes to the class.

Technology Resources

Have students visit **ClassZone.com** for reteaching of Key Concepts.

 CONTENT REVIEW

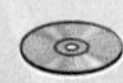 CONTENT REVIEW CD-ROM

CHAPTER INVESTIGATION

Focus

PURPOSE To recognize the features of a landscape by looking at contour lines on a topographic map

OVERVIEW Students will create a topographic map by tracing onto a plastic sheet the waterlines around a clay landscape model at various water levels. Student maps will show

- slopes
- changes in elevation
- relief of landforms
- tops of hills

Lab Preparation

- Have beakers or empty cans on hand so that students can use them to fill and partially empty their containers.
- Have students read through the investigation for homework the night before doing the experiment in class. Copy and distribute datasheets and rubrics as you see fit.

 UNIT RESOURCE BOOK, pp. 50–58

 SCIENCE TOOLKIT, F15

Lab Management

- Suggest that different groups form different types of landscapes so they can compare their maps at the end.
- Caution students to avoid dripping water on their clear plastic sheets, as this will wash away their inked lines.
- Tracing the contour lines onto paper is easier if students hold the sheets against a window so that light can shine through.

SAFETY Remind students to avoid spilling water on the floor and to immediately wipe up any spills that occur.

INCLUSION Students can prepare containers the day before to have more time to spend on the investigation.

Teaching with Technology

Use an overhead projector to display students' maps.

CHAPTER INVESTIGATION

Investigate Topographic Maps

OVERVIEW AND PURPOSE Topographic maps show the shape of the land. In this lab you will use what you have learned about how Earth's three-dimensional surface is represented on maps to

- make a terrain model out of clay
- produce a topographic map of the model

Procedure

1. Build a simple landscape about 6–8 cm high from modeling clay. Include a variety of land features. Make sure your model is no taller than the sides of the container.

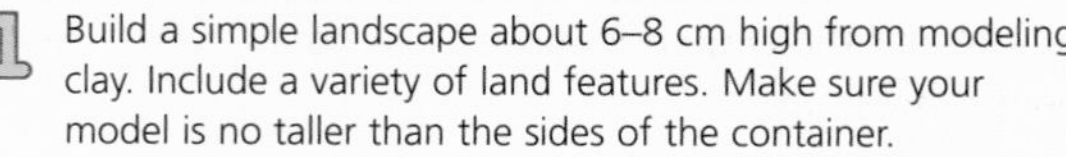

2. Place your model into the container. Stand a ruler upright inside the container and tape it in place.

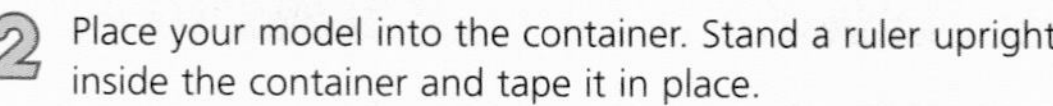

3. Lay the clear plastic sheet over the container and tape it on one side like a hinge. Carefully trace the outline of your clay model.

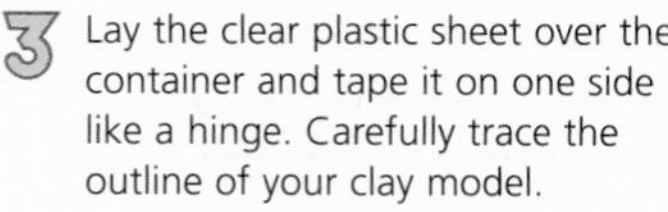

4. Add 2 cm of colored water to the container.

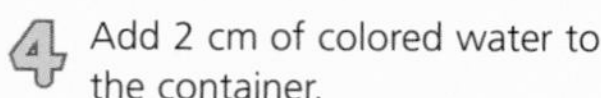

5. Insert spaghetti sticks into the model all around the waterline. Place the sticks about 3 cm apart. Make sure the sticks are vertical and are no taller than the sides of the container.

step 3

6. Lower the plastic sheet back over the container. Looking straight down on the container, make a dot on the sheet wherever you see a spaghetti stick. Connect the dots to trace the contour line accurately onto your map.

7. Continue adding water, 2 cm at a time. Each time you add water, insert the sticks into the model at the waterline and repeat step 6. Continue until the model landscape is underwater. Carefully drain the water when finished.

step 5

MATERIALS
- half-gallon cardboard juice container
- scissors
- modeling clay
- clear plastic sheet (transparency or sheet protector)
- cellophane tape
- ruler
- water
- food coloring
- box of spaghetti
- erasable marker pen

6.2.a, 6.7.f

168 Unit 2: Earth's Surface

INVESTIGATION RESOURCES

 CHAPTER INVESTIGATION, Investigate Topographic Maps
- Level A, pp. 50–53
- Level B, pp. 54–57
- Level C, p. 58

Advanced students should complete Levels B & C.

 Writing a Lab Report, D12–13

Technology Resources

Customize this student lab as needed or look for an alternative. Print rubrics to assess student lab reports.

 **Lab Generator CD-ROM**

Content Standard
6.2.a Students know water running downhill is the dominant process in shaping the landscape, including California's landscape.

Investigation Standard
6.7.f Read a topographic map and a geologic map for evidence provided on the maps and construct and interpret a simple scale map.

Observe and Analyze

1. Compare your topographic map with the three-dimensional model. Remember that contour lines connect points of equal elevation. What do widely spaced or tightly spaced contour lines mean? What does a closed circle mean?
2. Make a permanent record of your map to keep in your **Science Notebook** by carefully tracing the contour lines onto a sheet of white paper. To make reading the map easier, use a different color for an index contour line.
3. What is the contour interval of your model landscape? For example, each 2 centimeters might represent 20 meters in an actual landscape. Record the elevation of the index contour line on your map.

Conclude

Write It Up

1. **INFER** How would you determine the elevation of a point located halfway between two contour lines?
2. **EVALUATE** Describe any errors that you may have made in your procedure or any places where errors might have occurred.
3. **APPLY** Explain how you would use a topographic map if you were planning a hiking trip or a cross-country bike race.

INVESTIGATE Further

CHALLENGE Choose one feature on a topographic map—such as the map on page 166—to translate into a cross-sectional diagram.

1. Lay a piece of ruled paper across the center of the topographical feature.
2. Mark each of the contour lines on the ruled paper and label each mark with the elevation.
3. Mark the same elevations on the side of the paper, as shown in the example.
4. Use a ruler to draw a straight line down from each mark to the matching elevation on the side of the paper.
5. Connect the points to draw a profile of the landform.
6. Describe how you would expect the profile to change over time as water running downhill shapes the landscape.

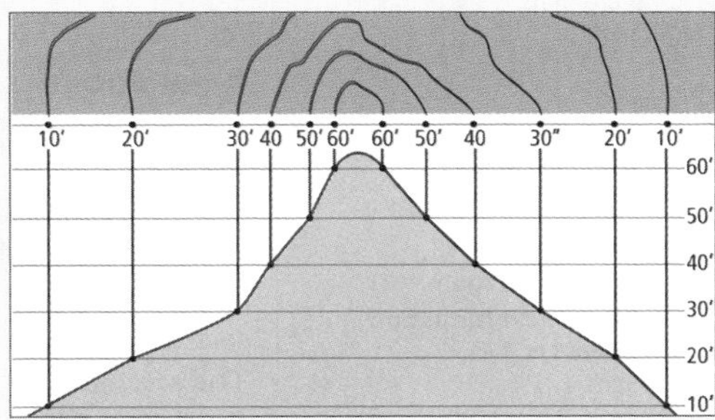

INVESTIGATE TOPOGRAPHIC MAPS
Observe and Analyze
Figure 1. Topographic Map of Model

Conclude

Observe and Analyze

1. Contour lines are widely spaced where slopes are gentle; closely spaced contour lines represent places where slopes are steep. Closed circles indicate a hilltop, mountaintop, or a depression center.

2. Students' maps should correspond to the landscapes they made in their cartons.

3. The contour interval is 2 cm. Elevation answers will vary but should match students' hypothetical contour intervals.

Conclude

1. Find the average (mean) of the elevations represented by the two lines.

2. Students should recognize that their lines are accurate only if they looked at the waterlines from straight above. Even the slightest angle in viewing will throw off the location of a line. Also, their maps are accurate only if they carefully filled the cartons to the specified levels.

3. For hiking or backpacking, a topographic map can help one avoid steep climbs and find the least strenuous route between points. In planning a cross-country race, one might want to choose more challenging slopes, easily identified by consulting the map.

INVESTIGATE Further

CHALLENGE 1–6. The profiles produced by this method will vary. Have students mark the elevation of each contour line beneath the point where it touches the sheet of ruled paper. This will make it easier for them to graph the topography. Be sure students use the vertical axis for elevation. The profiles would change over time as high areas got worn down and low areas got filled in with sediment.

Post-Lab Discussion

- Place the drained cartons, still containing the landscapes, on a lab bench. Use an overhead projector to display the plastic-sheet map produced by each group. Ask students to find the landscape that matches each map.
- Sketch your own map onto a plastic sheet and display it to the class. Ask students to describe the landscape it portrays.
- Discuss which rules of topographic maps students came to understand better while constructing their own maps.

5.3 FOCUS

Set Learning Goals

Students will

- Explain how remote-sensing images can provide detailed and accurate information about Earth.
- Explain how geographic data can be displayed in layers to build maps.

3-Minute Warm-Up

Display Transparency 37 or copy this exercise on the board:

Decide whether these statements are true. If not true, correct them.

1. Topographic maps show elevation but not relief. *Topographic maps show elevation, relief, and slope.*
2. Closely spaced contour lines indicate gradual slopes. *Closely spaced contour lines indicate steep slopes.*
3. Mountaintops are enclosed by circles on topographic maps. *true*

 3-Minute Warm-Up, p. T37

5.3 MOTIVATE

THINK ABOUT

PURPOSE To have students think about the wide range of information technology can provide

DISCUSS This image shows the Washington Monument, the Mall, and the Jefferson Memorial (the round building at bottom left). *Sample answers: buildings, roadways, bridges, and trees. Scientists could use such images to study the environment, mapmakers could use them to make maps, and engineers could study traffic patterns and urban growth.*

Ongoing Assessment

Explain how remote-sensing images can provide detailed and accurate information about Earth.

Ask: How has remote sensing changed the way in which maps are made? *Mapmakers used to have to draw the landscape. Today, remote sensing produces highly accurate images.*

KEY CONCEPT

Technology is used to map Earth.

CALIFORNIA Content Standard

6.7.f Read a topographic map and a geologic map for evidence provided on the maps and construct and interpret a simple scale map.

BEFORE, you learned

- Contour lines are used on topographic maps to show elevation, slope, and relief
- Contour lines follow certain rules
- Map symbols show many natural and human-made features

NOW, you will learn

- How remote-sensing images can provide detailed and accurate information about Earth
- How geographic data can be displayed in layers to build maps

VOCABULARY

remote sensing p. 170
sensor p. 171
false-color image p. 171
geographic information systems p. 173

THINK ABOUT

What can you see in this image?

Satellites can record all types of information about Earth's surface. This image shows a section of Washington, D.C. The satellite that collected the data is 680 kilometers (420 mi) above Earth. What familiar items can you see in the picture? How might images like this be useful to scientists, mapmakers, and engineers?

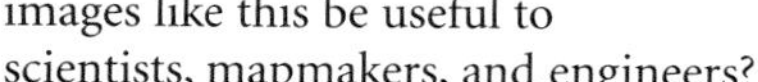

Remote sensing provides detailed images of Earth.

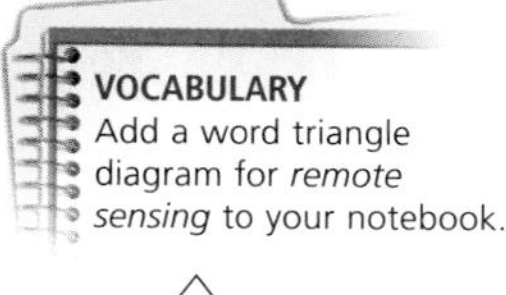

VOCABULARY
Add a word triangle diagram for *remote sensing* to your notebook.

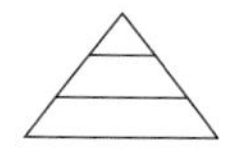

If you have ever looked at an object through a pair of binoculars, you have used remote sensing. **Remote sensing** is the use of scientific equipment to gather information about something from a distance. Remote-sensing technology can be as simple as a camera mounted on an airplane. It can be as complex as a satellite orbiting Earth.

Imagine that you are a mapmaker in the 1840s. You have been asked to draw a map of a state. You have no cameras or satellites to help you. To get a good view of the land, you have to climb to the highest points and carefully draw every hill, valley, river, and landform. It will take you months to map the state. Today, mapmakers use remote-sensing images from airplanes and satellites. With these, they can make highly detailed and accurate maps of Earth's surface.

RESOURCES FOR DIFFERENTIATED INSTRUCTION

Below Level

UNIT RESOURCE BOOK
- Reading Study Guide A, pp. 35–36
- Decoding Support, p. 47

AUDIO CDS

Advanced

UNIT RESOURCE BOOK
- Challenge and Extension, p. 41
- Challenge Reading, pp. 43–44

English Learners

UNIT RESOURCE BOOK
Spanish Reading Study Guide, pp. 39–40

AUDIO CDS
- Audio Readings in Spanish
- Audio Readings (English)

Airplane cameras use film to record data. Satellites use sensors to build images of Earth. A **sensor** is a mechanical or electrical tool that receives a signal, such as light, and responds to it. Satellite sensors detect far more than your eyes can see. They collect information about the different types of energy coming from Earth's surface. The satellite then sends that information to computers on Earth.

The computers turn the information into images, as shown in the illustration below. Satellite data can be used to build an image of the entire planet. It can show a single continent or a detail of your area. For example, the image on the right shows a close-up of the Jefferson Memorial in Washington, D.C.

One of the ways scientists study changes to Earth's surface is by using false-color images. In a **false-color image,** natural colors are replaced with artificial ones to show special features.

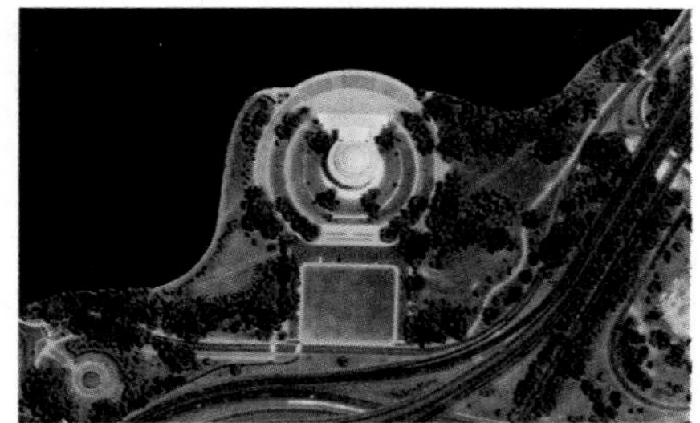

This satellite image includes the Jefferson Memorial, walkways, and roads. See if you can find the memorial in the image on page 170.

Satellite Imaging

Objects on Earth reflect or emit different types of energy. Satellite sensors can detect and record these energies.

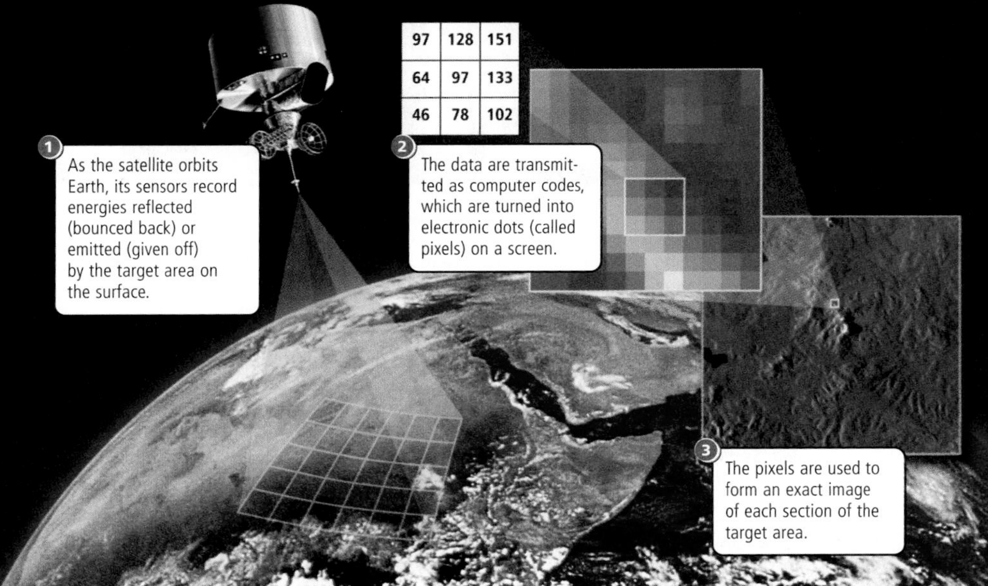

97	128	151
64	97	133
46	78	102
1 As the satellite orbits Earth, its sensors record energies reflected (bounced back) or emitted (given off) by the target area on the surface.
2 The data are transmitted as computer codes, which are turned into electronic dots (called pixels) on a screen.
3 The pixels are used to form an exact image of each section of the target area.

5.3 INSTRUCT

Teach the Standards

Technology and maps 6.7.f

In this section: Make sure students understand that current technology enables scientists to make highly accurate and detailed maps. Explain that geographic information systems arrange many kinds of data and display it in different types of maps.

- **previously taught:** technology in weather forecasting, pp. 134–139
- **future opportunities:** mapping and predicting earthquakes, pp. 320–321

Integrate the Sciences

Satellite imaging plays an important role in the monitoring of global climate change. One ongoing research project at Glacier National Park in Montana seeks to determine how a mountain wilderness responds to changes in climate. The latest in remote-sensing technologies, as well as GIS, have helped to produce 3-D maps and computer animations of the dynamics of the ecosystem—including data on snowpack density, stream discharge, and evapotranspiration. One clear pattern revealed by the satellite imaging is the retreat of the park's glaciers. Of the glaciers documented there in 1850, only a third remain. The remaining ones are far smaller than before and continue to shrink each year.

Teach from Visuals

To help students interpret the visual "Satellite Imaging," ask:

- What does the grid that is superimposed on Earth represent? *the target area for the satellite's sensors*
- What sort of data is the satellite collecting? *energies reflected by different objects on Earth*
- What is the relationship between the three inset images in the diagram? *The first shows data as computer codes; the second shows the data converted to pixels, the third shows an image formed from the pixels.*

DIFFERENTIATE INSTRUCTION

More Reading Support

A What do computers do with the information from sensors? *They change the information into images.*

English Learners To help English learners, revisit the three steps shown in the visual "Satellite Imaging." Use less technical, more familiar language to explain how an image is produced—for example, "The satellite looks at one spot on Earth. Then it records what levels of energy it sees. It sends the record to a computer, which changes the energy readings to dots on a screen. The dots combine to make a picture."

Teach from Visuals

To help students interpret the visual of satellite images, ask:

- How is snow depicted in the true- and false-color image? *Snow is white in the true-color image and bright blue in the false-color image.*
- How does the false-color image help viewers distinguish between plants and bare ground? *The false-color image uses bright green for plants and tan and pink for bare ground. This use of color provides a greater contrast between plants and bare ground than the true-color image does.*
- Why is the true-color image less useful than the false-color image for locating the coastline? *Rivers carry sediment and empty into the ocean. The sediment darkens the true color of the water and makes it more difficult to identify the coastline.*

Ongoing Assessment

READING VISUALS *Answer: Clouds and snow are both white in the true-color image. Clouds are white to light blue and snow is bright blue in the false-color image. Distinguishing between clouds and snow is important because knowing the accurate amount of snow cover can help officials estimate how much drinking water will be available in the spring.*

Satellite Images (?) B

People can compare true-color satellite images and false-color satellite images to see a wider range of detail. These images show the same area of California on March 7, 2004.

True Color

False Color

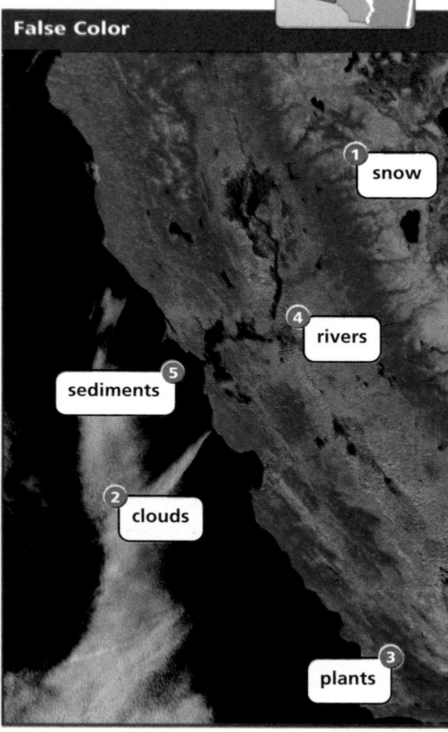

1. **Snow** In the true-color image, snow is white. In the false-color image, snow is bright blue. The amount of snow cover is important because the melting of snow in the spring provides California with much of its fresh water.
2. **Clouds** In the true-color image, clouds are white. They are white to light blue in the false-color image.
3. **Plants** In the false-color image, plants are bright green. This increases the contrast between areas covered by plants and areas of bare ground, which are shown in tan and pink.
4. **Rivers** In the false-color image, water is shown in dark blue and black. This makes the rivers in central California easier to see.
5. **Sediments** Rivers carry sediments to the ocean. Sediments in water can make the location of the coastline more difficult to see in the true-color image.

READING VISUALS How can you tell the difference between clouds and snow cover shown in these satellite images? Why might this be useful?

DIFFERENTIATE INSTRUCTION

(?) More Reading Support

B What does comparing true- and false-color images of an area provide? *a wider range of detail*

Inclusion Students with vision impairments may have difficulty seeing the rivers and contrasting the plants from the bare ground. Use projection equipment to place an enlarged image of these pictures on an overhead screen so that all students can participate in class discussion.

Challenge and Extension, p. 41

Geographic information systems display data in layers.

Find out more about how GIS is used.

Any good city map will show you what is on the surface—buildings, streets, parks, and other features. But suppose you need to know about tunnels under the city. Or maybe you want to know where the most students live. An ordinary map will not tell you what you want to know.

Instead, you would turn to geographic information systems. **Geographic information systems** (GIS) are computer systems that can store and arrange geographic data and show the data in many different types of maps. Scientists, city planners, and engineers all use GIS maps to help them make decisions. For example, suppose your city wants to build a new airport. It must be away from populated areas and near major highways. The illustration below shows how city officials might use GIS to pick the best site.

Geographic Information Systems

GIS can be used to produce maps that help people make decisions.

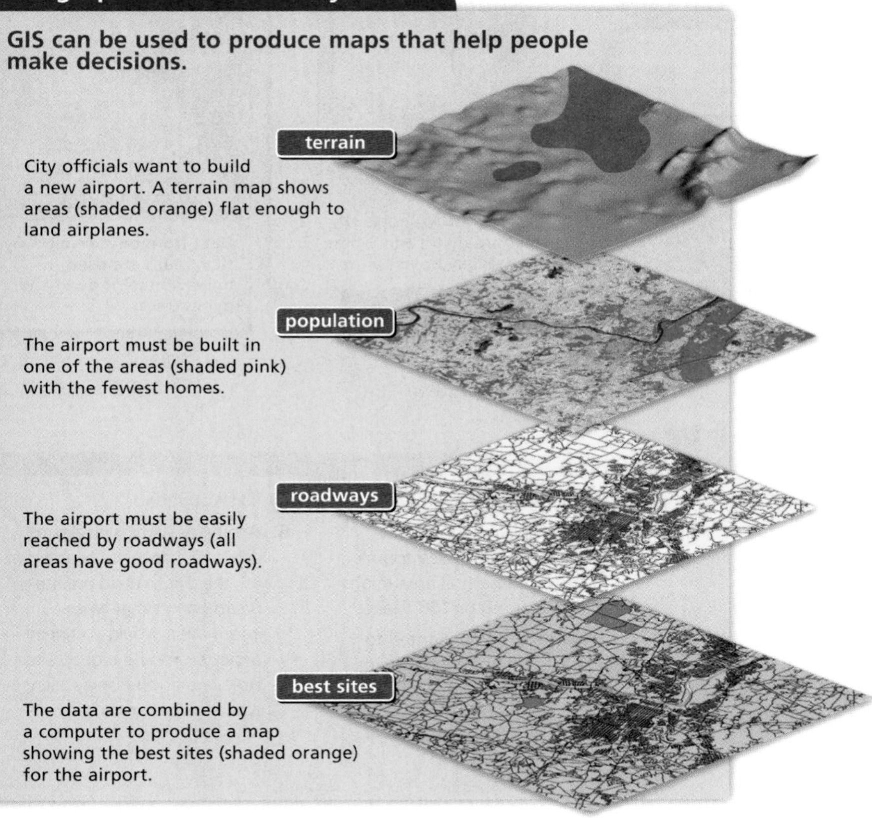

terrain
City officials want to build a new airport. A terrain map shows areas (shaded orange) flat enough to land airplanes.
population
The airport must be built in one of the areas (shaded pink) with the fewest homes.
roadways
The airport must be easily reached by roadways (all areas have good roadways).
best sites
The data are combined by a computer to produce a map showing the best sites (shaded orange) for the airport.

DIFFERENTIATE INSTRUCTION

More Reading Support

C What does *GIS* stand for? *geographic information systems*

Below Level The acronyms *GPS* and *GIS* might be confusing for some students. Write each acronym on the board, and have volunteers provide information to add under it. You might also have students make up their own memory aids to help them remember the difference between GIS and GPS. For instance, they might write "GIS" vertically to remind them it refers to data layers.

Advanced Have students who are interested in GIS and other mapping technologies read the following article:

 Challenge Reading, pp. 43–44

Teach Difficult Concepts

Students may have a hard time visualizing, on the basis of the description of data layers, how GIS works. Explain that GIS maps contain "made-to-order" information. To help students understand, try the following demonstration.

Teacher Demo

Display transparencies with an overhead projector to simulate GIS map layers. Tell students to suppose they are developers seeking to place a teen clothing store in the best possible location. On the first transparency, draw a simple map with the boundaries of a hypothetical community outlined in black. On a second transparency, draw roads and highways in blue and set it on top of the first transparency on the projector. Next, cluster some pink-outlined patches at one corner of the map near a highway. Tell students that these represent areas with more than 10 teens per 100 population. Note how arranging the data in layers makes it easy to decide where to locate the store. Have students agree on a suitable location.

Teach from Visuals

To help students interpret the visual about GIS, ask:

- Why is a terrain map included in this composite? *Airplanes need flat runways for landings.*
- How are the individual maps combined? *A computer stores the data in the individual maps and uses the data to build a composite map.*

Ongoing Assessment

Explain how geographic data can be displayed in layers to build maps.

Ask: How can combining the data in various map layers be useful? *It can help scientists, city planners, and engineers make decisions.*

Ongoing Assessment

Answer: GIS maps can help engineers, city planners, and scientists by combining different geographic information in one map that can be easily read, showing what is above and below the surface, presenting all the different types of information needed to make a decision, and indicating changes in the environment.

EXPLORE the BIG idea

Revisit "Internet Activity: Mapping" on p. 153. Have students summarize the technologies used to map Earth.

Reinforce the BIG idea

Have students relate the section to the Big Idea.

Reinforcing Key Concepts, p. 42

5.3 ASSESS & RETEACH

Assess

Section 5.3 Quiz, p. 102

Reteach

Ask students to come to the board to fill in frame game or four square note-taking organizers for each of the technological terms defined in this section. Include a definition, examples, nonexamples, and characteristics. *(Remote sensing: use of scientific equipment to gather information from a distance; camera or satellite; microscope; uses technology to gain a larger perspective)*

Technology Resources

Have students visit **ClassZone.com** for reteaching of Key Concepts.

CONTENT REVIEW

CONTENT REVIEW CD-ROM

Any geographic information can be entered into GIS and converted into a map. These systems are especially useful in showing information about changes in the environment.

For example, near Long Valley in California, the volcano known as Mammoth Mountain began giving off carbon dioxide, or CO_2. As the gas rose through the soil, it began killing the roots of trees nearby. Scientists measured the flow of CO_2 around Horseshoe Lake and other areas. They used computer software to build the maps shown below.

Summarize the ways GIS maps can be helpful to engineers, city planners, and scientists.

Mammoth Mountain

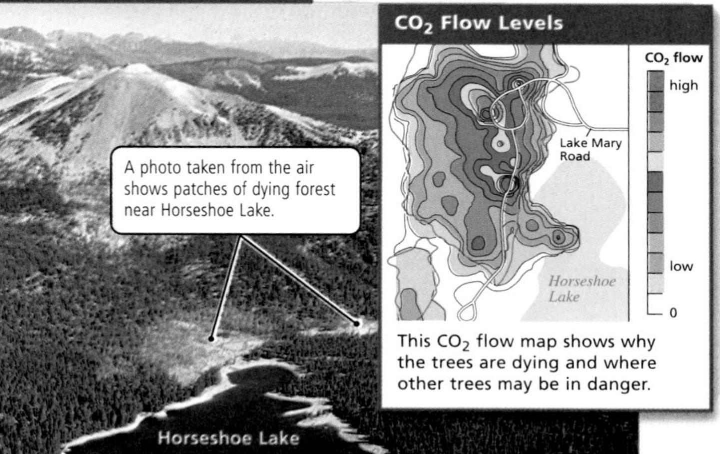

This CO_2 flow map shows why the trees are dying and where other trees may be in danger.

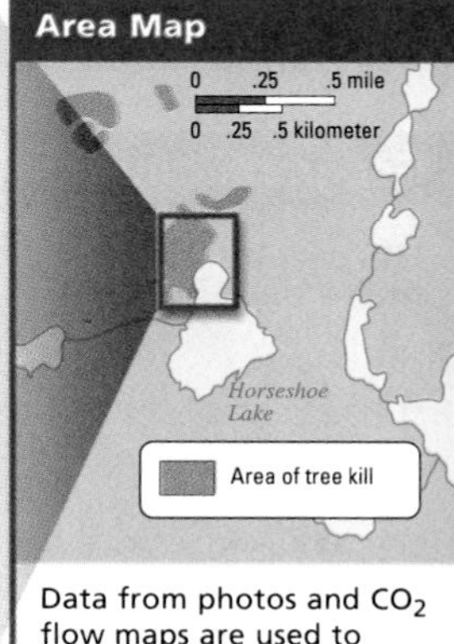

Data from photos and CO_2 flow maps are used to make a map of dead and dying trees.

5.3 Review

KEY CONCEPTS

1. How are satellites used to make images of Earth from outer space? (6.7.f)
2. What are some of the types of information obtained by remote sensing? (6.7.f)
3. Explain in your own words what a GIS map is. (6.7.f)

CRITICAL THINKING

4. **Infer** Explain how satellite images might be used to predict what a natural area might look like in 50 or 100 years.
5. **Evaluate** If you wanted to compare a region before and during a flood, how could false-color images help you?

CHALLENGE

6. **Analyze** Work with a small group. Suppose you wanted to ask the city to build a skateboard park. What types of information would you need in order to propose a good site? Draw a map to display each type of information.

ANSWERS

1. Satellites collect information about different types of energy.

2. surface features of Earth, changes in the environment, images for making maps

3. layers of data depicting different information, stacked on top of one another

4. They could reveal rates of change that would help in predicting what the same area might look like in the future.

5. They could highlight the wet areas before and during the flood.

6. Information needed might include which sites (1) have enough space for the park, (2) are near public transportation routes, and (3) are near schools.

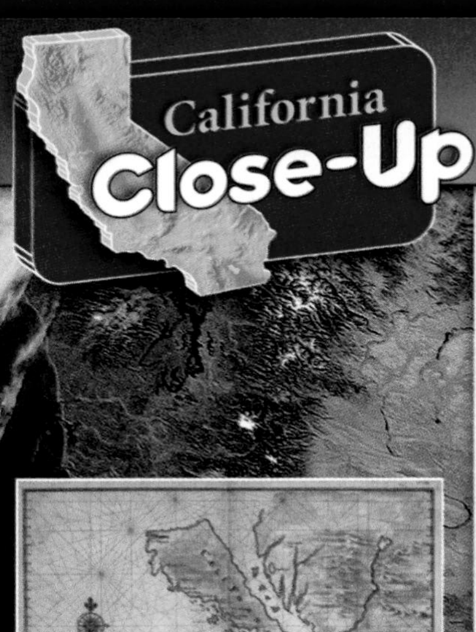

California Close-Up

MAPPING

The Big Picture

6.7.f Read a topographic map and a geologic map for evidence provided on the maps and construct and interpret a simple map scale.

In 1602 Spanish explorer Sebastian Vizcaíno sailed along the California coast. A journal from the voyage claimed that California was separated from the mainland by the "Sea of California." As a result, California was shown as an island on maps for over 100 years. In 1747 King Ferdinand VII of Spain declared that California was part of the mainland, and maps were corrected.

Today's mapmakers can do in minutes what used to take months or even years to do. Explorers in Vizcaíno's time probably made their maps by measuring the angles of elevation of stars at certain points and estimating distances from place to place. Remote sensing technology now allows scientists to make an extremely accurate map of most of Earth's surface in a matter of days.

In February 2000 an 11-day mission aboard the space shuttle *Endeavor* collected topographic data from more than 46 million square miles of Earth's surface. This Shuttle Radar Topography Mission (SRTM) was a joint project of NASA and the German and Italian space agencies. It was managed by NASA's Jet Propulsion Laboratory in Pasadena, California.

A specially modified radar system on the shuttle gathered data to make detailed 3-D maps of 80 percent of Earth's surface. These maps will have many applications, such as making better water drainage models and finding better locations for cell phone towers.

This map from about 1650 shows California as an island.

This view of the Los Angeles area was generated using data from the SRTM and a Landsat 5 satellite.

This satellite image of the California coast was taken in October 2000.

WRITING ABOUT SCIENCE

Suppose California really were an island, as shown on the old map. How would transportation technology change from the way it is today? Write a description of the necessary transportation system.

CALIFORNIA CLOSE-UP

Science in action in California

Set Learning Goal

To understand how accuracy in mapmaking has improved through technology

Present the Science

The shuttle's crew mapped most of Earth using a technique called *interferometry*. The shuttle bounced radar waves off Earth, and two antennae received the returning radar waves. The distance between Earth and the antennae differed according to Earth's geography. Because the antennae were at different distances, the returning signal was collected from two different angles. Scientists analyzed this information and created very accurate maps of Earth's surface.

Discussion Questions

Have students share their knowledge of and experience with California's geography.

- Ask: What possible problem may have introduced inaccuracy into Vizcaíno's method of using stars as the basis for estimating elevation? *As a result of Earth's rotation, the stars are not always at the same elevation in the sky.*
- Ask: How might aerial views of Earth help create better water drainage models? *Possible answers: Scientists will have better views of the land's slope and elevation, so they can better understand what causes water to drain toward the ocean.*

Close

Summarize what you have learned about how technology for mapping elevation has changed since Vizcaíno's exploration. *Possible answer: Vizcaíno was limited to mapping California from what he saw and from measurements based on the angles of the elevation of stars. Today, scientists can fly above Earth and use radar to obtain very accurate measurements of Earth's elevation.*

WRITING ABOUT SCIENCE

Writing Applications 6.1.f This assignment will give students practice in creative writing. Suggest that pairs of students read each other's descriptions and evaluate them in terms of readability and relevance to the topic.

The best descriptions will

- present creative solutions to the writing prompt
- clearly describe each idea

BACK TO

the BIG idea

Have students summarize the technologies used in mapping Earth and the benefits they provide. *Mapping technologies include satellites and other remote-sensing equipment, the Global Positioning System (GPS), and geographic information systems (GIS). They provide information about Earth's surface and the locations of specific places. Computer systems aid in the display of data.*

KEY CONCEPTS SUMMARY

SECTION 5.1

Explain the difference in accuracy between the globe and the map. *The shapes and sizes of landmasses and oceans are relatively accurate on the globe; shapes, sizes, or both are distorted on the map because it is flat.*

SECTION 5.2

How does the map shown here provide useful information? *The contour lines and symbols show the shape and features of the land.*

SECTION 5.3

What types of information might the satellite on the left gather for inclusion in the map layers on the right? *Sample answers: vegetation, waterways, forest fires, population, roadways, temperatures*

Review Concepts

- Big Idea Flow Chart, p. T33
- Chapter Outline, pp. T39–T40

5 Chapter Review

the BIG idea

Modern technology has changed the way we view and map Earth.

KEY CONCEPTS SUMMARY

1 Maps and globes are models of Earth.

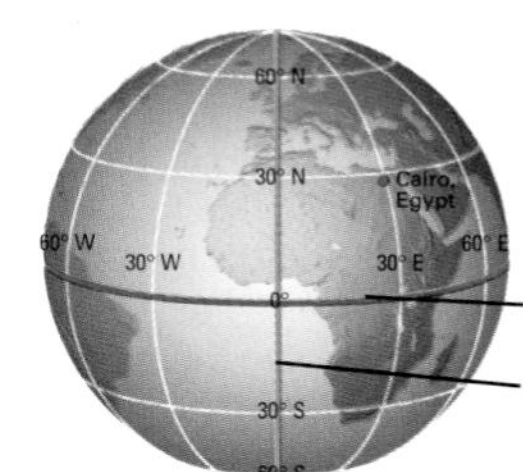

Latitude and longitude are used to locate any point on Earth.

equator

prime meridian

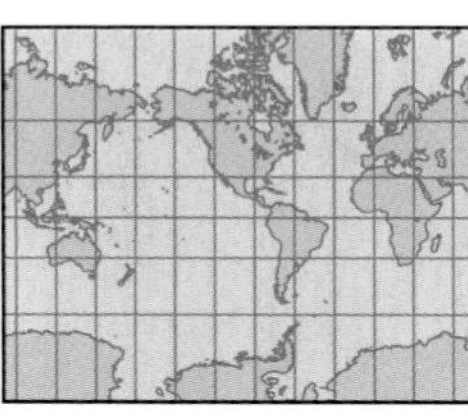

All map projections distort Earth's surface.

VOCABULARY
relief map p. 156
map scale p. 157
map legend p. 157
equator p. 158
latitude p. 158
prime meridian p. 159
longitude p. 159
projection p. 160

2 Topographic maps show the shape of the land.

Contour lines show elevation, slope, and relief.

Contour lines never cross.

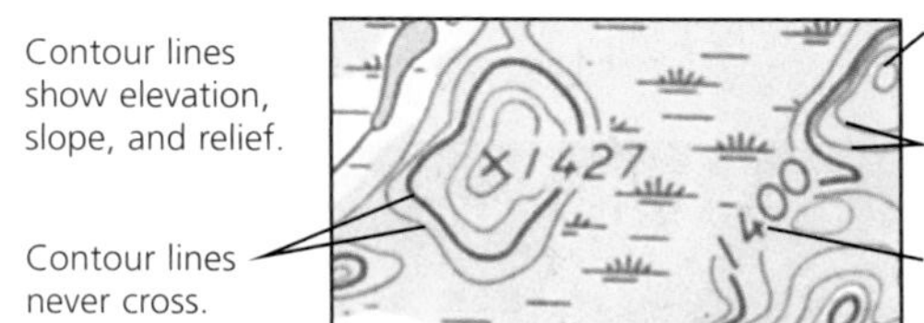

Closed circles represent hilltops.

Contour lines show steepness of slope.

Index contour lines show elevation.

VOCABULARY
topography p. 164
contour line p. 165
elevation p. 165
slope p. 165
relief p. 165
contour interval p. 166

3 Technology is used to map Earth.

Remote-sensing technology gathers accurate data about Earth.

Geographic information systems are computer programs used to merge layers of information.

VOCABULARY
remote sensing p. 170
sensor p. 171
false-color image p. 171
geographic information systems p. 173

Technology Resources

Have students visit **ClassZone.com** or use the CD-ROM for a cumulative review of concepts.

CONTENT REVIEW

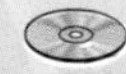
CONTENT REVIEW CD-ROM

Engage students in a whole-class interactive review of Key Concepts. Edit content as you wish.

POWER PRESENTATIONS

Reviewing Vocabulary

Copy and complete the chart below, using vocabulary terms from this chapter.

Term	Use	Appearance
map legend	*to explain map symbols*	*chart of symbols*
1. latitude	to show distance from the equator	
2. longitude		lines going from pole to pole
3.	to show land features	rippled and smooth areas
4. map scale	to represent distances	
5. equator		line at 0° latitude
6. prime meridian	to separate east and west hemispheres	
7.	to show height above sea level	line showing elevation
8. false-color image	to highlight information	

Reviewing Key Concepts

Multiple Choice *Choose the letter of the best answer.*

9. California is located in which of the following two hemispheres? (6.7.f)
- **a.** Southern and Eastern
- **b.** Northern and Eastern
- **c.** Northern and Western
- **d.** Southern and Western

10. The darkest contour lines on a topographic map are called (6.7.f)
- **a.** contour intervals
- **b.** topographic symbols
- **c.** hiking trails
- **d.** index contour lines

11. How is a steep slope depicted on a topographic map? (6.7.f)
- **a.** contour lines that are close together
- **b.** contour lines that are straight
- **c.** contour lines that are far apart
- **d.** contour lines are jagged

12. A flat map shows Earth's curved surface by means of (6.7.f)
- **a.** elevation
- **b.** topography
- **c.** relief
- **d.** projection

13. People use latitude and longitude lines mostly to identify (6.7.f)
- **a.** map scales
- **b.** country names
- **c.** exact locations
- **d.** distances

14. The most accurate way to show Earth's surface is a (6.7.f)
- **a.** globe
- **b.** conic projection
- **c.** cylindrical projection
- **d.** planar projection

15. One example of remote sensing is the use of (6.7.f)
- **a.** contour lines
- **b.** projections
- **c.** GIS
- **d.** binoculars

Short Answer *Write a few sentences to answer each question.*

16. How does the Global Positioning System work? In your answer use each of the following terms. Underline each term in your answer. (6.7.f)

24 satellites	computer	longitude
receiver	latitude	elevation

17. How do Mercator maps distort the view of Earth's surface? (6.7.f)

18. How do people use sensors in making maps? (6.7.f)

ASSESSMENT RESOURCES

ASSESSMENT BOOK
- Chapter Test A, pp. 103–106
- Chapter Test B, pp. 107–110
- Chapter Test C, pp. 111–114
- Alternative Assessment, pp. 115–116

STANDARDS REVIEW AND PRACTICE, pp. 3–4, 15–16, 55–56, 67–68

Technology Resources

Edit test items and answer choices.

Test Generator CD-ROM

Visit **ClassZone.com** to extend test practice.

Test Practice

Reviewing Vocabulary

1. lines parallel to the equator

2. to show distance from the prime meridian

3. relief map

4. a ratio or a bar

5. to separate north and south hemispheres

6. a line at 0° longitude

7. contour lines

8. artificial colors replacing Earth's natural colors

Reviewing Key Concepts

9. c

10. d

11. a

12. d

13. c

14. a

15. d

16. A network of 24 satellites sends signals that can be picked up by a receiver on Earth. Using these signals, a computer inside the receiver calculates the latitude, longitude, and elevation of its location.

17. Mercator maps make areas far away from the equator look much larger than they really are. For instance, Greenland is only one-eighth the size of South America, but it appears larger.

18. Sensors are mechanical or electrical devices that receive and respond to different types of energy. Since they can detect far more than human eyes can see, they provide more detailed information to use in making maps.

Thinking Critically

19. *E, because the contour lines are closest together near this hill*
20. *It is nearly flat.*
21. *They are near an unpaved road that leads to a paved road.*
22. *more than 1480 meters (in the loop that contains D)*
23. *E should look steep with a valley separating it from D; D should be slightly higher, with a gentler slope.*
24. *The main advantage is that the land is mostly flat; the main disadvantage is that it is a marsh.*
25. *Since there are several hills, mountain biking would be appropriate.*
26. *conic*
27. *cylindrical or Mercator*
28. *planar*
29. *cylindrical or Mercator*
30. *conic*

the BIG idea

31. *Students' responses should indicate what they have learned in this chapter.*
32. *Maps of the ocean floor and some other types of information might be considered new. Most of what people have learned from new technologies is more detailed and precise versions of older information.*
33. *Sample answer: Satellites have provided new information about each part of the Earth system and is probably the technology that has changed the way people view and map Earth the most.*

UNIT PROJECTS

Give students the appropriate Unit Project worksheets from the URB for their projects. Both directions and rubrics can be used as a guide.

 Unit Projects, pp. 5–10

Thinking Critically

Use the topographic map below to answer the next seven questions.

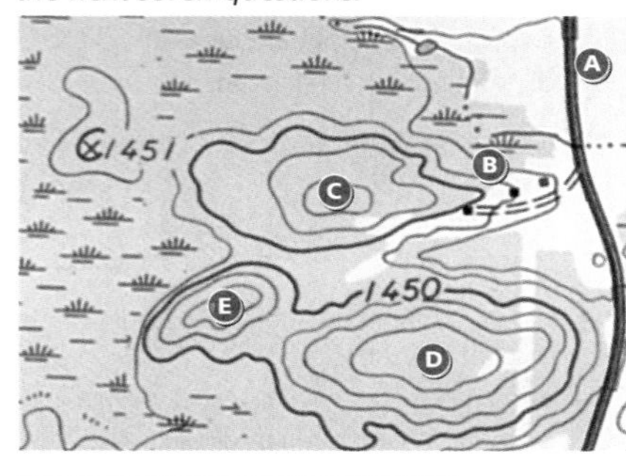

19. **APPLY** Imagine you are hiking through this area. Which hill—*C, D,* or *E*—has the steepest slope? How do you know? **(6.7.f)**
20. **ANALYZE** What is the topography of the land through which the curved road *A* goes? **(6.7.f)**
21. **IDENTIFY CAUSE** The squares at *B* represent buildings. Why do you think the buildings were placed here instead of somewhere else in the area? **(6.7.f)**
22. **APPLY** The contour interval is 10 meters. What is the elevation of the highest point on the map? **(6.7.f)**
23. **SYNTHESIZE** Sketch the two hills *D* and *E*. What would they look like to someone on the ground? **(6.7.f)**
24. **INFER** Suppose someone wanted to build a road through the terrain on the far left side of the map. What are the advantages and disadvantages of such a route? **(6.7.f)**
25. **EVALUATE** Do you think this area would be a good place to ride mountain bikes? Why or why not? **(6.7.f)**

CHART INFORMATION *On a separate sheet of paper, identify which map projection best matches each description.* **(6.7.f)**

Description	Projection
distorts landmasses farther from center point	*planar*
26. curved latitude and longitude lines	
27. distorts landmasses far from equator	
28. depicts polar regions accurately	
29. straight latitude and longitude lines	
30. distorts landmasses near equator	

the BIG idea

31. **APPLY** Look again at the photographs on pages 152–153. Now that you have finished the chapter, reread the question on the main photograph. What would you change in or add to your answer? **(6.7.f)**
32. **SYNTHESIZE** Describe some of the types of information that new technology has provided about Earth. **(6.7.f)**
33. **DRAW CONCLUSIONS** What type of technology do you think has done the most to change the way people view and map Earth? Explain your conclusion. **(6.7.f)**

UNIT PROJECTS

If you are doing a unit project, make a folder for your project. Include in your folder a list of the resources you will need, the date on which the project is due, and a schedule to track your progress. Begin gathering data.

MONITOR AND RETEACH

If students have trouble answering items 19–25, review the Mount Hood topographic map on p. 165 and the definitions of these words: *contour lines, elevation, slope,* and *relief.*

Students may benefit from summarizing one or more sections of the chapter.

 Summarizing the Chapter, pp. 68–69

Standards-Based Assessment

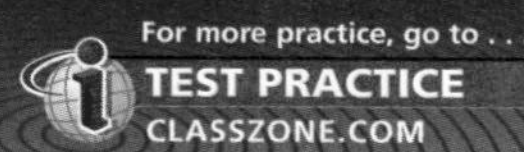

Using a Map Scale

The map shows the Cabrillo National Monument, a national park located on the Point Loma peninsula in San Diego, California. Use it to answer the questions below.

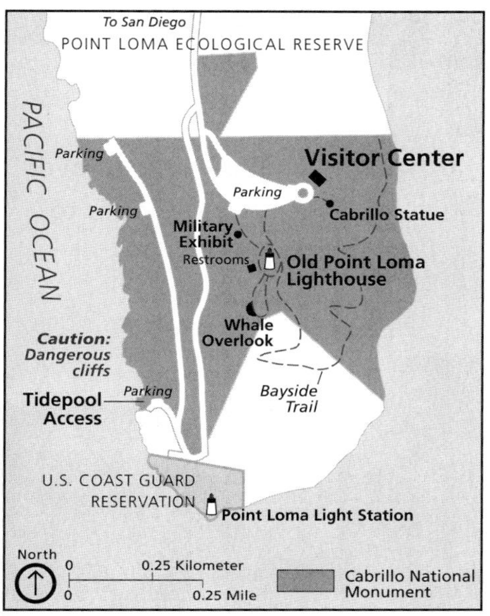

1. Which statement about the map is true?
- **a.** If it showed a larger area, it could show more detail.
- **b.** If it showed a smaller area, it could show more detail.
- **c.** If it showed a larger area, it would need a ratio scale.
- **d.** If it showed a smaller area, it would need an equivalent-units scale.

2. Notice that the map scale is in kilometers and miles. If the map showed only the Visitor Center, what measurements would it likely show?
- **a.** millimeters and inches
- **b.** centimeters and inches
- **c.** meters and yards
- **d.** kilometers and miles

3. Which type of scale does this map have?
- **a.** ratio
- **b.** bar scale
- **c.** detail scale
- **d.** equivalent-units scale

4. What is the distance between the parking lot in the northwest corner of the park and the parking lot that is closest to it?
- **a.** 0.25 km
- **b.** 0.50 km
- **c.** 0.75 km
- **d.** 1.25 km

5. Which is a natural feature on the map?
- **a.** Visitor Center
- **b.** Cabrillo Statue
- **c.** Pacific Ocean
- **d.** Old Point Loma Lighthouse

6. If you were at the Tidepool Access, in what direction would you have to travel to reach the restrooms?
- **a.** northwest
- **b.** northeast
- **c.** southwest
- **d.** southeast

7. If you walked in a straight line from the Cabrillo Statue to the Whale Overlook, about how many miles would you walk?
- **a.** 0.25 mile
- **b.** 0.50 mile
- **c.** 0.75 mile
- **d.** 1.25 miles

Extended Response

Answer the two questions below in detail.

8. If you were planning to hike the Bayside Trail, what other type of map would be useful to have? Explain why.

9. Describe a situation in which knowing how to use a map scale can benefit people.

REFLECTING ON THE CHAPTER

Have students answer the following questions in their **Science Notebook:**

1. What questions do you still have about maps and how maps represent Earth?
2. What surprised you about the technologies used to map Earth?
3. How do the concepts of this chapter relate to your Unit Project?

California Content Standard

6.7.F Read a topographic map and a geologic map for evidence provided on the maps and construct and interpret a simple scale map.

Analyzing a Diagram

1. b *2. c* *3. b* *4. a* *5. c* *6. b* *7. a*

Extended Response

8. RUBRIC

4 points for a response that names the correct type of map and explains three pieces of information on the map

Sample: A topographical map will show features such as the trail's elevation and slope, and the presence of any streams. This type of map will enable me to prepare appropriately for the hike.

3 points for a response that names the correct type of map and explains two pieces of information on the map

2 points for a response that names the correct type of map and explains one piece of information on the map

1 point for a response that names the correct type of map

9. RUBRIC

4 points for a response that correctly describes how to use a map scale and shows how using the scale can benefit people.

Sample: Bill is giving directions to a baseball game to his new neighbor, Joe. Using a map, Bill measures the distance between their street and the location of the baseball stadium. He then relates this distance to the actual distance by using the map's bar scale. The stadium is 12 miles away, so Joe will have to plan accordingly to arrive on time.

3 points for a response that mostly describes how to use a map scale and shows how using the scale can benefit people.

2 points for a response that partly describes how to use a map scale and shows how using the scale can benefit people.

1 point for a response that describes how to use a map scale or shows the benefit of using the scale.

CHAPTER

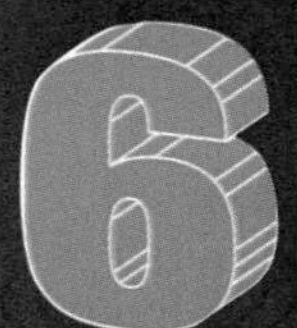

Minerals and Rocks

Earth Science UNIFYING PRINCIPLES

PRINCIPLE 1
Heat energy inside Earth and radiation from the Sun provide energy for Earth's processes.

PRINCIPLE 2
Physical forces, such as gravity, affect the movement of all matter on Earth and throughout the universe.

PRINCIPLE 3
Matter and energy move among Earth's rocks and soil, atmosphere, waters, and living things.

PRINCIPLE 4
Earth has changed over time and continues to change.

Unit: Earth's Surface BIG IDEAS

CHAPTER 5
Views of Earth Today
Modern technology has changed the way we view and map Earth.

CHAPTER 6
Minerals and Rocks
Minerals and rocks are basic building blocks of Earth.

CHAPTER 7
Erosion and Deposition
Water, wind, and ice shape Earth's surface.

CHAPTER 6 KEY CONCEPTS

SECTION 1

Minerals are all around us.

1. Minerals and rocks are part of daily life.
2. Minerals have four characteristics.
3. Minerals are grouped according to composition.
4. Most rocks are made of minerals.

SECTION 2

Rocks form in different ways.

1. Our world is built of rocks.
2. Rocks are classified by how they form.
3. Rocks can change into other types of rocks.

SECTION 3

Natural processes break down rocks.

1. Weathering helps change Earth's features over time.
2. Mechanical weathering produces physical changes in rocks.
3. Chemical weathering changes the mineral composition of rocks.
4. Weathering occurs at different rates.

SECTION 4

Geologic maps show Earth's surface features.

1. Geologic maps show information about rocks at and near Earth's surface.
2. Geologic maps show information about resources and hazards.

The Big Idea Flow Chart is available on p. T41 in the **TRANSPARENCY BOOK.**

Previewing Content

SECTION

Minerals are all around us. pp. 183–189

1. Minerals have four characteristics.
Minerals are the building blocks of most rocks. Minerals differ from **rocks** by having uniform compositions and orderly internal structures. The four characteristics of minerals are explained in the following chart:

Four Characteristics of Minerals

Characteristic	Example or Explanation
Forms in nature	Many minerals form when molten rock cools.
Is a solid	Ice is a mineral, but liquid water and water vapor are not minerals.
Has a definite chemical makeup	The mineral halite has one atom of the **element** sodium for every atom of the element chlorine.
Has a **crystal** structure	In all minerals, the atoms are arranged in an orderly, repeating, three-dimensional pattern.

2. Minerals are grouped according to composition.
Minerals are classified into groups on the basis of their chemical composition. The most common group is the silicates, which contain the elements oxygen and silicon joined together. These two elements are the most common ones in Earth's crust.

SECTION

Rocks form in different ways.
pp. 190–198

1. Our world is built of rocks.
Earth consists mostly of rock. Because rocks are common, long-lasting, and can be beautiful, they're used for many purposes, such as for constructing buildings, carving sculptures and monuments, and building roads. Rocks may contain minerals that are sources of metals or other valuable resources.

2. Rocks are classified by how they form.
There are three types of rock found on Earth, and each forms in a distinctive way. **Igneous rock** is formed when molten rock cools and becomes solid. **Sedimentary rock** is formed when pieces of minerals and rocks, plants, and other loose material get pressed or cemented together. **Metamorphic rock** is formed when heat or pressure causes older types of rock to change into new types of rock.

3. Rocks can change into other types of rocks.
The **rock cycle** describes the natural processes that form, change, break down, and re-form rocks. The following diagram shows the three types of rocks and the rock cycle.

The Rock Cycle

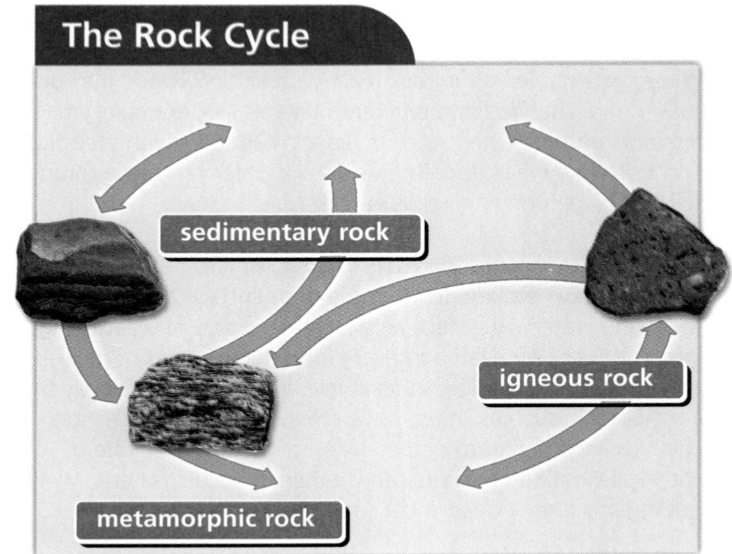

Common Misconceptions

MISCONCEPTION DATABASE
CLASSZONE.COM Background on student misconceptions

CHANGES IN ROCK Students may think that Earth has always been the way it is now, which means that rocks do not change. This misconception might come from observation of mountains, landforms, and rocks that appear to be permanent. In fact, rocks change as they move through the rock cycle.

This misconception is addressed on p. 196.

Previewing Content

SECTION

Natural processes break down rocks. pp. 199–205

1. **Weathering helps change Earth's features over time.** **Weathering** is the process by which natural forces break down rock into particles called *sediments*. The two main types of weathering are mechanical and chemical. **Mechanical weathering** involves a physical change in a rock. **Chemical weathering** changes the composition of rock.

2. **Mechanical weathering produces physical changes in rocks.** The agents of mechanical weathering include
   - ice wedging
   - plant root growth
   - pressure release
   - abrasion

   When water freezes in the cracks and pores of rocks, it expands, and ice breaks apart the rocks. Pressure release occurs when intrusive rocks are pushed to the surface; pressure on the rock is released and layers or sheets of rock gradually break off.

   Plants can take root in cracks of rocks and wedge the cracks open. Moving water can break up rocks by abrasion, which is the process of wearing down an object by friction.

3. **Chemical weathering changes the mineral composition of rocks.** When certain minerals in rock react with air and water, they dissolve or are changed into different minerals. For example, small amounts of atmospheric carbon dioxide can react with precipitation to form a weak acid. This acidic rainwater can move through soil and break down minerals in rocks.

4. **Weathering occurs at different rates.** When a rock is broken down, more of its surface area is exposed to air and water. As surface area increases, rates of weathering increase. Rates of weathering vary for different types of rocks—the igneous rock granite, for example, weathers more slowly than a softer rock, such as limestone. Because water is needed for chemical weathering to occur, and heat increases the rate of chemical weathering, chemical weathering occurs faster in wet, hot regions than it does in cold, dry regions.

SECTION

Geologic maps show Earth's surface features. pp. 206–213

1. **Geologic maps show information about rocks at and near Earth's surface.** A **geologic map** is a type of map that shows geologic features at or near Earth's surface for a specific region. The features can include the types and ages of rocks, as well as geologic structures such as fracture patterns within rock layers, the direction and angle at which rock layers are tilted, and faults.

2. **Geologic maps show information about resources and hazards.** Geologic maps are useful for evaluating potential resources and hazards that might be present in an area. Some examples of resources are oil or valuable minerals. Some examples of hazards are volcanoes (along with lava flow), landslides, and earthquakes.

Common Misconceptions

DENSITY OF WATER Students may think that the density of water does not change when it freezes. In fact, when water freezes, it becomes less dense as it expands. This is why ice is a powerful agent of mechanical weathering—water in the pores of rocks can freeze, expand, and split rocks apart.

 This misconception is addressed on p. 200.

MISCONCEPTION DATABASE
CLASSZONE.COM Background on student misconceptions

CHANGES IN ROCKS Some students might think that rocks do not change or break down over time by natural processes. They may not understand that smaller stones are the result of larger rocks breaking apart or that something so seemingly strong and unchanging as a boulder can be dissolved or broken apart by something so seemingly "weak" as water.

 This misconception is addressed on p. 201.

Previewing Labs

Lab Generator CD-ROM
Edit these Pupil Edition labs and generate alternative labs.

EXPLORE the BIG idea

What Makes Up Rocks?, p. 181 Students look for minerals in rocks.	**TIME** 10 minutes **MATERIALS** magnifying glass; three different rocks
Internet Activity: Rocks Students are introduced to how rocks form and change.	**TIME** 20 minutes **MATERIALS** computer with Internet access

SECTION 

EXPLORE Minerals, p. 183 Students examine salt to infer some of the characteristics of a mineral.	**TIME** 10 minutes **MATERIALS** colored paper, table salt, rock salt, magnifying glass
INVESTIGATE Crystal Shape, p. 186 Students observe different shapes that crystals have. **ALTERNATIVE:** Teacher Demonstration, URB p. 211	**TIME** 20 minutes **MATERIALS** 1 tablespoon, 2 cups or jars, 2 stirring rods, 1 tbs table salt, 1 tbs Epsom salts, 60 mL water, 2 pie plates, 2 sheets black paper, scissors

SECTION 

EXPLORE Rocks, p. 190 Students examine rock samples to see how rocks differ from one another.	**TIME** 20 minutes **MATERIALS** rock samples, magnifying glass
INVESTIGATE Sediment Layers, p. 194 Students examine how particle size determines how sedimentary layers form. **ALTERNATIVE:** Reading Activity, URB p. 211	**TIME** 20 minutes **MATERIALS** jar, measuring cup, water, 1/3 cup gravel, 1/3 cup sand

SECTION 

EXPLORE Weathering, p. 199 Students observe what causes a rock to break down.	**TIME** 20 minutes **MATERIALS** chalk, cup, vinegar
CHAPTER INVESTIGATION **Weathering,** pp. 204–205 Part One: Students observe the conditions that allow rusting to occur. Part Two: Students design an experiment to model the effects of mechanical and chemical weathering on different types of rocks. **ALTERNATIVE:** Direct Instruction, URB p. 212	**TIME** Part One: 20 minutes for setup, then results develop overnight; Part Two: 45 minutes for setup, then results develop overnight **MATERIALS** For Part One: steel wool, 3 cups, water, graduated cylinder; for Part Two: rock samples, dilute acids (such as vinegar, cola, lemon juice), plastic container and lid, duct tape, clear plastic sealable bag, balance, graduated cylinder, water

SECTION 

INVESTIGATE Landslide Areas, p. 211 Students analyze a geologic map to find out where landslides are most likely to affect a road. **ALTERNATIVE:** Teacher Demonstration, URB p. 212 Geologic Map of Highway 101, p. 111	**TIME** 20 minutes **MATERIALS** geologic map of Highway 101

 **Additional INVESTIGATION,** Modeling Rock Formation, A, B, & C, pp. 130–138; Teacher Instructions, pp. 211–212

Previewing Chapter Resources

	INTEGRATED TECHNOLOGY	LABS AND ACTIVITIES

CHAPTER 6 Minerals and Rocks

INTEGRATED TECHNOLOGY

CLASSZONE.COM
- eEdition Plus
- EasyPlanner Plus
- Misconception Database
- Content Review
- Test Practice
- Visualization
- Resource Centers
- Internet Activity: Rocks
- Math Tutorial

SCILINKS.ORG

SCILINKS

CD-ROMS
- eEdition
- EasyPlanner
- Power Presentations
- Content Review
- Lab Generator
- Test Generator

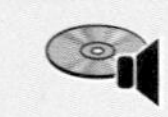

AUDIO CDS
- Audio Readings
- Audio Readings in Spanish

LABS AND ACTIVITIES

EXPLORE the Big Idea, p. 181
- What Makes Up Rocks?
- Internet Activity: Rocks

UNIT RESOURCE BOOK
Unit Projects, pp. 5–10

Lab Generator CD-ROM
Generate customized labs.

SECTION 1 Minerals are all around us.
pp. 183–189

 Lesson Plan, pp. 70–71

- **RESOURCE CENTER,** Minerals
- **MATH TUTORIAL**

TRANSPARENCY BOOK
- Big Idea Flow Chart, p. T41
- Daily Vocabulary Scaffolding, p. T42
- Note-Taking Model, p. T43
- 3-Minute Warm-Up, p. T44

- EXPLORE Minerals, p. 183
- INVESTIGATE Crystal Shape, p. 186
- Math in Science, p. 189

UNIT RESOURCE BOOK
- Datasheet, Crystal Shape, p. 79
- Math Support, p. 119
- Math Practice, p. 120

SECTION  2 Rocks form in different ways.
pp. 190–198

 Lesson Plan, pp. 81–82

- **RESOURCE CENTER,** Igneous, Sedimentary, and Metamorphic Rocks
- **VISUALIZATION,** Cooling Molten Rocks Form Crystals

TRANSPARENCY BOOK
- Daily Vocabulary Scaffolding, p. T42
- 3-Minute Warm-Up, p. T44

- EXPLORE Rocks, p. 190
- INVESTIGATE Sediment Layers, p. 194

UNIT RESOURCE BOOK
- Datasheet, Sediment Layers, p. 90
- Additional INVESTIGATION, Modeling Rock Formations, A, B, & C, pp. 130–138

SECTION   3 Natural processes break down rocks.
pp. 199–205

 Lesson Plan, pp. 92–93

RESOURCE CENTER, Weathering

TRANSPARENCY BOOK
- Daily Vocabulary Scaffolding, p. T42
- 3-Minute Warm-Up, p. T45
- "Mechanical Weathering" Visual, p. T46

- EXPLORE Weathering, p. 199
- CHAPTER INVESTIGATION, Weathering, pp. 204–205

UNIT RESOURCE BOOK
- CHAPTER INVESTIGATION, Weathering, pp.121–129

SECTION  4 Geologic maps show Earth's surface features.
pp. 206–213

 Lesson Plan, pp. 102–103

TRANSPARENCY BOOK
- Big Idea Flow Chart, p. T41
- Daily Vocabulary Scaffolding, p. T42
- 3-Minute Warm-Up, p. T45
- "Yosemite Geologic Map" Visual, p. T46
- Chapter Outline, pp. T47–T48

- INVESTIGATE Landslide Areas, p. 211

UNIT RESOURCE BOOK
- Datasheet, Geologic Maps of Highway 101, p. 111
- Datasheet, Landslide Areas, p. 112

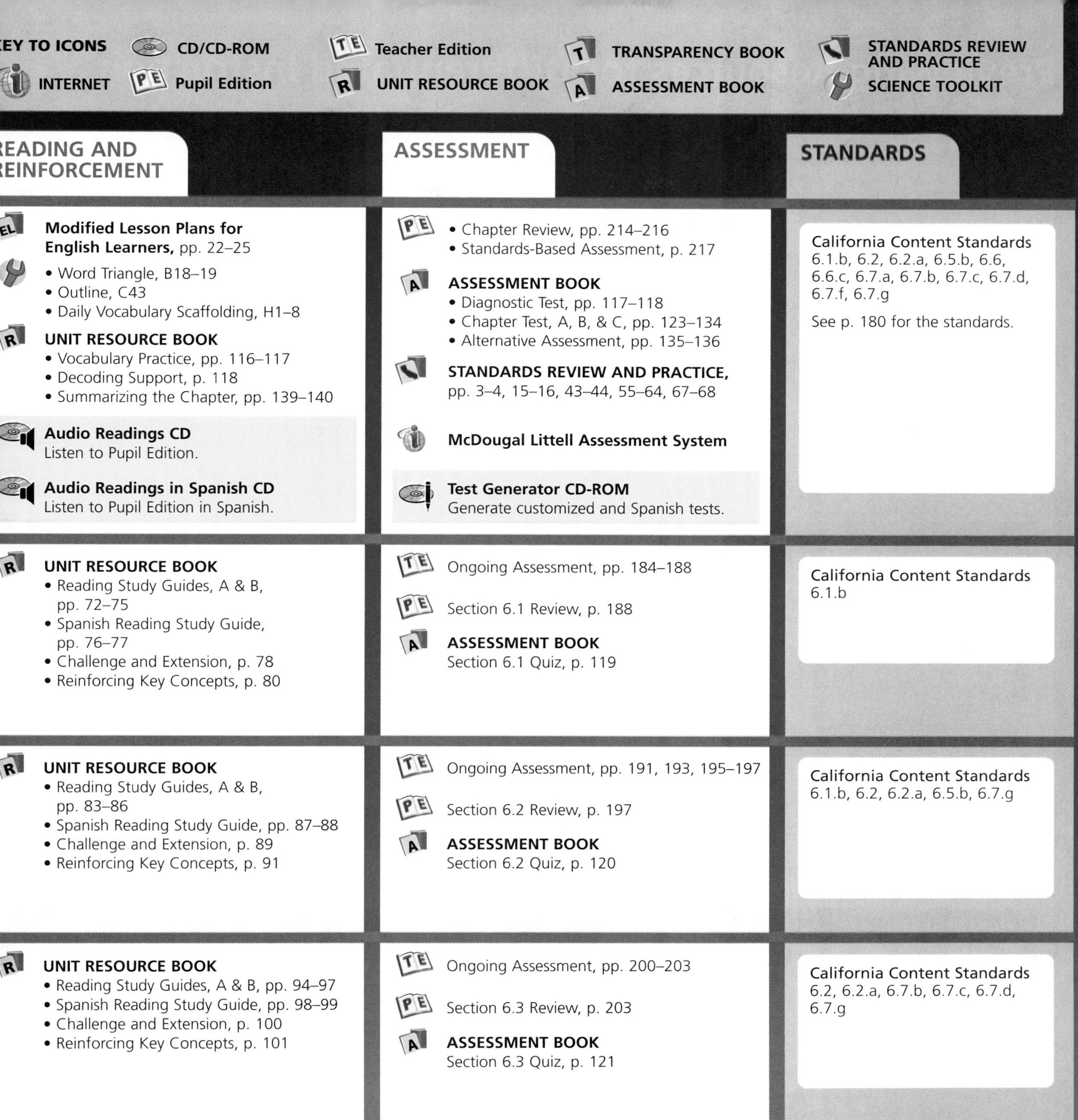

KEY TO ICONS: CD/CD-ROM · Teacher Edition · TRANSPARENCY BOOK · STANDARDS REVIEW AND PRACTICE · INTERNET · Pupil Edition · UNIT RESOURCE BOOK · ASSESSMENT BOOK · SCIENCE TOOLKIT

READING AND REINFORCEMENT	ASSESSMENT	STANDARDS
Modified Lesson Plans for English Learners, pp. 22–25 • Word Triangle, B18–19 • Outline, C43 • Daily Vocabulary Scaffolding, H1–8 **UNIT RESOURCE BOOK** • Vocabulary Practice, pp. 116–117 • Decoding Support, p. 118 • Summarizing the Chapter, pp. 139–140 **Audio Readings CD** Listen to Pupil Edition. **Audio Readings in Spanish CD** Listen to Pupil Edition in Spanish.	• Chapter Review, pp. 214–216 • Standards-Based Assessment, p. 217 **ASSESSMENT BOOK** • Diagnostic Test, pp. 117–118 • Chapter Test, A, B, & C, pp. 123–134 • Alternative Assessment, pp. 135–136 **STANDARDS REVIEW AND PRACTICE,** pp. 3–4, 15–16, 43–44, 55–64, 67–68 **McDougal Littell Assessment System** **Test Generator CD-ROM** Generate customized and Spanish tests.	California Content Standards 6.1.b, 6.2, 6.2.a, 6.5.b, 6.6, 6.6.c, 6.7.a, 6.7.b, 6.7.c, 6.7.d, 6.7.f, 6.7.g See p. 180 for the standards.
UNIT RESOURCE BOOK • Reading Study Guides, A & B, pp. 72–75 • Spanish Reading Study Guide, pp. 76–77 • Challenge and Extension, p. 78 • Reinforcing Key Concepts, p. 80	Ongoing Assessment, pp. 184–188 Section 6.1 Review, p. 188 **ASSESSMENT BOOK** Section 6.1 Quiz, p. 119	California Content Standards 6.1.b
UNIT RESOURCE BOOK • Reading Study Guides, A & B, pp. 83–86 • Spanish Reading Study Guide, pp. 87–88 • Challenge and Extension, p. 89 • Reinforcing Key Concepts, p. 91	Ongoing Assessment, pp. 191, 193, 195–197 Section 6.2 Review, p. 197 **ASSESSMENT BOOK** Section 6.2 Quiz, p. 120	California Content Standards 6.1.b, 6.2, 6.2.a, 6.5.b, 6.7.g
UNIT RESOURCE BOOK • Reading Study Guides, A & B, pp. 94–97 • Spanish Reading Study Guide, pp. 98–99 • Challenge and Extension, p. 100 • Reinforcing Key Concepts, p. 101	Ongoing Assessment, pp. 200–203 Section 6.3 Review, p. 203 **ASSESSMENT BOOK** Section 6.3 Quiz, p. 121	California Content Standards 6.2, 6.2.a, 6.7.b, 6.7.c, 6.7.d, 6.7.g
UNIT RESOURCE BOOK • Reading Study Guides, A & B, pp. 104–107 • Spanish Reading Study Guide, pp. 108–109 • Challenge and Extension, p. 110 • Reinforcing Key Concepts, p. 113 • Challenge Reading, pp. 114–115	Ongoing Assessment, pp. 207–208, 210–211 Section 6.4 Review, p. 212 **ASSESSMENT BOOK** Section 6.4 Quiz, p. 122	California Content Standards 6.6, 6.6.c, 6.7.f

Previewing Resources for Differentiated Instruction

CHAPTER INVESTIGATION

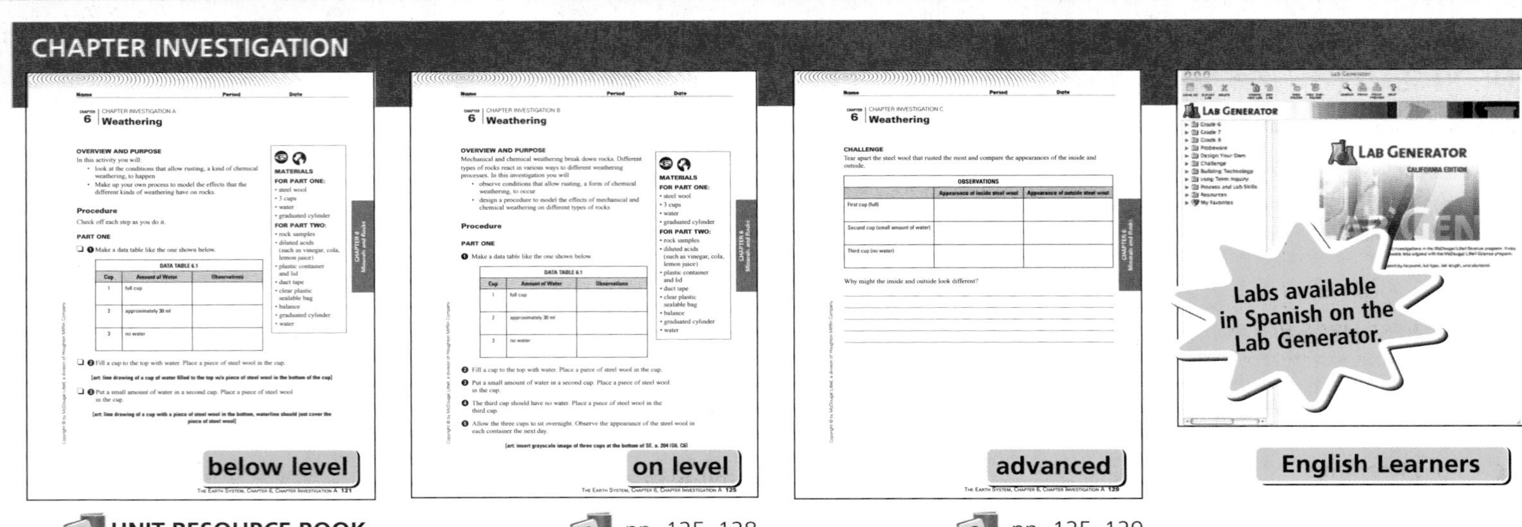

UNIT RESOURCE BOOK, pp. 121–124 | pp. 125–128 | pp. 125–129

READING STUDY GUIDE

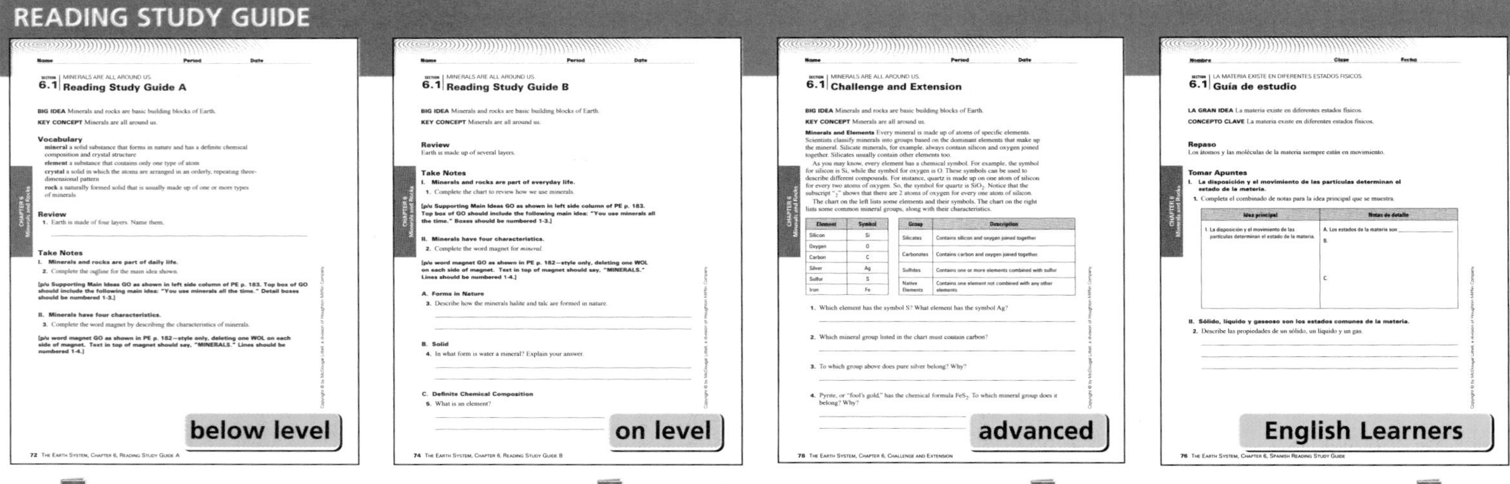

UNIT RESOURCE BOOK, pp. 72–73 | pp. 74–75 | p. 78 | p. 76

CHAPTER TEST

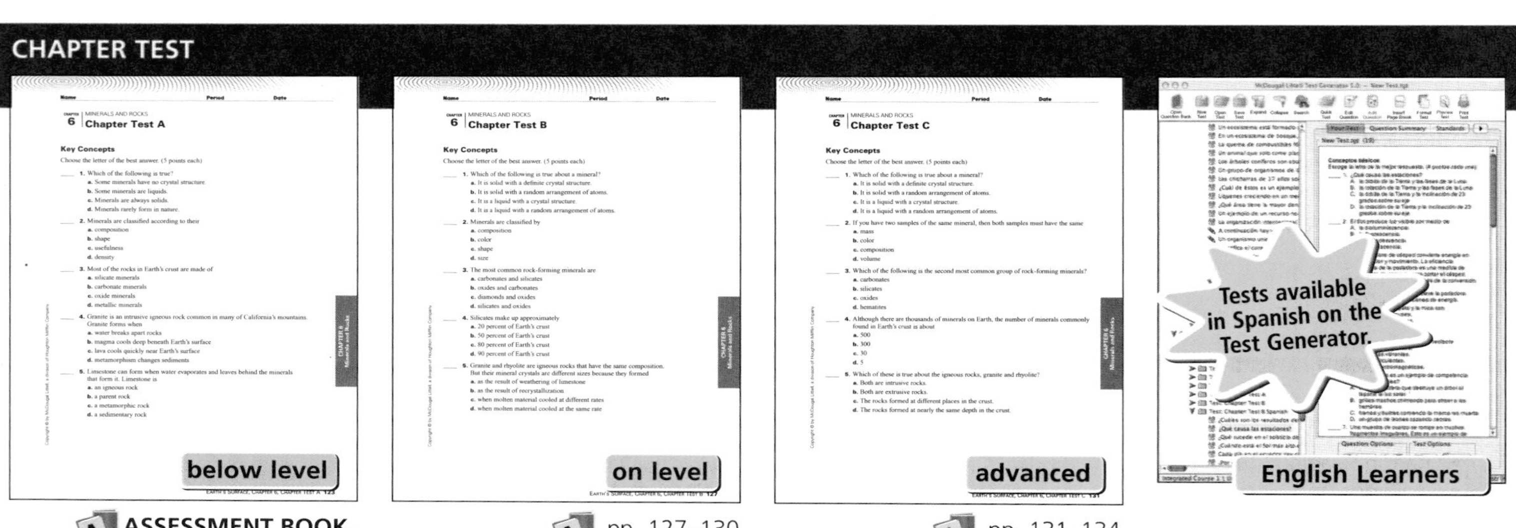

ASSESSMENT BOOK, pp. 123–126 | pp. 127–130 | pp. 131–134

TECHNOLOGY

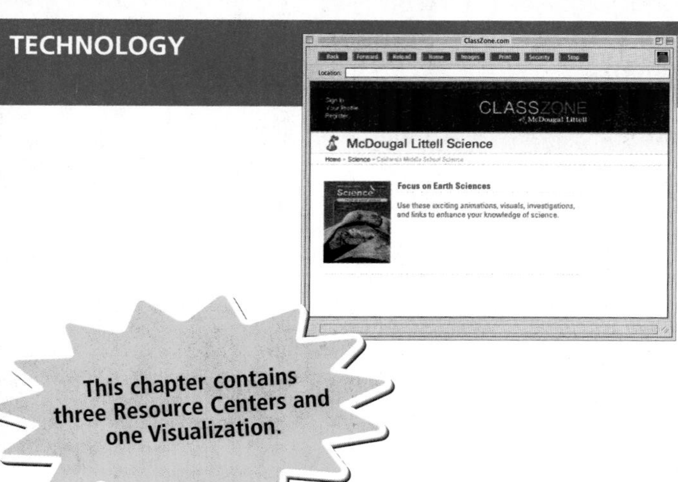

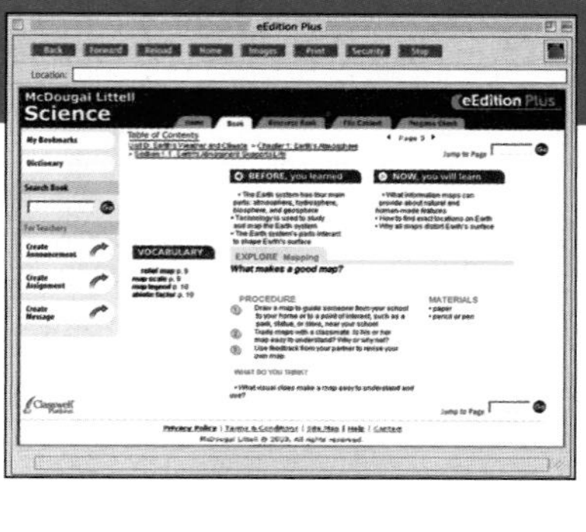

VISUAL CONTENT

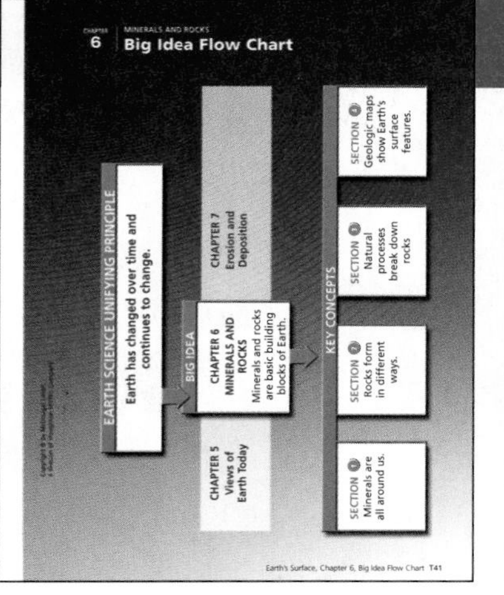

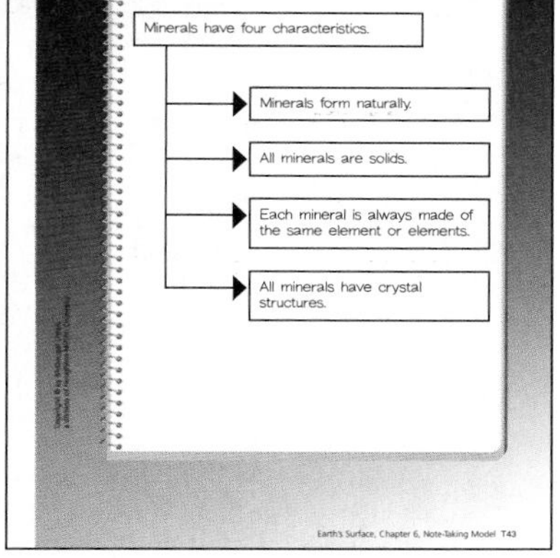

6 Note-Taking Model
SUPPORTING MAIN IDEAS
Minerals have four characteristics.
Minerals form naturally.
All minerals are solids.
Each mineral is always made of the same element or elements.
All minerals have crystal structures.

TRANSPARENCY BOOK, p. T41

p. T43

p. T46

MORE SUPPORT

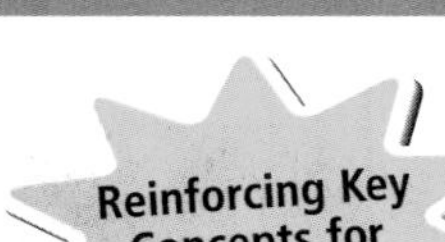

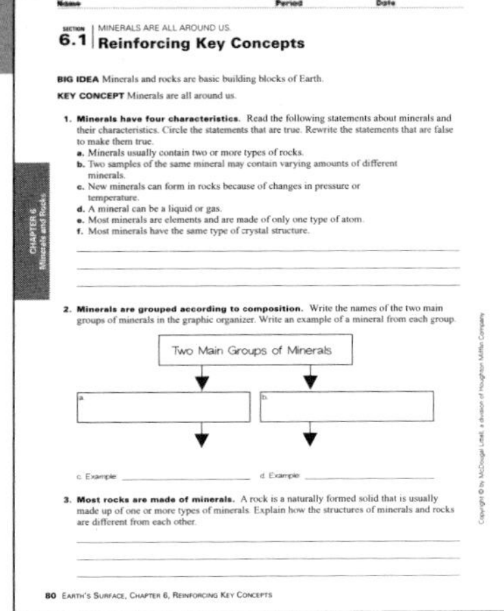

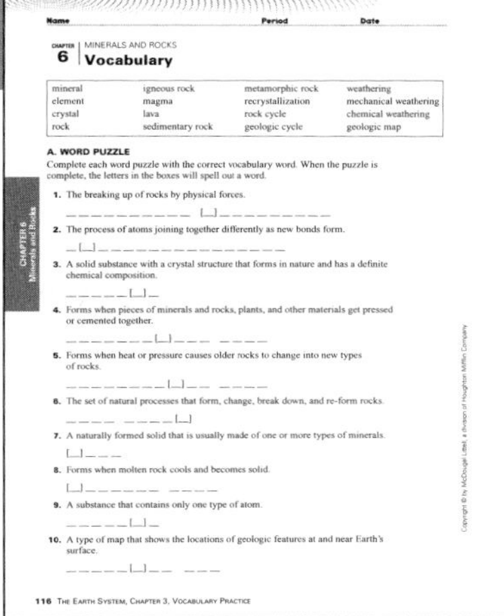

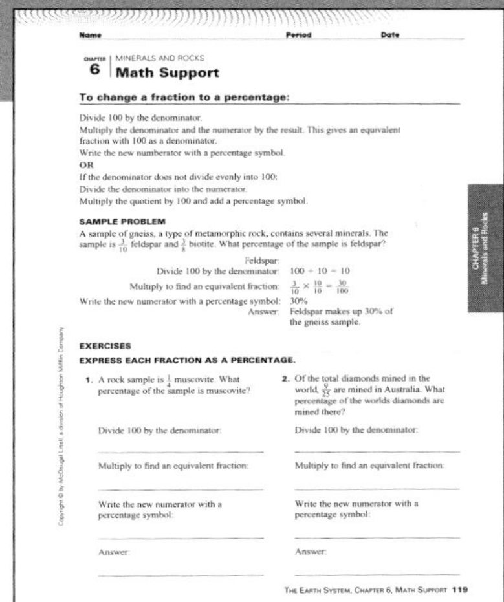

UNIT RESOURCE BOOK, p. 80

pp. 116–117

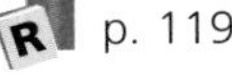

p. 119

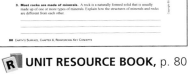

CHAPTER

Minerals and Rocks

INTRODUCE

the BIG idea

Have students look at the photograph of the boy panning for gold and discuss how the question in the box links to the Big Idea. Ask:

- What do you think happens to gold as the water is swirled in the pan?
- Why would the gold settle to the bottom?

California Content Standards

6.1.b Students know Earth is composed of several layers: a cold, brittle lithosphere; a hot, convecting mantle; and a dense, metallic core.

6.2 Topography is reshaped by the weathering of rock and soil and by the transportation and deposition of sediment.

6.2.a Students know water running downhill is the dominant process in shaping the landscape, including California's landscape.

6.5.b Students know matter is transferred over time from one organism to others in the food web and between organisms and the physical environment.

6.6 Sources of energy and materials differ in amounts, distribution, usefulness, and the time required for their formation.

6.6.c Students know the natural origin of the materials used to make common objects.

6.7.a Develop a hypothesis.

6.7.b Select and use appropriate tools and technology (including calculators, computers, balances, spring scales, microscopes, and binoculars) to perform tests, collect data, and display data.

6.7.c Construct appropriate graphs from data and develop qualitative statements about the relationships between variables.

6.7.d Communicate the steps and results from an investigation in written reports and oral presentations.

6.7.f Read a topographic map and a geologic map for evidence provided on the map and construct and interpret a simple scale map.

CHAPTER

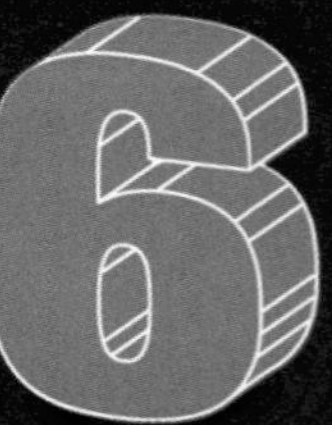

Minerals and Rocks

the BIG idea

Minerals and rocks are basic building blocks of Earth.

Key Concepts

SECTION

Minerals are all around us.
Learn about the characteristics all minerals share.

SECTION

Rocks form in different ways.
Learn about the three types of rocks and how they form.

SECTION

Natural processes break down rocks.
Learn about the mechanical and chemical processes that break down rocks.

SECTION

Geologic maps show Earth's surface features.
Learn how geologic maps show information about rocks, geologic structures, natural resources, and geologic hazards.

California ClassZone

CLASSZONE.COM

Chapter 6 online resources: Content Review, three Visualizations, three Resource Centers, Math Tutorial, Test Practice

Why might gold be found in this river?

180 Unit 2: **Earth's Surface**

INTERNET PREVIEW

CLASSZONE.COM For student use with the following pages:

Review and Practice

- Content Review, pp. 182, 214
- Math Tutorial: Percents and Fractions, p. 189
- Test Practice, p. 217

Activities and Resources

- Internet Activity: Rocks, p. 181
- Resource Centers: Minerals, p. 187; Igneous, Sedimentary, Metamorphic Rock, p. 194; Weathering, p. 200
- Visualization: Crystal Formation, p. 192

The Rock Cycle
Code: MDL015

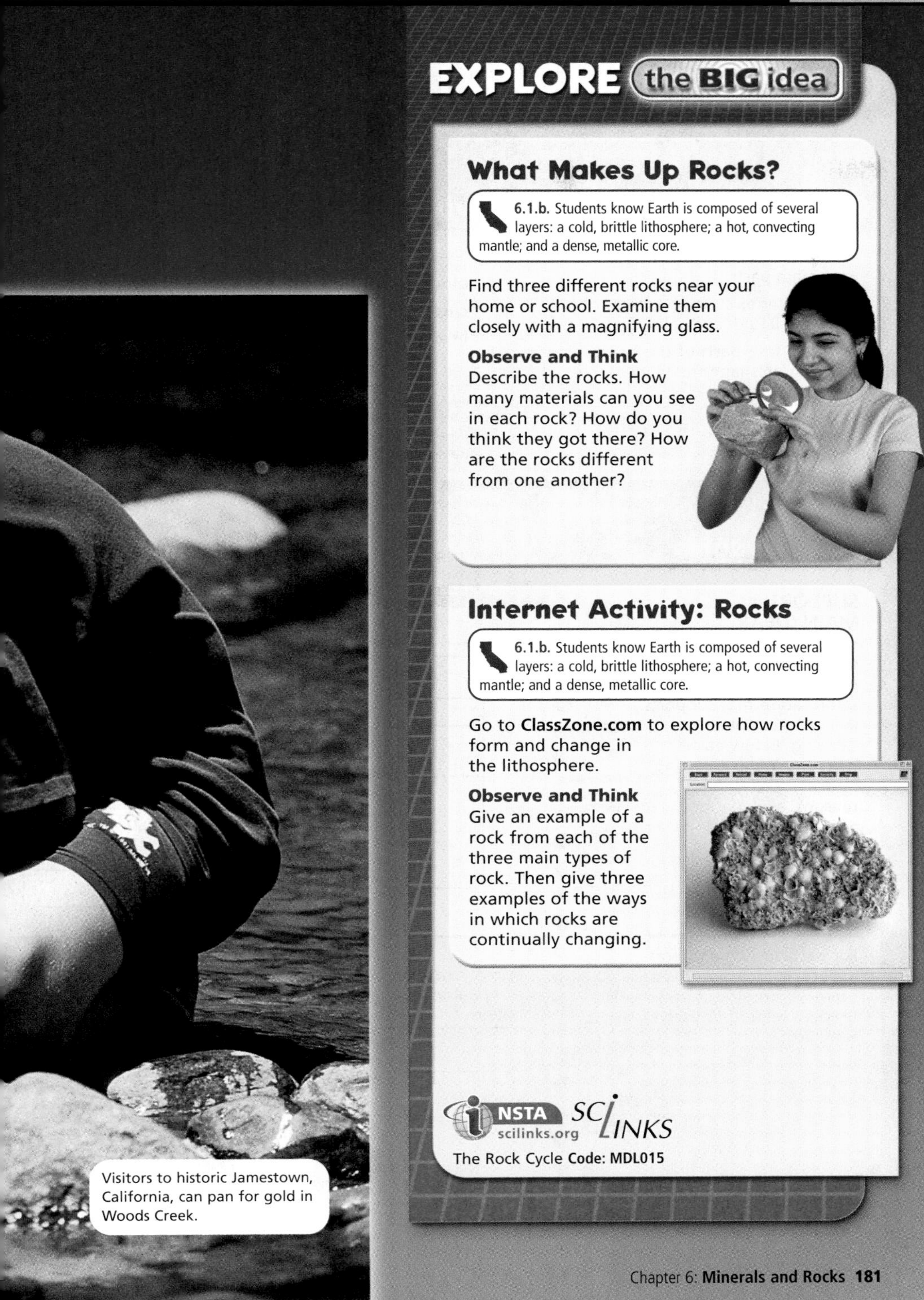

EXPLORE the BIG idea

What Makes Up Rocks?

6.1.b. Students know Earth is composed of several layers: a cold, brittle lithosphere; a hot, convecting mantle; and a dense, metallic core.

Find three different rocks near your home or school. Examine them closely with a magnifying glass.

Observe and Think
Describe the rocks. How many materials can you see in each rock? How do you think they got there? How are the rocks different from one another?

Internet Activity: Rocks

6.1.b. Students know Earth is composed of several layers: a cold, brittle lithosphere; a hot, convecting mantle; and a dense, metallic core.

Go to **ClassZone.com** to explore how rocks form and change in the lithosphere.

Observe and Think
Give an example of a rock from each of the three main types of rock. Then give three examples of the ways in which rocks are continually changing.

NSTA scilinks.org SCiLINKS
The Rock Cycle **Code: MDL015**

Visitors to historic Jamestown, California, can pan for gold in Woods Creek.

Chapter 6: **Minerals and Rocks 181**

EXPLORE the BIG idea

These inquiry-based activities are appropriate for use at home or as a supplement to classroom instruction.

What Makes Up Rocks?

PURPOSE To introduce students to materials that make up rocks. Students examine three rocks with a magnifying glass.

TIP *10 min.* Have students find three rock samples that look different.

Sample answer: Some rocks may look as though they are made up of only one material. Others may be made up of two or more materials that differ in color and texture. The materials are formed by natural processes within Earth or on Earth's surface. The rocks may differ in size, shape, color, weight, and texture.

REVISIT after p. 187.

Internet Activity: Rocks

PURPOSE To introduce students to the three main types of rocks, and the way in which rocks form and change.

TIP *20 min.* Ask students to list the three main types of rocks before they visit the Web site.

Sample answer: igneous, metamorphic, sedimentary; being worn down and broken apart, forming within Earth and then being exposed at the surface, and becoming another type of rock

REVISIT after p. 196.

EACHING WITH TECHNOLOGY

C Microscope If you have a PC microscope with appropriate software, use this technology to examine grains of salt while performing he activity on p. 183.

ideo Camera You might want to tape groups of students showing nd explaining the models they created for "Investigate Sediment ayers," p. 194. Play the videotape during an open house or during the vait time at parent conferences.

PREPARE

CONCEPT REVIEW

Activate Prior Knowledge

- Draw a diagram of Earth's four main parts on the board and ask students to identify them.
- Ask students to identify examples of three states of matter within the classroom, such as air (gas), a bottle of water (liquid), and a desk (solid).
- Have students list some of the different features of Earth's surface, such as rivers, lakes, and mountains.

TAKING NOTES

Supporting Main Ideas

Identifying supporting information for main ideas is a basic reading and study skill that not only helps students understand the concepts presented in the text but also prepares them for taking standardized tests. Encourage students to look for topic sentences and examples when filling in supporting information.

Vocabulary Strategy

The word magnet strategy will help students visualize the fact that a single word can have several concepts associated with it.

Vocabulary and Note-Taking Resources

- Vocabulary Practice, pp. 116–117
- Decoding Support, p. 118

- Daily Vocabulary Scaffolding, p. T42
- Note-Taking Model, p. T43

- Word Magnet, B24–25
- Supporting Main Ideas, C42
- Daily Vocabulary Scaffolding, H1–8

CHAPTER 6

Getting Ready to Learn

CONCEPT REVIEW

- The Earth system has four main parts.
- Matter exists in the forms of gas, liquid, and solid.
- The four parts of the Earth system shape the planet's surface.

VOCABULARY REVIEW

See Glossary for definitions.

atom

crust

lithosphere

Review concepts and vocabulary.

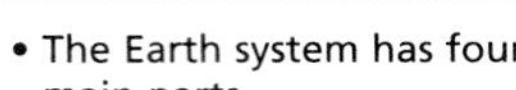

TAKING NOTES

SUPPORTING MAIN IDEAS

Make a chart to show each main idea and the information that supports it. Copy each blue heading. Below each heading, add supporting information, such as reasons, explanations, and examples.

VOCABULARY STRATEGY

For each vocabulary term, make a **magnet word** diagram. Write other terms or ideas related to that term around it.

See the Note-Taking Handbook on pages R45–R51.

SCIENCE NOTEBOOK

Minerals have four characteristics.
- Minerals form naturally.
- All minerals are solids.
- Each mineral is always made of the same element or elements.
- All minerals have crystal structures.

CRYSTAL
- atoms joined in a repeating 3-D pattern
- formed by all minerals

CHECK READINESS

Administer the Diagnostic Test to determine students' readiness for new science content and their mastery of requisite math skills.

 Diagnostic Test, pp. 117–118

Technology Resources

Students needing content and math skills should visit **ClassZone.com.**

- **CONTENT REVIEW**
- **MATH TUTORIAL**

 **CONTENT REVIEW CD-ROM**

KEY CONCEPT

Minerals are all around us.

CALIFORNIA Content Standard

Background for 6.1.b. Students know Earth is composed of several layers: a cold, brittle lithosphere; a hot, convecting mantle; and a dense, metallic core.

BEFORE, you learned

- Earth is made of layers
- Earth's outermost rocky layer is the crust

NOW, you will learn

- About the characteristics of minerals
- How minerals are classified into groups
- Which mineral group is most common

VOCABULARY

mineral p. 184
element p. 184
crystal p. 185
rock p. 187

EXPLORE Minerals (6.1.b)

What are some characteristics of a mineral?

PROCEDURE

1. Sprinkle some table salt on a sheet of colored paper. Look at a few grains of the salt through a magnifying glass. Then rub a few grains between your fingers.
2. In your notebook, describe all the qualities of the salt that you observe.
3. Examine the rock salt in the same way and describe its qualities in your notebook. How do the two differ?

MATERIALS

- colored paper
- table salt
- rock salt
- magnifying glass

WHAT DO YOU THINK?

Salt is a fairly common mineral in Earth's crust. From your observations of salt, what do you think are some characteristics of minerals?

Minerals and rocks are part of daily life.

SUPPORTING MAIN IDEAS
Enter this blue heading in a chart and record supporting information.

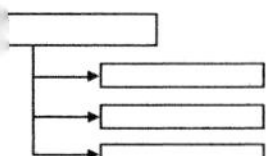

You use minerals all the time. Every time you turn on a microwave oven or a TV, you depend on minerals. The wires that carry electric current are made of copper, which is a mineral. Table salt, or halite (HAL-YT), is another mineral that you use in your everyday life.

Earth's lithosphere is made of rocks. As you will read later in this chapter, almost all rocks are made of minerals. People use rocks in many ways. If you look at large buildings, you might see that parts of their outside walls are made of rocks. Sometimes you can see minerals in the rocks. In a museum, you might see statues and other artworks carved from rocks.

6.1 FOCUS

Set Learning Goals

Students will

- Identify the characteristics of minerals.
- Explain how minerals are classified into groups.
- Identify which mineral group is most common.
- Observe through experimentation how crystals differ in shape.

3-Minute Warm-Up

Display Transparency T44 or copy this exercise on the board:

Decide if these statements are true. If not, correct them.

1. Latitude is a distance in degrees north or south of the equator. *true*
2. Relief maps use contour lines to show features. *Topographic maps use contour lines to show features.*
3. Geographic information systems display data in layers to build maps. *true*

3-Minute Warm-Up, p. T44

6.1 MOTIVATE

EXPLORE Minerals

PURPOSE To promote inquiry into the characteristics of minerals

TIP *10 min.* Organize the class into small groups to share observations.

WHAT DO YOU THINK? *Answers will vary but may include that minerals are solid and sparkly.*

Teaching with Technology

Students might use a PC microscope to examine the grains of salt.

RESOURCES FOR DIFFERENTIATED INSTRUCTION

Below Level

UNIT RESOURCE BOOK
Reading Study Guide A, pp. 72–73
Decoding Support, p. 118

AUDIO CDS

Advanced

UNIT RESOURCE BOOK
Challenge and Extension, p. 78

English Learners

UNIT RESOURCE BOOK
Spanish Reading Study Guide, pp. 76–77

AUDIO CDS

- Audio Readings in Spanish
- Audio Readings (English)

6.1 INSTRUCT

Teach the Standards

Lithosphere 6.1.b

In this section: Students build on what they know about the layers of Earth by learning in detail about minerals and rocks, which make up the lithosphere. Ask students to describe the lithosphere in their own words and contrast it with the mantle beneath it.

previously taught: Earth's layers, p. 44

future opportunities: plate tectonics, pp. 267–268; earthquakes, p. 303

Teach Difficult Concepts

Many texts state that one of the characteristic of minerals is that they are inorganic, not derived from living organisms. This is not strictly accurate because many living organisms produce minerals to form their shells, bones, and other hard parts. However, a substance that forms only by an organic process cannot be considered a mineral. For example, sugar forms organically; it never forms inorganically (without a process involving a living organism). Therefore, sugar is not a mineral, even though it has all of the other required characteristics. A substance must form from an inorganic process as well to be considered a mineral.

Teacher Demo

Place a handful of sugar on a sheet of colored paper and a handful of salt next to it. Ask whether both materials are minerals. Explain that the sugar is not a mineral but the salt is. All sugar comes from plants, which are living organisms. Thus, sugar is an organic product. Salt does not come from a living organism. It precipitates out of water.

Ongoing Assessment

Identify the characteristics of minerals.

Ask: What characteristics does ice have that make it a mineral? *It forms in nature, is a solid, has a definite chemical makeup, and has a crystal structure.*

Minerals have four characteristics.

A mineral can be so small that you need a microscope to see it, or it can be large. No matter what size a mineral is, it has four characteristics. A **mineral** is a substance that

- forms in nature
- is a solid
- has a definite chemical composition
- has a crystal structure

Forms in Nature

Minerals are formed by natural processes. Every type of mineral can form in nature by processes that do not involve living organisms. A few minerals can also be produced by organisms as part of their shells or bones.

Minerals form in many ways. Halite can form when water evaporates in a shallow part of the ocean, leaving behind the salt it contained. Many types of minerals develop when molten rock cools. Talc, a mineral that can be used to make baby powder, forms inside Earth as high pressure and temperature cause changes in solid rock.

READING TIP
Molten rock refers to rock that has become so hot that it has melted.

Solid

A mineral is a solid—that is, it has a definite volume and a rigid shape. Volume refers to the amount of space an object takes up. For example, a golf ball has a smaller volume than a baseball, and a baseball has a smaller volume than a basketball.

A substance that is a liquid or a gas is not a mineral. However, in some cases its solid form is a mineral. For example, liquid water is not a mineral, but ice is.

Definite Chemical Composition

Each mineral has a definite chemical makeup: it consists of a specific combination of atoms of certain elements. An **element** is a substance that contains only one type of atom. In turn, an atom is the smallest particle an element can be divided into.

Look at the illustration on page 185. You can see that some substances, including the minerals gold and copper, consist of just one element. However, most minerals are compounds, substances that consist of several elements in specific proportions. Notice that halite has one atom of sodium for every atom of chlorine.

REMINDER
You may remember *compound* from compound words—words formed by joining together smaller words: *note* + *book* = *notebook*. Likewise, a chemical compound has two or more elements joined together.

DIFFERENTIATE INSTRUCTION

More Reading Support

A How do minerals form? *by natural processes*

B Does a mineral exist as a solid, a liquid, or a gas? *solid*

English Learners This section has a number of phrasal verbs, such as *takes up* (p. 184) and *make up* (p. 185). English learners may read these phrases incorrectly by combining the meanings of the two words. Provide some synonyms for these phrasal verbs. If necessary, have students draw a sketch that helps them remember the meanings.

Atoms in Minerals

The mineral copper is made up of only copper atoms.

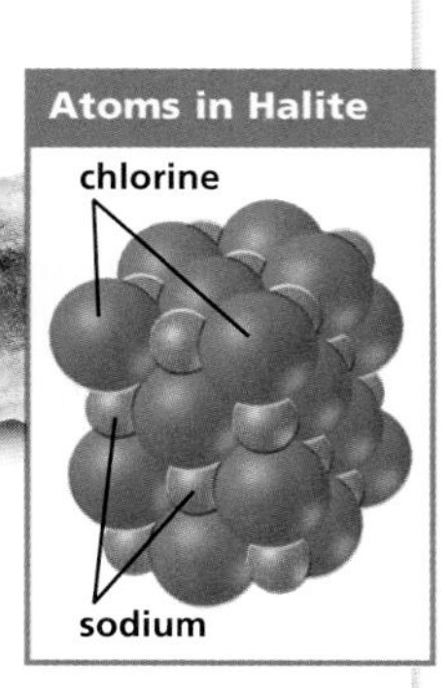

The mineral halite is made up of equal numbers of sodium and chlorine atoms.

Atoms in Halite

chlorine

sodium

READING VISUALS How do the diagrams show that copper consists of only one element and halite is a compound?

Crystal Structure

If you look closely at the particles of ice that make up frost, you will notice that they have smooth, flat surfaces. These flat surfaces form because of the arrangement of atoms in the ice, which is a mineral. This arrangement is a characteristic of minerals. It is the structure of a **crystal,** a solid in which the atoms are arranged in an orderly, repeating three-dimensional pattern.

Each mineral has its own type of crystal structure. In some cases, two minerals have the same chemical composition but different crystal structures. For example, both diamond and graphite consist of just one element—carbon. But the arrangements of the carbon atoms in these two minerals are not the same. Therefore, they have different crystal structures and very different properties. Diamonds are extremely hard and have a brilliant sparkle. Graphite is soft, gray, and dull.

CHECK YOUR READING Why do graphite and diamond have different properties?

In nature, a perfect crystal is rare. One can grow only when a mineral is free to form in an open space. This condition rarely exists within Earth's crust. The amount of space available for growth influences the shapes and sizes of crystals. Most crystals have imperfect shapes because their growth was limited by other crystals that formed next to them. But even though most crystals do not have perfect shapes, their atoms are still arranged in orderly crystal structures.

Integrate the Sciences

There are more than 100 chemical elements. Their atoms are made up of protons, neutrons, and electrons. It is the electron structure of an atom that determines the kind of bond it forms. Atoms form bonds either by sharing electrons or by transferring electrons.

Teach from Visuals

To help students interpret the diagrams of atoms in minerals, ask:

- What do the circles in each diagram represent? *atoms*
- Which atoms in halite are smaller? *sodium*

Ongoing Assessment

READING VISUALS *Answer: All the atoms in the copper diagram are the same color. The atoms in the halite diagram are two different colors.*

CHECK YOUR READING *Answer: The arrangement of carbon atoms in each mineral is different, so each has a different crystal structure and properties.*

DIFFERENTIATE INSTRUCTION

More Reading Support

C How can two minerals have the same chemical composition and still be different minerals? *They can have different crystal structures.*

Advanced Explain chemical formulas to students. The chemical formula of copper is Cu, and that of halite is NaCl. The proportion of an element in a compound is indicated by a number following the element symbol, such as H_2O for water. Have students use a mineral identification book to explain the chemical formulas of minerals mentioned in this chapter.

R Challenge and Extension, p. 78

INVESTIGATE Crystal Shape

PURPOSE To observe how crystal shapes can differ

TIPS *15 min.* Students will be able to see the desired results within one day.

- At the beginning of the experiment, have students record hypotheses and describe the results they expect to obtain.
- Have students revise their hypotheses as necessary after completing the experiment.

WHAT DO YOU THINK? *crystals; Crystals of table salt are cube-shaped; crystals of Epsom salts are long and thin. The crystals are different shapes because the substances have different crystal structures.*

CHALLENGE *Earth's crust and mantle contain mineral crystals.*

 Datasheet, Crystal Shape, p. 79

Technology Resources

Customize this student lab as needed. Print rubrics to assess student lab reports.

 **Lab Generator CD-ROM**

INVESTIGATE Crystal Shape

How do crystals differ in shape?

SKILL FOCUS
Observing (6.1.b)

PROCEDURE

1. Cut sheets of paper so that they fit inside the pie plates as shown. Place one sheet in each pie plate.
2. Observe the shape of the particles of the table salt then add the salt to 30 mL of water in a cup. Stir the water until the salt has dissolved.
3. Pour enough salt solution into one of the pie plates to completely cover the paper with a small film of liquid. Be careful not to pour into the plate any undissolved salt that may be in the bottom of the cup.
4. Repeat steps 2 and 3 with the Epsom salts. Let the plates dry overnight.

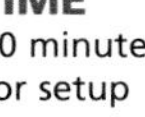

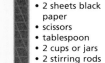

MATERIALS
- 2 pie plates
- 2 sheets black paper
- scissors
- tablespoon
- 2 cups or jars
- 2 stirring rods
- 1 tbs table salt
- 1 tbs Epsom salts
- 60 mL water

TIME
20 minutes for setup

WHAT DO YOU THINK?

- What do you see on the paper? Compare and describe the shapes of the crystals.
- Why are the shapes of the crystals the same as or different from the shapes in the materials you started with?

CHALLENGE Which layers of Earth contain mineral crystals?

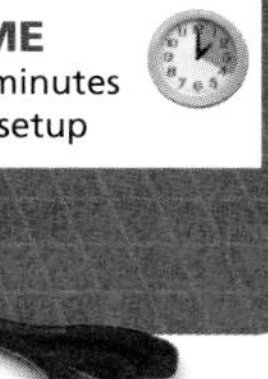

Minerals are grouped according to composition.

REMINDER
You can see a chart of common minerals and their properties on pages R66–R68.

Although there are thousands of different minerals, only about 30 are common in Earth's crust. These 30 minerals make up most of the rocks in the crust. For that reason, they are called rock-forming minerals. Scientists classify minerals into groups based on their compositions. Silicates (SIHL-ih-KAYTS) make up about 90 percent of the rocks in Earth's crust. They are the most common rock-forming minerals. Quartz, feldspar, and mica (MY-kuh) are common silicates. All the minerals in this group contain oxygen and silicon, the two most common elements in Earth's crust, joined together.

CHECK YOUR READING Which mineral group do most rock-forming minerals belong to?

The second most common group of rock-forming minerals is the carbonates. These minerals contain carbon and oxygen joined together. Some carbonate minerals are commonly produced by living things.

Ongoing Assessment

Explain how minerals are classified into groups.

Ask: How do scientists classify minerals into groups? *on the basis of their chemical makeups*

Identify which mineral group is most common.

Ask: What percentage of the rocks in Earth's crust are silicates? *about 90 percent*

 *Answer: silicates*

DIFFERENTIATE INSTRUCTION

More Reading Support

D How many minerals make up most of the rocks in Earth's crust? *30*

E What do all silicates contain? *oxygen and silicon joined together*

Alternative Assessment As an alternative to having students write answers to the questions for "Investigate Crystal Shape," you might have groups orally report and discuss their results and their responses to the questions.

For example, clams and oysters produce carbonate minerals such as calcite (KAL-SYT) when they form their shells. Carbonate minerals also form by processes that do not involve living things.

There are many other mineral groups. All are important, even though their minerals are not as common as silicates or carbonates. For example, the mineral group known as oxides contains the minerals from which most metals are refined. Examples of metals include tin and chromium. An oxide consists of an element, usually a metal, joined to oxygen. This group includes hematite (HEE-muh-TYT), a source of iron.

Find information on minerals.

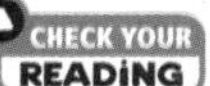

Why is the oxide mineral group important?

Most rocks are made of minerals.

You might think that minerals and rocks are the same things. But a mineral must have the four characteristics listed on page 184. A rock has only two of the four—it is a solid and it forms naturally. A **rock** is a naturally formed solid that is usually made up of one or more types of minerals.

Add a magnet word diagram for *rock* in your notebook.

Minerals in Rocks

Most rocks contain several types of minerals.

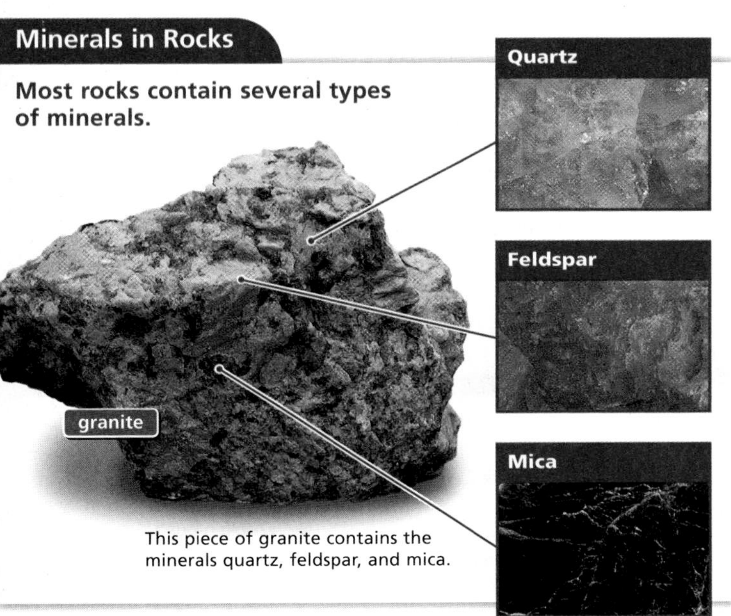

This piece of granite contains the minerals quartz, feldspar, and mica.

Integrate the Sciences

One interesting sea creature that produces its own carbonate shell is the chambered nautilus. With its distinctive banded spiral shell, the nautilus seems to be a close relative of the snail, although in reality it's most closely related to other cephalopods such as the squid and the octopus. The shell of the nautilus, like that of all mollusks, is composed of calcium carbonate. This shell provides the nautilus with protection. In addition, the shell's chambers contain gases that help the animal float in the water.

Teach from Visuals

To help students interpret the diagram of minerals in rocks, ask:

- How can you tell that the rock has different minerals in it? *It contains materials of different colors.*
- How do the minerals differ in appearance? *They differ in color and texture.*

Explore the BIG idea

Revisit "What Makes Up Rocks?" on p. 181. Have students explain the reasons for what they observed.

Ongoing Assessment

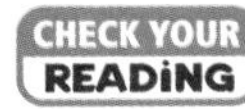

Answer: It is a source of metals.

DIFFERENTIATE INSTRUCTION

More Reading Support

F Why do some ocean animals produce the mineral calcite? *to form their shells*

G What are two characteristics of rocks? *They are solid and form naturally.*

Below Level Help students make the connection between the most common elements and the most common mineral group.

Most Common in Earth's Crust	
Elements	**Mineral Group**
oxygen, silicon	silicate (contain oxygen + silicon)

Teach from Visuals

Note that the two rocks pictured are examples of a common type of rock and an unusual type of rock. To help students interpret the visual, ask:

- How does the obsidian differ in appearance from the gabbro? *The obsidian appears more uniform in color and texture than the gabbro. The obsidian looks glassy, and the gabbro looks grainy.*
- How does this difference in appearance reflect their compositions? *The obsidian is a natural glass and contains no minerals. Gabbro is made up of several types of minerals, which results in grains of different colors.*

Ongoing Assessment

Answer: A mineral always has the same composition, but rocks do not.

ASSESS & RETEACH

Assess

Section 6.1 Quiz, p. 119

Reteach

- Hold up a sample of a mineral, such as a piece of chalk. Ask students what four characteristics it has that make it a mineral. List the four characteristics on the board and ask volunteers to explain each one.
- Hold up a common rock (make sure the rock is not limestone or another carbonate). Ask students what group the minerals in the rock most likely belong to. Have students explain what silicates contain and why they are the most common mineral group in Earth's crust.

Technology Resources

Have students visit **ClassZone.com** for reteaching of Key Concepts.

- **CONTENT REVIEW**
- **MATH TUTORIAL**

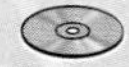

CONTENT REVIEW CD-ROM

READING TIP

Proportions show relationships between amounts. For example, a quartz crystal always has the same proportion of oxygen atoms to silicon atoms: two oxygen atoms for every silicon atom.

The structure of rocks is different from that of minerals. A mineral is always made of the same elements in the same proportions. All minerals have an orderly crystal structure. However, the proportion of different minerals in a certain type of rock may vary. Also, the minerals in a rock can be all jumbled together.

How are minerals different from rocks?

Gabbro, like most rocks, is made up of several types of minerals.

Obsidian is an unusual rock because it contains no minerals.

A few types of rocks are made up of one type of mineral. A few contain no minerals at all. Limestone, for example, can be made up entirely of the mineral calcite. Obsidian (ahb-SIHD-ee-uhn) is a rock that contains no minerals. It is made of natural glass, which is not a mineral because it does not have a crystal structure.

Coal is another rock that does not have a crystal structure. It is made up of the remains of ancient plants that were buried and pressed into rock. Coal started forming millions of years ago in swamps. As plants died, their remains fell on the remains of earlier plants. Then other materials buried the plant remains. Over time, the weight of the materials above pressed the plant remains into coal. You will read in Chapter 13 how people use coal as an energy source.

6.1 Review

KEY CONCEPTS

1. What are the four characteristics of a mineral? (6.1.b)
2. How are minerals classified? (6.1.b)
3. What is the most common group of minerals? What percentage of the crust do they make up? (6.1.b)

CRITICAL THINKING

4. **Classify** Can oil and natural gas be classified as minerals? Why or why not?
5. **Apply** When a piece of quartz is heated to a very high temperature, it melts into a liquid. Is it still a mineral? Why or why not?

CHALLENGE

6. **Interpret** You can see perfect crystals lining the inside of certain rocks when they are broken open. How do you think the crystals were able to form?

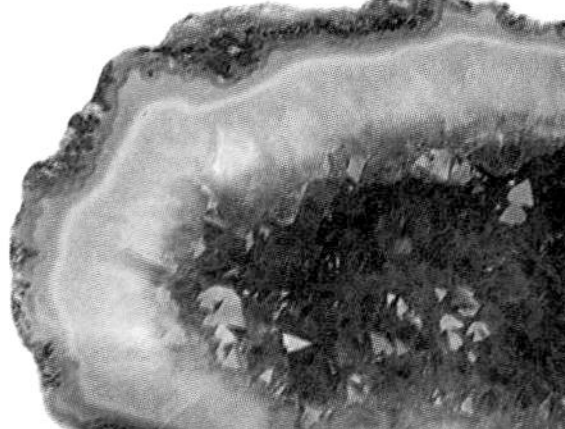

ANSWERS

1. A mineral forms in nature, is a solid, has a definite chemical makeup, and has a crystal structure.

2. Scientists classify minerals into groups on the basis of their chemical makeups.

3. The silicate group is the most common, and these minerals make up about 90% of the crust.

4. Oil and natural gas cannot be classified as minerals, because they are not solids, do not form crystals, and do not have a definite chemical makeup.

5. Melted quartz is not a mineral, because it is not a solid.

6. The minerals had room to grow into perfect crystals because the rocks are hollow

MATH TUTORIAL
CLASSZONE.COM
Click on Math Tutorial for more help with percents and fractions.

Math 6.NS.2.4

SKILL: WRITING FRACTIONS AS PERCENTS

Minerals in Rocks

Granite

Like most rocks, granite is a mixture of several minerals. Each mineral makes up a certain proportion, or fraction, of a granite sample. You can compare mineral amounts by expressing each mineral's fraction as a percentage.

Example

To change a fraction to a percentage, you must find an equivalent fraction with 100 as the denominator. Suppose, for example, you want to change the fraction $\frac{1}{5}$ to a percentage. First, divide 100 by the denominator 5, which gives you 20. Then multiply both the numerator and denominator by 20 to find the percentage.

$\frac{1}{5} \cdot \frac{20}{20} = \frac{20}{100}$ or 20% $\frac{1}{5}$ is 20%

The table below shows the fraction of each mineral in a granite sample.

Minerals in Granite Sample

Mineral	Fraction of Granite Sample	Percentage of Granite
Quartz	$\frac{1}{4}$	?
Feldspar	$\frac{13}{20}$	?
Mica	$\frac{3}{50}$	?
Dark minerals	$\frac{1}{25}$	?

Use the table to answer the following questions.

1. Copy the table. Calculate and fill in the percentage of each mineral in the granite sample.
2. Which minerals make up the greatest and smallest percentages of the granite?
3. In another granite sample, feldspar makes up $\frac{3}{5}$ and mica makes up $\frac{2}{25}$. What is the percentage of each mineral in the rock?

CHALLENGE The mineral hornblende is often one of the dark minerals in granite. If hornblende makes up $\frac{1}{32}$ of a granite sample, approximately what percentage of the rock is hornblende?

ANSWERS

1. *25%, 65%, 6%, 4%*
2. *greatest percentage: feldspar; smallest percentage: dark minerals*
3. *feldspar, $\frac{3}{5} \times \frac{20}{20} = \frac{60}{100}$ or 60%*
mica, $\frac{2}{25} \times \frac{4}{4} = \frac{8}{100}$ or 8%.

CHALLENGE *$\frac{1}{32} \times \frac{3.125}{3.125} = \frac{3.125}{100}$ or 3.125%*

MATH IN SCIENCE
Math Skills Practice for Science

Set Learning Goal
To find and compare the percentages of various minerals in a rock

Math Standard

6.NS.2.4 Determine the least common multiple and the greatest common divisor of whole numbers; use them to solve problems with fractions (e.g., to find a common denominator to add two fractions or to find the reduced form for a fraction).

Present the Science
The percentages of component minerals are one of the factors used in classifying rocks. The percentage of each component mineral typically varies within a certain range from sample to sample of the same type of rock. Granite is a common rock in Earth's crust.

Develop Algebra Skills
- Use the fraction $\frac{3}{10}$ to demonstrate on the board this method of changing a fraction to a percentage. First, divide 100 by the denominator, 10, which gives you 10. Then multiply the numerator and the denominator by 10 to find the percentage.

  $\frac{3}{10} \times \frac{3}{10} = \frac{30}{100}$ or 30%
- Students may have other methods of changing fractions to percentages. If so, have them share their methods.

Close
Ask: What does the percentage of a mineral in a rock tell you? *It tells you what portion of the rock is made up of that mineral.*

- Math Support, p. 119
- Math Practice, p. 120

Technology Resources

Students can visit **ClassZone.com** for practice in adding measurements.

MATH TUTORIAL

6.2 FOCUS

Set Learning Goals

Students will

- Identify the three types of rocks.
- Explain how one type of rock can change into another.
- Tell how common each rock type is in Earth's crust.
- Model how sedimentary layers form in an experiment.

3-Minute Warm-Up

Display Transparency 44 or copy this exercise on the board:

1. Draw and label a diagram that shows the relationship between minerals and rocks. *Students might draw a rock with specks of different sizes and shades, and label the specks as minerals and the entire object as a rock.*
2. Which of the following is *not* one of the four characteristics of minerals? forms in nature, solid, definite chemical composition, created as a result of the mineral cycle, crystal structure *created as a result of the mineral cycle.*

 3-Minute Warm-Up, p. T44

6.2 MOTIVATE

EXPLORE Rocks

PURPOSE To spark students' thinking about the differences between different types of rocks.

TIP *10 min.* If possible, choose rocks that clearly differ in shape, color, and texture.

WHAT DO YOU THINK? *Sample answers: Similarities: Different rocks are all solid. Differences: Rocks may differ in size, color, shape, texture, or appearance; student responses to second bullet will depend on what type of rocks they are analyzing.*

KEY CONCEPT

6.2 Rocks form in different ways.

CALIFORNIA Content Standards

Background for
6.1.b Students know Earth is composed of several layers: a cold, brittle lithosphere; a hot, convecting mantle; and a dense, metallic core.
6.2 Topography is reshaped by the weathering of rock and soil and by the transportation and deposition of sediment.

BEFORE, you learned

- Minerals and rocks are basic components of Earth
- Minerals have four characteristics
- Most rocks are made of minerals

NOW, you will learn

- About the three types of rocks
- How one type of rock can change into another
- How common each rock type is in Earth's crust

VOCABULARY

igneous rock p. 191
magma p. 191
lava p. 191
sedimentary rock p. 192
metamorphic rock p. 194
recrystallization p. 195
rock cycle p. 196

EXPLORE Rocks (6.1.b)

How do rocks differ from one another?

PROCEDURE

1. Closely examine the rock samples. What do you notice about the forms, shapes, colors, and textures of the rocks?
2. In your notebook, make lists of the characteristics of the rocks.

WHAT DO YOU THINK?

- What are the similarities and differences between the rocks?
- Which of Earth's layers did the rocks come from? How do you know?

MATERIALS

- rock samples
- magnifying glass

SUPPORTING MAIN IDEAS As you read, write each blue heading in a chart and record supporting information.

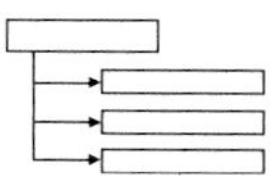

Our world is built of rocks.

Earth is built almost entirely of rock. When you look at Earth's surface, you can see soil, plants, rivers, and oceans. These surface features, however, form only a very thin covering on the planet. Between this thin layer and Earth's metallic core, Earth is made of solid and molten rock.

Because rocks are so common, it is not surprising that people use them for many different purposes, including using them as

- building materials for houses and skyscrapers
- sources of metals, such as iron, aluminum, and copper
- materials for statues and other works of art
- a base for pavement of roads and highways

RESOURCES FOR DIFFERENTIATED INSTRUCTION

Below Level

UNIT RESOURCE BOOK
- Reading Study Guide A, pp. 83–84
- Decoding Support, p. 118

AUDIO CDS

 **Additional INVESTIGATION,** Modeling Rock Formation, A, B, & C, pp. 130–138; Teacher Instructions, pp. 211–212

Advanced

UNIT RESOURCE BOOK
Challenge and Extension, p. 89

English Learners

UNIT RESOURCE BOOK
Spanish Reading Study Guide, pp. 87–88

- Audio Readings in Spanish
- Audio Readings (English)

People value rocks because rocks are strong and long-lasting, and because some are beautiful. Rock structures and carvings still exist from ancient times and give us a link to our distant past. Many famous monuments and sculptures are made from rocks. Granite blocks form part of the Great Wall of China. Limestone blocks make up the Great Pyramid in Egypt. The faces of four U.S. presidents are carved in the granite of Mount Rushmore.

Why do people use rocks for many different purposes?

This sculptor in Indonesia, like artists throughout the world, shapes rocks into lasting works of art.

Rocks are classified by how they form.

Earth has three types of rocks that form in distinct ways. As you read about these types of rocks, you will see that rocks do not last forever. Over time—usually thousands to millions of years—rocks change, break down, and re-form. But they still last longer than almost any other building material you can name, including iron.

Igneous Rock

Igneous rock (IHG-nee-uhs) forms when molten rock cools and becomes solid. Molten rock is a mixture of melted rock, solid mineral crystals, and dissolved gases. Igneous rock can form under Earth's surface, or it can form on the surface. Molten rock inside Earth is called **magma.** Molten rock that reaches Earth's surface is called **lava.**

Depending on where they form, igneous rocks are referred to as intrusive (ihn-TROO-sihv) or extrusive (ihk-STROO-sihv). The illustration on page 192 shows that an intrusive igneous rock is one that forms when magma cools inside Earth. An extrusive igneous rock is one that forms when lava cools on Earth's surface.

An intrusive igneous rock can have the same mineral composition as an extrusive igneous rock. However, the rocks will have different names, because the size of their mineral crystals will be very different. For example, granite is a common intrusive rock. If magma with the same composition reaches the surface, it forms an extrusive rock such as rhyolite.

READING TIP

The words *intrusive* and *extrusive* come from the Latin words *intrudere,* "to push in," and *extrudere,* "to push out." The prefix *in-* means "into," or "within." The prefix *ex-* means "outside," or "away from."

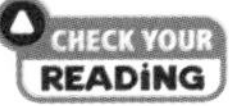

How are granite and rhyolite similar? How are they different?

6.2 INSTRUCT

Teach the Standards

Transportation and deposition of sediment 6.2

In this section: Help students understand that sedimentary rock, one of the three types of rock found on Earth, is formed by sediment—small particles that are carried and deposited by moving water or other natural forces.

- **previously taught:** landslides, p. 46
- **future opportunities:** stream channels, p. 232; alluvial fans and deltas, p. 233; shorelines, pp. 239–242; erosion of mountains, p. 339

Social Studies Connection

Have small groups of students research a famous world monument made of stone, such as the Great Wall of China, Stonehenge, the Egyptian Sphinx, the Egyptian or Mexican pyramids, Machu Picchu in Peru, or the Parthenon in Greece. Students should prepare short class presentations on the monument, in which they display a large drawing or photo of the monument, and explain when it was built, what type of stone it is made from, who built it, and for what purpose. Students can also include in their presentations a short guide for tourists wishing to visit the monument, including information on how to get to the monument and other key points of interest.

Ongoing Assessment

CHECK YOUR READING *Answer: Rocks have many uses because they last a long time and can be beautiful.*

CHECK YOUR READING *Answer: Both granite and rhyolite have the same mineral composition, but the size of their mineral crystals are very different.*

DIFFERENTIATE INSTRUCTION

More Reading Support

A Name a famous monument that is made from rock. *Great Wall of China, Great Pyramid of Egypt, Mount Rushmore*

English Learners English learners may have difficulty reading sentences that have introductory clauses and phrases. When this happens, have them find the comma that separates a clause from the rest of the sentence. Then have them locate the subject of the sentence. They might benefit from some examples on this page, such as *Depending on where they form…*and *If magma with the same composition reaches the surface….*

Have students who are interested in the formation of crystals in rock read the following article:

R Challenge Reading, pp. 114–115

History of Science

James Hutton, the Scottish physician and farmer regarded as the father of modern geology, was the scientist who deduced that granite formed from the cooling of molten rock deep within Earth. He observed intrusions of granite within sedimentary rock as he worked in his fields. He noticed that the granite seemed to have invaded fractures in the sedimentary rock while the granite was molten. He also noted the coarse texture of the granite, which would be expected from slow cooling and slow crystallization.

Teach from Visuals

To help students interpret the visual of cooling molten rock, ask:

- Because granite forms deep within Earth, would you expect it to have large or small mineral crystals? Why? *large, because mineral crystals grow larger with longer cooling times*
- Since rhyolite forms on Earth's surface, would you expect it to have large or small mineral crystals? Why? *small, because it cools quickly*

Crystal Size and Cooling Time

The more slowly molten rock cools, the larger the igneous rocks' mineral crystals will be.

shorter cooling time

Extrusive Rock

Molten rock that cools at Earth's surface hardens quickly, forming rocks that have small mineral crystals.

rhyolite

Intrusive Rock

Molten rock that cools inside Earth hardens slowly, forming rocks that have large mineral crystals.

granite

longer cooling time

Explore an animation showing how crystals form as molten rock cools.

You can see extrusive igneous rocks at Earth's surface. But intrusive igneous rocks form within Earth. How do they reach the surface? Forces inside Earth can push rocks up, as when mountains form. Also, water and wind break apart and carry away surface rocks. Then deeper rocks are uncovered at the surface.

B

Sedimentary Rock

Most **sedimentary rock** (SEHD-uh-MEHN-tuh-ree) forms when pieces of minerals and rocks, plants, and other loose materials get pressed or cemented together. Loose materials that are carried by water or wind and then settle on a surface are called sediments. Sediments build up in layers as they settle from water or wind. C

Younger layers of sediments form on top of older layers. The illustration on page 193 shows sediments carried by water. The distance that sediments are carried depends on the size of the sediments and the speed of the water. Large, heavy sediments settle quickly as the speed of the water decreases. Small, light sediments can be carried a long way—even by slowly flowing water.

Lower layers of sediments can get pressed into rock by the weight of layers of sediments above them. Also, new minerals can grow in the spaces between the sediments, cementing them together. Over time, sedimentary rocks can break apart into individual sediments. The sediments can then become part of new sedimentary rocks.

DIFFERENTIATE INSTRUCTION

B Where does intrusive igneous rock form? *within Earth*

C What are sediments? *loose materials carried by water or wind that settle to a surface*

Alternative Assessment Have students draw and label a diagram that shows how sedimentary rock is formed from layers. Students' diagrams should indicate how the bottom layer of sediments are pressed together by the layers above them and how minerals can grow in between sediments and cement them together.

Sorting Sediments by Size

The speed of water and the size of sediments determine how far sediments are carried.

1 Water in a lake usually moves fastest near the shore or where a river enters. In deeper areas, water moves slower.

gravel

sand

silt and clay

2 Gravel settles near the shore. Rock containing large sediment particles, such as gravel, is known as conglomerate.

3 Sand is carried farther from shore. Rock that forms from sand-sized particles is known as sandstone.

4 Silt and clay are carried into deep water. Rock that forms from silt- and clay-sized particles is known as shale.

READING VISUALS Is shale more likely to form near the shore or near the middle of a big lake or ocean?

Processes similar to the ones that produce sedimentary rocks from rock particles also produce rocks from fossils. Fossils are the remains or traces of organisms from long ago. Limestone is a rock that is usually made up of the fossils of ocean organisms. When the organisms die, their shells and skeletons settle to the ocean floor as layers of sediment. Over time, the layers become buried, pressed together, and cemented to form limestone. You have read that coal is made up of the remains of ancient plants that have been pressed into rock.

Sedimentary rocks form in ways other than being pressed or cemented together. Consider processes that take place along the edges of lakes and oceans where the climate is dry and water evaporates quickly. As water evaporates, it leaves behind materials that were dissolved in it. Minerals form as the materials combine into crystals. Over time, layers of minerals can build up and form sedimentary rocks, such as rock salt or gypsum. Under the city of Detroit, for example, is a thick layer of rock salt that developed when part of an ancient ocean dried up.

REMINDER

When material dissolves in water, it breaks into many tiny parts. When the water evaporates, the parts join together and the material becomes solid again.

What are three processes that can form sedimentary rock?

DIFFERENTIATE INSTRUCTION

More Reading Support

D Where does most limestone come from? *the shells and skeletons of ocean organisms*

Teach from Visuals

To help students interpret the visual showing sediment particles, ask:

- As water currents slow down, what size of particles settles first? *the largest, gravel*
- What size of particles settles next? *the next smallest, sand, and then silt and clay*
- What does the type of sedimentary rock that forms depend on? *the size of rock particles from which it forms*

Integrate the Sciences

The faster a current flows, the larger the particles it can carry. Gravity works against the ability of water to carry particles. A basic law of physics states that all particles, no matter what their size, fall to Earth at the same speed in a vacuum. But in a fluid such as water, larger particles settle faster than smaller ones. Density is also a factor; however, the most common minerals in sediments have similar densities.

Ongoing Assessment

READING VISUALS *Answer: in the middle, because silt and clay particles can settle only from very slow-moving water*

CHECK YOUR READING *Answer: Sedimentary rock can form when sediments are put under pressure, when sediments are cemented together by new minerals, or when water evaporates and leaves behind layers of minerals.*

INVESTIGATE Sediment Layers

PURPOSE To investigate how sedimentary layers form in water.

TIP *10 min.* Ask a student to help you demonstrate this activity for the class.

WHAT DO YOU THINK? *Size and density—the biggest, heaviest particles settle first, and then smaller and smaller ones. Particles would settle in a similar way, forming layers of sediments sorted by size and density.*

CHALLENGE *Sample answer: Where water is moving downhill quickly, large sediment particles, such as gravel, can be transported; where water is moving downhill more slowly, smaller particles, such as sand and silt, can be transported.*

 Datasheet, Sediment Layers, p. 90

Technology Resources

Customize this student lab as needed or look for an alternative. Print rubrics to assess student lab reports.

 **Lab Generator CD-ROM**

Teaching with Technology

If you have access to a video camera, you might tape groups of students performing the experiment and explaining the answers to the Investigate questions. You could show the videotape at an open house or play it during the wait time at parent conferences.

INVESTIGATE Sediment Layers

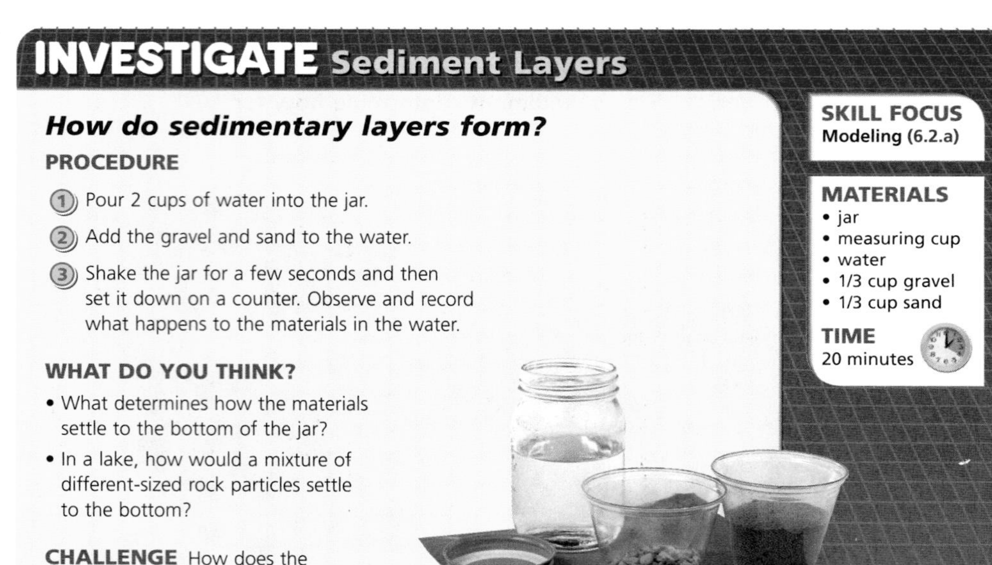

How do sedimentary layers form?

PROCEDURE

1. Pour 2 cups of water into the jar.
2. Add the gravel and sand to the water.
3. Shake the jar for a few seconds and then set it down on a counter. Observe and record what happens to the materials in the water.

WHAT DO YOU THINK?

- What determines how the materials settle to the bottom of the jar?
- In a lake, how would a mixture of different-sized rock particles settle to the bottom?

CHALLENGE How does the movement of sediment by water running downhill help shape the landscape?

SKILL FOCUS
Modeling (6.2.a)

MATERIALS
- jar
- measuring cup
- water
- 1/3 cup gravel
- 1/3 cup sand

TIME
20 minutes

Metamorphic Rock

READING TIP
Rocks change into other rocks by the process of metamorphism. A similar word, *metamorphosis,* refers to what happens when a caterpillar changes into a butterfly.

Metamorphic rock (MEHT-uh-MAWR-fihk) forms when heat or pressure causes older rocks to change into new types of rocks. For example, a rock can get buried deeper in the crust, where pressure and temperature are much greater. These conditions cause the structure of the rock to change so that new minerals grow in place of the original minerals. The rock becomes a metamorphic rock. The process by which this occurs is called metamorphism. Many metamorphic rocks form deep in the crust. They can reach Earth's surface over time as mountains are pushed up or as surface rocks are worn away, uncovering deeper rocks.

RESOURCE CENTER
CLASSZONE.COM
Find out more about the three types of rocks.

Most metamorphic changes occur over large areas in which both temperature and pressure are high. An example is a region where large blocks of the lithosphere are pressing together and pushing up mountain ranges. This process can affect an area hundreds of kilometers wide and tens of kilometers deep. When either high pressure or high temperature conditions occur alone, metamorphic changes tend to occur over smaller areas. For example, surface rock can be covered with a lava flow. The lava heats the rock it touches, causing metamorphism to occur. The changes are due to high temperature, not pressure.

DIFFERENTIATE INSTRUCTION

More Reading Support

E When do most metamorphic changes occur over very large areas? *when high temperature and high pressure are both present*

Below Level To help students visualize the way that rocks get pushed up into mountains, take a small stack of papers and push their ends so that they compress and bulge up.

During metamorphism, rocks undergo many changes. One type of change occurs when pressure causes a rock's minerals to line up in layers, as shown in the illustration below. Metamorphic changes occur while rocks remain solid. Rocks do not melt when they undergo metamorphism. If the temperature gets high enough to melt the rock, the end result is an igneous rock, not a metamorphic rock.

Heat and pressure can break the bonds that join atoms in minerals. Then the atoms can join together differently as new bonds form. This process is called **recrystallization.** It has two main results. First, individual mineral crystals can grow larger as more atoms join their crystal structures. Second, atoms can combine in different ways, and new minerals can form in place of older ones. For example, shale is a sedimentary rock that is formed from silt and clay. During recrystallization, garnet can form from these materials.

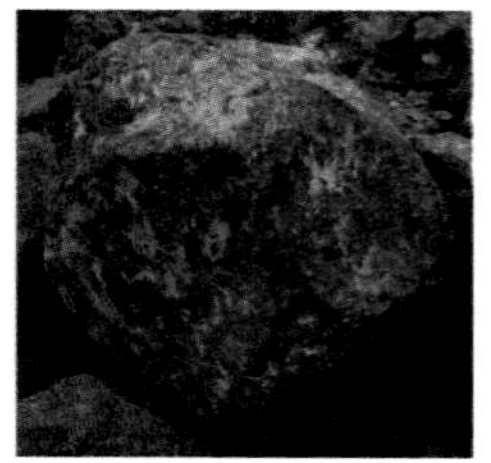

CALIFORNIA Focus

The state rock of California is a metamorphic rock known as serpentine. Serpentine is shiny and commonly has a green color. It contains minerals such as chromite, a source of chromium, and magnesite, a source of magnesium.

Metamorphic Changes

Because pressure and temperature increase with depth, rocks change when they are buried deeper in the crust.

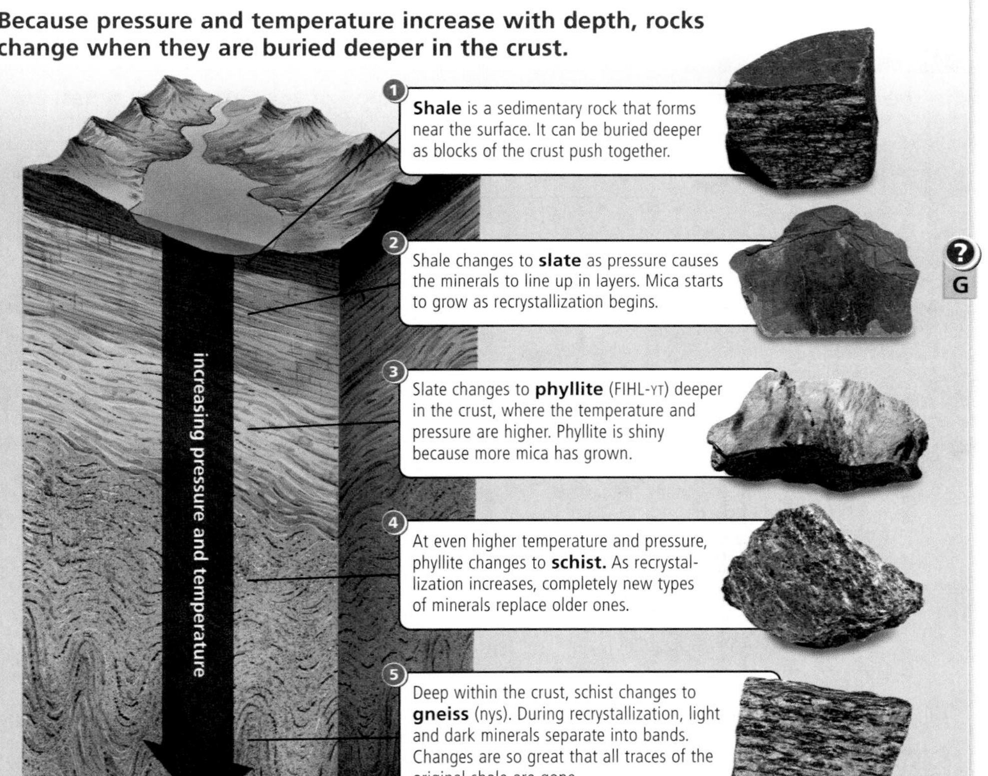

increasing pressure and temperature
1 **Shale** is a sedimentary rock that forms near the surface. It can be buried deeper as blocks of the crust push together.
2 Shale changes to **slate** as pressure causes the minerals to line up in layers. Mica starts to grow as recrystallization begins.
3 Slate changes to **phyllite** (FIHL-YT) deeper in the crust, where the temperature and pressure are higher. Phyllite is shiny because more mica has grown.
4 At even higher temperature and pressure, phyllite changes to **schist.** As recrystallization increases, completely new types of minerals replace older ones.
5 Deep within the crust, schist changes to **gneiss** (nys). During recrystallization, light and dark minerals separate into bands. Changes are so great that all traces of the original shale are gone.

G

Teach from Visuals

To help students interpret the visual about how rocks change, ask:

- What does the arrow on this illustration indicate? *that in Earth's crust, pressure and temperature increase with depth*
- How does the level of metamorphism change as the depth, temperature, and pressure increase? *The amount of metamorphism increases as depth, temperature, and pressure increase.*

Teacher Demo

As you discuss the illustration, show actual samples of shale, slate, phyllite, schist, and gneiss, if available. You might place the samples on each row of a bookshelf in the order shown to emphasize the fact that they form at different depths. Pass each rock around the room, and have students describe the differences they see among the five metamorphic rocks.

Ongoing Assessment

Identify the three types of rocks.

Ask: How do the three types of rocks differ? *They differ in the way they form. Igneous rock forms when molten rock cools and becomes solid. Most sedimentary rock forms as pieces of older rocks, plants, and other loose materials get pressed and cemented into rock. Metamorphic rock forms as heat or pressure or both cause older rocks to change into new types of rock.*

DIFFERENTIATE INSTRUCTION

More Reading Support

F Do rocks melt during metamorphism? *No, rocks remain solid during metamorphism.*

G What is a common parent rock for slate? *shale*

English Learners Have English learners write the words *metamorphism, recrystallization,* and *foliation* in their Science Word Dictionaries. They might also want to write abbreviated definitions for these and other terms in the chapter on index cards. Students can use these cards for quick reference.

Address Misconceptions

IDENTIFY Ask: How does a rock change over time? If students answer, "Rocks don't change" or "I can't think of any ways," they may hold the misconception that rocks are permanent and unchanging.

CORRECT As a class, review the definition of *rock cycle* on p. 196. Have students study the diagram of the rock cycle on the same page and discuss each step. Explain that the arrows show the different ways that rocks can move through the cycle.

REASSESS Ask: What kinds of changes does a rock go through over many years? *A rock changes into a different rock type or re-forms into the same rock type.* Why do rocks seem to be unchanging? *The rock cycle usually moves slowly. It is often hard to notice the changes.*

Technology Resources

Visit **ClassZone.com** for background on common student misconceptions.

MISCONCEPTION DATABASE

Teach from Visuals

To help students interpret the visuals of the rock cycle, ask: What do the arrows pointing in two directions mean? *The process could go either way.*

EXPLORE the BIG idea

Revisit "Internet Activity: Rocks" on p. 181. Have students relate their examples to the rock cycle diagram.

Ongoing Assessment

Explain how one type of rock can change into another.

Ask: How can metamorphic rock change into sedimentary rock? *At Earth's surface, metamorphic rock breaks into loose pieces. These loose pieces get pressed and cemented together to form sedimentary rock.*

READING VISUALS *Possible answer: change with heat and pressure; break down into loose particles*

Rocks can change into other types of rocks.

When rocks are raised to the surface, water and wind can break them down into sediments. Over time, the sediments might become sedimentary rock. When rocks at or near the surface are pushed deeper into the crust, they might become metamorphic rocks. Or they might melt and then cool into igneous rocks. For example, rocks can be raised up or pushed deeper when mountains are forming. You will read more about this topic in Chapter 8.

The Rock Cycle

READING TIP The word *cycle* comes from the Greek word *kuklos,* which means "circle." A cycle is made up of a set of repeating events.

The **rock cycle** is the set of natural processes by which rocks form, change, break down, and re-form. Rocks do not move through the rock cycle in a particular order. As you can see in the illustration below, a rock at any point in the cycle can change in two or three different ways. The rock cycle has no beginning or end. It goes on continually.

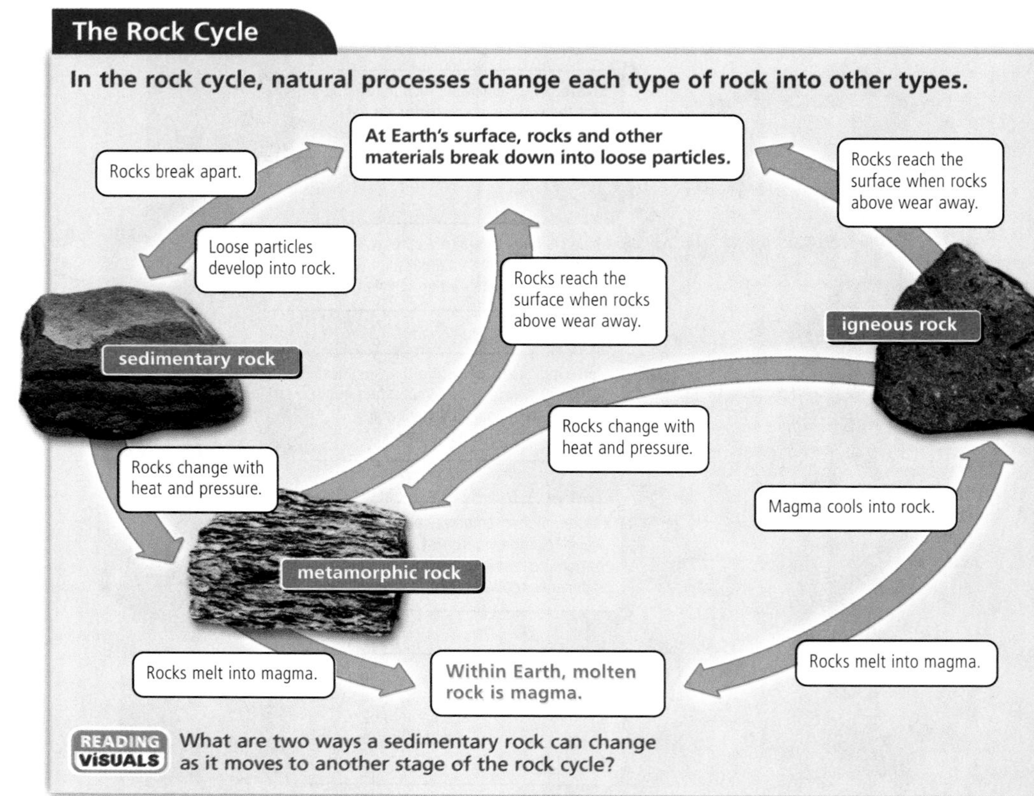
The Rock Cycle
In the rock cycle, natural processes change each type of rock into other types.
At Earth's surface, rocks and other materials break down into loose particles.
Rocks break apart.
Rocks reach the surface when rocks above wear away.
Loose particles develop into rock.
Rocks reach the surface when rocks above wear away.
igneous rock
sedimentary rock
Rocks change with heat and pressure.
Rocks change with heat and pressure.
Magma cools into rock.
metamorphic rock
Rocks melt into magma.
Within Earth, molten rock is magma.
Rocks melt into magma.

READING VISUALS What are two ways a sedimentary rock can change as it moves to another stage of the rock cycle?

DIFFERENTIATE INSTRUCTION

More Reading Support

H What is the rock cycle? *a set of natural processes that form, change, break down, and re-form rocks*

Additional Investigation To reinforce Section 6.2 learning goals, use the following full-period investigation:

R Additional Investigation, Modeling Rock Formation, A, B, & C, pp. 130–138, 211–212
(Advanced students should complete Levels B and C.)

Advanced Challenge students to create flow charts or PowerPoint presentations depicting the ways that rocks can move through the rock cycles:

R Challenge and Extension, p. 89

Rocks in the Crust

Even though sedimentary rock is common at Earth's surface, the crust as a whole consists mainly of igneous and metamorphic rock.

Rocks in the Crust

Igneous, sedimentary, and metamorphic rocks are all found in Earth's crust. But these rock types are not evenly distributed. Most of Earth's crust—95 percent of it—consists of igneous rock and metamorphic rock. Sedimentary rock, which forms a thin covering on Earth's surface, makes up only 5 percent of the crust.

REMINDER
The crust is the upper layer of the lithosphere. The uppermost mantle makes up the rest of the lithosphere.

The distribution of rock types is a reflection of the rock cycle. Sedimentary rocks are most common at the surface because they are formed by processes that occur at the surface. Most igneous rocks and metamorphic rocks are formed by processes that occur deeper within Earth.

CHECK YOUR READING Would you expect to find sedimentary rock deep in Earth's crust? Why or why not?

6.2 Review

KEY CONCEPTS

1. What are the three types of rock? (6.1.b)
2. Give an example of how one type of rock can change into another type. (6.1.b)
3. Which rock types are most common within Earth's crust? Which type is most common at Earth's surface? (6.1.b)

CRITICAL THINKING

4. **Analyze** Why is the set of natural processes by which rocks change into other types of rocks called a cycle?
5. **Infer** Which type of rock would be most likely to form on the bottom of a large, deep lake? Why?

CHALLENGE

6. **Synthesize** Draw a diagram showing how an igneous rock could change into a metamorphic rock and how the metamorphic rock could change into a sedimentary rock.

ANSWERS

1. igneous, sedimentary, metamorphic

2. Increasing pressure and temperature in Earth's crust can cause the sedimentary rock shale to become the metamorphic rock gneiss.

3. igneous and metamorphic; sedimentary

4. because the steps occur over and over and have no beginning or end

5. sedimentary; because layers of sediment can build up in the center of a large lake

6. The diagram should show the following: heat and/or pressure change the igneous rock into a metamorphic rock; the metamorphic rock reaches the surface as overlying rocks are worn away; at the surface, the metamorphic rock breaks down into sediments, which are then cemented together to form sedimentary rock.

Ongoing Assessment

Tell how common each rock type is in Earth's crust.

Ask: What percentage of Earth's entire crust is made of igneous and metamorphic rock? *95%*

CHECK YOUR READING *Answer: Sedimentary rock would not be found deep in Earth's crust because it forms at the surface. When it gets buried deep enough, it changes into igneous or metamorphic rock.*

Reinforce the BIG idea

Have students relate the section to the Big Idea.

R Reinforcing Key Concepts, p. 91

6.2 ASSESS & RETEACH

Assess

Section 6.2 Quiz, p. 120

Reteach

- Hold up a sedimentary rock and tell students that it is the most common type of rock on Earth's surface but the least common in Earth's crust as a whole. Explain that sedimentary rock forms as rock at Earth's surface gets broken into pieces. These rock particles are carried away by water or wind, settle in layers, and get pressed and cemented together.
- Next hold up an igneous rock and a metamorphic rock and tell students that these are the most common types of rock that make up Earth's crust. Explain that igneous rock forms when molten rock cools, and metamorphic rock forms when heat and pressure change another type of rock.

Technology Resources

Have students visit **ClassZone.com** for reteaching of Key Concepts.

CONTENT REVIEW

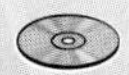
CONTENT REVIEW CD-ROM

CONNECTING SCIENCES
Integration of Sciences

Set Learning Goal
To understand that limestone can form from both organic and inorganic processes

Present the Science
Limestone is a biochemical sedimentary rock. Many marine organisms take in dissolved calcium carbonate from seawater and then secrete it to form their shells. Coral organisms, called polyps, do the same thing. Most coral polyps live in colonies, and the ones that form coral reefs attach themselves to one another. Coral reefs contain the skeletons of millions of coral polyps.

Discussion Questions
- Ask: Does the limestone in a coral reef form from sediment under heat or pressure? *Possible answer: No, it does not. The limestone in the coral reef is added directly to the reef by living animals. It is not loose sediment first.*
- Ask: How does the limestone in the formations in Mono Lake differ from the limestone in a coral reef? *Possible answer: The limestone in the Mono Lake formations is formed without the help of organisms. Minerals dissolved in the lake water crystallized and formed limestone.*

Close
Ask: Why is limestone an unusual type of rock? *Possible answer: Limestone is unusual because it can be formed by living organisms. Most rocks on Earth form only from inorganic processes.*

CONNECTING SCIENCES

EARTH SCIENCE AND LIFE SCIENCE

The skeletons of these tiny coral organisms eventually make huge coral reefs.

Coral Polyps Rock!

6.5.b Students know matter is transferred over time from one organism to others in the food web and between organisms and the physical environment.

What is a type of rock that comes from once-living organisms? Limestone! Limestone is made up of carbonate minerals, such as calcite—a major mineral in the shells and skeletons of sea organisms.

Coral Reefs and Coral Polyps
Coral organisms build their limestone skeletons one on top of another. Over time, countless skeletons of these organisms form coral reefs.

Coral polyps, the creatures that create reefs, are often only a few millimeters long, although some can grow much larger. Those that live in colonies are about 1–3 millimeters in diameter. Corals do not move because their bases are stuck to the reef surface. But their tentacles do move. Corals have stinging threads with tiny barbs on the tip. Those threads are filled with venom that can kill small animals. The tentacles move the food to the coral's mouth. Reef-building corals make their own cup-shaped skeletons out of carbonate minerals. The coral polyp can hide almost totally inside the skeleton. Huge numbers of these skeletons eventually become large formations of limestone. Imagine how many tiny corals it takes to build one huge coral reef!

Limestone Towers
Some limestone forms without the help of organisms. As water dries up, materials that had been dissolved in it can crystallize into minerals. Also, water can contain so many dissolved substances that minerals form in it. The towers of limestone in Mono Lake formed around the openings of underwater springs. The springs' water was rich in dissolved substances that formed into carbonate minerals.

These limestone towers in Mono Lake, California, formed underwater. They are now above the surface because the lake level has dropped.

EXPLORE
1. **COMPARE AND CONTRAST** Compare the pictures of the coral reef and the limestone towers. What similarities do you see? Contrast them with other pictures in the book showing other types of rock.
2. **CHALLENGE** Break up small pieces of coral and limestone. Place the coral and limestone into separate cups. Drop a few drops of vinegar in each cup. What happens? Why?

EXPLORE
*1. **COMPARE AND CONTRAST** Both coral and limestone appear light in color, with an uneven surface. They have a very different appearance from a rock such as rhyolite, for example, which is very smooth and dark in color, or granite, which contains very large mineral crystals that are easy to see.*
*2. **CHALLENGE** Both the coral and the limestone begin to bubble and dissolve when exposed to vinegar. This is due to a chemical reaction between an acid (vinegar) and a base (carbonate such as in coral or limestone).*

KEY CONCEPT

Natural processes break down rocks.

CALIFORNIA Content Standards

Background for 6.2. Topography is reshaped by the weathering of rock and soil and by the transportation and deposition of sediment.

6.2.a Students know water running downhill is the dominant process in shaping the landscape, including California's landscape.

BEFORE, you learned
- Minerals make up almost all rocks
- Different minerals have different properties
- Rocks are broken down to form sediments

NOW, you will learn
- About the relationship between weathering and the geological cycle
- How mechanical weathering breaks down rocks
- How chemical weathering changes rocks
- What factors affect the rate at which weathering occurs

VOCABULARY

geologic cycle p. 199
weathering p. 199
mechanical weathering p. 200
chemical weathering p. 202

EXPLORE Weathering (6.2)

What can cause a rock to break down?

PROCEDURE

1. Place a piece of chalk in a cup.
2. Pour vinegar over the chalk and observe any changes that occur.

WHAT DO YOU THINK?
- What happened to the chalk and why?
- What processes in nature might affect rocks in similar ways?

MATERIALS
- chalk
- cup
- vinegar

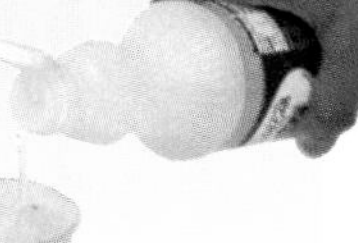

Weathering helps change Earth's features over time.

Earth's features change over time. For example, the actions of water, ice, and wind wear mountains down into small pieces of sediment. Eventually, the sediment is changed back into large bodies of rock again, and new mountains are pushed up. All of these changes and more are processes in the geologic cycle. The **geologic cycle** includes all the processes by which Earth's features are worn down and built up. The rock cycle is part of the geologic cycle.

Weathering is the set of natural processes that break down rocks. It is part of the geologic cycle too. Rocks must be broken down before sediments can be carried to new places, changing the shape of Earth's surface. One kind of weathering occurs when a rock is physically broken apart. Another kind occurs when a chemical reaction changes the composition of the rock.

VOCABULARY
Add a magnet word diagram for *geologic cycle* to your notebook.

RESOURCES FOR DIFFERENTIATED INSTRUCTION

Below Level

UNIT RESOURCE BOOK
- Reading Study Guide A, pp. 94–95
- Decoding Support, p. 118

AUDIO CDS

Advanced

UNIT RESOURCE BOOK
- Challenge and Extension, p. 100

English Learners

UNIT RESOURCE BOOK
Spanish Reading Study Guide, pp. 98–99

AUDIO CDS
- Audio Readings in Spanish
- Audio Readings (English)

6.3 FOCUS

Set Learning Goals

Students will
- Explain the relationship between weathering and the geological cycle.
- Describe how mechanical weathering breaks down rocks.
- Explain how chemical weathering changes rocks.
- Identify the factors that affect the rate at which weathering occurs.

3-Minute Warm-Up

Display Transparency 45 or copy this exercise on the board:

Decide if these statements are true. If not, correct them:

1. The set of natural processes that form, change, and re-form rocks is called the rock cycle. *true*
2. A rock is usually made up of only one type of mineral. *A rock is usually made up of more than one type of mineral.*
3. Igneous rock develops from layers of sediment. *Sedimentary rock develops from layers of sediment.*

3-Minute Warm-Up, p. T45

6.3 MOTIVATE

EXPLORE Weathering

PURPOSE To introduce students to the forces that break down rocks

TIP *10 min.* You can use antacid tablets instead of chalk for this experiment, as long as they contain carbonates.

WHAT DO YOU THINK? *Sample answers: The chalk in contact with vinegar fizzed. This is due to a chemical reaction between the chalk (which contains carbonates, a base), and the vinegar (an acid). In nature, naturally acidic water or acid rain might have the same effect on limestone.*

6.3 INSTRUCT

Teach the Standards

Breakdown of rock 6.2.a

In this section: Help students understand how mechanical and chemical weathering both play an important role in the shaping of the landscape, as both processes break down rocks on Earth's surface.

- **previously taught:** rock cycle, p. 44, p. 196
- **future opportunities:** soil formation, p. 356, pp. 380–381

Address Misconceptions

IDENTIFY Ask: What happens to the density of water when it freezes? If students say that the density remains the same, they may have difficulty understanding that ice can be an agent of mechanical weathering.

CORRECT Explain that when water freezes into ice, its density decreases as the ice expands and the water molecules move farther apart. Share the example of water in a covered plastic container that is placed in the freezer. As the water freezes, it will expand against the sides of the container until the lid pops off.

REASSESS Reinforce the connection between this example and mechanical weathering. Ask: How is what would happen to the frozen container similar to what might happen to a rock if water entered its cracks and pores and then froze? *The water would expand as it freezes, which could cause the rock to break apart.*

Technology Resources

Visit **ClassZone.com** for background on common student misconceptions.

MISCONCEPTION DATABASE

Ongoing Assessment

CHECK YOUR READING *Answer: Moving water can cause rocks to grind against one another. Water itself also causes abrasion.*

Mechanical weathering produces physical changes in rocks.

Learn more about weathering.

If you smash a walnut with a hammer, you will break it into a lot of small pieces. But you will not change what it is. Even though the pieces of the walnut are no longer connected, they are still made up of the same materials. **Mechanical weathering**—the breaking up of rocks by physical forces—works in much the same way. In this natural process, physical forces split rocks apart but do not change what they are made of. Ice wedging, pressure release, plant root growth, and abrasion can all cause mechanical weathering.

READING TIP The word *expand* means "to increase in size or volume."

1. **Ice Wedging** When water freezes, it expands. When water freezes in the cracks and pores of rocks, the force of its expansion is strong enough to split the rocks apart. This process, which is called ice wedging, can break up huge boulders. Ice wedging is common in places where temperatures rise above and fall below the freezing point for water, which is 0°C (32°F).
2. **Pressure Release** Rock deep within Earth is under great pressure from rocks around it. Over time, processes within Earth can push the rock up to the surface. At the same time, the rock above it can wear away. In either case, the pressure inside the rock is still high, but the pressure on the surface of the rock is released. This release of pressure causes the rock to expand. As the rock expands, cracks form in it, leading to exfoliation. Exfoliation (ehks-FOH-lee-AY-shuhn) is a process in which layers or sheets of rock gradually break off. This process is sometimes called onion-skin weathering. The rock surface breaks off in thin layers like the layers of an onion.
3. **Plant Root Growth** Trees, bushes, and other plants may take root in cracks in rocks. As the roots of these plants grow, they wedge open the cracks. The rock—even if it is large—can be split completely apart.
4. **Abrasion** Water can wear down rocks on riverbeds and along shorelines. Abrasion (uh-BRAY-zhuhn) is the process of wearing down by friction, the rubbing of one object or surface against another. The force of moving water alone can wear away particles of rock. Water also causes rocks to tumble downstream. The tumbling rocks wear down as they grind against the riverbed and against each other. Ocean waves beating against a rocky shore also wear down rocks by abrasion.

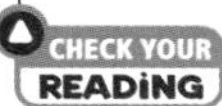

How does moving water weather rocks?

DIFFERENTIATE INSTRUCTION

More Reading Support

A Which type of weathering occurs when physical forces break apart rocks? *mechanical*

B Which physical force causes exfoliation? *pressure release*

English Learners This section has a number of phrasal verbs, such as *make up* and *break down*. While these terms might initially serve to simplify an idea for a student, they could in fact confuse an English learner. Instruct students not to read *up* and *down* as literal directions, and offer synonyms to clarify the meaning of these and other phrasal verbs.

Mechanical Weathering

Ice wedging, pressure release, plant root growth, and abrasion can all break apart rocks.

① Ice Wedging

Rainwater fills small cracks in a rock.

As the water freezes, it expands, widening the cracks and splitting apart the rock.

② Pressure Release

Earth's forces can push rock that formed deep underground up to the surface.

The release of pressure causes the rock to expand and crack.

③ Plant Root Growth

When plants grow in cracks in a rock, their roots can widen the cracks and force the rock apart.

④ Abrasion

Flowing water can move rocks, causing them to rub together and wear down into rounded shapes.

READING VISUALS What evidence of mechanical weathering can you see in each photograph above?

DIFFERENTIATE INSTRUCTION

Alternative Assessment Show students several samples of "beach glass" (or "sea glass"), but do not tell them what the samples are. Instead, explain that the smooth pieces once had sharp edges. Have students study the photographs in the visual "Mechanical Weathering." Then ask: Which physical force likely caused the mechanical weathering? Explain your answer. *Moving water likely weathered the pieces because water wears down rocks and other hard objects into smooth, rounded shapes.*

Teach from Visuals

To help students interpret the visual on mechanical weathering, ask:

- What do all these processes have in common? *They are physical forces.*
- Which two processes seem most alike? Why? *Mechanical weathering by ice and plant roots seem most similar. Both involve filling a crack in a rock and then splitting the rock apart.*

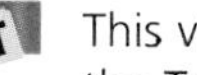

This visual is also available as T46 in the Transparency Book.

Address Misconceptions

IDENTIFY Ask: Where do pebbles and small particles of rock come from? If students do not say "larger rocks," they may hold the misconception that rocks do not change or break down naturally.

CORRECT Pass around a piece of sandstone. Ask students to describe it. *hard, solid, strong* Then hold another piece of sandstone and rub the rocks together over a sheet of black paper. Show students the grains that fall on the paper.

REASSESS Ask: What made the rocks break? *abrasion, or the friction from rubbing the rocks together* What makes rocks rub together in nature? *moving water, wind, glacial ice*

Technology Resources

Visit **ClassZone.com** for background on common student misconceptions.

MISCONCEPTION DATABASE

Ongoing Assessment

Describe how mechanical weathering breaks down rocks.

Ask: What happens to the composition of a rock during mechanical weathering? *It stays the same; mechanical weathering breaks down rocks physically, not chemically.*

READING VISUALS *Answer: Ice wedging: fine crack; no plant roots. Pressure release: "peeling" of rock in layers. Plant root growth: tree growing in a crack. Abrasion: moving water.*

Teach Difficult Concepts

Mechanical and chemical weathering are presented as two separate processes in this section. However, in nature, the two processes work together. To help students grasp this concept, remind them that mechanical weathering breaks rocks apart. As a result, more surface area is exposed to air and water. Ask: How would this affect the rates of chemical weathering? *Rates of chemical weathering would increase.*

Teacher Demo

Present students with a number of small metal items (for example, coins, steel wool, paper clips), and ask them to determine whether these objects would eventually rust if left outside in the rain. Provide students with magnets, and ask them to test which items are attracted to the magnets. Explain that the metal objects that are magnetic contain iron, which when combined with oxygen and water produces iron oxides or rust. Students can deduce that the non-magnetic metal items do not contain iron and therefore would not rust.

Ongoing Assessment

Explain how chemical weathering changes rocks.

Ask: What happens to some minerals in rocks when they react with air and water? *They dissolve or are changed into different minerals.*

CHECK YOUR READING *Answer: Pollutants in the air can react with water to form acid rain. Air and water can also react with iron to form rust.*

Chemical weathering changes the mineral composition of rocks.

If you have seen a rusty nail, you have seen the result of a chemical reaction. A chemical reaction causes a chemical change. The steel in the nail contains iron. Oxygen in air and water react with the iron to form rust.

C

Minerals in rocks also undergo chemical changes when they react with water and air. **Chemical weathering** is the breakdown of rocks by chemical reactions that change the rocks' composition. When minerals in rocks come into contact with air and water, some dissolve. Others react and are changed into different minerals.

Dissolving

Water is the main cause of chemical weathering. Some minerals completely dissolve in ordinary water. Many more minerals dissolve in water that is slightly acidic. In the atmosphere, small amounts of carbon dioxide dissolve in rainwater. The water and carbon dioxide react to form a weak acid. After falling to Earth, the rainwater moves through the soil, picking up more carbon dioxide. The slightly acidic water breaks down minerals in rocks. In the process, the rocks may also break apart into smaller pieces.

The rocks in Oak Creek Canyon are reddish because iron in the rocks reacted with water and air to produce iron oxides.

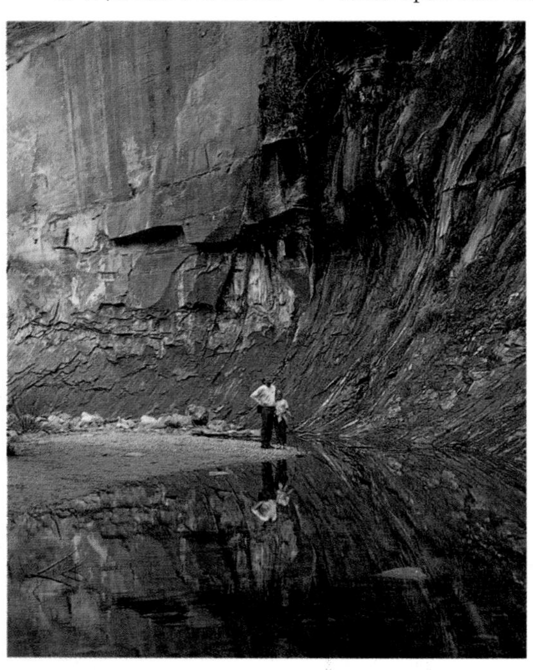

Air pollution can make rainwater more acidic than it is naturally. Power plants and automobiles produce gases such as sulfur dioxide and nitric oxide. These gases react with water vapor in the atmosphere to form acid rain. Acid rain causes rocks to weather much faster than they would otherwise.

Rusting

The oxygen in the air is also involved in chemical weathering. Many common minerals contain iron. When these minerals dissolve in water, oxygen in the air and the water combines with the iron to produce iron oxides, or rust. The iron oxides form a coating that colors the weathered rocks. Notice the colors in the photograph of Oak Creek Canyon in Arizona.

CHECK YOUR READING How is air involved in chemical weathering?

DIFFERENTIATE INSTRUCTION

More Reading Support

C Which type of weathering changes the makeup of a rock? *chemical weathering*

D Which gas in the air helps produce rust? *oxygen*

Advanced Ask students to find out which weak acid is formed as a result of chemical weathering of rocks containing carbonate minerals. *carbonic acid* Where else is carbonic acid found? *soft drinks* How does the weathering of minerals by carbonic acid in rocks connect to students' lives? *It chemically weathers tooth enamel and leads to decay.*

Challenge and Extension, p. 100

Weathering occurs at different rates.

Most weathering processes occur over long periods of time. For example, it can take hundreds or thousands of years for a very hard rock to wear down only a few millimeters—a few times the thickness of your fingernail. But the rate of weathering is not the same for all rocks. Factors such as surface area, rock composition, and climate influence the rate of weathering.

SUPPORTING MAIN IDEAS Enter this blue heading in a chart and record supporting information.

Surface Area The more of a rock's surface that is exposed to air and water, the faster the rock will break down. A greater surface area allows chemical weathering to affect more of a rock.

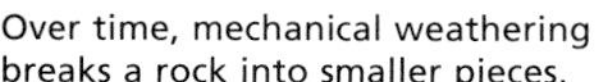

1 Over time, mechanical weathering breaks a rock into smaller pieces.

2 As a result, the rock has more surface area exposed to chemical weathering.

Rock Composition Different kinds of rock break down at different rates. Granite, for example, breaks down much more slowly than limestone. Both of these rocks are often used for tombstones and statues.

Climate Water is needed for chemical weathering to occur, and heat speeds up chemical weathering. As a result, chemical weathering occurs faster in hot, wet regions than it does in cold, dry regions. However, mechanical weathering caused by freezing and thawing occurs more in cold regions than in hot regions.

6.3 Review

KEY CONCEPTS

1. How is weathering related to the geologic cycle? **(6.2)**
2. What are four causes of mechanical weathering? **(6.2)**
3. How do water and air help cause chemical weathering? **(6.2.a)**
4. Describe three factors that affect the rate at which weathering occurs. **(6.2)**

CRITICAL THINKING

5. **Infer** How does mechanical weathering affect the rate of chemical weathering?
6. **Predict** Would weathering affect a marble sculpture inside a museum? Explain your answer.

CHALLENGE

7. **Infer** The word *weather* is most commonly used to refer to the state of the atmosphere at a certain time. Why do you think the same word is used to refer to the breakdown of rocks?

ANSWERS

1. Weathering is one part of the geologic cycle, which includes all processes by which Earth's features are worn down and built up.

2. ice wedging, pressure release, plant root growth, abrasion

3. They can cause rusting and acid rain.

4. Surface area: The more of a rock's surface that is exposed, the faster the rock will weather. Rock composition: Certain types of rock break down more quickly than others. Climate: Temperature and moisture in a location affect the rate of weathering.

5. It breaks up rocks and increases the surface area of the rock. More rock is exposed to air and water, so the rate of chemical weathering increases.

6. No; the sculpture would be protected from rain, heat, and wind.

7. Characteristics of weather, such as rain and temperature, help to break down rock.

Ongoing Assessment

Identify factors that affect the rate at which weathering occurs.

Ask: What are three factors that influence the rate of weathering? *surface area, rock composition, and climate*

Reinforce the BIG idea

Have students relate the section to the Big Idea.

 Reinforcing Key Concepts, p. 101

6.3 ASSESS & RETEACH

Assess

 Section 6.3 Quiz, p. 121

Reteach

Make two separate description wheels—one for mechanical weathering and one for chemical weathering. On the spokes for the mechanical weathering wheel, include the terms *ice wedging, pressure release, plant root growth,* and *abrasion.* For chemical weathering, include *dissolving, rusting, chemical reactions,* and *weak acids.* Use the wheels to discuss the characteristics of the two types of weathering and the differences between the two. Then have students write one or two sentences that compare and contrast the two types of weathering. *Sample sentences: Both kinds of weathering break down rocks naturally. Mechanical weathering breaks rocks apart without changing their composition, but chemical weathering changes their composition.*

Technology Resources

Have students visit **ClassZone.com** for reteaching of Key Concepts.

 **CONTENT REVIEW**

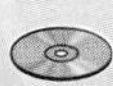 **CONTENT REVIEW CD-ROM**

CHAPTER INVESTIGATION

Focus

PURPOSE To design an experiment to model the effects of mechanical and chemical weathering

OVERVIEW Students will conduct a simple experiment to observe the conditions that allow rusting to occur. Students will also design their own experiment to model the effects of both mechanical and chemical weathering on rock. Students will find the following:

- Exposure to both water and air will cause steel wool to rust.
- Exposure to various acids can cause chemical weathering of rock.
- Mechanical weathering of rocks can occur as a result of abrasion.

Lab Preparation

On the day before this experiment, collect rock samples.

Prior to the investigation, have students read the investigation and prepare their data tables. Or you may wish to copy and distribute datasheets and rubrics.

 UNIT RESOURCE BOOK, pp. 121–129

 SCIENCE TOOLKIT, F13

Lab Management

- For best results, use inexpensive steel wool with thin fibers for Part One.
- Draw Table 1 on the board and fill it in with student observations so students can compare their observations.

SAFETY Tell students to be certain the lid of the plastic container is sealed carefully before they shake it. Do not allow students to hit rocks with a hammer.

Teaching with Technology

If you have access to a video camera, you might tape groups of students performing their designed experiments and record their observations and conclusions. You could show the videotape at an open house or play it during the wait time at parent conferences.

CHAPTER INVESTIGATION

Weathering

OVERVIEW AND PURPOSE Mechanical and chemical weathering break down rocks. Different types of rocks react in various ways to different weathering processes. In this investigation you will

- observe conditions that allow rusting, a form of chemical weathering, to occur
- design a procedure to model the effects of mechanical and chemical weathering on different types of rocks

MATERIALS

for Part One:
- steel wool
- 3 cups
- water
- graduated cylinder

for Part Two:
- rock samples
- dilute acids (such as vinegar, cola, lemon juice)
- plastic container and lid
- duct tape
- clear plastic sealable bag
- balance
- graduated cylinder
- water

6.2, 6.7.b, 6.7.c, 6.7.d

Procedure

PART ONE

1. Make a data table like the one shown in the Science Notebook on page 205.
2. Fill a cup almost to the top with water. Place a piece of steel wool in the cup.
3. Put a small amount of water in a second cup. Place a piece of steel wool in the cup.
4. The third cup should have no water. Place a piece of steel wool in the third cup.
5. Allow the three cups to sit overnight. Observe the appearance of the steel wool in each container the next day.

INVESTIGATION RESOURCES

 CHAPTER INVESTIGATION, Weathering
- Level A, pp. 121–124
- Level B, pp. 125–128
- Level C, p. 129

Advanced students should complete Levels B & C.

 Writing a Lab Report, D12–13

Technology Resources

Customize this student lab as needed or look for an alternative. Print rubrics to assess student lab reports.

 **Lab Generator CD-ROM**

Content Standard
6.2 Topography is reshaped by the weathering of rock and soil and by the transportation and deposition of sediment.

Investigation Standard
6.7.b Select and use appropriate tools and technology (including calculators, computers, balances, spring scales, microscopes, and binoculars) to perform tests, collect data, and display data.

PART TWO

1 Design a procedure to model the effects of different weathering processes on several rock samples. You might use some or all of the materials available. Your procedure should enable you to collect data, determine if the rocks changed, and describe how they changed.

2 Record your procedure in your Science Notebook.

3 Create a data table to organize the data you will collect.

4 Measure and record the mass or volume of each rock sample. Record this information in your notebook.

5 Carry out your procedure. Make both qualitative and quantitative observations. Be aware that acids can irritate the skin and eyes. Be sure to wear your safety goggles when using an acid and when modeling mechanical weathering processes.

Observe and Analyze

Write It Up

1. **RECORD OBSERVATIONS** Complete your data table for Part One.
2. **COMPARE** What happened to the steel wool in each cup?
3. **IDENTIFY VARIABLES** What was the independent variable—the factor you changed—in Part One? What was the dependent variable—the factor you measured?
4. **RECORD OBSERVATIONS** Make sure your data table for Part Two is completed.

Conclude

1. **ANALYZE** Judging by the appearance of the pieces of steel wool in Part One, what do you think is necessary for rusting to occur?
2. **APPLY** What can you conclude about the best way to protect metal objects, such as bicycles, from rusting?
3. **IDENTIFY** Which processes in Part Two were models of mechanical weathering? chemical weathering?
4. **IDENTIFY LIMITS** What limitations of materials or methods could have affected your results from modeling different weathering processes?
5. **PREDICT** Based on your observations, predict how weathering processes affect common types of rocks near your home or school. How might these weathering processes affect the local topography?

INVESTIGATE Further

CHALLENGE Tear apart the steel wool that rusted the most and compare the appearances of the inside and outside. Why might the inside and outside look different?

CHEMICAL WEATHERING
Observe and Analyze
Table 1. Formation of Rust

Cup	Amount of Water	Observations
1	full cup	
2	approximately 30 mL	
3	no water	

Observe and Analyze

1. *Make sure students' data tables for Part One are complete.*
2. *Cup 1: no rusting was observed; cup 2: rusting was observed; cup 3: no rusting was observed.*
3. *independent variable: the amount of water in the cup; dependent variable: the amount of rusting that occurred*
4. *Make sure students' data tables for Part Two are complete.*

Conclude

1. *In order for rusting to occur, iron or an iron-containing rock or metal must be exposed to both water and air.*
2. *The best way to protect metal objects from rusting is to limit their exposure to water.*
3. *Answers will vary depending on the types of experiments performed. Sample answers: Shaking rocks together in the sealed plastic container was a model of mechanical weathering. Exposing rocks to various acidic liquids was a model of chemical weathering.*
4. *Sample answer: The experiments modeled the effects of weathering in a very short period of time. True weathering of rocks usually occurs over a very long period of time.*
5. *Sample answers: If the rock samples used in the experiment were taken from an area nearby, then similar weathering processes in nature might affect the rocks outside in a similar way. These weathering processes might break down rocks into sediment, which will then be washed downstream by water, where they may eventually build up again, forming sedimentary rock.*

INVESTIGATE Further

CHALLENGE The steel wool inside was less exposed to both the water in the cup and oxygen in the air, and therefore rusted less.

Post-Lab Discussion

Ask students to think about the differences they observed between the effects of the different acidic solutions on the different rock samples.

- What might you conclude about the differences between the liquids? *Some are more acidic than others.*
- What might you conclude about the differences between the rock samples? *Some rocks are more reactive with acid than other rocks.*

6.4 FOCUS

Set Learning Goals

Students will

- Describe what a geologic map shows about Earth's surface.
- Explain how a geologic map shows information about resources.
- Explain how a geologic map shows information about hazards.
- Analyze where landslides are most likely to affect a road.

3-Minute Warm-Up

Display Transparency 45 or copy this exercise on the board:

Complete each statement.

1. Ice wedging is a form of _____ weathering. *mechanical*
2. The process of water wearing down rocks is known as ______. *abrasion*
3. Rusting is caused by a reaction between iron, water, and ______ in the air. *oxygen*

3-Minute Warm-Up, p. T45

6.4 MOTIVATE

THINK ABOUT

PURPOSE To understand what a geologic map might be used for

DEMONSTRATE Tell students they are not expected to know the "right" answer, but should feel free to speculate. *Students may answer that a geologic map of the area pictured might show the types of rock or minerals found in the sea cliffs. The map might be used to study how mechanical and chemical weathering affect the sea cliffs.*

KEY CONCEPT

Geologic maps show Earth's surface features.

CALIFORNIA Content Standards

6.7.f Read a topographic map and a geologic map for evidence provided on the maps and construct and interpret a simple scale map.

6.6 Sources of energy and materials differ in amounts, distribution, usefulness, and the time required for their formation.

BEFORE, you learned

- A topographic map shows the shape of the land
- A map key explains the meanings of map symbols
- Rocks are classified by how they formed

NOW, you will learn

- What a geologic map shows about Earth's surface
- How a geologic map shows information about resources
- How a geologic map shows information about hazards

VOCABULARY

geologic map p. 206

THINK ABOUT

Why do people make geologic maps?

People make many different kinds of maps. City maps include the locations of streets and important landmarks. Topographic maps show the shape of the land. A geologic map shows features of Earth's surface, including rock types. The photograph shows Point Loma, California. What would a geologic map of this area look like? What might the map be used for?

Geologic maps show information about rocks at and near Earth's surface.

The geologic features of your area make up your landscape. The shape of the land depends in large part on the types of rock at Earth's surface. The types of rock at the surface help determine the types of plants that grow best in an area. Some geologic features, such as faults, can greatly affect people who live nearby. People feel shaking caused by an earthquake when blocks of rock suddenly move past one another along a fault.

VOCABULARY Add a magnet word diagram for *geologic map* to your notebook.

A **geologic map** is a type of map that shows the locations of geologic features at and near Earth's surface. In many areas, plants and soil cover geologic features such as rocks and faults. A geologic map shows what you would see if the plants and soil were removed. It often also includes towns, roads, and topographic contour lines.

RESOURCES FOR DIFFERENTIATED INSTRUCTION

Below Level

UNIT RESOURCE BOOK

- Reading Study Guide A, pp. 104–105
- Decoding Support, p. 118

AUDIO CDS

Advanced

UNIT RESOURCE BOOK

Challenge and Extension, p. 110

English Learners

UNIT RESOURCE BOOK

Spanish Reading Study Guide, pp. 108–109

AUDIO CDS

- Audio Readings in Spanish
- Audio Readings (English)

Types and Ages of Rocks

On the right is a geologic map that shows the San Diego area. The map uses colors and symbols to show geologic features. Each color stands for a type of rock of a certain age or age range. For example, the map uses yellow and peach to show sedimentary rocks of different ages. The map's key lists the types of rock shown by each color. A key often includes a short description of the types of rock shown on the map.

The map of the San Diego area uses only color to show different rock types. As you will see later in this section, many geologic maps use special letter codes as well as colors to give information about types of rocks and their ages.

What do different colors show on a geologic map?

Geologic Map of San Diego Area

San Jacinto Fault
Elsinore Fault
PENINSULAR RANGES
San Diego
Point Loma
0 5 10 miles

Geologic Structure
— Fault
······ Covered fault

Rock Type	Approximate Age
Sedimentary rocks and sediment deposits	2–65 million years
Sedimentary rocks	65–155 million years
Sedimentary and volcanic rocks that in places have been metamorphosed	210–248 million years
Metamorphic rocks	Older than 65 million years
Granite and similar intrusive igneous rocks	65–248 million years

Geologic Structures

The term *geologic structure* refers to features of rocks and the relationships among them. Geologic structures include fracture patterns within a rock layer, the direction and angle at which rock layers are tilted, and faults. Geologic maps use symbols to show these geologic structures.

What symbols are used to show the locations of faults on the map of the San Diego area? Faults are shown by solid lines and by dotted lines. Solid lines show faults that cut through Earth's surface. Dotted lines show faults that are covered by rock layers or sediment layers.

Arrows show the relative direction of movement of rocks on either side of a fault. Find the San Jacinto Fault on the map. The arrows show how rocks on one side of the fault are moving in relation to rocks on the other side of the fault. You will read more about how rocks move along faults in Chapter 9.

6.4 INSTRUCT

Teach the Standards

Interpreting maps 6.7.f

In this section: Help students understand how to interpret the features commonly included on a geologic map.

- **previously taught:** map scales and symbols, p. 157; map projections, pp. 160–162; topographic maps, pp. 164–167
- **future opportunities:** tectonic plate boundaries map, p. 275, p. 291; epicenter map, p. 313; tsunami travel time map, p. 319

Teach from Visuals

To help students interpret the information shown in the geological map of the San Diego area, ask:

- What do the different colors in the geologic map of San Diego represent? *different types of rock and their approximate ages*
- On this map, what do the thick black lines and dotted lines represent? *fault lines in Earth's crust*
- Why would knowing where the fault lines exist be especially important in a state like California? *Possible answer: because California has many earthquakes, and earthquakes occur along fault lines*

Ongoing Assessment

Describe what a geologic map shows about Earth's surface.

Ask: What kinds of features would you include in a geologic map of the area where you live? *Answers will vary. Students may say types of rocks found at the surface, ages of the rocks, or the location of fault lines if they are known to be nearby.*

different types of rock

DIFFERENTIATE INSTRUCTION

More Reading Support

A What term is used to describe features of rocks and the relationships among rocks? *geologic structure*

English Learners Students who are English learners may have trouble with the pronunciation of the word *geologic*. Explain to them that the prefix *geo-* means "earth" or "ground." Invite them to look through a dictionary to find other words with this prefix and explain each word's connection to "earth." Some examples include *geography, geology, geode,* and *geometry* (literally meaning "to measure the earth").

Geography Connection

Formed by glaciers some 10,000 years ago, Yosemite Valley was declared a national park in 1890 after a successful campaign by famed naturalist John Muir. The valley itself is about 900 meters (3000 feet) deep and 1.6 to 3.2 kilometers (1 to 2 miles) wide. It provides visitors with a variety of interesting rock formations, waterfalls, meadows, and forests, including groves of giant sequoia trees, the largest living things on Earth.

At more than 1220 meters (4000 feet) and 915 meters (3000 feet) high, respectively, the steep cliffs of both Half Dome and El Capitan dominate the landscape. Other well-known rock formations popular with visitors to Yosemite include Cathedral Rocks and Spires, The Three Brothers, and Sentinel Rock. There are also many popular waterfalls at the park, two of the most famous being Yosemite Falls and Bridalveil Falls. Many species of wildlife make Yosemite their home, and visitors to the park may encounter deer, coyotes, and even the occasional bear.

Develop Critical Thinking

Help students apply what they have learned by asking what two different types of rock indicated by letter codes beginning with "K" such as Khd (Half Dome Granodiorite) and Kec (El Capitan Granite) might have in common? *Answer: They both come from the same geologic time period.*

Ongoing Assessment

with colors, patterns, or letter codes

READING TIP

The geologic time scale is a chart that divides Earth's history into sections. You can see a chart of the geologic time scale on pages R62–R63.

Geologic Map of Yosemite

The map on page 209 shows the geology of part of Yosemite National Park. It uses colors, patterns, and letter codes to show the types of rocks at Earth's surface. Like most geologic maps, this map has been printed on top of a topographic map.

How are different types of rock shown on a geologic map?

Each type of rock is given a name. The name often comes from a place where the rock's characteristics are easiest to see or where the rock was first studied. The letter code for a type of rock includes a short form of the rock's name.

? B

Half Dome The steep cliff of Half Dome is one of Yosemite's most famous sights. It is shown on the eastern side of the map.

1. The type of rock that makes up Half Dome is known as Half Dome Granodiorite (GRAN-uh-DY-uh-RYT). As you can see on the map, Half Dome takes up only a very small part of the total area covered by Half Dome Granodiorite.
2. The letter code for Half Dome Granodiorite is Khd. The first letter refers to the age of the rock on the geologic time scale. The "K" refers to the Cretaceous (krih-TAY-shuhs) Period. You may have heard of this period in connection with dinosaurs. At the end of this period, dinosaurs became extinct.

READING TIP

The letter code for the El Capitan Granite is Kec. The first letter refers to the geologic time period in which the rock formed. The next two letters abbreviate the name of the rock.

Cretaceous Half Dome
↓ ↓ ↓
K h d

? C

Yosemite Valley The bottom of Yosemite Valley is covered by sediments, which are shown in yellow on the map.

3. The contour lines are far apart at the bottom of the valley. The land there is fairly flat. The contour lines around the valley are close together. The sides of the valley are steep.
4. Most of the sediments in the middle of the valley were deposited by streams. Sediments along the sides of the valley are made up of pieces of rocks that fell from nearby cliffs.
5. Because sediments form at Earth's surface, they lie in a fairly thin layer on top of the rocks underneath. Suppose you could remove the sediments shown in yellow from the eastern side of Yosemite Valley. You would probably find Half Dome Granodiorite lying underneath the sediments.

El Capitan The tall cliff of El Capitan is popular with rock climbers. It is shown near the western edge of the map.

6. El Capitan is made up mainly of the rock known as El Capitan Granite. The letter code for this rock type is Kec. This rock type contains granite and granodiorite.

DIFFERENTIATE INSTRUCTION

B What is the name of the steep cliff that is one of Yosemite's most famous sights? *Half Dome*

C What covers the bottom of Yosemite Valley? *sediments*

Advanced Have advanced students search reference source and the Internet to investigate another national park. Ask them to research the kinds of rock found in the park and compare them to the different rock types found in Yosemite. Have students draw a simple geologic map of the national park they research. Students should create a map key that explains the colors, patterns, and letter codes they used to distinguish between rock types.

 Challenge and Extension, p. 110

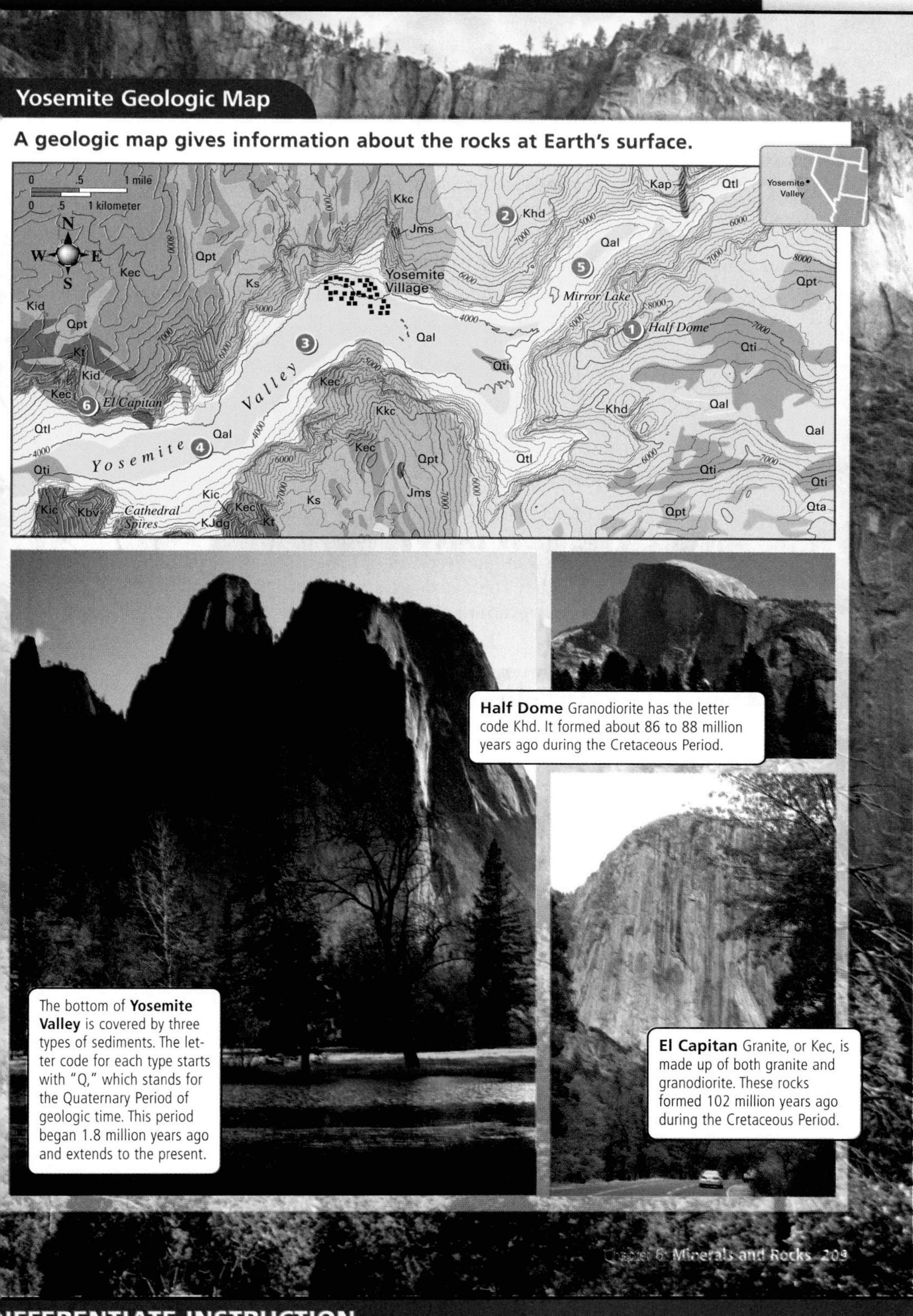

Half Dome Granodiorite has the letter code Khd. It formed about 86 to 88 million years ago during the Cretaceous Period.

The bottom of **Yosemite Valley** is covered by three types of sediments. The letter code for each type starts with "Q," which stands for the Quaternary Period of geologic time. This period began 1.8 million years ago and extends to the present.

El Capitan Granite, or Kec, is made up of both granite and granodiorite. These rocks formed 102 million years ago during the Cretaceous Period.

Teach from Visuals

To help students interpret the information presented on the Yosemite geologic map, ask

- What kind of rock is found in the area near Half Dome? ***granodiorite (Khd)***
- What does the letter Q stand for in the codes for the three types of sediment found at the bottom of Yosemite Valley? ***the Quaternary Period***

Real World Example

If possible, bring in small samples of the types of rocks mentioned here. Allow students to handle the samples and ask them to compare the rocks with one another. What differences or similarities do they observe in color, hardness, and texture? Are they able to observe different mineral crystals in any of the rocks?

IFFERENTIATE INSTRUCTION

elow Level To help below level students better understand a geo-gical map, prepare an "empty" map of Yosemite National Park with the fferent geologic feature landmarks indicated. Using colored crayons or arkers, students can color in areas on the map where various types of ɔck can be found, using different colors to represent different rock types. sk students to prepare a key to help readers know which color represents hich rock type.

Integrate the Sciences

The Mojave Desert contains not only a range of mineral resources and rocks, but also a wide variety of interesting reptiles. These reptiles include snakes such as the red racer, the Mojave rattlesnake, and the Mojave Desert sidewinder; lizards such as the chuckwalla, the desert iguana, and the southern desert horned lizard; and tortoises, such as the endangered desert tortoise.

Teach from Visuals

To help students interpret the geologic map of the Mojave Desert, ask:

- What are some resources shown on the geologic map of the Mojave Desert? *gypsum, gold, silver, salt, boron*
- What part of California is the Mojave Desert found in? How do you know? *The Mojave Desert is found in the southern part of the state; You can tell this by looking at the map detail shown in the upper right corner.*

Ongoing Assessment

Explain how a geologic map shows information about resources.

Ask: When people are planning to mine for a specific metal in an area, why might it be helpful to consult a geologic map of the area first? *The geologic map will show them where the area's resources, including bodies of rock likely to contain the metal, are located.*

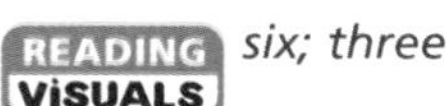

six; three

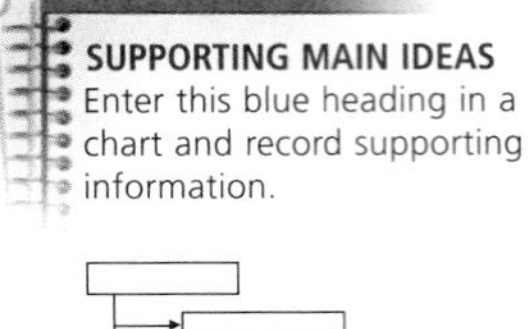

SUPPORTING MAIN IDEAS
Enter this blue heading in a chart and record supporting information.

Geologic maps show information about resources and hazards.

Geologic maps show information about the types and ages of rocks in an area. Therefore, they are useful for locating natural resources such as oil and minerals. Suppose a valuable mineral has been found in a certain type of rock. A geologic map can be used to find other places where that rock is at or near the surface.

Geologic maps are also useful for studying geologic hazards. A hazard is a possible source of danger. For example, areas on either side of a stream are often covered by sediment deposits left by floods. These areas might not be safe for building. People can see the size of these deposits on a geologic map. They can use the map when deciding whether to build houses or a park near the stream.

Resources

The geologic map below shows some of the mineral resources in the Mojave Desert area of California. This type of map is useful when people want an overview of the geology and resources of a large area. They could also get a more detailed map with information about a location.

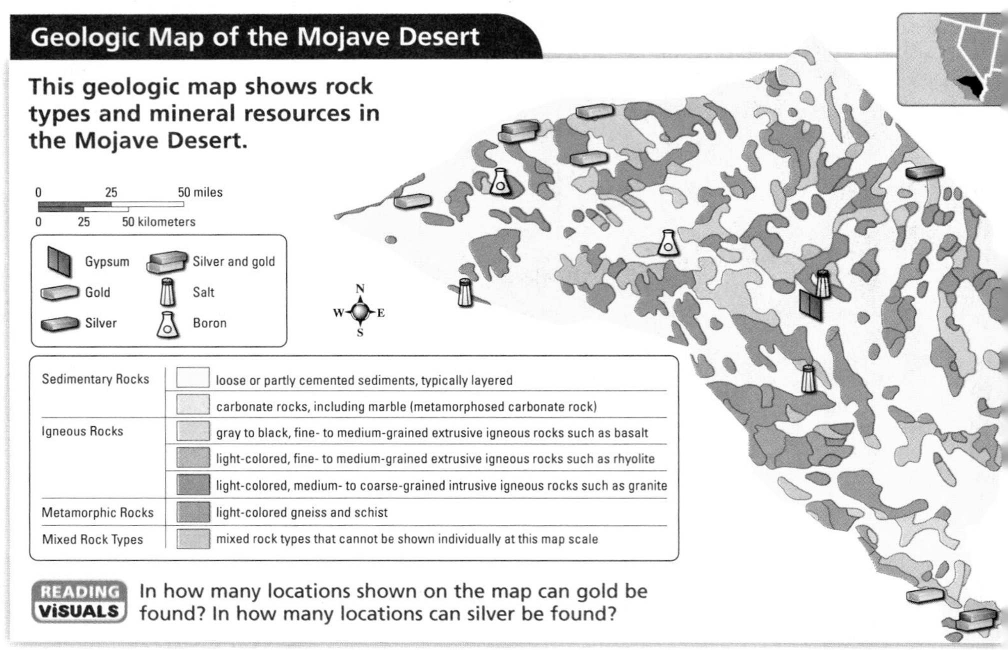

DIFFERENTIATE INSTRUCTION

More Reading Support

D What are some examples of natural resources? *oil, minerals*

E What is meant by a hazard? *a possible source of danger*

Hazards

Geologic maps show many types of hazards. For example, a map of an active volcano would show the locations of lava flows and other hazards related to eruptions. The data shown on the map can tell how powerful the volcano's eruptions tend to be and how often they happen. You will read more about volcanic eruptions and hazards in Chapter 10.

Landslides are another type of hazard shown on a geologic map. Areas where landslides have happened are marked. People can use the maps to get data about the landslides. The maps can show the types of rocks involved, the angle and direction at which the rock layers were tilted, and the slope of the land. People can then use these data to identify areas where new landslides are likely to occur.

CHECK YOUR READING Name two types of hazards that might be shown on a geologic map.

INVESTIGATE Landslide Areas

Where are landslides most likely to affect a road?

SKILL FOCUS
Analyzing (6.7.f)

MATERIALS
Geologic Map of Highway 101

TIME
20 minutes

PROCEDURE

1. Look at the geologic map of part of Highway 101. Use the map key to identify the geologic units shown on the map.
2. On the lines provided, write two ways in which the rocks that make up units KJFb and KJFm are similar.
3. On the map, mark the locations where there is a border between different landslide areas. On the line provided, write the number of borders between landslides.
4. Use the map scale to estimate the length of Highway 101 that goes through landslide areas shown on the map. Write your estimate on the line provided.
5. Determine which individual landslide covered the greatest distance. Mark that landslide on the map. On the line provided, write the distance covered by the landslide.

WHAT DO YOU THINK?

- Why is it important to show landslide areas on a geologic map?
- Why do some landslide areas share a border? Did the landslides overlap? Explain.

CHALLENGE At what elevation did the landslide that covered the greatest distance begin? At what elevation did it stop? How does the change in elevation affect the path of a landslide?

DIFFERENTIATE INSTRUCTION

More Reading Support

F What kind of information about an active volcano might a geologic map reveal? *how violent the volcano's eruptions are; how often the eruptions occur*

Alternative Assessment Group students into pairs or teams and have them compare each other's map markings and answers to the investigation questions. Then reproduce the map on the board and invite individual students to redraw their markings for the class.

INVESTIGATE Landslide Areas

PURPOSE To analyze a geologic map and determine how changes in elevation affect landslides

TIPS *20 min.* You may want to provide students with a road map of California so they can see where the stretch of highway in the geologic map is located.

- Review the use of map scales to make sure students are able to measure distances on the map.
- The map's contour interval is 40 feet.
- Students do not need to come up with identical estimates.

PROCEDURE *2. They contain sedimentary rocks that are similar in age.*

3. students should mark borders between landslides near the center of the map; 2

4. about 2.75 mi or 4.5 km

5. students should mark the large landslide near the top of the map; about 0.6 mi or 1 km

WHAT DO YOU THINK? *to indicate dangerous areas where people should be careful or where landslides might re-occur; a second landslide likely occurred in the same area, partly covering an earlier landslide.*

CHALLENGE *The landslide started at an elevation of about 980 feet and ended at about 120 feet in elevation. A landslide stops where the land becomes fairly flat.*

- Datasheet, Landslide Areas, p. 112
- Geologic Map of Highway 101, p. 111

Technology Resources

Customize this student lab as needed or look for an alternative. Print rubrics to assess student lab reports.

 **Lab Generator CD-ROM**

Ongoing Assessment

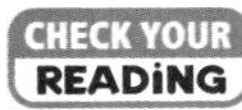

volcanic lava flow, landslides

Teach from Visuals

To help students interpret the earthquake hazard map of the Bay Area, ask:

- According to the map, what kind of soil would cause the greatest increase in shaking during an earthquake? *soils, water-saturated mud, and artificial landfill*
- Where is such soil type generally found? *close to water*
- What kind of surface would shake the least during an earthquake? *volcanic rock, sedimentary rock, and sands*

Reinforce the BIG idea

Have students relate the section to the Big Idea.

 Reinforcing Key Concepts, p. 113

6.4 ASSESS & RETEACH

Assess

 Section 6.4 Quiz, p. 122

Reteach

Help students review this section's concepts by writing the following three headings on the board: "Geologic Features," "Resources," and "Hazards." Have students list examples from the chapter under each heading. *Sample answers: Geologic Features: rocks, fracture patterns, faults; Resources: gold, silver, oil; Hazards: volcanoes, landslides, water-saturated mud*

Technology Resources

Have students visit **ClassZone.com** for reteaching of Key Concepts.

 CONTENT REVIEW

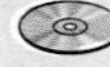 CONTENT REVIEW CD-ROM

Earthquake Hazard Map

This geologic map of an area of central California shows soil types and how they are likely to react during an earthquake.

Surface Rock or Soil Type	Predicted Reaction During an Earthquake
volcanic rock, sedimentary rock, and sands	may cause an increase in shaking
soils, including muds, sands, gravels, and silts	moderate increase in shaking
soils, including water-saturated mud and artificial landfill	greatest increase in shaking

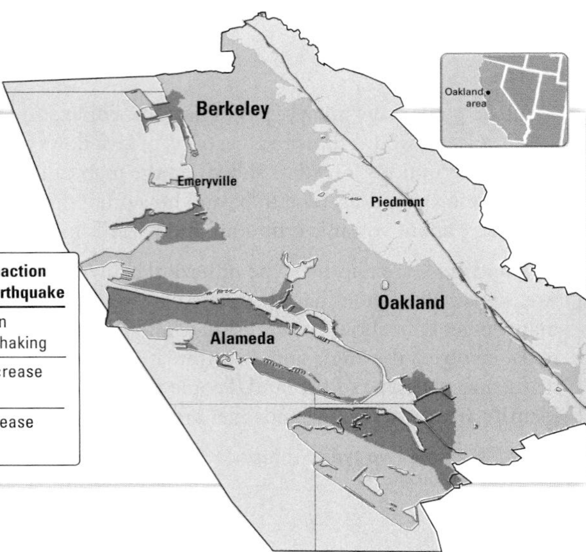

Some geologic maps focus on a specific type of hazard. The map above shows the amount of shaking that is likely to take place during an earthquake. This map gives information about soils rather than just about rock. Some types of soil can cause the ground to shake more during an earthquake.

People can use this type of map to get an idea of the shaking hazard for an area. For detailed information about the hazard at a certain place, people study soil samples. They also check factors not shown on the map, such as soil depth. You will read more about earthquake hazards, as well as how people build structures to resist earthquake damage, in Chapter 9.

6.4 Review

KEY CONCEPTS

1. What sorts of information are usually shown on a geologic map? (6.7.f)
2. How can a geologic map be used to find natural resources? (6.6)
3. How can a geologic map be used to analyze potential hazards such as landslides or floods? (6.7.f)

CRITICAL THINKING

4. **Analyze** Why do geologic maps usually show features such as towns or topographic contour lines?
5. **Infer** Describe three ways in which letter codes on geologic maps are useful.

CHALLENGE

6. **Evaluate** What is a geologic hazard in your area? How might it be shown on a map?

ANSWERS

1. information about rocks and geologic structures at or near Earth's surface

2. Because it shows information about types and ages of rocks in an area, people can use the map to locate mineral resources that those rocks might contain.

3. Geologic maps show where landslides are common, and they show where floods have deposited sediments.

4. to help map readers more easily recognize the area shown on the geologic map

5. They are easy to read; they are informative because they reveal the type of rock shown; they are more useful on black-and-white geologic maps, because colors cannot be used to indicate different rock types.

6. Answers will vary. These hazards might be indicated on a geologic map using colors or symbols.

MINERALS UNDERGROUND

Gold Fever!

6.6.c Students know the natural origin of the materials used to make common objects.

It is 1848. A man races through the town, waving a small container of gold. Gold has been discovered near Sutter's Mill. The California gold rush is on!

At that time, gold could be used as money. Soon, gold seekers from the East traveled across the mountains to California or sailed there around the southern tip of South America. In the foothills of the Sierra Nevada, prospectors claimed mines and got to work.

Until 1847 San Francisco was called Yerba Buena. About 460 people lived there. Two years later, about 79,000 people lived in the city. The successful prospectors used their gold to buy homes and businesses.

AN ACCOUNT OF
CALIFORNIA,
AND THE
WONDERFUL GOLD REGIONS,
A New Arrival at the Gold Diggings.
WITH A DESCRIPTION OF
The Different Routes to California;
Information about the Country, and the Ancient and Modern Discoveries of Gold;
How to Test Precious Metals; Accounts of Gold Hunters;
TOGETHER WITH MUCH OTHER
Useful Reading for those going to California, or having Friends there.
ILLUSTRATED WITH MAPS AND ENGRAVINGS.
BOSTON:
PUBLISHED BY J. B. HALL, 66 CORNHILL.
For Sale at Skinner's Publication Rooms, 601 Cornhill.
Price, 12½ cents.

The mining region was called the Mother Lode. A lode is a deposit of a valuable mineral within a body of rock. Movement along earthquake faults in the area caused rocks to crack. Over time, gold that was dissolved in water settled into the cracks. These cracks became veins of gold. Some veins were 5 feet wide. One was 40 feet long! The gold formed as lumpy nuggets. Most nuggets were small, but a few were as big as a fist.

Much of the gold in the Mother Lode region weathered out of the rock in which it formed. Eventually it was washed into streams and rivers, where it built up in sedimentary deposits. Such deposits in the Mother Lode region are associated with many streams and rivers, include the Feather, American, and Yuba rivers.

Gold is still mined in California today. Gold is commonly used in jewelry, and it also has many other uses that people might not know about. For example, small amounts of gold are used in many common electronic products, including computers, telephones, and cellular phones.

This gold nugget is still partly attached to the rock in which it formed.

The Castle Mountain open-pit gold mine is located in the Mojave Desert near Ivanpah, California.

WRITING ABOUT SCIENCE

Gold is used in electronics, lasers, communications satellites, and medicine. Research one of the uses of gold. Write a description of how and why gold is used in that way.

WRITING ABOUT SCIENCE

Writing Applications 6.2.2 This assignment will give students practice in writing a descriptive essay. Suggest that partners read each other's descriptions and evaluate them in terms of organization and clarity.

The best essays will

- state the thesis or purpose
- follow an organizational pattern

CALIFORNIA CLOSE-UP

Science in Action in California

Set Learning Goal

To understand the natural origin of gold and some of its many uses.

Present the Science

Gold is a mineral that has been prized since ancient times for its beauty. Gold is also an element (chemical symbol Au), because pure gold contains only gold atoms. Early prospectors sometimes found underground "veins" of gold, which were actually cracks in rock that had once been filled by hot water from within Earth's crust containing dissolved gold. As the water cooled, the gold became solid again and was left behind in the cracks.

Discussion Questions

Have students share their knowledge and experience with gold and the California gold rush period.

- Ask: Why do you think gold was so valuable during the time of the California gold rush? *because it was rare and because it could be used as money*
- Ask: What connection can you make between the high density of gold in California and its tendency to build up in sedimentary deposits? *Possible answer: Because gold is dense and heavy, it is more likely to settle to the bottom of a river, while lighter sediments are washed away.*
- Ask: What are some modern uses for gold? *Possible answers: jewelry, computers, telephones, cellular phones*

Fun Facts

Gold prospectors were often referred to as "forty-niners," named after the year in which most of them headed west—1849.

Close

Ask students to name instances when they may have seen or handled gold. Remind them that the discovery of gold was instrumental to the early formation of California as a U.S. state.

BACK TO

the BIG idea

Ask students to give examples of minerals and rocks that they see in nature, wear on their bodies, and use in their homes. *Sample answers: quartz in a granite rock, gold in a necklace, and slate stones in a walkway*

KEY CONCEPTS SUMMARY

SECTION 6.1

Ask: What does it mean to say that a mineral has a definite chemical makeup? *The mineral consists of a specific combination of atoms of certain elements.*

Ask: What is a crystal? *a solid in which atoms are arranged in an orderly, repeating three-dimensional pattern*

SECTION 6.2

Ask: Where do metamorphic rocks form? *in areas of high heat or pressure, or both*

Ask: The process of rocks changing continuously from one type of rock to another is called what? *the rock cycle*

SECTION 6.3

Ask: Which type of weathering involves a physical change in rocks? *mechanical*

Ask: Acid rain causing color change in an outdoor marble statue is an example of what? *chemical weathering*

SECTION 6.4

Ask: How are geologic maps different from standard maps? *Standard maps normally show many human-made things such as roads, highways, cities, and towns; geologic maps show things such as types and ages of rocks and geologic structures.*

6 Chapter Review

Minerals and rocks are basic building blocks of Earth.

KEY CONCEPTS SUMMARY

1 Minerals are all around us.

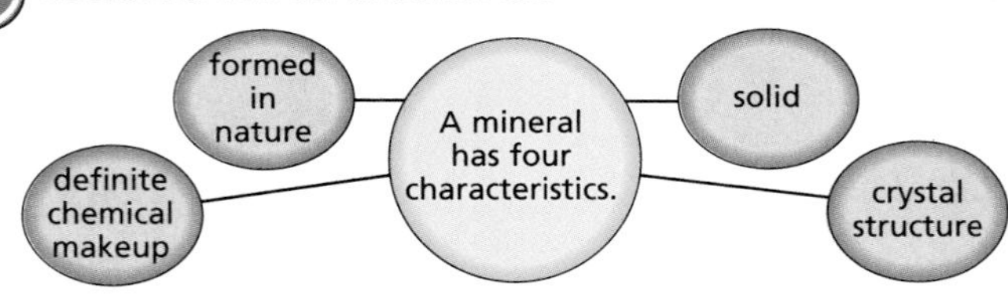

VOCABULARY
mineral p. 184
element p. 184
crystal p. 185
rock p. 187

2 Rocks form in different ways.

There are three types of rocks.

Igneous rocks form from molten rock.

Sedimentary rocks form from earlier rocks.

Metamorphic rocks form as existing rocks change.

VOCABULARY
igneous rock p. 191
magma p. 191
lava p. 191
sedimentary rock p. 192
metamorphic rock p. 194
rock cycle p. 196

3 Natural processes break down rocks.

Over time, **mechanical weathering** breaks a rock into smaller pieces.

Chemical weathering affects exposed rock surfaces.

VOCABULARY
geologic cycle p. 199
weathering p. 199
mechanical weathering p. 200
chemical weathering p. 202

4 Geologic maps show Earth's surface features.

Geologic maps show
- types and ages of rocks
- geologic structures
- resources and hazards

VOCABULARY
geologic map p. 206

214 Unit 2: **Earth's Surface**

Review Concepts

- Big Idea Flow Chart, p. T41
- Chapter Outline, pp. T47–T48

Technology Resources

Have students visit **ClassZone.com** or use the CD-ROM for a cumulative review of concepts.

CONTENT REVIEW

CONTENT REVIEW CD-ROM

Engage students in a whole-class interactive review of Key Concepts. Edit content as you wish.

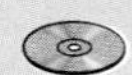
POWER PRESENTATIONS

Reviewing Vocabulary

On a separate sheet of paper, write a sentence or two describing the relationship between the two terms.

1. mineral, crystal
2. magma, lava
3. intrusive, extrusive
4. igneous rock, metamorphic rock
5. geologic cycle, weathering
6. mechanical weathering, chemical weathering
7. geologic map, topographic map

Reviewing Key Concepts

Multiple Choice *Choose the letter of the best answer.*

8. A crystal structure is characteristic of (6.6)
   a. an element
   b. a rock
   c. magma
   d. a mineral
9. How is it possible for two different minerals to have the same chemical composition? (6.6)
   a. They have different crystal structures.
   b. One is formed only by organisms.
   c. Only one is a rock-forming mineral.
   d. They have different appearances.
10. The rock cycle shows how rocks continually (6.1.b)
    a. increase in size
    b. increase in number
    c. become more complex
    d. change over time
11. Which kind of rock forms by recrystallization? (6.1.b)
    a. intrusive igneous
    b. extrusive igneous
    c. sedimentary
    d. metamorphic
12. Rock salt is an example of a sedimentary rock that develops from dissolved minerals as (6.1.b)
    a. water evaporates
    b. magma cools
    c. sediments break down
    d. sand settles in water
13. The force of expanding water in the cracks and pores of a rock is an example of (6.2.a)
    a. chemical weathering
    b. mechanical weathering
    c. oxidation
    d. crystallization
14. The breakdown of rock by acidic water is an example of (6.2.a)
    a. chemical weathering
    b. mechanical weathering
    c. oxidation
    d. crystallization
15. Three factors that affect the rate of weathering are (6.2.a)
    a. microorganisms, plants, and animals
    b. weather, landforms, and rainfall
    c. surface area, rock composition, and climate
    d. texture, color, and pore space
16. The term *geologic structure* refers to (6.1.b)
    a. types and ages of rocks
    b. characteristics of minerals
    c. patterns of weathering in rocks
    d. features of rocks and relationships among rocks

Short Answer *Write a short answer for each question.*

17. Why aren't all solids minerals? Include the term *crystal structure* in your answer. (6.6)
18. What is the difference between a rock and a mineral? (6.1.b)
19. Compare the distribution of rock types at Earth's surface with their distribution in the entire crust. How are any differences related to processes that take place in the rock cycle? (6.1.b)

ASSESSMENT RESOURCES

ASSESSMENT BOOK

- Chapter Test A, pp. 123–126
- Chapter Test B, pp. 127–130
- Chapter Test C, pp. 131–134
- Alternative Assessment, pp. 135–136

STANDARDS REVIEW AND PRACTICE, pp. 3–4, 15–16, 43–44, 55–64, 67–68

Technology Resources

Edit test items and answer choices.

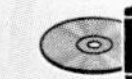 **Test Generator CD-ROM**

Visit **ClassZone.com** to extend test practice.

 **Test Practice**

Reviewing Vocabulary

Sample answers:

1. *All minerals form crystals.*
2. *Magma is molten rock inside Earth, and lava is molten rock at Earth's surface.*
3. *Intrusive igneous rock forms inside Earth, and extrusive igneous rock forms on Earth's surface.*
4. *Igneous rock can be transformed into metamorphic rock through heat and pressure. Metamorphic rock can also melt into magma, and then cool again to form igneous rock.*
5. *Weathering, the set of natural processes that breaks down rocks, is part of the geologic cycle.*
6. *Mechanical weathering uses physical forces to break down rock. Chemical weathering breaks down rock by changing its composition through chemical reactions.*
7. *A topographic map shows the shape of the land, and a geologic map shows features on Earth's surface, including rock types.*

Reviewing Key Concepts

8. d	*11. d*	*14. a*
9. a	*12. a*	*15. c*
10. d	*13. b*	*16. d*

17. *Not all solids have atoms arranged in crystal structures—that is, in orderly, repeating three-dimensional patterns.*
18. *A mineral must form in nature, be solid, have a definite chemical composition, and have a crystal structure. A rock must be solid and form naturally. Most rocks are made of minerals.*
19. *Most of the rocks at Earth's surface are sedimentary, but the crust as a whole is made up almost entirely of igneous and metamorphic rocks. The processes that produce sedimentary rocks occur only at the surface; when these rocks are buried, they are subjected to metamorphism.*

Thinking Critically

20. *topographic and geologic*
21. *sedimentary rock*
22. *magma; the large crystals formed as molten rock slowly cooled within Earth*
23. *14 million years (102 million years–88 million years)*
24. *Water and gravity move sediments downhill.*
25. *The deposits were left by many floods that occurred over a long time.*
26. *Physical weathering processes such as ice wedging might have broken apart rocks at the top of cliffs.*
27. *The layers of salt were left after the ancient ocean dried up.*
28. *Mechanical weathering involves a physical change in rocks. Chemical weathering involves a chemical change. Both break up rocks.*
29. *Sample answer: A rabbit eats a plant, and then dies and decays to form humus. Humus provides the nutrients needed for new plant growth.*

the BIG idea

30. *Minerals are not basic components of gas-giant planets. One of the characteristics of minerals is that they are solids.*
31. *Now there are a lot of products made from metals, such as cars, electronic equipment for music and television, and furnaces and air conditioners. These products would be much harder to find and much more expensive if minerals with metals were rare. Many of those products would never have been invented if metals were rare.*
32. *Gold could form in a rock that is later broken apart by weathering. Water could carry the gold to the river.*

UNIT PROJECTS

Collect schedules, materials lists, and questions. Be sure dates and materials are obtainable, and questions are focused.

 Unit Projects, pp. 5–10

Thinking Critically

Use the map and key to answer the next seven questions. (6.7.f)

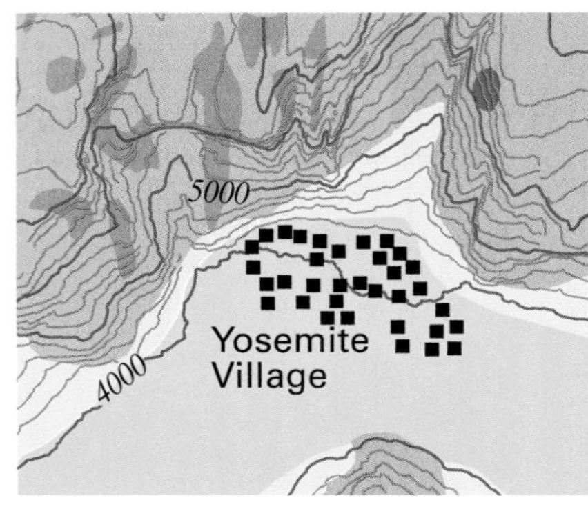

Sediment or Rock Type	Approximate Age
Sediment deposits mainly left by streams	0–2 million years
Sediment deposits made up of rocks fallen from cliffs	0–10,000 years
Igneous rock: granodiorite	88 million years
Igneous rock: granodiorite	93 million years
Igneous rock: granite and granodiorite	102 million years
Metamorphic rock formed from sedimentary rock	144–206 million years

20. **APPLY** Which two types of maps have been combined to make this map? (6.7.f)
21. **APPLY** From what type of rock did the metamorphic rock form?
22. **INTERPRET** All of the igneous rocks have large mineral crystals. Did they form from magma or from lava? Explain.
23. **CALCULATE** What is the difference in age between the youngest and oldest types of igneous rock?
24. **SYNTHESIZE** Why are sediments likely to be found at the lowest elevations? (6.2.a)
25. **DRAW CONCLUSIONS** The age of the sediment deposits left by streams is given as a range. What is a likely reason why it is not given as a single age? (6.2.b)
26. **SYNTHESIZE** How might weathering processes help form the sediment deposits made up of rocks fallen from cliffs? (6.2.a)
27. **HYPOTHESIZE** Thick layers of halite are mined near Detroit, Michigan. At one time, seawater covered the area. Write a hypothesis that explains how the halite formed there. (6.7.a)
28. **COMPARE AND CONTRAST** How does mechanical weathering differ from chemical weathering? How are the two processes similar? (6.2.a)
29. **SYNTHESIZE** A cycle is a series of events or actions that repeats regularly. Describe a cycle that involves living things. (6.2.a)

the BIG idea

30. **ANALYZE** Minerals are basic components of planets such as Earth and Mars. Other planets in our solar system, such as Jupiter and Saturn are called gas giants because they are made up mainly of the gases hydrogen and helium. They do not have solid surfaces. Do you think that minerals are basic components of gas giants? Why or why not? (6.6)
31. **INFER** Minerals make up much of Earth. People use minerals as sources of many materials, such as metals. Some metals are used to make machine parts or build houses. How would your life be different if minerals that contain metals were rare in Earth's crust? (6.6.c)
32. **SYNTHESIZE** Use your knowledge of the rock cycle and weathering to explain why loose pieces of gold might be found in a river.

UNIT PROJECTS

If you need to do an experiment for your unit project, gather the materials. Be sure to allow enough time to observe results before the project is due.

MONITOR AND RETEACH

If students have trouble applying the concepts in items 20–26, have them review geologic maps and discuss the kinds of information these maps can show. Refer students to the map on p. 207. Invite volunteers to formulate questions about the map for the rest of the class to answer.

Students may benefit from summarizing one or more sections of the chapter.

 Summarizing the Chapter, pp. 139–140

Standards-Based Assessment

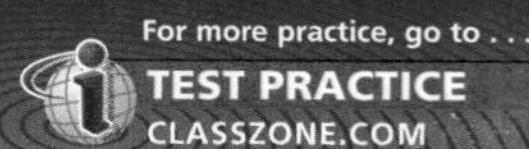

Analyzing a Diagram

6.1.b

This diagram shows a simple version of the rock cycle. Use it to answer the questions.

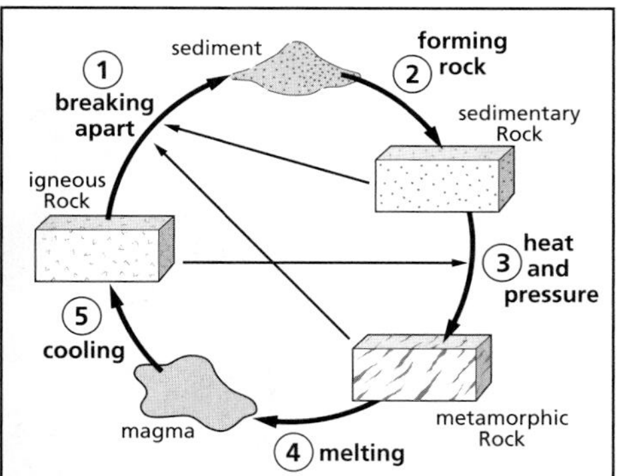

1. Where are loose materials developing into rock?
a. 1 **c.** 4
b. 2 **d.** 5

2. Where are sand and other small particles forming from rock?
a. 1 **c.** 4
b. 2 **d.** 5

3. Where is magma developing into rock?
a. 1 **c.** 4
b. 3 **d.** 5

4. Where is molten rock forming?
a. 1 **c.** 4
b. 3 **d.** 5

5. Where are heat and pressure changing solid rock into another type of rock without melting it?
a. 1 **c.** 4
b. 3 **d.** 5

6. According to the diagram, what can happen to sedimentary rock?
a. It can become sediment or magma.
b. It can become igneous rock or magma.
c. It can become sediment or metamorphic rock.
d. It can become sediment, metamorphic rock, or magma.

7. How could you change the diagram to show that igneous rock can become magma again?
a. Add an arrow from igneous rock to metamorphic rock.
b. Add an arrow from heat and pressure to igneous rock.
c. Add an arrow from igneous rock to melting.
d. Add an arrow from melting to igneous rock.

8. What must happen to rock that formed inside Earth before it can become sediment?
a. It must reach the surface as rock above it wears away.
b. It must become magma and erupt from a volcano.
c. Heat and pressure must change it into sediment.
d. It must become sedimentary rock while inside Earth.

Extended Response

Answer the two questions below in detail.

9. In the water cycle, different forms of water cycle between Earth's surface and the atmosphere. For example, liquid water from oceans and lakes changes into gas and enters the atmosphere. How is this cycle similar to the rock cycle? How is it different?

10. Melba is trying to decide whether an igneous rock formed deep inside Earth or at the surface. What should she look for? Why?

REFLECTING ON THE CHAPTER

Have students answer the following questions in their **Science Notebook:**

1. Look around the outside of your home or school. Can you find any minerals that you did not notice before reading this chapter? Make a list of any minerals you see and briefly describe why you believe each is a mineral.
2. Did anything you learned about minerals and rocks in this chapter surprise you? If so, what surprised you and why?
3. How do the concepts in this chapter relate to your Unit Project?

California Content Standard

6.1.b Students know Earth is composed of several layers: a cold, brittle lithosphere; a hot, convecting mantle; and a dense, metallic core.

Analyzing a Diagram

1. b	*3. d*	*5. b*	*7. c*
2. a	*4. c*	*6. c*	*8. a*

Extended Response

9. RUBRIC

4 points for a response that correctly answers the question and explains at least three concepts accurately

Sample: The water cycle is similar to the rock cycle in that water can change from one form to another (for example, ice to liquid water to gas). Like the rock cycle, the water cycle has no beginning and no ending. It is different in that changes in the water cycle can occur very quickly, and it is temperature that causes the water to change form. In addition to temperature, the rock cycle involves both pressure inside Earth and weathering at Earth's surface.

3 points correctly answers the question and explains two concepts accurately
2 points correctly answers the question and explains one concept accurately
1 point correctly answers the question but does not explain any concepts accurately

10. RUBRIC

4 points for a response that correctly answers the question and explains how the size of mineral crystals in igneous rocks is related to cooling time

Sample: Melba should look at the igneous rock's texture. If it has small mineral crystals, it is a surface rock that had a quick cooling time. If it has large mineral crystals, it was formed deep within Earth and had a slow cooling time.

3 points for a response that correctly answers the question and gives a mostly accurate explanation
2 points for a response that correctly answers the question and gives a partly correct explanation
1 point for a correct response with no explanation

FOCUS

Set Learning Goals

Students will

- Describe how scientists have studied fossils over time.
- Explain the application of technology used to study fossils.
- Analyze layers of sediment.

California Content Standards

6.1.a Students know evidence of plate tectonics is derived from the fit of the continents; the location of earthquakes, volcanoes, and midocean ridges; and the distribution of fossils, rock types, and ancient climatic zones.

6.1.e Students know major geologic events, such as earthquakes, volcanic eruptions, and mountain building, result from plate motions.

INSTRUCT

The top half of the timeline shows major events in the study of fossils. The bottom half discusses advances in the technology used in this study, including various technological applications. Note that technology developed many years ago is still useful and continues to be refined.

Application

1669 In addition to his work on sedimentary layers, Nicolaus Steno analyzed fossils. He gathered rocks from the Mediterranean area and, by careful comparison, concluded that they were shaped like the teeth of living sharks. Steno suggested that the rocks were the remains of ancient shark-like creatures. His theory was widely ridiculed. Ask students why they think new ideas in science are often initially discounted. *Because new ideas challenge deeply held beliefs, many people resist them at first.*

TIMELINES in Science

6.1.a, 6.1.e

THE STORY OF FOSSILS

Fossils are an important source of information about the history of life on Earth. The first observer to suggest that fossils provided clues to the past was Xenophanes. He lived in Greece around 500 B.C. Today, knowledge about fossils helps people find deposits of oil and understand changes in weather patterns. Above all, fossils reveal information about plants and animals that lived in the past.

The timeline shows a few events in the history of the study of fossils. Tools that were invented for other purposes, such as radar and CT scanners, have helped scientists learn more about fossils. The boxes below the timeline highlight the role of technology, along with applications of knowledge about fossils.

1669

Scientist Notes Importance of Rock Layers

Danish-born scientist Nicolaus Steno recognizes that sediments form new layers of rock on top of old layers. Therefore, digging down provides a way to move back in time. Scientists plan to build on Steno's discovery to determine the ages of fossils found in rock layers.

EVENTS

1640 1660 1680 1700

APPLICATIONS AND TECHNOLOGY

This sandstone formation in Utah displays layers of sediment that were laid down one on top of another.

218 Unit 2: Earth's Surface

DIFFERENTIATE INSTRUCTION

Below Level To help students organize the information in this timeline, point out that new applications of technology are linked to gains in scientific knowledge. For example, William Smith published the first large map showing underground layers of soil and rock in England. People then began to understand the importance of underground layers, and they developed better ways to study and map Earth's layers.

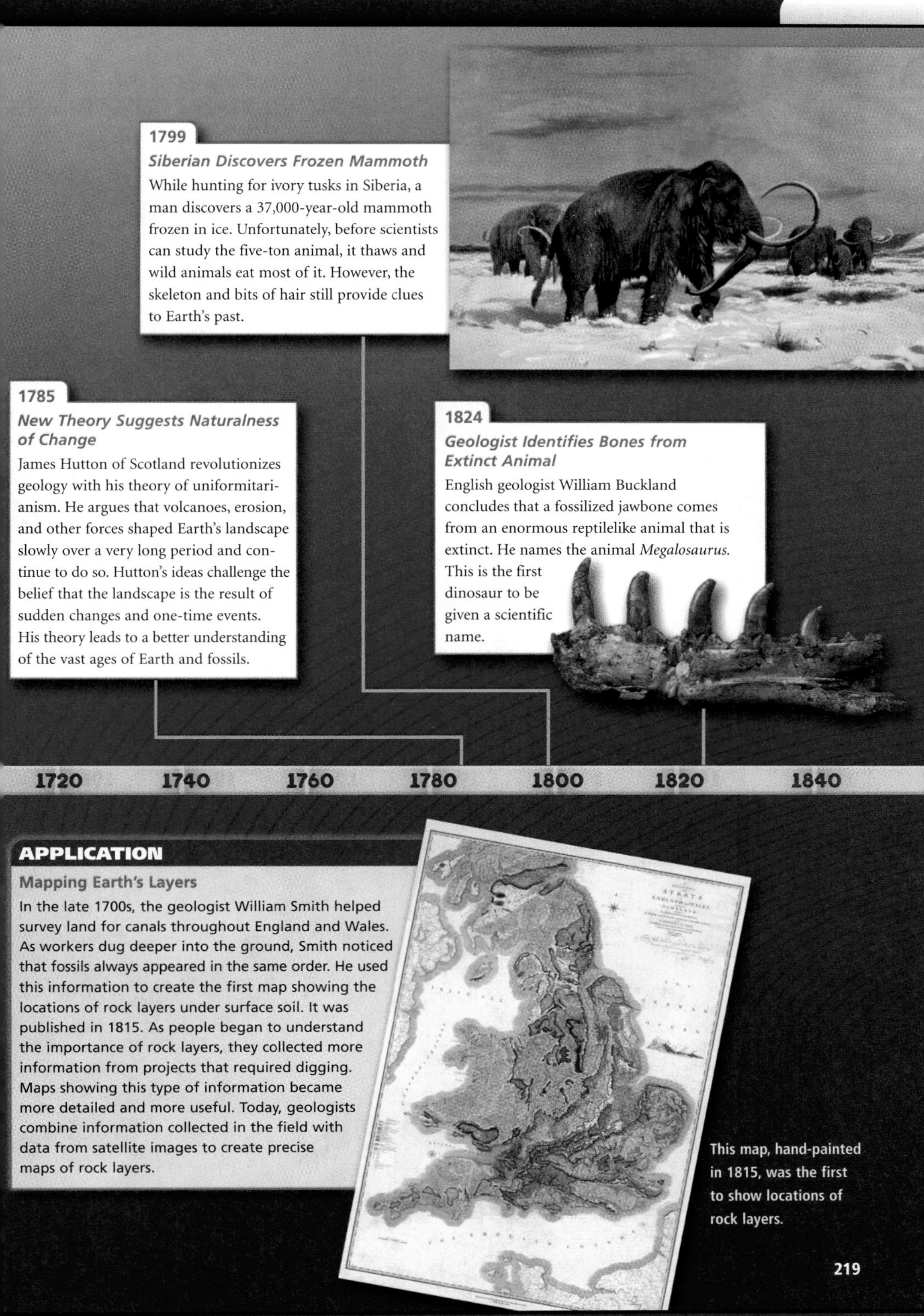

1799
Siberian Discovers Frozen Mammoth
While hunting for ivory tusks in Siberia, a man discovers a 37,000-year-old mammoth frozen in ice. Unfortunately, before scientists can study the five-ton animal, it thaws and wild animals eat most of it. However, the skeleton and bits of hair still provide clues to Earth's past.
1785
New Theory Suggests Naturalness of Change
James Hutton of Scotland revolutionizes geology with his theory of uniformitarianism. He argues that volcanoes, erosion, and other forces shaped Earth's landscape slowly over a very long period and continue to do so. Hutton's ideas challenge the belief that the landscape is the result of sudden changes and one-time events. His theory leads to a better understanding of the vast ages of Earth and fossils.
1824
Geologist Identifies Bones from Extinct Animal
English geologist William Buckland concludes that a fossilized jawbone comes from an enormous reptilelike animal that is extinct. He names the animal Megalosaurus. This is the first dinosaur to be given a scientific name.
1720
1740
1760
1780
1800
1820
1840
APPLICATION
Mapping Earth's Layers
In the late 1700s, the geologist William Smith helped survey land for canals throughout England and Wales. As workers dug deeper into the ground, Smith noticed that fossils always appeared in the same order. He used this information to create the first map showing the locations of rock layers under surface soil. It was published in 1815. As people began to understand the importance of rock layers, they collected more information from projects that required digging. Maps showing this type of information became more detailed and more useful. Today, geologists combine information collected in the field with data from satellite images to create precise maps of rock layers.
This map, hand-painted in 1815, was the first to show locations of rock layers.
219

DIFFERENTIATE INSTRUCTION

English Learners **1785** Students may find the term *uniformitarianism* confusing because the word *uniform* implies that things do not change, yet the theory deals with changes over time. Explain that Hutton's theory describes how the same changes that occurred in the past continue today. Ask students to explain in their own words why uniformitarianism is a good name for Hutton's theory.

Scientific Process

1824 After students have read how William Buckland identified the fossilized jawbone, ask: Why do you think that Buckland concluded that the jawbone came from an extinct species rather than an existing one? *The jawbone did not match the jawbones of existing species.*

Integrate the Sciences

In 1999, scientists excavated a complete frozen mammoth in Siberia. The specimen, estimated to be 20,000 years old, is currently being studied by an international team. Various proposals for the mammoth include cloning its cells to produce a living specimen. Sperm cells, if available, could be used to fertilize a modern elephant.

Technology

NEW TIME SCALE Discuss how Boltwood's geologic time scale might have changed the way scientists viewed Earth. Ask: Would knowing that Earth was billions of years old have made scientists' work easier or harder? Explain. *Sample answer: It may have made their work easier. Certain biological and physical processes, such as evolution and mountain building, take place over vast amounts of time. Knowing that Earth was billions of years old helped explain how these processes could occur.*

Science Process

Tell students that scientists disagree over the relationship between dinosaurs and birds. Some propose that birds evolved from small dinosaurs. Others hypothesize that a common ancestor links the two species—they are related, but evolved separately. Recent fossil discoveries of dinosaurs with apparent feathers strengthens the argument that birds descended from dinosaurs.

Mathematics Connection

Tell students that the half-life of carbon 14 is 5730 years. Ask: If the age of an artifact is equivalent to five carbon 14 half-lives, how old is the artifact? *28,650 years*

Scientific Process

CT SCANS Ask students to give an example of how technology was used to disprove a hypothesis. *Sample answer: Many scientists had long thought that dinosaurs were cold-blooded. A CT scan of a dinosaur heart suggested that dinosaurs were warm-blooded.*

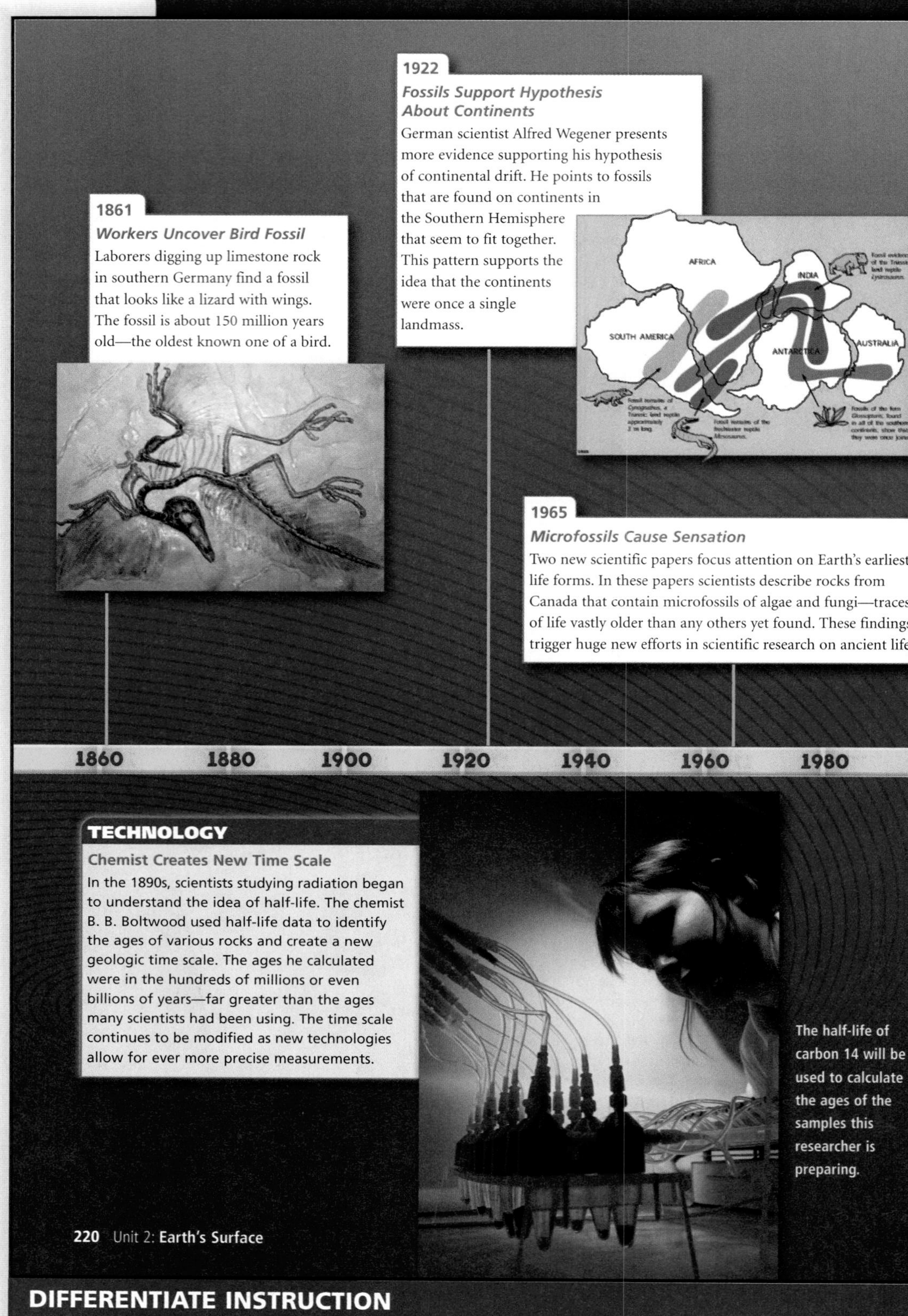

1861
Workers Uncover Bird Fossil
Laborers digging up limestone rock in southern Germany find a fossil that looks like a lizard with wings. The fossil is about 150 million years old—the oldest known one of a bird.

1922
Fossils Support Hypothesis About Continents
German scientist Alfred Wegener presents more evidence supporting his hypothesis of continental drift. He points to fossils that are found on continents in the Southern Hemisphere that seem to fit together. This pattern supports the idea that the continents were once a single landmass.

1965
Microfossils Cause Sensation
Two new scientific papers focus attention on Earth's earliest life forms. In these papers scientists describe rocks from Canada that contain microfossils of algae and fungi—traces of life vastly older than any others yet found. These findings trigger huge new efforts in scientific research on ancient life

TECHNOLOGY
Chemist Creates New Time Scale
In the 1890s, scientists studying radiation began to understand the idea of half-life. The chemist B. B. Boltwood used half-life data to identify the ages of various rocks and create a new geologic time scale. The ages he calculated were in the hundreds of millions or even billions of years—far greater than the ages many scientists had been using. The time scale continues to be modified as new technologies allow for ever more precise measurements.

The half-life of carbon 14 will be used to calculate the ages of the samples this researcher is preparing.

220 Unit 2: Earth's Surface

DIFFERENTIATE INSTRUCTION

Advanced Give students copies of the geologic time scale. Have them classify the organisms mentioned on pp. 218–219 according to their proper place on the scale. *Dinosaurs were dominant during the Mesozoic Era. The first birds and mammals appeared during that era. Microorganisms first developed during Precambrian time.*

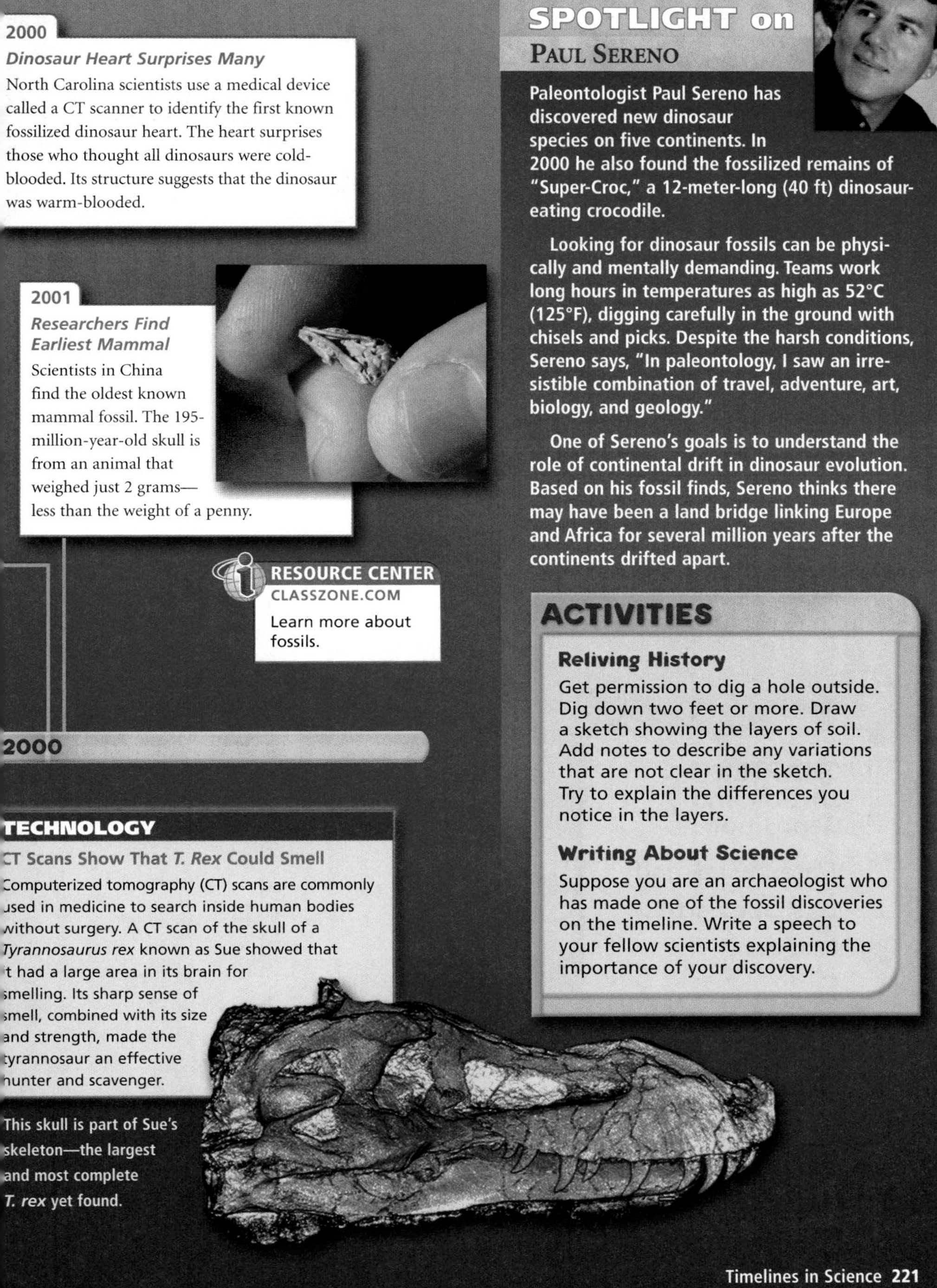

2000

Dinosaur Heart Surprises Many

North Carolina scientists use a medical device called a CT scanner to identify the first known fossilized dinosaur heart. The heart surprises those who thought all dinosaurs were cold-blooded. Its structure suggests that the dinosaur was warm-blooded.

2001

Researchers Find Earliest Mammal

Scientists in China find the oldest known mammal fossil. The 195-million-year-old skull is from an animal that weighed just 2 grams—less than the weight of a penny.

RESOURCE CENTER
CLASSZONE.COM
Learn more about fossils.

2000

TECHNOLOGY

CT Scans Show That *T. Rex* Could Smell

Computerized tomography (CT) scans are commonly used in medicine to search inside human bodies without surgery. A CT scan of the skull of a *Tyrannosaurus rex* known as Sue showed that it had a large area in its brain for smelling. Its sharp sense of smell, combined with its size and strength, made the tyrannosaur an effective hunter and scavenger.

This skull is part of Sue's skeleton—the largest and most complete *T. rex* yet found.

SPOTLIGHT on

PAUL SERENO

Paleontologist Paul Sereno has discovered new dinosaur species on five continents. In 2000 he also found the fossilized remains of "Super-Croc," a 12-meter-long (40 ft) dinosaur-eating crocodile.

Looking for dinosaur fossils can be physically and mentally demanding. Teams work long hours in temperatures as high as 52°C (125°F), digging carefully in the ground with chisels and picks. Despite the harsh conditions, Sereno says, "In paleontology, I saw an irresistible combination of travel, adventure, art, biology, and geology."

One of Sereno's goals is to understand the role of continental drift in dinosaur evolution. Based on his fossil finds, Sereno thinks there may have been a land bridge linking Europe and Africa for several million years after the continents drifted apart.

ACTIVITIES

Reliving History

Get permission to dig a hole outside. Dig down two feet or more. Draw a sketch showing the layers of soil. Add notes to describe any variations that are not clear in the sketch. Try to explain the differences you notice in the layers.

Writing About Science

Suppose you are an archaeologist who has made one of the fossil discoveries on the timeline. Write a speech to your fellow scientists explaining the importance of your discovery.

Timelines in Science 221

Spotlight on

Students may enjoy seeing photographs of Paul Sereno's discoveries at his Web site and in *National Geographic*. Also included are photographs of paleontologists at work in Sereno's Dinosaur Lab at the University of Chicago and in the field in South America, Africa, and Asia.

In 1999 Sereno and his wife, educator Gabrielle Lyon, founded Project Exploration, a "living classroom" with the goal of making science accessible to the public—with a special emphasis on interesting girls and urban students in science. The program has taken inner-city students to Montana and Wyoming to participate in paleontology fieldwork. Project Exploration, based in Chicago, also holds professional development workshops for teachers.

ACTIVITIES

Reliving History

In many areas, electrical and telephone lines are buried. A two-foot hole can disrupt such lines. It might be best to select one location for digging and have the class as a whole sketch and describe the exposed layers of sediment. Contact your local electric company before digging the hole; they will mark the location of underground lines.

Writing About Science

Allow students to pick any of the discoveries and encourage them to think about its importance. Then remind them that a speech usually begins with an attention-getter. They should order their reasons of importance logically. If time permits, allow them to give their speeches.

DIFFERENTIATE INSTRUCTION

Alternative Writing Projects Have students imagine that they are scientists in the field who have just discovered an amazing new fossil. Have them write a journal entry describing their find.

Inclusion Students with physical impairments may have trouble digging holes. Take photographs of exposed layers of sediment or use pictures of underground layers taken from magazines or textbooks. Give students the pictures and have them sketch and describe the layers.

Technology Resources

Students can visit **ClassZone.com** for information about fossils.

CHAPTER

Erosion and Deposition

Earth Science
UNIFYING PRINCIPLES

PRINCIPLE 1
Heat energy inside Earth and radiation from the Sun provide energy for Earth's processes.

PRINCIPLE 2
Physical forces, such as gravity, affect the movement of all matter on Earth and throughout the universe.

PRINCIPLE 3
Matter and energy move among Earth's rocks and soil, atmosphere, waters, and living things.

PRINCIPLE 4
Earth has changed over time and continues to change.

Unit: Earth's Surface
BIG IDEAS

CHAPTER 5
Views of Earth Today
Modern technology has changed the way we view and map Earth.

CHAPTER 6
Minerals and Rocks
Minerals and rocks are basic building blocks of Earth.

CHAPTER 7
Erosion and Deposition
Water, wind, and ice shape Earth's surface.

CHAPTER 7
KEY CONCEPTS

SECTION 1

Processes wear down and build up Earth's surface.
1. Natural forces move and deposit sediments.
2. Gravity can move large amounts of rock and soil.

SECTION 2

Moving water shapes land.
1. Streams shape Earth's surface.
2. Water moving underground forms caverns.

SECTION 3

Waves and wind shape land.
1. Waves and currents shape shorelines.
2. Wind shapes land.

SECTION 4

Glaciers carve land and move sediments.
1. Glaciers are moving bodies of ice.
2. Glaciers deposit large amounts of sediment.

The Big Idea Flow Chart is available on p. T49 in the **TRANSPARENCY BOOK.**

SECTION

Processes wear down and build up Earth's surface. pp. 225–229

1. Natural forces move and deposit sediments.
Weathered rock and soil is constantly moving from place to place in the process of **erosion.**
- Erosion is carried out by the action of water, wind, and ice.
- Water, wind, and ice move and deposit eroded material.
- Gravity plays a role in all types of erosion and **deposition.**

2. Gravity can move large amounts of rock and soil.
Gravity can pull rock and soil downhill by several types of **mass wasting.**
- Rockfalls and rockslides occur on steep slopes and involve small or large masses of rock.
- Mudflows occur when rocks, soil, and plants flow downhill with enough water to form a muddy mixture. Mudflows move quickly down steep slopes and can have devastating effects on towns in their path.
- Creep is the slow movement of soil down a gentle hillside. Its effects are slow but noticeable, as in these tilted fence posts.

1 Originally, the fence posts stand vertically in the ground.

2 Over many years, the soil holding the posts slowly shifts downhill, and the posts lean.

SECTION

Moving water shapes land. pp. 230–237

1. Streams shape Earth's surface.
Running water shapes the landscape over most of Earth. Systems of streams drain water and move sediment from a **drainage basin.**
- As streams flow and carry sediment, they form valleys and **floodplains.**
- As a stream continues on its course, it usually slows down, picking up less sediment and depositing more. The slope becomes flatter, the stream and valley become wider, and the stream forms meanders, or looping curves.
- Where the stream enters the ocean, it builds up sediment in a **delta.**
- At the base of mountains, streams can flatten out and form **alluvial fans.**

Drainage basins come in all sizes, depending on what part of the stream you look at. In the continental view below, three basins are shown. But each river and small stream also has its own basin, divided by higher land.

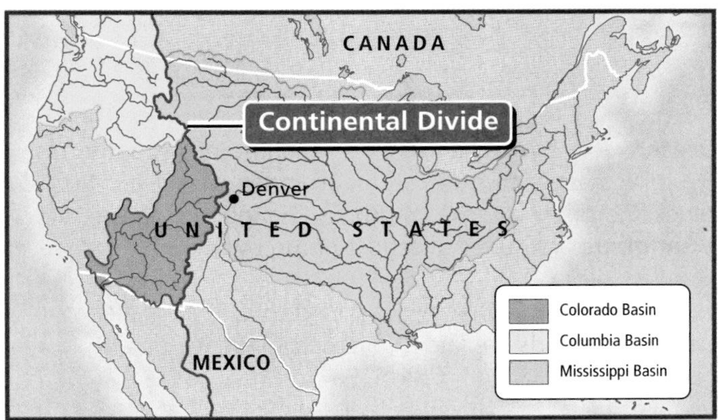

2. Water moving underground forms caverns.
Not all rainwater flows into streams. Some of it evaporates, some is absorbed by plants, and some becomes groundwater. Groundwater that is slightly acidic can dissolve some rocks. This process hollows out rock, creating caves and caverns. In limestone areas, caverns are not uncommon. **Sinkholes** may form when the roof of a cavern near the surface collapses.

Common Misconceptions

MISCONCEPTION DATABASE
CLASSZONE.COM Background on student misconceptions

THE ROLE OF GRAVITY Many students think about gravity's role only in obvious cases, such as a free-falling object. They often don't consider the role gravity plays in more subtle downward movements, such as flowing rivers or settling sediments.

 This misconception is addressed on p. 228.

GROUNDWATER Students commonly visualize groundwater as an underground lake or stream. While such features do exist in some caverns, most groundwater fills cracks and pores in rock and the spaces between rock and soil particles.

 This misconception is addressed on p. 234.

Previewing Content

SECTION

Waves and wind shape land.
pp. 238–244

1. Waves and currents shape shorelines.
The energy of waves, powered by wind, shapes shorelines through erosion and deposition. Pounding waves break cliffs into small rocks and grains of sand. Waves and currents carry away this sediment and deposit it along the shore, building up beaches. **Longshore drift** is the movement of sand along the shore in a zigzag pattern, as shown below. **Longshore current** is the movement of water along a shore as waves strike the shore at an angle.

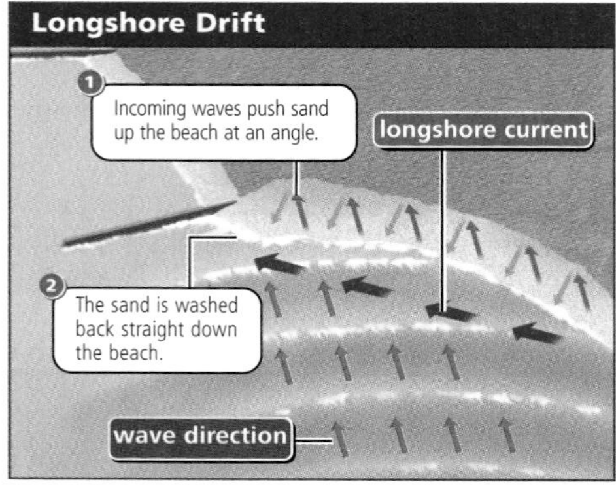

Longshore Drift
1
Incoming waves push sand up the beach at an angle.
longshore current
2
The sand is washed back straight down the beach.
wave direction

Ocean waves and currents shape sand into many landforms. Typically, these features build up over many years, but hurricanes and other storms can quickly change their shape.

- **Sandbars** are ridges of sand built up by the action of waves and currents.
- Spits are above-water ridges joined to land at one end.
- **Barrier islands** are large, emerged sandbars, parallel to the shore.

2. Wind shapes land.
Wind erosion and deposition are greatest in dry areas with few plants to hold the soil in place. High-energy wind scoops up sand and dust and deposits them as the wind energy wanes.

- **Dunes** are mounds of sand. They form on ocean and lake shores and in deserts.
- Layers of dust, called **loess,** can become fertile soil.
- Desert pavement is a layer of gravel and larger stones, left behind when dry winds blow away fine-grained sediments.

SECTION

Glaciers carve land and move sediments. pp. 245–251

1. Glaciers are moving bodies of ice.
Glaciers build up in cold regions where more snow falls each year than melts. Today glaciers cover about 10 percent of Earth, in mountain ranges and near the poles. During the last ice age, however, glaciers covered almost 30 percent of the land surface.

- Alpine glaciers flow down mountain valleys, widening narrow V-shaped valleys into deeper U-shaped valleys.
- Continental glaciers spread out into broad sheets. They cover most of Greenland and Antarctica.

2. Glaciers deposit large amounts of sediment.
A melting glacier leaves behind different kinds of **moraines,** landforms made of sediment. These moraines form a variety of hills, ridges, and blankets of **till.** Retreating glaciers also leave behind lakes of many sizes.

- Small **kettle lakes** form from blocks of ice that melt, leaving bowl-like depressions.
- Large lakes form when glaciers gouge river valleys into huge depressions and fill them with water. The Great Lakes are one example, shown in this series of drawings.

The ice sheet covering a land of river valleys began to retreat.

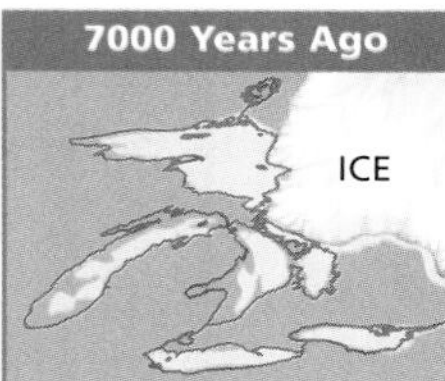

Water filled the bowls carved out by the ice.

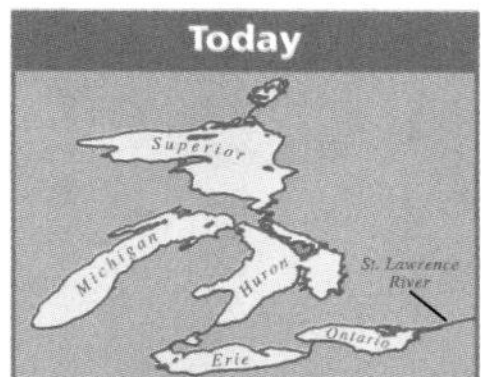

The Great Lakes contain 20 percent of the world's fresh lake water.

Common Misconceptions

MISCONCEPTION DATABASE
CLASSZONE.COM Background on student misconceptions

WAVES Many students think waves are a major means by which water moves. However, waves are a movement of energy through water, not a movement of the water itself.

 This misconception is addressed on p. 239.

RETREATING GLACIERS Some students think that when a glacier retreats, it actually moves backward. In fact, a glacier retreats by melting at its leading edge—the glacier does not "back up."

 This misconception is addressed on p. 248.

Previewing Labs

Lab Generator CD-ROM
Edit these Pupil Edition labs and generate alternative labs.

EXPLORE the BIG idea

Where Has Water Been? p. 223 Students observe the effects of water flowing on the ground.	**TIME** 10 minutes **MATERIALS** none
How Do Waves Shape Land? p. 223 Students make a model beach and observe how waves affect shorelines.	**TIME** 10 minutes **MATERIALS** sand and gravel, pie tin, water, cup
SECTION  **INVESTIGATE** Erosion, p. 226 Students design an experiment to find out how the slope of the land is affected by the action of rainwater. **ALTERNATIVE:** Reading Activity, URB p. 212	**TIME** 25 minutes **MATERIALS** soil, 2 large trays, pitcher of water
SECTION  **EXPLORE** Divides, p. 230 Students make a model divide and observe how a divide works.	**TIME** 10 minutes **MATERIALS** sheet of paper, tape, several paper clips
CHAPTER INVESTIGATION  **Creating Stream Features,** pp. 236–237 Students set up a stream table and observe the formation of different features in a model stream. **ALTERNATIVE:** Teacher Modeling, URB p. 212	**TIME** 40 minutes **MATERIALS** stream table with hose attachment or recirculating pump, sieve (optional), wood blocks, sand (at least 2 lbs), ruler, water, sink with drain, pitcher (optional), bucket (optional)
SECTION  **INVESTIGATE** Longshore Drift, p. 240 Students push a coin up a slope to model how sand moves along a beach. **ALTERNATIVE:** Direct Instruction, URB p. 212	**TIME** 15 minutes **MATERIALS** 2 or 3 books, coin
SECTION  **EXPLORE** Glaciers, p. 245 Students observe how a model glacier changes landscapes as it erodes and deposits material.	**TIME** 5 minutes **MATERIALS** modeling clay, paper towel, ice cube containing sand and gravel
INVESTIGATE Kettle Lake Formation, p. 249 Students design an experiment to show how kettle lakes form. **ALTERNATIVE:** Reading Activity, URB p. 212	**TIME** 30 minutes **MATERIALS** shallow tray, ice cubes, modeling clay, sand, gravel, flexible lamp or hair dryer (optional), water

R **Additional INVESTIGATION,** Rivers Change the Land, A, B, & C, pp. 200–208; Teacher Instructions, pp. 211–212

Previewing Chapter Resources

CHAPTER 7
Erosion and Deposition

INTEGRATED TECHNOLOGY

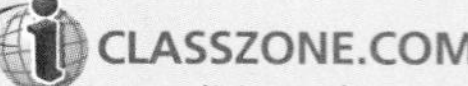
CLASSZONE.COM
- eEdition Plus
- EasyPlanner Plus
- Misconception Database
- Content Review
- Test Practice
- Visualizations
- Resource Centers
- Math Tutorial

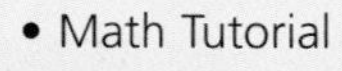
SCILINKS.ORG

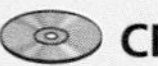
CD-ROMS
- eEdition
- EasyPlanner
- Power Presentations
- Content Review
- Lab Generator
- Test Generator

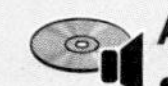
AUDIO CDS
- Audio Readings
- Audio Readings in Spanish

LABS AND ACTIVITIES

EXPLORE the Big Idea, p. 223
- Where Has Water Been?
- How Do Waves Shape Land?

UNIT RESOURCE BOOK
Unit Projects, pp. 5–10

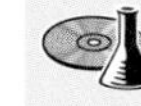

Lab Generator CD-ROM
Generate customized labs.

SECTION

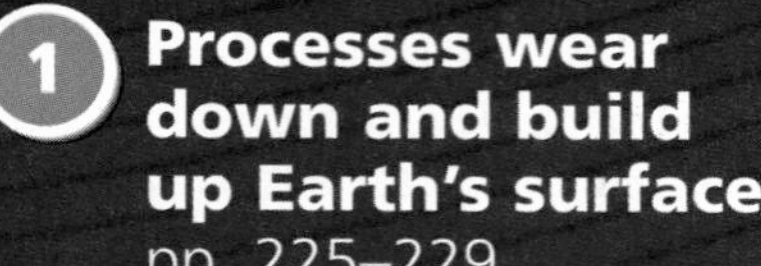

1 Processes wear down and build up Earth's surface.
pp. 225–229

Lesson Plan, pp. 141–142

RESOURCE CENTER, Mudflows

TRANSPARENCY BOOK
- Big Idea Flow Chart, p. T49
- Daily Vocabulary Scaffolding, p. T50
- Note-Taking Model, p. T51
- 3-Minute Warm-Up, p. T52

INVESTIGATE Erosion, p. 226

UNIT RESOURCE BOOK
Datasheet, Erosion, p. 150

SECTION

2 Moving water shapes land.
pp. 230–237

Lesson Plan, pp. 152–153

- **RESOURCE CENTER,** Rivers and Erosion
- **VISUALIZATION,** Cave Formation

TRANSPARENCY BOOK
- Daily Vocabulary Scaffolding, p. T50
- 3-Minute Warm-Up, p. T52

- EXPLORE Divides, p. 230
- CHAPTER INVESTIGATION, Creating Stream Features, pp. 236–237

UNIT RESOURCE BOOK
- CHAPTER INVESTIGATION, Creating Stream Features, A, B, & C, pp. 191–199
- Additional INVESTIGATION, Rivers Change the Land, A, B, & C, pp. 200–208

SECTION

3 Waves and wind shape land.
pp. 238–244

Lesson Plan, pp. 162–163

TRANSPARENCY BOOK
- Daily Vocabulary Scaffolding, p. T50
- 3-Minute Warm-Up, p. T53

- INVESTIGATE Longshore Drift, p. 240
- California Close-up, p. 244

UNIT RESOURCE BOOK
Datasheet, Longshore Drift, p. 171

SECTION

4 Glaciers carve land and move sediments.
pp. 245–251

Lesson Plan, pp. 173–174

- **RESOURCE CENTER,** Glaciers
- **MATH TUTORIAL,** Making Line Graphs

TRANSPARENCY BOOK
- Big Idea Flow Chart, p. T49
- 3-Minute Warm-Up, p. T53
- "Types of Glaciers and Movement" Visual, p. T54
- Chapter Outline, pp. T55–T56

- EXPLORE Glaciers, p. 245
- INVESTIGATE Kettle Lake Formation, p. 249
- Math in Science, p. 251

UNIT RESOURCE BOOK
- Datasheet, Kettle Lake Formation, p. 182
- Math Support & Practice, pp. 189–190

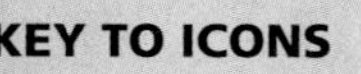 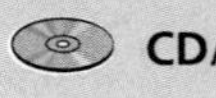   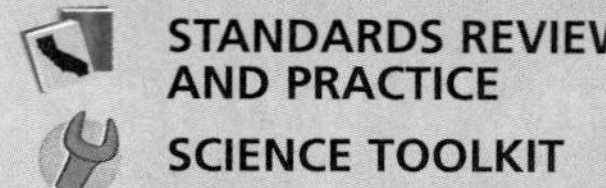 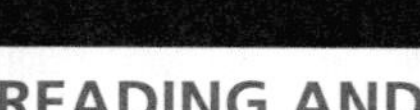

KEY TO ICONS: CD/CD-ROM · Teacher Edition · TRANSPARENCY BOOK · STANDARDS REVIEW AND PRACTICE · INTERNET · Pupil Edition · UNIT RESOURCE BOOK · ASSESSMENT BOOK · SCIENCE TOOLKIT

READING AND REINFORCEMENT	ASSESSMENT	STANDARDS
 **Modified Lesson Plans for English Learners,** pp. 26–29  • Four Square, B22–23 • Choose Your Own Strategy, C36–C42 • Daily Vocabulary Scaffolding, H1–8  **UNIT RESOURCE BOOK** • Vocabulary Practice, pp. 186–187 • Decoding Support, p. 188 • Summarizing the Chapter, pp. 209–210  **Audio Readings CD** Listen to Pupil Edition.  **Audio Readings in Spanish CD** Listen to Pupil Edition in Spanish.	 • Chapter Review, pp. 253–254 • Standards-Based Assessment, p. 255  **ASSESSMENT BOOK** • Diagnostic Test, pp. 137–138 • Chapter Test, A, B, & C, pp. 143–154 • Alternative Assessment, pp. 155–156 • Unit Test, A, B, & C, pp. 157–168  **STANDARDS REVIEW AND PRACTICE,** pp. 15–22, 59–60, 71–72  **McDougal Littell Assessment System** 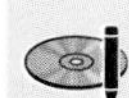 **Test Generator CD-ROM** Generate customized and Spanish tests.	California Content Standards 6.2.a, 6.2.b, 6.2.c, 6.2.d, 6.7.b, 6.7.h, 6.7.g See p. 222 for the standards.
 **UNIT RESOURCE BOOK** • Reading Study Guide, A & B, pp. 143–146 • Spanish Reading Study Guide, pp. 147–148 • Challenge and Extension, p. 149 • Reinforcing Key Concepts, p. 151	 Ongoing Assessment, pp. 226–229  Section 7.1 Review, p. 229  **ASSESSMENT BOOK** Section 7.1 Quiz, p. 139	California Content Standards 6.2.a, 6.2.d, 6.7.g
 **UNIT RESOURCE BOOK** • Reading Study Guide, A & B, pp. 154–157 • Spanish Reading Study Guide, pp. 158–159 • Challenge and Extension, p. 160 • Reinforcing Key Concepts, p. 161	Ongoing Assessment, pp. 232–233, 235  Section 7.2 Review, p. 235  **ASSESSMENT BOOK** Section 7.2 Quiz, p. 140	California Content Standards 6.2.a, 6.2.b, 6.2.d, 6.7.b
 **UNIT RESOURCE BOOK** • Reading Study Guide, A & B, pp. 164–167 • Spanish Reading Study Guide, pp. 168–169 • Challenge and Extension, p. 170 • Reinforcing Key Concepts, p. 172	Ongoing Assessment, pp. 239, 241–243  Section 7.3 Review, p. 243  **ASSESSMENT BOOK** Section 7.3 Quiz, p. 141	California Content Standards 6.2.c, 6.2.d, 6.7.g, 6.7.h
 **UNIT RESOURCE BOOK** • Reading Study Guide, A & B, pp. 175–178 • Spanish Reading Study Guide, pp. 179–180 • Challenge and Extension, p. 181 • Reinforcing Key Concepts, p. 183 • Challenge Reading, pp. 184–185	 Ongoing Assessment, pp. 246–248, 250  Section 7.4 Review, p. 250  **ASSESSMENT BOOK** Section 7.4 Quiz, p. 142	California Content Standards 6.2.a, 6.7.h

Previewing Resources for Differentiated Instruction

CHAPTER INVESTIGATION

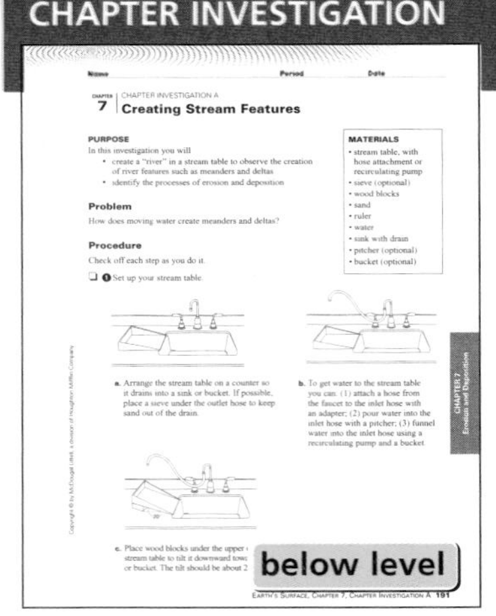

UNIT RESOURCE BOOK, pp. 191–194

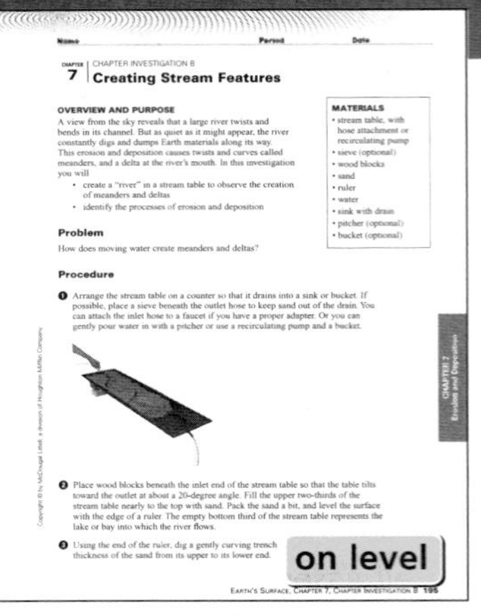

pp. 195–198

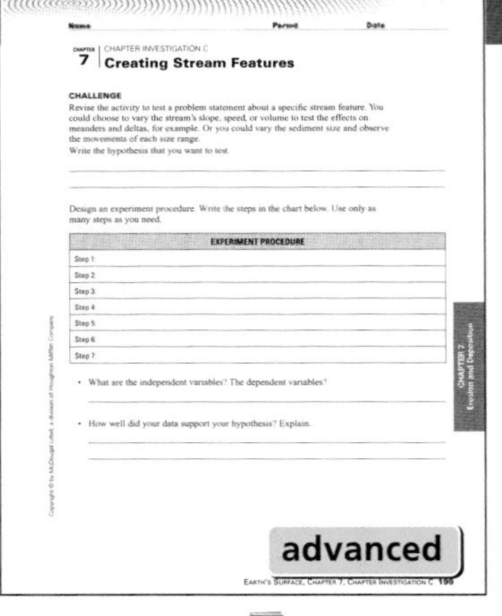

pp. 195–199

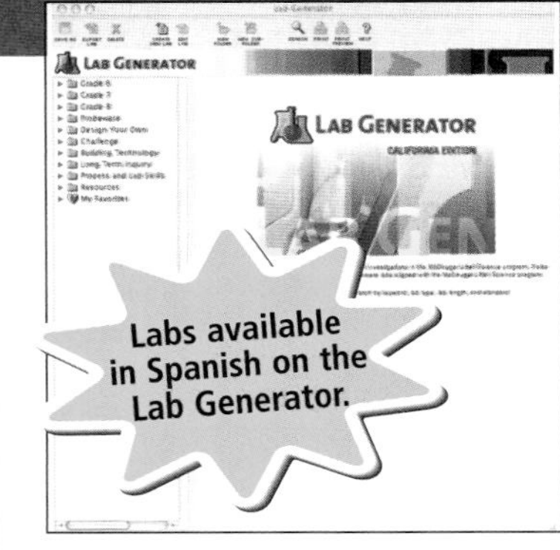

English Learners

READING STUDY GUIDE

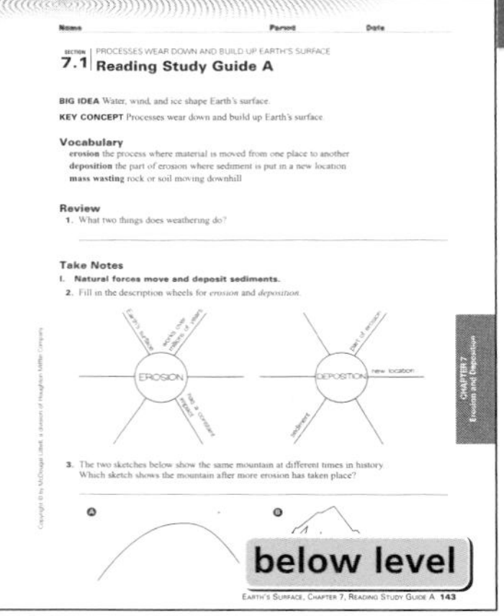

UNIT RESOURCE BOOK, pp. 143–144

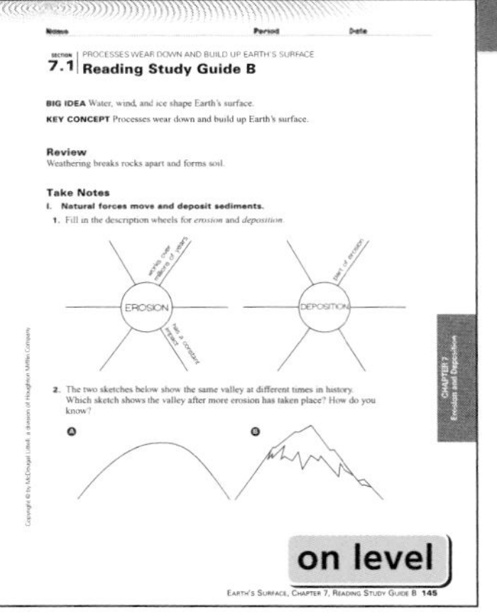

pp. 145–146

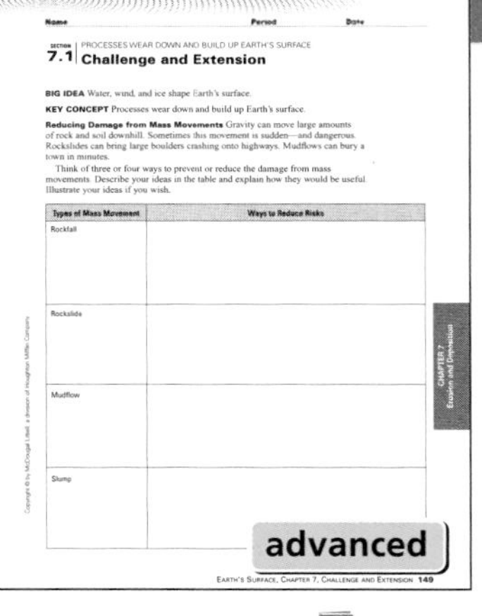

p. 149

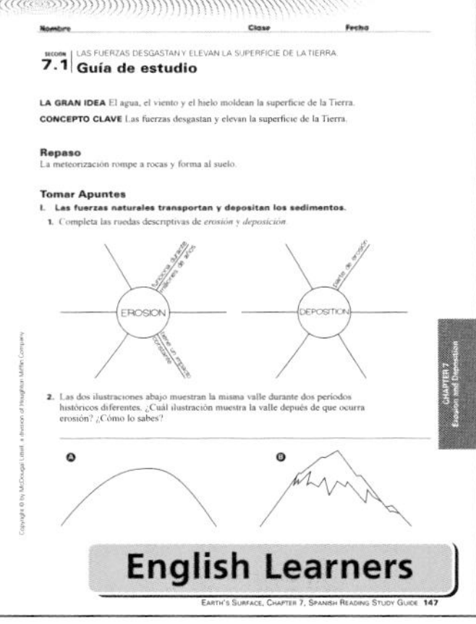

p. 147

CHAPTER TEST

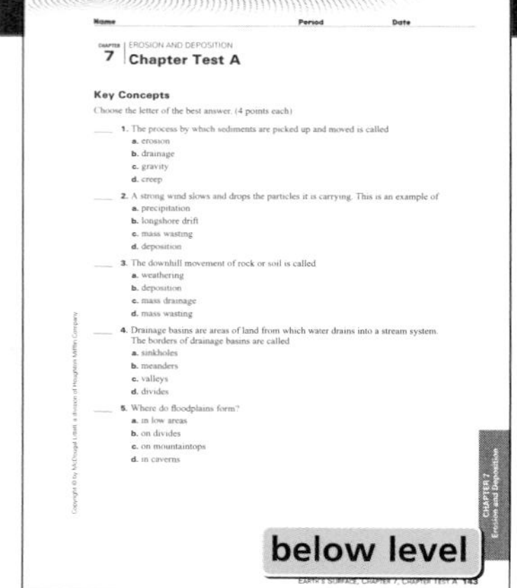

ASSESSMENT BOOK, pp. 143–146

pp. 147–150

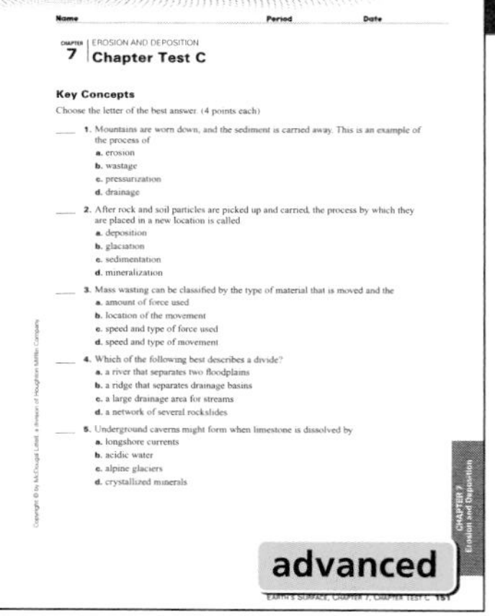

pp. 151–154

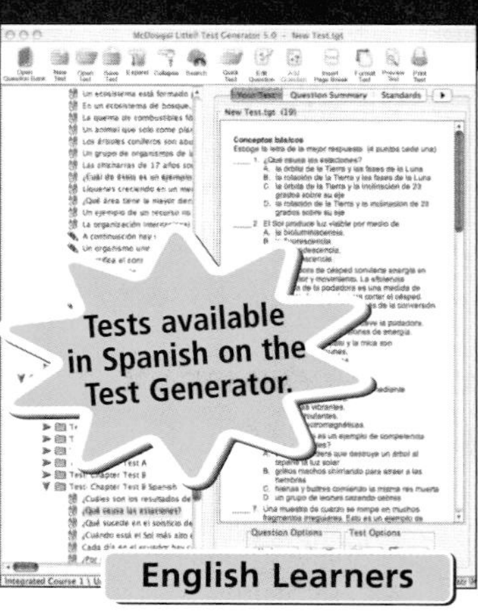

English Learners

TECHNOLOGY

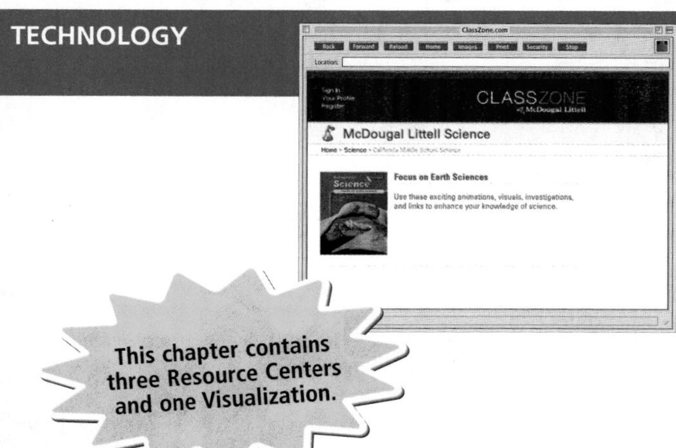

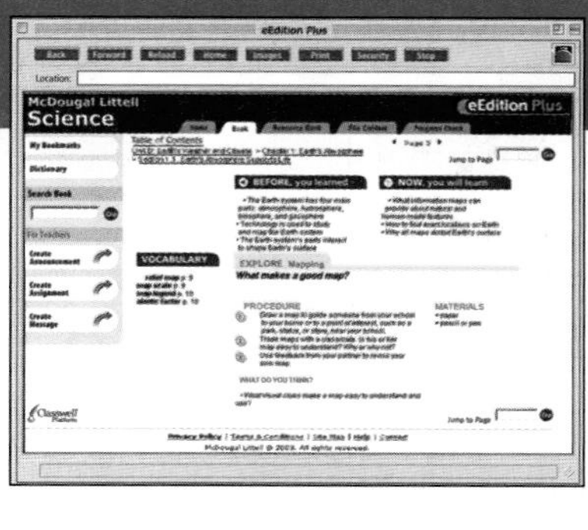

VISUAL CONTENT

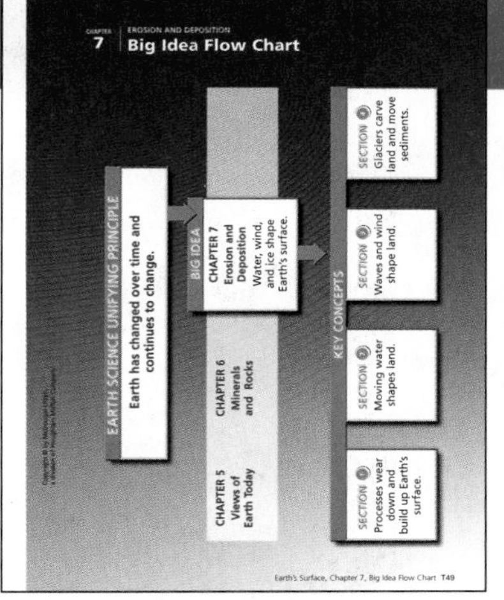

TRANSPARENCY BOOK, p. T49

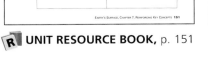

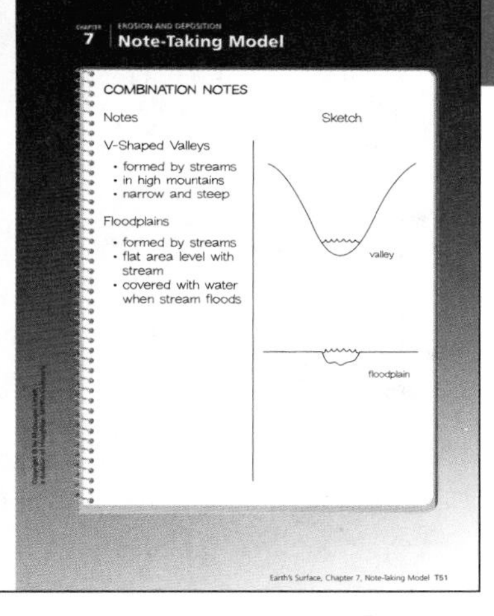

p. T51

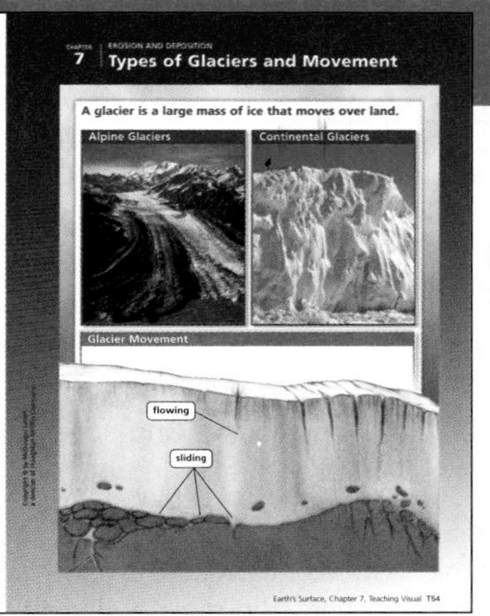

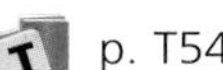
p. T54

MORE SUPPORT

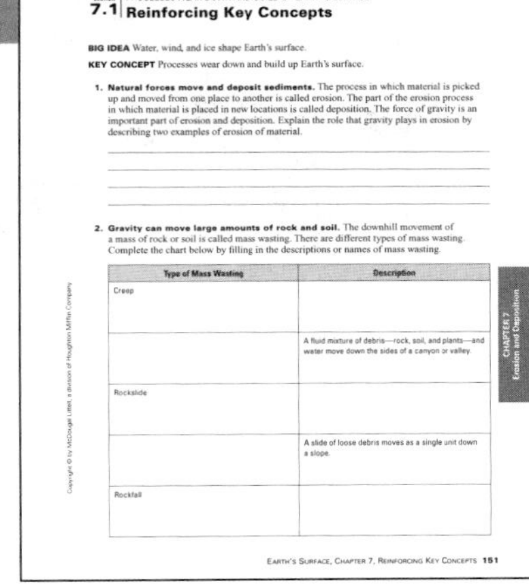

UNIT RESOURCE BOOK, p. 151

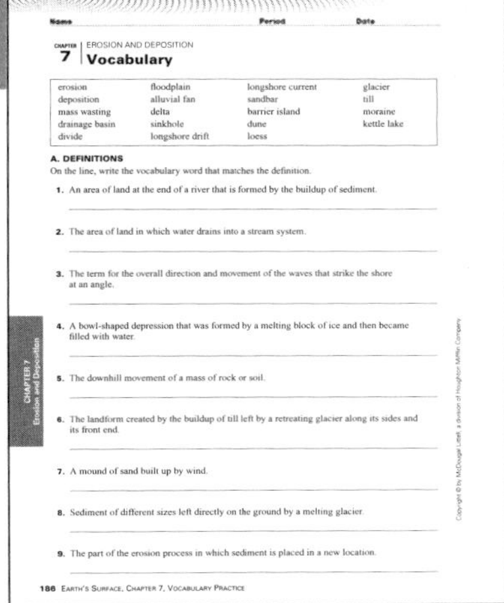

pp. 186–187

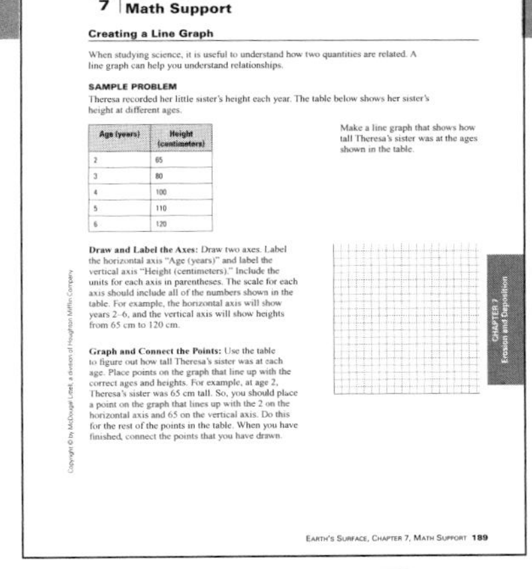

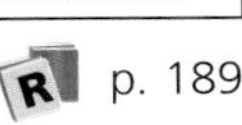
p. 189

CHAPTER 7

Erosion and Deposition

INTRODUCE

the BIG idea

Have students look at the photograph of the glacier and discuss how the question in the box links to the Big Idea:

- How thick do you think the ice is?
- How long do you think the ice has been here?
- Do you think the ice moves quickly or slowly?

California Content Standards

6.2.a Students know water running downhill is the dominant process in shaping the landscape, including California's landscape.

6.2.b Students know rivers and streams are dynamic systems that erode, transport sediment, change course, and flood their banks in natural and recurring patterns.

6.2.c Students know beaches are dynamic systems in which the sand is supplied by rivers and moved along the coast by the action of waves.

6.2.d Students know earthquakes, volcanic eruptions, landslides, and floods change human and wildlife habitats.

6.7.b Select and use appropriate tools and technology (including calculators, computers, balances, spring scales, microscopes, and binoculars) to perform tests, collect data, and display data.

6.7.h Identify changes in natural phenomena over time without manipulating the phenomena (e.g., a tree limb, a grove of trees, a stream, a hillslope).

CHAPTER

Erosion and Deposition

Water, wind, and ice shape Earth's surface.

Key Concepts

SECTION 1 **Processes wear down and build up Earth's surface.** Learn how natural forces shape and change the land.

SECTION 2 **Moving water shapes land.** Learn about the effects of water moving over land and underground.

SECTION 3 **Waves and wind shape land.** Discover how waves and wind affect land.

SECTION 4 **Glaciers carve land and move sediments.** Learn about the effect of ice moving over land.

California ClassZone

CLASSZONE.COM

Chapter 7 online resources: Content Review, one Visualization, three Resource Centers, Math Tutorial, Test Practice

222 Unit 2: Earth's Surface

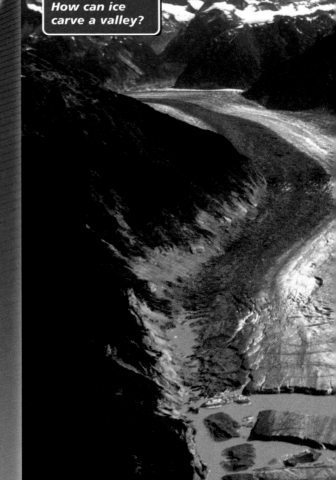

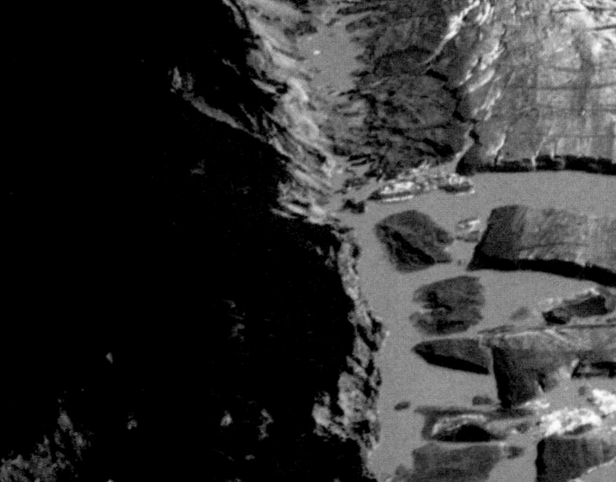

How can ice carve a valley?

INTERNET PREVIEW

CLASSZONE.COM For student use with the following pages:

Review and Practice
- Content Review, pp. 224, 252
- Math Tutorial: Making Line Graphs, p. 251
- Test Practice, p. 255

Activities and Resources
- Resource Centers: Mudflows, p. 228; Rivers and Erosion, p. 232; Glaciers, p. 246
- Visualization: Cave Formation, p. 234

Wind Erosion
Code: MDL017

EXPLORE the BIG idea

Where Has Water Been?

6.2.a Students know water running downhill is the dominant process in shaping the landscape, including California's landscape.

Think about what water does when it falls and flows on the ground. Go outside your school or home and look at the ground and pavement carefully. Look in dry places for evidence of where water has been.

Observe and Think What evidence did you find? How does it show that water was in a place that is now dry?

How Do Waves Shape Land?

6.2.c Students know beaches are dynamic systems in which the sand is supplied by rivers and moved along the coast by the action of waves.

Pile a mixture of sand and gravel on one side of a pie tin to make a "beach." Slowly add water away from the beach until the tin is about one-third full. Use your hand to make waves in the tin and observe what happens.

Observe and Think What happened to the beach? How did the waves affect the sand and gravel?

NSTA scilinks.org SCILINKS
Wind Erosion **Code: MDL017**

EXPLORE the BIG idea

These inquiry-based activities are appropriate for use at home or as a supplement to classroom instruction.

Where Has Water Been?

PURPOSE To introduce students to the concept that moving water shapes the land. Students observe the effects of water flowing on the ground.

TIP *10 min.* Suggest students make drawings of the evidence they find.

Sample answer: Water moved soil and other materials and deposited them. The evidence was grooves in the dirt along a curb and leaves gathered around a storm-drain cover.

REVISIT after p. 233.

How Do Waves Shape Land?

PURPOSE To demonstrate how the action of waves shape the landscape. Students make a model beach and observe how waves affect shorelines.

TIP *10 min.* Suggest students make waves in different directions so that the waves hit the beach at different angles.

Answer: Materials on the beach shifted position. The waves pulled some of the sand away from the beach or moved it from one area of the beach to another. The gravel moved a little, but less than the sand.

REVISIT after p. 239.

TEACHING WITH TECHNOLOGY

CBL and Probeware If you have a CBL and a turbidity probe, measure the lack of clarity in a stream after teaching p. 232.

PREPARE

CONCEPT REVIEW

Activate Prior Knowledge

- Set out two cookies, one whole and one that has been crumbled into tiny pieces.
- Tell students that the intact cookie represents a rock. Ask what the crumbled cookie might represent. *smaller rocks and rock particles*
- Discuss what processes changed the crumbled cookie and relate these processes to weathering of rock.

TAKING NOTES

Choose Your Own Strategy

Allowing students to choose their own note-taking strategy will help build confidence in their ability to take notes that are meaningful for them. Encourage students to experiment with their own strategies based on those they have encountered in earlier chapters. Remind them that different strategies may be appropriate for different topics or sections in the chapter.

Vocabulary Strategy

Having students use four square diagrams will help them see more than simple definitions of words. Students will get a more complete view of vocabulary terms in the context of the section.

Vocabulary and Note-Taking Resources

- Vocabulary Practice, pp. 186–187
- Decoding Support, p. 188

- Daily Vocabulary Scaffolding, p. T50
- Note-Taking Model, p. T51

- Four Square, B22–23
- Choose Your Own Strategy, C36–C42
- Daily Vocabulary Scaffolding, H1–8

CHAPTER 7

Getting Ready to Learn

CONCEPT REVIEW

- Energy can be transferred by the movement of matter.
- Weathering breaks down rocks.
- Water and ice are agents of weathering.

VOCABULARY REVIEW

weathering p. 199

See Glossary for definitions.

gravity, sediment, soil

CONTENT REVIEW
CLASSZONE.COM

Review concepts and vocabulary.

TAKING NOTES

CHOOSE YOUR OWN STRATEGY

Take notes using one or more of the strategies from earlier chapters, such as **main idea and detail notes, supporting main ideas,** or **main idea web.** Feel free to mix and match the strategies, or use an entirely different note-taking strategy.

VOCABULARY STRATEGY

Write each new vocabulary term in the center of a **four square** diagram. Write notes in the squares around each term. Include a definition, some characteristics, and some examples of the term. If possible, write some things that are not examples of the term.

See the Note-Taking Handbook on pages R45–R51.

SCIENCE NOTEBOOK

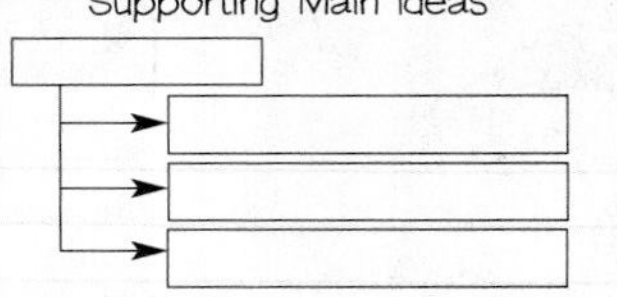

Definition process in which weathered particles are picked up and moved	Characteristics gravity is important part; wind and ice are agents
EROSION	
Examples mass wasting, mudflow, slump, creep	Nonexamples topography, weathering

CHECK READINESS

Administer the Diagnostic Test to determine students' readiness for new science content and their mastery of requisite math skills.

 Diagnostic Test, pp. 137–138

Technology Resources

Students needing content and math skills should visit **ClassZone.com.**

- **CONTENT REVIEW**
- **MATH TUTORIAL**

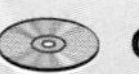 **CONTENT REVIEW CD-ROM**

KEY CONCEPT

Processes wear down and build up Earth's surface.

CALIFORNIA Content Standards

6.2.a Students know water running downhill is the dominant process in shaping the landscape, including California's landscape.

6.2.d Students know earthquakes, volcanic eruptions, landslides, and floods change human and wildlife habitats.

BEFORE, you learned

- Weathering breaks rocks apart
- Water can move sediment from one place to another

NOW, you will learn

- How erosion moves and deposits rock and soil
- How gravity causes movement of large amounts of rock and soil

VOCABULARY

erosion p. 225
deposition p. 225
mass wasting p. 227

THINK ABOUT

How did natural forces shape this landform?

This valley in Iceland was formed by the action of water. How long might it have taken to form? Where did the material that once filled the valley go?

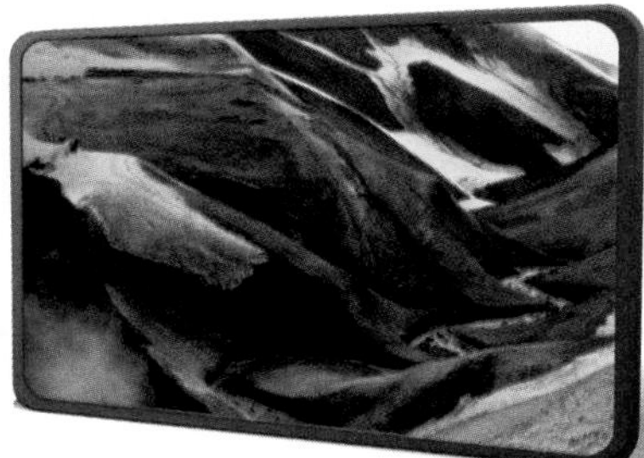

Natural forces move and deposit sediments.

The valley in the photograph was formed by the movement of water. The water flowed over the land and carried away weathered rock and soil. This shaped a valley where the water flows. In this section you will learn about the processes that shape landscapes.

The process in which weathered particles are picked up and moved from one place to another is called **erosion** (ih-ROH-zhuhn). Erosion has a constant impact on Earth's surface. Over millions of years, it wears down mountains by removing byproducts of weathering and depositing them elsewhere. The part of the erosion process in which sediment is placed in a new location, or deposited, is called **deposition** (DEHP-uh-ZIHSH-uhn).

VOCABULARY
Use four square diagrams to take notes about the terms *erosion* and *deposition*.

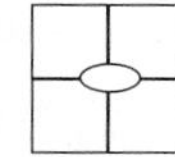

The force of gravity is an important part of erosion and deposition. Gravity causes water to move downward, carrying and depositing sediment as it flows. Gravity can pull huge masses of ice slowly down mountain valleys. And gravity causes dust carried by the wind to fall to Earth.

RESOURCES FOR DIFFERENTIATED INSTRUCTION

Below Level

UNIT RESOURCE BOOK
- Reading Study Guide A, pp. 143–144
- Decoding Support, p. 188

AUDIO CDS

Advanced

UNIT RESOURCE BOOK
Challenge and Extension, p. 149

English Learners

UNIT RESOURCE BOOK
Spanish Reading Study Guide, pp. 147–148

AUDIO CDS
- Audio Readings in Spanish
- Audio Readings (English)

7.1 FOCUS

Set Learning Goals

Students will

- Describe how erosion and deposition move rock and soil.
- Explain how gravity causes the mass movement of rock and soil.
- Design an experiment that shows how rainwater affects sloping land.

3-Minute Warm-Up

Display Transparency 52 or copy this exercise on the board:

Decide if the statements are true. If not true, correct them.

1. Weathering can be caused by mechanical and chemical processes. *true*
2. Weathering breaks rocks apart. *true*
3. Weathering proceeds most quickly in warm, dry areas. *most slowly*

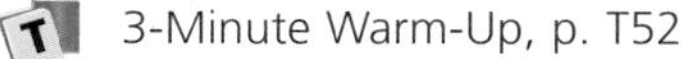

3-Minute Warm-Up, p. T52

7.1 MOTIVATE

THINK ABOUT

PURPOSE To introduce the idea that natural forces shape the landscape

DISCUSS Ask students to describe situations that show the ability of moving water to transport materials. Discuss where the material ends up. *Examples might include a canoe traveling downstream, sediment traveling downstream, ocean waves moving beach sand, raindrops pitting a sandy beach, a hose washing dirt off a car. Water flows over the surface, carries away rock and soil, and deposits it downhill.*

Answer: The valley probably took a very long time to form. Material was carried away by the stream.

7.1 INSTRUCT

Teach the Standards

Water and erosion 6.2.a

In this section: Make sure that students understand how erosion of weathered rock occurs through the movement of water, wind, and ice.

- **previously taught:** weathering, pp. 199–203
- **future opportunities:** erosion of mountains, p. 339

INVESTIGATE Erosion

PURPOSE To design an experiment that shows the effects of rainwater on various slopes

TIPS *25 min.*

- You may want to have students measure the height or angle of their slope.
- Encourage students to pour the water slowly, so that they can examine what the water does to the soil particles and how it flows through the soil.

WHAT DO YOU THINK? *More soil eroded on the sloping land than on the flat land. Variables included the slope of the soil, the amount of water poured on the soil, where it was poured, and the force of the water. The erosion caused by water is greater on slopes than on flat land.*

CHALLENGE *Sample answer: Use soil in tray to build river channels and land. Add water to the river until it overflows its banks. Observe the movement of sediment.*

 Datasheet, Erosion, p. 150

Technology Resources

Customize this student lab as needed or look for an alternative. Print rubrics to assess student lab reports.

 **Lab Generator CD-ROM**

Ongoing Assessment

 *Answer: water, wind, and ice*

A Erosion of weathered rock by the movement of water, wind, and ice occurs in three major ways:

- **Water** Rainwater and water from melting snow flow down sloping land, carrying rock and soil particles. The water makes its way to a river, which then carries the sediment along. The sediment gets deposited on the river's bottom, banks, or floodplain, or near its mouth. Waves in oceans and lakes also carry sediment and deposit it to form beaches and other features.
- **Wind** Strong winds lift tiny particles of dust and carry them long distances. When the wind dies down, the particles drop to the ground. Wind can also push larger particles of sand along the ground.
- **Ice** As ice moves slowly downhill, it transports rock and soil particles that are contained in it.

READING TIP A floodplain is a flat area of land on either side of a stream that becomes flooded when a river overflows its banks. You will learn more about river and stream features in Section 7.2.

CHECK YOUR READING What are the three major ways in which erosion moves sediment?

INVESTIGATE Erosion

How does the effect of rainwater on sloping land differ from its effect on flat land?

DESIGN YOUR OWN EXPERIMENT

Streams cause much of the erosion on Earth. Design an experiment to show the effect that rainwater has on sloping land.

SKILL FOCUS Designing experiments (6.2.a)

MATERIALS
- soil
- 2 large trays
- pitcher of water

TIME 25 minutes 

PROCEDURE

1. Figure out how to use the soil, water, and trays to test the effects of rainwater on sloping land and on flat land.
2. Write up your procedure.
3. Carry out your experiment.

WHAT DO YOU THINK?

- What were the results of your experiment? Did it work? Why or why not?
- What were the variables in your experiment?
- What does your experiment demonstrate about erosion and running water?

CHALLENGE How would you design an experiment to demonstrate the relationship between floods and erosion?

DIFFERENTIATE INSTRUCTION

More Reading Support

A What carries rock and soil particles? *rainwater and water from melting snow, wind, and ice*

English Learners To be sure that English learners understand the difference between erosion and deposition, place the terms on the classroom's Science Word Wall with brief definition for each word. English learners may be unfamiliar with certain idioms used in the English language. The phrase "wind dies down" on p. 226 may be confusing to someone reading it literally. Help English learners recognize idioms and understand their meanings.

Gravity can move large amounts of rock and soil.

Along the California coast many homes are built atop cliffs, backed by mountains and looking out to the sea. These homes are in beautiful areas. However, their location is risky.

The California coast region and other mountainous areas have many landslides. A landslide is one type of **mass wasting**—the downhill movements of masses of rock and soil.

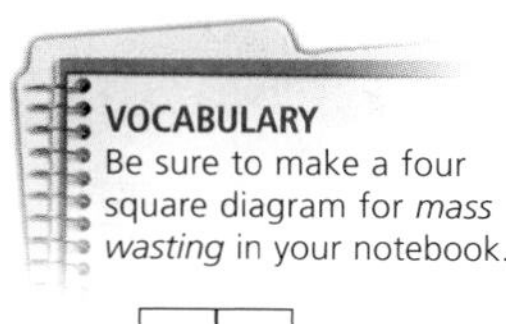

VOCABULARY
Be sure to make a four square diagram for *mass wasting* in your notebook.

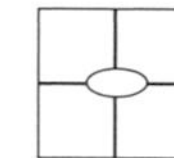

In mass wasting, gravity pulls material downward. A triggering event, such as heavy rain or an earthquake, might loosen the rock and soil. As the material becomes looser, it gives way to the pull of gravity and moves downward.

Mass wasting can occur suddenly or gradually. It can involve tons of rock sliding down a steep mountain slope or moving little by little down a gentle hillside. One way to classify a mass wasting event is by the type of material that is moved and the speed of the movement. A sudden, fast movement of rock and soil is called a landslide. Movements of rock are described as slides or falls. Movement of mud or soil is described as a mudflow or a mudslide.

Mass Wasting of Rock

Mass wasting of rock includes rockfalls and rockslides:

- In a rockfall, individual blocks of rock drop suddenly and fall freely down a cliff or steep mountainside. Weathering can break a block of rock from a cliff or mountainside. The expansion of water that freezes in a crack, for example, can loosen a block of rock.
- In a rockslide, a large mass of rock slides as a unit down a slope. A rockslide can reach a speed of a hundred kilometers per hour. Rockslides can be triggered by earthquakes.

Mass wasting of rock often takes place in high mountains. In some places, rocks can fall or slide onto roads. You might also see evidence of rockfalls and rockslides at the base of steep cliffs, where piles of rock slope outward.

Rockslides, such as this one near Yosemite National Park in California, can drop huge amounts of rock onto highways.

Teach from Visuals

To help students interpret the photograph of a rockslide, ask:

- How would you describe the area? *steep slopes, loose rock*
- What type of mass wasting is shown? *rockslide*
- Why is this movement not called a rockfall? *The mass of rock is too great.*

Teacher Demo

Demonstrate how water acts as a lubricant to trigger mass wasting. Place a layer of soil and gravel mixture on a board. Pack the mixture tightly. Tilt the surface slightly, so that the mixture does not move. Ask students to predict what will happen when you pour a small amount of water near the top of the surface. Test their predictions. The water should lubricate the mixture enough to start it sliding down the surface.

Teach Difficult Concepts

The various forms of mass wasting are not always distinctly different. The difference between a rockfall and a rockslide, for example, is that the former involves small blocks of rock while the latter involves a large mass of rock. Ask: What do rockfalls and rockslides have in common? *They both involve rocks being pulled down steep slopes by gravity.*

Ongoing Assessment

Describe how erosion and deposition move rock and soil.

Ask: How does erosion and deposition occur in a creek? *The flowing water picks up and moves sediment. Some sediment gets deposited along the creek bottom or along its banks.*

DIFFERENTIATE INSTRUCTION

More Reading Support

B What force causes mass wasting? *gravity*

C What are two forms of mass wasting? *rockfall, rockslide*

Below Level The term *mass wasting* may be difficult for students to understand. Discuss the meaning of each word in the term. *Mass* refers to a large amount of material. *Wasting* refers to destruction. Together, the words refer to the destruction of a large amount of material, or the destruction of a hillside.

Real World Example

The mudflow in the town of Armero, Colombia, was one of the greatest natural disasters in South American history. About 23,000 people died—20,000 in Armero and 3,000 in other valleys. Armero lay directly in the path of the 40-meter-high wall of mud traveling 40 kilometers per hour. It struck just after 11 P.M., when most people were asleep. The mud buried all but the highest parts of the town in 15 minutes.

Develop Critical Thinking

APPLY Ask students what might be done to limit the damage done by mudflows. Answers may include limiting the amount of development in valleys prone to mudflows, developing a warning system, and constructing barriers along the path that dangerous mudflows are likely to take. Point out that such barriers are common in Japan.

Address Misconceptions

IDENTIFY Ask: What force causes creep? If students do not say gravity, they may hold the misconception that gravity causes downward motion only in obvious cases, such as a free-falling object.

CORRECT Hold out a ball and drop it. Ask students what caused the ball to drop. Then let the ball roll down a surface that is barely tilted. Ask what caused the ball to roll. Point out that gravity acts on the ball regardless of the angle at which it is allowed to fall.

REASSESS Ask: Why does a slow-moving river flow? *Gravity pulls it downhill.*

Technology Resources

Visit **ClassZone.com** for background on common student misconceptions.

MISCONCEPTION DATABASE

Ongoing Assessment

CHECK YOUR READING *Answer: Mudflows can occur as a flow of water moves down a mountainside or valley and picks up debris from soaked land or ash from a volcano.*

Mudflows in 1999 in Venezuela happened very quickly and took as many as 30,000 lives.

Mudflow

Sometimes a mountain slope collapses. Then a mixture of rock, soil, and plants—called debris (duh-BREE)—falls or slides down. Like mass wasting of rock, mass movements of debris are common in high mountains with steep slopes.

D

RESOURCE CENTER CLASSZONE.COM

Learn more about mudflows.

E

A major type of mass wasting of debris is a mudflow. A mudflow consists of debris with a large amount of water. Mudflows often happen in mountain canyons and valleys after heavy rains. The soil becomes so heavy with water that the slope can no longer hold it in place. The mixture of soil, water, and debris flows downward, picking up sediment as it rushes down. When it reaches a valley, it spreads in a thin sheet over the land.

Mudflows also occur on active volcanoes. In 1985, a huge mudflow destroyed the town of Armero, Colombia, and killed more than 20,000 people. When a volcano erupted there, the heat melted ice and snow near the top of the volcano. This released a large amount of water that mixed with ash from the volcano. The mixture of ash and water rushed down the volcano and picked up debris. It formed gigantic mudflows that poured into all the surrounding valleys.

Mount St. Helens, a volcanic mountain in the state of Washington, is a place where large mudflows have occurred. During an eruption in 1980, some mudflows from the volcano traveled more than 90 kilometers (56 mi) from the mountain.

What causes a mudflow to occur?

In this example of slump, at Mesa Verde National Park in Colorado, a huge mass of rock and soil moved downward.

Slumps and Creep

Slumps and creep are two other main types of mass wasting on hilly land. These forms of mass wasting can be much less dramatic than rockslides or mudflows. But they are the types of mass movement that you are most likely to see evidence of.

DIFFERENTIATE INSTRUCTION

More Reading Support

D What is debris made of? *rock, soil, and plants*

E What is a mudflow made of? *water and debris*

Advanced Have students find on a map the places mentioned in the text (Armero, Colombia, and Mount St. Helens in Washington). Then have them find on the map other places they think would be prone to mudflows. They should look not only in mountainous areas but in areas with active volcanoes.

Challenge and Extension, p. 149

A slump is a slide of loose debris that moves as a single unit. Slumps can occur along roads and highways where construction has made slopes unstable. They can cover sections of highway with debris. Like other types of mass movement, slumps can be triggered by heavy rain.

The slowest form of mass movement of soil or debris is creep. The soil or debris moves at a rate of about 1 to 10 millimeters a year—a rate too slow to be seen. But evidence of creep can be seen on hillsides that have old fences or telephone poles. The fences or poles may lean downward, or some may be out of line. They have been moved by the creeping soil. The soil closer to the surface moves faster than the soil farther down, which causes the fences or poles to lean.

1 Originally, the fence posts stand vertically in the ground.

2 Over many years, the soil holding the posts slowly shifts downhill, and the posts lean.

Even the slight slope of this land in Alberta, Canada, caused these posts to tilt because of creep.

Creep can affect buildings as well. The weight of a heavy mass of soil moving slowly downhill can be great enough to crack a building's walls. Creep affects all hillsides covered with soil, but its rate varies. The wetter the soil, the faster it will creep downhill.

7.1 Review

KEY CONCEPTS

1. How does erosion change landscapes? (6.2.a)
2. Describe why weathering is important in erosion. (6.2.a)
3. How can gravity move large amounts of rock and soil? (6.2.d)

CRITICAL THINKING

4. **Compare and Contrast** What is the main difference between erosion and mass wasting?
5. **Infer** What force and what cause can contribute to both erosion and mass wasting?

CHALLENGE

6. **Rank** Which of the four locations would be the best and worst places to build a house? Rank the four locations and explain your reasoning.

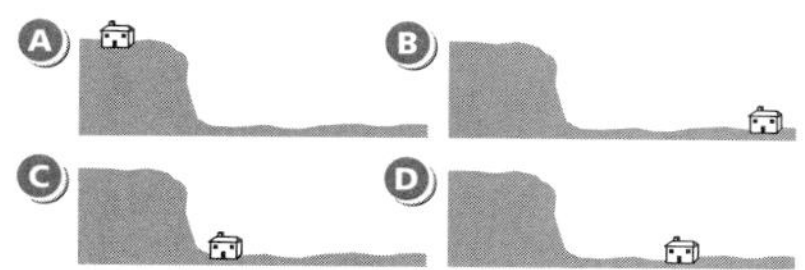

ANSWERS

. Forces of erosion move oil, sediment, and rock from ne place to another.

. Weathering breaks down ock into pieces, which may be arried away and deposited.

3. Gravity moves large amounts of rock and soil downhill as the rock and soil loosen for various reasons.

4. Mass wasting involves only the force of gravity whereas erosion occurs with movement of another material such as water, air, or ice.

5. the force of gravity and the downhill movement of water

6. ABDC or BADC; if land is very stable, A is a good location

Ongoing Assessment

Explain how gravity causes the mass movement of rock and soil.

Ask: Where would you expect to see a road sign saying, "Caution: Falling Rock"? *in rocky areas with steep slopes*

Reinforce the BIG idea

Have students relate the section to the Big Idea.

 Reinforcing Key Concepts, p. 151

7.1 ASSESS & RETEACH

Assess

 Section 7.1 Quiz, p. 139

Reteach

Create a chart that compares the different kinds of mass wasting: rockfall, rockslide, mudflow, slump, creep. Include columns headed Type of Mass Wasting, Type of Material, Speed, and Evidence. Have students fill in individual charts, or make the chart on the board.

Technology Resources

Have students visit **ClassZone.com** for reteaching of Key Concepts.

 **CONTENT REVIEW**

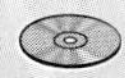 **CONTENT REVIEW CD-ROM**

7.2 FOCUS

Set Learning Goals

Students will

- Explain how moving water shapes Earth's surface.
- Explain how water moving underground forms natural features.
- Discover through experimentation how streams shape the landscape.

3-Minute Warm-Up

Display Transparency 52 or copy this exercise on the board:

1. What four things cause erosion of small rock particles? *rain, snow, wind, ice*
2. What force causes mass wasting, mudflows, slump, creep? *gravity*

 3-Minute Warm-Up, p. T52

7.2 MOTIVATE

EXPLORE Divides

PURPOSE To introduce the concept of a divide

TIP *10 min.* The height from which students drop the paper clips is not important as long as the clips land close to the paper ridge.

WHAT DO YOU THINK? *Water falling on a natural ridge must also flow to one side or the other.*

KEY CONCEPT

7.2 Moving water shapes land.

CALIFORNIA Content Standards

6.2.a Students know water running downhill is the dominant process in shaping the landscape, including California's landscape.

6.2.b Students know rivers and streams are dynamic systems that erode, transport sediment, change course, and flood their banks in natural and recurring patterns.

6.2.d Students know earthquakes, volcanic eruptions, landslides, and floods change human and wildlife habitats.

BEFORE, you learned

- Erosion is the movement of rock and soil
- Gravity causes mass movements of rock and soil

NOW, you will learn

- How moving water shapes Earth's surface
- How water moving underground forms caves and other features

VOCABULARY

drainage basin p. 231
divide p. 231
floodplain p. 232
alluvial fan p. 233
delta p. 233
sinkhole p. 235

NOTE-TAKING STRATEGY
A main idea and detail notes chart would be a good strategy to use for taking notes about streams and Earth's surface.

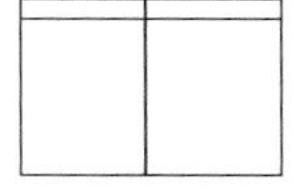

EXPLORE Divides (6.2.a)

How do divides work?

PROCEDURE

1. Fold the sheet of paper in thirds and tape it as shown to make a "ridge."
2. Drop the paper clips one at a time directly on top of the ridge from a height of about 30 cm. Observe what happens and record your observations.

WHAT DO YOU THINK?
How might the paper clips be similar to water falling on a ridge?

MATERIALS

- sheet of paper
- tape
- paper clips

Streams shape Earth's surface.

If you look at a river or stream, you may be able to notice something about the land around it. The land is higher than the river. If a river runs through a steep valley, you can easily see that the river is the low point. But even in very flat places, the land slopes down to the river, which itself runs downhill in a low path through the land.

Running water is the major force shaping the landscape over most of Earth. From the broad, flat land around the lower Mississippi River to the steep mountain valleys of the Himalayas, water running downhill changes the land. Running water shapes a variety of landforms by moving sediment in the processes of erosion and deposition. In this section, you will learn how water on land flows in systems of streams and rivers and how water shapes and changes landscapes. You also will learn that water can even carve out new features underground.

RESOURCES FOR DIFFERENTIATED INSTRUCTION

Below Level

UNIT RESOURCE BOOK

- Reading Study Guide A, pp. 154–155
- Decoding Support, p. 188

AUDIO CDS

 **Additional INVESTIGATION,** Rivers Change the Land, A, B, & C, pp. 200–208; Teacher Instructions, pp. 211–212

Advanced

UNIT RESOURCE BOOK

Challenge and Extension, p. 160

English Learners

UNIT RESOURCE BOOK

Spanish Reading Study Guide, pp. 158–159

 **AUDIO CDS**

- Audio Readings in Spanish
- Audio Readings (English)

Drainage Basins and Divides

When water falls or ice melts on a slope, some of the water soaks into the ground and some of it flows down the slope in thin sheets. But within a short distance, this water becomes part of a channel that forms a stream. A stream is any body of water—large or small—that flows down a slope along a channel.

READING TIP

One meaning of *channel* is "the bed or bottom of a body of water." The word *channel* comes from the Latin word *canālis*, meaning "tube." The word *canal* comes from the same Latin word.

Streams flow into one another to form complex drainage systems, with small streams flowing into larger ones. The area of land in which water drains into a stream system is called a **drainage basin.** In most drainage basins, the water eventually drains into a lake or an ocean. For example, in the Mississippi River drainage basin, water flows into the Mississippi and then drains into the Gulf of Mexico, which is part of the ocean.

Drainage basins are separated by ridges called divides, which are continuous lines of high land. A **divide** is a ridge from which water drains to one side or the other. Divides can run along high mountains. On flatter ground, a divide can simply be the highest line of land and can be hard to see.

Divides are the borders of drainage basins. A basin can be just a few kilometers wide or can drain water from a large portion of a continent. The Continental Divide runs from Alaska to Mexico. Most water that falls west of the Continental Divide ends up draining into the Pacific Ocean. Most water that falls east of it drains into the Gulf of Mexico and the Atlantic Ocean.

Divides and Drainage Basins

Divides are ridges that form the borders of drainage basins.

Denver, Colorado, sits just east of the Rocky Mountains and the Continental Divide.

DIFFERENTIATE INSTRUCTION

More Reading Support

A What makes up a stream system? *all the streams that drain water from one area of land*

B What do you call the area drained by a stream system? *a drainage basin*

Additional Investigation To reinforce Section 7.2 learning goals, use the following full-period investigation:

Additional INVESTIGATION, Rivers Change the Land, A, B, & C, pp. 200–208, 211–212
(Advanced students should complete Levels B and C.)

English Learners Many sentences in this section begin with introductory clauses of phrases that tell when or where, such as *When water falls or ice melts on a slope.* Help students separate these phrases and understand their relation as modifiers to the main clause of the sentence, which contains the subject.

7.2 INSTRUCT

Teach the Standards

Sediment 6.2.b

In this section: Help students see how moving water shapes Earth's surface by causing erosion and deposition of sediments. Explain that the sediment deposited from moving water creates floodplains, alluvial fans, and deltas.

- **previously taught:** sedimentary rocks, pp. 192–193
- **future opportunities:** erosion of mountains, p. 339

Real World Example

The formation of stream channels can be seen on a small scale on a barren hill at a construction site. After several rainfalls, a pattern of channels usually develops down the hillsides. Many of the smaller channels join the larger ones at an angle, forming a system of gullies.

Teach from Visuals

To help students interpret the map of the United States, ask:

- Where does water drain from the Columbia Basin? (First, show the students where the Pacific and Atlantic oceans and Gulf of Mexico are.) *the Pacific Ocean*
- Is our community included in one of the drainage basins shown here? If so, which one? If not, why not? *If not, it is because water in that area drains into a different river system.*
- Can two rivers be part of the same drainage basin? Explain your answer. *Yes, because divides cause water to flow in one direction. Water flows into various streams that are all part of one system.*

Teach Difficult Concepts

A divide is easy to visualize along a mountain ridge, but students may have a harder time visualizing a divide on relatively flat land. Explain that even on flat or gently rolling land, there will be a continuous line that is higher than the surrounding land that functions as a divide.

Teach Difficult Concepts

Distinguish a V-shaped valley from other kinds of valleys. Explain that the V shape refers to a cross section of the valley, that is, a "slice" across the valley. Show students a picture of a typical V-shaped valley, such as the Yellowstone River valley.

Teach from Visuals

To help students interpret the photograph of the meanders and oxbow lakes, ask:

- How might the river have looked thousands of years ago? *Its course was different, and the oxbow lakes were part of the river.*
- How might the river look thousands of years from now? *Its course will be different, and some of the meanders will probably be cut off as oxbow lakes.*

Teaching with Technology

To measure the lack of clarity in a stream with sediments, use a CBL and a turbidity probe.

Ongoing Assessment

CHECK YOUR READING *Answer: Floods deposit sediment onto the floodplain, which makes that land good for growing crops.*

Downtown Davenport, Iowa, sits in the floodplain of the Mississippi River. The city was covered with water when the river flooded in 1993.

Valleys and Floodplains

As streams flow and carry sediment from the surface of the land, they form valleys. In high mountains, streams often cut V-shaped valleys that are narrow and steep walled. In lower areas, streams may form broad valleys that include floodplains. A **floodplain** is an area of land on either side of a stream that is underwater when the stream floods. The floodplain of a large river may be many kilometers wide.

When a stream floods, it deposits much of the sediment that it carries onto its floodplain. This sediment can make the floodplain very fertile, or able to support a lot of plant growth. In the United States, the floodplains of the Mississippi River are some of the best places for growing crops.

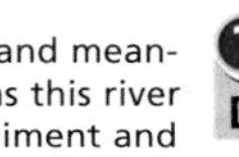

RESOURCE CENTER CLASSZONE.COM

Find out more about rivers and erosion.

CHECK YOUR READING Why is fertile land often found on flat land around rivers?

Stream Channels

? D

As a stream flows through a valley, its channel may run straight in some parts and curve in other parts. Curves and bends that form a twisting, looping pattern in a stream channel are called meanders (mee-AN-duhrz). The moving water erodes the outside banks and deposits sediment along the inside banks. Over many years, meanders shift position.

Oxbow lakes and meanders formed as this river deposited sediment and changed course.

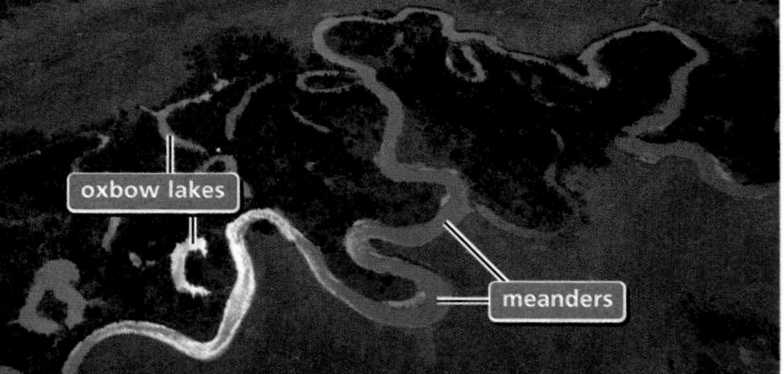

During a flood, the stream may cut a new channel that bypasses a meander. The cut-off meander forms a curved lake called an oxbow lake. An oxbow is a U-shaped piece of wood that fits under the neck of an ox. An oxbow lake has a similar shape.

DIFFERENTIATE INSTRUCTION

More Reading Support

C What area of land floods when a stream overflows its banks? *floodplain*

D What do you call curves and bends in a stream channel? *meanders*

Advanced Have students draw a sequence of three to five diagrams showing how an oxbow lake can form. The drawings should show how erosion of the outside banks of two meanders can form a loop so that the meanders meet, allowing the water to take a shorter course and cutting off the loop to form an oxbow lake.

Challenge and Extension, p. 160

Alluvial Fans and Deltas

Besides shaping valleys and forming oxbow lakes, streams also create landforms called alluvial fans and deltas. Both of these landforms are formed by the deposition of sediment.

An **alluvial fan** (uh-LOO-vee-uhl) is a fan-shaped deposit of sediment at the base of a mountain. It forms where a stream leaves a steep valley and enters a plain. The stream slows down and spreads out on the flatter ground. As it slows down, it can carry less sediment. The slower-moving water drops some of its sediment, leaving it at the base of the slope.

This alluvial fan was formed by a stream flowing into the Jago River in Alaska.

A **delta** is an area of land formed by the buildup of sediment at the end, or mouth, of a river. When a river enters the ocean, the river's water slows down, and the river drops much of its sediment. This sediment gradually builds up to form a plain. Like alluvial fans, deltas tend to be fan-shaped. Over a very long time, a river may build up its delta far out into the sea. A large river, such as the Mississippi, can build up a huge delta. Like many other large rivers on Earth, the Mississippi has been building up its delta out into the sea for many thousands of years.

From Divide to Delta

On their path to the ocean, streams and rivers slow down and flatten out.

1. Rainwater falls, or snow and ice melt. Streams form.
2. In high areas, streams flow through V-shaped valleys and are narrow and somewhat straight.
3. As land flattens, streams and rivers widen and take curvier paths.
4. Rivers form deltas as they empty into the ocean and deposit sediment.

READING VISUALS Where does the illustration show meanders?

233

Teach from Visuals

To help students interpret the diagram of the divide and delta, ask:

- Why are there no waterfalls in area 3? *The land is too flat.*
- Why are streams fast-flowing in area 2? *The land is steep.*
- Which areas would be good for white-water rafting? *1 and 2*
- Why does the river get wider farther downstream? *Other streams join it, bringing more water and sediment.*
- Do you think every river looks like this one? Explain. *No; every major river has these characteristics to some degree, but each river is different depending on the shape of the land, the climate, human interference, and so on.*

EXPLORE the BIG idea

Revisit "Where Has Water Been?" on p. 223. Have students use the terms they have learned to explain where water has been.

Ongoing Assessment

Explain how moving water shapes Earth's surface.

Ask: How is a river like a sculptor? *A river carves out valleys and shapes Earth's surface like a sculptor carves out rock or clay and shapes that material into different forms.*

Answer: at area 3, where the land flattens

DIFFERENTIATE INSTRUCTION

More Reading Support

E Why does an alluvial fan form where a stream enters a much flatter area? *The stream slows down and deposits much of its sediment.*

Alternative Assessment

Have students draw pictures to answer these questions.

- What does an oxbow lake look like?
- How does a meandering river look compared to a nonmeandering river?
- What shape do an alluvial fan and a delta have?
- How does a river valley in the fast-moving part of the river look compared to the slow-moving part of the river?

Address Misconceptions

IDENTIFY Have students draw a picture of what water usually looks like underground. If they show water as a large pool, lake, or free-flowing stream, they may hold the misconception that groundwater usually forms large open-air reservoirs.

CORRECT Show students a jar half-filled with potting soil on top of some pebbles. Ask what the jar will look like after you pour a cup of water into it. Pour the water. It will soak into the soil and reach the spaces between the pebbles. Explain that this is the usual condition of groundwater. Mention that water fills the pores of some kinds of solid rock.

REASSESS Ask: What model best shows water underground: a bathtub filled with water or a bathtub filled with rocks and a bucket of water poured over the rocks? *the tub of rocks and water*

Technology Resources

Visit **ClassZone.com** for background on common student misconceptions.

MISCONCEPTION DATABASE

Teach from Visuals

To help students interpret the visual of cavern formation, ask:

- How can rainwater soak into the ground? *It trickles through the spaces between soil and rock particles.*
- Where is the water table in this diagram? *in the caves at the bottom of the diagram, at the level of the stream*
- What might happen as the caves near the surface get larger? *The ground above might collapse.*

Teacher Demo

Place a few drops of vinegar on a piece of limestone. The limestone will fizz, showing that it is dissolving. Ask why the vinegar is so effective at dissolving the limestone. *Vinegar contains acid.*

Water moving underground forms caverns.

Not all rainwater runs off the land and flows into surface streams. Some of it evaporates, some is absorbed by plants, and some soaks into the ground and becomes groundwater. At a certain depth below the surface, the spaces in soil and rock become completely filled with water. The top of this water-filled region is called the water table. The water below the water table is called groundwater. **F**

The water table is at different distances below the surface in different places. Its level can change over time in the same location, depending on changes in rainfall. Below the water table, groundwater flows slowly through underground beds of rock and soil, where it causes erosion to take place.

VISUALIZATION CLASSZONE.COM

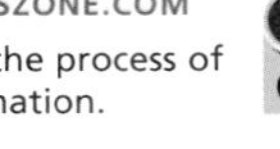
Observe the process of cave formation.

You have read that chemicals in water and air can break down rock. As you read in Chapter 6, rainwater is slightly acidic. This acidic water can dissolve certain rocks, such as limestone. In some areas, where the underground rock is limestone, the groundwater can dissolve some of the limestone and carry it away. Over time, this process **G**

Cavern Formation

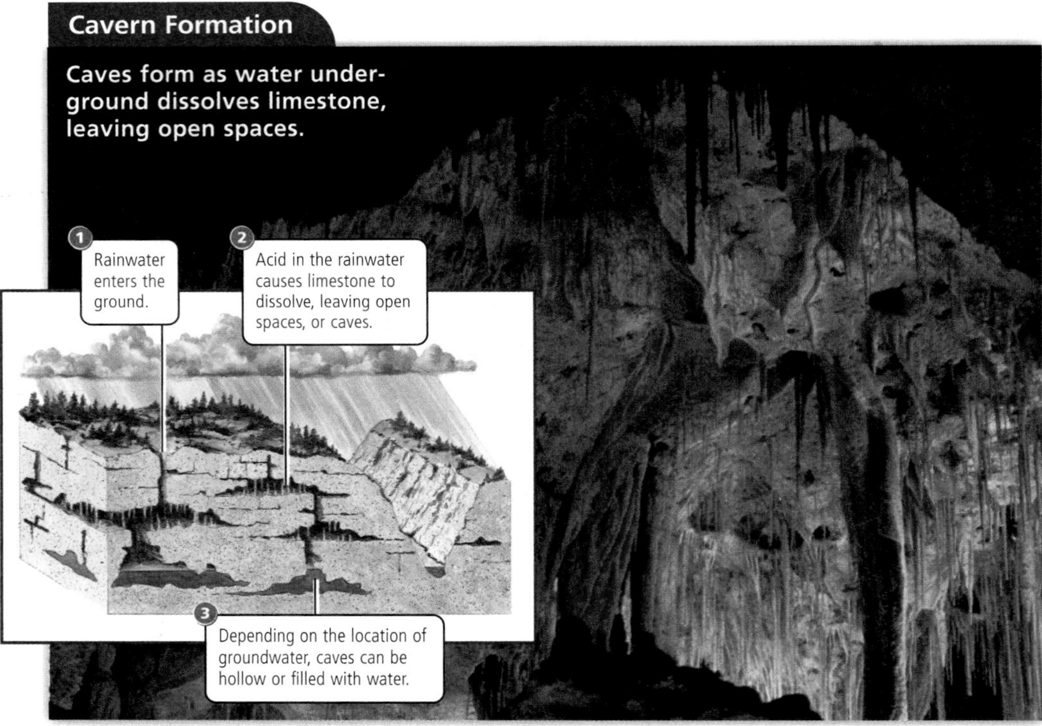

Caves form as water underground dissolves limestone, leaving open spaces.
1 Rainwater enters the ground.
2 Acid in the rainwater causes limestone to dissolve, leaving open spaces, or caves.
3 Depending on the location of groundwater, caves can be hollow or filled with water.

DIFFERENTIATE INSTRUCTION

More Reading Support

F What is the name of the highest level of water underground? *water table*

G Why can groundwater dissolve limestone? *Rainwater is acidic.*

Advanced Have students investigate and explain the forma tion of the slender deposits that form on the ceiling and floor o caves (stalactites and stalagmites).

This sinkhole took down a large part of a parking lot in Atlanta, Georgia.

produces open spaces, or caves. Large caves are called caverns. If the water table drops, a cavern may fill with air.

Some caverns have huge networks of rooms and passageways. Mammoth Cave in Kentucky, for example, is part of a cavern system that has more than 560 kilometers (about 350 mi) of explored passageways. Within the cavern are lakes and streams.

A surface feature that often occurs in areas with caverns is a sinkhole. A **sinkhole** is a basin that forms when the roof of a cave becomes so thin that it suddenly falls in. Sometimes it falls in because water that supported the roof has drained away. Landscapes with many sinkholes can be found in southern Indiana, south central Kentucky, and central Tennessee. In Florida, the collapse of shallow underground caverns has produced large sinkholes that have destroyed whole city blocks.

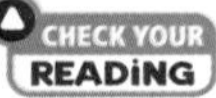
Why do caverns form in areas with limestone?

7.2 Review

KEY CONCEPTS

1. What is the difference between a drainage basin and a divide? (6.2.b)
2. How do streams change as they flow from mountains down to plains? (6.2.b)
3. How do caverns form? (6.2.a)

CRITICAL THINKING

4. **Sequence** Draw a cartoon with three panels showing how a sinkhole forms.
5. **Compare and Contrast** Make a Venn diagram to compare and contrast alluvial fans and deltas.

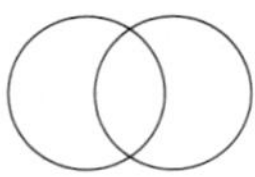

CHALLENGE

6. **Apply** During a flood, a river drops the largest pieces of its sediment on the floodplain close to its normal channel. Explain why. (**Hint:** Think about the speed of the water.)

ANSWERS

. A drainage basin is an area into which water flows from divide. A divide forms a border of drainage basins.

. As streams flow toward flat plains, they are in valleys that are V-shaped. Streams then become less steep and then wider and curvier.

3. Rainwater that is slightly acidic dissolves limestone underground, creating caverns.

4. Drawings should show that a cavern fills with water, the water drains, and the "ceiling" falls in.

5. alluvial fan: base of mountain; delta: mouth of river; both: formed by deposition when water slows, fan-shaped

6. Faster water has more power to carry large pieces. Water is faster in its channel than it is on the floodplain.

Ongoing Assessment

Explain how water moving underground forms natural features.

Ask: How does acid in rainwater affect the land underground? *The acidic water dissolves rock and forms open spaces called caves.*

CHECK YOUR READING *Answer: Limestone is a rock that is dissolved by acid in rainwater.*

Integrate the Sciences

Cave formation involves a chemical reaction between rainwater and limestone. Carbon dioxide in the air mixes with rainwater to form a weak solution of carbonic acid. The rainwater becomes even more acidic from carbon dioxide in decaying vegetation. This acidic water reacts with the mineral calcite in the limestone, dissolving the rock.

Reinforce the BIG idea

Have students relate the section to the Big Idea.

 Reinforcing Key Concepts, p. 161

7.2 ASSESS & RETEACH

Assess

 Section 7.2 Quiz, p. 140

Reteach

Show students a map of the United States. Ask them to identify any specific basins, floodplains, or deltas mentioned in this section, and point out where they think other ones are likely to exist.

Technology Resources

Have students visit **ClassZone.com** for reteaching of Key Concepts.

 CONTENT REVIEW

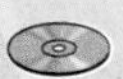 CONTENT REVIEW CD-ROM

CHAPTER INVESTIGATION

Focus

PURPOSE To observe the formation of meanders, deltas, and alluvial fans in a model stream

OVERVIEW Students will construct a model stream in a stream table. They will observe the processes of erosion and deposition over the life of the stream. Students will find the following:

- The river channel and valley widen with time.
- Meanders widen with time.
- Alluvial fans and deltas form.

Lab Preparation

- The ideal source of water is from a narrow hose attached to a tap or pump. The flow from a pitcher is harder to control, but students could slowly pour water into a funnel attached to a hose.
- If draining the stream table into a sink, be sure to use a fine sieve or nylon stocking to prevent sand from going into the drain.

Prior to the investigation, have students read through the investigation. You may wish to copy and distribute datasheets and rubrics.

 UNIT RESOURCE BOOK, pp. 191–199

 SCIENCE TOOLKIT, F15

Lab Management

- The channel students dig should be fairly deep.
- Encourage students to conduct this experiment slowly, starting with a stream of water poured slowly at as shallow an angle as possible.

SAFETY Water is bound to get on the floor during this experiment. Students should wipe up spills immediately.

INCLUSION Students with visual impairments could gently feel the various features being formed in the stream table.

CHAPTER INVESTIGATION

Creating Stream Features

OVERVIEW AND PURPOSE A view from the sky reveals that a large river twists and bends in its channel. But as quiet as it might appear, the river constantly digs up and dumps Earth materials along its way. This erosion and deposition may cause twists and curves called meanders and form a delta at the river's mouth. In this investigation you will

- create a "river" in a stream table to observe the formation of meanders and deltas
- identify the processes of erosion and deposition

Problem

Write It Up

How does moving water create meanders and deltas?

MATERIALS
- stream table, with hose attachment or recirculating pump
- sieve (optional)
- wood blocks
- sand
- ruler
- water
- sink with drain
- pitcher (optional)
- bucket (optional)

6.2.a, 6.2.b, 6.7.b

Procedure

1. Arrange the stream table on a counter so that it drains into a sink or bucket. If possible, place a sieve beneath the outlet hose to keep sand out of the drain. You can attach the inlet hose to a faucet if you have a proper adapter. Or you can gently pour water in with a pitcher or use a recirculating pump and a bucket.

2. Place wood blocks beneath the inlet end of the stream table so that the table tilts toward the outlet at about a 20-degree angle. Fill the upper two-thirds of the stream table nearly to the top with sand. Pack the sand a bit, and level the surface with the edge of a ruler. The empty bottom third of the stream table represents the lake or bay into which the river flows.

3. Using the end of the ruler, dig a gently curving channel halfway through the thickness of the sand from its upper to its lower end.

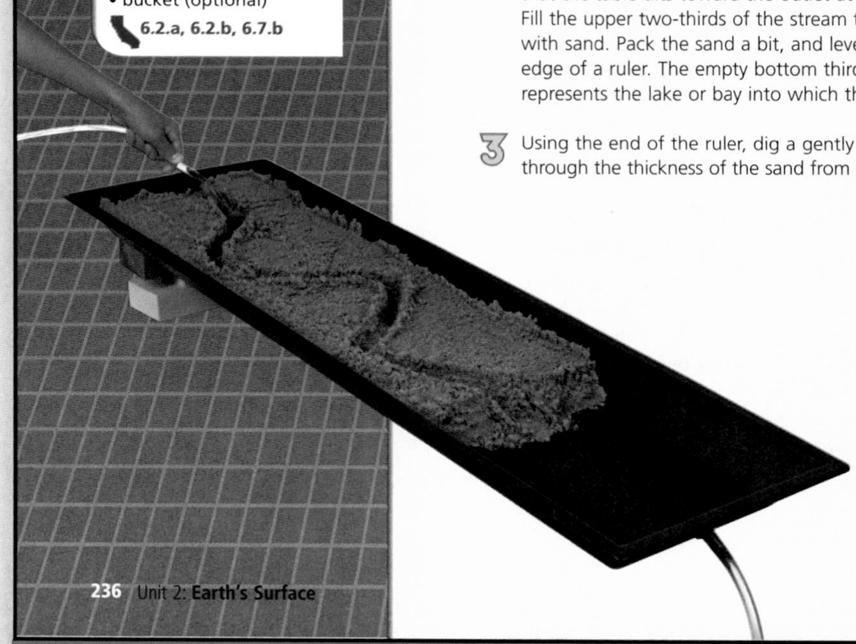

INVESTIGATION RESOURCES

 CHAPTER INVESTIGATION, Creating Stream Features
- Level A, pp. 191–194
- Level B, pp. 195–198
- Level C, p. 199

Advanced students should complete Levels B & C.

 Writing a Lab Report, D12–13

Technology Resources

Customize this student lab as needed or look for an alternative. Print rubrics to assess student lab reports.

 **Lab Generator CD-ROM**

Content Standard
6.2.a Students know water running downhill is the dominant process in shaping the landscape, including California's landscape.

Investigation Standard
6.7.b Select and use appropriate tools and technology (including calculators, computers, balances, spring scales, microscopes, and binoculars) to perform tests, collect data, and display data.

4 Direct a gentle flow of tap water into the upper end of the channel. Increase the flow slightly when the water begins to move through the channel. You may have to try this several times before you find the proper rate of flow to soak the sand and fill the stream channel. Avoid adding so much water that it pools at the top before moving into the channel. You can also change the stream table's tilt.

5 Once you are successful in creating a river, observe its shape and any movement of the sand. Continue pouring water until the top part of the sand is completely washed away and your river falls apart. Scrape the sand back into place with the ruler and repeat the procedure until you thoroughly understand the stream and sand movements.

Observe and Analyze

Write It Up

1. **RECORD** Make a series of drawings showing changes in your river over time. Be sure to label the river's features, as well as areas of erosion and deposition. Be sure to diagram what happens to the sand at the river's mouth.
2. **RECORD** Write a record of the development of your river from start to finish. Include details such as the degree of tilt you used, your method of introducing water into the stream table, and features you observed forming.

Conclude

Write It Up

1. **EVALUATE** How do you explain the buildup of sand at the mouth of your river? Use the words *speed, erosion,* and *deposition* in your answer. Did the slope of the stream change over time?
2. **INTERPRET** Where in your stream table did you observe erosion occurring? deposition? What features did each process form?
3. **INFER** What might have happened if you had increased the amount of the water flowing into your river? the speed?
4. **IDENTIFY LIMITS** In what ways was your setup a simplified version of what would actually occur on Earth? Describe how an actual stream would be more complex.
5. **APPLY** Based on what you observed in this investigation, write two statements that relate the age of a stream to (1) the number of its meanders and (2) to the size of its delta or alluvial fan.

INVESTIGATE Further

CHALLENGE Revise this activity to test a problem statement about a specific stream feature. You might choose to vary the stream's slope, speed, or volume to test the effects on meanders and deltas. Or you could vary the sediment size and observe the movements of each size. Write a hypothesis and design an experimental procedure. Identify the independent and dependent variables.

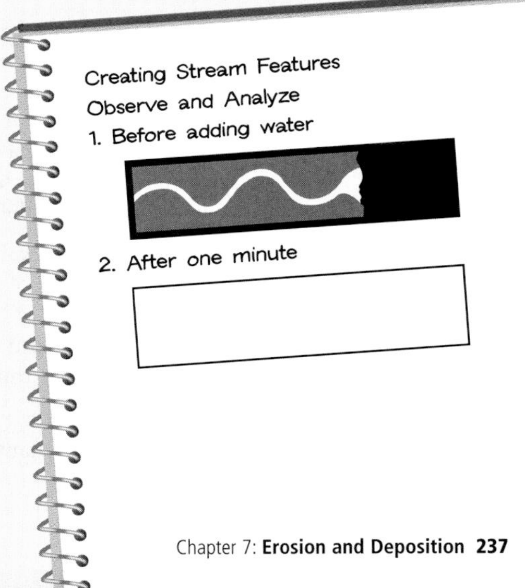

Creating Stream Features
Observe and Analyze
1. Before adding water
2. After one minute

Post-Lab Discussion

Ask: How might scientists use stream tables to gather information or to solve a problem? *Stream tables can be used to study the effects of sediment of different sizes or the slope of a stream on how the stream changes over time. Stream tables can be useful for modeling how a dam or pollution might affect a river.*

Observe and Analyze

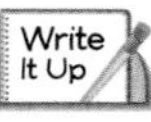

1. *Observe students' diagrams. They will likely show a widening of the stream channel and meanders over time. Students might use two colors to show the original stream channel and the new stream after water flows. They should show where material has been picked up by erosion and where it has been put down by deposition.*
2. *Students should identify where erosion and deposition occur, where meanders might have formed or changed, and where a delta might have formed.*

Conclude

1. *As the speed of the stream slows, the sand that is carried by the river in the process of erosion settles out by the process of deposition at the river's mouth. The slope may have flattened and been reduced by buildup of sand, although unlike real river valleys, the tray has a constant slope.*
2. *Erosion occurred along most of the stream banks, especially at the outside of the curves, which may have formed into new meanders. Deposition occurred at the inside of the meanders and especially at the mouth (end) of the river, where a delta would form.*
3. *more erosion, a deepening of the channel, possibly a flood*
4. *The setup had only one stream, the surface was only sand and spread evenly; the stream was very short, and the amount of time was brief. An actual stream would have water flowing into it from other streams and down its banks, the structure of the land would be different and variable, the stream and land would be exposed to weather, and changes would occur over a long time.*
5. *The older the stream, the more extreme its meanders will be and the larger its delta or alluvial fan will be.*

INVESTIGATE Further

CHALLENGE Experimental design should vary one aspect of the stream, keeping other conditions constant.

7.3 FOCUS

Set Learning Goals

Students will

- Describe how waves and currents shape shorelines.
- Explain how wind shapes landscapes.
- Observe in an experiment how sand moves along a beach.

3-Minute Warm-Up

Display Transparency 53 or copy this exercise on the board:

Draw a map of a river. Label the river with an arrow to show its direction of flow. Add three small streams that join the river. Label each stream with an arrow to show its direction of flow. *Maps should show each stream meeting the river at an angle, producing a tree-like pattern. The flow of the streams should be the same as that of the main river.*

 3-Minute Warm-Up, p. T53

7.3 MOTIVATE

THINK ABOUT

PURPOSE To introduce waves as a force of erosion

DISCUSS Ask students what probably surrounded the stone pillars millions of years ago. Ask: Why do you think these are left over from large areas of rock? *The pillars are made of hard rock that was among softer or fractured rock that was easier to weather and disintegrate.*

KEY CONCEPT

7.3 Waves and wind shape land.

CALIFORNIA Content Standards

6.2.c Students know beaches are dynamic systems in which the sand is supplied by rivers and moved along the coast by the action of waves.

6.2.d Students know earthquakes, volcanic eruptions, landslides, and floods change human and wildlife habitats.

6.7.h Identify changes in natural phenomena over time without manipulating the phenomena (e.g., a tree limb, a grove of trees, a stream, a hillslope).

BEFORE, you learned

- Stream systems shape Earth's surface
- Groundwater creates caverns and sinkholes

NOW, you will learn

- How waves and currents shape shorelines
- How wind shapes land

VOCABULARY

longshore drift p. 239
longshore current p. 239
sandbar p. 240
barrier island p. 240
dune p. 241
loess p. 242

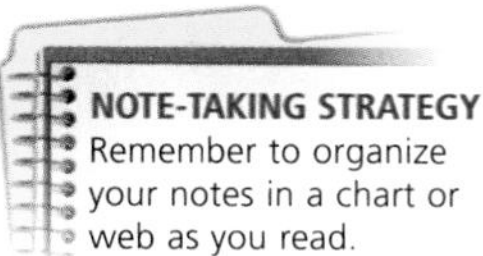
NOTE-TAKING STRATEGY Remember to organize your notes in a chart or web as you read.

THINK ABOUT

How did these pillars of rock form?

The rock formations in this photograph stand along the shoreline of Garrapata State Park in California. What natural process created these stone pillars? What evidence of this process can you see in the photograph?

Waves and currents shape shorelines.

The stone pillars, or sea stacks, in the photograph above add to the scenic beauty of Garrapata State Park, which is located at the northern end of the Big Sur coastline. They were formed by the movement of water. The constant action of waves breaking against the cliffs slowly wore rock away, leaving behind pillarlike formations. Waves continue to wear down the pillars and cliffs. In the years to come, the waves will likely wear away the stone pillars completely.

The force of waves, powered by wind, can wear away rock and move thousands of tons of sand on beaches. The force of wind can change the look of the land. Moving air can pick up sand particles and move them around to build up dunes. Wind can carry huge amounts of fine sediment thousands of kilometers.

In this section, you'll read more about how waves and wind shape shorelines and many other landforms.

RESOURCES FOR DIFFERENTIATED INSTRUCTION

Below Level

UNIT RESOURCE BOOK

- Reading Study Guide A, pp. 164–165
- Decoding Support, p. 188

 **AUDIO CDS**

Advanced

UNIT RESOURCE BOOK

Challenge and Extension, p. 170

English Learners

UNIT RESOURCE BOOK

Spanish Reading Study Guide, pp. 168–169

 **AUDIO CDS**

- Audio Readings in Spanish
- Audio Readings (English)

horelines

Some shorelines, such as the Big Sur coastline, are steep and rocky. As waves crash against the rock, they wear away the bottom of the cliffs. Eventually, parts of the cliffs above break away and fall into the water, where they are worn down and carried away by the water.

While high, rocky coasts get worn away, low coastlines often get built up. As you read earlier, when a stream flows into an ocean or a lake, it deposits sediment near its mouth. This sediment mixes with the sediment formed by waves beating against the coast. Waves and currents move this sediment along the shore, building up beaches. Beaches are dynamic, or ever-changing, systems. Two terms are used to describe the movement of sediment and water along a shore: *longshore drift* and *longshore current.*

- **Longshore drift** is the zigzag movement of sand along a beach. Waves formed by wind blowing across the water far from shore may hit a shoreline at an angle. These angled waves carry sand up onto the shore. Then gravity pulls the water and sand straight back into the water. The sand gradually moves down the beach. The illustration below shows longshore drift.
- A **longshore current** is movement of water along a shore as waves strike the shore at an angle. The direction of the longshore current can change from day to day as the direction of the waves striking the shore changes.

Longshore drift moves large amounts of sand along beaches. It can cause a beach to shrink at one location and grow at another.

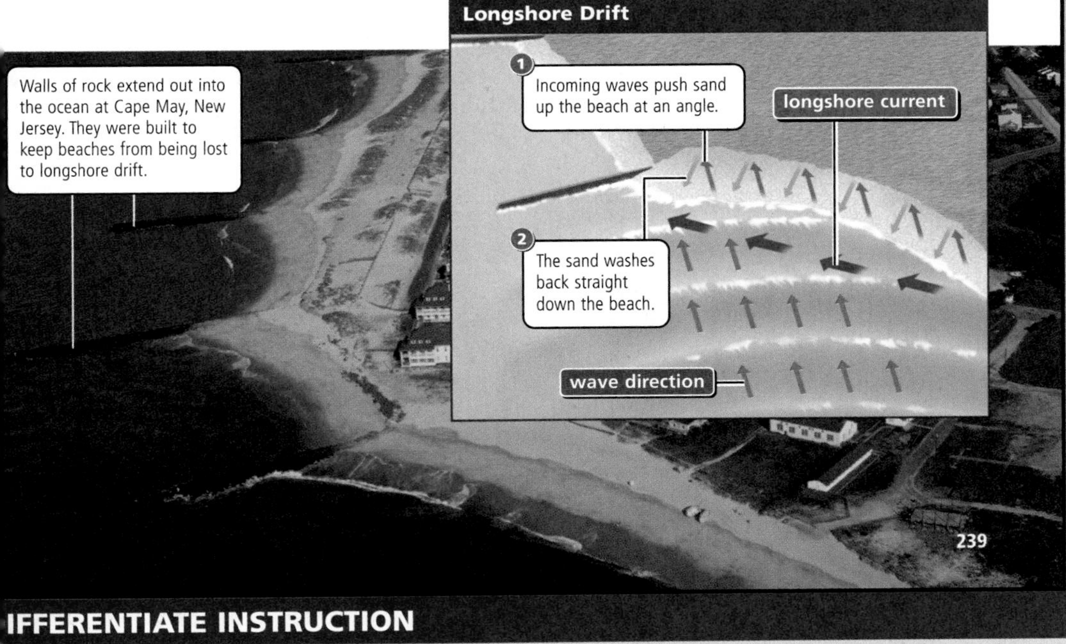

Longshore Drift
1 Incoming waves push sand up the beach at an angle.
longshore current
2 The sand washes back straight down the beach.
wave direction
239

Walls of rock extend out into the ocean at Cape May, New Jersey. They were built to keep beaches from being lost to longshore drift.

7.3 INSTRUCT

Teach the Standards

Shorelines 6.2.c

In this section: Help students understand that shorelines are dynamic features. Point out that water affects beaches by moving sand.

- **previously taught:** sorting of sediment, pp. 192–193
- **future opportunities:** estuaries, p. 404

Address Misconceptions

IDENTIFY Ask: Are ocean waves a movement of energy or water? If students do not say energy, they may hold the misconception that waves move masses of water forward.

CORRECT Set up a long trough of water and place a cork or other float in the middle. Use your hand to create a gentle wave to demonstrate that the float rises and falls on the wave but does not move forward.

REASSESS Remind students that water waves move energy, not material. Ask: How might a message in a bottle thrown into the sea near Europe end up on the shores of the United States? *Currents, rather than waves, could take it there.*

Ongoing Assessment

Describe how waves and currents shape shorelines.

Ask: How do waves erode cliffs along a shoreline? *The waves crash into the rocky cliffs over and over again, breaking away large chunks of rock that fall into the water and are carried away.*

Technology Resources

Visit **ClassZone.com** for background on common student misconceptions.

MISCONCEPTION DATABASE

EXPLORE the BIG idea

Revisit "How Do Waves Shape Land?" on p. 223. Have students explain their results.

IFFERENTIATE INSTRUCTION

More Reading Support

A Where does beach sand come from? *from sediment brought to the shore by rivers and from rocks eroded along the shoreline*

Below Level Have students model longshore drift by moving their finger diagonally across their desk, straight back, diagonally across, and so on until they reach the edge of the desk. Ask them how many kinds of movements they made. *three: diagonal, straight back, and the general movement across the desk* Compare these movements to those of longshore drift.

INVESTIGATE Longshore Drift

PURPOSE To model the concept of longshore drift

TIP *15 min.* Tell students to place the books far up on their desk, so that the coin falls onto the desk instead of the floor.

WHAT DO YOU THINK? *The coin moved at an angle on its way up and generally straight back, perpendicular to the edge of the book, on its way down. The book surface is the beach, the coin is the sand, and the movement of the finger is the wave.*

CHALLENGE *From right to left; flick from the lower left corner to change the current's direction.*

 Datasheet, Longshore Drift, p. 171

Technology Resources

Customize this student lab as needed or look for an alternative. Print rubrics to assess student lab reports.

 **Lab Generator CD-ROM**

Teach from Visuals

To help students interpret the diagram of sand deposition, ask: How are sandbars and barrier islands related? *Barrier islands build up as sandbars parallel to a coastline accumulate enough deposition to rise above the surface. Sandbars are buildups of sand and may be underwater. They are not always parallel to the coast and do not always become barrier islands.*

INVESTIGATE Longshore Drift

How does sand move along a beach?

SKILL FOCUS
Observing (6.2.c)

MATERIALS
- 2 or 3 books
- coin

TIME
15 minutes

PROCEDURE

1. Prop up a book as shown.
2. Hold a coin with your finger against the bottom right corner of the book.
3. Gently flick the coin up the slope of the book at an angle. The coin should slide back down the book and fall off the bottom. If necessary, change the angle of the book and the strength with which you are flicking the coin.
4. Repeat step 3 several times. Observe the path the coin takes. Record your observations. Include a diagram that shows the path the coin takes as it slides up and down the book.

WHAT DO YOU THINK?

- What path did the coin take on its way up? on its way down?
- In this model of longshore drift, what represents the beach? What represents the sand? What represents a wave?

CHALLENGE In this model, in which direction will the longshore current move? How could you change the model to change the direction of the current?

Sandbars and Barrier Islands

As ocean waves and currents transport sand, they shape a variety of coastal landforms. Longshore currents, for example, often deposit sand along shorelines. The sand builds up to form sandbars. A **sandbar** is a ridge of sand built up by the action of waves and currents. A sandbar that has built up above the water's surface and is joined to the land at one end is called a spit. The tip of Cape Cod, Massachusetts, is a spit.

B

Strong longshore currents that move mostly in one direction may produce sandbars that build up over time into barrier islands. A **barrier island** is a long, narrow island that develops parallel to a coast.

C

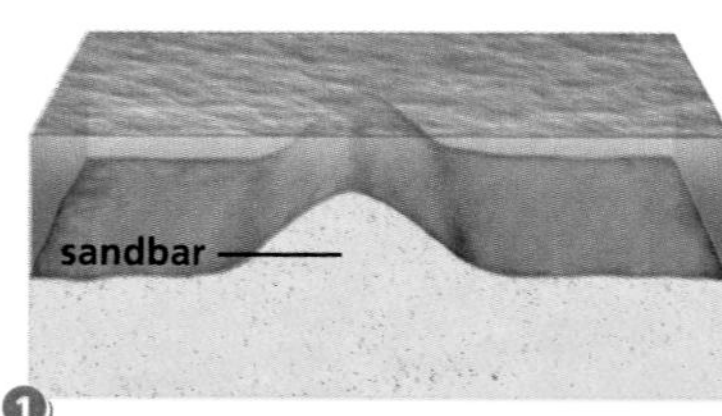

1 Waves and currents move and build up sand deposits to form a sandbar under the water surface.

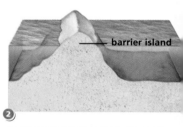

2 As more sand is deposited, the sandbar rises above the surface to become a barrier island.

DIFFERENTIATE INSTRUCTION

More Reading Support

B Where might you see a spit? *extending from a beach*

C From what structure do both spits and barrier islands form? *sandbars*

Below Level Show students a large-scale map of Massachusetts and point out Cape Cod. Have students find and point out the spit at the cape's tip. Use maps of other places along the East Coast to point out spits and barrier islands.

Advanced Have students develop a PowerPoint presentation, using scanned photographs of a variety of spits and barrier islands. They should include photographs of jetties, the shape of beaches that result, and maps that show the locations.

 Challenge and Extension, p. 170

This lighthouse on a barrier island in North Carolina had to be moved because of beach erosion. The photograph shows the lighthouse before it was moved.

A barrier island gets its name from the fact that it forms a barrier between the ocean waves and the mainland. As a barrier island builds up, grasses, bushes, and trees begin to grow on it.

Barrier islands are common along gently sloping coasts around the world. They occur along the coasts of New Jersey and North Carolina and along the coastline of the Gulf of Mexico. Padre Island in Texas is a barrier island about 180 kilometers (110 mi) in length.

Barrier islands constantly change shape. Hurricanes or other storms can speed up the change. During large storms, waves can surge across the land, carrying away huge amounts of sediment and depositing it elsewhere. Houses on beaches can be destroyed in storms.

CHECK YOUR READING How and where do barrier islands form?

Wind shapes land.

At Indiana Dunes National Lakeshore, not far from the skyscrapers of Chicago, you can tumble or slide down huge sand dunes. First-time visitors to the Indiana dunes find it hard to believe that sand formations like these can be found so far from a desert or an ocean. What created this long stretch of dune land along the southern shore of Lake Michigan? The answer: wind. A **dune** is a mound of sand built up by wind.

Like water, wind has the power to transport and deposit sediment. Although wind is a less powerful force of erosion than moving water, it can still shape landforms. This often happens in dry regions and in areas that have few or no plants to hold soil in place. Wind can build up dunes, deposit layers of dust, or make a land surface as hard as pavement.

Develop Critical Thinking

CONNECT Grasses, bushes, and trees grow on some barrier islands. Ask: Do you think the plants have any effect on erosion of the islands? Explain. *Plants slow erosion by anchoring the sediments with their roots and by blocking waves and wind.*

Ongoing Assessment

Answer: Barrier islands form as wave action builds up sandbars above the water surface. They form parallel to lowland coasts around the world.

DIFFERENTIATE INSTRUCTION

More Reading Support

D What causes spits and barrier islands to change shape quickly? *hurricanes and other storms*

E What force creates sand dunes? *wind*

English Learners Some students have never seen the ocean; help them with background knowledge of the concepts of shore, waves, and so on. Discuss words associated with erosion: *wear away, worn down, built up, deposit.* Many such terms are phrased as verbs with interchangeable parts.

Teach from Visuals

To help students interpret the dune diagram and photograph, ask:

- Which side of the dune in the diagram has the most gentle slope? *the side that the wind blows into*
- On the steep side of the dune, why doesn't the wind blow the sand away, making a gentle slope? *because the dune blocks the wind*
- From which side do you think the wind blows in the area shown in the photograph? Why do you think so? *from left to right because the gentler slopes are on the left*

Teacher Demo

Use a hair dryer and a tray of dry sand to demonstrate how a dune forms around an obstacle. Place a stone in the tray and blow sand against it (starting from a distance to avoid causing a mess). A dune will form. Ask: Once the stone is covered, why does sand continue to collect? *The small dune itself acts as an obstacle.*

SAFETY Make sure the hair dryer and windblown sand are directed away from students.

Ongoing Assessment

Describe how wind shapes landscapes.

Ask: How are sand dunes formed? *Strong winds pick up sand particles and carry them away. When the wind dies down or runs into something, the sand is dropped. Over time, as more sand is dropped in the same location, a dune forms.*

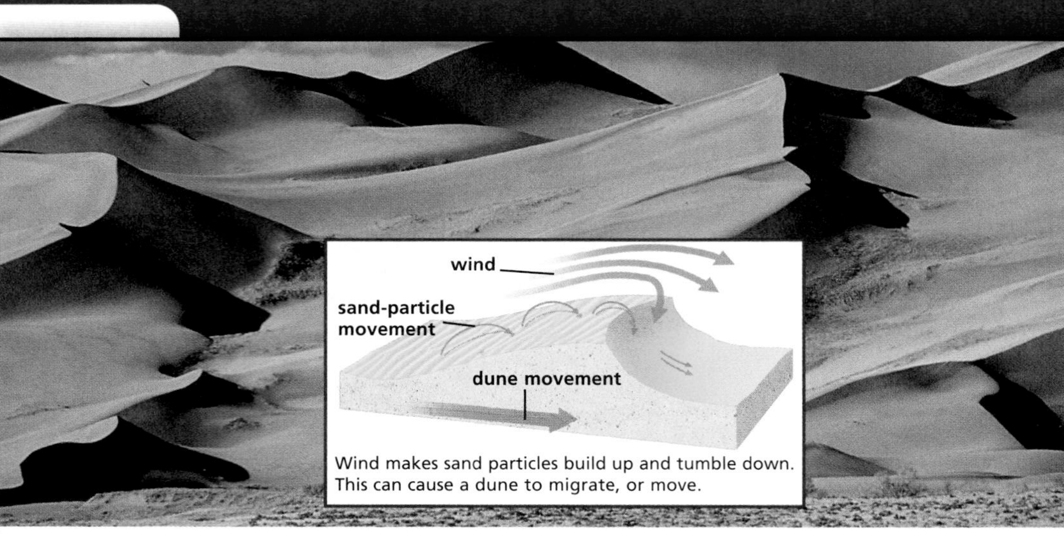

Wind makes sand particles build up and tumble down. This can cause a dune to migrate, or move.

These hills of sand are at the Great Sand Dunes National Monument in Colorado.

Dune Formation

Even a light breeze can carry dust. A moderate wind can roll and slide grains of sand along a beach or desert, creating ripples. Only a strong wind can actually pick up and carry sand particles. When the wind dies down or hits something—such as a cliff or a hill—it drops the sand. Over time, the deposits of sand build up to create dunes.

Some dunes start out as ripples that grow larger. Others form as wind-carried sand settles around a rock, log, or other obstacle. In climates with enough rainfall, plants begin to grow on dunes a short distance from beaches.

CALIFORNIA Focus

The Imperial Sand Dunes are the largest group of sand dunes in California. The dune system is more than 64 kilometers (40 mi) long. Some dunes are more than 91 meters (300 ft) tall.

 F

Dunes form only where there are strong winds and a constant supply of loose sand. They can be found on the inland side of beaches of oceans and large lakes, on the sandy floodplains of large rivers, and in sandy deserts.

Dunes can form in a variety of sizes and shapes. They can reach heights of up to 300 meters (about 1000 ft). Some dunes are curved; others are long, straight ridges. Still others are mound-shaped hills. A dune usually has a gentle slope on the side that faces the wind and a steeper slope on the side sheltered from the wind.

Loess

G

Besides forming dunes, wind also changes the soil over large regions of Earth by depositing dust. A strong windstorm can move millions of tons of dust. As the wind dies down, the dust drops to the ground. Deposits of fine wind-blown sediment are called **loess** (LOH-uhs).

In some regions, deposits of loess have built up over thousands and even millions of years. Loess is a valuable resource because it forms good soil for growing crops.

DIFFERENTIATE INSTRUCTION

More Reading Support

F What two conditions are needed for dunes to form? *strong winds and loose sand*

G What are deposits of wind-blown sediment? *loess*

Below Level Students may have a hard time appreciating the size that sand dunes can reach. Compare the size of the tallest dunes (300 meters, or 1000 feet) to something familiar, such as a skyscraper or a local hill.

English Learners Remind students that these words are generalizations that mean nearly the same thing: *mostly, mainly, typically, usually, often, commonly.*

This loess deposit in Iowa built up over many thousands of years.

Loess covers about 10 percent of the land surface of Earth. China has especially large deposits of loess, covering hundreds of thousands of square kilometers. Some of the deposits are more than 300 meters (about 1000 ft) thick. Such thick deposits take a long time to develop. Some of the loess deposits in China are 2 million years old. Winds blowing over the deserts and dry regions of central Asia carried the dust that formed these deposits.

Parts of east central Europe and the Mississippi Valley in the United States also contain large loess deposits. In the central United States, loess deposits are between 8 and 30 meters (25 and 100 ft) thick.

Desert Pavement

Wind does not only shape land surfaces by depositing dust. It also shapes land surfaces by removing dust. When wind blows away all the smallest particles from a mixture of sand, silt, and gravel, it leaves behind a layer of stones and gravel. This stony surface is called desert pavement because it looks like a cobblestone street. The coarse gravel and rocks are too large to be picked up by wind.

Desert pavement is made up of particles too large to be picked up by wind.

CHECK YOUR READING How are both loess and desert pavement formed by wind?

7.3 Review

KEY CONCEPTS

1. What kinds of landforms do longshore drift and longshore currents produce? (6.2.c)
2. How do dunes form? (6.7.h)
3. How does loess form, and why is it important? (6.7.h)

CRITICAL THINKING

4. **Identify Cause and Effect** Is longshore drift the cause or the effect of a longshore current? Explain.
5. **Predict** What effect would a barrier island have on the shoreline of the mainland?

CHALLENGE

6. **Hypothesize** The southern and eastern shores of Lake Michigan have large areas of sand dunes, but the northern and western shores do not. Write a hypothesis that explains why. You might want to use a map and draw the shape of Lake Michigan to explain.

ANSWERS

1. beaches, sandbars, barrier islands, and spits

2. Strong winds pile up sand in mounds.

3. Loess forms as winds deposit fine sediments from elsewhere. It can form thick deposits of fertile soil.

4. It is the effect. Longshore drift is the movement of sand, which is caused by longshore current, which is the force of the water moving in a direction.

5. It might lessen the force of the waves on the mainland shore, especially during storms.

6. North and west: wind is blowing sand toward the water, so areas of dunes don't form. South and east: wind is blowing inland, where there is room for sand to pile up into dunes.

Ongoing Assessment

CHECK YOUR READING *Answer: Wind picks up fine-grained sediment and deposits it as loess. Desert pavement forms when wind blows away all fine-grained sediment, leaving rocks.*

Reinforce the BIG idea

Have students relate the section to the Big Idea.

R Reinforcing Key Concepts, p. 172

7.3 ASSESS & RETEACH

Assess

A Section 7.3 Quiz, p. 141

Reteach

Provide samples of different sediments including large pebbles, medium-sized pebbles, small pebbles, sand grains, and loess. (Loess particles are about the size of talcum powder particles.) Create a chart that lists each kind of grain. Have students fill in the chart to show how each type of grain is affected by erosion and deposition in wind, waves, and water.

Technology Resources

Have students visit **ClassZone.com** for reteaching of Key Concepts.

CONTENT REVIEW

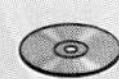

CONTENT REVIEW CD-ROM

CALIFORNIA CLOSE-UP
Science in Action in California

Set Learning Goal

To explain how ocean waves erode cliffs and how scientists measure changes in shorelines

Present the Science

Cliff erosion results from the force of ocean waves crashing against cliffs. Erosion occurs at different rates along a cliff. Scientists use lasers to measure how erosion and deposition affect beach shorelines. Planes bounce laser light off the ground and measure how long it takes the light to bounce back.

Discussion Questions

Have students share their knowledge and experiences with sand and cliff erosion along the California coast.

- Ask: What is a possible cause for the different rates of cliff erosion? *Waves might crash against one part of a cliff with more force than in other parts. Also, some parts of the cliff might be made of rocks that are more resistant to erosion.*
- Ask: What do scientists measure to determine the patterns of erosion and deposition of beaches? *They measure the changes in the shoreline's height.*
- Ask: If laser light that is bounced off one area of the beach takes longer to bounce back compared with other areas, scientists conclude that the height of that part of the shoreline is lower. How do they know this? *They convert the time measurement to a distance. The laser will take longer to bounce back because there is a greater distance for the laser to travel between the beach and the plane. Therefore, the shoreline must be lower than in other places.*

Close

Ask students what examples of erosion they have seen in their area.

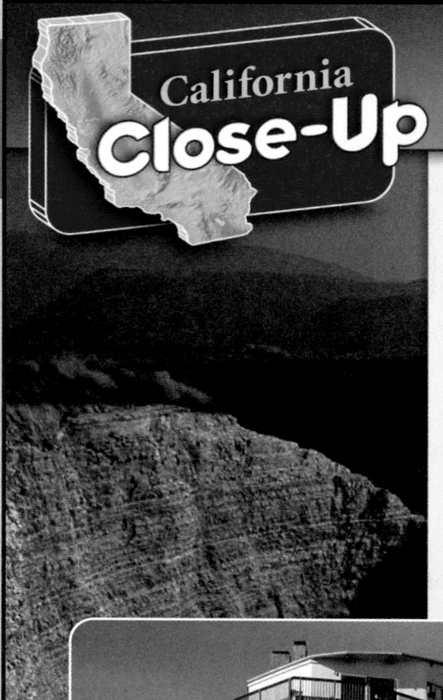

EROSION

The Changing Shoreline

6.2.c Students know beaches are dynamic systems in which the sand is supplied by rivers and moved along the coast by the action of waves.

A natural cycle of erosion and deposition shapes beaches and cliffs along the California coast. Rivers carry sand and silt down to the ocean. Ocean currents move sand along the shoreline. In the winter, storms can move sand offshore. The large storm waves also cause cliff erosion.

Where's the Beach?

Cliffs erode as waves crash against the cliff and break up the rocks. Different parts of a cliff can erode at different rates. In 1998, after an unusual number of winter storms, scientists measured the changes in a cliff near Pacifica. Part of the cliff suffered from erosion equal to 50 years of normal erosion. Meanwhile, a nearby part of the cliff had almost no erosion at all. Even normal erosion takes place at different rates along a cliff. Scientists have studied the cliff erosion rates in Isla Vista over many years. Some parts of the cliff erode as quickly as 38 centimeters (15 in.) a year. Other areas erode less than 5 centimeters (2 in.) in a year.

This photograph of a house in Isla Vista was taken in January 2005. In January 2002, the cliff edge was about where the pillars are.

Measuring Ups and Downs

To study the patterns of erosion and deposition, scientists measure the change in height along the shoreline. LIDAR, which stands for LIght Detection And Ranging, is an instrument that helps scientists measure the change in a shoreline. LIDAR is like radar except it uses laser light instead of radio waves. An airplane flies over a beach, and the LIDAR on the plane bounces light off the ground and measures how long it takes for the light to bounce back and reach the plane. This time measurement can be converted to a distance. With LIDAR, scientists can accurately measure shoreline changes.

WRITING ABOUT SCIENCE

Sometimes people build seawalls to protect cliffs from erosion. Waves break against the seawall instead of against the cliff. How might a seawall affect ocean and shore life? Write a few paragraphs that discuss the effects a seawall might have on the coastal ecosystem.

WRITING ABOUT SCIENCE

Writing Applications 6.2.2 This assignment will give students practice in writing a cause-effect essay. Suggest that peers read each other's essays and evaluate them in terms of how clearly the cause is linked to the effects.

The best essays will

- *clearly explain how the cause and the effects are related.*
- *explain the science behind the cause and effects.*

KEY CONCEPT

Glaciers carve land and move sediments.

CALIFORNIA Content Standard

6.2.a Students know water running downhill is the dominant process in shaping the landscape, including California's landscape.

BEFORE, you learned
- Running water shapes landscapes
- Wind changes landforms

NOW, you will learn
- How moving ice erodes land
- How moving ice deposits sediment and changes landforms

VOCABULARY

glacier p. 245
till p. 248
moraine p. 248
kettle lake p. 249

EXPLORE Glaciers (6.2.a)

How do glaciers affect land?

PROCEDURE

1. Flatten the clay on top of a paper towel.
2. Drag the ice cube across the clay as shown. Record your observations.
3. Leave the ice cube to melt on top of the clay.

MATERIALS
- modeling clay
- paper towel
- ice cube containing sand and gravel

WHAT DO YOU THINK?
- What happened when you dragged the ice cube across the clay?
- What happened to the sand and gravel in the ice cube as it melted?

VOCABULARY
Remember to add a four square diagram for *glacier* to your notebook.

Glaciers are moving bodies of ice.

You might not think of ice as something that moves. But think about what happens to an ice cube on a table. The cube begins to melt, makes a small puddle, and may slide a little. The water under the cube makes the table surface slippery, which allows the ice cube to slide.

A similar process happens on a much larger scale with glaciers. A **glacier** is a large mass of ice that moves over land. A glacier forms in a cold region when more snow falls than melts each year. As the snow builds up, its weight presses the snow on the bottom into ice. On a mountain, the weight of a heavy mass of ice causes it to flow downward, usually slowly. On flatter land, the ice spreads out as a sheet. As glaciers form, move, and melt away, they shape landscapes.

7.4 FOCUS

Set Learning Goals

Students will
- Explain how moving ice erodes land.
- Explore different ways that moving ice deposits sediment and changes landforms.
- Design an experiment to show how kettle lakes form.

3-Minute Warm-Up

Display Transparency 53 or copy this exercise on the board:

Draw two cross sections, one of a mountain stream and one of a meandering stream. Label as many landforms as you can. *The mountain stream should be V-shaped and the meandering stream should be relatively flat, with a floodplain.*

3-Minute Warm-Up, p. T53

7.4 MOTIVATE

EXPLORE Glaciers

PURPOSE To model how a glacier changes landscapes

TIP *5 min.* To make the ice, place a mixture of sand and gravel in the bottom of ice cube trays before adding water. Angular grains will work better than smooth ones.

WHAT DO YOU THINK? *Sediment in the ice cube scraped the clay. Some clay may have built up along the sides and at the end of the path. As the ice melted, sediment was deposited.*

RESOURCES FOR DIFFERENTIATED INSTRUCTION

Below Level

UNIT RESOURCE BOOK
Reading Study Guide A, pp. 175–176
Decoding Support, p. 188

AUDIO CDS

Advanced

UNIT RESOURCE BOOK
- Challenge and Extension, p. 181
- Challenge Reading, pp. 184–185

English Learners

UNIT RESOURCE BOOK
Spanish Reading Study Guide, pp. 179–180

AUDIO CDS
- Audio Readings in Spanish
- Audio Readings (English)

7.4 INSTRUCT

Teach the Standards

Glaciers 6.2.a

In this section: Make sure students understand that glaciers move by the processes of flowing and sliding. Explain that glaciers can erode the landscape, create moraines, and form lakes.

previously taught: water stored in glaciers, p. 42

Teach from Visuals

To help students interpret the visual "Ice Age in North America," display a political map of your area. Ask:

- Was our area covered with ice during the last ice age? *Answers will vary.*
- If an area was not covered by ice, can you assume that the landscape was unaffected by the glaciers? Explain. *No; areas free of ice might have been affected by water from melted ice or by wind-blown sediment.*

Real World Example

Evidence of glaciers during the last ice age are seen throughout North America. Grooves gouged into rocks can be seen in New York City's Central Park. Mounds of glacial sediment are scattered throughout the Midwest and New England. The fertile soils of the Great Plains are largely a result of thick deposits of loess, sediment that was pulverized by glaciers and then blown far away.

Teacher Demo

Show students a handful of snow or finely crushed ice. Squeeze the material into a ball. Ask:

- What does squeezing do to the particles? *It presses them together.*
- How is this like what happens in a glacier? *A glacier forms as snow is compacted.*

Ongoing Assessment

CHECK YOUR READING *alpine glaciers, which form in mountain valleys, and continental glaciers, which form on large landmasses near the poles*

Extent of Glaciers

Glaciers can exist only in places where it is cold enough for water to stay frozen year-round. Glaciers are found in mountain ranges all over the world and in land regions near the north and south poles.

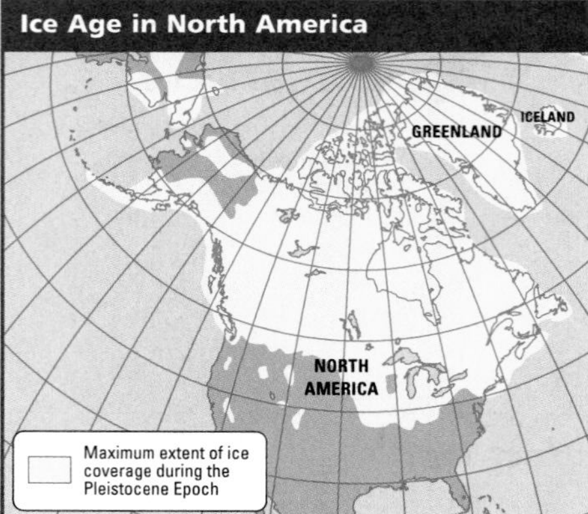

Today, glaciers cover about 10 percent of Earth's land surface. However, the amount of land surface covered by glaciers has varied greatly over Earth's history. Glaciers have expanded during long cold periods called ice ages and have disappeared during long warm periods. About 30,000 years ago—during the last major ice age—glaciers extended across the northern parts of North America, Europe, and Asia. They covered nearly 30 percent of the present land surface of Earth.

There are two major types of glaciers: alpine glaciers and continental glaciers.

RESOURCE CENTER CLASSZONE.COM

Learn more about the movement and effects of glaciers.

Alpine Glaciers

A Alpine glaciers are also called valley glaciers. They form in mountains and flow down through valleys. As these glaciers move, they cause erosion by breaking up rock and carrying away the resulting sediment. Over time, an alpine glacier can change a V-shaped mountain valley into a U-shaped valley with a wider, flatter bottom.

Some glaciers extend all the way down into the lower land at the bases of mountains. At an alpine glacier's lower end, where temperatures are warmer, melting can occur. The melting glacier drops sediment, and streams flowing from the glacier carry some of the sediment away. If an alpine glacier flows into the ocean, big blocks may break off and become icebergs.

Continental Glaciers

Continental glaciers are also called ice sheets. They are much larger than alpine glaciers. They can cover entire continents, including all but the highest mountain peaks. An ice sheet covered most of Canada and the northern United States during the last ice age. This ice sheet melted and shrank about 10,000 years ago.

B Today, ice sheets cover most of Greenland and Antarctica. Each of these glaciers is shaped like a wide dome over the land. The ice covering Antarctica is as much as 4500 meters (15,000 ft) thick.

CHECK YOUR READING What are the two major types of glaciers and where do they form?

DIFFERENTIATE INSTRUCTION

More Reading Support

A Where do alpine glaciers form? *in mountain valleys*

B What areas do continental glaciers cover today? *most of Greenland and Antarctica*

English Learners Note that English learners may be confused by words that function as both nouns and verbs. For example, in "Investigate Kettle Lake Formation" on p. 249, the word *model* can be found as a noun and a verb. The phrase "design a model of the process" uses the word as a noun. But the phrase "model how sediment builds up around ice blocks" uses the word as a verb.

Types of Glaciers and Movement

A glacier is a large mass of ice that moves over land.

Alpine Glaciers

A glacier, such as this one in Alaska, changes the landscape as it moves down a mountain valley.

Continental Glaciers

Huge sheets of ice cover the continent of Antarctica and other land regions.

Glacier Movement

Gravity causes the ice in a glacier to move downhill. Two different processes cause glaciers to move: flowing and sliding.

Flowing The ice near the surface of a glacier is brittle, and cracks often form in it. However, deep inside a glacier, ice does not break as easily because it is under great pressure from the weight of the ice above it. Instead of breaking, ice inside a glacier flows like toothpaste being squeezed in its tube.

As a glacier moves, it breaks up rock and pushes and carries sediment.

Sliding The weight of a glacier and heat from Earth cause ice at the bottom of a glacier to melt. A layer of water forms under the glacier. The glacier slides along on this layer of water just as an ice cube might slide on a countertop.

READING VISUALS In the illustration, why are cracks shown near the surface of the glacier and not at the bottom?

DIFFERENTIATE INSTRUCTION

Below Level Some students may not grasp what 10 percent and 30 percent land coverage means. Draw two circle graphs showing each of these quantities. Then transfer these concepts to maps of the world's landmasses.

Teach from Visuals

To help students interpret the diagram of glacier movement, ask:

- What causes the dark lines on the alpine glacier? *rocks picked up by the glacier along its route*
- When do cracks form in the top of the glacier? *when the glacier flows over a large bump in the rocky bed*
- Where would you find water in a glacier? *under the ice*

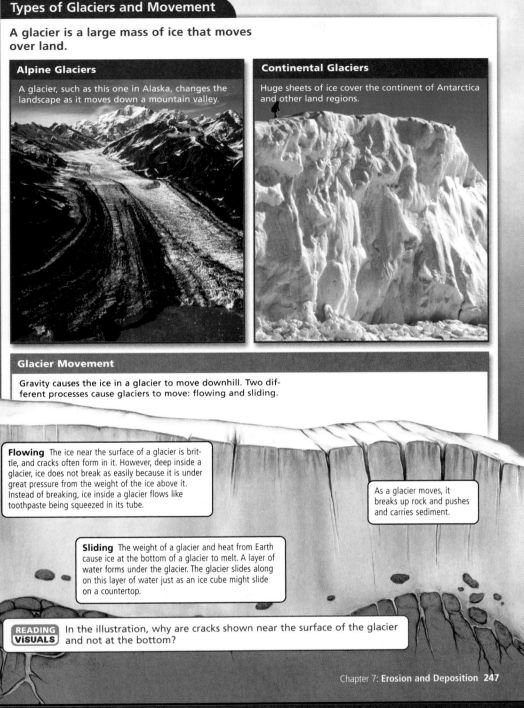 This visual is also available as T54 in the Transparency Book, Grade 6.

Integrate the Sciences

During the ice ages, large mammals such as woolly mammoths and saber-toothed cats roamed the plains and open woodlands that existed in North America just south of the glaciers. When the glaciers melted at the end of the last ice age, about 10,000 years ago, these large mammals became extinct. Some scientists think the change to a warmer climate led to extinctions, perhaps by changing the habitat and food sources. Some researchers think the mammals were hunted to extinction by humans. Others suggest that humans may have introduced deadly diseases into mammal populations. Perhaps a combination of factors is to blame.

Ongoing Assessment

Explain how moving ice erodes land.

Ask: How is an alpine glacier like a plow? *The glacier scoops up rock and soil and plucks rocks from the sides of valleys. The sediment moves with the glacier.*

READING VISUALS *Near the bottom of the glacier, the ice is under so much pressure that it flows instead of cracking. Near the surface, the ice is brittle and cracks.*

Address Misconceptions

IDENTIFY Ask students how a glacier moves as it retreats. If they describe the glacier as backing up, they may hold the misconception that glaciers move backward.

CORRECT Tell students that in order for a glacier to move backward, it would have to move against gravity. It can't do that. Remind students that a glacier retreats by melting at its leading edge, where it is warmer. A retreating glacier is melting at the bottom at a faster rate than it can accumulate ice at the top.

REASSESS Give students a mass of modeling clay and a plastic knife. The clay represents an alpine glacier. Have students demonstrate how a glacier retreats. *Students should use the knife to cut off slices of the glacier at its leading edge.*

Technology Resources

Visit **ClassZone.com** for background on common student misconceptions.

MISCONCEPTION DATABASE

Ongoing Assessment

Explore different ways that moving ice deposits sediments and changes landforms.

Ask: How would an alpine glacier change a V-shaped river valley? *The glacier would widen and deepen the valley and leave moraines.*

CHECK YOUR READING *Sketches should show lateral moraines on the sides of the glacier, end moraine at the farthest advance, and ground moraines underneath.*

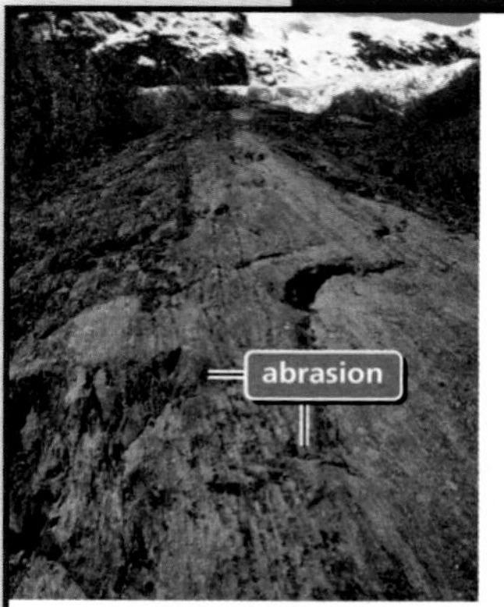

A moving glacier left abrasion lines on this rock.

Glaciers deposit large amounts of sediment.

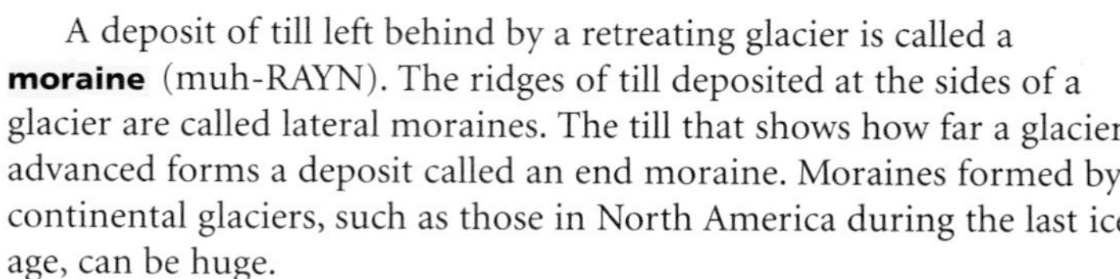

As glaciers have melted, they have shaped the landscapes of many places on Earth. As a glacier moves or expands, it transports a vast amount of sediment—a mix of boulders, small rocks, sand, and clay. It acts like a plow, pushing rock and soil and plucking out big blocks of rock. As a glacier moves over rock, it scratches and scrapes the rock in a process called abrasion. Abrasion leaves grooves on rock surfaces.

Moraines

When glaciers expand and advance and then melt and retreat, they affect both the land underneath them and the land around them. A glacier pushes huge amounts of sediment to its sides and front. When the glacier retreats, the deposits of sediment remain as visible evidence that ice once moved through. The sediment left directly on the ground surface by a retreating glacier is called **till.**

? C

? D

A deposit of till left behind by a retreating glacier is called a **moraine** (muh-RAYN). The ridges of till deposited at the sides of a glacier are called lateral moraines. The till that shows how far a glacier advanced forms a deposit called an end moraine. Moraines formed by continental glaciers, such as those in North America during the last ice age, can be huge.

The blanket of till that a glacier deposits along its bottom is called a ground moraine. Rock deposits from glaciers can often be identified as till because the till rocks are different from the rock that was present before the glacier formed.

CHECK YOUR READING Draw a sketch of a glacier and label where lateral, end, and ground moraines would form.

A glacier scooped out this valley in the Sierra Nevada and left behind lateral moraines.

DIFFERENTIATE INSTRUCTION

More Reading Support

C What is till made of? *sediment of different sizes left by a glacier*

D What do you call a buildup of till left by a glacier? *a moraine*

Below Level Help students understand the difference between the moraines discussed in the text. Make a table that lists *lateral moraine, end moraine,* and *ground moraine* and their definitions. Ask students to think of analogies to help them distinguish between the different types, such as relating *lateral* to a lateral pass in football, which is a short pass to the side.

Lakes

Besides ridges, hills, and blankets of till, melting glaciers also leave behind holes, or depressions, of various sizes that can become lakes. Landscapes shaped by glaciers are often dotted with small kettle lakes as well as larger lakes. A **kettle lake** is a bowl-shaped depression that was formed by a block of ice from a glacier and then became filled with water.

The last ice sheet in North America formed many kettle lakes in some regions. Kettle lakes are common in Michigan, Wisconsin, and Minnesota.

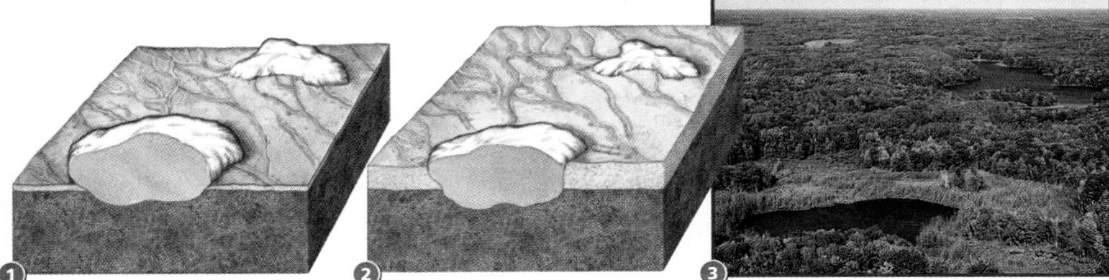

1 As a glacier moves away, it leaves huge blocks of ice.

2 Over time, sediment builds up around the ice.

3 The ice melts, leaving behind holes that become kettle lakes. These lakes are in Wisconsin.

INVESTIGATE Kettle Lake Formation

How do kettle lakes form?

DESIGN —YOUR OWN—

Kettle lakes form when sediment builds up around blocks of ice left behind by a retreating glacier. Use what you know about kettle lake formation to design a model of the process.

PROCEDURE

1. Use the tray, the ice cubes, and the other materials to model how sediment builds up around ice blocks.
2. Write a description of the process you used to make your model.

WHAT DO YOU THINK?

- Describe how your model worked. What did you do first? What happened next?
- Did your model accurately represent the formation of kettle lakes? Did it work? Why or why not?
- What were the limitations of your model? Are there any aspects of kettle lake formation that are not represented? If so, what are they?

SKILL FOCUS
Designing models (6.2.a)

MATERIALS
- shallow tray
- ice cubes
- modeling clay
- sand
- gravel
- water

TIME
30 minutes

249

DIFFERENTIATE INSTRUCTION

More Reading Support

E What is kettle lake? *a small bowl-shaped depression that was formed by a glacier and then became filled with water*

Advanced Encourage students to research what North America was like during the last ice age. Have them make a poster depicting how this area was different during that time. Challenge some students to make a three-dimensional topographical map of the area.

- Challenge and Extension, p. 181
- Challenge Reading, pp. 184–185

Teach from Visuals

To help students interpret the diagram of kettle lake formation, ask:

- What does the huge block of ice left behind a retreating glacier do to the ground? *It leaves a depression.*
- What makes the depression that the ice is in even deeper? *Sediments build up around the ice.*

History of Science

In the 1830s, Louis Agassiz, a biologist, began studying glaciers in Switzerland. He hypothesized that glaciers in the upper valleys at one time extended down the valleys, gouging them out and pushing rocks forward like a huge plow. After studying glaciated areas throughout Europe and North America, he also hypothesized the existence of an ice age.

INVESTIGATE Kettle Lake Formation

PURPOSE To design an experiment to show how kettle lakes form

TIPS *30 min.*

- Suggest to students that they use the clay to represent the land in which the ice becomes embedded.
- To speed up the experiment, use a hair dryer or lamp to melt the ice. Exercise caution using electrical devices around the melting ice.

WHAT DO YOU THINK? *Answers will vary. An experiment might be to place ice cube in pan, build up clay and materials around it, and use a lamp to melt the cube. The model's limitations might include that materials collapsed where the ice was. Groundwater and rain to fill the lake were not represented.*

Datasheet, Kettle Lake Formation, p. 182

Technology Resources

Customize this student lab as needed or look for an alternative. Print rubrics to assess student lab reports.

Lab Generator CD-ROM

Ongoing Assessment

CHECK YOUR READING *Answer: It gouged out great depressions of land and dammed them with rock. The weight of ice made the land sink.*

Reinforce the BIG idea

Have students relate the section to the Big Idea.

 Reinforcing Key Concepts, p. 183

7.4 ASSESS & RETEACH

Assess

A Section 7.4 Quiz, p. 142

Reteach

Draw a Venn diagram on the board. Label one side Alpine Glaciers and the other Continental Glaciers. List these terms: till, moraine, kettle lake, erosion, deposition, valley, ice sheet, icebergs, Greenland, abrasion, Finger Lakes, Lake Superior, and Lake Michigan. Have students place each term in the diagram in its appropriate place under Alpine Glaciers, Continental Glaciers, or in the middle overlapping portion to show the term applies to both glacier types.

Technology Resources

Have students visit **ClassZone.com** for reteaching of Key Concepts.

 **CONTENT REVIEW**

 **CONTENT REVIEW CD-ROM**

Great Lakes Formation

① 14,000 Years Ago

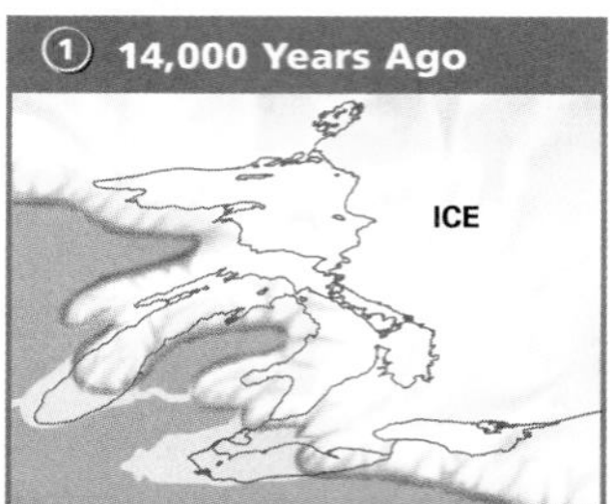

The ice sheet covering a land of river valleys began to retreat.

② 7000 Years Ago

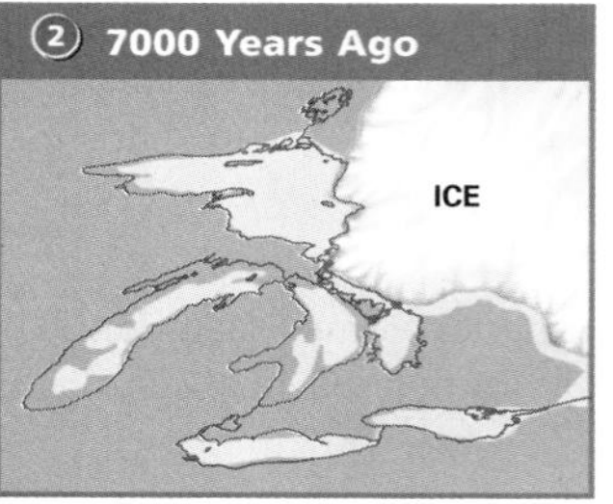

Water filled the holes carved out by the ice.

③ Today

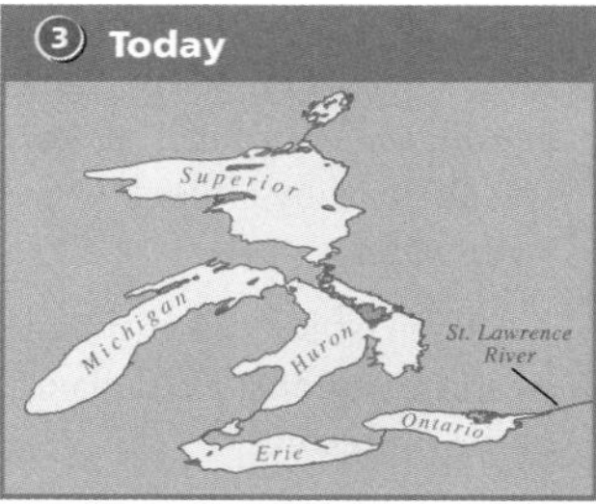

The Great Lakes contain 20 percent of the world's fresh lake water.

Many large lakes are the result of ice ages. In some places, lakes formed after glaciers in valleys melted. Moraines were left behind that blocked water from draining out. Many of these lakes are long and narrow, like the Finger Lakes in New York, which are named for their slender shape.

The Great Lakes were formed thousands of years ago as an ice sheet moved over the land and then melted. A million years ago, the region of the Great Lakes had many river valleys. The ice sheet dug out large depressions in the land and left piles of rock and debris that blocked water from draining out. In some areas, the enormous weight of the glacier actually caused the land to sink as much as one kilometer.

The ice sheet started to melt about 14,000 years ago. By about 7000 years ago, it had melted past what would become Lake Erie and Lake Ontario, the lakes farthest to the east.

 What are two ways an ice sheet formed the Great Lakes?

7.4 Review

KEY CONCEPTS

1. Describe the two processes that cause glaciers to move. (6.2.a)
2. What are the two major types of glaciers, and where are they found? (6.2.a)
3. Describe the land features left behind by glaciers that have melted and shrunk. (6.7.h)

CRITICAL THINKING

4. **Compare and Contrast** Identify two ways in which the erosion effects of glaciers differ from those of rivers.
5. **Predict** How would glaciers be affected by changes in climate, such as global warming and global cooling?

CHALLENGE

6. **Infer** Regions near the equator are generally the warmest on Earth. However, in one small area of Africa, there are glaciers close to the equator. Form a hypothesis to explain why these glaciers exist.

ANSWERS

1. Gravity and water make the bottom slippery and cause flowing and sliding.

2. Alpine glaciers: mountain valleys; continental glaciers: most of Antarctica and Greenland

3. Glaciers leave behind U-shaped valleys, moraines, abrasions, till, and kettle lakes.

4. Glaciers crush rock and move large rocks; rivers move smaller sediments. Glaciers pile up distinctive features called moraines; rivers create sandbars, meanders, and deltas.

5. Warming melts glaciers and shrinks ice sheets; cooling causes glaciers to expand and form in new places.

6. Temperatures cool at high altitudes. High mountains could be cold enough year-round for glaciers to form near the equator.

MATH TUTORIAL
CLASSZONE.COM
Click on Math Tutorial for more help with making line graphs.

Math 6.MR.2.4
Science 6.2.a

SKILL: CREATING A LINE GRAPH

Snow Line Elevation and Latitude

Glaciers form above the snow line, the lowest elevation at which there is permanent snow in the summer. The snow line elevation depends on temperature and precipitation. In the hot tropics the snow line is high in the mountains, while at the poles it is near sea level. The table shows the snow line elevations at different locations on Earth. The latitude of each location indicates how far the location is from the equator. The latitude of the equator is 0 degrees, and the latitude of the North Pole is 90 degrees.

Location	Latitude (degrees north)	Snow Line Elevation (meters)
North Pole	90	0
Juneau, Alaska	58	1050
Glacier National Park	49	2600
Sierra Nevada	37	3725
Himalayas (East Nepal)	28	5103
Ecuador	0	4788

Follow the steps below to make a line graph of the data.

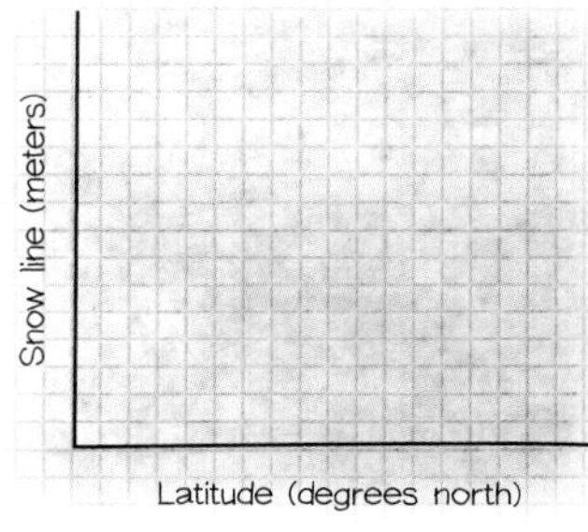

(1) On a sheet of graph paper, draw and label axes. Show latitude on the horizontal axis and snow line elevation on the vertical axis.

(2) Choose and mark a scale for each axis.

(3) Graph each point.

(4) Draw line segments to connect the points.

Use your graph to answer the following questions.

1. Mount Kenya is very close to the equator. Estimate the snow line elevation on Mount Kenya.

2. Mount Rainier is at 47 degrees north latitude and is 4389 meters tall. Can there be glaciers on Mount Rainier? If so, estimate the elevation above which the glaciers form.

3. Mount Washington in New Hampshire is at 45 degrees north latitude and is 1917 meters tall. Can there be glaciers on Mount Washington? If so, estimate their lowest elevation.

CHALLENGE **Temperatures are hotter at the equator than at 28 degrees north latitude. Why is the snow line lower at the equator in Ecuador? (Hint: The answer involves precipitation.)**

ANSWERS

. about 5000 meters

. yes; about 3000 meters

. No; the snow line is well above 1917 meters (snow line at 49 degrees is 2600 meters).

HALLENGE More precipitation in the moist tropics means more now builds up, so it might not all melt in summer, leading to a lacier.

MATH IN SCIENCE
Math Skills Practice for Science

Set Learning Goal
To create and interpret a line graph showing how snow-line elevation relates to latitude

Math Standard

6.MR.2.4 Use a variety of methods, such as words, numbers, symbols, charts, graphs, tables, diagrams, and models, to explain mathematical reasoning.

Present the Science
Glaciers need not only cold temperatures to form but sufficient precipitation. Moist, cold air tends to drop most of its snow on the windward side of coastal mountain ranges. The leeward side has a much drier climate. Therefore, in regions where wind generally blows from west to east, glaciers are likely to be more abundant on western slopes of a mountain range.

Develop Graphing Skills
Guide students to set up a scale that makes sense. For example, each scale has to include at least the lowest and highest values they are graphing. It is usually a good idea to mark a scale that goes a little beyond the highest value. Degrees of latitude, however, only go up to 90.

DIFFERENTIATION TIP Students may need to review how to plot coordinate points. Demonstrate how the grid of graph paper makes it easy to follow lines up and across to plot points.

Close
Have students look at the line that connects all the points. Ask: If you plotted the snow line elevation of 20 more mountains, how would you expect the line on the graph to change? *The general shape of the line would be the same.*

- Math Support, p. 189
- Math Practice, p. 190

Technology Resources

Students can visit **ClassZone.com** to practice creating a line graph.

 **MATH TUTORIAL**

BACK TO

the BIG idea

Have students look at the photograph at the bottom of p. 248. Ask them to describe the different kinds of erosion that have occurred in this area in the past and that are going on today. Students should cite evidence where possible. *Lateral moraines and U-shaped valley are evidence of glacier erosion. Streams continue to erode the valley floor. Mass wasting probably happens along the valley walls. Wind erodes exposed rock somewhat.*

KEY CONCEPTS SUMMARY

SECTION 7.1

Ask: What forces created the landscape shown in the photograph? *erosion caused by moving water, wind, and ice*

SECTION 7.2

Ask: How did the features on the left side of the diagram form? *Rainwater, slightly acidic, trickled through ground, dissolved limestone to form caves.*

Ask: How did the feature on the right side of the diagram form? *Flowing water of a stream eroded land and formed a steep-walled V-shaped valley.*

SECTION 7.3

Ask: Why are these stone formations separated from the cliff to the left? *Waves breaking against rock wore some away, leaving stone pillars.*

Ask: What happens to the rocks that the waves erode? *They may eventually become sand and form beaches.*

SECTION 7.4

Ask: How do glaciers change landscapes through erosion and deposition? *Glaciers widen/deepen valleys, create lakes, deposit sediment as ridges.*

Review Concepts

- Big Idea Flow Chart, p. T49
- Chapter Outline, pp. T55–T56

7 Chapter Review

the BIG idea

Water, wind, and ice shape Earth's surface.

KEY CONCEPTS SUMMARY

1 Processes wear down and build up Earth's surface.

Water, wind, and ice move sediment in the process called **erosion**. The placement of sediment in a new location is **deposition**, part of the erosion process.

VOCABULARY
erosion p. 225
deposition p. 225
mass wasting p. 227

2 Moving water shapes land.

Water drains from land in **drainage basins**, which are separated by **divides.** As water flows over land and underground, it moves sediment and changes land features.

VOCABULARY
drainage basin p. 231
divide p. 231
floodplain p. 232
alluvial fan p. 233
delta p. 233
sinkhole p. 235

3 Waves and wind shape land.

The action of water moves sand and builds up new landforms, such as **sandbars** and **barrier islands.** Wind forms **dunes.**

VOCABULARY
longshore drift p. 239
longshore current p. 239
sandbar p. 240
barrier island p. 240
dune p. 241
loess p. 242

4 Glaciers carve land and move sediments.

Glaciers are large bodies of ice that change landscapes as they move.

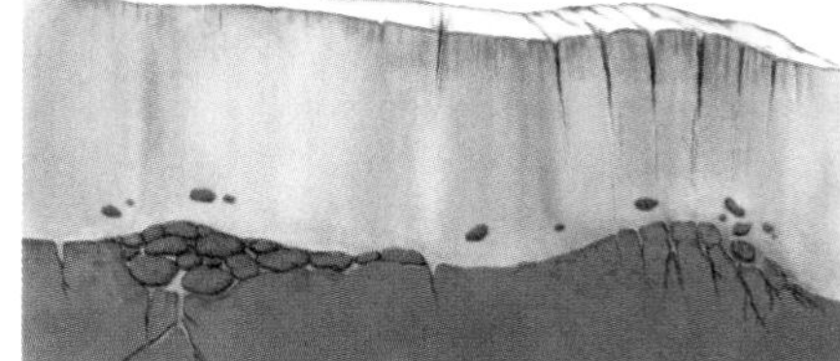

VOCABULARY
glacier p. 245
till p. 248
moraine p. 248
kettle lake p. 249

252 Unit 2: Earth's Surface

Technology Resources

Have students visit **ClassZone.com** or use the CD-ROM for a cumulative review of concepts.

CONTENT REVIEW

CONTENT REVIEW CD-ROM

Engage students in a whole-class interactive review of Key Concepts. Edit content as you wish.

POWER PRESENTATIONS

Reviewing Vocabulary

Copy and complete the chart below. Explain how each landscape feature is formed.

Feature	How It Forms
EXAMPLE delta	A river deposits sediment as it enters the ocean.
1. alluvial fan	
2. sinkhole	
3. sandbar	
4. barrier island	
5. dune	
6. loess	
7. moraine	
8. kettle lake	

Reviewing Key Concepts

Multiple Choice *Choose the letter of the best answer.*

9. The first stage in the erosion process is **(6.2.a)**
- **a.** deposition
- **b.** mass wasting
- **c.** drainage
- **d.** weathering

10. The main natural force responsible for mass movements of rocks and debris is **(6.2.d)**
- **a.** rainwater **c.** gravity
- **b.** wind **d.** fire

11. A sinkhole is formed by the collapse of **(6.2.a)**
- **a.** an alluvial fan
- **b.** a cavern
- **c.** a moraine
- **d.** a kettle lake

12. Rivers transport sediment to **(6.2.b)**
- **a.** drainage basins
- **b.** oceans and lakes
- **c.** the water table
- **d.** moraines

13. Drainage basins are separated by a **(6.2.b)**
- **a.** moraine **c.** tributary
- **b.** divide **d.** barrier island

14. In high mountains, a valley carved by a stream has the shape of a **(6.2.b)**
- **a.** U **c.** plate
- **b.** crescent **d.** V

15. An oxbow lake is formed by the cutting off of a **(6.2.b)**
- **a.** meander **c.** sinkhole
- **b.** drainage basin **d.** glacier

16. Sandbars, spits, and barrier islands can all be built up by **(6.2.c)**
- **a.** glaciers **c.** wind
- **b.** ocean waves **d.** mass wasting

17. A dune is a sand mound built up primarily by **(6.7.h)**
- **a.** gravity **c.** glaciers
- **b.** running water **d.** wind

18. Strong winds can transport large quantities of **(6.7.h)**
- **a.** gravel **c.** dry sand
- **b.** wet sand **d.** clay

19. A mountain valley carved by a glacier has the shape of a **(6.7.h)**
- **a.** U **c.** bowl
- **b.** crescent **d.** V

Short Answer *Answer each of the following questions in a sentence or two.*

20. How is deposition part of the erosion process? **(6.2.a)**

21. How can rainwater in the Rocky Mountains end up in the ocean? **(6.2.a)**

22. What is the effect of a longshore current on a beach? **(6.2.c)**

23. Why is a mass movement of mud called a flow? **(6.2.d)**

24. What visual evidence is a sign of creep? **(6.2.d)**

25. What is the connection between icebergs and glaciers? **(6.7.h)**

ASSESSMENT RESOURCES

ASSESSMENT BOOK
- Chapter Test A, pp. 143–146
- Chapter Test B, pp. 147–150
- Chapter Test C, pp. 151–154
- Alternative Assessment, pp. 155–156
- Unit Test, A, B, & C, pp. 157–168

STANDARDS REVIEW AND PRACTICE, pp. 15–22, 59–60, 71–72

Technology Resources

Edit test items and answer choices.

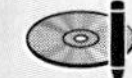

Test Generator CD-ROM

Visit **ClassZone.com** to extend test practice.

Test Practice

Reviewing Vocabulary

1. *Water flows from a steep slope onto flat ground and deposits sediment in a fan shape.*
2. *The ceiling above a cavern falls in, often because the water that supported the ceiling drops.*
3. *Sand builds up from the action of waves and currents.*
4. *Longshore current builds up a sandbar above the water's surface parallel to shore.*
5. *Strong winds pile up sand in a mound.*
6. *Wind transports and deposits fine-grained sediment.*
7. *A glacier piles up sediment along its sides and end and underneath on the ground.*
8. *Sediment builds up around a block of ice left behind by a glacier.*

Reviewing Key Concepts

9. *d*
10. *c*
11. *b*
12. *b*
13. *b*
14. *d*
15. *a*
16. *b*
17. *d*
18. *c*
19. *a*
20. *Deposition is the stage of erosion in which material is dropped at a new place.*
21. *Rain falls to the ground, flows into a stream or streams in the drainage basin, and flows from stream to stream until it reaches the ocean.*
22. *It can shift sand along the shore.*
23. *It contains water, which makes it flow downhill.*
24. *fence posts and telephone poles standing at an angle or cracks in buildings*
25. *Icebergs occur as ice breaks off glaciers at the ocean shoreline.*

Thinking Critically

26. Arrow should point toward the ocean bay at the bottom of the picture.
27. along the sides of the glaciers, the dark bands inside of them
28. on either side of the main glacier
29. because it ends in the bay
30. B is narrower, more V-shaped. A is in a U-shaped valley. B might not be glaciated.
31. U-shaped valley, abrasion marks, till, rocks different from underlying rocks, moraines, kettle or large lakes
32. Both are deposits of material moved in erosion. Till is carried by glacial ice; deltas are near rivers.
33. Advantage: river-deposited sediment for good soil. Disadvantage: river might flood and ruin crops.
34. Similar: movement of large amounts of material, powered by gravity. Mudflows mix water, sediment. Mass wasting of rock can be dry rocks sliding downhill.
35. In eastern part; wind slows down, drops sediment, forms loess.
36. Is the ground loose or wet? Is slope steep, causing creep?
37. Erosion: sediment carried to site of ice block. Deposition: sediment is deposited around the ice.

the BIG idea

38. The snow falls onto either side of the divide. Meltwater, including glacier water, flows downhill, moves sediment (erosion). Water flows into streams, which lead to ocean. Streams deposit material.
39. Sample answer: (1) A stream moves sediment down a hill and spreads it. Gravity pulls the water down. (2) Wind carries sediment. When the wind loses strength, gravity pulls sediment to the ground. (3) Gravity pulls alpine glaciers down valley.

UNIT PROJECTS

Use the appropriate rubrics from the URB to evaluate their presentations.

R Unit Projects, pp. 5–10

Thinking Critically

This photograph shows two glaciers joining to form one (A). Make a sketch of the glaciers to answer the next three questions.

26. APPLY Place an arrow to show in which direction the main glacier (A) is moving. (6.7.h)

27. ANALYZE Mark the places where you think till would be found. (6.7.h)

28. APPLY Mark the location of a lateral moraine. (6.7.h)

29. ANALYZE Why does the main glacier not have an end moraine? (6.7.h)

30. COMPARE AND CONTRAST Compare the main glacier valley in the photograph with the valley at the far right (B). How are the valleys different? Explain why they might be different. (6.7.h)

31. APPLY In exploring an area of land, what clues would you look for to determine whether glaciers were once there? (6.7.h)

32. COMPARE AND CONTRAST How is a deposit of till from a glacier similar to a river delta? How is it different? (6.2.b)

33. EVALUATE If you were growing crops on a field near a slow-moving, curvy river, what would an advantage of the field's location be? What might be a disadvantage? (6.2.b)

34. COMPARE AND CONTRAST How are mudflows and mass wasting of rock similar? How are they different? Include references to speed and types of material in your answer. (6.2.d)

35. INFER If the wind usually blows from west to east over a large area of land, and the wind usually slows down over the eastern half of the area, where would you be likely to find loess in the area? Explain your answer. (6.7.h)

36. APPLY If you were considering a location for a house and were concerned about creep, what two factors about the land would you consider? (6.2.d)

37. SYNTHESIZE Describe how the processes of erosion and deposition are involved in the formation of kettle lakes. (6.2.b)

the BIG idea

38. SYNTHESIZE Describe how snow falling onto the Continental Divide in the Rocky Mountains can be part of the process of erosion and deposition. Include the words *divide, glacier, stream,* and *ocean* in your answer. (6.2.a)

39. PROVIDE EXAMPLES Choose three examples of erosion processes—one each from Sections 7.2, 7.3, and 7.4. Explain how gravity is involved in each of these processes. (6.2.d)

UNIT PROJECTS

Evaluate all the data, results, and information in your project folder. Prepare to present your project. Be ready to answer questions posed by your classmates about your results.

MONITOR AND RETEACH

If students are having trouble applying the concepts in items 26–30, refer them to the photograph of an alpine glacier on p. 247 and review the discussion about moraines on p. 248. Have them compare the lateral moraines in the photograph on p. 248 with those on the glacier on p. 247.

Students may benefit from summarizing one or more sections of the chapter.

 Summarizing the Chapter, pp. 209–210

254 Unit 2: **Earth's Surface**

Standards-Based Assessment

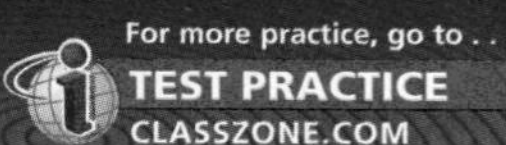

Analyzing a Diagram

Use the diagram to answer the questions below.

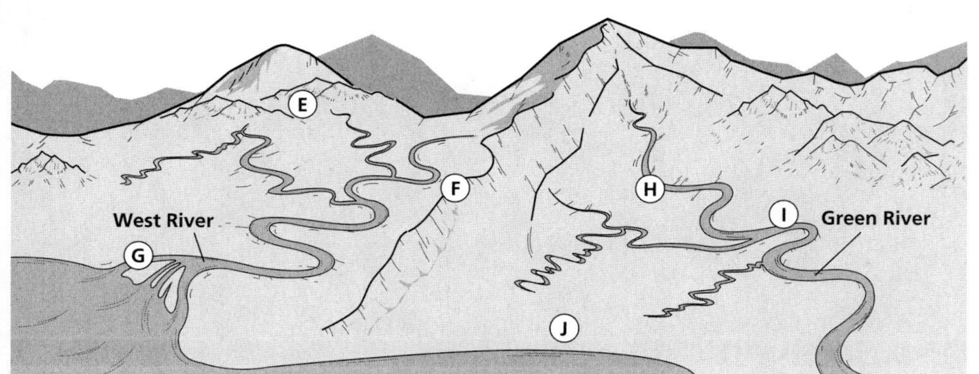

1. Where would a glacier be most likely to form?
- **a.** E
- **b.** F
- **c.** G
- **d.** H

2. Where is a divide?
- **a.** E
- **b.** F
- **c.** H
- **d.** I

3. Where is a delta?
- **a.** E
- **b.** F
- **c.** G
- **d.** J

4. Which process could move sediment from point E to point G?
- **a.** weathering
- **b.** erosion
- **c.** deposition
- **d.** drifting

5. Which word best describes the building up of sediment at point G?
- **a.** weathering
- **b.** erosion
- **c.** deposition
- **d.** drifting

6. Why might the water in the Green River move faster at point H than at point I?
- **a.** The river at point H is warmer.
- **b.** The river at point H is smaller.
- **c.** The slope at point H is steeper.
- **d.** More rain falls at point H.

Extended Response

Answer the two questions below in detail. Include some of the terms shown in the word box. In your answers, underline each term you use.

ocean waves	currents	barrier island
grass	glaciers	kettle lakes

7. Each year, Clark and his family visit the ocean. Clark notices that a sandbar near the coast is slightly larger each year. Predict what will happen if this trend continues.

8. Annika often goes fishing at one of several small, round lakes that are within 20 miles of her house in Minnesota. How might these lakes have formed?

REFLECTING ON THE CHAPTER

Have students answer the following questions in their **Science Notebook:**

1. How did the activities in this chapter help you learn about erosion and deposition?
2. What information about erosion and deposition could help you the most in the future?
3. How are the concepts of erosion and deposition part of your Unit Project?

California Content Standards

6.2.a Students know water running downhill is the dominant process in shaping the landscape, including California's landscape.

6.2.b Students know rivers and streams are dynamic systems that erode, transport sediment, change course, and flood their banks in natural and recurring patterns.

6.2.c Students know beaches are dynamic systems in which the sand is supplied by rivers and moved along the coast by the action of waves.

6.2.d Students know earthquakes, volcanic eruptions, landslides, and floods change human and wildlife habitats.

Analyzing a Diagram

1. a *3. c* *5. c*

2. b *4. b* *6. c*

Extended Response

7. RUBRIC

4 points for a response that correctly describes the development of a barrier island and uses the terms accurately.

***Sample answer:** Currents will move sand along the shore and deposit it on the sandbar. Eventually, the sandbar might be built up above the water surface and become a barrier island. Ocean waves might deposit more sediment, and the island will grow. As the island builds up, grass and other plants will grow.*

3 points describes the development adequately and uses two terms accurately

2 points describes the development partially and uses one term accurately

1 point describes the development partially but uses no terms

8. RUBRIC

4 points for a response that correctly identifies three processes and uses the terms.

***Sample answer:** During the last ice age, huge glaciers advanced over parts of North America. As these ice sheets melted, huge blocks of ice were left. Sediment was deposited around the blocks. When the blocks melted, they left bowl-shaped depressions that became kettle lakes.*

3 points describes two processes correctly and uses both terms accurately

2 points describes one process correctly and uses both terms accurately

1 point describes one process partially and uses one term accurately

The Changing Earth

LAVA

hot spot

geosphere

Contents Overview

Unit 3 Scientific Background

Below is an in-depth look at some subtopics of the concepts presented in this unit.

PLATE TECTONICS: West Coast Terranes

The continents consist of blocks of lithospheric rock that vary in age, size, and composition. Older rocks make up the interiors of most continents, while younger rocks form the continental margins. The older, more stable continental interiors are called *cratons*.

Some of the continental margins consist of fragments of oceanic crust, volcanic island arcs, or mountain ranges that collided with and became attached to cratons as a result of the movement of the lithospheric plates. Such crustal fragments with geologic characteristics distinct from those of adjoining blocks of rock are called *terranes*. Terranes are actually broken-off pieces of lithosphere plates, and they may be oceanic or continental in origin.

The process by which terranes become attached to continents or to other terranes is called *accretion*. This process has contributed to the buildup of many mountainous regions around the Pacific Ocean.

Some continental margins have a chaotic arrangement of terranes. For example, the type of rocks and fossils in one terrane may be entirely different from those in adjacent terranes, even though the rocks and fossils are from the same geologic period. Such terranes are called *exotic*.

The West Coast of North America has a patchwork of exotic terranes that traveled long distances after the breakup of Pangaea, which began about 200 million years ago. Many of the terranes found along the coast were formerly spread throughout the eastern Pacific Ocean. Since the breakup of Pangaea, North America has been moving westward, adding terranes to its western coast. These crustal fragments are found from the Baja Peninsula to northern Alaska and consist of oceanic lithosphere, volcanic island arcs, and displaced pieces of continents. The exotic terranes make the West Coast a complex geologic region.

EARTHQUAKES: Seismic Waves

The study of seismic waves not only provides information about the size of earthquakes, it also gives scientists a way to learn about Earth's interior. Most of what scientists know about the interior structure of Earth has come from the study of seismic waves, specifically the behavior of P and S waves traveling through Earth's interior.

Studying Earth's Interior If Earth were uniform in composition, seismic waves would travel through it at a constant speed and direction. But instead, the speed of the waves increases with depth, and some waves are refracted, or bent, while others are reflected. Abrupt changes in velocity, called *discontinuities,* occur at certain depths. These facts indicate that Earth has layers that differ in composition and physical state.

Although the velocity of seismic waves generally increases with depth, distinct discontinuities and changes in the rate of increase provide clues to the composition and physical state of the different layers. An abrupt increase in velocity marks the boundary separating the crust from the mantle. This boundary is called the *Moho*. The bending of P waves marks the boundary between the mantle and the core, which is called the *shadow zone*. The fact that S waves cannot travel through the core indicates that at least part of the core is liquid. A deeper region where P waves are reflected marks the boundary between the outer and inner core. This boundary is called the Lehmann discontinuity.

Information from seismic waves also allows scientists to calculate the size of Earth's different layers. However, the study of seismic waves alone does not reveal the composition of the inner layers. Scientists must combine information from the study of seismic waves with data from such sources as laboratory experiments and models and the study of meteorites to speculate on the composition of Earth's inner layers.

Earthquake Magnitude Scales Of course, the primary reason for studying seismic waves is to measure the size of earthquakes. The first scales used to measure the size of earthquakes were based on *intensity,* a measure of the amount of ground shaking, which was estimated from the damage done. Since the effects of an earthquake depend not only on the amount of ground shaking but also on the design of buildings, the composition of the soil, and other factors, intensity scales were not reliable for comparing earthquakes. Magnitude scales, which use seismic records to calculate the amount of energy released at the source of an earthquake, were developed to overcome this problem.

The Richter scale was the first magnitude scale based on seismic records. The Richter scale was originally designed for measuring shallow-focus earthquakes in southern California. Although its purpose was broadened, it was not a good tool for distinguishing the sizes of large earthquakes.

The moment magnitude scale overcomes this limitation of the Richter scale. Its measurement of earthquake magnitude is based on the amount of displacement along a fault. It can be calculated from seismographs by examining long-period seismic waves and verified in the field by measuring the fault displacement. The moment magnitude scale is widely used by seismologists because it distinguishes between large earthquakes much better than the Richter scale does, and it gives a more accurate measure of the amount of energy released by an earthquake.

MOUNTAINS AND VOLCANOES: Magma Formation

Since the rock in Earth's crust and mantle is solid, not liquid, a logical question arises: Where does magma come from? Magma forms when solid rock in the crust or mantle melts. Most magma forms in the upper mantle, where plate motions produce changes in temperature, pressure, or water content that cause rock to melt.

How Magma Forms Even though the temperature increases with depth inside Earth, additional heat is needed to melt rock in Earth's outer layers. This additional heat is produced at subduction zones, where the friction of two plates moving against each other creates enough heat to melt rock. Crustal rocks also heat up and melt when they sink into the mantle at subduction zones. In addition, crustal rocks may melt and form magma when hot mantle rocks rise and intrude into them. However, most magma forms not because of additional heat, but because of changes in pressure or water content.

The greater the pressure on rock, the higher its melting temperature. So a decrease in pressure can lower a rock's melting temperature. When mantle rock rises as a result of convection, it moves into an area of lower pressure and undergoes what is called *decompression melting*. This process occurs at spreading centers, where plates move apart in the ocean.

Water content also affects the melting temperature of rock. Rock with high water content has a much lower melting temperature than rock with low water content does. At subduction zones, an oceanic plate sinks under another plate. Water from the descending crustal rock moves into the hot mantle rock, lowering its melting temperature enough to produce magma. If this magma rises and pools under crustal rocks, it can cause these rocks to melt also.

Magma Composition The minerals that make up rock vary in their melting points. So when a rock melts, its component minerals melt at different temperatures. Often, not all the minerals that make up a rock melt. Most magmas result from partial melting, which affects the composition of the magma. In general, partial melting produces magma with a higher silica content than the original rock because silicates have low melting points.

The partial melting of mantle rock produces basaltic magma. However, as magma rises through continental crust, it may incorporate crustal rocks that are rich in silica and so change to andesitic or rhyolitic magma.

FRONTIERS in Science

VIDEO SUMMARY

SCIENTIFIC AMERICAN FRONTIERS

"Paradise Postponed" is a segment of the *Scientific American Frontiers* series that aired on PBS stations. The "paradise" of the title is the Caribbean island of Montserrat. Like the Hawaiian Islands, Montserrat was formed by volcanic activity millions of years ago. Montserrat's volcano had not erupted for 400 years. Then a series of massive eruptions beginning in 1995 produced hot steam and ash that melted buildings and destroyed towns. Two-thirds of the residents have moved away from the island for safety reasons. Around 3000 people live in the northern third of the island, as far away from the volcano as possible. They are not allowed into the evacuated area around the volcano, known as the "exclusion zone." Scientists from the Montserrat Volcano Observatory risk their lives to collect data and predict the likelihood of future eruptions.

California Content Standards

6.1.d Students know that earthquakes are sudden motions along breaks in the crust called faults and that volcanoes and fissures are locations where magma reaches the surface.

6.2.d Students know earthquakes, volcanic eruptions, landslides, and floods change human and wildlife habitats.

FRONTIERS in Science

Studying VOLCANOES with Satellites

New ways of viewing Earth are giving scientists powerful tools for learning about and predicting volcanic eruptions.

California Content Standards

6.1.d Students know that earthquakes are sudden motions along breaks in the crust called faults and that **volcanoes and fissures are locations where magma reaches the surface.**

6.2.d Students know earthquakes, **volcanic eruptions,** landslides, and floods change human and wildlife habitats.

SCIENTIFIC AMERICAN FRONTIERS

View the video segment "Paradise Postponed" to learn how scientists study volcanoes and predict eruptions.

During a 1997 eruption of the Soufrière Hills volcano on Montserrat, volcanic material flowed all the way to the ocean.

258 Unit 3: **The Changing Earth**

ADDITIONAL RESOURCES

Technology Resources

Scientific American Frontiers Video: *Paradise Postponed:* 20-minute video segment that introduces the unit.

ClassZone.com
CAREER LINK, Volcanologist

Guide student viewing and comprehension of the video:

Video Teaching Guide, pp. 1–2; Video Viewing Guide, p. 3; Video Wrap-Up, p. 4

Scientific American Frontiers Video Guide, pp. 25–28

Unit projects procedures and rubrics:

Unit Projects, pp. 5–10

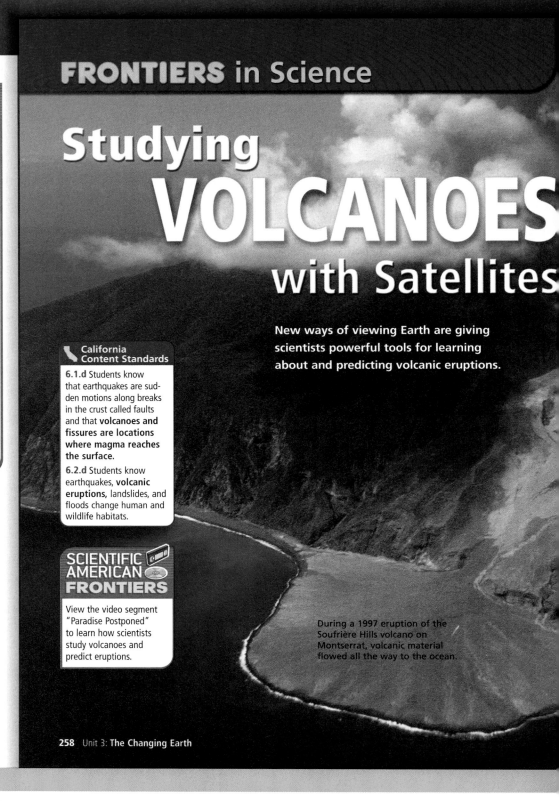

This photograph was taken from a satellite on October 29, 2002. It shows a plume of volcanic ash and gases rising from Soufrière Hills volcano in Montserrat.

Deadly Eruptions

On the island of Montserrat in the Caribbean Sea, small eruptions of the Soufrière Hills volcano began in 1995. These early warnings gave people time to move away several months before the first of the large explosions. A

People living in the towns near Nevado del Ruiz volcano in Colombia were not so lucky. On a night in November 1985, a storm hid the snow-covered volcano. No one could see the start of an eruption. Huge amounts of snow and ice melted and mixed with volcanic ash to form mudflows that killed 25,000 people. The flow that buried much of the town of Armero traveled 74 kilometers in just two and one-half hours.

Throughout history volcanic eruptions have caused some of the world's worst disasters. Warnings might have saved hundreds of thousands of lives. But in most cases people had no idea that falling rocks, toxic gases, or other deadly effects of an erupting volcano would soon surround their area. By the time people realized that a volcano was erupting, it was too late to get away. Today, scientists monitor volcanoes around the world to help avoid such tragedies. B

FOCUS

Set Learning Goals

Students will

- Determine how satellite data are used to predict and monitor volcanic eruptions.
- Discuss effects of volcanic eruptions.
- Complete a unit project relating to evaluating information about volcanic eruptions, mapmaking, or fossil preservation.

Tell students that scientific frontiers often involve areas of study that directly benefit society. Point out that the eruption of the Nevado del Ruiz volcano killed as many as 25,000 people. After students have viewed the video "Paradise Postponed," discuss why there is a need to predict volcanic eruptions.

INSTRUCT

Scientific Process

Ask: Why do scientists want to predict volcanic eruptions? *to save lives*

Technology Design

Have students compare the eruptions of Soufrière Hills and the Nevado del Ruiz volcano. Ask:

- What factor made the Nevado del Ruiz eruption so deadly? *The start of the eruption was not visible.*
- How do scientists hope to avert great loss of human life from volcanoes? *They monitor activity that may warn of a large eruption.*

Teach from Visuals

Have students study the photograph and related captions on pp. 258–259. Ask: Is Soufrière Hills Volcano still active? How do you know? *The volcano is probably still active. It has had several large, recent eruptions.*

DIFFERENTIATE INSTRUCTION

More Reading Support

A Why did people move away from the Soufrière Hills volcano? *They realized its danger.*

B Why do scientists monitor volcanoes? *to save human lives*

Advanced Have students locate Montserrat and Nevado del Ruiz on a world map. Give them a second map showing Earth's plate boundaries. Ask students to describe any relationships they see. *Montserrat and Nevado del Ruiz are on or near plate boundaries.*

Integrate the Sciences

Major volcanic eruptions release clouds of dust that can block sunlight for years, affecting global climate. Volcanic gases can react with atmospheric moisture to produce acid rain. Scientists hypothesize that these combined effects may have caused major extinctions in the past. In fact, some scientists hypothesize that the largest extinction on Earth, which occurred about 250 million years ago, was related to a series of huge volcanic eruptions.

Scientific Process

Volcanologists use observation and analysis to find signals to predict volcanic eruptions. Ask:

- Why did scientists predict that the Pavlof Volcano would soon erupt? *A weather satellite detected an area of increased heat on the volcano.*
- What system is now in place to alert scientists in this situation? *Computers check satellite data and send e-mails when they detect any unusually hot areas.*

Sharing Results

Ask students to give an example of how scientists in different fields share information. *Sample answer: Meteorologists use satellites to measure cloud temperatures. When a satellite detected increased heat on Pavlof Volcano, meteorologists shared the information with volcanologists.*

C A 1996 eruption of Alaska's Pavlof volcano was the first to be predicted by using data from space. The satellite image recorded during the eruption shows a hot area on the volcano in red.

Predicting Volcanic Eruptions

Scientists who study volcanoes paid close attention when an instrument on a weather satellite unexpectedly "saw" hot ground in 1996. The instrument's usual function is to measure cloud temperatures. But in this case it detected an area of increased heat on Alaska's Pavlof volcano. The scientists predicted that the volcano would soon erupt. Three days later, it did. This eruption was the first to be predicted by using information from space. Now computers check satellite data as they receive the data. Any unusually hot areas trigger an automatic e-mail alert to scientists.

In 1999 NASA launched the *Terra* satellite as part of a program to study Earth's surface and atmosphere. Among *Terra*'s instruments is one that detects heat given off by Earth's surface. When scientists observe an unusual increase in surface temperature, they find out whether magma, or melted rock, is rising underground. In some cases unusual heat has been the first sign that a volcano may soon erupt.

After an Eruption

Satellites are also used to monitor eruptions as they happen. Lava flows show up clearly, as you can see in the *Terra* image on page 261. In addition, satellites are used to track the locations of volcanic ash and gas clouds. Airplanes flying into this material can be severely damaged, so pilots need to know where it is. Volcanic material in

View the "Paradise Postponed" segment of your *Scientific American Frontiers* video to learn how scientists monitor volcanic eruptions.

IN THIS SCENE FROM THE VIDEO **Scientist Barry Voigt looks at the effects of a powerful eruption that happened a few days earlier.**

STUDYING VOLCANOES Until 1995 the Caribbean island of Montserrat was a peaceful vacation spot. Then the island's volcano began to erupt. Over the next two years, the volcano erupted dozens of times. Hot ash, rocks, and gases came pouring out. These eruptions destroyed most of the island's towns and drove away many of the people who lived there.

Scientists from around the world have gone to Montserrat to find out how well they can predict eruptions. Seismic stations buried near the volcano detect earthquakes. An earthquake can be a sign that the volcano is about to erupt. Scientists can also predict an eruption by studying changes in the lava that has built up on top of the volcano. When an eruption does occur, scientists visit the site to collect rocks and measure the volcanic ash flow.

DIFFERENTIATE INSTRUCTION

More Reading Support

C Which eruption was the first to be predicted from information from space? *Pavlof volcano in 1996*

English Learners Have students identify scientific process words found in the text, such as *detect, predict, determine, observe,* and *monitor.* Review the meanings of these terms. Have students use each word in a different context.

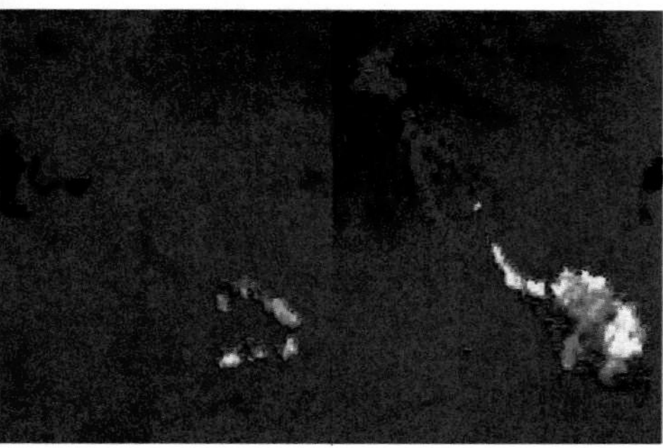

Data collected by the *Terra* satellite show how a Hawaiian lava flow moved. It entered the ocean on May 13, 2000 (left). It is shown again on August 1, 2000 (right).

the air can be hard to see or to tell from normal clouds, especially at night. Satellites are very helpful in identifying and tracking eruptions in areas where there are few or no people.

Explosive Neighbors

Scientists use satellites such as *Terra* to monitor restless volcanoes near cities. Mount Rainier, a volcano in Washington, is located near the cities of Seattle and Tacoma. In the past, heat from eruptions has melted large amounts of the ice and snow at the top of the volcano. This created mudflows that destroyed everything in their paths. Another extremely dangerous volcano is Mount Vesuvius in Italy. Warnings before eruptions of such volcanoes can allow the millions of people who live near them to get to a safe place.

UNANSWERED Questions

Even when scientists predict that a volcano will erupt soon, many questions still cannot be answered.

- How powerful will the next eruption be?
- On what day (or even during what week) will the volcano erupt?
- How much magma is rising under the volcano? How fast is it rising? Will it stop?

UNIT PROJECTS

As you study this unit, work alone or with a group on one of the projects listed below.

Review Movie Science (6.7.d, 6.7.e)

Review a movie that includes a volcanic eruption. Evaluate how accurate the movie's depiction of a volcano is.

- Visit the U.S. Geological Survey Web site for a list of movies about volcanoes, such as *Dante's Peak*.
- Evaluate one movie and prepare a radio or TV report.

Earthquake Report (6.7.b, 6.7.d)

Make a map of the volcanic eruptions and earthquakes that occur around the world while you are studying this unit.

- Write a news script and create a chart to show the events' locations and intensities.
- Present your findings as a special TV report for an evening news program.

Ash-Fall Fossil Exhibit (6.7.b, 6.7.f)

Prepare an exhibit showing how volcanic ash can preserve fossils of the organisms it buries. You could begin by researching Ashfall Fossil Beds State Historical Park in Nebraska.

- Create a poster that shows the major steps in the formation of fossils of organisms in volcanic ash.
- Make models or tracings of some ash-fall fossils.
- Display the poster and models as a classroom or Web-site exhibit.

Learn more about careers in volcanology.

UNANSWERED Questions

Have students read the questions and think of some of their own. Remind them that scientists always end up with more questions—that inquiry is the driving force of science.

- With the class, generate on the board a list of new questions.
- Students can add to the list after they watch the *Scientific American Frontiers* Video.
- Students can use the list as a springboard for choosing their Unit Projects.

UNIT PROJECTS

Encourage students to pick the project that most appeals to them. Point out that each will take several weeks to complete. You might group or pair students to work on projects. Each project has two worksheet pages, including a rubric. Use the pages to guide students through criteria, process, and schedule.

 Unit Projects, pp. 5–10

REVISIT concepts introduced in this article:

Chapter 8
- Movement of tectonic plates, pp. 274–284

Chapter 10
- Volcano formation, pp. 346–355
- Effects of volcanoes, pp. 356–362

DIFFERENTIATE INSTRUCTION

More Reading Support

D Where could satellite monitoring of volcanoes save the most lives? *near cities*

Differentiate Unit Projects Projects are appropriate for varying abilities. Allow students to choose the ones that interest them most and let them vary their product. Encourage below level students to give visual or oral presentations or to record audio presentations about their topic.

Below Level Encourage students to try "Review Movie Science."

Advanced Challenge students to complete "Earthquake Report."

CHAPTER

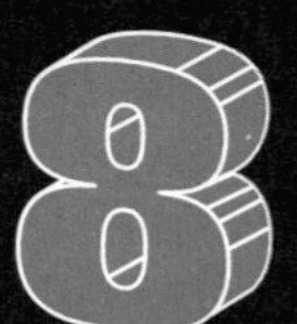

Plate Tectonics

Earth Science UNIFYING PRINCIPLES

PRINCIPLE 1
Heat energy inside Earth and radiation from the Sun provide energy for Earth's processes.

PRINCIPLE 2
Physical forces, such as gravity, affect the movement of all matter on Earth and throughout the universe.

PRINCIPLE 3
Matter and energy move among Earth's rocks and soil, atmosphere, waters, and living things.

PRINCIPLE 4
Earth has changed over time and continues to change.

Unit: The Changing Earth BIG IDEAS

CHAPTER 8
Plate Tectonics
The movement of tectonic plates causes geologic changes on Earth.

CHAPTER 9
Earthquakes
Earthquakes release stress that has built up in rocks.

CHAPTER 10
Mountains and Volcanoes
Mountains and volcanoes form as tectonic plates move.

CHAPTER 8 KEY CONCEPTS

SECTION 1

Earth has several layers.

1. Earth is made up of materials with different densities.
2. Earth's layers have different properties.
3. The lithosphere is made up of many plates.

SECTION 2

Continents change position over time.

1. Continents join together and split apart.
2. The theory of plate tectonics explains how plates and their continents move.

SECTION 3

Plates move apart.

1. Tectonic plates have different boundaries.
2. The sea floor spreads apart at divergent boundaries.
3. Continents split apart at divergent boundaries.
4. Hot spots can be used to track plate movements.

SECTION 4

Plates converge or scrape past each other.

Tectonic plates:

1. push together at convergent boundaries.
2. scrape past each other at transform boundaries.
3. The theory of plate tectonics helps geologists today.

The Big Idea Flow Chart is available on p. T57 in the **TRANSPARENCY BOOK.**

Previewing Content

SECTION

Earth has several layers. pp. 265–269

1. Earth is made up of materials with different densities.
Scientists theorize that Earth began as a spinning mass of rocks and dust about 5 billion years ago. Explosions from comets and asteroids crashing into its surface, along with the pressure of Earth's gravity, produced enough heat to melt materials inside Earth. Over time, dense material sank to the center of Earth and less dense material moved toward the surface, forming Earth's layers.

2. Earth's layers have different properties.
The table below shows how Earth's layers differ in composition, temperature, and thickness. Earth's crust and the top of the mantle form the **lithosphere,** which sits on a layer of hotter, softer rock in the upper mantle called the **asthenosphere.**

Earth's Layers

Layer of Earth	Composition	Temp/Thickness
inner core	solid metals	7000°–8000° C 2400 km diameter
outer core	liquid metals	4400°–6100° C 2300 km thick
mantle	heated rock	870°–4400° C 2900 km thick
crust	cooler rock	0°–700° C 6–70 km thick

3. The lithosphere is made up of many plates.
The lithosphere is split into large and small slabs of rocks called **tectonic plates,** which fit together like a jigsaw puzzle. Most of the large tectonic plates contain both continental and oceanic crust. The discovery of Earth's layers and tectonic plates helped scientists answer the mystery of how the continents moved to their present positions.

SECTION

Continents change position over time. pp. 270–277

1. Continents join together and split apart.
A German scientist named Alfred Wegener proposed the hypothesis of **continental drift** in the early 1900s, stating that Earth's continents were once joined in a single landmass and gradually moved apart. Fossils, studies of ancient climates, and rock formations provided evidence for continental drift. For example, rock formations in Brazil matched rock formations in western Africa, showing that the two continents had once been joined and moved apart.

2. The theory of plate tectonics explains how plates and their continents move.
Scientists combined Wegener's continental drift hypothesis with information they gained from mapping the sea floor to develop the **theory of plate tectonics.** Along spreading centers in the sea floor, melted rock rises through cracks, cools, and forms new crust that builds up **mid-ocean ridges.** Old crust gets pushed aside, and the sea floor slowly spreads apart. Earth doesn't get larger, however, because oceanic crust is destroyed along deep-ocean trenches, where the oceanic plates sink into the asthenosphere. The diagram shows how the motions of convection currents, ridge push, and slab pull move Earth's huge tectonic plates.

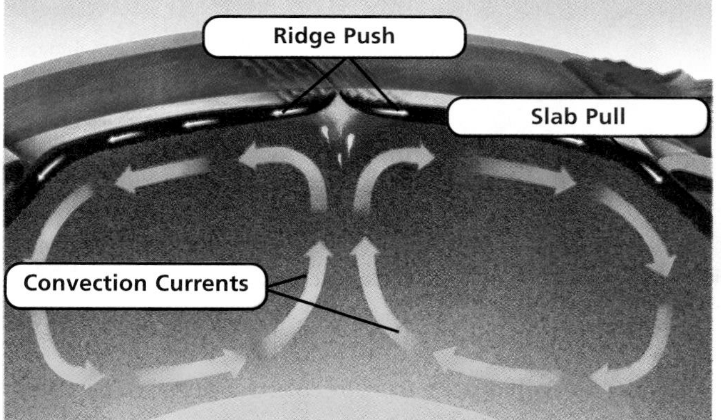

Common Misconceptions

MISCONCEPTION DATABASE
CLASSZONE.COM Background on student misconceptions

CHANGES IN SCIENCE Students may think that scientific changes mainly involve facts and occur mostly through the invention of new technology for observation and measurement. In reality, entire theories sometimes change because of new observations or reinterpretations of previous evidence.

 This misconception is addressed on p. 272.

Previewing Content

SECTION

Plates move apart. pp. 278–285

1. Tectonic plates have different boundaries.
A plate boundary is where the edges of two plates meet. A **divergent boundary** occurs where plates move apart. Most divergent boundaries are found in the ocean. A **convergent boundary** occurs where plates push together. A **transform boundary** occurs where two plates scrape past each other.

2. The sea floor spreads apart at divergent boundaries.
Mid-ocean ridges and **rift valleys** occur at divergent boundaries in the ocean. Mid-ocean ridges form the longest mountain chains on Earth. Most contain a rift valley along their center. From studying sea-floor rock, scientists discovered that Earth's magnetic north and south poles have switched places a number of times over the planet's long history. These switches are called **magnetic reversals** and are caused by changes in Earth's magnetic field. As the diagram below shows, bands of rock on either side of a mid-ocean ridge record periods of magnetic reversals. As molten material at a divergent boundary cools, some magnetic minerals line up with the Earth's magnetic field. When the material hardens, these minerals are permanently fixed like tiny compass needles pointing north and south.

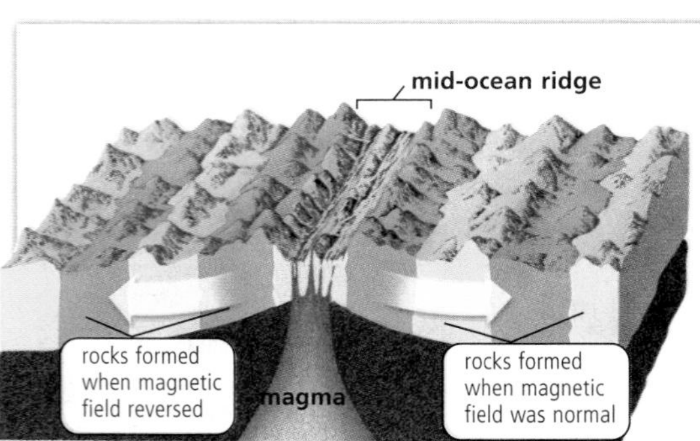

3. Continents split apart at divergent boundaries.
Divergent boundaries on continents also produce rift valleys. Magma rising through cracked, thinned crust forms volcanoes. As rift valleys grow wider, the continent begins to split apart. If a rift valley continues to widen, the thinned valley floor sinks below sea level and water from a nearby ocean or river may fill the valley and form a sea or lake.

4. Hot spots can be used to track plate movements.
A **hot spot** is an area of volcanic activity that develops above where magma rises in a plume from the mantle. A hot spot can be used to measure plate movement because it generally stays in one place while the tectonic plate above it keeps moving. Hot spots can provide a fixed point for measuring the speed and direction of plate movements.

SECTION

Plates converge or scrape past each other. pp. 286–293

1. Tectonic plates push together at convergent boundaries.
There are three types of convergent boundaries.

- **Continental-continental collisions** occur where two continental plates collide, crumpling and folding the rock between them. If the rocks push high enough, they form mountains.
- **Oceanic-oceanic subductions** occur where two oceanic plates collide and the older, denser plate sinks beneath the top plate, forming deep-ocean trenches and island arcs.
- **Oceanic-continental subductions** occur where an oceanic plate sinks beneath a continental plate, forming a deep-ocean trench and volcanic coastal mountains.

2. Tectonic plates scrape past each other at transform boundaries.
At a transform boundary, two plates move past each other in opposite directions, and their edges scrape and grind against each other. No crust is formed or destroyed at a transform boundary. This type of boundary occurs on the sea floor and on land. The following chart compares the different types of plate boundaries.

Plate Boundaries

Divergent
- plates move apart
- occurs in ocean and on land
- produces mid-ocean ridges, rift valleys, volcanoes, earthquakes

Transform
- plates move past each other in opposite directions
- occurs in ocean and on land

Convergent

Continental-Continental Collision
- crumples and folds crust
- produces mountains, earthquakes

Subduction
- **Oceanic-oceanic**—older, denser plate sinks; produces deep-ocean trench, island arcs
- **Oceanic-continental**—oceanic plate sinks under continental plate, forms deep-ocean trench, volcanic coastal mountains

3. The theory of plate tectonics helps geologists today.
The plate tectonics theory enables geologists to understand how Earth's continents and ocean basins formed. It also helps them to predict earthquakes and volcanic activity.

Previewing Labs

Lab Generator CD-ROM
Edit these Pupil Edition labs and generate alternative labs.

EXPLORE the BIG idea

Convection in Action, p. 263 Students observe convection currents.	**TIME** 10 minutes **MATERIALS** medium-size pot, water, sponge, hot plate
Internet Activity: Interior of Earth, p. 263 Students are introduced to the latest ideas about how Earth formed and the properties of Earth's layers.	**TIME** 20 minutes **MATERIALS** computer with Internet access

SECTION 

EXPLORE Density, p. 265 Students pour salt water into fresh water to observe that a denser material sinks.	**TIME** 15 minutes **MATERIALS** 2 clear plastic cups for water, 1 tsp table salt, measuring spoons, food coloring
INVESTIGATE Earth's Different Layers, p. 268 Students model how the varying density of materials helped to form Earth's layers. **ALTERNATIVE:** Diagramming Activity, URB p. 202	**TIME** 15 minutes **MATERIALS** clear plastic cup, 1/4 cup small colored wooden beads, 2/3 cup fine gravel, stirring stick

SECTION 

EXPLORE Movements of Continents, p. 270 Students model how the outlines of land masses can be a clue to the movement of continents.	**TIME** 20 minutes **MATERIALS** 1 sheet of paper per group, 3–4 colored marking pens, scissors
CHAPTER INVESTIGATION **Convection Currents and Plate Movement,** pp. 276–277 Students observe how convection currents can move floating objects above. **ALTERNATIVE:** Teacher Demonstration, URB p. 202	**TIME** 40 minutes **MATERIALS** rectangular glass baking dish, 2 oblong pans or 2 bricks, 2 small candles, matches, liquid food coloring, 2 sponges, 3–4 pushpins, scissors, water

SECTION 

EXPLORE Divergent Boundaries, p. 278 Students model how plates move apart at a divergent boundary.	**TIME** 15 minutes **MATERIALS** small oatmeal box with a slit cut in the side, piece of striped paper, scissors, tape
INVESTIGATE Magnetic Reversals, p. 281 Students explore mapping the sequences of magnetic reversals. **ALTERNATIVE:** Reading Activity, URB p. 202 R Sea-floor Model Instructions, p. 41	**TIME** 20 minutes **MATERIALS** 10 cm of string, masking tape, bar magnet, marking pen, sea-floor model

SECTION 

EXPLORE Tectonic Plates, p. 286 Students model the collision of tectonic plates and observe the effects.	**TIME** 10 minutes **MATERIALS** 6 square napkins
INVESTIGATE Convergent Boundaries, p. 289 Students design models to show subduction. **ALTERNATIVE:** Reading Activity, URB p. 202	**TIME** 30 minutes **MATERIALS** box of clay in 3 or more colors, poster board, marker pens

 **Additional INVESTIGATION,** Magnetic Patterns on the Ocean Floor, A, B, & C, pp. 71–79; Teacher Instructions, p. 202

Previewing Chapter Resources

CHAPTER 8
Plate Tectonics

INTEGRATED TECHNOLOGY

CLASSZONE.COM
- eEdition Plus
- EasyPlanner Plus
- Misconception Database
- Content Review
- Test Practice
- Visualizations
- Resource Centers
- Internet Activity: Interior of Earth
- Math Tutorial

SCILINKS.ORG

SCILINKS

CD-ROMS
- eEdition
- EasyPlanner
- Power Presentations
- Content Review
- Lab Generator
- Test Generator

AUDIO CDS
- Audio Readings
- Audio Readings in Spanish

LABS AND ACTIVITIES

EXPLORE the Big Idea, p. 263
- Convection in Action
- Internet Activity: Interior of Earth

UNIT RESOURCE BOOK
- Family Letter, p. vii
- Spanish Family Letter, p. viii
- Unit Projects, pp. 5–10

Lab Generator CD-ROM
Generate customized labs.

SECTION

1 Earth has several layers. pp. 265–269

Lesson Plan, pp. 11–12

TRANSPARENCY BOOK
- Big Idea Flow Chart, p. T57
- Daily Vocabulary Scaffolding, p. T58
- Note-Taking Model, p. T59
- 3-Minute Warm-Up, p. T60

- EXPLORE Density, p. 265
- INVESTIGATE Earth's Different Layers, p. 268

UNIT RESOURCE BOOK
Datasheet, Earth's Different Layers, p. 20

SECTION
2 Continents change position over time. pp. 270–277

Lesson Plan, pp. 22–23

VISUALIZATION, Continental Movement Over Time

TRANSPARENCY BOOK
- Daily Vocabulary Scaffolding, p. T58
- 3-Minute Warm-Up, p. T60

- EXPLORE Movements of Continents, p. 270
- CHAPTER INVESTIGATION, Convection Currents and Plate Movement, pp. 276–277

UNIT RESOURCE BOOK
CHAPTER INVESTIGATION, Convection Currents and Plate Movement, A, B, & C, pp. 62–70

SECTION

3 Plates move apart. pp. 278–285

Lesson Plan, pp. 32–33

MATH TUTORIAL, Rates

TRANSPARENCY BOOK
- Daily Vocabulary Scaffolding, p. T58
- 3-Minute Warm-Up, p. T61

- EXPLORE Divergent Boundaries, p. 278
- INVESTIGATE Magnetic Reversals, p. 281
- Math in Science, p. 285

UNIT RESOURCE BOOK
- Sea-Floor Model Instructions, p. 41
- Datasheet, Magnetic Reversals, p. 42
- Math Support & Practice, pp. 60–61
- Additional INVESTIGATION, Magnetic Patterns on the Ocean Floor, A, B, & C, pp. 71–79

SECTION

4 Plates converge or scrape past each other. pp. 286–293

Lesson Plan, pp. 44–45

- **VISUALIZATION,** Plate Boundaries
- **RESOURCE CENTER,** Effects of Plate Movement

TRANSPARENCY BOOK
- Big Idea Flow Chart, p. T57
- Daily Vocabulary Scaffolding, p. T58
- 3-Minute Warm-Up, p. T61
- "Tectonic Plate Boundaries" Visual, p. T62
- Chapter Outline, pp. T63–T64

- EXPLORE Tectonic Plates, p. 286
- INVESTIGATE Convergent Boundaries, p. 289
- Think Science, p. 293

UNIT RESOURCE BOOK
Datasheet, Convergent Boundaries, p. 53

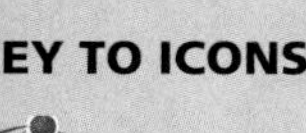 

KEY TO ICONS CD/CD-ROM · INTERNET ·  Pupil Edition ·  Teacher Edition ·  UNIT RESOURCE BOOK ·  TRANSPARENCY BOOK ·  ASSESSMENT BOOK ·  STANDARDS REVIEW AND PRACTICE · 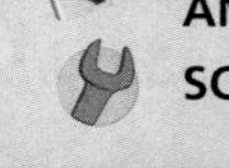 SCIENCE TOOLKIT

READING AND REINFORCEMENT	ASSESSMENT	STANDARDS
Modified Lesson Plans for English Learners, pp. 31–34 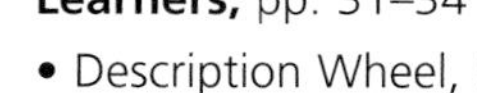 • Description Wheel, B20–21 • Supporting Main Ideas, C42 • Daily Vocabulary Scaffolding, H1–8  **UNIT RESOURCE BOOK** • Vocabulary Practice, pp. 57–58 • Decoding Support, p. 59 • Summarizing the Chapter, pp. 80–81 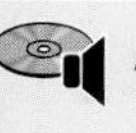  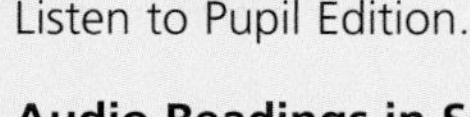 **Audio Readings CD** Listen to Pupil Edition.  **Audio Readings in Spanish CD** Listen to Pupil Edition in Spanish.	 • Chapter Review, pp. 295–296 • Standards-Based Assessment, p. 297  **ASSESSMENT BOOK** • Diagnostic Test, pp. 174–175 • Chapter Test, A, B, & C, pp. 180–191 • Alternative Assessment, pp. 192–193  **STANDARDS REVIEW AND PRACTICE,** pp. 1–12, 27–28, 57–58, 61–64, 71–72  **McDougal Littell Assessment System** 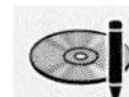 **Test Generator CD-ROM** Generate customized and Spanish tests.	California Content Standards 6.1.a, 6.1.b, 6.1.c, 6.1.d, 6.1.e, 6.1.f, 6.3.c, 6.7.a, 6.7.c, 6.7.d, 6.7.e, 6.7.g, 6.7.h See p. 262 for the standards.
UNIT RESOURCE BOOK • Reading Study Guide, A & B, pp. 13–16 • Spanish Reading Study Guide, pp. 17–18 • Challenge and Extension, p. 19 • Reinforcing Key Concepts, p. 21	Ongoing Assessment, pp. 266–268 Section 8.1 Review, p. 269 **ASSESSMENT BOOK** Section 8.1 Quiz, p. 176	California Content Standards 6.1.a, 6.1.b, 6.7.a
UNIT RESOURCE BOOK • Reading Study Guide, A & B, pp. 24–27 • Spanish Reading Study Guide, pp. 28–29 • Challenge and Extension, p. 30 • Reinforcing Key Concepts, p. 31	Ongoing Assessment, pp. 271–275  Section 8.2 Review, p. 275  **ASSESSMENT BOOK** Section 8.2 Quiz, p. 177	California Content Standards 6.1.a, 6.1.b, 6.1.c, 6.1.f, 6.3.c, 6.7.a, 6.7.d, 6.7.g
UNIT RESOURCE BOOK • Reading Study Guide, A & B, pp. 34–37 • Spanish Reading Study Guide, pp. 38–39 • Challenge and Extension, p. 40 • Reinforcing Key Concepts, p. 43 • Challenge Reading, pp. 55–56	Ongoing Assessment, pp. 279, 281, 284  Section 8.3 Review, p. 284  **ASSESSMENT BOOK** Section 8.3 Quiz, p. 178	California Content Standards 6.1.a, 6.1.b, 6.1.c, 6.1.d, 6.1.e, 6.7.e, 6.7.g
UNIT RESOURCE BOOK • Reading Study Guide, A & B, pp. 46–49 • Spanish Reading Study Guide, pp. 50–51 • Challenge and Extension, p. 52 • Reinforcing Key Concepts, p. 54	Ongoing Assessment, pp. 287–292  Section 8.4 Review, p. 292  **ASSESSMENT BOOK** Section 8.4 Quiz, p. 179	California Content Standards 6.1.a, 6.1.e, 6.1.f, 6.7.g

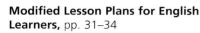

Previewing Resources for Differentiated Instruction

CHAPTER INVESTIGATION

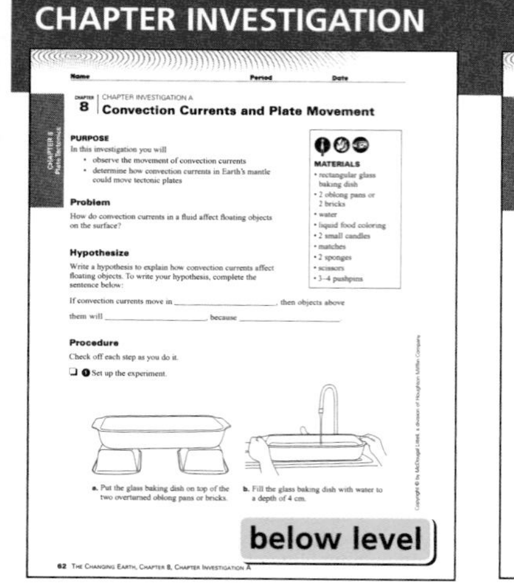

below level

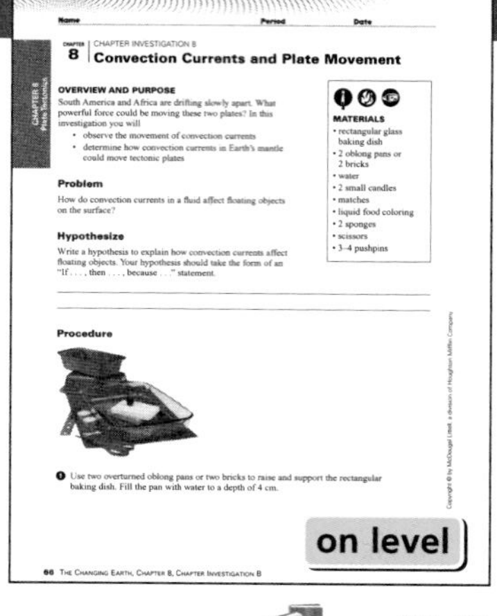

on level

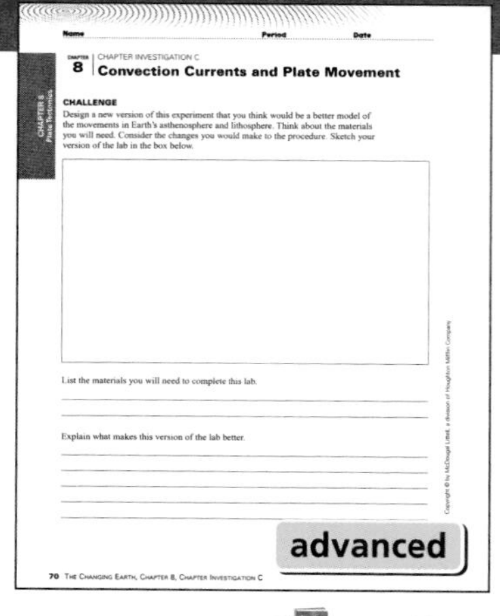

advanced

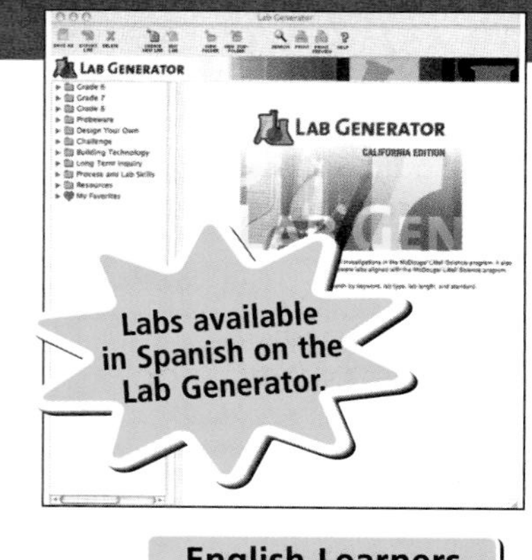

Labs available in Spanish on the Lab Generator.

English Learners

UNIT RESOURCE BOOK, pp. 62–65

pp. 66–69

pp. 66–70

READING STUDY GUIDE

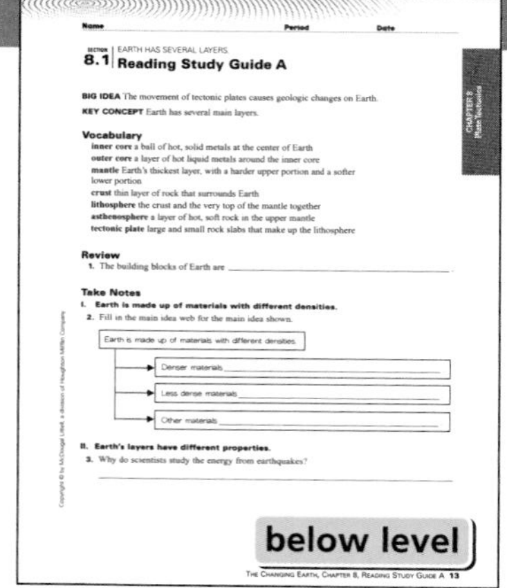

below level

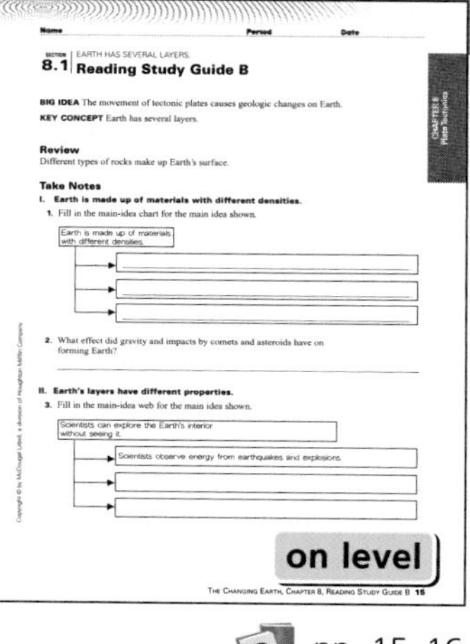

on level

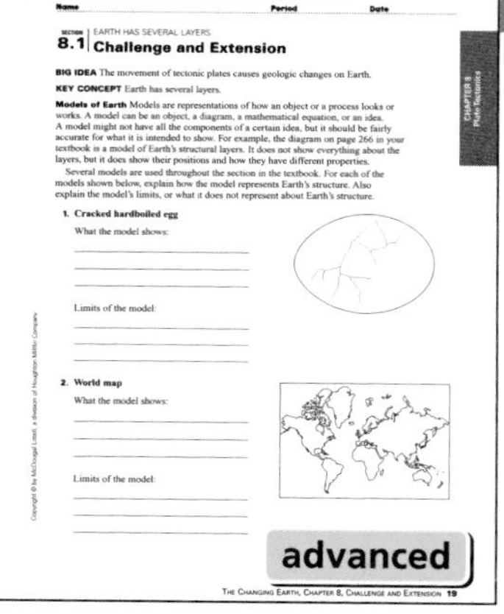

advanced

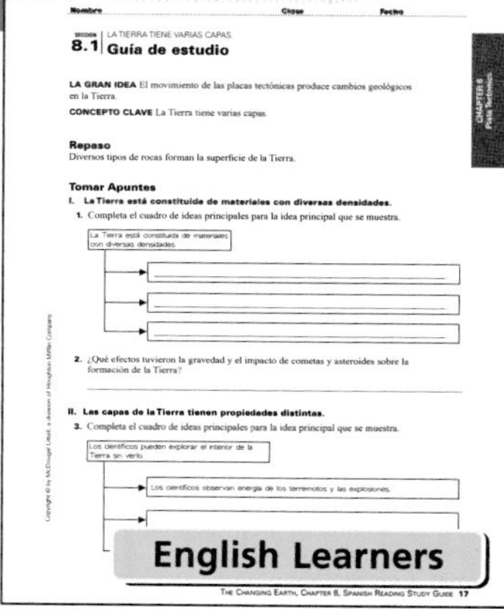

English Learners

UNIT RESOURCE BOOK,

pp. 13–14

pp. 15–16

p. 19

p. 17

CHAPTER TEST

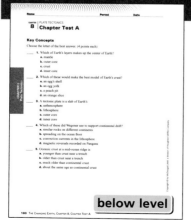

below level

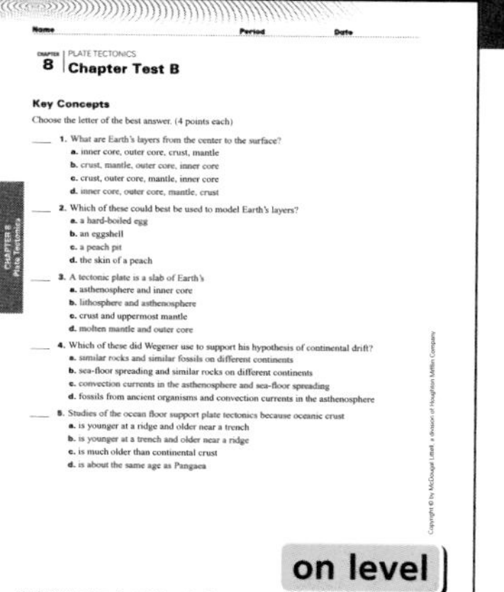

on level

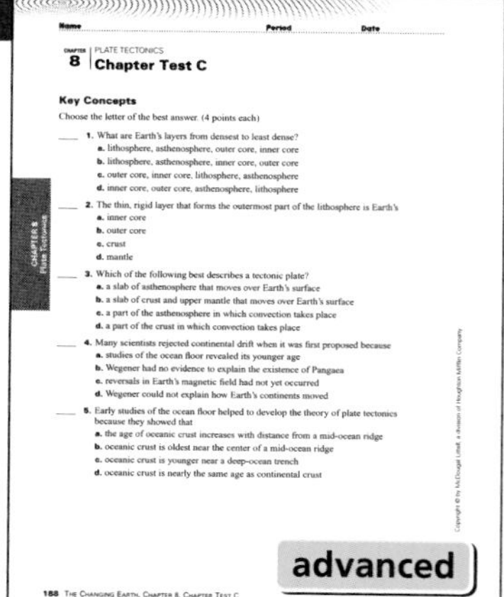

advanced

Tests available in Spanish on the Test Generator.

English Learners

ASSESSMENT BOOK, pp. 180–183

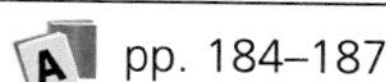

pp. 184–187

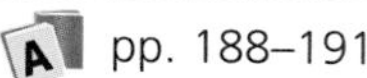

pp. 188–191

TECHNOLOGY

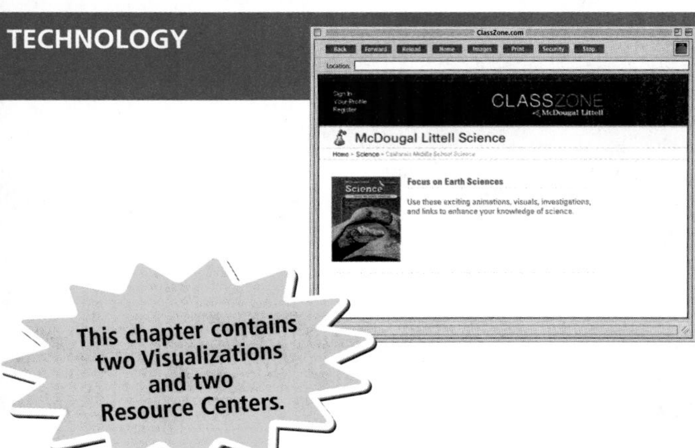

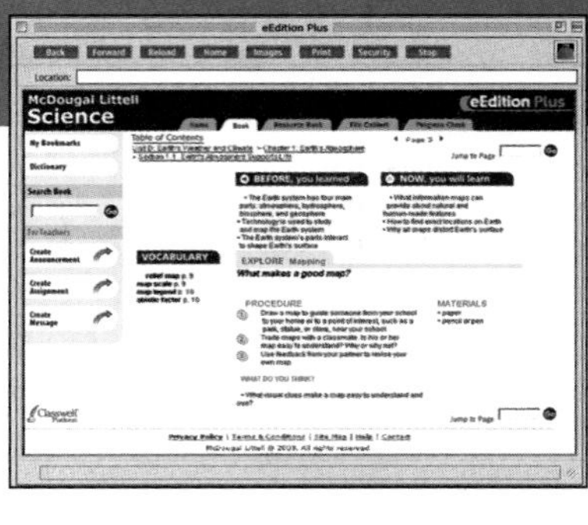

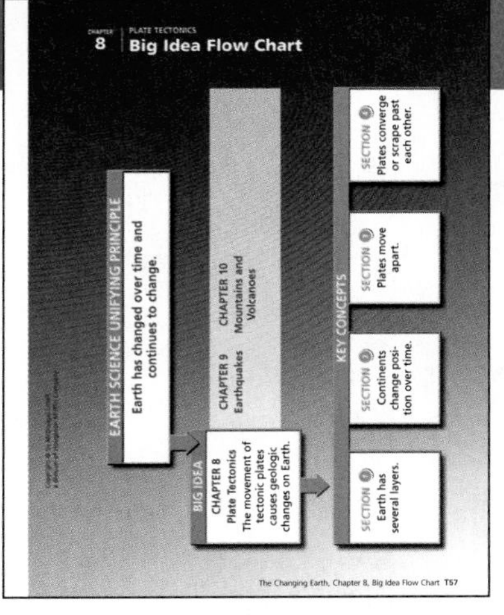

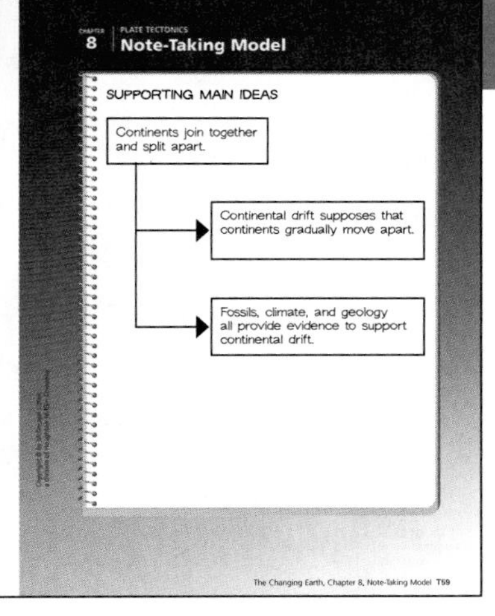

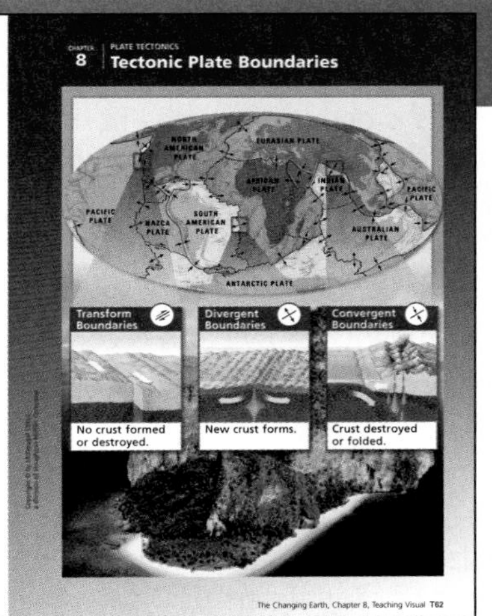

TRANSPARENCY BOOK, p. T57

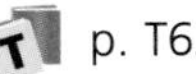

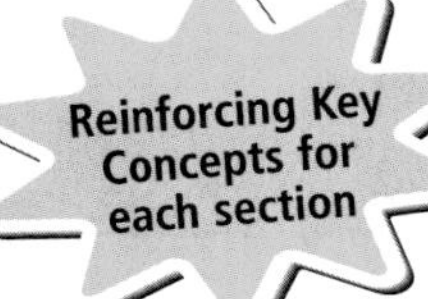

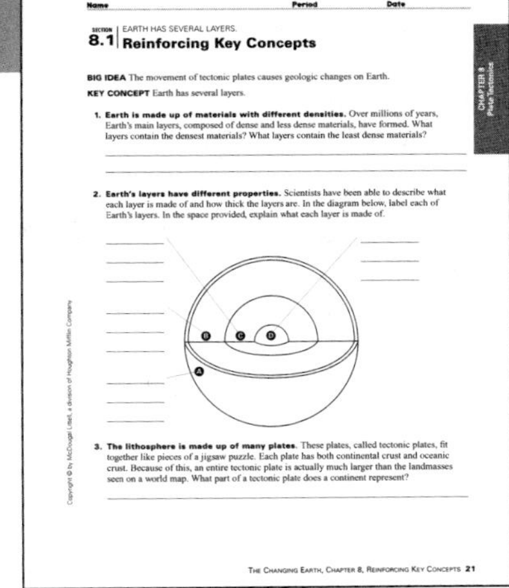

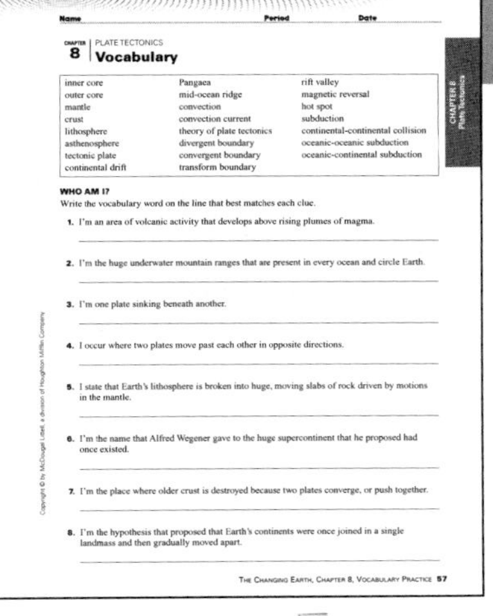

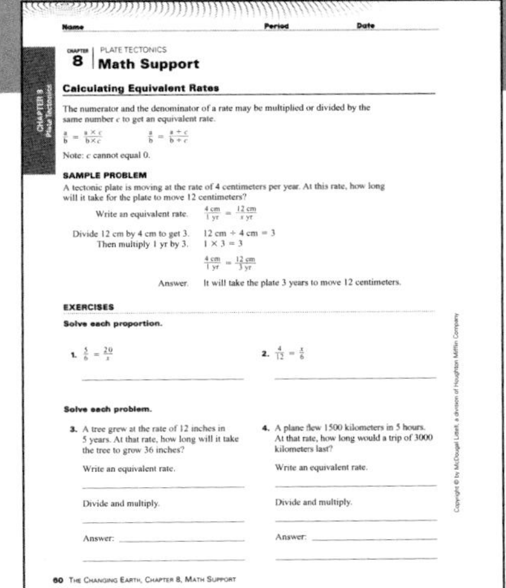

UNIT RESOURCE BOOK, p. 21

pp. 57–58

p. 60

CHAPTER 8

Plate Tectonics

INTRODUCE

the BIG idea

Have students look at the photograph of a huge crack in Earth's surface and discuss how the question in the box links to the Big Idea:

- Have you seen similar cracks? What caused them?
- What clues would you look for to determine the cause of the crack in the photograph?

California Content Standards

6.1.a Students know evidence of plate tectonics is derived from the fit of the continents; the location of earthquakes, volcanoes, and midocean ridges; and the distribution of fossils, rock types, and ancient climatic zones.

6.1.b Students know Earth is composed of several layers: a cold, brittle lithosphere; a hot, convecting mantle; and a dense, metallic core.

6.1.c Students know lithospheric plates the size of continents and oceans move at rates of centimeters per year in response to movements in the mantle.

6.1.d Students know that earthquakes are sudden motions along breaks in the crust called faults and that volcanoes and fissures are locations where magma reaches the surface.

6.1.e Students know major geologic events, such as earthquakes, volcanic eruptions, and mountain building, result from plate motions.

6.1.f Students know how to explain major features of California geology (including mountains, faults, volcanoes) in terms of plate tectonics.

6.3.c Students know heat flows in solids by conduction (which involves no flow of matter) and in fluids by conduction and by convection (which involves flow of matter).

CHAPTER

Plate Tectonics

the BIG idea

The movement of tectonic plates causes geologic changes on Earth.

Key Concepts

SECTION

Earth has several layers.
Learn about Earth's interior and its rigid surface plates.

SECTION

Continents change position over time.
Learn how continental drift and plate tectonics changed the way people view Earth.

SECTION

Plates move apart.
Learn about the three types of plate boundaries and what happens when plates move apart.

SECTION

Plates converge or scrape past each other.
Learn what geologic events occur at these plate boundaries.

California ClassZone

CLASSZONE.COM

Chapter 8 online resources: Content Review, two Visualizations, two Resource Centers, Math Tutorial, Test Practice

What might have made this huge crack in Earth's surface?

INTERNET PREVIEW

CLASSZONE.COM For student use with the following pages:

Review and Practice

- Content Review, pp. 264, 294
- Math Tutorial: Rates, p. 285
- Test Practice, p. 297

Activities and Resources

- Internet Activity: Interior of Earth, p. 263
- Visualizations: Continental Movement Over Time, p. 272; Plate Boundaries, p. 289
- Resource Centers: Earth's Layers, p. 263; Effects of Plate Movement, p. 293

Plates **Code: MDL052**

EXPLORE the BIG idea

Convection in Action

6.3.c Students know heat flows in solids by conduction (which involves no flow of matter) and in fluids by conduction and by convection (which involves flow of matter).

Put a medium-sized pot of water on to boil. Place a small wet sponge on the water. Watch the water and sponge as the water heats.

Observe and Think
What happened to the water as it heated? What happened to the sponge as the water became hotter? How do the movements of the water and the sponge relate to convection?

Internet Activity: Interior of Earth

6.1.b Students know Earth is composed of several layers: a cold, brittle lithosphere; a hot, convecting mantle; and a dense, metallic core.

Go to **ClassZone.com** to explore Earth's layers. Find out how scientists learned what the interior, or inside, of Earth is like.

Observe and Think
Science fiction books and movies show people traveling to the center of Earth. Do you think this can happen any time soon? Give an explanation of your answer using what you've found out about the properties of Earth's interior.

NSTA scilinks.org SCILINKS
Plates **Code: MDL052**

EXPLORE the BIG idea

These inquiry-based activities are appropriate for use at home or as a supplement to classroom instruction.

Convection in Action

PURPOSE To give students experience watching convection currents in a fluid.

TIP *10 min.* Ask students to observe what happens as the water begins to heat up. Do this as a demonstration, or tell students to be very careful.

Answer: Students should notice that water begins to form bubbles, then streams of bubbles, then begins to roll faster and faster as it boils. The sponge will move to the side of the pan and keep moving. As the water at the bottom of the pan heats up, it becomes less dense and rises to the surface, where it cools and sinks. This continuous rise and fall keeps the sponge in motion.

REVISIT after p. 274.

Internet Activity: Interior of Earth

PURPOSE To introduce students to the latest ideas about the formation and properties of Earth's layers.

TIP *20 min.* Students should appreciate the complexity of Earth's layers and the fact that scientists still have many unanswered questions.

Answer: No. Earth's interior is far too hot for any living thing to survive. Also, the increase in pressure from the outer crust to the core would also make survival impossible.

REVISIT after p. 269.

TEACHING WITH TECHNOLOGY

CD-ROM While teaching p. 279, use a computer to display a map of the ocean floor on CD-ROM for students to study the Mid-Atlantic Ridge and its rift valley.

Video Camera You might film groups of students showing and describing the models they develop for the investigation on p. 289.

PREPARE

CONCEPT REVIEW

Activate Prior Knowledge

- Place an igneous, a metamorphic, and a sedimentary rock on your desk.
- Ask students to describe how each type of rock might change into another type.

TAKING NOTES

Supporting Main Ideas

Identifying main ideas and supporting details is a basic reading comprehension skill students will need to master if they are to perform well on standardized tests. If students have a hard time remembering the information they put in their charts, they may be including too much information with the supporting details they identify.

Vocabulary Strategy

Description wheels can include definitions, uses, examples, and other kinds of details. Students can include as many spokes as they want, and each spoke should be a different detail. Description wheels can be useful study aids when students review their notes.

Vocabulary and Note-Taking Resources

- Vocabulary Practice, pp. 57–58
- Decoding Support, p. 59

- Daily Vocabulary Scaffolding, p. T58
- Note-Taking Model, p. T59

- Description Wheel, B20–21
- Supporting Main Ideas, C42
- Daily Vocabulary Scaffolding, H1–8

CHAPTER 8

Getting Ready to Learn

CONCEPT REVIEW

- Most rocks are made of minerals.
- Different types of rocks are formed under different temperatures and pressures.
- Earth's surface has changed over millions of years.

VOCABULARY REVIEW

density p. 28
mineral p. 184
rock p. 187
magma p. 191

Review concepts and vocabulary.

TAKING NOTES

SUPPORTING MAIN IDEAS

Make a chart to show main ideas and the information that supports them. Copy each blue heading. Below each heading, add supporting information, such as reasons, explanations, and examples.

VOCABULARY STRATEGY

Place each vocabulary term at the center of a **description wheel** diagram. Write some words describing it on the spokes.

SCIENCE NOTEBOOK

Earth is made up of materials with different densities.

- Dense materials—such as iron and nickel—sink toward center
- Less dense materials rise toward surface

INNER CORE: at center of Earth; hot, solid ball; dense iron and nickel; under great pressure; 2400 km diameter

See the Note-Taking Handbook on pages R45–R51.

CHECK READINESS

Administer the Diagnostic Test to determine students' readiness for new science content and their mastery of requisite math skills.

 Diagnostic Test, pp. 174–175

Technology Resources

Students needing content and math skills should visit **ClassZone.com.**

- **CONTENT REVIEW**
- **MATH TUTORIAL**

KEY CONCEPT

Earth has several layers.

CALIFORNIA Content Standards

6.1.a Students know evidence of plate tectonics is derived from the fit of the continents; the location of earthquakes, volcanoes, and midocean ridges; and the distribution of fossils, rock types, and ancient climatic zones.

6.1.b Students know Earth is composed of several layers: a cold, brittle lithosphere; a hot, convecting mantle; and a dense, metallic core.

BEFORE, you learned

- Minerals and rocks are the building blocks of Earth
- Different types of rocks make up Earth's surface

NOW, you will learn

- About the different properties of Earth's layers
- About the plates that make up Earth's outermost layers

VOCABULARY

inner core p. 266
outer core p. 266
mantle p. 267
crust p. 267
lithosphere p. 267
asthenosphere p. 267
tectonic plate p. 268

EXPLORE Density (6.1.b)

Will a denser material sink or float?

PROCEDURE

1. Add equal amounts of water to the cups. Add 3 spoonfuls of salt to one of the cups. Stir until the salt is dissolved.
2. Add 10 drops of food coloring to the cup with the salt water.
3. Gently pour about one-third of the colored salt water into the cup of fresh water. Observe what happens.

WHAT DO YOU THINK?

- What did you observe when the two types of water were mixed?
- What does this activity tell you about materials with different densities in Earth's layers?

MATERIALS

- 2 clear plastic cups
- tap water
- table salt
- plastic spoon
- food coloring

Earth is made up of materials with different densities.

SUPPORTING MAIN IDEAS
Support the main ideas about Earth's layers with details and examples.

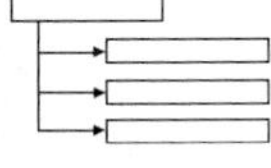

Scientists think that Earth formed about 4.6 billion years ago. Bits of material ran into each other and stuck together. The planet grew larger as more and more material was added. Intense heat was produced by these impacts, radioactive decay, and Earth's gravity. The young planet became a glowing ball of melted rock.

In time, denser materials, such as iron and nickel, sank toward the center of Earth. Less dense materials moved toward the surface. Other materials settled between the planet's center and its surface. Slowly, Earth's main layers formed—the core, the mantle, and the crust.

RESOURCES FOR DIFFERENTIATED INSTRUCTION

Below Level

UNIT RESOURCE BOOK

- Reading Study Guide A, pp. 13–14
- Decoding Support, p. 59

AUDIO CDS

Advanced

UNIT RESOURCE BOOK
Challenge and Extension, p. 19

English Learners

UNIT RESOURCE BOOK
Spanish Reading Study Guide, pp. 17–18

AUDIO CDS

- Audio Readings in Spanish
- Audio Readings (English)

8.1 FOCUS

Set Learning Goals

Students will

- Describe the different properties of Earth's layers.
- Describe the plates that make up Earth's outermost layers.
- Model Earth's layers in an experiment.

3-Minute Warm-Up

Display Transparency 60 or copy this exercise on the board:

Decide if each statement is true. If not, correct it.

1. The rock cycle describes the natural processes that form, change, break down, and form rocks again. *true*
2. The most common types of rocks in Earth's crust are sedimentary and igneous. *The most common types of rocks in Earth's crust are igneous and metamorphic. (Sedimentary rock is the most common type only at Earth's surface.)*
3. Heat or pressure can change a rock into another type of rock. *true*

 3-Minute Warm-Up, p. T60

8.1 MOTIVATE

EXPLORE Density

PURPOSE To observe how a dense material will sink when combined with a less dense material

TIP *15 min.* To avoid disturbing the layers of water, students should pour the water gently and not shake or stir the water.

WHAT DO YOU THINK? *The salt water sank to the bottom because it contains more matter in the form of salt, making it denser than the fresh water. Deeper layers of Earth are generally denser than shallower layers. When denser material does exist above less dense material, the denser material will sink.*

8.1 INSTRUCT

Teach the Standards

Earth's layers 6.1.b

In this section: Help students remember and identify the properties of these layers of Earth: the dense, metallic core; the hot, convecting mantle; and the cold, brittle lithosphere. Explain that each layer has parts.

previously taught: geosphere, p. 44; rocks in the crust, p. 197

future opportunities: earthquakes, p. 303

Integrate the Sciences

The difference in pressure between the inner core and outer core accounts for the different states of matter in the two layers. The more pressure there is, the less atoms can move. The less atoms move, the more solid the material remains despite intense heat. Scientists do not know for sure what causes the intense heat in Earth's core. It may be due partly to the radioactive decay of some materials in the core.

Teach from Visuals

To help students interpret the diagram of Earth's layers, ask:

- How does the density of material differ from the inner core to the crust? *It becomes less dense.*
- How does the temperature of the material change from the inner core to the crust? *It decreases.*
- Which layer of Earth is the thinnest? *the crust*

Ongoing Assessment

READING VISUALS *Answer: Greater pressure in the inner core squeezes atoms together so closely that the core remains solid. Less pressure in the outer core allows the metals to remain liquid.*

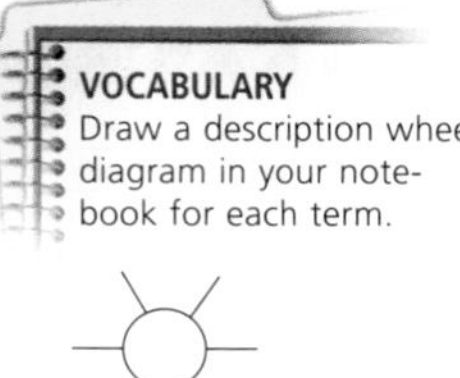

VOCABULARY
Draw a description wheel diagram in your notebook for each term.

Earth's layers have different properties.

How do scientists know what Earth's deep interior is like? After all, no one has seen it. To explore the interior, scientists study the energy from earthquakes. The energy travels through Earth in the same way that ripples move through a pond. The energy moves slower through less dense materials or liquids. It moves faster through denser materials or solids. In this way, scientists can figure out what each layer is made of and how thick the layers are.

Core, Mantle, Crust

A

The core is Earth's densest region and is made up of two parts. The **inner core** is a ball of hot, solid metals. There is great pressure at the center of Earth. This squeezes the atoms of the metals so closely together that the core remains solid despite the intense heat.

The **outer core** is a layer of liquid metals around the inner core. The temperature and pressure in the outer core are lower than in the inner core. The lower pressure allows the metals to remain liquid.

Earth's Layers

Earth's layers formed as denser materials sank toward the center and less dense materials rose toward the surface.

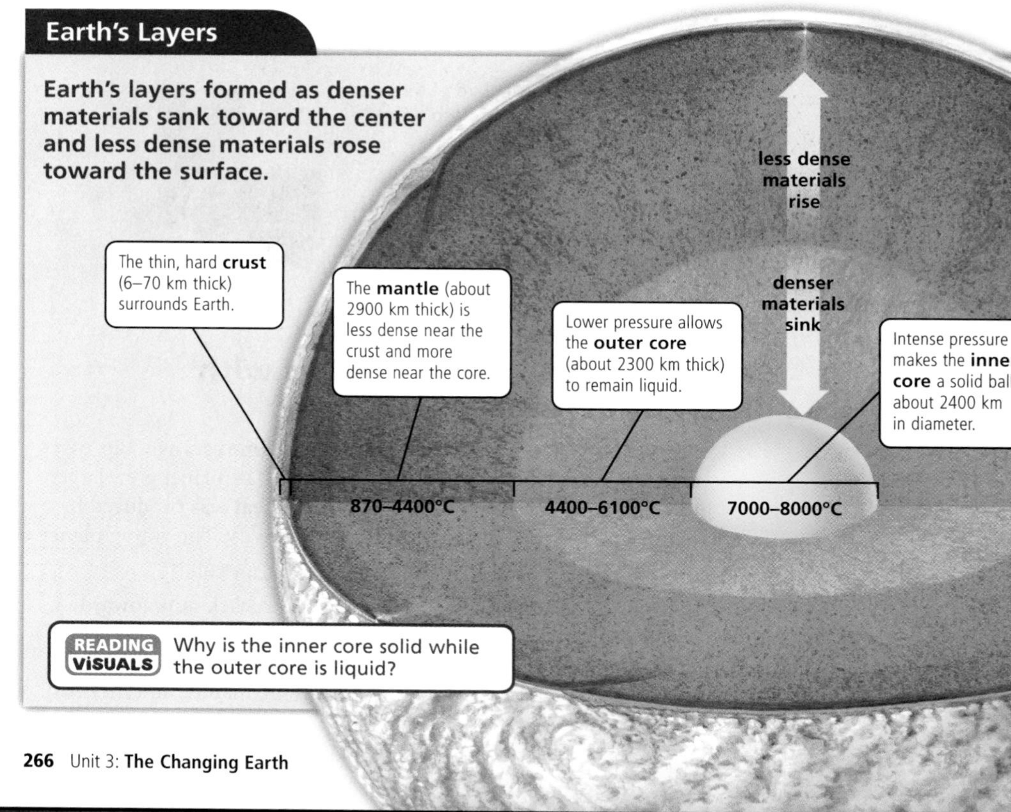

less dense materials rise
denser materials sink
The thin, hard crust (6–70 km thick) surrounds Earth.
The mantle (about 2900 km thick) is less dense near the crust and more dense near the core.
Lower pressure allows the outer core (about 2300 km thick) to remain liquid.
Intense pressure makes the inner core a solid ball about 2400 km in diameter.
870–4400°C
4400–6100°C
7000–8000°C

READING VISUALS Why is the inner core solid while the outer core is liquid?

DIFFERENTIATE INSTRUCTION

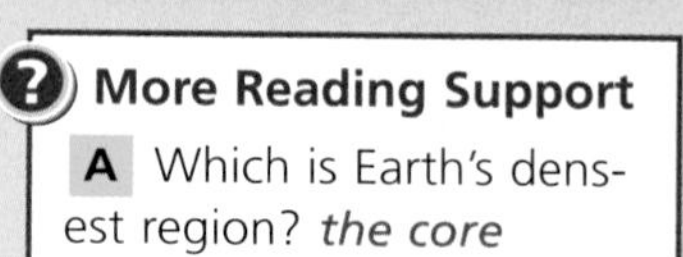

More Reading Support

A Which is Earth's densest region? *the core*

English Learners Make sure English learners understand how to read and follow activity directions. Some students may be unfamiliar with the imperative mood of a verb used in most activities when the subject "you" is understood but not stated. For example, students are directed to "Stir the beads and gravel . . ." (p. 268). Tell students this means the reader, or "you," should stir the beads and gravel.

The **mantle** is Earth's thickest layer. It is nearly 2900 kilometers (1700 mi) thick. The mantle is made of hot rock and is less dense than the thick core, which is made of metals. The very top part of the mantle is cool and hard. Just below that, the rock is hot and soft enough to move like a thick paste.

The **crust** is a thin layer of cool rock. It surrounds Earth like a shell surrounds an egg. There are two basic types of crust. Continental crust includes all continents and some major islands. Oceanic crust makes up the ocean floor. Look at the diagram below. You can see that Earth's crust is thinnest under the ocean and thickest under continental mountain ranges. The crust is home to life on Earth.

Lithosphere and Asthenosphere

The **lithosphere** (LIHTH-uh-SFEER) is made up of Earth's crust and the very top of the mantle. This layer is cold and brittle. The lithosphere sits on top of the **asthenosphere** (as-THEHN-uh-SFEER). This is a layer of hotter, softer rock in the upper mantle. The asthenosphere is soft enough to flow slowly like hot tar. You can imagine the lithosphere as solid pieces of pavement resting on hot tar.

READING TIP
The Greek prefix *litho-* means "stone" or "rock." The Greek word *asthenēs* means "weak."

Lithosphere and Asthenosphere

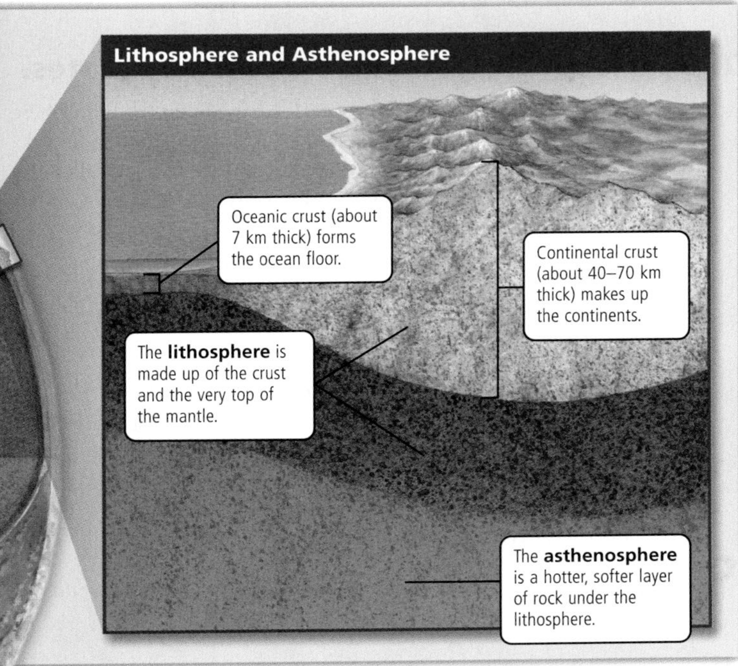
Oceanic crust (about 7 km thick) forms the ocean floor.
Continental crust (about 40–70 km thick) makes up the continents.
The lithosphere is made up of the crust and the very top of the mantle.
The asthenosphere is a hotter, softer layer of rock under the lithosphere.

Teach Difficult Concepts

Some students may have difficulty understanding the composition of the asthenosphere. Explain that the asthenosphere has properties of both a liquid and a solid. The material in the asthenosphere can flow slowly like a hot, thick paste, such as tar. Some other materials that have properties of both liquids and solids are toothpaste and rubber cement.

Teach from Visuals

To help students interpret the diagram of Earth's top layers, ask:

- Where is Earth's crust thinnest? *under the oceans*
- Where is it thickest? *under mountains*

Ongoing Assessment

Describe the different properties of Earth's layers.

Ask: What are Earth's four layers like? *The inner core is a ball of hot, solid metals; the outer core is liquid metals; the mantle has a layer of cool, rigid rock at the top and a layer of hotter, softer rock below it; and the crust is a thin layer of cool rock that surrounds Earth. The layers become less dense and less hot from the center to the outermost layer.*

Ask: What layer is home to all life on Earth? *the crust*

DIFFERENTIATE INSTRUCTION

More Reading Support

B What is Earth's thickest layer? *the mantle*

C What does the lithosphere consist of? *the crust and the very top of the mantle*

Inclusion To visually model the nature of the asthenosphere and lithosphere, spread a layer of toothpaste on top of a rubber ball. Then place a small piece of paper on top of the toothpaste. Explain that the toothpaste represents the asthenosphere, and the paper represents the lithosphere. The ball represents the lower mantle and the inner and outer cores.

Advanced

 Challenge and Extension, p. 19

INVESTIGATE Earth's Different Layers

PURPOSE To create a model of how Earth's layers formed

TIP *15 min.* Advise students to pour the water slowly down the inside of the cup to avoid disturbing the layers.

WHAT DO YOU THINK? *The wooden beads separated from the gravel and rose to the surface. The model shows that denser materials sink to the bottom (or center) and less dense materials rise to the top.*

CHALLENGE *Students might place a solid layer of clay in the bottom of the cup to represent the solid core.*

Datasheet, Earth's Different Layers, p. 20

Technology Resources

Customize this student lab as needed or look for an alternative. Print rubrics to assess student lab reports.

Lab Generator CD-ROM

Real World Example

The lithospheric plates that make up Earth's crust could also be compared to a sheet of ice on a river or lake. When the ice first starts to break up, it forms many moving pieces. The pieces still form a surface that covers the water.

Ongoing Assessment

Describe the plates that make up Earth's outermost layers.

Ask: What is the lithosphere like? *It is split into many large and small slabs of rock.*

Answer: The oceanic crust of the plates is underwater.

INVESTIGATE Earth's Different Layers

How can you model Earth's layers?

SKILL FOCUS
Modeling (6.1.b)

MATERIALS
- clear plastic cup
- small colored wooden beads
- gravel
- stirring stick
- tap water

TIME
15 minutes

PROCEDURE

1. Put a layer of wooden beads about 1 centimeter thick at the bottom of a clear plastic cup or small jar.
2. Put a layer of gravel about 2 centimeters thick on top of the wooden beads. Stir the beads and gravel until they are well mixed.
3. Put another layer of gravel about 1 centimeter thick on top of the mix. Do NOT mix this layer of gravel.
4. SLOWLY fill the cup about two-thirds full of water. Be sure not to disturb the layers in the cup.
5. Stir the beads and gravel with the stick. Observe what happens.

WHAT DO YOU THINK?
- What happened to the materials when you stirred them?
- How do you think this model represents the layers of Earth?

CHALLENGE What could you add to the model to represent Earth's solid core?

The lithosphere is made up of many plates.

READING TIP
The word *tectonic* comes from the Greek word *tecktōn,* which means "builder." Tectonic plates are constantly building and changing landforms and oceans on Earth.

As scientists studied Earth's surface, they discovered that the lithosphere does not form a continuous shell around Earth. Instead, they found that the lithosphere is broken into many large slabs of rock called **tectonic plates** (tehk-TAHN-ihk). Scientists think that these giant plates formed early in Earth's history.

Tectonic plates fit together like a jigsaw puzzle. You could compare the lithosphere to the cracked shell of a hard-boiled egg. The shell may be broken into many pieces, but it still forms a "crust" around the egg itself.

D

Most large tectonic plates include both continental crust and oceanic crust, as shown in the diagram on page 269. Most of the continental crust rises above the ocean. The rest of the plate is thin oceanic crust, or sea floor, and is underwater. The next time you look at the continents on a world map, remember you are seeing only the part of Earth's crust that rises above the ocean.

Why do you see only part of Earth's crust on a typical world map?

DIFFERENTIATE INSTRUCTION

More Reading Support

D What two types of crust do most large tectonic plates contain? *oceanic and continental*

Below Level To help students understand the discussion of continental and oceanic crust, use a world map with ocean basins to show how much of Earth's crust lies underwater. Point out where the African Plate's oceanic crust forms part of the sea floor of the Atlantic and Indian Oceans and the Mediterranean Sea (discussed on p. 269).

African Plate

Most tectonic plates have both continental and oceanic crust.

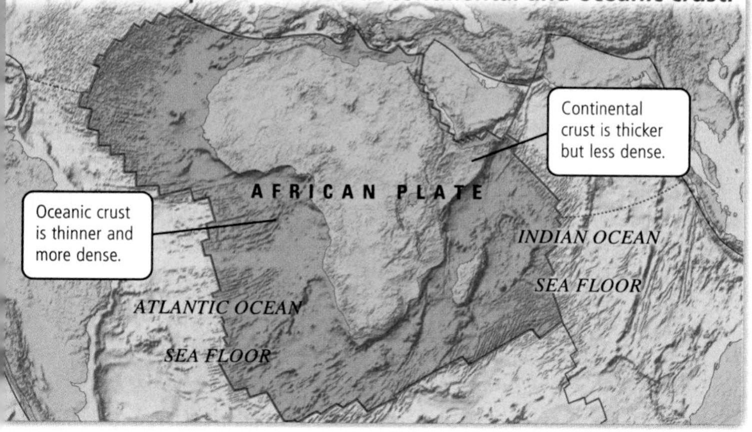

Continental crust is thicker but less dense.

AFRICAN PLATE

Oceanic crust is thinner and more dense.

INDIAN OCEAN SEA FLOOR

ATLANTIC OCEAN SEA FLOOR

In the diagram above, much of the African Plate is shaded dark blue. This part lies underwater. The continent of Africa, which looks large on a world map, is actually about half the size of the entire plate. The plate's oceanic crust forms part of the sea floor of the Atlantic and Indian oceans and of the Mediterranean Sea. The ocean crusts of other plates make up the rest of the sea floors.

Earth's layers and tectonic plates are two of the most important discoveries in geology. They helped solve a mystery that had puzzled people for nearly 400 years. The mystery involved two questions. Have the continents always been where they are today? If not, how did they move to their present positions? In Section 8.2, you will find out how scientists are answering these questions.

Review

KEY CONCEPTS

1. Briefly describe the inner and outer cores, the mantle, and the crust. (6.1.b)
2. In what ways is the lithosphere different from the asthenosphere? (6.1.b)
3. Describe the structure of most tectonic plates. (6.1.b)

CRITICAL THINKING

4. **Draw Conclusions** Suppose you are looking at a scene that has mountains near an ocean. Where do you think the crust would be the thickest? Why?
5. **Hypothesize** What would Earth look like if most of its crust was above sea level?

CHALLENGE

6. **Predict** You have learned that Earth's lithosphere is made up of many plates. How do you think this fact might help scientists solve the mystery of the moving continents?

NSWERS

hot, dense, solid inner re; hot liquid outer core; ick mantle of heated rock; in, rigid crust

lithosphere: made up of the gid crust and very top part the mantle; asthenosphere: eaker, softer rock just below e lithosphere

3. They have both thinner oceanic crust and thicker continental crust.

4. thickest under the mountains because the crust is thickest on the continents

5. There would be low plains and valleys surrounding all continents because that part of the crust uncovered by oceans is thinner and lower than the continental crust.

6. If Earth's crust was all in one piece, the continents could not move. But since the crust is made up of many plates, the plates might be able to move separately.

Teach from Visuals

To help students interpret the map of tectonic plates, ask:

- Does the African Plate include all of Africa? *yes*
- Does the African Plate include only Africa? *No, it also includes much of the Atlantic and Indian Oceans.*

EXPLORE the BIG idea

Revisit "Internet Activity: Interior of Earth" on p. 263. Have students describe what they would experience on an imaginary trip to the center of Earth.

Reinforce the BIG idea

Have students relate the section to the Big Idea.

 Reinforcing Key Concepts, p. 21

8.1 ASSESS & RETEACH

Assess

 Section 8.1 Quiz, p. 176

Reteach

Help students review this section's concepts by showing them a hardboiled egg that has been cut in half. Keep the shell on and make sure it is cracked. Ask students how this egg can be seen as a useful model of Earth's structure. *Parts of the egg can be used to represent layers of Earth.* Ask what each part of the egg represents. *yolk: core; egg white: mantle; shell: crust; sections of cracked shell: tectonic plates*

Technology Resources

Have students visit **ClassZone.com** for reteaching of Key Concepts.

 CONTENT REVIEW

 CONTENT REVIEW CD-ROM

8.2 FOCUS

Set Learning Goals

Students will

- Explain how the continental drift hypothesis was developed.
- Explain evidence for plate movement scientists have gathered from observations of the sea floor.
- Describe how scientists developed the theory of plate tectonics.

3-Minute Warm-Up

Display Transparency 60 or copy this exercise on the board:

Draw a diagram showing and labeling Earth's four layers. Identify the lithosphere and the asthenosphere on your diagram. *Diagram should show the inner core, outer core, mantle, and crust. The crust and the top part of the mantle should be labeled lithosphere. The adjacent part of the mantle should be labeled asthenosphere.*

 3-Minute Warm-Up, p. T60

8.2 MOTIVATE

EXPLORE Movements of Continents

PURPOSE To model how the shape of coastlines and land features could be a clue to the movement of continents

TIP *20 min.* Make sure students draw some of their land features, such as mountain ranges, large enough to cross from one side of the landmass to the other. Their drawings should be complex enough to be a challenge to put together.

WHAT DO YOU THINK? *Clues would include outlines of the pieces and landforms drawn on the pieces. Students should notice that Africa and South America seem to fit together.*

KEY CONCEPT

8.2 Continents change position over time.

CALIFORNIA Content Standards

6.1.a Students know evidence of plate tectonics is derived from the fit of the continents; the location of earthquakes, volcanoes, and midocean ridges; and the distribution of fossils, rock types, and ancient climatic zones.

6.3.c Students know heat flows in solids by conduction (which involves no flow of matter) and in fluids by conduction and by convection (which involves flow of matter).

BEFORE, you learned

- Earth's main layers are the core, the mantle, and the crust
- The lithosphere and asthenosphere are the topmost layers of Earth
- The lithosphere is made up of tectonic plates

NOW, you will learn

- How the continental drift hypothesis was developed
- About evidence for plate movement from the sea floor
- How scientists developed the theory of plate tectonics

VOCABULARY

continental drift p. 270
Pangaea p. 272
mid-ocean ridge p. 272
convection p. 273
convection current p. 273
theory of plate tectonics p. 274

EXPLORE Movements of Continents (6.1.a)

How do you put together a giant continent?

PROCEDURE

1. Work with a small group. Draw the outline of a large landmass. Fill in mountains, rivers, lakes, and any other features you like.
2. Cut out your landmass. Then tear the drawing into several pieces and mix the pieces up. Ask another group to put the puzzle together.

WHAT DO YOU THINK?

- What clues helped you fit the pieces together?
- Do any lands on a world map seem to fit together?

MATERIALS

- sheet of paper
- colored marking pens
- scissors

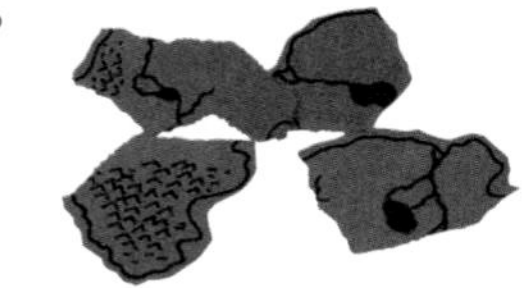

Continents join together and split apart.

The idea that Earth's surface might be moving is not new. As far back as the 1500s, when mapmakers started including North and South America on their world maps, they noticed something odd. The western coast of Africa and the eastern coast of South America seemed to fit together like pieces of a puzzle. Were these continents joined at one time?

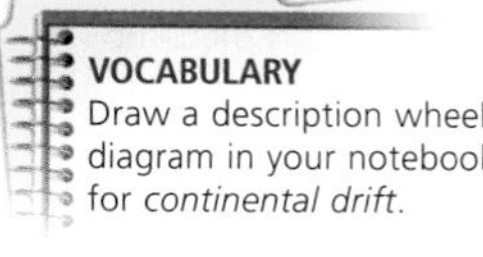

VOCABULARY Draw a description wheel diagram in your notebook for *continental drift.*

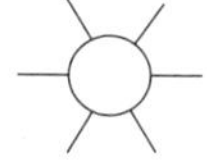

In the late 1800s, German scientist Alfred Wegener (VAY-guh-nuhr) began studying this question. In 1912 he proposed a hypothesis known as **continental drift.** According to Wegener's hypothesis, Earth's continents were once joined in a single landmass. They gradually moved, or drifted, apart. For many years, people did not accept Wegener's ideas. In the mid-1900s scientists found new evidence that made them take continental drift more seriously.

RESOURCES FOR DIFFERENTIATED INSTRUCTION

Below Level

UNIT RESOURCE BOOK

- Reading Study Guide A, pp. 24–25
- Decoding Support, p. 59

 **AUDIO CDS**

Advanced

UNIT RESOURCE BOOK

Challenge and Extension, p. 30

English Learners

UNIT RESOURCE BOOK

Spanish Reading Study Guide, pp. 28–29

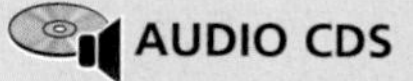 **AUDIO CDS**

- Audio Readings in Spanish
- Audio Readings (English)

Evidence for Continental Drift

Wegener gathered evidence for his hypothesis from fossils, from studies of ancient climate, and from the geology of continents.

Fossils Wegener learned that the fossils of an ancient reptile, *Mesosaurus* (MEHZ-uh-SAWR-uhs), had been discovered in South America and western Africa. This small reptile lived about 270 million years ago. Its fossils were not found anywhere else in the world. Wegener said this fact could easily be explained if South America and Africa were once joined. See the map below.

Climate Evidence of climate change also supported Wegener's hypothesis. For example, Greenland today lies near the Arctic Circle and is mostly covered in ice. Yet fossils of tropical plants can be found on its shores. In contrast, South Africa today has a warm climate. Yet its rocks were deeply scratched by ice sheets that once covered the area.

> **READING TIP**
> *Climate* refers to a pattern of wind, temperature, and rain or snow that occurs in a region over time. Earth's climates have changed many times in the planet's long history.

Wegener suggested that these continents had moved, carrying their fossils and rocks with them. For example, Greenland had once been near the equator and had slowly moved to the Arctic Circle. South Africa, once closer to the South Pole, had moved slowly north to a warmer region.

Geology Wegener's best evidence for continental drift came from the kinds of rocks that make up the continents. He showed that the rock found in Brazil matched the rock found in western Africa. Also, limestone layers in the Appalachian Mountains of North America were exactly like the limestone in Scotland's Highlands.

CHECK YOUR READING Which evidence for continental drift do you think is the most convincing? Explain your answer.

AFRICA

SOUTH AMERICA

Areas in which *Mesosaurus* fossils have been found

The reptile *Mesosaurus* was about 45 cm (18 in.) long. This fossil was found in Brazil, South America.

DIFFERENTIATE INSTRUCTION

More Reading Support

A From what three sources did Wegener gather evidence for his continental drift hypothesis? *fossils, studies of ancient climate, and the geology of continents*

English Learners Help English learners with words such as *still, yet, instead, in contrast, but,* and *however,* which signal a clause or a sentence with a contrasting meaning to the clause or sentence that precedes these words. For example, ". . . South Africa today has a warm climate. *Yet* its rocks were deeply scratched by ice sheets. . . ." *Yet* signals a contrast between "warm climate" and "ice sheets."

8.2 INSTRUCT

Teach the Standards

Tectonic plates 6.1.a

In this section: Make sure students understand the theory of plate tectonics. Then point out the evidence presented in this section: the movement of continents and the distribution of fossils, ancient climate zones, rock types, and ocean trenches.

previously taught: rock formation, pp. 191–195

future opportunities: earthquakes, p. 302; mountain belts, p. 338

Teach from Visuals

To help students interpret the outline map of South America and Africa, ask:

- What do the shaded areas on the outline maps of South America and Africa represent? *where Mesosaurus fossils have been found*
- What do you notice about the location of the shaded areas and the coastlines of the two continents? *The shaded areas are located where the coastlines fit together.*
- What does this evidence suggest? *The two continents were once joined.*

History of Science

During Wegener's time, many scientists were aware that fossils of identical plants and animals from the same time period had been found in South America and in Africa. Wegener's critics came up with their own hypotheses, such as the following: land bridges once connected the continents; plants and animals reached distant lands by floating on rafts of driftwood; animals swam across thousands of miles of ocean. There was no evidence for any of these hypotheses, yet Wegener's critics continued to reject his ideas until the 1960s.

Ongoing Assessment

Answer: Answers will vary, but students should be able to give reasons for their choices.

Teach from Visuals

To help students interpret the four maps of Pangaea and continental drift, ask:

- What was Earth like 200 million years ago? *It had one large continent and one huge ocean.*
- By 180 million years ago, how had Earth changed? *It had split into two continents.*
- How long ago did most of the major continents become separate? *65 million years ago*

Address Misconceptions

IDENTIFY Ask students to give examples of scientific changes that they have noticed in the past few years. If they cite examples that focus solely on inventions of new technology, they may hold the misconception that technology or new discoveries are necessary for scientific change.

CORRECT Point out that scientific changes also involve developing new theories to explain observations or to reinterpret previous evidence. The facts may not change, but the explanation of those facts changes and can alter how we see the world.

REASSESS Ask: How is Wegener's work an example of how science changes? *Wegener made new observations and reinterpreted existing evidence to develop his hypothesis of continental drift.*

Technology Resources

Visit **ClassZone.com** for background on common student misconceptions.

 **MISCONCEPTION DATABASE**

Ongoing Assessment

Explain how the continental drift hypothesis was developed.

Ask: How did Wegener develop the continental drift hypothesis? *To explain the fact that the western coast of Africa and the eastern coast of South America seemed to fit together, Wegener gathered evidence from fossils, from studies of ancient climate, and from the rock formations on both continents.*

Examine continental movement over the past 150 million years.

Pangaea and Continental Drift

For Wegener, all the evidence pointed to a single conclusion. The continents had once been joined in a huge supercontinent he called **Pangaea** (pan-JEE-uh). *Pangaea* comes from the Greek word meaning "all lands." This giant continent reached from pole to pole and was centered over the area where Africa lies today.

Pangaea began to split apart some 200 million years ago. In time, the continents moved to where they are today. Yet Wegener could not explain *how* the continents moved. Because of this, his critics called continental drift "a fairy tale" and rejected his hypothesis.

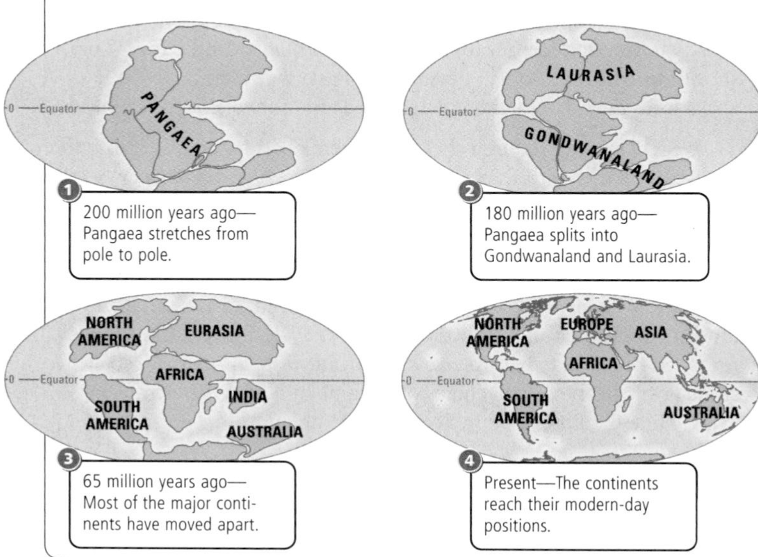

1 200 million years ago—Pangaea stretches from pole to pole.

2 180 million years ago—Pangaea splits into Gondwanaland and Laurasia.

3 65 million years ago—Most of the major continents have moved apart.

4 Present—The continents reach their modern-day positions.

The theory of plate tectonics explains how plates and their continents move.

For many years, Wegener's ideas were pushed aside. Then in the mid-1900s, scientists proved that tectonic plates move. They also offered explanations about how the plates move. Their work eventually led to the theory of plate tectonics, which built on some of Wegener's ideas.

Evidence from the Sea Floor

Scientists began mapping the sea floor in detail in the 1950s. They expected the floor to be smooth and level. Instead, they found huge underwater mountain ranges, called **mid-ocean ridges.** These ridges appeared in every ocean, circling Earth like seams in a baseball.

DIFFERENTIATE INSTRUCTION

 **More Reading Support**

B What is Pangaea? *Wegener's name for the supercontinent that once reached from pole to pole.*

Advanced Challenge students to add to the visual presentation on p. 272 by drawing a fifth map showing how the continents might look 100 million years from now. Refer students to the map on p. 275 to see the directions in which the major plates are moving. You might also refer them to pp. 282–283 for a discussion of rift valleys. *Maps should show a wider Atlantic Ocean. They might also show that the Red Sea has widened, the Mediterranean has narrowed, and a long narrow sea has formed in the Great Rift Valley as eastern Africa begins to split from the continent.*

Sea-Floor Spreading Scientists learned that the ridges form along cracks in the crust. Molten rock rises through these cracks. Then it cools and forms new oceanic crust. The old crust is pulled away, making room for new material. In this way, the sea floor slowly spreads apart. Scientists call these areas spreading centers. You will read more about spreading centers in Section 8.3.

Age of the Sea Floor Further evidence that the sea floor is spreading apart came from the age of the rocks in the crust. Scientists drilled into the sea floor from a specially equipped ship called the *Glomar Challenger.* The rock samples revealed that the youngest rock is closest to the ridge. The oldest rock is farthest away.

The samples also showed that even the oldest ocean floor is young—only 160 to 180 million years old. Continental crust is much older—up to 4 billion years old. These data confirmed that the ocean floor is constantly forming and moving away from the mid-ocean ridges like a conveyor belt. As the sea floor moves, the tectonic plates and their continents also move.

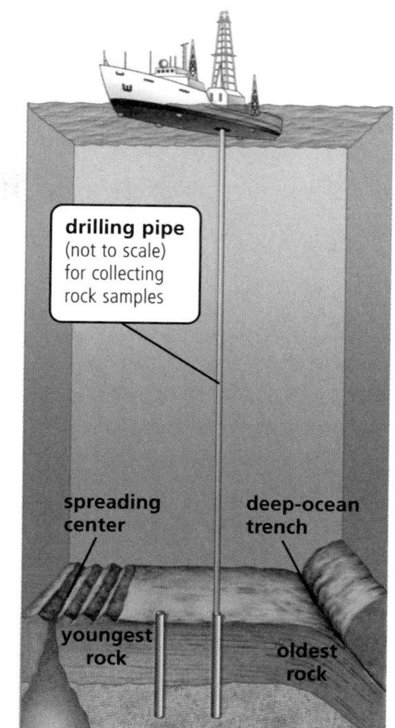

Scientists drill into the sea floor to obtain rock samples. The different ages of the rocks prove that plates move.

Ocean Trenches If the sea floor has been spreading for millions of years, why isn't Earth getting larger? Scientists discovered the answer at huge trenches in the sea floor. At these sites, dense oceanic crust is sinking into the asthenosphere. Old crust is being destroyed at the same rate that new crust is forming. As a result, Earth remains the same size.

Scientists now had evidence that tectonic plates move. But the same question remained. *How* could the plates move thousands of kilometers around the planet? The asthenosphere provided a possible answer.

CHECK YOUR READING How does the age of the sea floor show that plates move?

Causes of Plate Movement

Tectonic plates rest on the asthenosphere, a layer of soft, hot rock. Rock in this layer and in the mantle just below it moves by convection. **Convection** is the transfer of energy by the movement of a material. You have seen convection if you have ever boiled a pot of water. The water at the bottom of the pot heats up, becomes less dense, and rises. At the surface, it cools, becomes denser, and sinks. Then the water is heated and rises again.

The rock in the asthenosphere acts in a similar way. The hot, soft rock rises, cools, and sinks. Then it is heated and rises again. If this sinking and rising continues, it is called a **convection current**—a motion that transfers heat energy in a material.

Teach from Visuals

To help students interpret the drilling diagram, ask:

- What kind of rock samples did scientists find closest to a spreading center? *youngest rock*
- What kind of rock samples did scientists find farther from the spreading center? *old rock*
- What did this evidence indicate? *that new rock was being created at the spreading center and older rock was being pushed away from the spreading center*

History of Science

Scientific knowledge of the ocean floor increased greatly during World War II (1939–1945). Ships with echo-sounding devices measured the depth of the ocean at various locations. They recorded the time it took for sound to reach the ocean floor and bounce back. The recordings showed that a mountain chain existed in the central Atlantic Ocean. As exploration of the sea floor expanded in the 1950s, scientists discovered that this mountain chain nearly circled the Earth.

Ongoing Assessment

CHECK YOUR READING *Answer: Rock is youngest near the ridge, and older as you get farther away, showing that the older rock was carried away from the ridge some time ago.*

DIFFERENTIATE INSTRUCTION

More Reading Support

C What happens at a spreading center? *sea floor slowly spreads apart*

D How does rock in the asthenosphere move? *by convection*

Below Level To help students see how Wegener's ideas moved from a hypothesis to a theory, outline on the board the mounting evidence that supported his idea. Emphasize that a hypothesis is an unproved explanation of observations and evidence. A theory is a well-tested and widely accepted explanation that is consistent with available evidence. It can explain all or most of the data and can be used to predict future events.

EXPLORE the BIG idea

Revisit "Convection in Action" on p. 263. Have students explain their results.

Teach from Visuals

To help students interpret the plate movement diagram, ask:

- In what direction do convection currents move on each side of a spreading center? *outward from the center*
- In what direction would the plates move as a result? *in opposite directions away from the spreading center*

Ongoing Assessment

Describe how scientists developed the theory of plate tectonics.

Ask: What did geologists in the late 1960s combine to develop the theory of plate tectonics? *information about tectonic plates, about the sea floor, and about movements in the mantle*

READING VISUALS *Answer: Higher temperatures near the bottom heat up the material and cause it to rise. Lower temperatures near the surface cool the material and cause it to sink.*

Convection currents in the mantle are much slower than those in boiling water. The rock creeps only a few centimeters a year. The diagram below shows convection currents circulating. The tectonic plates in the lithosphere are carried on the asthenosphere like long, heavy boxes moved on huge rollers. Over millions of years, convection currents carry the plates thousands of kilometers.

Scientists suspect that two other motions help move these huge plates. The motions are called slab pull and ridge push. Slab pull takes place where gravity pulls the edge of a cool, dense plate into the asthenosphere. Because plates are hard, the entire plate is dragged along. Ridge push occurs when material from a mid-ocean ridge slides downhill from the ridge. The material pushes the rest of the plate.

Putting the Theory Together

REMINDER
A scientific theory is a well-tested explanation that is consistent with all available evidence.

 E

Geologists combined their knowledge of Earth's plates, the sea floor, and the asthenosphere to develop the **theory of plate tectonics.** The theory states that Earth's lithosphere is made up of huge plates that move over the surface of Earth.

The map on page 275 shows Earth's major tectonic plates and the directions in which they move. They are the African, Antarctic, Australian, Indian, Eurasian, Nazca, North and South American, and Pacific plates.

Causes of Plate Movement

Convection currents, slab pull, and ridge push move Earth's huge tectonic plates.

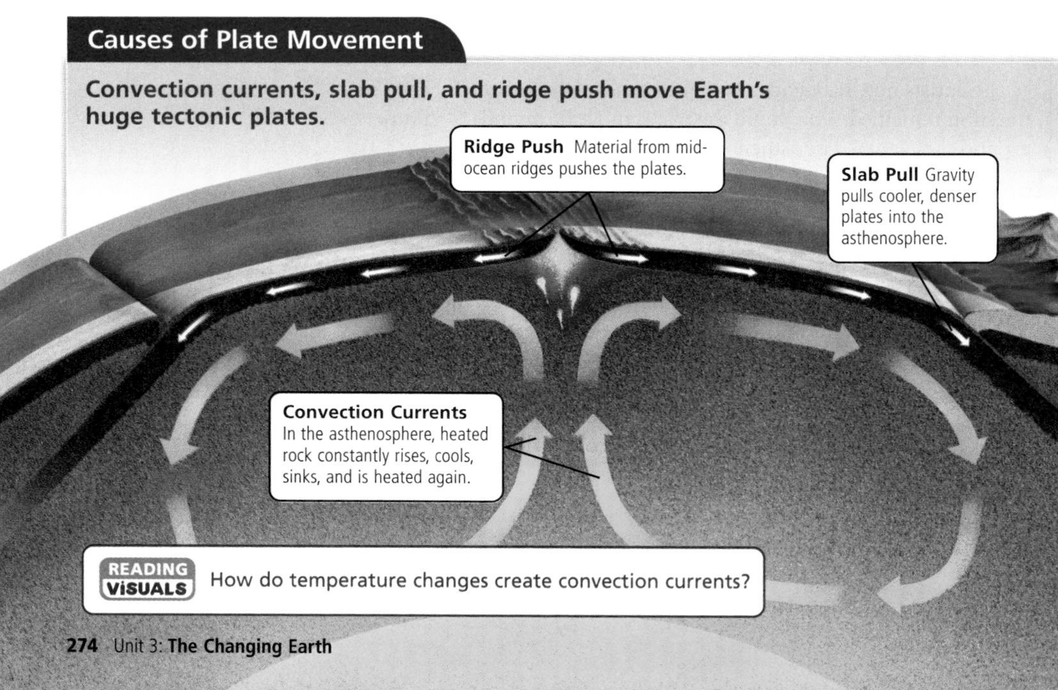
Ridge Push Material from mid-ocean ridges pushes the plates.
Slab Pull Gravity pulls cooler, denser plates into the asthenosphere.
Convection Currents In the asthenosphere, heated rock constantly rises, cools, sinks, and is heated again.

READING VISUALS How do temperature changes create convection currents?

274 Unit 3: The Changing Earth

DIFFERENTIATE INSTRUCTION

More Reading Support

E What does the theory of plate tectonics state? *Earth's lithosphere is made up of huge, moving plates that are carried over Earth's surface.*

Advanced Have students who excel in mathematics calculate how far a plate would move in 200 million years if it moved at the rate of 3 cm per year. *Answer: 200,000,000 × 3 cm = 600,000,000 cm. 600,000,000 ÷ 100,000 = 6000 km* Ask students to consult reference sources to find out the width of the Atlantic Ocean. Then have them discuss how their calculations and findings relate to the theory of plate tectonics. *(The width of the Atlantic Ocean varies from about 2900 to 8800 km.)*

 Challenge and Extension, p. 30

Tectonic Plates

Earth's lithosphere is made up of moving plates.

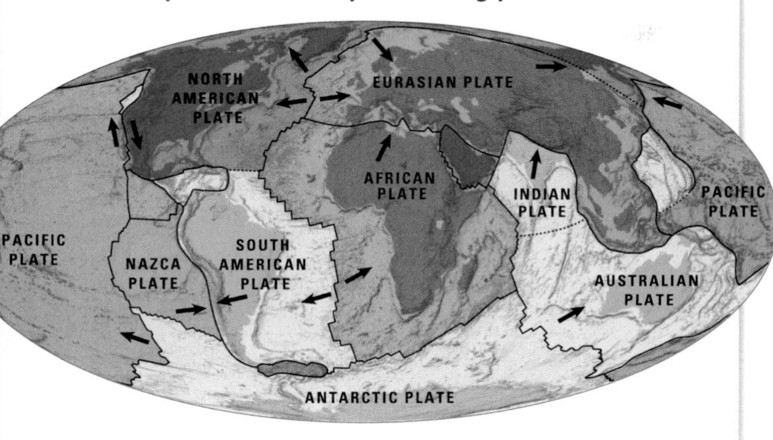

READING VISUALS Where on the map are two plates moving apart? pushing together? scraping past each other?

As scientists studied the plates, they realized that one plate could not shift without affecting the others nearby. They found that plates can move apart, push together, or scrape past each other. The arrows on the map above show each type of plate motion.

Plate movements cause great changes in Earth's crust. Most major earthquakes, volcanoes, and mountain ranges appear where tectonic plates meet. You will learn why as you read more about plate movements.

CALIFORNIA Focus

Most of California is on the North American Plate, but the part west of the San Andreas Fault is on the Pacific Plate. The plates are moving past each other in opposite directions at an average rate of about 5 cm per year.

8.2 Review

KEY CONCEPTS

1. What evidence did Wegener gather to support his continental drift hypothesis? (6.1.a)
2. Give three types of evidence from the sea floor that prove Earth's tectonic plates move. (6.1.a)
3. Explain how motions in the asthenosphere can move tectonic plates around Earth. (6.1.c)

CRITICAL THINKING

4. **Apply** A friend tells you he read on a Web site that Earth is getting smaller. What can you tell him that shows Earth's size is not changing?
5. **Evaluate** What other types of scientists, besides geologists, would find the theory of plate tectonics useful in their work?

CHALLENGE

6. **Infer** Use the arrows on the map above and your knowledge of sea-floor spreading and ocean trenches to answer these questions: What is happening to the size of the Atlantic Ocean? What can you infer is happening to the size of the Pacific Ocean? Explain your answers.

ANSWERS

. ancient climate clues that showed continents had once been in different locations; the same rock layers and fossils appeared on two widely separated continents.

. sea-floor spreading, different ages of sea-floor rock, ocean trenches

3. Circulation of heated and cooling material forms convection currents that can carry tectonic plates.

4. The oceanic crust is sinking into trenches, but at the same time, the sea floor is spreading. Both happen at the same rate, so Earth stays the same size.

5. biologists and oceanographers

6. Because of sea-floor spreading the Atlantic Ocean is getting wider; the Pacific Ocean must be getting narrower because the size of Earth stays roughly the same.

Ongoing Assessment

READING VISUALS *Sample answer: the North and South American plates are moving apart from the Eurasian and African plates; the Nazca Plate and the South American Plate are pushing together; the Pacific Plate and the North American Plate are scraping past each other.*

Teach from Visuals

To help students interpret the map of Earth's tectonic plates, ask:

- How many major plates are shown on the map? *9*
- How large are the major plates? *larger than continents*

Reinforce the BIG idea

Have students relate the section to the Big Idea.

 Reinforcing Key Concepts, p. 31

8.2 ASSESS & RETEACH

Assess

 Section 8.2 Quiz, p. 177

Reteach

Help students review this section's concepts by writing these heads on the board: "Evidence for Continental Drift" and "Evidence for Plate Tectonics." Call on students to identify the main ideas for each. *Evidence for Continental Drift: fossils, climate, rock formations. Evidence for Plate Tectonics: sea-floor spreading, sea-floor rock of different ages, ocean trenches.*

Technology Resources

Have students visit **ClassZone.com** for reteaching of Key Concepts.

 **CONTENT REVIEW**

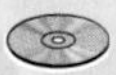 **CONTENT REVIEW CD-ROM**

CHAPTER INVESTIGATION

Focus

PURPOSE To observe the movement of convection currents in order to determine how they move tectonic plates

OVERVIEW Students will use candles to heat water in a pan and create convection currents to move drops of food coloring and sponges. Students will find the following:

- Heat creates convection currents in water.
- These currents move objects on the surface of the water.

Lab Preparation

- Work with the class as a group to write the hypothesis for the experiment.
- Have students create their own lab datasheets. They should make a full-page, two-column chart with the column headings *Cold Water* and *Hot Water* and the row headings *Food Coloring* and *Sponges.*
- Create two stations, each with a set of the materials listed.
- Prior to the investigation, have students read through the investigation and prepare their data tables. Or you may wish to copy and distribute datasheets and rubrics.

UNIT RESOURCE BOOK, pp. 62–70

SCIENCE TOOLKIT, F14

Lab Management

- If possible, students should work in small groups. Each student should have the chance to do something in the experiment—for example, light the candles, hold the sponges, write the observations, and so on.
- Tell students to line up the matching "coastlines" so they are centered lengthwise over the candles.

SAFETY Advise students to be careful with the matches and to return them to you as soon as they finish.

CHAPTER INVESTIGATION

Convection Currents and Plate Movement

OVERVIEW AND PURPOSE South America and Africa are drifting slowly apart. What powerful force could be moving these two plates? In this investigation you will

- observe the movement of convection currents
- determine how convection currents in Earth's mantle could move tectonic plates

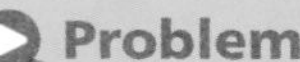

Problem

How do convection currents in a fluid affect floating objects on the surface?

Hypothesize

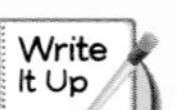

Write a hypothesis to explain how convection currents affect floating objects. Your hypothesis should take the form of an "If . . . , then . . . , because . . ." statement.

MATERIALS
- rectangular glass baking dish
- 2 oblong pans or 2 bricks
- ruler
- water
- liquid food coloring
- 2 small candles
- matches
- 2 sponges
- scissors
- 3–4 pushpins

6.1.c, 6.3.c, 6.7.a, 6.7.c, 6.7.d

Procedure

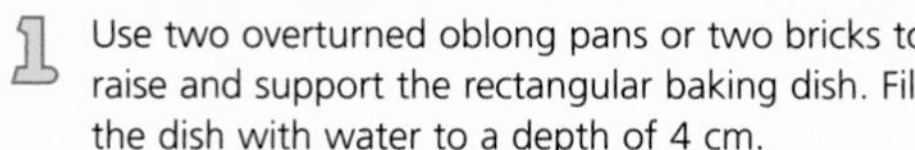

1. Use two overturned oblong pans or two bricks to raise and support the rectangular baking dish. Fill the dish with water to a depth of 4 cm.
2. Hold the food coloring over the middle of the dish. Squeeze several drops into the water. Be careful not to touch or disturb the water with the plastic tip or your hands. Write down your observations.
3. Light the two candles and place them beneath the center of the dish. Then squeeze several more drops of food coloring into the middle of the dish.

step 3

4. Observe what happens for a few minutes, and then write down your observations. After you have finished, blow out the candles and wait until the water cools.
5. Moisten the two sponges. Cut one into the shape of South America and the other into the shape of Africa. Insert the pushpins as shown in the photo.

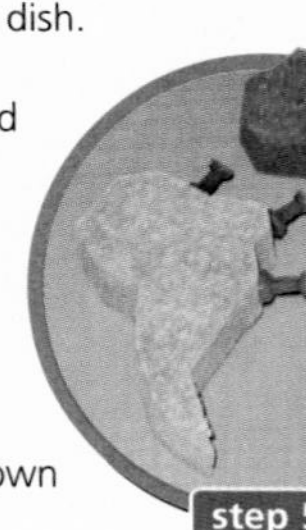
step 5

INVESTIGATION RESOURCES

CHAPTER INVESTIGATION, Convection Currents and Plate Movement
- Level A, pp. 62–65
- Level B, pp. 66–69
- Level C, p. 70

Advanced students should complete Levels B & C.

Writing a Lab Report, D12–13

Technology Resources

Customize this student lab as needed or look for an alternative. Print rubrics to assess student lab reports.

Lab Generator CD-ROM

Content Standard
6.3.c Students know heat flows in solids by conduction (which involves no flow of matter) and in fluids by conduction and by convection (which involves flow of matter).

Investigation Standard
6.7.a Develop a hypothesis.

6 Place the sponges on top of the water in the center of the dish. Fit the two sponges together along their coastlines.

7 Gently hold the sponges together until the water is still. Then let go. Observe them for a few minutes and record what you saw.

8 Light the candles again. Place them under the dish and directly beneath the two sponges.

9 Gently hold the sponges together again until the water heats up. Then carefully let go of the sponges, trying not to disturb the water.

10 Observe the sponges for a few minutes. Then record your observations.

Observe and Analyze

Write It Up

1. **RECORD** Draw diagrams to show how the food coloring and the sponges moved in cold water and in heated water. Use arrows to indicate any motion.
2. **ANALYZE** Did the food coloring and the sponges move more with or without the candles? Use what you have learned about convection to explain the role of the candles.

Conclude

Write It Up

1. **EVALUATE** Water is a fluid, but the asthenosphere is not. What properties of the asthenosphere allow it to move like a fluid and form convection currents?
2. **COMPARE AND CONTRAST** How is your setup like Earth's asthenosphere and lithosphere? How is your setup different?
3. **ANALYZE** Compare your results with your hypothesis. Do your observations support your hypothesis? Why or why not?
4. **INTERPRET** Write an answer to your problem statement.
5. **IDENTIFY CONTROLS** Did your experiment include controls? If so, what purpose did they serve?
6. **APPLY** In your own words, explain how the African continent and the South American continent are drifting apart.
7. **APPLY** Suppose you own an aquarium. You want to make sure your fish are warm whether they swim near the top or near the bottom of the aquarium. The pet store sells two types of heaters. One heater extends 5 cm below the water's surface. The other heater rests on the bottom of the aquarium. Based on what you learned in this activity, which heater would you choose? Why?

INVESTIGATE Further

CHALLENGE Design a new version of this experiment that you think would be a better model of the movements in Earth's asthenosphere and lithosphere. What materials will you need? What changes would you make to the procedure? Sketch your experiment, and explain what makes it better.

Convection Currents and Plate Movement
Problem How do convection currents in a fluid affect floating objects on the surface?
Hypothesize
Observe and Analyze
Diagram 1. Sponges on Unheated Water
Conclude

Chapter 8: **Plate Tectonics** **277**

Observe and Analyze

SAMPLE DATA Drops of food coloring and sponges do not move in cold water. They move apart in heated water.

1. *Diagrams will show no motion in cold water, and will show objects moving apart in heated water.*
2. *More with the candles. Candles heated the water at the bottom; hot water rose to the surface where it cooled; the cool water sank, only to be heated once again. Candles keep convection currents going.*

Conclude

1. *The heated rock is soft and able to move, so it can circulate slowly.*
2. *Similar: heat source, layers, objects on the surface. Different: water is more fluid, the candles are concentrated in one spot, the sponges are much smaller and don't cover the surface area.*
3. *Students should explain why their hypothesis was supported or not.*
4. *Student answers should mention the fact that convection currents move objects on the surface.*
5. *Yes, the controls were the food coloring and the sponges in cold water. The controls served to show there was not another cause of movement.*
6. *At the mid-ocean ridge, the new crust is pushing the old crust aside. The spreading center moves the oceanic crust like a conveyor belt. As the crust moves, the continents are carried farther and farther apart.*
7. *Heater that rests on bottom—it will create convection currents that circulate warm water throughout the entire aquarium.*

INVESTIGATE Further

CHALLENGE Students can work in small groups to design new versions of the experiment. Ask them to present their versions to the class. If possible, have them conduct their experiments and report on the results.

ost-Lab Discussion

sk students the following questions:

- What difficulties or errors did you encounter when doing this lab? *Students may say holding the continents together or getting them centered over the candles.*
- How did this experiment affect your understanding of convection currents? *Answers will vary, but students should mention how watching the action of the food coloring or sponges moving made convection currents more clear.*

8.3 FOCUS

Set Learning Goals

Students will

- Identify different plate boundaries.
- Explain what happens when plates move apart.
- Determine how to measure the direction and speed of plates.
- Model the magnetic reversal of Earth's poles in an experiment.

3-Minute Warm-Up

Display Transparency 61 or copy this exercise on the board:

Match each definition with the correct term.

Definitions

1. huge landmass in which all continents were once joined *a*
2. hypothesis that Earth's continents were once joined in a single landmass and gradually moved apart *d*
3. theory that Earth's lithosphere is made up of huge, moving plates that are carried around the planet by motions in the mantle *b*

Terms

a. Pangaea c. sea-floor spreading
b. plate tectonics d. continental drift

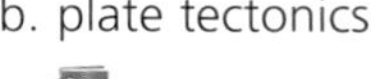

3-Minute Warm-Up, p. T61

8.3 MOTIVATE

EXPLORE Divergent Boundaries

PURPOSE To model how plates move apart at a divergent boundary

TIP *15 min.* Make sure students pull the pieces out slowly enough to see how the two sides match.

WHAT DO YOU THINK? *The two pieces of paper move away from the crack in the center at the same rate. There might be a similar formation of new crust pushing the old crust back.*

KEY CONCEPT

8.3 Plates move apart.

CALIFORNIA Content Standards

6.1.c Students know lithospheric plates the size of continents and oceans move at rates of centimeters per year in response to movements in the mantle.

6.1.e Students know major geologic events, such as earthquakes, volcanic eruptions, and mountain building, result from plate motions.

BEFORE, you learned

- The continents join and break apart
- The sea floor provides evidence that tectonic plates move
- The theory of plate tectonics helps explain how the plates move

NOW, you will learn

- About different plate boundaries
- What happens when plates move apart
- How the direction and speed of plates can be measured

VOCABULARY

divergent boundary p. 278
convergent boundary p. 278
transform boundary p. 278
rift valley p. 279
magnetic reversal p. 280
hot spot p. 283

EXPLORE Divergent Boundaries (6.1.c)

What happens when plates move apart?

PROCEDURE

1. Cut the piece of striped paper into two symmetrical pieces slightly less wide than the slit in the oatmeal box.
2. Match up the lines of the two pieces and tape the pieces together at one edge. Push the taped edge into the box until only a few centimeters of the free edges show at the top.
3. Grasp each piece of paper, one in each hand. Slowly pull the two pieces horizontally out of the cylinder, pulling them in opposite directions.

WHAT DO YOU THINK?

How is your model similar to the process of sea-floor spreading?

MATERIALS

- scissors
- piece of striped paper
- tape
- small oatmeal box with slit cut in side

READING TIP

Use word meanings to help remember science terms.

diverge = to go in different directions

converge = to come together from different directions

transform = to change

Tectonic plates have different boundaries.

A plate boundary is where the edges of two plates meet. After studying the way plates move, geologists identified three types of boundaries.

- A **divergent boundary** (dih-VUR-juhnt) occurs where plates move apart. Most divergent boundaries are found in the ocean.
- A **convergent boundary** (kuhn-VUR-juhnt) occurs where plates push together.
- A **transform boundary** occurs where plates scrape past each other.

In this section, you will discover what happens at divergent boundaries in the ocean and on land. You will read more about convergent and transform boundaries in Section 8.4.

RESOURCES FOR DIFFERENTIATED INSTRUCTION

Below Level

UNIT RESOURCE BOOK

- Reading Study Guide A, pp. 34–35
- Decoding Support, p. 59

AUDIO CDS

Advanced

UNIT RESOURCE BOOK

- Challenge and Extension, p. 40
- Challenge Reading, pp. 55–56

English Learners

UNIT RESOURCE BOOK

Spanish Reading Study Guide, pp. 38–39

AUDIO CDS

- Audio Readings in Spanish
- Audio Readings (English)

Additional INVESTIGATION, Magnetic Patterns on the Ocean Floor, A, B, & C, pp. 71–79; Teacher Instructions, pp. 202

The sea floor spreads apart at divergent boundaries.

In the ocean, divergent boundaries are also called spreading centers. Mid-ocean ridges mark these sites where the ocean floor is spreading apart. As the ridges continue to widen, a gap called a **rift valley** forms. Here, hot material rises to build new crust.

Mid-Ocean Ridges and Rift Valleys

Mid-ocean ridges are the longest chain of mountains on Earth. Most of these ridges contain a rift valley along their center. See the rift valley in the diagram below. When hot material rises from the asthenosphere, cold ocean water cools the rock until it becomes solid. As the plates move apart, new cracks open in the solid rock. More hot material rises and hardens. The growing ridge stands high above the sea floor.

The world's longest ridge is the Mid-Atlantic Ridge. This ridge runs the length of the Atlantic Ocean. Here, the North and South American plates are moving away from the Eurasian and African plates. The ridge extends nearly 11,000 kilometers (6214 mi) from Iceland to near Antarctica. The rift valley is 24 kilometers (15 mi) wide and 9 kilometers (6 mi) deep. That is about 7 kilometers (4 mi) deeper than the Grand Canyon!

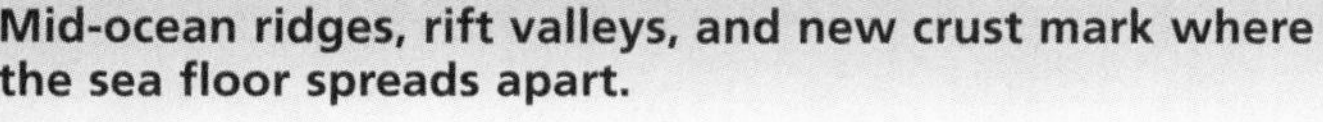

Divergent Boundary in the Ocean

Mid-ocean ridges, rift valleys, and new crust mark where the sea floor spreads apart.

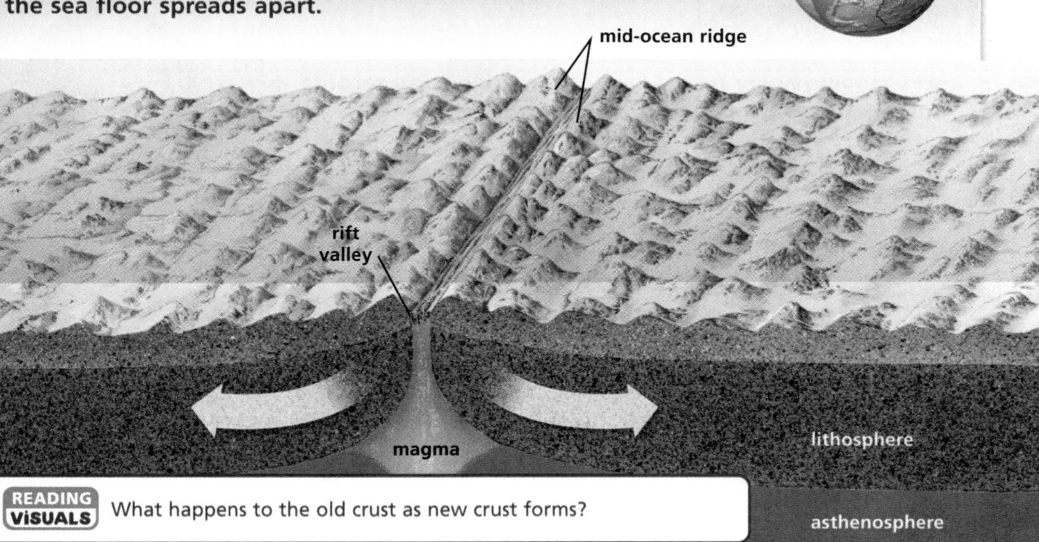

READING VISUALS What happens to the old crust as new crust forms?

DIFFERENTIATE INSTRUCTION

More Reading Support

A What features are found at divergent boundaries in the ocean? *mid-ocean ridges and rift valleys*

English Learners The paragraphs on this page have a variety of introductory clauses and phrases. For example, "As the ridges continue to widen, a gap called a rift valley forms." Have English learners find the comma that separates the introductory clause or phrase from the rest of the sentence. Then help them locate the subject of the sentence. Photocopy and distribute this and other pages and have students practice identifying introductory clauses and phrases.

8.3 INSTRUCT

Teach the Standards

Plate movement 6.1.c

In this section: Help students understand how plates move in response to movements in the mantle. Point out the evidence from mid-ocean ridges and how hot-spot volcanoes can be used to track plate movement.

- **previously taught:** mantle, p. 44; causes of plate movement, pp. 273–274
- **future opportunities:** volcanoes, pp. 346–353

Real World Example

A divergent boundary might be compared to a crack in a sidewalk where a tree has pushed through. The tree will eventually spread the sidewalk and stretch the crack wider and wider. As the tree keeps growing, it will carry the broken edges of the sidewalk upward with it, creating a type of "ridge."

Teaching with Technology

Provide students with a map of the ocean floor on CD-ROM so that they can study the Mid-Atlantic Ridge and its rift valley. Have students zoom in on the ridge to examine it more closely.

Teach from Visuals

To help students interpret the divergent boundary diagram, ask:

- What creates a rift valley? *plates pulling away from each other*
- What does the globe show? *the location of the Mid-Atlantic Ridge*

Ongoing Assessment

Explain what happens when oceanic plates move apart.

Ask: How do rift valleys and mid-ocean ridges form at spreading centers? *Rift valleys form as plates move apart. Rising magma enters the rift and cools. As the plates continue to move, more magma flows into the rift.*

Answer: Plate movement carries it away from the ridge.

Teach Difficult Concepts

Students may have difficulty understanding magnetic reversals and the difference between the Earth's magnetic poles and geographic poles. Use a globe to explain that the Earth's geographic poles mark the ends of an imaginary "pole" around which the Earth spins. The magnetic poles mark the "top" and "bottom" of Earth's magnetic field. They are located *near* the geographic poles but not at the same points. Earth's magnetic field is constantly shifting and moving, causing the magnetic poles to change location as well.

Integrate the Sciences

Physical scientists believe that the circulating flow of molten metals in the outer core produces Earth's magnetism. The outer core, being liquid, rotates at a different speed than the more solid layers. Scientists theorize that these differences in rotation produce the fluctuation in Earth's magnetic field. But as yet no one knows exactly why or how the changes occur.

Teach from Visuals

To help students interpret the magnetic reversals diagram, ask:

- What do the arrows in the two globes represent? *the direction of magnetic north on Earth*
- What pattern can you see on each side of the mid-ocean ridge? *The magnetic reversals have been recorded in identical patterns on both sides of the ridge.*

Sea-Floor Rock and Magnetic Reversals

You read earlier that the sea floor is younger near a mid-ocean ridge and older farther away. As scientists continued to study the sea-floor rock, they made a surprising discovery about Earth's magnetic field.

To understand Earth's magnetic field, you can compare the planet to a bar magnet. Like a magnet, it has a north pole and a south pole. Earth's magnetic field affects the entire planet. Notice in the diagram below that Earth's geographic and magnetic poles are not in the same place.

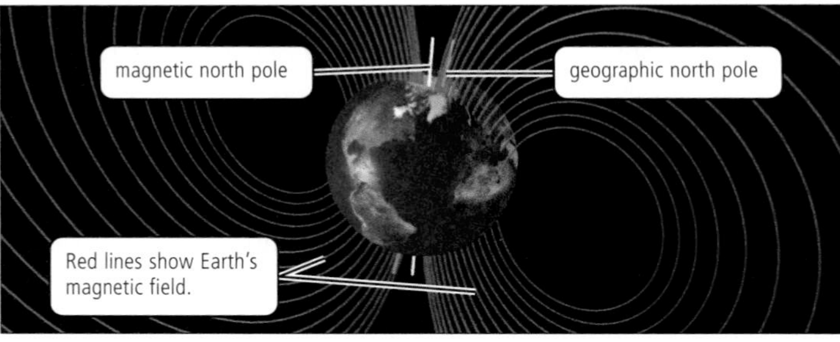

Unlike a bar magnet, Earth's magnetic poles sometimes switch places. The north pole becomes the south pole, and the south pole becomes the north pole. This switch in direction is called a **magnetic reversal.** Such reversals are caused by changes in Earth's magnetic field. No one knows why these changes happen. In contrast, Earth's geographic poles never change places.

B

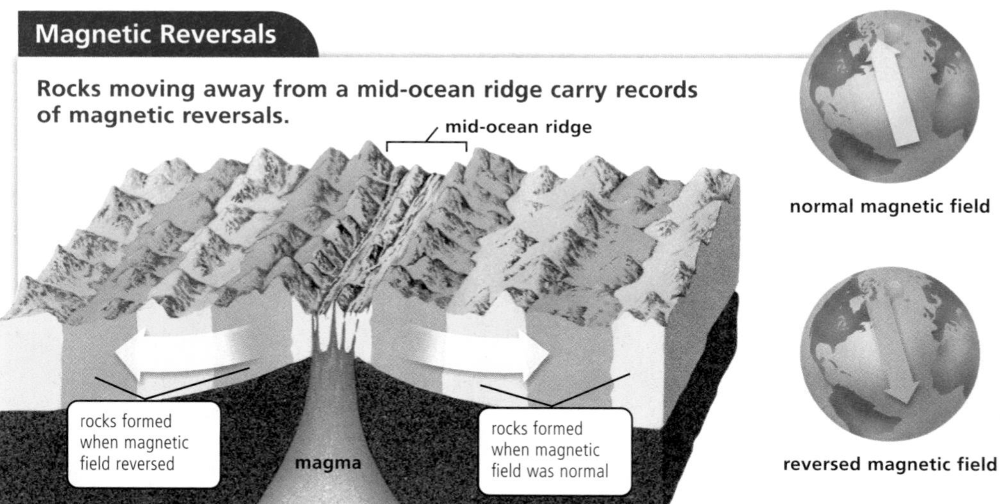

DIFFERENTIATE INSTRUCTION

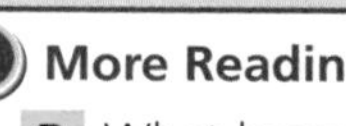

More Reading Support

B What happens in a magnetic reversal? *Earth's magnetic north and south poles switch places.*

Below Level Provide a bar magnet and iron filings so students can see how a magnetic field works. Have students use a compass to mark the north end of the magnet. Then have them reverse the bar magnet and observe how the compass needle switches direction to follow the new north.

Advanced Have students who are interested in magnetic reversals read the following article.

 Challenge Reading, pp. 55–56

Scientists found that each magnetic reversal is recorded in the sea-floor rock. These records are especially clear at some mid-ocean ridges. As the hot material rises and cools, some magnetic minerals line up with Earth's magnetic field. When the material hardens, these minerals stay in place like tiny compass needles pointing north and south. Whenever the magnetic field reverses, the cooling minerals record the change.

As shown in the diagram on page 280, the records of magnetic reversals line up like stripes in the rock. As the two plates move away from a mid-ocean ridge, each plate carries a record of magnetic reversals with it. The records are the same on either side of the ridge.

As scientists continued to map the ocean floor, they found more records of magnetic reversals. By finding the age of the rock, scientists had more evidence of plate movement. The youngest rock records the most recent reversal, which happened only about 760,000 years ago. The oldest rock records reversals that happened more than 150 million years ago.

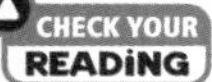
Explain how records of magnetic reversals show that plates move apart.

INVESTIGATE Magnetic Reversals

How can you map magnetic reversals?

SKILL FOCUS
Modeling (6.1.a)

MATERIALS
- string
- bar magnet
- masking tape
- marking pen
- sea-floor model

TIME
20 minutes

PROCEDURE

1. Wrap one end of the string around the middle of the bar magnet. Tape the string in place as shown.
2. Place a small piece of tape on one end of the magnet. Label the tape "N" to represent north.
3. Hold the bar magnet over one end of the sea-floor model as shown. Move the magnet SLOWLY toward the other end of the sea-floor model. Record your observations.

WHAT DO YOU THINK?

- What did the magnet reveal about the sea-floor model? Draw a diagram showing any pattern that you might have observed.
- Which part of the model represents the youngest sea floor? Which part represents the oldest sea floor?

CHALLENGE If Earth's magnetic field had never reversed in the past, how would the sea-floor model be different?

DIFFERENTIATE INSTRUCTION

More Reading Support

C Where is each magnetic reversal recorded? *in the sea-floor rock*

Additional Investigation To reinforce Section 8.3 learning goals, use the following full-period investigation:

Additional INVESTIGATION, Magnetic Patterns on the Ocean Floor, A, B, & C, pp. 71–79, 202
(Advanced students should complete Levels B and C.)

Advanced Challenge students to explain how the sea-floor model for the investigation on this page was made.

History of Science

In the 1950s, scientists mapping the ocean floor began using magnetometers that were adapted from submarine-detecting devices developed during World War II. Their discovery of the magnetic striping of the ocean floor surprised and puzzled scientists. Then in 1963, two English and two Canadian scientists independently proposed the idea that the pattern of magnetic striping corresponded to episodes of magnetic reversals in Earth's history.

INVESTIGATE Magnetic Reversals

PURPOSE To explore the effects of magnetic reversals

TIPS *20 min.* Make the sea-floor model before class using the instructions on p. 41 of the Unit Resource Book. Have students hold the magnet in the center of the model and move it *slowly* from one end to the other. If students move it too quickly, they will not see the magnet flip directions.

WHAT DO YOU THINK? *magnetic reversals; diagrams should show striped pattern that is the same on both sides. youngest: near the mid-ocean ridge; oldest: closest to the outside edges of the model*

CHALLENGE *The model would show one uniform direction for magnetic north and south.*

- Sea-floor Model Instructions, p. 41
- Datasheet, Magnetic Reversals, p. 42

Technology Resources

Customize this student lab as needed or look for an alternative. Print rubrics to assess student lab reports.

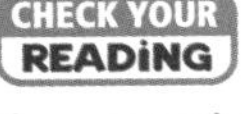
Lab Generator CD-ROM

Ongoing Assessment

Answer: The farther away from the ridge, the older the record of reversals on both sides of the ridge. This shows that the plates move away from the center.

Real World Example

You might compare the bulging and sinking of the crust at a continental divergent boundary to an asphalt road in winter. As water under the road freezes and expands, it causes the land and the asphalt to rise. When the water melts, it creates a small crater into which the road sinks. A pothole results.

Integrate the Sciences

The Great Rift Valley is not only a remarkable geological feature, it also supports a rich diversity of vegetation and wildlife. Mountain gorillas live in the rain forests on volcanic mountains. The grasslands of the Serengeti are home to herds of antelope, wildebeest, zebras, gazelles, and elephant as well as lions, leopards, and cheetahs.

Teach from Visuals

To help students interpret the divergent boundary diagrams, ask:

- In what direction are the plates moving in the large diagram? *away from each other*
- Do rift valleys grow wider or narrower as magma rises? *wider*
- What happens to the valley floor as the rift widens? *thins and sinks*

Ongoing Assessment

Explain what happens when continental plates move apart.

Ask: What happens to the crust when a continental plate begins to split? *The crust bulges and then splits and falls inward, creating a rift valley.*

CHECK YOUR READING *The valley can be flooded by waters from nearby oceans or rivers, eventually forming a lake or sea.*

Continents split apart at divergent boundaries.

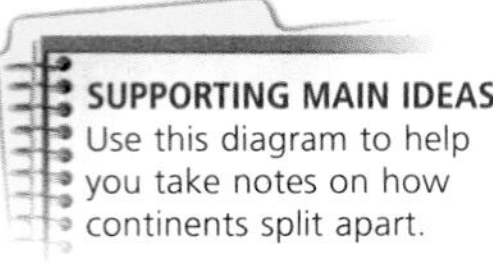

SUPPORTING MAIN IDEAS
Use this diagram to help you take notes on how continents split apart.

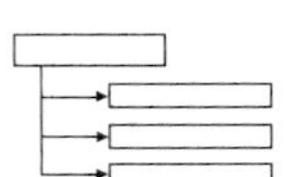

Like the sea floor, continents spread apart at a divergent boundary. The boundary begins to form when hot material rises from deep in the mantle. This heat causes the crust to bulge upward. The crust cracks as it is stretched, and a rift valley forms. This is shown in the diagram below. Magma rises through the cracked, thinned crust and forms volcanoes. As the rift valley grows wider, the continent begins to split apart.

If the rift valley continues to widen, the thinned valley floor sinks lower and lower until it is below sea level. Water from nearby oceans or rivers may fill the valley and form a sea or a lake. In the Middle East, the Arabian Plate and African Plate have been moving apart for several million years. Over time, the waters of the Indian Ocean gradually filled the rift valley, forming the Red Sea. This sea is slowly getting wider as the plates continue to move apart.

CHECK YOUR READING What happens when the floor of a rift valley sinks below sea level?

Divergent Boundary on Land

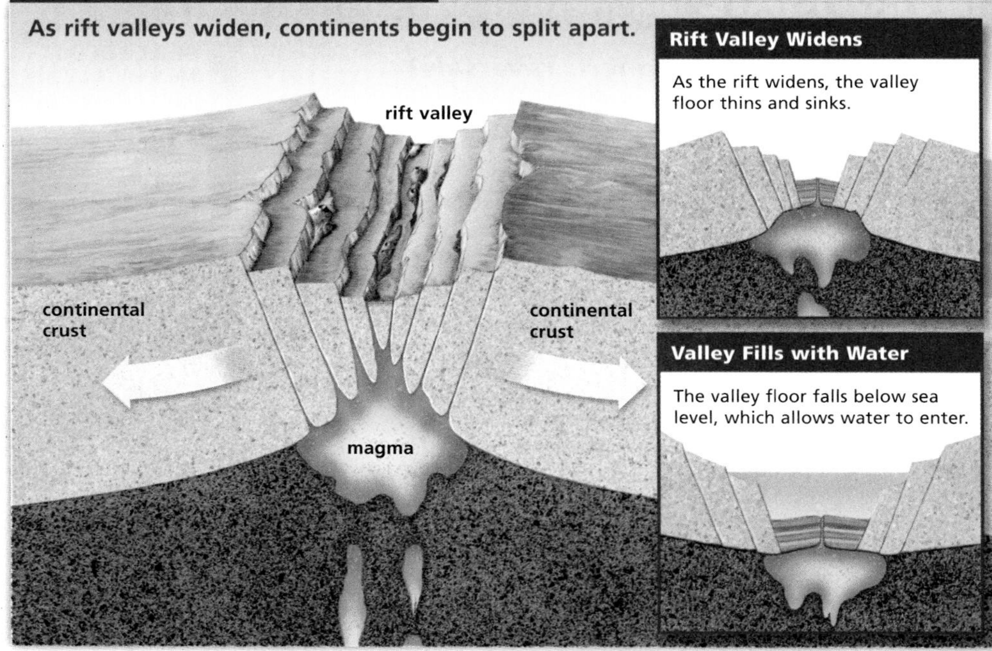

DIFFERENTIATE INSTRUCTION

More Reading Support

D What is slowly happening to the Red Sea? *It is getting wider.*

Below Level On a physical map, point out the location of the Red Sea and note that it is part of the Great Rift Valley system that extends from Syria to Mozambique. Students should be able to visualize from the map how Saudi Arabia split away from Africa and water from the Indian Ocean formed the Red Sea.

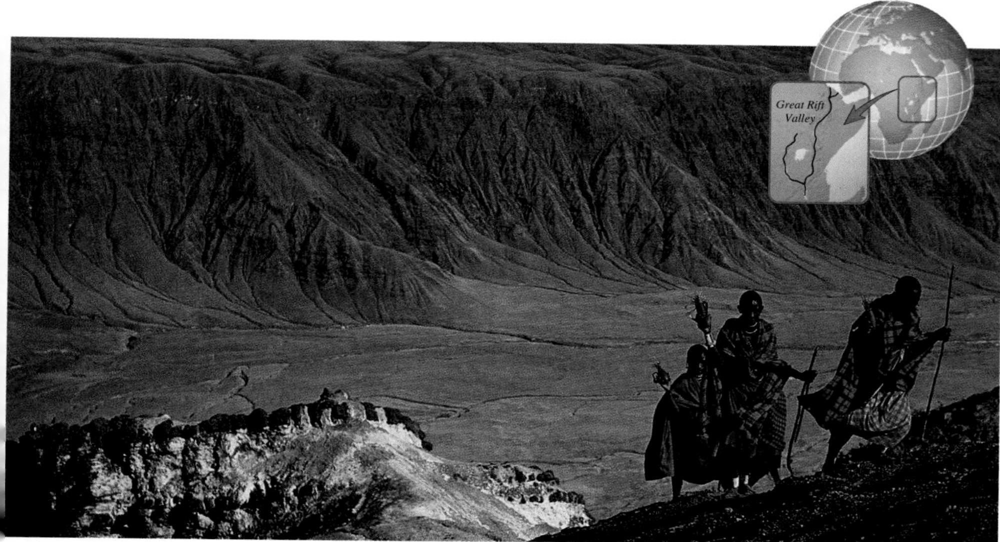

The Great Rift Valley in eastern Africa is a good example of a continental rift valley. It is getting wider as the African Plate splits apart. This huge valley is thousands of kilometers long and as much as 1800 meters (5900 ft) deep.

PREDICT Rift valleys, like the Great Rift Valley in Africa, occur where plates are moving apart. What will happen to the Rift Valley when it gets deep enough?

Hot spots can be used to track plate movements.

Hot spots are places where heated rock rises from the mantle in plumes, or thin columns. Volcanoes often develop above the plume. Although most hot spots occur far from plate boundaries, they offer a way to measure plate movement. This is because a hot spot generally stays in one place while the tectonic plate above it keeps moving.

At a hot spot, the heat from the plume partly melts some of the rock in the tectonic plate above it. Magma formed in this way can rise all the way through the plate. If the plate stays over the hot spot long enough, the rock above it will melt and a volcano will form at the surface of the plate.

After repeated eruptions, a hot-spot volcano that forms on the ocean floor may become high enough to rise above the sea as an island. For example, the Hawaiian Islands are being built as the Pacific Plate moves slowly over a hot spot.

The Hawaiian islands are located in the middle of the Pacific Plate. The largest island, Hawaii, is still over the hot spot.

IFFERENTIATE INSTRUCTION

More Reading Support

E What is a hot spot? *volcanic activity that develops above a plume, which is a stream of magma rising from the mantle*

Advanced Have students draw diagrams that show how a hot spot can be used to track plate movements. Ask them to mark which landforms (volcanic islands or volcanic mountains) were created first, second, and so on. Ask students to assign a direction and speed to their tectonic plate and calculate the ages of the landforms, starting from a specific point in time, say, 100,000,000 years ago.

R Challenge and Extension, p. 40

Teach Difficult Concepts

The idea of hot spot volcanoes may be difficult for students to understand. You might have students view an animation of the process on the Internet or you might try the following demonstration.

Teacher Demo

Demonstrate the concept of a hot spot using a candle and wax tablet. As you hold a lit candle under a tablet of wax, tell students that the wax tablet is like a tectonic plate, and the candle is a like plume of magma rising from the mantle. The tablet melts under the hot candle just as the rock of a tectonic plate would melt under a hot spot. When you move the tablet, another spot starts to melt.

Ongoing Assessment

PHOTO CAPTION Answer: If the Rift Valley sinks low enough, water from the Red Sea will flood the valley.

Ongoing Assessment

Determine how to measure the direction and speed of plates.

Ask: What do hot spots have that allows scientists to measure speed and movement? *a fixed point*

READING VISUALS *Answer: feature farthest from the hot spot; Plate movement carries the first islands or landforms away from the hot spot as new ones form.*

CHECK YOUR READING *Answer: A plume of magma from the mantle melts the rock in the plate above it.*

Teach from Visuals

To help students interpret the diagram of hot spots, ask: How might the Hawaiian Islands be different a million years from now? Why? *Another island or two might form over the hot spot as plate movement carries the Big Island away.*

Reinforce the BIG idea

Have students relate the section to the Big Idea.

 Reinforcing Key Concepts, p. 43

8.3 ASSESS & RETEACH

Assess

 Section 8.3 Quiz, p. 178

Reteach

Help students review this section's concepts by encouraging them to draw diagrams of the features discussed on pp. 279–280, 282, and 284.

Technology Resources

Have students visit **ClassZone.com** for reteaching of Key Concepts.

 CONTENT REVIEW

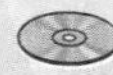 CONTENT REVIEW CD-ROM

Hot Spots

Tectonic plates move over hot spots in the mantle.

Oceanic Hot Spot

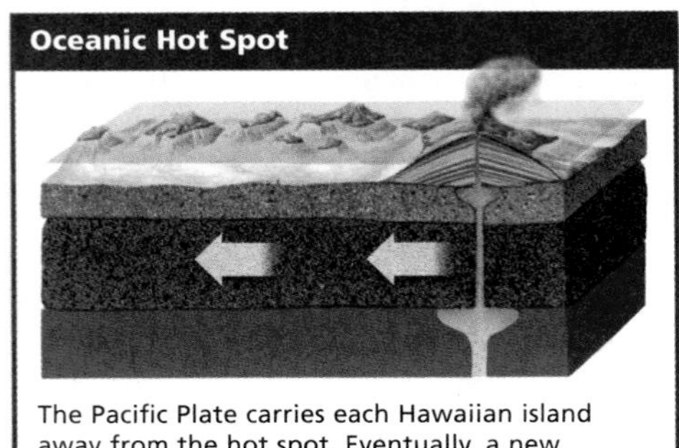

The Pacific Plate carries each Hawaiian island away from the hot spot. Eventually, a new volcano forms over the plume.

Continental Hot Spot

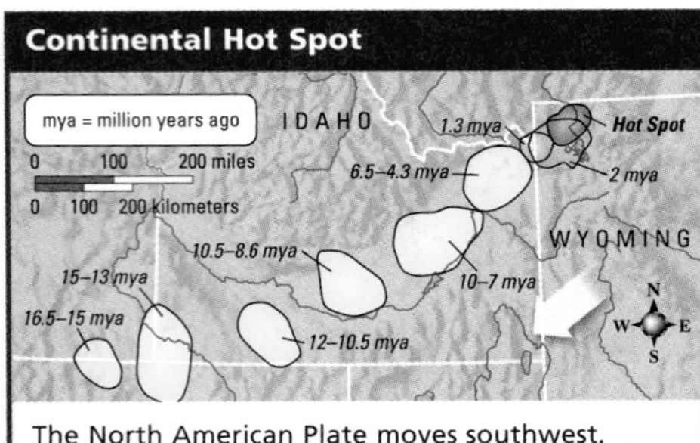

The North American Plate moves southwest, carrying each inactive volcano away from the Yellowstone hot spot.

READING VISUALS Which island or landform in each diagram was formed first? How do you know?

When the plate moves on, it carries the first volcano away from the hot spot. Heat from the plume will then melt the rock at a new site, forming a new volcano. The diagram on the left shows this process.

Many hot spots have a fixed point that scientists can use to measure the speed and direction of plate movements. For example, the Yellowstone hot spot under the North American Plate has formed a chain of inactive volcanoes. These are shown in the diagram on the right. Scientists estimate that the North American Plate is moving southwest at about 2.3 cm (1 in.) per year.

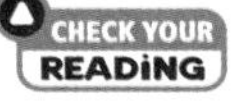 How does a hot-spot volcano form?

8.3 Review

KEY CONCEPTS

1. Name and describe the three types of plate movements. (6.1.b)
2. Create a two-column chart with these headings: Divergent Boundary, Features. Fill in the chart for divergent boundaries at sea and on land. (6.1.a)
3. How are hot spots used to track plate motion? (6.1.e)

CRITICAL THINKING

4. **Predict** Suppose a magnetic reversal occurred today. How would new rocks at mid-ocean ridges differ from rocks that formed last year?
5. **Infer** A huge crack runs through Iceland, an island that lies above the Mid-Atlantic Ridge. What do you think is happening to this country?

CHALLENGE

6. **Hypothesize** Look carefully at the diagram above and the Hawaiian Islands picture on page 283. Notice that some hot-spot islands or landforms are larger than other islands or landforms in the same chain. Develop a hypothesis, based on plate movement, that might explain this fact.

ANSWERS

1. divergent, moving apart; convergent, pushing together; transform, scraping past

2. Oceanic: mid-ocean ridges, rift valleys, new crust; Continental: rift valleys, volcanoes, new crust

3. provide a fixed point to measure speed and motion of plate above

4. The magnetic minerals in the new rocks would be aligned in the opposite direction.

5. The Mid-Atlantic Ridge is a divergent boundary, so the island would be pulling apart into two sections.

*6. Sample: **If** melted rock rising through the crust builds islands or landforms, **then** a larger island or landform would have to be over the hot spot longer **because** it would need more time to acquire material before being carried away.*

his satellite photograph shows where the Arabian Plate and he African Plate are moving apart. As a result, the Red Sea s slowly growing wider.

SKILL: CALCULATING EQUIVALENT RATES

Tracking Tectonic Plates

Scientists use lasers to track the movements of tectonic plates. They bounce laser light off satellites and measure the distance from each satellite to the ground. As the plates move, the distance changes. With this tracking system, scientists know exactly how far tectonic plates move each year.

You can use equivalent rates to predict how far two divergent plates will move over a given time. A rate is a ratio of two measures expressed in different units, such as

$$\frac{10 \text{ cm}}{4 \text{ yr}}$$

This 0.61-meter-wide satellite is covered with mirrors to reflect laser light back to Earth.

Example

If Boston, Massachusetts, and Lisbon, Portugal, are moving apart at an average rate of 10 cm every 4 years, how much farther apart will they move in 20 years?

Solution

Write an equivalent rate.

$$\frac{10 \text{ cm}}{4 \text{ yr}} = \frac{?}{20 \text{ yr}}$$

Divide 20 yr by 4 yr to get 5, then multiply 10 cm by 5.

$$20 \div 4 = 5$$

$$10 \text{ X } 5 = 50$$

$$\frac{10 \text{ cm}}{4 \text{ yr}} = \frac{50 \text{ cm}}{20 \text{ yr}}$$

ANSWER Boston and Lisbon will move 50 centimeters farther apart in 10 years.

Answer the following questions.

1. If New York, New York, and London, England, are moving apart at an average rate of 5 cm every 2 years, how much farther apart will they move in 8 years?
2. If Miami, Florida, and Casablanca, Morocco, are moving apart at an average rate of 25 cm every 10 years, how much farther apart will they move in 30 years?
3. If Portland, Maine, and Dublin, Ireland, are moving apart at an average rate of 50 cm every 20 years, how much farther apart will they move in 10 years?

CHALLENGE If Halifax, Nova Scotia, and Birmingham, England, are moving apart at an average rate of 5 cm every 2 years, how long will it take them to move 35 cm farther apart?

ANSWERS

1. 20 cm *2. 75 cm* *3. 25 cm*

CHALLENGE 14 years

$$\frac{5 \text{ cm}}{2 \text{ yr}} = \frac{35 \text{ cm}}{?}$$

$$\frac{35}{5} = 7$$

$$7 \cdot 2 = 14$$

$$\frac{5 \text{ cm}}{2 \text{ yr}} = \frac{35 \text{ cm}}{14 \text{ yr}}$$

MATH IN SCIENCE

Math Skills Practice for Science

Set Learning Goal

To use ratios to predict how much farther apart two tectonic plates will move

Math Standards

6.NS.2.2 Explain the meaning of multiplication and division of positive fractions and perform the calculations (e.g., $\frac{5}{8} \div \frac{15}{16} = \frac{5}{8} \times \frac{16}{15} = \frac{2}{3}$).

6.NS.2.3 Solve addition, subtraction, multiplication, and division problems, including those arising in concrete situations, that use positive and negative integers and combinations of these operations.

Present the Science

The field of *space geodesy*—space-based techniques of precisely measuring widely separated points on Earth—grew rapidly in the late 1970s. The techniques are based on military and aerospace technology. Besides satellite laser ranging, the Global Positioning System (GPS) is also used to measure plate movement.

Develop Algebra Skills

- Remind students that equivalent rates are like equivalent fractions. In the example problem, you are finding an equivalent fraction by multiplying the numerator by the same factor as the denominator.
- Ask: How many centimeters are in an inch? *2.54* About how many inches is 10 centimeters? *about 4*

Close

Ask students how scientists might use long-range predictions of plate movements. *to predict sites of earthquakes or volcanic activity or where new hot-spot volcanoes or mountains might form*

- Math Support, p. 60
- Math Practice, p. 61

Technology Resources

Students can visit **ClassZone.com** for practice in writing equivalent rates.

MATH TUTORIAL

 FOCUS

Set Learning Goals

Students will

- Describe what happens when two continental plates converge.
- Identify what happens when an oceanic plate converges with another plate.
- Explain what happens when one plate scrapes past another plate.
- Design an experiment to model converging plates.

3-Minute Warm-Up

Display Transparency 61 or copy this exercise on the board:

Decide if these statements are true. If not, correct them.

1. At a divergent boundary, tectonic plates collide. *At a divergent boundary, tectonic plates move apart.*
2. Rift valleys form at divergent boundaries in the ocean and on land. *true*
3. Divergent boundaries in the ocean are also called spreading centers. *true*

T 3-Minute Warm-Up, p. T61

 MOTIVATE

EXPLORE Tectonic plates

PURPOSE To model the collision of tectonic plates and observe the effects

TIPS *10 min.* Advise students not to hold the napkins too close to the edges. They should push the napkins together slowly so they can watch what happens when the edges meet. If they get only one kind of action, such as one set of napkins going under the other set, have them do the activity more slowly or more quickly to get a variety of actions.

WHAT DO YOU THINK? *Napkins should slide under, over, or bunch up together. Students should be able to infer that tectonic plates will move in similar ways.*

KEY CONCEPT

Plates converge or scrape past each other.

CALIFORNIA Content Standards

6.1.a Students know evidence of plate tectonics is derived from the fit of the continents; the location of earthquakes, volcanoes, and midocean ridges; and the distribution of fossils, rock types, and ancient climatic zones.

6.1.e Students know major geologic events, such as earthquakes, volcanic eruptions, and mountain building, result from plate motions.

6.1.f Students know how to explain major features of California geology (including mountains, faults, volcanoes) in terms of plate tectonics.

BEFORE, you learned

- Plates move apart at divergent boundaries
- In the oceans, divergent boundaries mark where the sea floor spreads apart
- On land, continents split apart at divergent boundaries

NOW, you will learn

- What happens when two continental plates converge
- What happens when an oceanic plate converges with another plate
- What happens when one plate scrapes past another plate

VOCABULARY

subduction p. 286
continental-continental collision p. 287
oceanic-oceanic subduction p. 288
oceanic-continental subduction p. 289

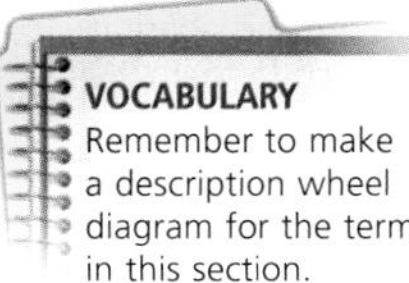

VOCABULARY
Remember to make a description wheel diagram for the terms in this section.

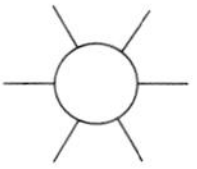

EXPLORE Tectonic Plates (6.1.e)

What happens when tectonic plates collide?

PROCEDURE

1. Arrange six square napkins in two rows.
2. Slowly push the two rows of napkins together. Observe what happens.

WHAT DO YOU THINK?

- In what ways did the napkin edges move?
- How might your observations relate to the movement of tectonic plates?

MATERIALS
6 square napkins

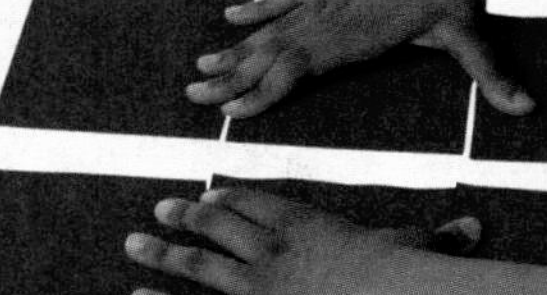

Tectonic plates push together at convergent boundaries.

You read earlier that new crust forms at divergent boundaries where plates move apart. At convergent boundaries, plates push together. Here, crust is either folded or destroyed.

When two plates with continental crust collide, they crumple and fold the rock between them. A plate with older, denser oceanic crust will sink beneath another plate. The crust melts in the asthenosphere and is destroyed. When one plate sinks beneath another, it is called **subduction.** The word is based on the Latin prefix *sub-*, meaning "under," and the Latin *ducere,* meaning "to lead." Therefore, subduction is a process in which one plate is "led under" another.

There are three types of convergent boundaries: where two continental plates meet, where two oceanic plates meet, or where an oceanic plate and a continental plate meet. Major geologic events occur at all three types of boundaries.

RESOURCES FOR DIFFERENTIATED INSTRUCTION

Below Level

UNIT RESOURCE BOOK
- Reading Study Guide A, pp. 46–47
- Decoding Support, p. 59

 **AUDIO CDS**

Advanced

UNIT RESOURCE BOOK
Challenge and Extension, p. 52

English Learners

UNIT RESOURCE BOOK
Spanish Reading Study Guide, pp. 50–51

 **AUDIO CDS**

- Audio Readings in Spanish
- Audio Readings (English)

Continental-Continental Collision

A **continental-continental collision** occurs where two plates carrying continental crust push together. Because both crusts are the same density, neither plate can sink beneath the other. If the plates keep moving, their edges crumple and fold. See the diagram below.

You can see the same effect if you put two blocks of clay on a table and push them together. If you push hard enough, one or both of the blocks will buckle. One cannot sink under the other, so the clay folds under the pressure.

In some cases, the folded crust can be pushed up high enough to form mountains. Some of the world's largest mountains appear along continent-continent boundaries. The European Alps, shown in the photograph at right, are found where the African and Eurasian plates are colliding. The tallest mountains in the world are the Himalayas. They first formed when the Indian Plate began colliding with the Eurasian Plate.

Alps

The European Alps began rising nearly 40 million years ago as a section of the African Plate collided with the Eurasian Plate.

The Himalayas and the Alps are still forming today. As long as the plates keep moving, these mountains will keep rising higher.

CHECK YOUR READING Explain how colliding plates form mountain ranges.

Convergent Boundary—Collision

Rocks crumple and fold to form mountains.

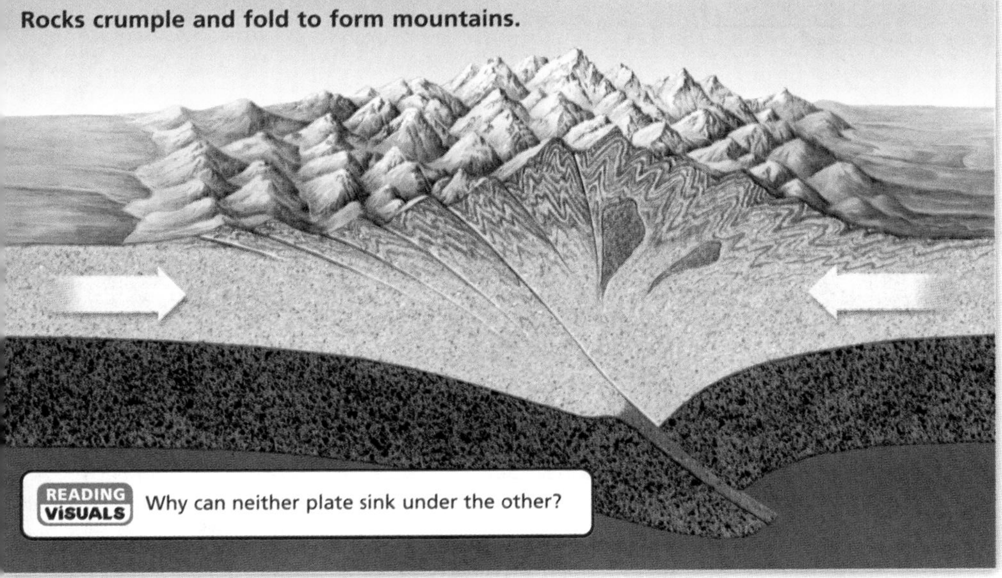

READING VISUALS Why can neither plate sink under the other?

8.4 INSTRUCT

Teach the Standards

Plate movement 6.1.e

In this section: Help students see how plate movements cause mountain building, earthquakes, and volcanic eruptions.

- **previously taught:** hot spots, pp. 283–284
- **future opportunities:** earthquakes, pp. 302–305; mountain building, pp. 337–339; volcanic eruptions, pp. 346–348

History of Science

The Burgess Shale is an important site where thousands of fossils of sea animals have been found in a mountain range. Located in Yoho National Park in the Rocky Mountains in British Columbia, the site contains fossils that are more than 500 million years old. The fossils formed in an underwater mudslide that preserved not just the hard skeletons but also the soft body parts of the animals. When the animals were buried, the area formed a reef near the coast of North America, which at that time was located near the equator.

Teach from Visuals

To help students interpret the continental collision diagram, ask:

- What does the diagram show is happening to the rocks in the crust? *The wavy lines show how the rocks are bent and folded as the two plates push together.*
- What kind of landform occurs at a collision zone? *mountain range*

Ongoing Assessment

Describe what happens when two continental plates converge.

Ask: What happens to the plate edges when two continental plates collide? *Because neither plate can sink under the other, the edges crumple and fold.*

CHECK YOUR READING *Answer: Plates push together until rocks crumple and fold, rising higher and eventually forming mountain ranges.*

READING VISUALS *Answer: Both plates are the same density so neither one can sink under the other.*

DIFFERENTIATE INSTRUCTION

More Reading Support

A What is an area where two continental plates push together? *a continental-continental collision*

B When does folded crust form mountains? *when it is pushed up high*

English Learners Point out to English learners the different word forms found in this section. For example, *collide* and *collision, subduct* and *subduction, converge* and *convergent,* and *ocean* and *oceanic.* Help students understand how the different word forms relate to parts of speech and to understanding a sentence.

Teach Difficult Concepts

Students may have difficulty understanding the formation of volcanoes at subduction zones. Emphasize that volcanoes can appear fairly far from where the plates originally meet because the leading edge of the subducted plate is melting some distance from the initial point of subduction. Melted rock can rise through the crust to form volcanoes at the surface.

Teach from Visuals

To help students interpret the diagram of oceanic subduction, ask:

- What kinds of plates are involved in subduction? *either two oceanic plates or an oceanic plate and a continental plate*
- What features occur when an oceanic plate sinks beneath another oceanic plate? *a trench and volcanic islands*
- What features occur when an oceanic plate sinks beneath a continental plate? *a trench and coastal mountains and volcanoes*

Ongoing Assessment

READING VISUALS *Answer: Crust is being formed at the mid-ocean ridge and where magma reaches the surface to slowly form islands and coastal volcanoes. Crust is being destroyed where plates subduct and melt.*

Oceanic-Oceanic Subduction

An **oceanic-oceanic subduction** occurs where one plate with oceanic crust sinks under another plate with oceanic crust. The older plate sinks because it is colder and denser than the younger plate. When the older crust reaches the asthenosphere, it melts in the intense heat. Two main features form at oceanic-oceanic subductions: deep-ocean trenches and island arcs.

Deep-Ocean Trenches These trenches are like deep canyons that form in the ocean floor as a plate sinks. Most deep-ocean trenches are found in the Pacific Ocean. One example is the Mariana Trench. There, the Pacific Plate is sinking under the Philippine Plate. This trench is the deepest place in the world's oceans. It extends nearly 11,000 meters (36,000 ft) into the sea floor.

Island Arcs Chains of volcanic islands form on the top plate, parallel to a deep-ocean trench. As oceanic crust of the sinking plate melts, magma rises through the top plate. Over time, the flows build up a series of islands. Island arcs include the Philippine Islands, the Aleutian Islands of Alaska, and the islands of Japan.

Convergent Boundaries—Subduction

Sinking plates form deep-ocean trenches, island arcs, and coastal mountains.

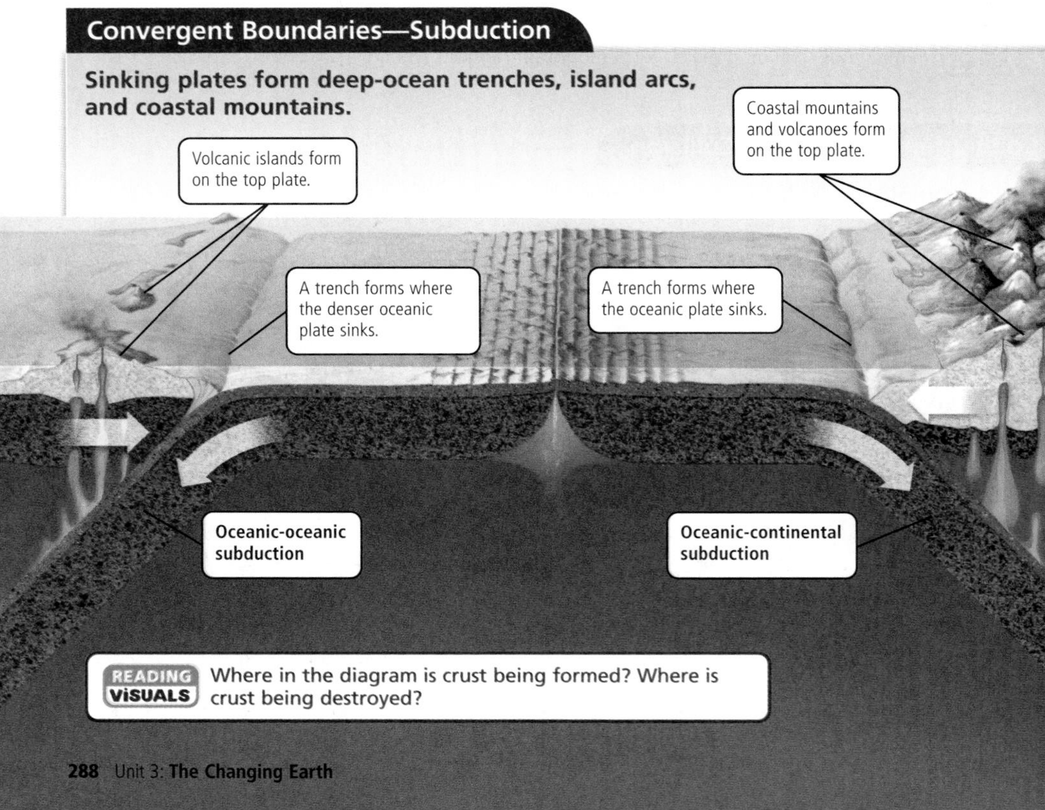
Volcanic islands form on the top plate.
Coastal mountains and volcanoes form on the top plate.
A trench forms where the denser oceanic plate sinks.
A trench forms where the oceanic plate sinks.
Oceanic-oceanic subduction
Oceanic-continental subduction

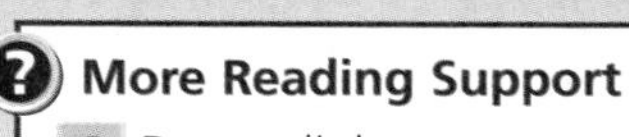

READING VISUALS Where in the diagram is crust being formed? Where is crust being destroyed?

DIFFERENTIATE INSTRUCTION

More Reading Support

C Does a lighter or denser plate sink? *the denser plate*

D Chains of volcanic islands that form parallel to a deep-ocean trench are called what? *island arcs*

Below Level Have students give an oral summary of what they just read about sinking plates and deep-ocean trenches. Explain that the melted rock of the sinking plate is lighter or less dense than the surrounding rock. It will rise up through cracks in the crust of the top plate and form either volcanic island arcs or coastal volcanoes.

Oceanic-Continental Subduction

An **oceanic-continental subduction** occurs when ocean crust sinks under continental crust, as shown in the diagram on page 288. The oceanic crust sinks because it is colder and denser than the continental crust. At these sites, deep-ocean trenches and coastal mountains form.

Explore what happens along plate boundaries.

Deep-Ocean Trenches Some of the world's youngest trenches are in the eastern Pacific Ocean. Here, the Pacific Plate is sinking under the North American Plate. As the oceanic crust moves, it often causes underwater earthquakes.

Coastal Mountains As oceanic crust sinks under a continent, the continental crust buckles to form a range of mountains. Like island arcs, these mountains are parallel to a deep-ocean trench. Some of these mountains are volcanoes, which form as melted oceanic crust rises through the top plate.

The Cascade Mountains in California, Oregon, and Washington are coastal mountains. They formed as the Juan de Fuca Plate began sinking under the North American Plate. Some of these peaks, such as Mount St. Helens in Washington, are active volcanoes.

CHECK YOUR READING Why do deep-ocean trenches form at both types of subduction?

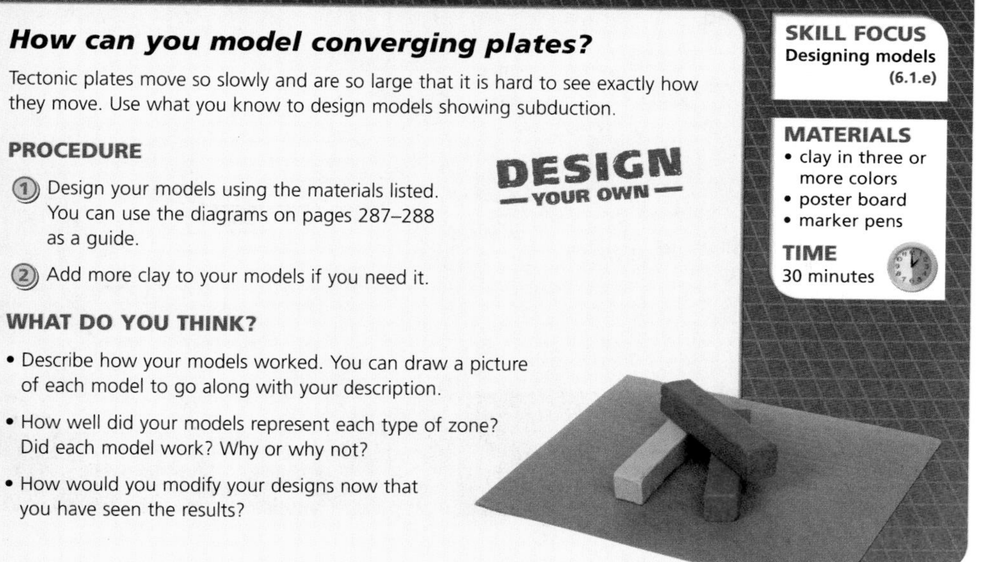

INVESTIGATE Convergent Boundaries

How can you model converging plates?

Tectonic plates move so slowly and are so large that it is hard to see exactly how they move. Use what you know to design models showing subduction.

PROCEDURE

1. Design your models using the materials listed. You can use the diagrams on pages 287–288 as a guide.
2. Add more clay to your models if you need it.

WHAT DO YOU THINK?

- Describe how your models worked. You can draw a picture of each model to go along with your description.
- How well did your models represent each type of zone? Did each model work? Why or why not?
- How would you modify your designs now that you have seen the results?

SKILL FOCUS
Designing models (6.1.e)

MATERIALS
- clay in three or more colors
- poster board
- marker pens

TIME
30 minutes

INVESTIGATE Convergent Boundaries

PURPOSE To design models to show how plates collide and subduct in collision and subduction zones

TIP *30 min.* Have students label their models.

WHAT DO YOU THINK? *Student answers will vary.*

 Datasheet, Convergent Boundaries, p. 53

Technology Resources

Customize this student lab as needed or look for an alternative. Print rubrics to assess student lab reports.

 **Lab Generator CD-ROM**

Teaching with Technology

Film groups of students showing and describing the models they created for the investigation on this page. Have the video available for parents to watch at conference time.

Ongoing Assessment

Identify what happens when an oceanic plate converges with another plate.

Ask: What causes volcanic islands and mountains to form? *Answer: The crust of the subducting plate melts and rises through cracks in the top plate, forming a series of volcanic islands or coastal volcanoes.*

CHECK YOUR READING *Answer: In both types of subduction, one plate sinks beneath another, forming a deep-ocean trench.*

FFERENTIATE INSTRUCTION

More Reading Support

E What are sites of
requent earthquakes?
leep-ocean trenches

Alternative Assessment Have groups of students present their models and answer the investigation questions orally.

Teacher Demo

To help students visualize the movement along a transform boundary, demonstrate the movement or have them demonstrate the movement using two blocks of wood or two books.

Develop Critical Thinking

INFER Have students infer how scientists know that Los Angeles will be closer to where San Francisco is today in about 10 million years.

Teach from Visuals

To help students interpret the transform boundary diagram, ask:

What kind of movement occurs at a transform boundary? *Two plates slide past each other in opposite directions.*

What landform on the diagram shows how far the plates have moved? *The riverbed—as the plates move, the riverbed is offset along part of the fault.*

Ongoing Assessment

Explain what happens when one plate scrapes past another plate.

What happens as plates scrape past one another? *The rocks grind against each other, but no crust is formed or destroyed.*

CHECK YOUR READING *Answer: The Pacific Plate and North American Plate are scraping past each other along the San Andreas Fault. Crust is not being formed or destroyed.*

Tectonic plates scrape past each other at transform boundaries.

You learned that crust is formed at a divergent boundary. It is folded or destroyed at a convergent boundary. At a transform boundary, crust is neither formed nor destroyed. Here, two plates move past each other in opposite directions, as shown in the diagram below. As the plates move, their edges scrape and grind against each other.

Transform boundaries occur mostly on the sea floor near mid-ocean ridges. They also occur on land, where some are clearly visible as long cracks in Earth's surface. The San Andreas Fault in California is a transform boundary that runs from the Gulf of California through the San Francisco area. It marks where the Pacific Plate and part of the North American Plate are moving in opposite directions. If the plates keep moving at their present rate, Los Angeles will be a neighbor of San Francisco in about 10 million years.

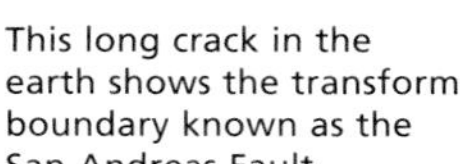

This long crack in the earth shows the transform boundary known as the San Andreas Fault.

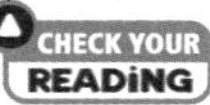

What makes the San Andreas Fault a transform boundary?

Transform Boundary

Plate edges grind and scrape past each other. Crust is neither formed nor destroyed.

valley

riverbed offset as plates move

DIFFERENTIATE INSTRUCTION

More Reading Support

F Where do two plates move past each other in opposite directions? *at a transform boundary*

G Where do transform boundaries occur? *on the sea floor and on land*

Advanced Have interested students learn about and report on current research on the San Andreas Fault.

Challenge and Extension, p. 52

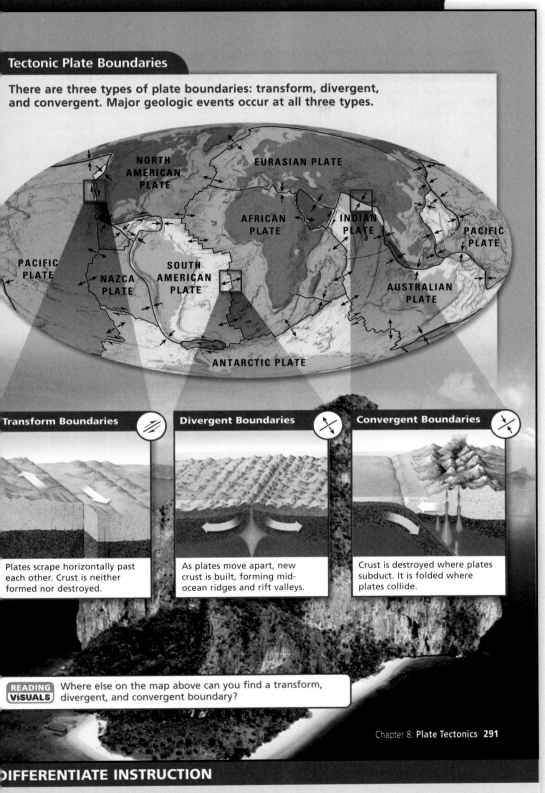

Tectonic Plate Boundaries

There are three types of plate boundaries: transform, divergent, and convergent. Major geologic events occur at all three types.

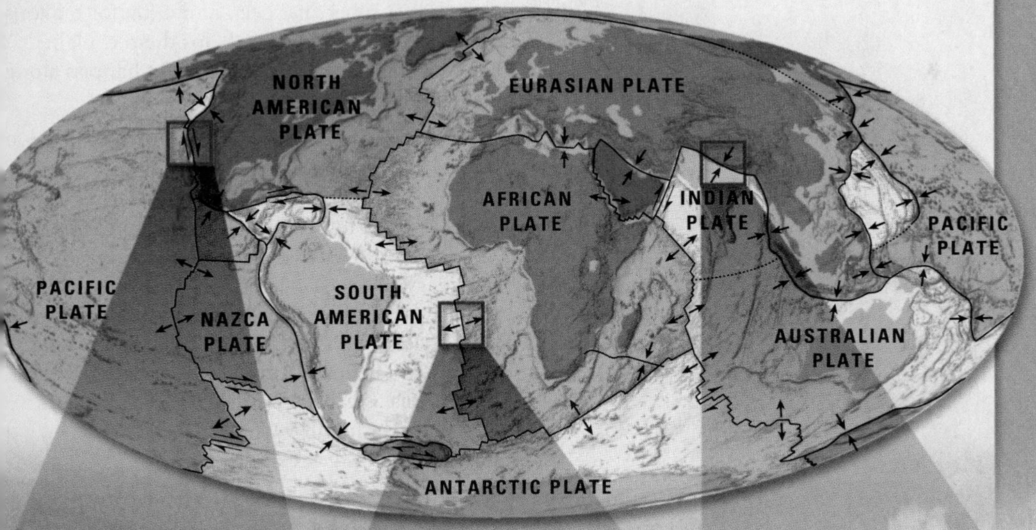

NORTH AMERICAN PLATE
EURASIAN PLATE
AFRICAN PLATE
INDIAN PLATE
PACIFIC PLATE
PACIFIC PLATE
NAZCA PLATE
SOUTH AMERICAN PLATE
AUSTRALIAN PLATE
ANTARCTIC PLATE

Transform Boundaries

Plates scrape horizontally past each other. Crust is neither formed nor destroyed.

Divergent Boundaries

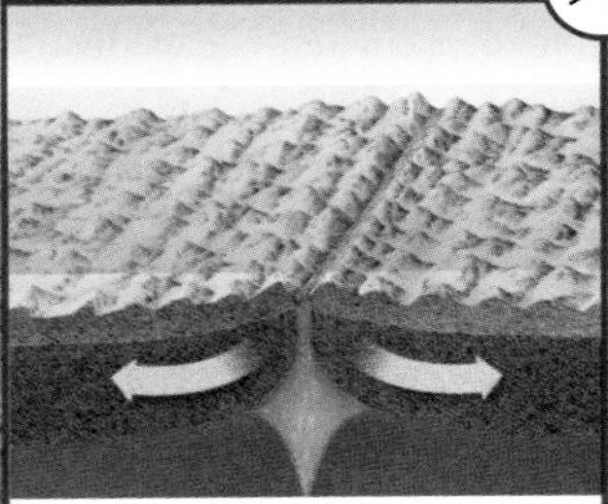

As plates move apart, new crust is built, forming mid-ocean ridges and rift valleys.

Convergent Boundaries

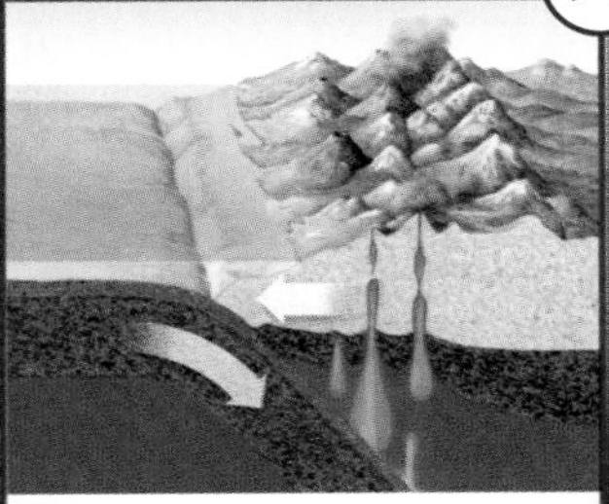

Crust is destroyed where plates subduct. It is folded where plates collide.

READING VISUALS Where else on the map above can you find a transform, divergent, and convergent boundary?

IFFERENTIATE INSTRUCTION

nclusion For students who benefit from physical demonstrations of oncepts, have them use wooden blocks to show the three types of late movements. They should push two blocks into each other to emonstrate a convergent boundary, move the blocks apart for a divergent boundary, and slide the blocks horizontally past each other to how a transform boundary.

Teach from Visuals

To help students interpret the diagrams of tectonic plate boundaries and review what they have learned about different types of boundaries, ask:

- In what direction do plates move in convergent boundaries? *toward each other*
- In what direction do plates move in divergent boundaries? *away from each other*
- In what direction do plates move in transform boundaries? *horizontally past each other*
- What features occur with each type of boundary on continents? *convergent—folded mountains; divergent—rift valley; transform—surface fault*
- What features occur with convergent and divergent boundaries in the ocean? *convergent—trench, volcanic island arc, coastal volcanoes and mountains; divergent—mid-ocean ridge, rift valley*

This visual is also available as T62 in the Transparency Book.

Ongoing Assessment

READING VISUALS *Possible answers: transform boundary: between the North American Plate and the small plate below it; divergent boundary: in the ocean between the African Plate and the Australian Plate; convergent boundary: between the Eurasian Plate and the African Plate.*

Ongoing Assessment

CHECK YOUR READING *Answer: Sites of future volcanoes, earthquakes, mountain building*

History of Science

Although scientists can forecast the likelihood of an earthquake over a certain period of time, they cannot pinpoint exactly when and where an earthquake will occur. In 1990, an American scientist named Iben Browning predicted that a large earthquake would strike the New Madrid Fault Zone on about December 3, 1990. His prediction was widely publicized and taken seriously by many people in the region. Many people bought earthquake insurance policies; and hundreds of schools, shops, and businesses closed on that date. More than a decade after the date, a large earthquake still had not hit the area.

Reinforce the BIG idea

Have students relate the section to the Big Idea.

 Reinforcing Key Concepts, p. 54

8.4 ASSESS & RETEACH

Assess

 Section 8.4 Quiz, p. 179

Reteach

Help students review this section's concepts by pairing the students and having them use the visual on p. 291 to quiz each other about the kind of movement and the types of features associated with each kind of tectonic plate boundary.

Technology Resources

Have students visit **ClassZone.com** for reteaching of Key Concepts.

 CONTENT REVIEW

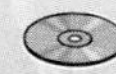 CONTENT REVIEW CD-ROM

Current U. S. Eastern Coastline

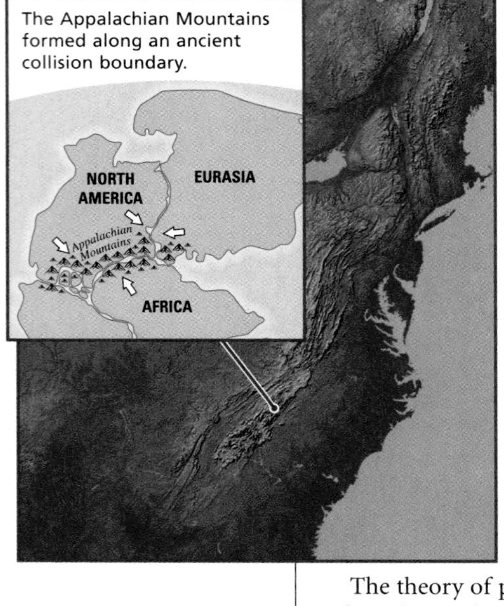

The theory of plate tectonics helps geologists today.

The theory of plate tectonics changed the way that scientists view Earth. They learned that the planet's lithosphere has been in motion for millions of years. Today, the theory helps them explain Earth's past and predict what might happen along plate boundaries in the future.

By studying rock layers and using the theory, geologists can uncover the history of any region on Earth. In the eastern United States, the deformed and folded rocks in the Appalachian Mountains show there was once a convergent boundary there. Geologists discovered that these rocks are the same type and age as rocks in northwest Africa. These facts reveal that the mountains formed when North America collided with Africa and Eurasia as part of Pangaea. Where the plates pulled apart, the rift valleys formed part of the current U.S. eastern coastline.

The theory of plate tectonics also gives scientists a way to study and predict geologic events. For example, scientists can predict that there are likely to be more earthquakes where plates slide past each other. They can look for volcanic activity where plates are sinking beneath other plates. And they can predict that mountains will continue to rise where plates push together.

 What future events can scientists predict using the theory of plate tectonics? Give two examples.

8.4 Review

KEY CONCEPTS

1. What are the three types of convergent boundaries? (6.1.e)
2. Describe what happens at a transform boundary. (6.1.e)
3. Why is the theory of plate tectonics so important to geologists? (6.1.a)

CRITICAL THINKING

4. **Compare and Contrast** Use a Venn diagram to compare and contrast oceanic-oceanic and oceanic-continental subduction boundaries.
5. **Interpreting Visuals** Look again at the map on page 291. Identify the plates and type of boundary that formed the Andes Mountains on the west coast of South America.

CHALLENGE

6. **Synthesize** Sketch a diagram of the following landscape and label all the features. A plate with oceanic crust is sinking beneath a plate with continental crust. Farther inland on the continent, a transform boundary can be seen in Earth's crust.

ANSWERS

1. where two continental plates meet, two oceanic plates meet, an oceanic and continental plate meet

2. Two plates move past each other in opposite directions.

3. gives geologists a new way to explain past and future geologic events; helps geologists understand why major geologic events happen along plate boundaries.

4. compare: both form trenches; contrast: oceanic–oceanic form volcanic islands, oceanic–continental form coastal mountains and volcanoes

5. South American and Nazca plates; convergent boundary

6. Sketches will vary, but should show a trench formed where the oceanic plate sinks under the continental plate, coastal mountains and volcanoes, and two inland plates scraping against each other, moving in opposite directions

Think SCIENCE

A volcanic coastal mountain spews out ash.

RESOURCE CENTER
CLASSZONE.COM

Learn more about the effects of plate movement.

SKILL: EVALUATING CONCLUSIONS

What on Earth Is Happening Here?

6.7.e Recognize whether evidence is consistent with a proposed explanation.

When tectonic plates move, they cause major changes in Earth's surface. The ground shakes, magma erupts on the surface, crust is built or destroyed, and mountains or islands form. Read the observations about plate movements below. Then evaluate the conclusions given.

Observations

Scientists made these observations about a region where two major tectonic plates move.

a. The region is on the coast of a landmass.
b. Along the coast is a deep-ocean trench.
c. The mountains on the coast are volcanic.
d. A line connecting these mountains is fairly straight.
e. The mountains are getting higher.
f. Far out at sea, a mid-ocean ridge is forming.

Conclusions

Here are three possible conclusions about the movement of tectonic plates in the region.

- One plate is pulling away from the other.
- One plate is sinking under the other.
- One plate is scraping past the other.

Evaluate Each Conclusion

On Your Own Decide how well the observations support each conclusion. Note any observations that don't support a conclusion.

As a Group Decide which conclusion is most reasonable. Discuss your ideas in a small group, and see if the group can agree.

CHALLENGE What further observations would support or weaken each conclusion? How could you make these observations? What other geologic events might this conclusion help explain?

ANSWERS

On Your Own Students should be able to support their choice of conclusions with observations.

As a Group Groups should be able to choose a logical conclusion based on the observations. If there are disagreements, ask students to draw a diagram based on the observations.

CHALLENGE Further observations might include: Is crust being formed or destroyed at the site? Are the volcanoes active? Are plates moving past each other? Observations could be made by measurement of plate movements, deep-sea explorations, and so on. Other geological events might include earthquakes, hot springs, steam vents.

THINK SCIENCE

Scientific Methods of Thinking

Set Learning Goal

To read observations about plate movements and evaluate the conclusions that could be drawn from the data

Present the Science

Distinct geologic features occur at the three types of tectonic plate boundaries. In this activity, students will apply what they have learned about the geologic features associated with each type of boundary.

Guide the Activity

- Advise students to begin by making a list or chart of the geologic features associated with each type of plate boundary.
- Remind students that if any one of the observations does not fit with a conclusion, then the conclusion is not justified.

COOPERATIVE LEARNING STRATEGY

Divide the class into groups of 3–4 students. Tell groups to begin the discussion by allowing each group member to present his or her notes. Have each group select a reporter to present the group's opinion to the class.

Close

Ask: What is the name of the type of boundary that fits the observations? *convergent boundary—oceanic-continental subduction*

Technology Resources

Have students visit **ClassZone.com** to learn more about the effects of plate movement.

 RESOURCE CENTER

BACK TO

the BIG idea

Refer students back to the photograph on pp. 262–263. Ask them to use what they have learned about tectonic plate movements to summarize what is happening to Iceland, as shown in this picture. *Sample answer: Iceland is located on the Mid-Atlantic Ridge, where two plates are moving apart. As the plates slowly move, the island country is being torn in two. The large crack represents where the divergent boundary appears on land.*

KEY CONCEPTS SUMMARY

SECTION 8.1

What layers are the most dense? *inner and outer core*

What does the lithosphere include? *the crust and very top part of the mantle*

SECTION 8.2

What motions cause the tectonic plates to move? *convection currents, ridge push, and slab pull*

Why does Earth stay roughly the same size? *Crust is destroyed at about the same rate as it is formed.*

SECTION 8.3

Name the three types of plate boundaries. *divergent, convergent, and transform boundaries*

Where do most divergent boundaries occur? *in the oceans*

SECTION 8.4

Why does one plate sink beneath another at a subduction boundary? *The plate that sinks is more dense than the top plate.*

What is the main plate motion at a transform boundary? *Plates scrape past each other horizontally in opposite directions.*

Review Concepts

- Big Idea Flow Chart, p. T57
- Chapter Outline, pp. T63–T64

8 Chapter Review

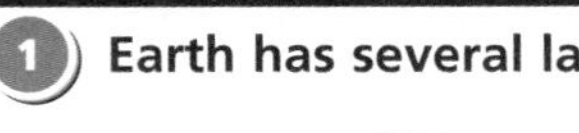

The movement of tectonic plates causes geologic changes on Earth.

KEY CONCEPTS SUMMARY

1 Earth has several layers.

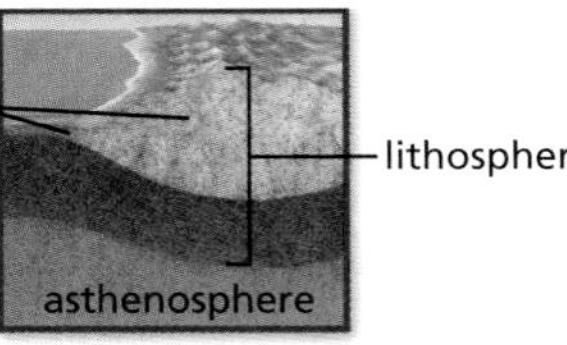

The lithosphere is made up of tectonic plates, which rest on the asthenosphere.

VOCABULARY
inner core p. 266
outer core p. 266
mantle p. 267
crust p. 267
lithosphere p. 267
asthenosphere p. 267
tectonic plate p. 268

2 Continents change position over time.

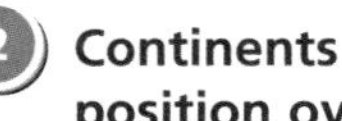

Gravity and motions in the asthenosphere move tectonic plates over Earth's surface.

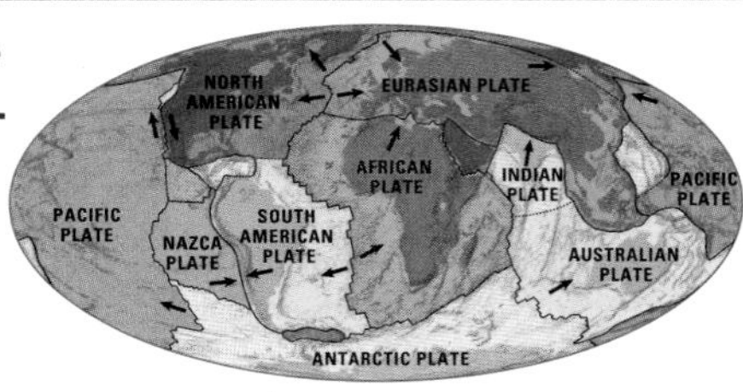

VOCABULARY
continental drift p. 270
Pangaea p. 272
mid-ocean ridge p. 272
convection p. 273
convection current p. 273
theory of plate tectonics p. 274

3 Plates move apart.

New crust is formed at divergent boundaries. Features include:
- mid-ocean ridges
- records of magnetic reversals
- rift valleys

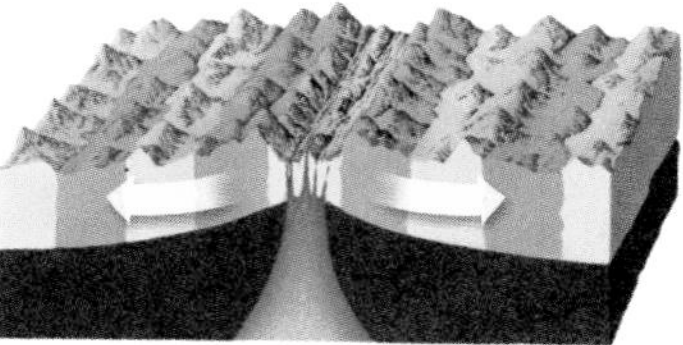

VOCABULARY
divergent boundary p. 278
convergent boundary p. 278
transform boundary p. 278
rift valley p. 279
magnetic reversal p. 280
hot spot p. 283

4 Plates converge or scrape past each other.

Crust is destroyed or folded at convergent boundaries.
- Subduction boundaries form island arcs, deep-ocean trenches, and coastal mountains.
- Collision boundaries can form mountains.

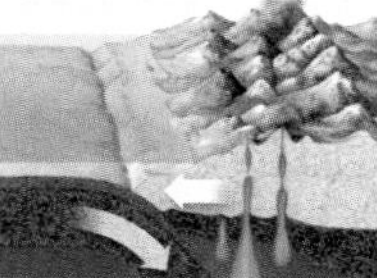

Crust is neither formed nor destroyed at transform boundaries.

VOCABULARY
subduction p. 286
continental-continental collision p. 287
oceanic-oceanic subduction p. 288
oceanic-continental subduction p. 289

Technology Resources

Have students visit **ClassZone.com** or use the CD-ROM for a cumulative review of concepts.

 **CONTENT REVIEW**

CONTENT REVIEW CD-ROM

Engage students in a whole-class interactive review of Key Concepts. Edit content as you wish.

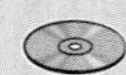 **POWER PRESENTATIONS**

Reviewing Vocabulary

Make a magnet word diagram for each of the vocabulary terms listed below. Write the term in the magnet. Write other terms or ideas related to it on the lines around the magnet.

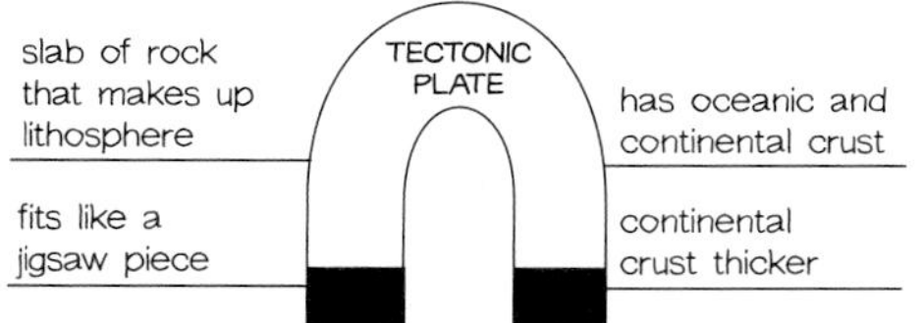

1. mantle
2. lithosphere
3. mid-ocean ridge
4. convection current
5. divergent boundary
6. convergent boundary

Reviewing Key Concepts

Multiple Choice *Choose the letter of the best answer.*

7. Which of the following best describes Earth's mantle? **(6.1.a)**
   a. the densest of Earth's layers
   b. the home of all life on Earth
   c. the thickest layer of hot rock
   d. the thinnest and hottest layer

8. Tectonic plates make up Earth's **(6.1.a)**
   a. lower mantle
   b. lithosphere
   c. asthenosphere
   d. inner core

9. Why did many scientists reject Wegener's continental drift hypothesis? **(6.1.a)**
   a. He could not explain how the continents moved.
   b. The geology of continents did not support his hypothesis.
   c. Fossil evidence showed that the continents were never joined.
   d. The climates of the continents have remained the same.

10. What evidence from the sea floor shows that tectonic plates move? **(6.1.a)**
    a. The sea floor is much older than any of the continents.
    b. The sea floor is youngest near a mid-ocean ridge and older farther away.
    c. Mid-ocean ridges circle Earth like seams in a baseball.
    d. The sea floor is thinner than continental crust.

11. A mid-ocean ridge forms where plates **(6.1.a)**
    a. move apart
    b. push together
    c. scrape past each other
    d. subduct

12. Plate motion is caused partly by **(6.1.c)**
    a. magnetic reversals
    b. convection currents
    c. continental drift
    d. volcanic hot spots

13. Which of the following is formed at a collision zone? **(6.1.e)**
    a. mountain range
    b. volcanic island chain
    c. deep-ocean trench
    d. continental rift valley

14. What happens when two oceanic plates meet? **(6.1.e)**
    a. Both plates sink into the asthenosphere.
    b. The colder, denser plate sinks.
    c. Both plates fold the rock between them.
    d. One plate slides past the other.

15. Where is crust neither formed nor destroyed? **(6.1.e)**
    a. mid-ocean ridge
    b. continental rift valley
    c. transform boundary
    d. subduction zone

Short Answer *Write a short answer to each question.*

16. How does the theory of plate tectonics help geologists predict future geologic events? **(6.1.e)**

17. How do rocks record changes in Earth's magnetic field? **(6.1.a)**

18. Explain what happens when a continental plate splits apart. **(6.1.c)**

ASSESSMENT RESOURCES

ASSESSMENT BOOK
- Chapter Test A, pp. 180–183
- Chapter Test B, pp. 184–187
- Chapter Test C, pp. 188–191
- Alternative Assessment, pp. 192–193

STANDARDS REVIEW AND PRACTICE, pp. 1–12, 27–28, 57–58, 61–66, 71–72

Technology Resources

Edit test items and answer choices.

Test Generator CD-ROM

Visit **ClassZone.com** to extend test practice.

Test Practice

Reviewing Vocabulary

Sample answers

1. mantle—thickest layer; hotter, denser near core; cooler, more rigid near top

2. lithosphere—crust plus topmost layer of mantle; broken into tectonic plates; home to all life

3. mid-ocean ridge—divergent boundary; new crust formed; rift valley; ridges circle Earth

4. convection current—a motion in which heated material rises, cools, sinks; allows tectonic plates to move

5. divergent boundary—two plates move apart; ocean—mid-ocean ridges, rift valleys; land—rift valleys, splits continents apart

6. convergent boundary—plates push together; crust is folded or destroyed; continent-continent collision—mountains; oceanic-oceanic subduction—trenches, island arcs; oceanic-continent subduction—trenches, coastal mountains

Reviewing Key Concepts

7. c
8. b
9. a
10. b
11. a
12. b
13. a
14. b
15. c

16. Geologists can use the theory to predict the amount of geologic activity along divergent, convergent, and transform boundaries, including volcanic eruptions, earthquakes, and other events.

17. Magnetic minerals in molten rock line up with magnetic north and south like tiny compass needles. When the rock cools, a record of the direction of the magnetic field at that time is preserved.

18. Hot materials rises in the mantle and causes the plate above it to bulge. The crust splits, forming a rift valley. Over time the valley floor may sink below sea level. Water can enter to form a sea.

Thinking Critically

19. *Answers will vary but should include oceanic-continental subduction, magma rising through the crust and erupting through volcanoes on the surface.*
20. *Yes, if the plates keep moving as they are, creating more magma. No, if the plates stop moving, magma would also stop forming and rising.*
21. *The oceanic plate is sinking parallel to the coastline.*
22. *offshore, parallel to the coastline; where the oceanic plate is sinking beneath the continental plate.*
23. *reject; island arcs form where one oceanic plate sinks beneath another.*
24. *Students should draw a divergent boundary far out at sea, showing a mid-ocean ridge or spreading center.*
25. *If the South American and Pacific plates continue to converge, the Andes will grow taller in the future. If the plates stop moving, wind and water will wear down the mountains, making them shorter.*
26. *divergent*
27. *convergent—subduction*
28. *divergent*
29. *convergent*
30. *convergent—subduction*
31. *none*

the BIG idea

32. *A divergent boundary may be splitting the land as two plates move apart.*
33. *Student diagrams will vary but should include one or two supercontinents with students' own labels for the landmasses.*

UNIT PROJECTS

Give students the appropriate Unit Project worksheets from the Unit Resource Book for their projects. Both directions and rubrics can be used as a guide.

 Unit Projects, pp. 5–10

Thinking Critically

Use the diagram to answer the next six questions.

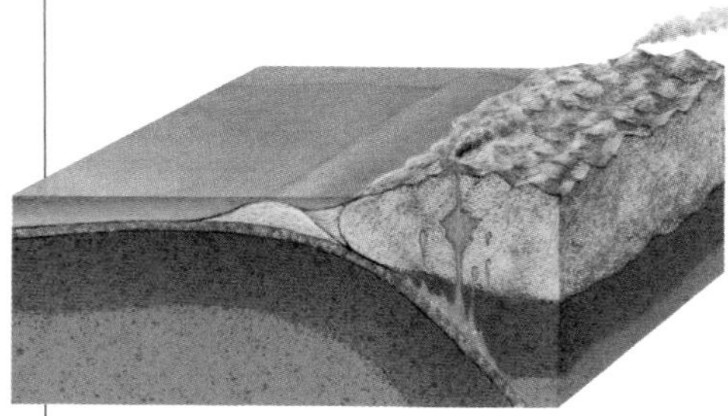

19. **ANALYZE** Write your own explanation of how the coastal mountains formed. (6.1.e)
20. **PREDICT** Would you expect the volcanoes on this coastline to continue to be active? Why or why not? (6.1.d)
21. **APPLY** Looking at the diagram above, why do you think the coastal mountains are in a fairly straight line? (6.1.e)
22. **APPLY** On the diagram above, where would you expect to find a deep ocean trench? Why? (6.1.e)
23. **APPLY** A friend looks at the diagram and tells you that there should be an island arc forming off the coast. Use your own knowledge and the map above to support or reject your friend's statement. (6.1.e)
24. **SYNTHESIZE** On a separate piece of paper, extend the diagram to the left. Draw the type of plate boundary that someone might find far out at sea. (6.1.e)
25. **PREDICT** Will the Andes Mountains on the west coast of South America become taller or shorter in the future? Use the theory of plate tectonics to explain your answer. (6.1.e)

APPLY Copy the chart below. Fill in the type of boundary—divergent, convergent, or transform—where each formation is likely to appear. (6.1.f)

Formation	Type of Boundary
26. Mid-ocean ridge	
27. Volcanic island arc	
28. Rift valley on land	
29. Mountains	
30. Deep-ocean trench	
31. Hot-spot volcano	

the BIG idea

32. **IDENTIFY CAUSE AND EFFECT** Look again at the photograph on pages 262–263. Now that you have finished the chapter, explain what may be forming this crack in Earth's surface. (6.1.e)
33. **PREDICT** Use the map on page 275, which shows Earth's tectonic plates and the directions in which they are moving. Based on the plate movements, where do you think the continents might be in a few million years? Draw a map that illustrates your prediction. You might want to give your landmasses names. (6.1.c)

UNIT PROJECTS

If you are doing a unit project, make a folder for your project. Include in your folder a list of the resources you will need, the date on which the project is due, and a schedule to keep track of your progress. Begin gathering data.

MONITOR AND RETEACH

If students are having trouble using the concepts in Chapter Review items 19–25, ask them what kind of plate boundary is shown in the diagram. *convergent* Point out the two tectonic plates and discuss what is happening regarding these plates. *An oceanic plate is sinking beneath a continental plate.* Then have students review the discussion of oceanic-continental subduction on p. 289.

Students may benefit from summarizing one or more sections of the chapter.

 Summarizing the Chapter, pp. 80–81

Standards-Based Assessment

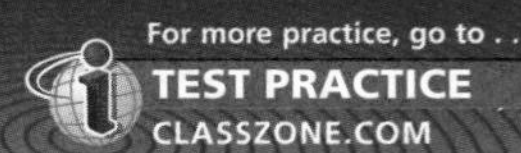

Analyzing a Diagram

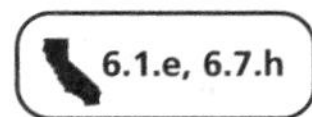

The diagram shows several tectonic plates. The arrows indicate the direction each plate is moving. Study the diagram and answer the questions below.

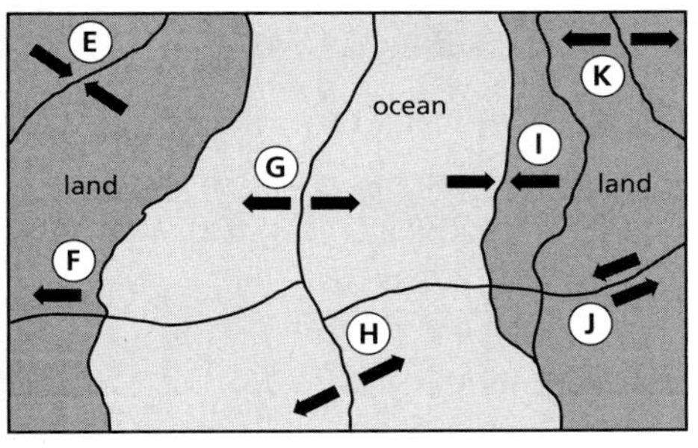

1. Where is an ocean trench most likely to form?
a. F **c.** H
b. G **d.** I

2. Where is a continental rift valley most likely to form?
a. E **c.** J
b. F **d.** K

3. Where would you find a convergent boundary?
a. E **c.** H
b. F **d.** K

4. Where is a mid-ocean ridge most likely to form?
a. G **c.** I
b. J **d.** F

5. What is a good example of a transform boundary?
a. E **c.** J
b. I **d.** K

6. Which is most likely to happen at I?
a. Island arcs will form parallel to a trench.
b. A spreading center will create a rift valley.
c. Continental crust will be destroyed.
d. Subduction will cause oceanic crust to melt.

7. Why are earthquakes likely to occur at J?
a. Two plates are spreading away from each other.
b. Two plates are colliding with each other.
c. Two plates are scraping past each other.
d. One plate is sliding under another plate.

8. Why are mountains likely to form at E?
a. A rift valley is forming.
b. Two plates are colliding.
c. Magma is flowing upward.
d. One plate is sinking.

9. Which is most likely to happen at G?
a. Rising magma will create new crust.
b. Subduction will cause a deep trench.
c. Colliding plates will cause rocks to crumple.
d. Moving plates will create island arcs.

Extended Response

Answer the two questions below in detail. Include some of the terms shown in the word box. In your answer, underline each term you use.

tectonic plates	subduction	magma	crust
continental drift	hot spot	mantle	

10. Two island chains are separated by a deep ocean trench. Although they are close to each other, the islands have very different fossils and types of rock. Explain why these island chains have such different geologic features.

11. Andrea lives near a chain of mountains located far from plate boundaries. The closest mountain is an active volcano. The other mountains used to be volcanoes. The farther away a mountain is in the chain, the older it is. Explain these facts.

REFLECTING ON THE CHAPTER

Have students answer the following questions in their **Science Notebook:**

1. What information in this chapter helped explain some of the geologic features of places you have visited or seen in pictures?
2. How did the models you made in the activities help you understand the concepts in the chapter?
3. What key concepts from this chapter will you use in your Unit Project?

California Content Standards

6.1.e Students know major geologic events, such as earthquakes, volcanic eruptions, and mountain building, result from plate motions.

6.7.h Identify changes in natural phenomena over time without manipulating the phenomena (e.g., a tree limb, a grove of trees, a stream, a hillslope).

Analyzing a Diagram

1. d	*4. a*	*7. c*
2. d	*5. c*	*8. b*
3. a	*6. d*	*9. a*

Extended Response

10. RUBRIC
4 points for a response that correctly explains why the island chains have different geologic features and uses these terms accurately: *tectonic plates, continental drift, subduction.*

Sample answer: The trench between the island chains suggests that the chains are on different tectonic plates that are moving toward each other. These movements used to be called continental drift. One plate is now sinking under the other in a motion called subduction. The islands were once far apart, which explains why their geology is so different.

3 points provides an adequate explanation and uses two terms accurately
2 points provides a partial explanation and uses two terms accurately
1 point provides a partial explanation and uses one term accurately

11. RUBRIC
4 points for a response that correctly explains the facts and uses these terms accurately: *hot spot, mantle, magma, crust.*

Sample answer: The mountain range is on a tectonic plate that is moving over a hot spot. As the plate moves, magma from the mantle melts the rock overhead and may form a new volcano on the crust. The mountains farthest away are oldest because they formed first.

3 points explains the facts adequately and uses three terms accurately
2 points explains the facts partially and uses two terms accurately
1 point explains the facts partially and uses one term accurately

CHAPTER

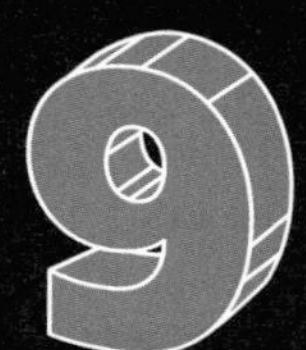

Earthquakes

Earth Science UNIFYING PRINCIPLES

PRINCIPLE 1
Heat energy inside Earth and radiation from the Sun provide energy for Earth's processes.

PRINCIPLE 2
Physical forces, such as gravity, affect the movement of all matter on Earth and throughout the universe.

PRINCIPLE 3
Matter and energy move among Earth's rocks and soil, atmosphere, waters, and living things.

PRINCIPLE 4
Earth has changed over time and continues to change.

Unit: The Changing Earth BIG IDEAS

CHAPTER 8
Plate Tectonics
The movement of tectonic plates causes geologic changes on Earth.

CHAPTER 9
Earthquakes
Earthquakes release stress that has built up in rocks.

CHAPTER 10
Mountains and Volcanoes
Mountains and volcanoes form as tectonic plates move.

CHAPTER 9 KEY CONCEPTS

SECTION 1

Earthquakes occur along faults.

1. Rocks move along faults.
2. Faults are classified by how rocks move.

SECTION 2

Earthquakes release energy.

1. Energy from earthquakes travels through Earth.
2. Seismic waves can be measured.

SECTION 3

Earthquake damage can be reduced.

1. Earthquakes can cause severe damage and loss of life.
2. Scientists work to monitor and predict earthquakes.
3. Structures can be designed to resist earthquake damage.

The Big Idea Flow Chart is available on p. T65 in the **TRANSPARENCY BOOK.**

Previewing Content

SECTION

Earthquakes occur along faults.

pp. 301–306

1. Rocks move along faults.

The Earth's lithosphere contains huge breaks, or **faults,** along which movement of blocks of rock occurs. In some places along faults, movement is slow and continuous. In other places, movement stops because the blocks of rock on the two sides of the fault lock together. The pressure of the blocks of rock pushing or pulling on each other causes **stress** to build up. Eventually, the stored-up energy is released and causes an **earthquake,** a sudden ground motion, and the blocks of rock along the fault suddenly jerk past each other.

2. Faults are classified by how rocks move.

- Along a normal fault, the block of rock above the fault plane moves down relative to the other block. This motion is caused by the two blocks of rock being pulled apart. See the diagram below.

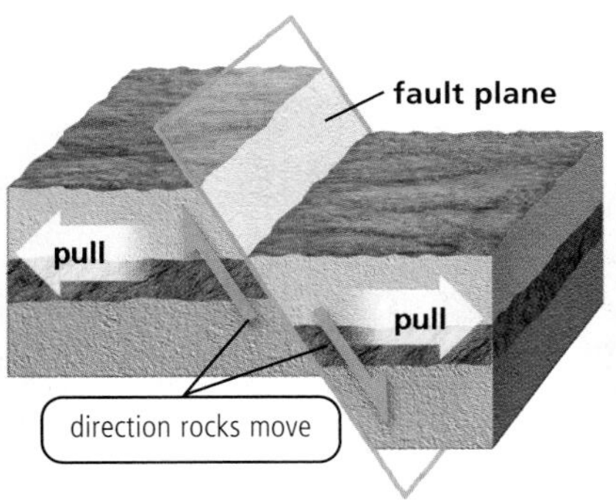

- Along a reverse fault, the block of rock above the fault plane moves up relative to the other block. This motion is caused by the two blocks of rock being pushed together.
- Along a strike-slip fault, the blocks of rock move horizontally on either side of the fault plane. This motion is caused by the rocks being pushed horizontally.

SECTION

Earthquakes release energy.

pp. 307–315

1. Energy from earthquakes travels through Earth.

The location underground where an earthquake begins is the **focus** of the earthquake. The crust breaks at the focus, and the released energy radiates outward in all directions in the form of **seismic waves.** The point on Earth's surface directly above the focus is the **epicenter.** There are three types of seismic waves:

- Primary waves travel the fastest and therefore arrive first at any location. These waves can travel through any material.
- Secondary waves travel more slowly than primary waves and arrive second. They do not travel through liquids and gases. Both primary waves and secondary waves travel through Earth.
- Surface waves travel along the surface of the crust and cause the most damage. They arrive last.

2. Seismic waves can be measured.

- A **seismograph** is an instrument used to detect and record ground movements. When an earthquake occurs, the shaking of the ground is recorded on paper, magnetic tape, or some other recording material. Separate seismographs record horizontal and vertical movement. The two types are shown in the diagram.

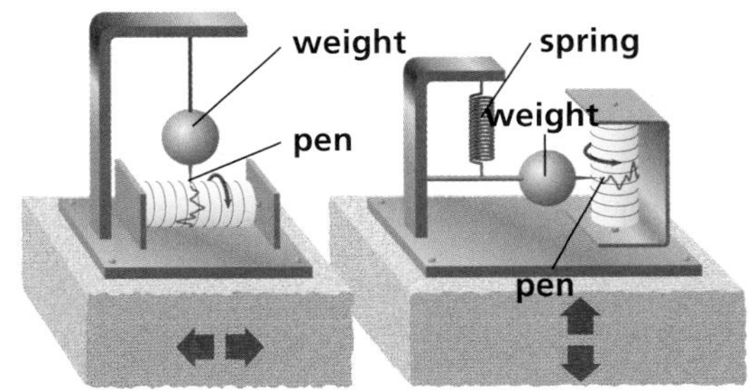

This seismograph records side-to-side movements. This seismograph records up-and-down movements.

- Seismograms recorded by seismographs at three different locations, or seismic stations, are needed to locate the epicenter of an earthquake. The difference in arrival time between primary and secondary waves is measured and used to calculate the distance to the epicenter. A circle with a radius corresponding to that distance is drawn around each seismic station, and the intersection of all three circles is the location of the epicenter.

Common Misconceptions

MISCONCEPTION DATABASE
CLASSZONE.COM Background on student misconceptions

EFFECT OF POWERFUL EARTHQUAKES Students may think that a powerful earthquake could cause a landmass such as western California to break off and fall into the ocean. Landmasses do not float on the ocean—they are parts of Earth's surface at higher elevations. The ocean comprises land at lower elevations that is covered by seawater.

This misconception is addressed on p. 304.

Previewing Content

SECTION

Earthquake damage can be reduced. pp. 316–325

1. Earthquakes can cause severe damage and loss of life.

- Earthquakes vary in size, or magnitude. Earthquake magnitude scales are used to describe the amount of energy an earthquake releases. Most scientists today prefer to use the moment magnitude scale.
- The movement of blocks of rock on opposite sides of a fault and the shaking of the ground can damage roads, dams, buildings, and other structures. Fires can break out, landslides often occur, and structures may sink or slide due to **liquefaction,** which causes soil to act like a liquid. Often, a strong earthquake is followed by weaker earthquakes, or **aftershocks.**
- Earthquakes may trigger water waves known as **tsunamis.** A tsunami moves quickly and may come ashore as a series of waves of varying heights.

2. Scientists work to monitor and predict earthquakes.

- Some of the signs that can help scientists predict the probability of a significant earthquake in a particular area include changes in the elevation of the ground, slow movement of blocks of rock, and the formation of small cracks in the ground.
- An area along an otherwise active fault where few or no earthquakes have occurred for a long time is known as a seismic gap. A gap may be an indicator that stress is building up and that a powerful earthquake might occur soon. The diagrams to the right show a seismic gap that was filled in by a large earthquake and its aftershocks.

3. Structures can be designed to resist earthquake damage.

- In areas where earthquakes are common, rules have been developed for building safer structures. For example, small buildings need to be firmly fastened to their foundations.
- Several methods are used to make large buildings more safe. Base isolators between a building and its foundation absorb much of the ground motion. An open space around a building lets the building shake more gently than the ground it is built on. Shear walls that contain steel supports add strength, as do cross braces, or X-shaped supports.

fault plane

seismic gap

fault plane

Large earthquake

1 Over several years many earthquakes have occurred along this fault. However, one section of the fault has had little earthquake activity. Stress is building up along this section.

2 A large earthquake and its aftershocks have occurred, releasing built-up stress. Over just a few weeks the seismic gap has been filled in.

Common Misconceptions

PREVENTING EARTHQUAKE DAMAGE Some students may think that it is now possible to construct earthquake-proof buildings. In reality, buildings can be designed and constructed to withstand some, but not all, earthquakes. Earthquake damage is always a possibility, especially in very strong earthquakes.

This misconception is addressed on p. 322.

MISCONCEPTION DATABASE

CLASSZONE.COM Background on student misconceptions

Previewing Labs

Lab Generator CD-ROM
Edit these Pupil Edition labs and generate alternative labs.

EXPLORE the BIG idea

Can You Bend Energy? p. 299 Students observe how light bends as it passes through air and water.	**TIME** 5 minutes **MATERIALS** clear glass, water, flashlight
Internet Activity: Earthquakes, p. 299 Students use the Internet to understand the frequency with which earthquakes occur.	**TIME** 20 minutes **MATERIALS** computer with Internet access

SECTION 1

EXPLORE Pressure, p. 301 Students observe how a stick bends and then breaks in response to added pressure.	**TIME** 10 minutes **MATERIALS** wooden craft stick
INVESTIGATE Faults, p. 303 Students use model blocks to explore how rocks can move along fault lines. **ALTERNATIVE:** Teacher Demonstration, URB p. 203	**TIME** 15 minutes **MATERIALS** 2 triangular blocks of wood that fit together to form a rectangle, masking tape, marker

SECTION 2

EXPLORE Movement of Energy, p. 307 Students use a spring toy to observe how energy moves through a solid material.	**TIME** 10 minutes **MATERIALS** large spring toy
INVESTIGATE Subduction-Zone Earthquakes, p. 309 Students use an earthquake map and data to examine how earthquake depths change within a subduction zone. **ALTERNATIVE:** Teacher Demonstration, URB p. 203 Earthquake Map, p. 102	**TIME** 20 minutes **MATERIALS** Earthquake Map; three pieces of different colored string, 16 cm, 24 cm, and 60 cm long; scissors; ruler; tape

SECTION 3

EXPLORE Shaking, p. 316 Students use sand, a rock, and a washer to compare the reactions of various materials to shaking.	**TIME** 10 minutes **MATERIALS** sand, newspaper, flat rock, washer
CHAPTER INVESTIGATION **How Structures React in Earthquakes,** pp. 324–325 Students design and build a structure, attempting to make it earthquake resistant, and observe how long it can withstand shaking. **ALTERNATIVE:** Teacher Modeling, URB p. 203	**TIME** 40 minutes **MATERIALS** modeling clay, 20–30 stirrer straws, piece of thin cardboard 15 cm on each side, scissors, ruler, shake table

Additional INVESTIGATION, Earthquake Depths, A, B, & C, pp. 131–139; Teacher Instructions, pp. 202–203

Previewing Chapter Resources

INTEGRATED TECHNOLOGY | **LABS AND ACTIVITIES**

CHAPTER 9
Earthquakes

Integrated Technology

CLASSZONE.COM
- eEdition Plus
- EasyPlanner Plus
- Misconception Database
- Content Review
- Test Practice
- Visualizations
- Resource Centers
- Internet Activity: Earthquakes
- Math Tutorial

SCILINKS.ORG

CD-ROMS
- eEdition
- EasyPlanner
- Power Presentations
- Content Review
- Lab Generator
- Test Generator

AUDIO CDS
- Audio Readings
- Audio Readings in Spanish

Labs and Activities

EXPLORE the Big Idea, p. 299
- Can You Bend Energy?
- Internet Activity: Earthquakes

UNIT RESOURCE BOOK
Unit Projects, pp. 5–10

Lab Generator CD-ROM
Generate customized labs.

SECTION

1 Earthquakes occur along faults.
pp. 301–306

Lesson Plan, pp. 82–83

Integrated Technology

VISUALIZATION, Fault Motion

TRANSPARENCY BOOK
- Big Idea Flow Chart, p. T65
- Daily Vocabulary Scaffolding, p. T66
- Note-Taking Model, p. T67
- 3-Minute Warm-Up, p. T68

Labs and Activities

- EXPLORE Pressure, p. 301
- INVESTIGATE Faults, p. 303
- Extreme Science, p. 306

UNIT RESOURCE BOOK
Datasheet, Faults, p. 91

SECTION

2 Earthquakes release energy.
pp. 307–315

Lesson Plan, pp. 93–94

Integrated Technology

- **VISUALIZATION,** Primary-Wave and Secondary-Wave Motion
- **RESOURCE CENTER,** Seismology
- **MATH TUTORIAL,** Multiplication

TRANSPARENCY BOOK
- Daily Vocabulary Scaffolding, p. T66
- 3-Minute Warm-Up, p. T68
- "Seismic Waves" Visual, p. T70

Labs and Activities

- EXPLORE Movement of Energy, p. 307
- INVESTIGATE Subduction-Zone Earthquakes, p. 309
- Math in Science, p. 315

UNIT RESOURCE BOOK
- Earthquake Map, p. 102
- Datasheet, Subduction-Zone Earthquakes, p. 103
- Math Support & Practice, pp. 120–121
- Additional INVESTIGATION, Earthquake Depths, A, B, & C, pp. 131–139

SECTION

3 Earthquake damage can be reduced.
pp. 316–325

Lesson Plan, pp. 105–106

Integrated Technology

RESOURCE CENTER, Explore Tsunamis

TRANSPARENCY BOOK
- Big Idea Flow Chart, p. T65
- Daily Vocabulary Scaffolding, p. T66
- 3-Minute Warm-Up, p. T69
- Chapter Outline, pp. T71–T72

Labs and Activities

- EXPLORE Shaking, p. 316
- CHAPTER INVESTIGATION, How Structures React in Earthquakes, pp. 324–325

UNIT RESOURCE BOOK
CHAPTER INVESTIGATION, How Structures React in Earthquakes, A, B, & C, pp. 122–130

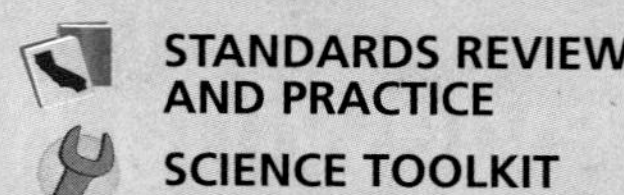

KEY TO ICONS: CD/CD-ROM; Teacher Edition; TRANSPARENCY BOOK; STANDARDS REVIEW AND PRACTICE; INTERNET; Pupil Edition; UNIT RESOURCE BOOK; ASSESSMENT BOOK; SCIENCE TOOLKIT

READING AND REINFORCEMENT	ASSESSMENT	STANDARDS
 **Modified Lesson Plans for English Learners,** pp. 35–37 • Magnet Word, B24–25 • Main Idea and Detail Notes, C37 • Daily Vocabulary Scaffolding, H1–8 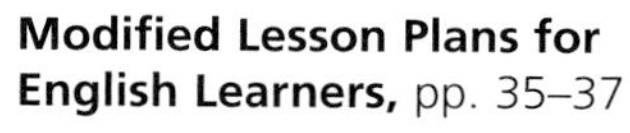 **UNIT RESOURCE BOOK** • Vocabulary Practice, pp. 117–118 • Decoding Support, p. 119 • Summarizing the Chapter, pp. 140–141  **Audio Readings CD** Listen to Pupil Edition. 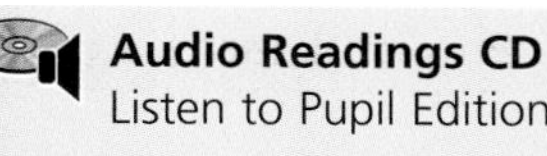 **Audio Readings in Spanish CD** Listen to Pupil Edition in Spanish.	• Chapter Review, pp. 327–328 • Standards-Based Assessment, p. 329  **ASSESSMENT BOOK** • Diagnostic Test, pp. 194–195 • Chapter Test, Levels A, B, & C, pp. 199–210 • Alternative Assessment, pp. 211–212  **STANDARDS REVIEW AND PRACTICE,** pp. 1–14, 21–24, 57–58  **McDougal Littell Assessment System**  **Test Generator CD-ROM** Generate customized and Spanish tests.	California Content Standards 6.1.a, 6.1.b, 6.1.c, 6.1.d, 6.1.e, 6.1.f, 6.1.g, 6.2.d, 6.3.a, 6.7.a, 6.7.d See p. 298 for the standards.
UNIT RESOURCE BOOK • Reading Study Guide, A & B, pp. 84–87 • Spanish Reading Study Guide, pp. 88–89 • Challenge and Extension, p. 90 • Reinforcing Key Concepts, p. 92	 Ongoing Assessment, pp. 301–303, 305  Section 9.1 Review, p. 305  **ASSESSMENT BOOK** Section 9.1 Quiz, p. 196	California Content Standards 6.1.a, 6.1.b, 6.1.d, 6.1.e, 6.1.f
UNIT RESOURCE BOOK • Reading Study Guide, A & B, pp. 95–98 • Spanish Reading Study Guide, pp. 99–100 • Challenge and Extension, p. 101 • Reinforcing Key Concepts, p. 104	Ongoing Assessment, pp. 308, 310–313  Section 9.2 Review, p. 314  **ASSESSMENT BOOK** Section 9.2 Quiz, p. 197	California Content Standards 6.1.a, 6.1.c, 6.1.e, 6.1.g, 6.3.a
UNIT RESOURCE BOOK • Reading Study Guide, A & B, pp. 107–110 • Spanish Reading Study Guide, pp. 111–112 • Challenge and Extension, p. 113 • Reinforcing Key Concepts, p. 114 • Challenge Reading, pp. 115–116	Ongoing Assessment, pp. 317–323  Section 9.3 Review, p. 323  **ASSESSMENT BOOK** Section 9.3 Quiz, p. 198	California Content Standards 6.1.d, 6.1g, 6.2.d, 6.3.a, 6.7.a, 6.7.d

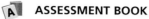

Previewing Resources for Differentiated Instruction

CHAPTER INVESTIGATION

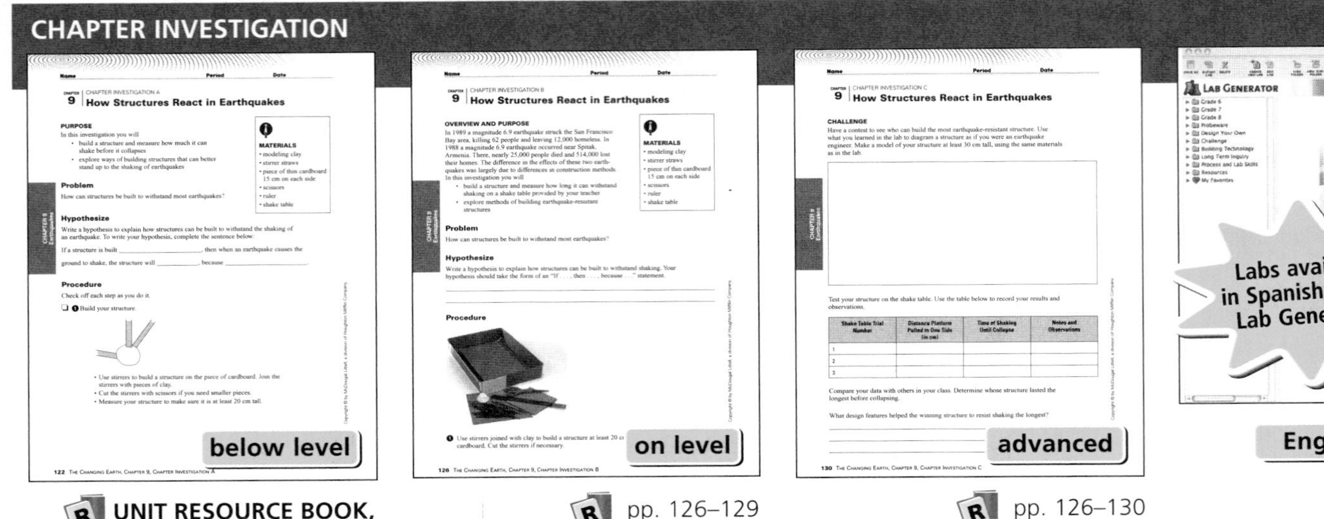

UNIT RESOURCE BOOK, pp. 122–125

pp. 126–129

pp. 126–130

READING STUDY GUIDE

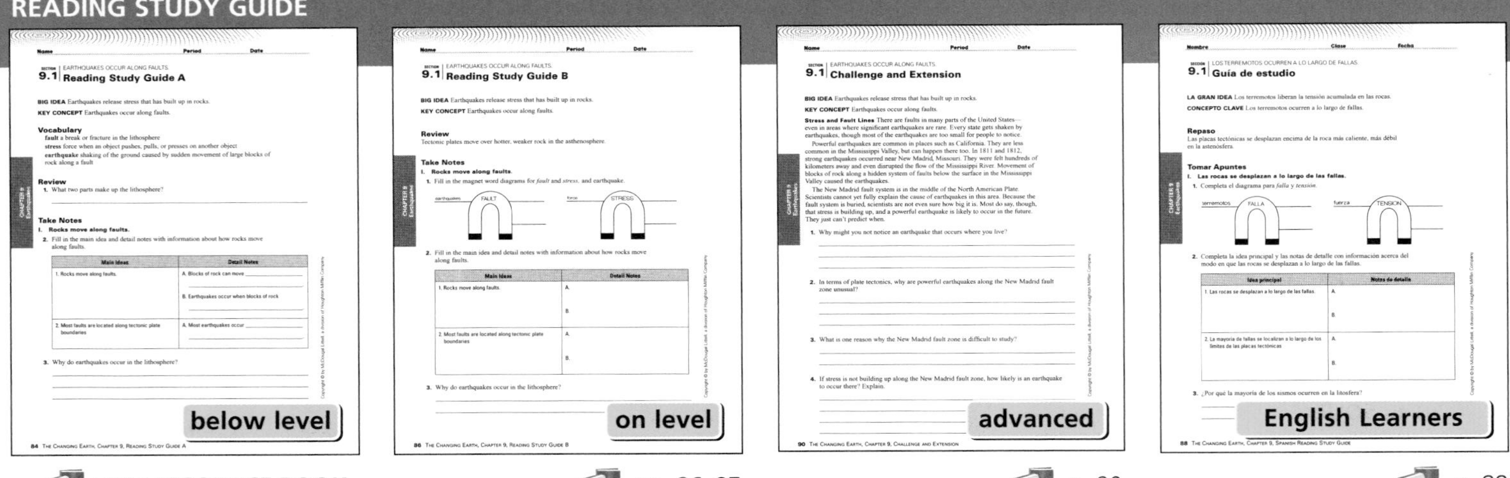

UNIT RESOURCE BOOK, pp. 84–85

pp. 86–87

p. 90

p. 88

CHAPTER TEST

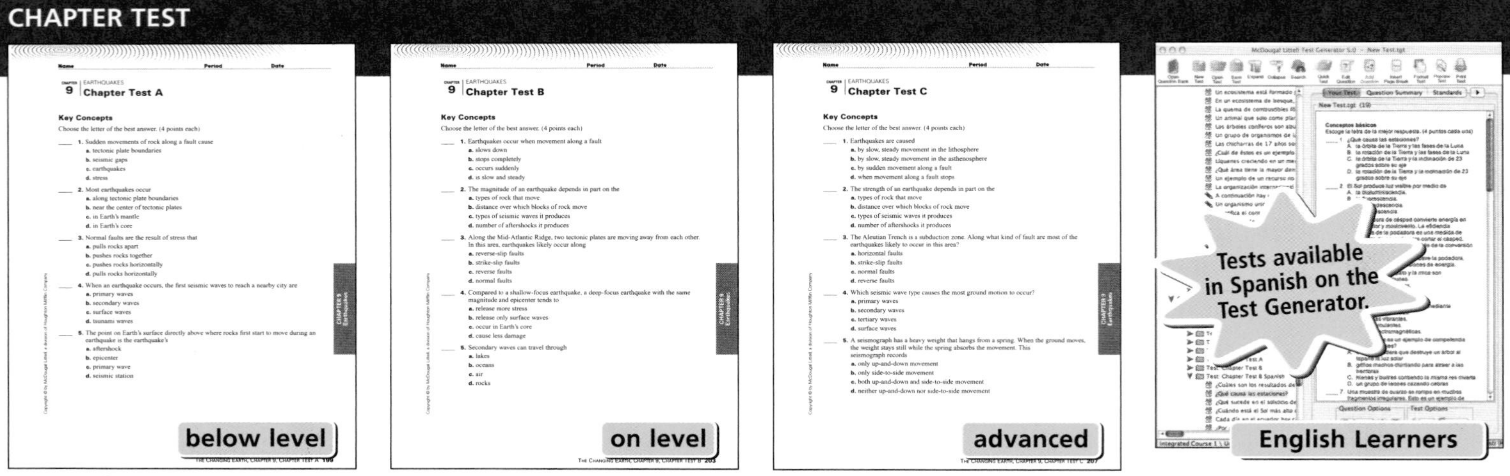

ASSESSMENT BOOK, pp. 199–202

pp. 203–206

pp. 207–210

TECHNOLOGY

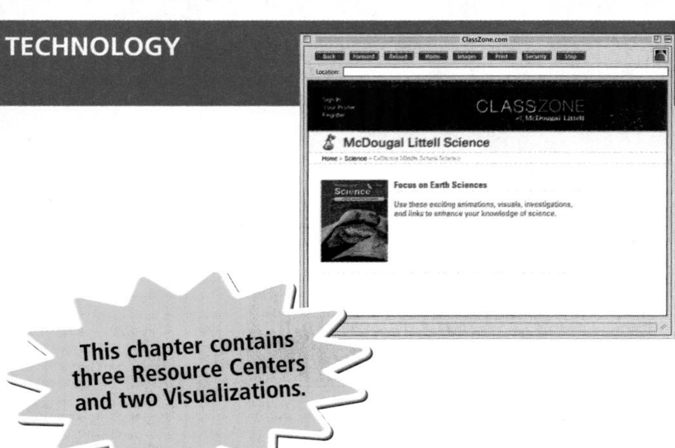

This chapter contains three Resource Centers and two Visualizations.

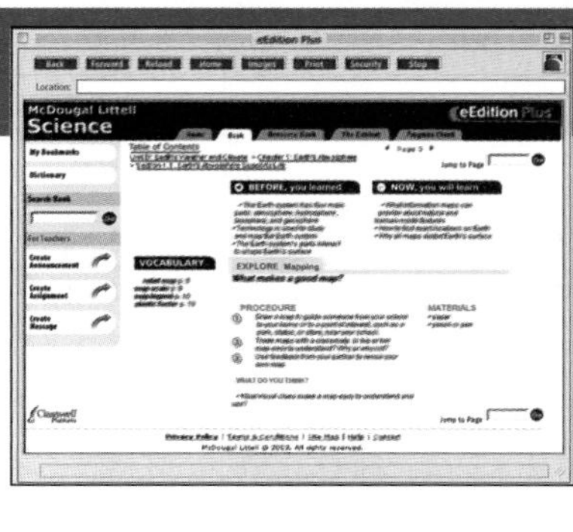

VISUAL CONTENT

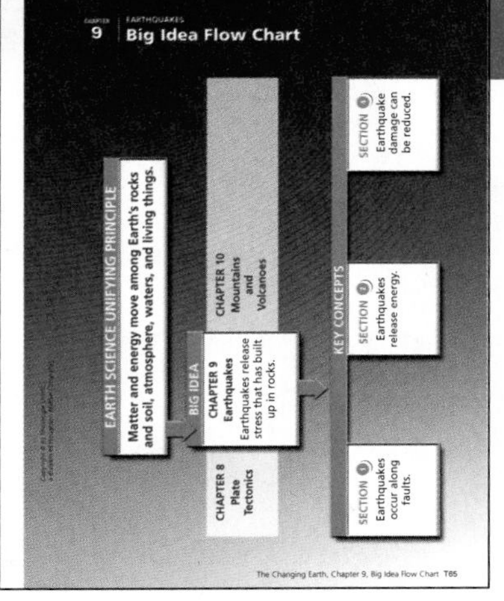

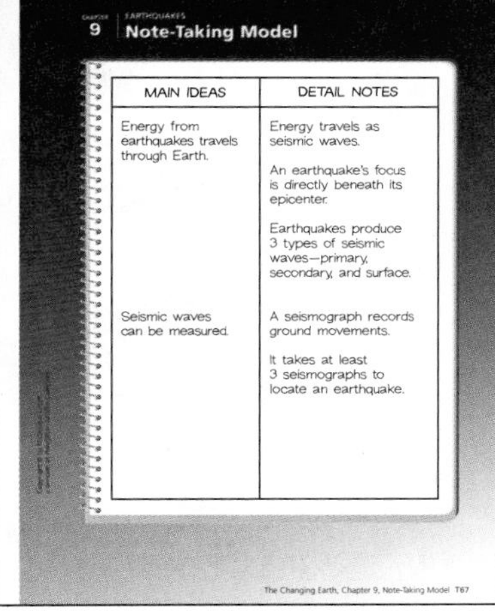

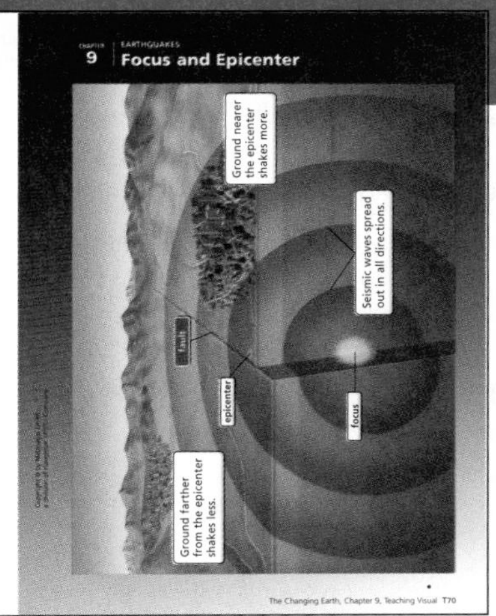

TRANSPARENCY BOOK, p. T65

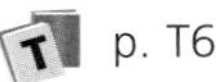

p. T67

p. T70

MORE SUPPORT

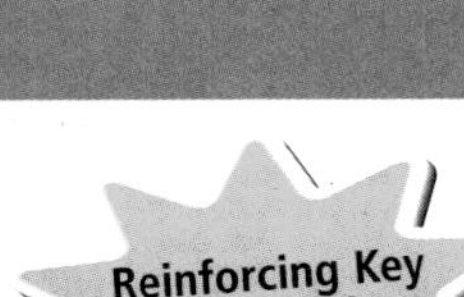

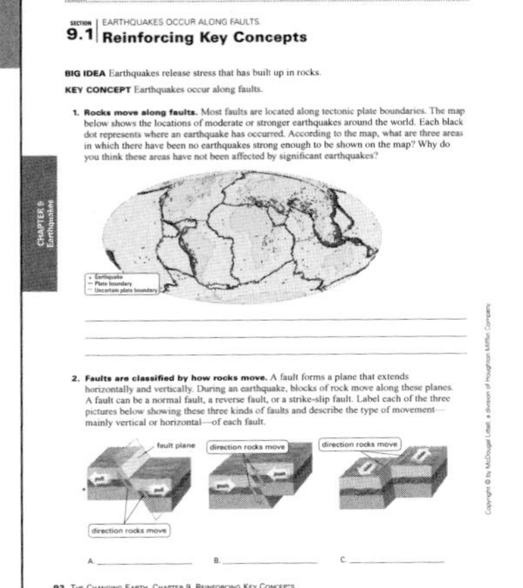

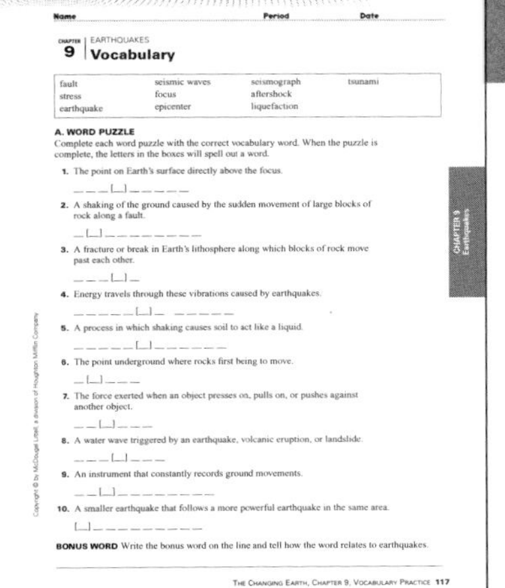

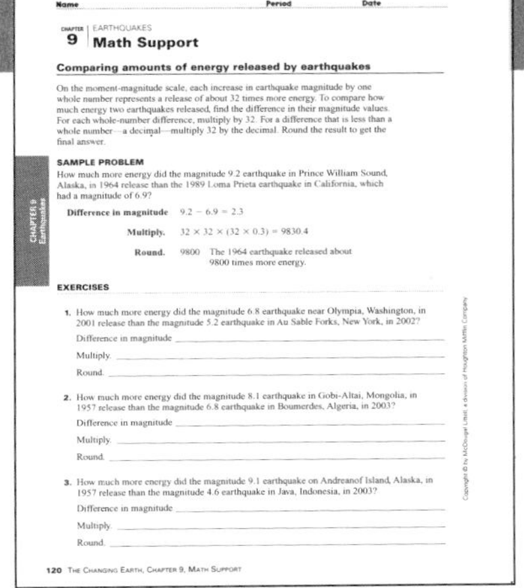

UNIT RESOURCE BOOK, p. 92

pp. 117–118

p. 120

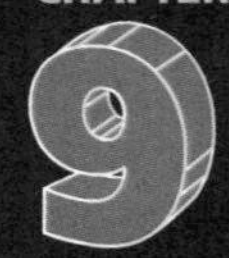

Earthquakes

INTRODUCE

the BIG idea

Discuss how the question in the box links to the Big Idea.

- What was the source of the energy needed to destroy this building?
- What are other kinds of earthquake damage?

California Content Standards

6.1.a Students know evidence of plate tectonics is derived from the fit of the continents; the location of earthquakes, volcanoes, and midocean ridges; and the distribution of fossils, rock types, and ancient climatic zones.

6.1.b Students know Earth is composed of several layers: a cold, brittle lithosphere; a hot, convecting mantle; and a dense, metallic core.

6.1.c Students know lithospheric plates the size of continents and oceans move at rates of centimeters per year in response to movements in the mantle.

6.1.d Students know that earthquakes are sudden motions along breaks in the crust called faults and that volcanoes and fissures are locations where magma reaches the surface.

6.1.e Students know major geologic events, such as earthquakes, volcanic eruptions, and mountain building, result from plate motions.

6.1.f Students know how to explain major features of California geology (including mountains, faults, volcanoes) in terms of plate tectonics.

6.1.g Students know how to determine the epicenter of an earthquake and know that the effects of an earthquake on any region vary, depending on the size of the earthquake, the distance of the region from the epicenter, the local geology, and the type of construction in the region.

6.2.d Students know earthquakes, volcanic eruptions, landslides, and floods change human and wildlife habitats.

6.3.a Students know energy can be carried from one place to another by heat flow or by waves, including water, light and sound waves, or by moving objects.

6.7.a Develop a hypothesis.

CHAPTER

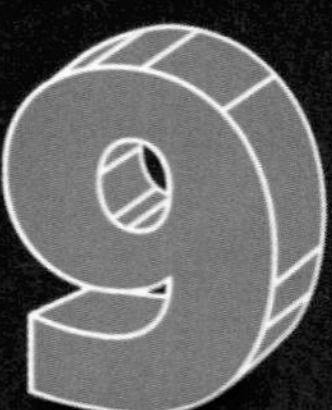

Earthquakes

the BIG idea

Earthquakes release stress that has built up in rocks.

Key Concepts

SECTION 1 **Earthquakes occur along faults.** Learn how rocks move along different kinds of faults.

SECTION 2 **Earthquakes release energy.** Learn how energy from an earthquake is used to determine its location and size.

SECTION 3 **Earthquake damage can be reduced.** Learn how structures are built to better withstand earthquakes.

What caused the damage to these buildings in San Francisco?

California ClassZone

CLASSZONE.COM

Chapter 9 online resources: Content Review, two Visualizations, three Resource Centers, Math Tutorial, Test Practice

298 Unit 3: The Changing Earth

INTERNET PREVIEW

CLASSZONE.COM For student use with the following pages:

Review and Practice

- Content Review, pp. 300, 326
- Math Tutorial: Multiplication, p. 315
- Test Practice, p. 329

Activities and Resources

- Internet Activity: Earthquakes, p. 299
- Visualizations: Fault Motion, p. 305; Wave Motion, p. 310 Resource Centers: Seismology, p. 312; Tsunamis, p. 319

Earthquakes

Code: MDL053

EXPLORE the BIG idea

Can You Bend Energy?

6.1.b Students know Earth is composed of several layers: a cold, brittle lithosphere; a hot, convecting mantle; and a dense, metallic core.

Put a clear glass filled with water on a table. Holding a flashlight at an angle to the glass, shine light through the water so that an oval of light forms on the table.

Observe and Think Did the light, which is a form of energy, travel in a straight line through the layers of air and water? Do you think other forms of energy travel in straight lines through layers inside Earth?

Internet Activity: Earthquakes

6.1.d Students know that earthquakes are sudden motions along breaks in the crust called faults and that volcanoes and fissures are locations where magma reaches the surface.

Go to **ClassZone.com** to see maps of recent earthquakes around the world, in the United States, and in your own area.

Observe and Think Where and when did the largest earthquakes occur? Summarize California's recent earthquake activity. Compare it with Alaska's for the same time period. What conclusions can you draw?

NSTA scilinks.org SCILINKS
Earthquakes **Code: MDL053**

EXPLORE the BIG idea

These inquiry-based activities are appropriate for use at home or as a supplement to classroom instruction.

Can You Bend Energy?

PURPOSE To help students recognize that energy does not always travel in straight lines.

TIP *5 min.* Darken the room to make the beam of light more easily visible.

Answers will vary. Students should report that the light did not travel in a straight line through the water to the table. Other types of energy bend as they pass through boundaries between layers in Earth.

REVISIT after p. 310.

Internet Activity: Earthquakes

PURPOSE To help students understand that earthquakes happen every day somewhere on Earth.

TIP *20 min.* Revisit the map of recent earthquakes in a week or two and see how it has changed.

Sample answer: Where and when the largest earthquakes occur will change over time as new earthquakes are reported.

REVISIT after p. 321.

EACHING WITH TECHNOLOGY

nternet Search Engine After teaching p. 319, ave students use a search engine and search he Internet to find an animation of a tsunami.

Presentation Software After teaching p. 322, have students use a computer with Internet access to find and download graphics of earthquake-resistant building structures. Have them use presentation software to present their findings to the class.

PREPARE

CONCEPT REVIEW

Activate Prior Knowledge

Review what students have learned about tectonic plates. Ask:

- What kind of plates is Earth's lithosphere made of? *tectonic plates*
- How do tectonic plates move and interact? *pull apart, push together, scrape past one another*
- Where do most major geologic events happen? *along tectonic plate boundaries*

TAKING NOTES

Main Idea and Detail Notes

Recording main ideas and details in a chart will help students organize and review key concepts and distinguish them from supporting details. Have students exchange charts and test each other.

Vocabulary Strategy

Students can include in their diagram as many other terms or ideas relating to the vocabulary term as they want.

Vocabulary and Note-Taking Resources

- Vocabulary Practice, pp. 117–118
- Decoding Support, p. 119

- Daily Vocabulary Scaffolding, p. T66
- Note-Taking Model, p. T67

- Magnet Word, B24–25
- Main Idea and Detail Notes, C37
- Daily Vocabulary Scaffolding, H1–8

CHAPTER 9

Getting Ready to Learn

CONCEPT REVIEW

- Earth's lithosphere is broken into tectonic plates.
- Tectonic plates pull apart, push together, and scrape past one another.
- Major geologic events occur along tectonic plate boundaries.

VOCABULARY REVIEW

lithosphere p. 267
tectonic plate p. 268
mid-ocean ridge p. 272
subduction p. 286

Review concepts and vocabulary.

TAKING NOTES

MAIN IDEA AND DETAIL NOTES

Make a two-column chart. Write the main ideas, such as those in the blue headings, in the column on the left. Write details about each of those main ideas in the column on the right.

VOCABULARY STRATEGY

For each vocabulary term, make a **magnet word** diagram. Write other terms or ideas related to that term around it.

See the Note-Taking Handbook on pages R45–R51.

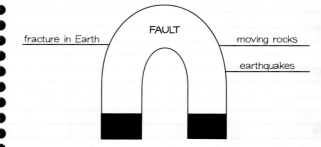

SCIENCE NOTEBOOK

MAIN IDEAS	DETAIL NOTES
1. Rocks move along faults.	1. Blocks of rock can move past one another slowly and constantly. 1. Blocks of rock can get stuck and then break free, causing earthquakes.
2. Most faults are located along tectonic plate boundaries.	2. 2. 2.

FAULT
fracture in Earth
moving rocks
earthquakes

CHECK READINESS

Administer the Diagnostic Test to determine students' readiness for new science content and their mastery of requisite math skills.

 Diagnostic Test, pp. 194–195

Technology Resources

Students needing content and math skills should visit **ClassZone.com.**

- **CONTENT REVIEW**
- **MATH TUTORIAL**

KEY CONCEPT

Earthquakes occur along faults.

CALIFORNIA Content Standards

6.1.b Students know Earth is composed of several layers: a cold, brittle lithosphere; a hot, convecting mantle; and a dense, metallic core.

6.1.d Students know that earthquakes are sudden motions along breaks in the crust called faults and that volcanoes and fissures are locations where magma reaches the surface.

6.1.e Students know major geologic events, such as earthquakes, volcanic eruptions, and mountain building, result from plate motions.

BEFORE, you learned

- The crust and uppermost mantle make up the lithosphere
- The lithosphere is cold and rigid
- Tectonic plates move over hotter, weaker rock in the asthenosphere

NOW, you will learn

- Why earthquakes occur
- Where most earthquakes occur
- How rocks move during earthquakes

EXPLORE Pressure (6.1.d)

How does pressure affect a solid material?

PROCEDURE

1. Hold a wooden craft stick at each end.
2. Bend the stick very slowly. Continue to put pressure on the stick until it breaks.

MATERIALS

wooden craft stick

WHAT DO YOU THINK?

- How did the stick change before it broke?
- How might rocks react to pressure?

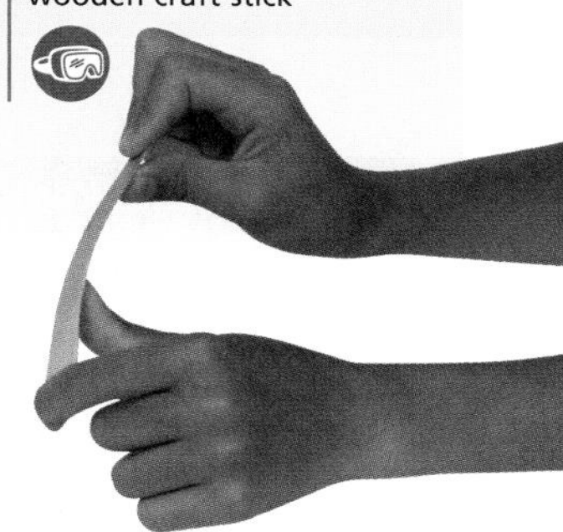

VOCABULARY

fault p. 301
stress p. 301
earthquake p. 301

VOCABULARY
Add magnet word diagrams for *fault, stress,* and *earthquake* to your notebook.

Rocks move along faults.

Sometimes when you pull on a drawer, it opens smoothly. At other times, the drawer sticks shut. If you pull hard enough, the drawer suddenly flies open. Rocks along faults behave in a similar way. A **fault** is a fracture, or break, in Earth's lithosphere. Blocks of rock move past each other along a fault.

Along some parts of a fault, the rocks on either side may slide along slowly and constantly. Along other parts of the fault, the rocks may stick, or lock together. The rocks bend as stress is put on them. **Stress** is the force exerted when an object presses on, pulls on, or pushes against another object. As stress increases, the rocks break free. A sudden release of stress in the lithosphere causes an earthquake. An **earthquake** is a shaking of the ground caused by the sudden movement of large blocks of rock along a fault.

RESOURCES FOR DIFFERENTIATED INSTRUCTION

Below Level

UNIT RESOURCE BOOK
- Reading Study Guide A, pp. 84–85
- Decoding Support, p. 119

AUDIO CDS

Advanced

UNIT RESOURCE BOOK
Challenge and Extension, p. 90

English Learners

UNIT RESOURCE BOOK
Spanish Reading Study Guide, pp. 88–89

AUDIO CDS

- Audio Readings in Spanish
- Audio Readings (English)

9.1 FOCUS

Set Learning Goals

Students will

- Explain why earthquakes occur.
- Identify where most earthquakes occur.
- Describe how rocks move during earthquakes.
- Model how movement occurs along the three main types of faults.

3-Minute Warm-Up

Display Transparency 68 or copy this exercise on the board:

Decide whether these statements are true. If not, correct them.

1. Earth's lithosphere consists of the uppermost mantle and core. *Earth's lithosphere consists of the crust and the uppermost mantle.*
2. Earth's lithosphere is hot and liquid. *Earth's lithosphere is cold and rigid.*
3. Tectonic plates move over the asthenosphere. *true*

3-Minute Warm-Up, p. T68

9.1 MOTIVATE

EXPLORE Pressure

PURPOSE To introduce the concept that rocks can bend before they break

TIP *10 min.* Caution students to avoid injuries by pointing the stick away from themselves or other students as they bend it slowly.

WHAT DO YOU THINK? *Answers will vary, but may include that the stick bent and cracked. Students may suggest that rocks can also bend and then break when subjected to pressure.*

Ongoing Assessment

Explain why earthquakes occur.

Ask: What must happen along a fault for an earthquake to occur? *sudden movement of large blocks of rock*

9.1 INSTRUCT

Teach the Standards

Faults (6.1.d)

In this section: Make sure students understand that a fault is a fracture or break in Earth's crust where blocks of rock have moved past each other. Help students understand that the sudden movement of rock along faults causes earthquakes. Ask students to name the three types of faults and describe the motion of rocks at each type.

- **previously taught:** effects of earthquakes, p. 47; earthquake faults and geologic hazards, pp. 206–207, 212; lithosphere, pp. 265–269
- **future opportunities:** volcanoes, pp. 342–344, 346–360

Teach from Visuals

To help students interpret the map showing plate boundaries, ask:

- Where in the Atlantic Ocean do most earthquakes occur? Why? *Most occur in the middle of the ocean where there is a plate boundary, the mid-Atlantic Ridge.*
- Why are so few earthquakes shown along the eastern coast of North America? *There are no plate boundaries and therefore few earthquakes along that coast.*

Ongoing Assessment

Identify where most earthquakes occur.

Ask: Where on Earth do most earthquakes take place? *along tectonic plate boundaries*

READING VISUALS *Answer: They are next to plate boundaries.*

Most faults are located along tectonic plate boundaries, so most earthquakes occur in these areas. However, the blocks of rock that move during an earthquake are much smaller than a tectonic plate. A plate boundary can be many thousands of kilometers long. During even a very powerful earthquake, blocks of rock might move only a few meters past each other along a distance of several hundred kilometers. The strength of an earthquake depends in part on

- how much stress builds up before the rocks move
- the distance the rocks move along the fault

? B

About 80 percent of all earthquakes occur in a belt around the edges of the Pacific Ocean. In the United States, the best-known fault in this belt is the San Andreas (san an-DRAY-uhs) Fault in California. It forms part of the boundary between the North American Plate and the Pacific Plate. Unlike many other faults, parts of the San Andreas Fault can be seen on the surface of the ground.

CALIFORNIA Focus

The San Andreas Fault is not one long fault. Instead, it is a zone consisting of three main segments: southern, central, and northern. The San Andreas Fault zone is more than 1288 kilometers (800 mi) long. Notable earthquakes occurred along the fault in 1857, 1906, and 1989.

A small percentage of earthquakes occurs along faults within plates. As you read in Chapter 8, a tectonic plate is hard, or rigid. Therefore, stress along a plate's boundary can cause rocks to break and move along weak areas toward the middle of the plate.

Where Earthquakes Occur

This map shows the locations of moderate to intense earthquakes for a ten-year period.

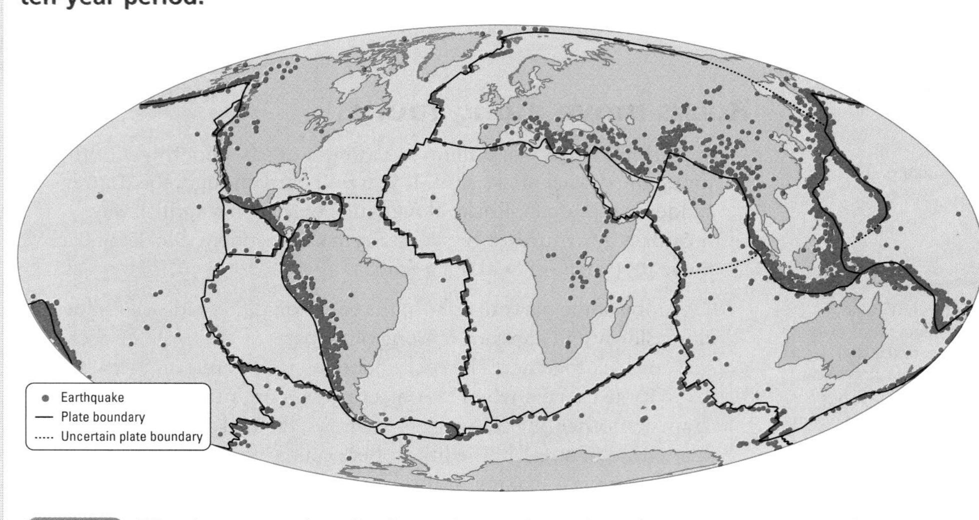

READING VISUALS Why do most earthquakes in North America and South America occur near the continents' western coasts?

302 Unit 3: The Changing Earth

DIFFERENTIATE INSTRUCTION

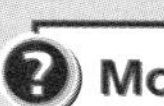

More Reading Support

A Where are most faults located? *along plate boundaries*

B Where do most earthquakes occur? *in a belt around the edges of the Pacific Ocean*

Inclusion Enlarge the "Where Earthquakes Occur" illustration on a photocopy machine, and give copies to students with visual impairments.

All earthquakes occur in the lithosphere. To understand why, you might compare a tectonic plate to a piece of cold, hard caramel. Like cold caramel, the plate is rigid and brittle. The rocks can break and move suddenly, causing an earthquake. Now compare the asthenosphere below the plate to warm, soft caramel. In the asthenosphere, hot rock bends and flows rather than breaks. A few earthquakes occur far below the normal depth of the lithosphere only because tectonic plates sinking in subduction zones are still cold enough to break.

CHECK YOUR READING Why don't earthquakes occur in the asthenosphere?

Faults are classified by how rocks move.

The blocks of rock along different types of faults move in different directions, depending on the kinds of stress they are under. Scientists classify a fault according to the way the rocks on one side move in relation to the rocks on the other side.

The three main types of faults are normal faults, reverse faults, and strike-slip faults. More than one type of fault may be present along the same plate boundary. However, the type of fault that is most common along a boundary depends on whether plates are pulling apart, pushing together, or scraping past one another at that boundary.

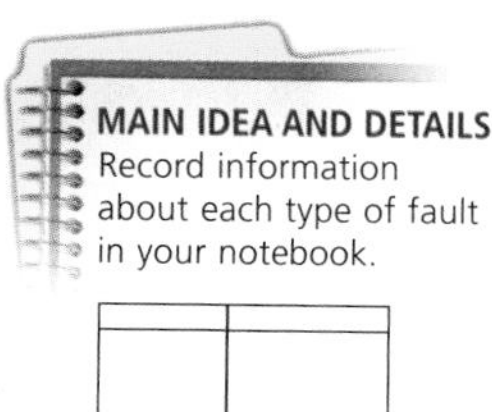

MAIN IDEA AND DETAILS Record information about each type of fault in your notebook.

INVESTIGATE Faults

How can rocks move along faults?

PROCEDURE

1. Place one block of wood against the other to form a rectangle.
2. Put two pieces of masking tape across both blocks. Draw a different pattern on each piece of tape. Break the tape where it crosses the blocks.
3. Keep the blocks in contact and slide one block along the other.
4. Repeat step 3 until you find three different ways the blocks can move relative to each other. Draw diagrams showing how the blocks moved. Include the tape patterns.

WHAT DO YOU THINK?

- How can you use the tape patterns to find the relative directions in which the blocks were moved?
- In each case, what sort of stress (such as pulling) did you put on the blocks?

CHALLENGE Compare the ways you moved the blocks with the ways tectonic plates move at their boundaries.

SKILL FOCUS
Modeling (6.1.e)

MATERIALS
- 2 triangular blocks of wood
- masking tape
- marker

TIME
15 minutes

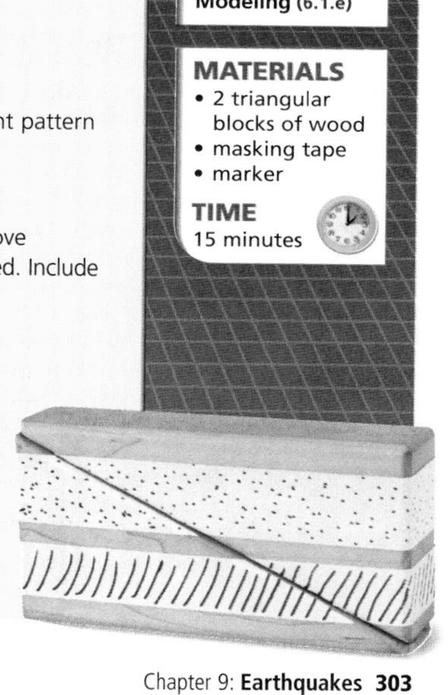

INVESTIGATE Faults

PURPOSE To model the three main types of faults

TIP *15 min.* Remind students to include in their drawings the patterns they draw on the masking tape.

WHAT DO YOU THINK? *by comparing how the layers are offset; pulling, pushing, sliding*

CHALLENGE *Pulling the blocks models the way plates move at a divergent boundary, pushing the blocks models the way plates move at a convergent boundary, and sliding the blocks models the way plates move at a transform boundary.*

 Datasheet, Faults, p. 91

Technology Resources

Customize this student lab as needed or look for an alternative. Print rubrics to assess student lab reports.

 **Lab Generator CD-ROM**

Ongoing Assessment

CHECK YOUR READING *Answer: The rock is hot enough to bend and flow rather than break.*

IFFERENTIATE INSTRUCTION

More Reading Support

C How are faults classi-
ied? *by the way the ocks on one side of the ault move relative to the ocks on the other side*

Alternate Assessment Have students use the wood blocks to demonstrate for the class both physically and orally the answers to the questions in "Investigate Faults."

Advanced

 Challenge and Extension, p. 90

Teach from Visuals

To help students interpret the diagrams and photographs of normal and reverse faults and to compare and contrast block movement, ask:

- In each diagram on this page, how does the block on the left move relative to the block on the right? *For the normal fault, the block on the left moves up relative to the block on the right. For the reverse fault, the block on the left moves down relative to the block on the right.*
- In which type of fault are the blocks moving apart? *normal fault*

Address Misconceptions

IDENTIFY Point out the San Andreas Fault on a large map. Ask: What effects are likely as powerful earthquakes continue to occur in western California? Students who say that western California will fall into the ocean hold the misconception that a single earthquake can break off part of a continent, and that the surfaces of continents and adjacent ocean floors are not continuous.

CORRECT Show a cross-section of Earth that includes continental crust and oceanic crust. Point out that the edge of a continent is not a shelf of land extending over the ocean, so it cannot break off and fall in. Remind students that the San Andreas is a strike-slip fault, along which landmasses move past one another horizontally.

REASSESS Ask: What will happen to western California as movement continues along the San Andreas Fault? *It will slide northward relative to the rest of North America and may eventually become an island.*

Technology Resources

Visit **ClassZone.com** for background on common student misconceptions.

 **MISCONCEPTION DATABASE**

READING TIP The word *plane* comes from the Latin word *planum,* which means "flat surface."

The illustrations on this page and page 305 show that a fault forms a flat surface, or plane, that extends both horizontally and vertically. Blocks of rock move along the fault plane during an earthquake. Along a normal or reverse fault, the blocks move up or down. Along a strike-slip fault, the blocks move sideways.

Normal Faults

 D

Along a normal fault, the block of rock above the fault plane slides down in relation to the other block. Stress that pulls rocks apart causes normal faults. Earthquakes along normal faults are common near boundaries where tectonic plates are moving apart, such as in the Great Rift Valley of Africa.

READING TIP Compare the directions of the arrows in the diagrams with the directions of the arrows on the photographs.

As rocks are pulled apart (white arrows), normal faults form. The block on the right has moved down in relation to the block on the left.

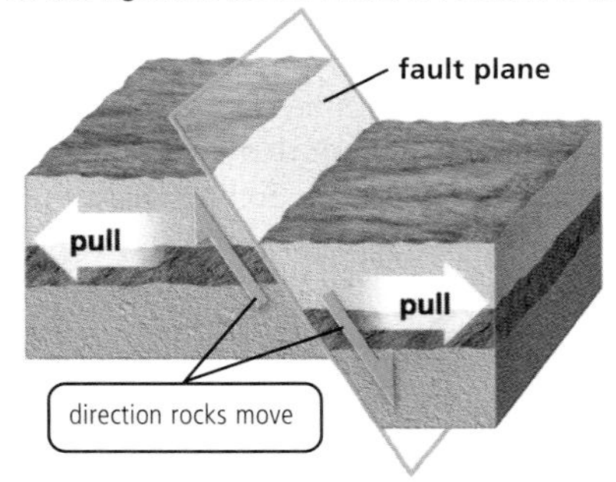

Reverse Faults

Along a reverse fault, the block of rock above the fault plane moves up in relation to the other block. Stress that presses rocks together causes reverse faults. These faults can occur near collision-zone boundaries.

As rocks are pushed together (white arrows), reverse faults form. The block on the right has moved up in relation to the block on the left.

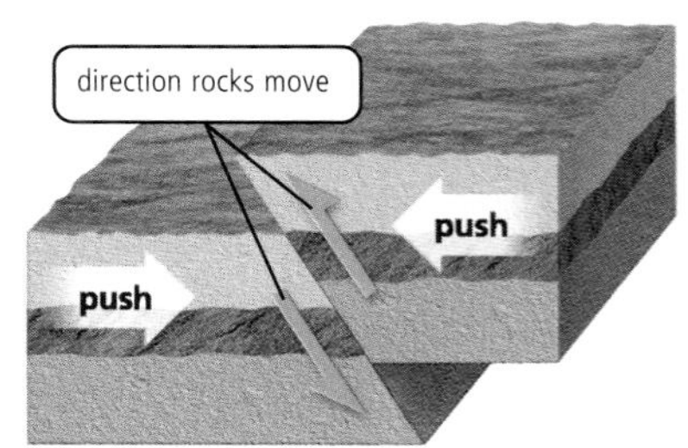

DIFFERENTIATE INSTRUCTION

 **More Reading Support**

D Along a normal fault, how do the blocks move? *One slides down relative to the other.*

English Learners English learners may have difficulty with words that have more than one meaning. The terms *fault* and *stress* from this section have other, more common meanings that students may be familiar with. Have students look up the terms in the dictionary and read all the definitions for each one. Help students identify which definition is used here.

Make sure English learners understand the meaning of *along*—"over the length of" (pp. 301–305).

For example, the Himalaya Mountains rise in the area where the Indian Plate is pushing into the Eurasian Plate. The Himalayas have many earthquakes along reverse faults.

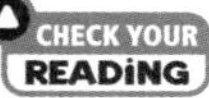

What type of stress produces reverse faults?

Strike-Slip Faults

Along a strike-slip fault, blocks of rock move sideways on either side of the fault plane. Stresses that push blocks of rock horizontally cause earthquakes along strike-slip faults. These faults can occur where plates scrape past each other. The San Andreas Fault is a strike-slip fault.

Explore animations showing fault motion.

As rocks are pushed horizontally in opposite directions, strike-slip faults form. The block on the right has moved to the right with respect to the block on the left.

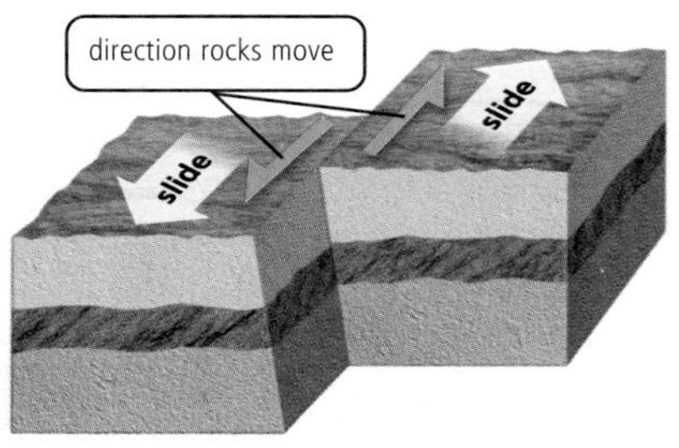

Over time, movement of rocks along normal and reverse faults can push up mountains and form deep valleys. As rocks move along strike-slip faults, rocks that were once in continuous layers can become separated by hundreds of kilometers.

9.1 Review

KEY CONCEPTS

1. What causes earthquakes? (6.1.e)
2. Why do most earthquakes occur along tectonic plate boundaries? (6.1.d)
3. What is the main direction of stress on blocks of rock at normal faults, reverse faults, and strike-slip faults? (6.1.d)

CRITICAL THINKING

4. **Compare and Contrast** Make a chart showing the similarities and differences between normal and reverse faults.
5. **Connect** Japan is near a subduction zone. What type of faults would you expect to be responsible for many of the earthquakes there? Explain.

CHALLENGE

6. **Analyze** What evidence from rock layers could show a scientist that earthquakes had occurred in an area before written records were kept?

ANSWERS

. sudden release of stress that had built up in rocks

. Most faults are at or near plate boundaries.

. normal faults: pulling part; reverse faults: pressing ogether; strike-slip faults: orizontal sliding

4. similarities: movement of rock is mainly vertical, fault plane is at an angle, both are related to plate movements; differences: main direction of stress is opposite, direction of relative movement of blocks is opposite, each is common at a different type of plate boundary

5. reverse faults, because plates are pushing together along a subduction zone

6. Layers of rock that are broken and offset indicate that earthquakes have occurred.

Ongoing Assessment

Describe how rocks move during earthquakes.

Ask: How does movement along a reverse fault compare to movement along a strike-slip fault? *Movement along a reverse fault is mainly vertical whereas movement along a strike-slip fault is horizontal.*

Answer: stress that presses rocks together

Reinforce the BIG idea

Have students relate the section to the Big Idea.

 Reinforcing Key Concepts, p. 92

9.1 ASSESS & RETEACH

Assess

 Section 9.1 Quiz, p. 196

Reteach

Help students review the three kinds of faults introduced in this section by creating on the board a three-column table with the following column heads: *Normal Fault, Reverse Fault,* and *Strike-Slip Fault.* In each column, have volunteers fill in how blocks of rock move along the fault and what kind of stress causes earthquakes along the fault. *Normal Fault: one block slides down relative to the other; stress: pulling. Reverse Fault: one block moves up relative to the other; stress: pushing together. Strike-Slip Fault: blocks move sideways; stress: pushing horizontally.*

Technology Resources

Have students visit **ClassZone.com** for reteaching of Key Concepts.

 CONTENT REVIEW

 CONTENT REVIEW CD-ROM

EXTREME SCIENCE
Fun and Motivating Science

Purpose
To understand the incredible power of earthquakes

Present the Science
The 11 largest earthquakes in the world since 1900 include the five listed in the chart and the following 6:

- off the coast of Ecuador, 1906, 8.8
- Rat Islands, Alaska, 1965, 8.7
- India-China border, 1950, 8.6
- Kamchatka Peninsula, 1923, 8.5
- Banda Sea, Indonesia, 1938, 8.5
- Kuril Islands, 1963, 8.5

With the exception of the 1950 earthquake near the India-China border, all of these earthquakes occurred near subduction-zone boundaries. The 1950 earthquake was related to the convergence of India and Asia.

Discussion Questions
Ask: Where and when was the most powerful earthquake in the United States? *Prince William Sound, Alaska, 1964*

Ask: In this earthquake, how far did the plates move? *9 meters*

Ask: How high was the 1964 tsunami in Valdez Inlet, and what caused it? *67 meters—taller than a 20-story building; a landslide*

Ask: How strong was the most powerful earthquake ever recorded? *An earthquake in Chile in 1960 had about 10 times more energy than the Alaskan earthquake of 1964.*

Close
Ask students what they can conclude about earthquakes from their reading. *Earthquakes can be very powerful, can cause a great deal of destruction, and can be felt a long distance away. Such powerful earthquakes do not happen very often.*

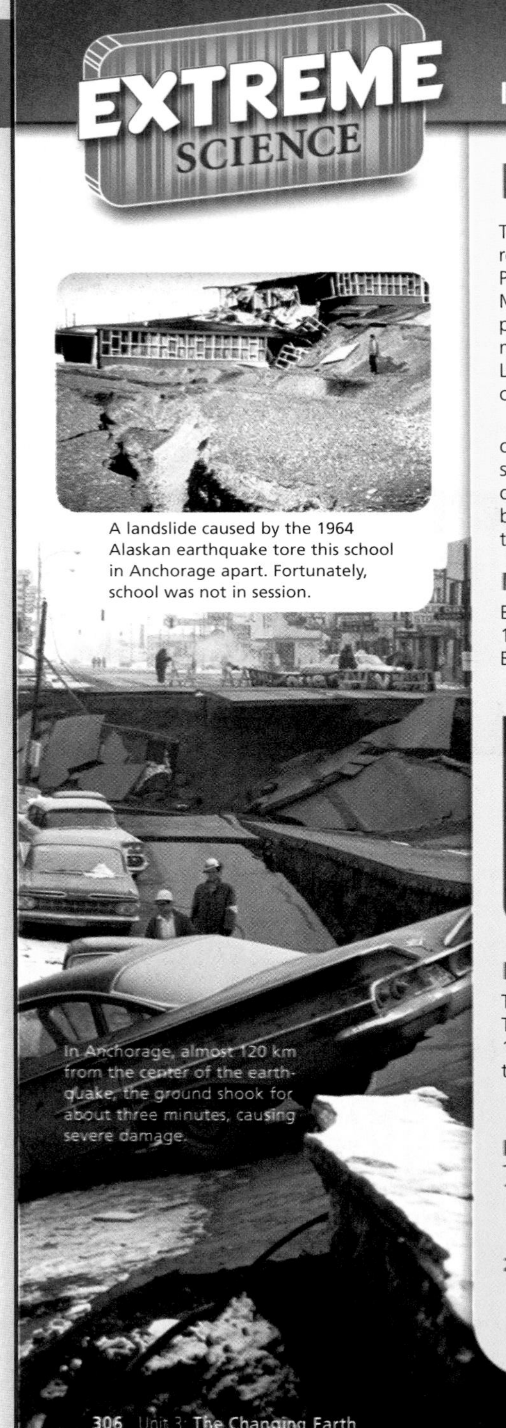

A landslide caused by the 1964 Alaskan earthquake tore this school in Anchorage apart. Fortunately, school was not in session.

In Anchorage, almost 120 km from the center of the earthquake, the ground shook for about three minutes, causing severe damage.

INCREDIBLE EARTHQUAKES

Earth Shakes

6.1.e Students know major geologic events, such as earthquakes, volcanic eruptions, and mountain building, result from plate motions.

The most powerful earthquake ever recorded in the United States struck Prince William Sound in Alaska on March 27, 1964. Plates that had been moving a few centimeters per year lurched 9 meters (30 ft), causing the ground to shake for more than three minutes. Energy from the earthquake reached Louisiana, more than 5000 kilometers (3000 mi) away. There, it caused waves high enough to sink fishing boats in a harbor.

The 1964 Alaskan earthquake caused buildings to crumble and collapse. It also produced tsunamis—water waves caused by a sudden movement of the ground during an earthquake, landslide, or volcanic eruption. In Alaska's Valdez Inlet, a landslide triggered by the earthquake produced a tsunami 67 meters (220 ft) high—taller than a 20-story building.

Missouri Earthquakes Ring Massachusetts Bells
Earthquakes were recorded near New Madrid, Missouri, in 1811 and 1812. The energy from the quakes caused church bells to ring in Boston, Massachusetts—nearly 1600 kilometers (1000 mi) away.

Five Largest Earthquakes Since 1900

Location	Date	Moment Magnitude
Off the coast of Chile	1960	9.5
Prince William Sound, Alaska	1964	9.2
Andreanof Islands, Alaska	1957	9.1
Kamchatka Peninsula, Russia	1952	9.0
Off the coast of Sumatra	2004	9.0

Largest Earthquake Ever
The most powerful earthquake ever recorded hit Chile in 1960. This earthquake released almost 10 times as much energy as the 1964 earthquake in Alaska. This was about 600 times the energy of the earthquake that destroyed much of San Francisco in 1906.

EXPLORE
1. **EXPLAIN** How were the 1964 Alaskan earthquake and the 1960 Chilean earthquake related to movements along tectonic plate boundaries?
2. **CHALLENGE** An inlet is a narrow body of water connected to a lake or ocean. Why might a tsunami be higher in an inlet than along the coastline around it?

EXPLORE
1. *EXPLAIN Both earthquakes occurred at subduction-zone boundaries where plates push together.*
2. *CHALLENGE The water cannot spread out, so it must rise higher.*

KEY CONCEPT

Earthquakes release energy.

CALIFORNIA Content Standards

6.1.g Students know how to determine the epicenter of an earthquake and know that the effects of an earthquake on any region vary, depending on the size of the earthquake, the distance of the region from the epicenter, the local geology, and the type of construction in the region.

6.3.a Students know energy can be carried from one place to another by heat flow or by waves, including water, light and sound waves, or by moving objects.

BEFORE, you learned

- Most earthquakes occur along tectonic plate boundaries
- Different directions of stress cause normal, reverse, and strike-slip faults

NOW, you will learn

- How energy from an earthquake travels through Earth
- How an earthquake's location is determined

VOCABULARY

seismic wave p. 307
focus p. 308
epicenter p. 308
seismograph p. 312

EXPLORE Movement of Energy (6.3.a)

How does energy travel?

PROCEDURE

1. On a flat surface, hold one end of a spring toy while a partner holds the other end. Stretch the spring, then squeeze some coils together and release them.
2. Again, hold one end of the spring while your partner holds the other end. Shake your end of the spring back and forth.

MATERIALS
spring toy

WHAT DO YOU THINK?

- How did energy travel along the spring when you gathered and released some coils?
- How did energy travel along the spring when you shook one end back and forth?

Energy from earthquakes travels through Earth.

MAIN IDEA AND DETAILS Record information about the energy released by earthquakes.

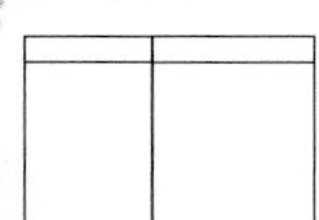

When you throw a rock into a pond, waves ripple outward from the spot where the rock hits the water. The energy released by an earthquake travels in a similar way through Earth. Unlike the pond ripples, though, earthquake energy travels outward in all directions—up, down, and to the sides. The energy travels as **seismic waves** (SYZ-mihk), which are vibrations caused by earthquakes. Seismic waves from even small earthquakes can be recorded by sensitive instruments around the world.

9.2 FOCUS

Set Learning Goals

Students will

- Explain how energy from an earthquake travels through Earth.
- Understand how an earthquake's location is determined.
- Analyze in an experiment how the locations of earthquakes are related to structures and processes inside Earth.

3-Minute Warm-Up

Display Transparency 68 or copy this exercise on the board:

Choose the correct term to fill in the blank.

Terms
faults
plate boundaries
stress
earthquake

1. All earthquakes occur along ____ . *faults*
2. The force exerted when an object pushes, pulls, or presses against another object is called ____ . *stress*
3. Most faults are located along ____ . *plate boundaries*

3-Minute Warm-Up, p. T68

9.2 MOTIVATE

EXPLORE Movement of Energy

PURPOSE To model how energy travels in primary and secondary waves

TIP *10 min.* Ask students to think about how the movement they see might relate to earthquakes.

WHAT DO YOU THINK? *in a straight line down the spring; back and forth perpendicular to the spring*

RESOURCES FOR DIFFERENTIATED INSTRUCTION

Below Level

UNIT RESOURCE BOOK
- Reading Study Guide A, pp. 95–96
- Decoding Support, p. 119

AUDIO CDS

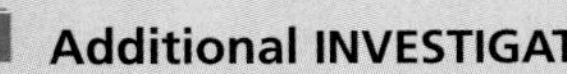

Additional INVESTIGATION, Earthquake Depths, A, B, & C, pp. 131–139; Teacher Instructions, pp. 202–203

Advanced

UNIT RESOURCE BOOK
Challenge and Extension, p. 101

English Learners

UNIT RESOURCE BOOK
Spanish Reading Study Guide, pp. 99–100

AUDIO CDS
- Audio Readings in Spanish
- Audio Readings (English)

9.2 INSTRUCT

Teach the Standards

Earthquakes and Energy (6.3.a)

In this section: Remind students that an earthquake's epicenter is the point on Earth's surface directly above the focus—the point at which the rocks first began to move. Explain to students that energy from an earthquake moves out in all directions from the focus in the form of seismic waves.

previously taught: transfer of energy, pp. 11, 18–24, 48–49; Earth's layers, pp. 265–269

future opportunities: effects of earthquakes, pp. 316–325; energy tranfer in ecosystem, pp. 390–396, 471–481

Teach from Visuals

To help students interpret the visual showing the focus and epicenter, ask:

- Where is the fault in relation to the focus and the epicenter? *They are lined up in the same place.*
- What happens after an earthquake begins? *The seismic waves spread out in all directions from the focus.*

Mathematics Connection

Point out that a fault can be thought of as a plane on which the focus is located as a point.

Ongoing Assessment

READING VISUALS *Answer: The focus is where movement starts inside Earth; the epicenter is the point on Earth's surface above the focus.*

All earthquakes start beneath Earth's surface. The **focus** of an earthquake is the point underground where rocks first begin to move. Seismic waves travel outward from the earthquake's focus. The **epicenter** (EHP-ih-SEHN-tuhr) is the point on Earth's surface directly above the focus. Scientists often name an earthquake after the city that is closest to its epicenter.

READING TIP The prefix *epi-* comes from a Greek word meaning "on top of." An earthquake's epicenter is directly over its focus.

If two earthquakes of equal strength have the same epicenter, the one with the shallower focus usually causes more damage. Seismic waves from a deep-focus earthquake lose more of their energy as they travel farther up to Earth's surface.

The depths of earthquakes along tectonic plate boundaries are related to the directions in which the plates move. For example, an earthquake along a mid-ocean spreading center has a shallow focus. There, the plates are pulling apart, and the new crust that forms is thin. Subduction zones have a wide range of earthquake depths, from shallow to very deep. Earthquakes can occur anywhere along the sinking plates.

Focus and Epicenter

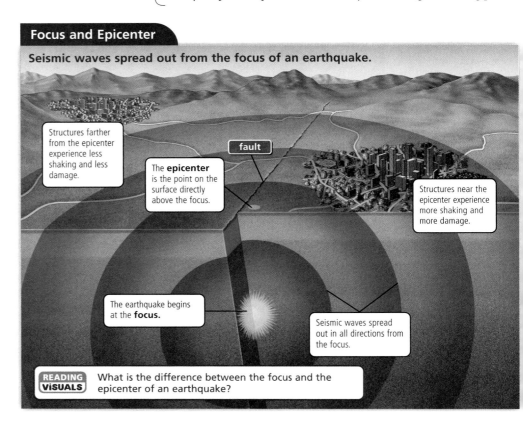

Seismic waves spread out from the focus of an earthquake.

READING VISUALS What is the difference between the focus and the epicenter of an earthquake?

DIFFERENTIATE INSTRUCTION

More Reading Support

A Where do all earthquakes start? *focus*

B Which causes more damage, a shallow- or deep-focus earthquake? *shallow*

Additional Investigation To reinforce Section 9.2 learning goals, use the following full-period investigation:

Additional INVESTIGATION, Earthquake Depths, A, B, & C, pp. 131–139, 202–203 (Advanced students should complete Levels B and C.)

English Learners To help students identify the subject of complicated sentences, have them find commas that separate introductory phrases and subordinate clauses from the main clause. For example, "When you throw a rock into a pond, waves ripple outward. . . ." (p. 307)

INVESTIGATE Subduction-Zone Earthquakes

Why are some earthquakes deeper than others?

PROCEDURE

1. Cut the first string into 4 pieces that are 4 cm long. Cut the second string into 3 pieces that are 8 cm long. Cut the third string into 4 pieces that are 15 cm long.
2. Use the key on the Earthquake Map to match string lengths with earthquake depths.
3. Tape one end of the pieces of string to the map at the earthquake locations, as shown. Always cover the same amount of string with tape.
4. Hold the map upside down, with the strings hanging down. Observe the patterns of earthquake locations and depths.

WHAT DO YOU THINK?

- What patterns among the strings do you observe? How do you explain them?
- How might the earthquake depths relate to the sinking of a tectonic plate in a subduction zone?

CHALLENGE Draw a line on the map, showing where the subduction zone might be at Earth's surface. How might the depths of the earthquakes be different if the subduction zone were on the other side of the island?

SKILL FOCUS
Analyzing (6.1.a)

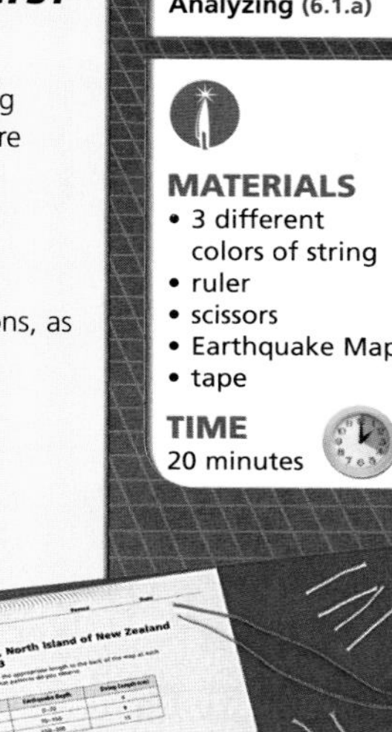

MATERIALS
- 3 different colors of string
- ruler
- scissors
- Earthquake Map
- tape

TIME
20 minutes

Waves and Energy

Waves are part of your everyday life. For example, music reaches your ears as sound waves. All waves, including seismic waves, carry energy from place to place. As a wave moves through a material, particles of the material move out of position for a short time. This causes the particles next to them to move. After each particle moves, it returns to its original position. In this way, energy moves through the material, but matter does not.

On October 17, 1989, an earthquake stopped baseball's World Series at Candlestick Park in San Francisco. As the seismic waves arrived, fans heard a low rumble. Then for about 15 seconds, the stadium shook from side to side and up and down. About 20 minutes after the earthquake was felt at the stadium, the seismic waves had traveled to the other side of Earth. There, the waves did not shake the ground hard enough for people to notice. The waves could be detected only by scientific instruments.

DIFFERENTIATE INSTRUCTION

More Reading Support

C What do waves carry from place to place? *energy*

Advanced Have students search in news sources or on the Internet for information about recent earthquakes. Have them identify the epicenter of each quake and the fault along which it occurred. Then ask them to use a large map of the world to present their findings to the class. Have them lead a discussion about where earthquakes are likely to occur.

 Challenge and Extension, p. 101

INVESTIGATE Subduction-Zone Earthquakes

PURPOSE To examine how the locations of earthquakes are related to structures and processes inside Earth

TIPS *20 min.* Provide rulers for measuring the string. Tell students to be careful when using the scissors. Use pieces of string with obviously different colors (such as primary colors).

INCLUSION Use strings with different thicknesses for students who are color-blind or who have visual impairments.

WHAT DO YOU THINK? *Earthquakes are deeper on one side of the island and shallower on the other. Earthquakes are occurring along a tilted plane under the island; earthquakes get deeper as a plate sinks in a subduction zone.*

CHALLENGE *The line should be drawn to the east (right) of the island. The depths of earthquakes across the island would be reversed if the subduction zone were on the other side.*

- Earthquake Map, p. 102
- Datasheet, Subduction-Zone Earthquakes, p. 103

Technology Resources

Customize this student lab as needed or look for an alternative. Print rubrics to assess student lab reports.

 **Lab Generator CD-ROM**

Real World Example

Scientists have developed a system to provide a warning that seismic waves from an earthquake that just occurred are about to arrive, but the method's effectiveness depends on the location of earthquake sensors. If the sensors are at the epicenter, there can be no warning. But if the epicenter is, for example, 60 kilometers (37 mi) away from the sensors, there will be about 16 seconds' warning. This is enough time for automatic systems to shut off gas valves and for people to move to safer areas within buildings.

Integrate the Sciences

While discussing primary and secondary waves, remind students that solids, liquids, and gases are made up of tiny particles of matter. Particles of a solid are close together and have strong bonds between them. They vibrate in place but cannot overcome the bonds. Solids have a definite size and shape. Particles of a liquid are close together but move faster and overcome some of the forces of attraction between the particles. The particles slide past each other. Liquids have a definite size but not a definite shape. Particles of a gas are far apart, move very fast, and have very little or no attraction to other particles. Gases have no definite size or shape.

Develop Critical Thinking

COMPARE Have students make a chart in which they compare the similarities and differences of the three types of seismic waves. ***Sample answer:***

Name	*Primary*	*Secondary*	*Surface*
Speed	*Fastest*	*Medium*	*Slowest*
Location	*Earth's interior*	*Earth's interior*	*Earth's surface*
Type of material	*All*	*Solids*	———
Type of movement	*Push/pull*	*Up/down; side/side*	*Up/down; side/side*
Damage	*Some*	*Some*	*Most*

EXPLORE the BIG idea

Revisit "Can You Bend Energy?" on p. 299. Have students relate their results to seismic wave movement.

Ongoing Assessment

CHECK YOUR READING *Answer: Particles in liquids and gases do not return to their original positions after being moved.*

Earthquakes produce three types of seismic waves: primary waves, secondary waves, and surface waves. Each type moves through materials differently. The waves can reflect, or bounce, off boundaries between different layers. The waves can also bend as they pass from one layer into another. Scientists learn about Earth's layers by studying the paths and speeds of seismic waves traveling through Earth.

Primary Waves

One meaning of *primary* is "first." Primary waves arrive before secondary waves.

The fastest seismic waves are called primary waves, or P waves. These waves are the first to reach any location after an earthquake occurs. Primary waves travel through Earth's crust at an average speed of about 5 kilometers per second (3 mi/s). Primary waves can travel through solids, liquids, and gases. As they pass through a material, the particles of the material are slightly pushed together and pulled apart. Buildings also experience this push and pull as primary waves pass through the ground they are built on.

Secondary Waves

VISUALIZATION CLASSZONE.COM

Explore primary-wave and secondary-wave motion.

Secondary waves are the second seismic waves to arrive at any location after an earthquake. This is true even though they start at the same time as primary waves. Secondary waves travel through Earth's interior at about half the speed of primary waves. Secondary waves are also called S waves. As they pass through a material, the material's particles are shaken up and down or from side to side. Secondary waves rock small buildings back and forth as they pass.

Secondary waves can travel through rock, but they cannot travel through liquids or gases. Look at the illustrations on page 311. As a primary wave passes through a material, the volume and density of the material change slightly. But as a secondary wave passes, the material changes slightly in shape. Liquids and gases do not have definite shapes. These materials flow—that is, particles in them do not return to their original positions after being moved. When scientists learned that secondary waves cannot pass through Earth's outer core, they realized that the outer core is not solid.

CHECK YOUR READING Why can't secondary waves travel through liquids or gases?

Surface Waves

E

Surface waves are seismic waves that move along Earth's surface, not through its interior. They make the ground roll up and down or shake from side to side. Surface waves cause the largest ground movements and the most damage. Surface waves travel more slowly than the other types of seismic waves.

DIFFERENTIATE INSTRUCTION

More Reading Support

D Which waves arrive first? *primary*

E Which waves do the most damage? *surface*

Alternative Assessment Modify the activity in "Develop Critical Thinking." Put students in groups and give each group a list, from the sample answer, of the main features of all waves. Then give them the chart without the wave labels. Have them figure out which wave is described in each column and complete the chart.

Seismic Waves

Earthquakes produce three types of seismic waves.

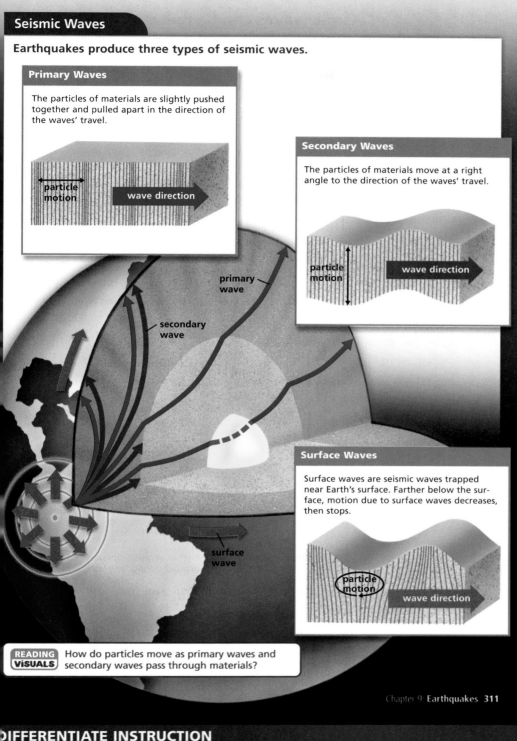

Primary Waves

The particles of materials are slightly pushed together and pulled apart in the direction of the waves' travel.

particle motion

wave direction

Secondary Waves

The particles of materials move at a right angle to the direction of the waves' travel.

particle motion

wave direction

primary wave

secondary wave

surface wave

Surface Waves

Surface waves are seismic waves trapped near Earth's surface. Farther below the surface, motion due to surface waves decreases, then stops.

particle motion

wave direction

READING VISUALS How do particles move as primary waves and secondary waves pass through materials?

IFFERENTIATE INSTRUCTION

Advanced Have students start a small wave in a pan of water that ontains one or two objects. Then have them relate the reflections of ne wave from the objects and the sides of the pan to the reflections f seismic waves inside Earth. Ask them to explain how reflections of eismic waves can be used to study Earth's structure.

Teach from Visuals

To help students with the visual on seismic waves, ask:

- How do particles move when primary waves pass through? *slightly pushed and pulled in direction the waves travel*
- How do particles move as secondary waves pass through? *at a right angle to direction the waves travel*
- How does depth affect motion due to surface waves? *As depth increases, motion decreases.*

The visual "Seismic Waves" is also available as T70 in the Transparency Book.

Integrating Sciences

Seismic waves are just one kind of wave. Sound and light also move in waves. Different types of waves have similar traits.

Develop Geometry Skills

Draw several angles on the board. Include two right angles, but in different positions. Ask students to identify the right angles.

Ongoing Assessment

Explain how energy from an earthquake travels through Earth.

Ask: What are three ways in which energy from an earthquake moves through Earth? *primary waves, secondary waves, surface waves*

READING VISUALS *Answer: Primary wave: particles are slightly pushed together and pulled apart in the direction the wave is moving. Secondary wave: particles move at a right angle to the direction the wave is moving.*

Teacher Demo

Have two students hold a sheet of white cardboard vertically without moving it. Have another student place a marker against the cardboard and jump up and down to create a drawing like a seismogram. Ask: Which type of seismograph did we model? *one with a heavy weight hanging from a spring that bounces up and down as the ground moves and measures up-and-down movements* Ask: What would we need to do differently to model the other kind of seismograph? *Place the paper horizontally and hold the marker from above to measure side-to-side movements, as does a seismograph with a heavy weight suspended by a wire that stays still as the ground moves back and forth.*

Teach from Visuals

To help students interpret the visual showing two seismographs, ask:

- What do the seismographs measure? *ground movements*
- What is similar about the two seismographs? *Both have a weight with a pen attached for recording movements onto a paper.*
- What is different about the two seismographs? *One has a weight hanging from a wire, and the other has a weight hanging from a spring that absorbs Earth's up-and-down motion.*

Ongoing Assessment

CHECK YOUR READING *Answer: One type measures horizontal movements and another measures vertical movements.*

Seismic waves can be measured.

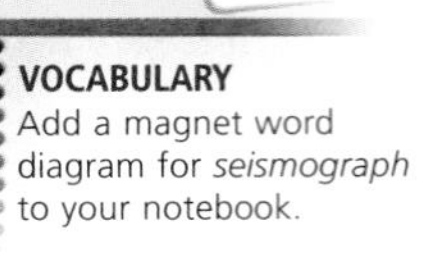

VOCABULARY Add a magnet word diagram for *seismograph* to your notebook.

Without listening to the news, scientists at seismic stations all over the world know when an earthquake occurs. Seismic stations are places where ground movements are measured. A **seismograph** (SYZ-muh-GRAF) is an instrument that constantly records ground movements. The recording of an earthquake looks like a group of wiggles in a line. The height of the wiggles indicates the amount of ground movement produced by seismic waves at the seismograph's location.

Using Seismographs

RESOURCE CENTER CLASSZONE.COM

Learn more about seismology.

Separate seismographs are needed to record side-to-side movements and up-and-down movements. A seismograph that measures side-to-side movements has a heavy weight hanging from a wire. The weight remains almost still as the ground moves back and forth beneath it. A pen attached to the weight records the movements. A seismograph that records up-and-down movements has a heavy weight hanging from a spring. As the ground moves, the weight stays almost still as the spring absorbs the movement by getting longer or shorter. A pen attached to the weight records the changes in distance between the ground and the weight.

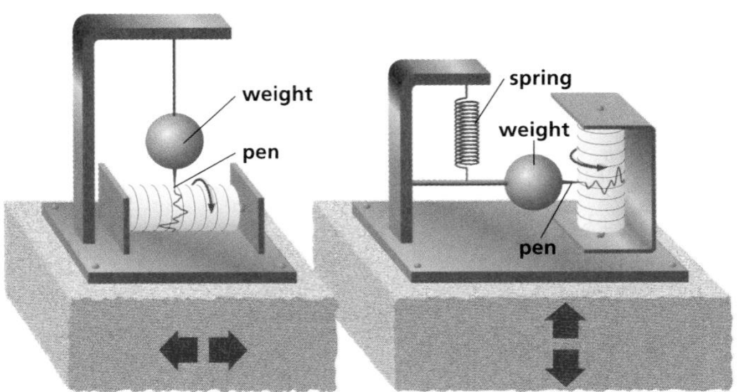

This seismograph records side-to-side movements.

This seismograph records up-and-down movements.

CHECK YOUR READING Why is more than one kind of seismograph needed to record all the movements of the ground during an earthquake?

Scientists use seismographs to measure thousands of earthquakes, large and small, every year. Some seismographs can detect ground movements as small as one hundred-millionth of a centimeter. The recording produced by a seismograph is called a seismogram. By studying seismograms, scientists can determine the locations and strengths of earthquakes.

DIFFERENTIATE INSTRUCTION

More Reading Support

F What instrument is used to measure ground movements? *seismograph*

G How many earthquakes are measured each year? *thousands*

Below Level Find a seismogram in a book, or print one from the Internet. Have students first tell what it is and what instrument produced it. Then identify when the earthquake started and stopped. Ask them to identify what moved to cause the lines on the paper. *the ground*

Locating an Earthquake

To locate the epicenter of an earthquake, scientists must have seismograms from at least three seismic stations. The procedure for locating an epicenter has three steps:

1. Scientists find the difference between the arrival times of the primary and the secondary waves at each of the three stations.
2. The time difference is used to determine the distance of the epicenter from each station. The greater the difference in time, the farther away the epicenter is.
3. A circle is drawn around each station. Each circle has a radius corresponding to the epicenter's distance from that station. The point where the three circles meet is the epicenter.

Finding an Epicenter

Seismograms provide data used to find an earthquake's epicenter.

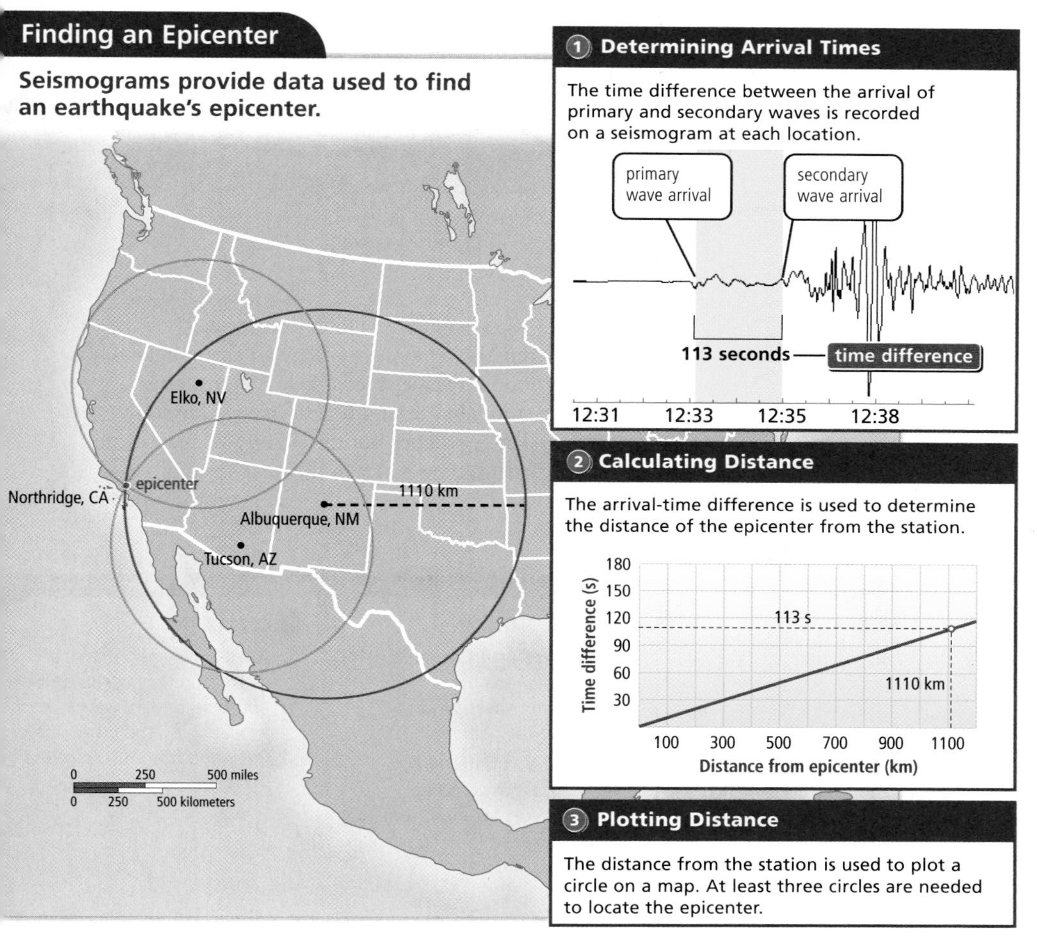

1 Determining Arrival Times

The time difference between the arrival of primary and secondary waves is recorded on a seismogram at each location.

2 Calculating Distance

The arrival-time difference is used to determine the distance of the epicenter from the station.

3 Plotting Distance

The distance from the station is used to plot a circle on a map. At least three circles are needed to locate the epicenter.

Develop Geometry Skills

Have students draw three points on a sheet of paper to represent three seismic stations. Give students a compass and have them draw three circles large enough to intersect, each with its center at a seismic station. Ask: Why are at least three seismic stations needed to find the location of an epicenter? *Two circles would overlap in two places.* Ask: What would happen if your circles were too small to intersect? *They wouldn't be useful for locating the earthquake's epicenter.*

Teach from Visuals

To help students interpret the visual about finding an epicenter, ask:

- Why is there a difference in arrival time at the seismograph between the primary and secondary waves? *Primary waves move faster.*
- What does the difference in arrival time between the two waves mean? *The greater the time difference, the farther away the epicenter is.*
- What is the distance used for? *It is used as the radius of a circle around the seismic station.*

Ongoing Assessment

Understand how an earthquake's location is determined.

How many seismic stations must record an earthquake in order to locate the epicenter of an earthquake? *three*

IFFERENTIATE INSTRUCTION

More Reading Support

H What type of seismic wave arrives first at a seismic station? *primary*

Advanced Challenge students to use the Internet to locate a map of California showing the locations of seismic stations. Challenge them to explain why there are so many of these stations.

History of Science

The first device for registering the occurrence of an earthquake was invented in about A.D. 132 by a Chinese scientist, Chang Heng. Heng's invention was called the dragon jar. The jar had eight dragon heads, each with a ball in its mouth, around the brim. Around the bottom of the jar were eight frogs. Each frog was directly beneath a dragon head. When an earthquake shook the ground, a ball dropped out of a dragon's mouth and fell into the mouth of a frog.

Reinforce the BIG idea

Have students relate the section to the Big Idea.

 Reinforcing Key Concepts, p. 104

9.2 ASSESS & RETEACH

Assess

 Section 9.2 Quiz, p. 197

Reteach

Write the following terms on the board in any order: *focus, epicenter, P wave, S wave, surface wave, seismograph,* and *seismogram.* Then create a three-column table with the following headings: *Location of Earthquake, Seismic Waves,* and *Measuring Earthquakes.*

- Invite students to place each of the terms from the list in the appropriate column. *Location of Earthquake: focus, epicenter; Seismic Waves: P wave, S wave, surface wave; Measuring Earthquakes: seismograph, seismogram*
- Have students explain why the terms belong in a particular column.

Technology Resources

Have students visit **ClassZone.com** for reteaching of Key Concepts.

 **CONTENT REVIEW**

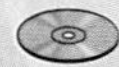 **CONTENT REVIEW CD-ROM**

Scientists can also use seismograph data to locate the focus of an earthquake. They study seismograms to identify waves that have reflected off boundaries inside Earth. Some of these waves help the scientists to determine the earthquake's depth.

A seismogram records the time when the first primary wave arrives. This wave travels by a direct path. The data also show when the first reflected primary wave arrives. After leaving the focus, this wave reflects from Earth's surface and then travels to the seismic station. The reflected wave takes a longer path, so it arrives slightly later. The difference in arrival times indicates the depth of the focus. Scientists usually use computers to calculate the location of an earthquake's epicenter and focus.

An earthquake's depth is determined from the difference in arrival times of direct and reflected seismic waves.

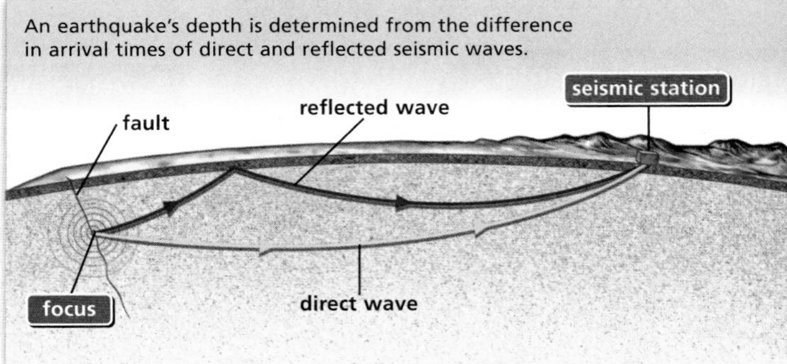

READING TIP
The word *magnitude* comes from the Latin word *magnitudo,* meaning "greatness."

Scientists also use seismograms to determine earthquakes' magnitudes, or strengths. The more energy an earthquake releases, the greater the ground movement recorded. The greatest movement determines the earthquake's strength on a magnitude scale. Stronger earthquakes get higher numbers. You will read more about earthquake magnitude scales in the next section.

9.2 Review

KEY CONCEPTS

1. Why does the greatest shaking of the ground occur near an earthquake's epicenter? **(6.1.g)**
2. What information do you need to completely describe where an earthquake started? **(6.1.e)**
3. What types of information can a scientist get by studying seismograms? **(6.3.a)**

CRITICAL THINKING

4. **Compare and Contrast** How are primary and secondary waves similar? How are they different?
5. **Apply** What information could you get about an earthquake's location from only two seismic stations' data? Explain.

CHALLENGE

6. **Apply** Why might an earthquake's primary waves, but not its secondary waves, reach a location on the other side of the world from the epicenter?

ANSWERS

1. Seismic waves lose more energy the farther they travel.

2. its epicenter and depth (focus)

3. where earthquakes start and how strong they are

4. Both travel out from the focus of an earthquake; both can travel through Earth's interior. Only primary waves can pass through areas inside Earth that are not solid.

5. Circles showing distances from two stations to the epicenter will usually intersect in two places, only one of which can be the actual epicenter.

6. Secondary waves cannot pass through Earth's outer core, but primary waves can.

MATH in SCIENCE

SKILL: MULTIPLICATION

Earthquake Energy

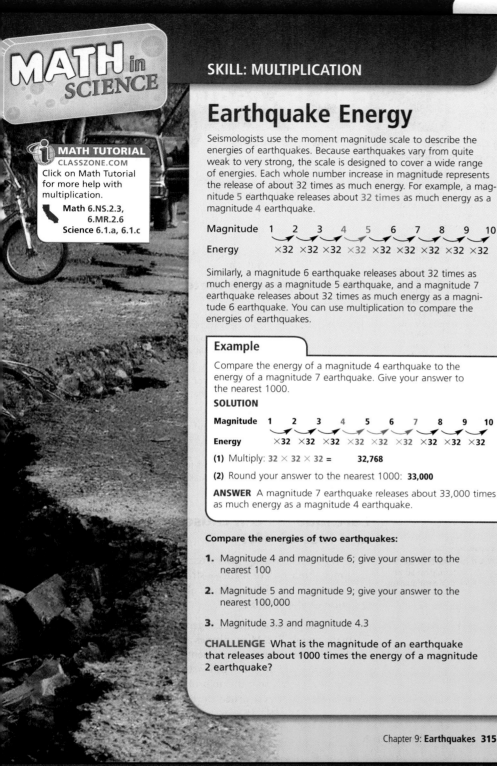

MATH TUTORIAL
CLASSZONE.COM
Click on Math Tutorial for more help with multiplication.

Math 6.NS.2.3, 6.MR.2.6
Science 6.1.a, 6.1.c

Seismologists use the moment magnitude scale to describe the energies of earthquakes. Because earthquakes vary from quite weak to very strong, the scale is designed to cover a wide range of energies. Each whole number increase in magnitude represents the release of about 32 times as much energy. For example, a magnitude 5 earthquake releases about 32 times as much energy as a magnitude 4 earthquake.

Magnitude	1	2	3	4	5	6	7	8	9	10
Energy	×32	×32	×32	×32	×32	×32	×32	×32	×32	

Similarly, a magnitude 6 earthquake releases about 32 times as much energy as a magnitude 5 earthquake, and a magnitude 7 earthquake releases about 32 times as much energy as a magnitude 6 earthquake. You can use multiplication to compare the energies of earthquakes.

Example

Compare the energy of a magnitude 4 earthquake to the energy of a magnitude 7 earthquake. Give your answer to the nearest 1000.

SOLUTION

Magnitude	1	2	3	4	5	6	7	8	9	10
Energy	×32	×32	×32	×32	×32	×32	×32	×32	×32	

(1) Multiply: **32 × 32 × 32 =** **32,768**

(2) Round your answer to the nearest 1000: **33,000**

ANSWER A magnitude 7 earthquake releases about 33,000 times as much energy as a magnitude 4 earthquake.

Compare the energies of two earthquakes:

1. Magnitude 4 and magnitude 6; give your answer to the nearest 100

2. Magnitude 5 and magnitude 9; give your answer to the nearest 100,000

3. Magnitude 3.3 and magnitude 4.3

CHALLENGE What is the magnitude of an earthquake that releases about 1000 times the energy of a magnitude 2 earthquake?

NSWERS

Magnitude 6 releases about 1000 times as much energy as a magnitude 4: 32 × 32 = 1024

Magnitude 9 releases about 1,000,000 times as much energy as a magnitude 5: 32 × 32 × 32 × 32 = 1,048,576

Magnitude 4.3 releases 32 times as much energy as magnitude 3.3.

***HALLENGE** A release of 1000 times more energy represents two eps higher on a magnitude scale; 2 + 2 = 4.*

MATH IN SCIENCE
Math Skills Practice for Science

Set Learning Goal

To use multiplication to compare the energies of earthquakes

Math Standards

6.NS.2.3 Solve addition, subtraction, multiplication, and division problems, including those arising in concrete situations, that use positive and negative integers and combinations of these operations.

6.MR.2.6 Indicate the relative advantages of exact and approximate solutions to problems and give answers to a specified degree of accuracy.

Present the Science

A magnitude scale compares the heights of waves on a seismogram. An increase of one unit of magnitude represents a 10-fold increase in wave height. The energy released by an earthquake can cause damage. An increase of one unit of magnitude represents a release of about 32 times more energy. An increase of 0.1 in magnitude represents a release of about 1.4 times more energy.

Develop Calculation Skills

Remind students that digits of 5 or higher are rounded up.

Close

Ask students to use what they have learned about the energy released by earthquakes to compare the destructive power of large- and small-magnitude earthquakes. *A large-magnitude earthquake will be much more destructive than a small-magnitude one because it releases so much more energy.*

- Math Support, p. 120
- Math Practice, p. 121

Technology Resources

Students can visit **ClassZone.com** to practice multiplying and rounding whole numbers.

MATH TUTORIAL

9.3 FOCUS

Set Learning Goals

Students will

- Explain how an earthquake's magnitude is related to the damage it causes.
- Describe how structures are built to withstand most earthquakes.
- Understand how scientists estimate the earthquake risk in an area.

3-Minute Warm-Up

Display Transparency 69 or copy this exercise on the board:

Decide if these statements are true. If not, correct them.

1. The epicenter is the point underground where rocks first begin to move. *The focus is the point underground where rocks first begin to move.*
2. Secondary waves move faster than primary waves. *Primary waves move faster than secondary waves.*
3. Three circles, each drawn around a different seismic station, meet at the epicenter of an earthquake. *true*

3-Minute Warm-Up, p. T69

9.3 MOTIVATE

EXPLORE Shaking

PURPOSE To model how structures built on different types of ground behave during earthquakes

TIP *10 min.* Remind students to be careful that sand does not get in their eyes. Students should rinse their hands after working with sand.

WHAT DO YOU THINK? *Pieces of sand moved around and the washer sank down; the washer was less affected when it was on the rock. Buildings on loose soil are likely to be more damaged during earthquakes than are buildings on more stable surfaces such as rock.*

KEY CONCEPT

9.3 Earthquake damage can be reduced.

CALIFORNIA Content Standards

6.1.g Students know how to determine the epicenter of an earthquake and know that the effects of an earthquake on any region vary, depending on the size of the earthquake, the distance of the region from the epicenter, the local geology, and the type of construction in the region.

6.2.d Students know earthquakes, volcanic eruptions, landslides, and floods change human and wildlife habitats.

BEFORE, you learned

- Seismic waves travel through Earth
- An earthquake's location and magnitude can be determined

NOW, you will learn

- How an earthquake's magnitude is related to the damage it causes
- How structures are built to withstand most earthquakes
- How scientists estimate the earthquake risk in an area

VOCABULARY

aftershock p. 318
liquefaction p. 318
tsunami p. 318

EXPLORE Shaking (6.1.g)

What happens as materials are shaken?

PROCEDURE

1. Pour a pile of sand on a newspaper. Place a metal washer on top of the sand. Shake the paper and observe what happens to the sand and the washer.
2. Now place the washer on top of a flat rock. Shake the rock and observe what happens.

MATERIALS

- sand
- newspaper
- flat rock
- washer

WHAT DO YOU THINK?

- How did the washer, the sand, and the rock react differently to shaking?
- How might the washer, the sand, and the rock model what happens to buildings and land during earthquakes?

Earthquakes can cause severe damage and loss of life.

MAIN IDEA AND DETAILS Record information about the effects of earthquakes in your notebook.

Every year, on average, an extremely powerful earthquake—one with a magnitude of 8 or higher—strikes somewhere on Earth. Such an earthquake can destroy almost all the buildings near its epicenter and cause great loss of life.

Earthquakes are most dangerous when they occur near areas where many people live. Most injuries and deaths due to earthquakes are not directly caused by the movement of the ground. They are caused by collapsing buildings and other structures and by fires. After an earthquake, fires may start due to broken natural-gas lines, broken electrical power lines, or overturned stoves.

RESOURCES FOR DIFFERENTIATED INSTRUCTION

Below Level

UNIT RESOURCE BOOK

- Reading Study Guide A, pp. 107–108
- Decoding Support, p. 119

AUDIO CDS

Advanced

UNIT RESOURCE BOOK

- Challenge and Extension, p. 113
- Challenge Reading, pp. 115–116

English Learners

UNIT RESOURCE BOOK

Spanish Reading Study Guide, pp. 111–112

AUDIO CDS

- Audio Readings in Spanish
- Audio Readings (English)

316 Unit 3: The Changing Earth

Earthquake Magnitude

A very powerful earthquake can release more energy than 1 million weak earthquakes combined. Earthquake magnitude scales give scientists and engineers a simple way to describe this huge range in energy.

The first scale of earthquake magnitude was developed in California during the 1930s by the scientists Charles Richter (RIHK-tuhr) and Beno Gutenberg. This scale is called the Richter scale. An earthquake's magnitude is based on how fast the ground moves at a seismic station. However, most scientists today prefer to use a newer, more accurate scale: the moment magnitude scale. This scale is based on the total amounts of energy released by earthquakes. The moment magnitude scale is used for all earthquake magnitudes given in this chapter.

Both the Richter scale and the moment magnitude scale are often shown with a top value of 10. However, neither actually has a maximum value. On each scale, an increase of one whole number indicates an increase of 32 times more energy. For example, a magnitude 5 earthquake releases 32 times as much energy as a magnitude 4 earthquake and about 1000 times as much energy as a magnitude 3 earthquake.

Magnitude and Effects Near Epicenter

More powerful earthquakes have higher magnitude values.

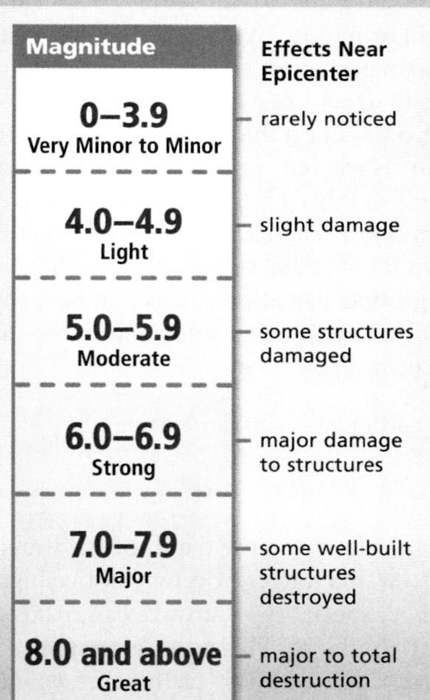

Magnitude	Effects Near Epicenter
0–3.9 Very Minor to Minor	rarely noticed
4.0–4.9 Light	slight damage
5.0–5.9 Moderate	some structures damaged
6.0–6.9 Strong	major damage to structures
7.0–7.9 Major	some well-built structures destroyed
8.0 and above Great	major to total destruction

Damage from Powerful Earthquake

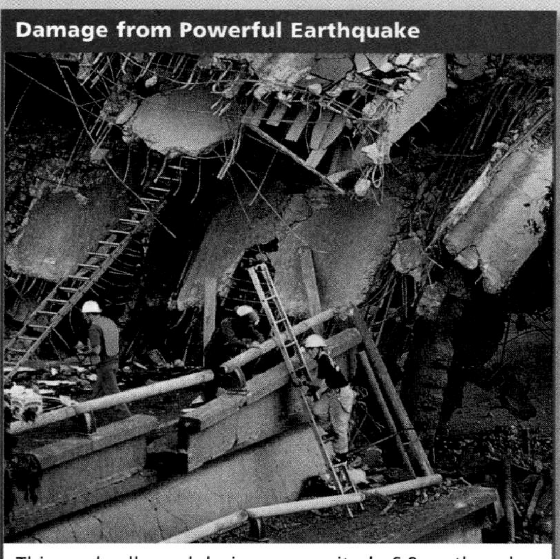

This road collapsed during a magnitude 6.9 earthquake in California on October 17, 1989. About 140 earthquakes with magnitudes of 6 or higher occur each year around the world.

9.3 INSTRUCT

Teach the Standards

Effects of Earthquakes (6.2.d)

In this section: Students learn about the devastating effects an earthquake can have on a region. Ask students to describe some of these effects. Explain that scientists are able to make maps of areas detailing past earthquakes and potential hazards; knowing this information enables buildings to be constructed that can better withstand earthquake damage.

- **previously taught:** geologic hazard, pp. 46, 211–212; effects of earthquakes, p. 47; movement of plates, pp. 278–293; determining epicenter, pp. 313–314
- **future opportunities:** fault-block mountains, pp. 342–344; impact on habitats, pp. 356–362

History of Science

The scientists who created the Richter scale used only one type of seismograph, limited their study to small earthquakes in Southern California, and used only one set of data—the distance the seismograph needle moved. They then adjusted for nearby and distant earthquakes. Over the next 20 years, this scale was refined so that it worked for newer seismographs, other regions, and different kinds of seismic waves. The moment magnitude scale was invented in 1977 by Hiroo Kanamori.

Teach from Visuals

To help students interpret the visual on this page, ask:

- What magnitude does an earthquake need to have to be noticed by most people? *4.0*
- At what magnitude does an earthquake cause total destruction of even well-built structures? *8.0 and above*

Ongoing Assessment

Explain how an earthquake's magnitude is related to the damage it causes.

Ask: What is the relationship between an earthquake's magnitude and the damage it causes? *The greater the magnitude, the greater the damage that is caused.*

DIFFERENTIATE INSTRUCTION

More Reading Support

A What is measured with the moment magnitude scale? *the total energy released by an earthquake*

English Learners Write the words *earthquake, aftershock,* and *overturned* on the board. Tell students that these are compound words—that is, made up of two words that can stand alone. Help students understand that breaking compound words into the words that make them up can help them figure out the meanings of the words. Have students locate other compound words in this section, such as *firefighters* (p. 318), *landslide* (p. 318), and *sometimes* (p. 320).

Teach Difficult Concepts

Some students may have a hard time understanding liquefaction. Explain that the energy of the earthquake moves the soil particles apart; they no longer touch each other, so they lose their support. To help students understand this process, try the following demonstration.

Teacher Demo

Fill a loaf pan almost to the top with sand. Add water to just below the sand's surface. Push the narrow end of a brick into the sand so it stands up like a building. Wait a few minutes. Tap the side of the pan with a mallet. Have students observe what happens. Ask: What does pounding with the hammer represent? *an earthquake*

Explain that the energy from the hammer tries to push the sand particles together, but then the water needs to be pushed out. In an earthquake, seismic waves try to push soil particles together very fast, and the water doesn't have time to get out. The water pressure increases, decreasing the strength of the contact between the sand particles, so they can't hold up the building.

Develop Critical Thinking

APPLY Have students apply their knowledge of the ways in which earthquakes can cause damage by having them suggest ways people could help protect themselves if they are in an area where earthquakes are common. *Sample answer: Stay in open areas. Build strong buildings. Make strong, flexible water pipes or have alternate sources of water for fighting fires. Avoid hills covered with unstable rocks or soil.*

Ongoing Assessment

CHECK YOUR READING *Answer: It is more accurate for large earthquakes, and it can be applied to past earthquakes.*

CHECK YOUR READING *Answer: movement of the ground, collapse of structures, fire, landslide, liquefaction*

VOCABULARY Add magnet word diagrams for *aftershock* and *liquefaction* to your notebook.

The moment magnitude scale is more accurate for larger earthquakes than the Richter scale. Another advantage of the moment magnitude scale is that it can be used for earthquakes that occurred before seismographs were invented. Geologists can measure the strength of the rocks and the length they moved along a fault to calculate a past earthquake's magnitude. This information is important for geologists to know when they determine an area's earthquake risk.

What are two advantages of the moment magnitude scale over the Richter scale?

Damage from Earthquakes

Movement of the blocks of rock on either side of a fault can crack roads, buildings, dams, and any other structures on the fault. As blocks of rock move, they can also raise, lower, or tilt the ground surface. Sometimes structures weakened by an earthquake collapse during shaking caused by aftershocks. An **aftershock** is a smaller earthquake that follows a more powerful earthquake in the same area. Also, fires that break out can cause great damage if broken water pipes keep firefighters from getting water. In the 1906 San Francisco earthquake, fires caused more than 90 percent of the building damage.

Earthquakes can cause major damage by affecting the soil and other loose materials. For example, landslides often occur as a result of earthquakes. A landslide is a movement of soil and rocks down a hill or mountain. Earthquakes can cause soil **liquefaction,** a process in which shaking of the ground causes soil to act like a liquid. For a short time the soil becomes like a thick soup. Liquefaction occurs only in areas where the soil is made up of loose sand and silt and contains a large amount of water. As the shaking temporarily changes the wet soil, structures either sink down into the soil or flow away with it. Shaking of the ground also affects areas that have mixtures of soils. Some soil types pack together more than others when shaken.

This building in Venezuela tilted and sank as the ground beneath it collapsed during an earthquake in 1967.

List five ways in which earthquakes can cause damage.

Damage from Tsunamis

If you sit on an ocean beach, you can watch the depth of the water change as waves come in. If you watch longer, you may notice bigger changes as the tide rises or falls. A special type of wave can make water rise higher than a 20-story building. This wave, a **tsunami** (tsu-NAH-mee), is a water wave triggered by an earthquake, volcanic eruption, or landslide. Tsunamis are sometimes called tidal waves.

318 Unit 3: **The Changing Earth**

DIFFERENTIATE INSTRUCTION

More Reading Support

B What is a process in which shaking causes soil to act like a liquid? *liquefaction*

C What is a water wave triggered by an earthquake? *a tsunami*

Advanced Have students look for fact sheets and information about earthquake safety on the U.S. Geological Survey's Web site. Challenge them to explain how maps of expected ground-shaking intensity are made and used.

Below Level Ask students what the effects of earthquakes are and list their responses on the board. Have students discuss each effect and explain what happens as a result of it.

However, they are not caused by the forces that produce tides. A tsunami may not be a single wave but several waves that can have different heights and can arrive hours apart.

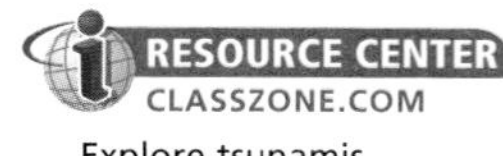

Explore tsunamis.

Tsunamis move quickly and can travel thousands of kilometers without weakening. In deep water, they can reach speeds of about 700 kilometers per hour (430 mi/h). A tsunami in the deep water of the open ocean may be less than one meter (3 ft) in height at the surface. As a tsunami reaches shallow water around an island or continent, it slows down and its height greatly increases.

A 1946 earthquake on Alaska's coast caused a tsunami that swept across the entire Pacific Ocean. In less than five hours, the tsunami reached Hawaii as a series of waves. Because people did not know of the danger, no one had evacuated, and 159 people were killed. A 2004 earthquake off the coast of Sumatra caused a tsunami in the Indian Ocean. The earthquake and tsunami killed more than 280,000 people.

In 2004 a tsunami devastated many coastal areas, including this beach in Madras, India.

Many earthquakes occur around the edges of the Pacific Ocean. Therefore, Hawaii and other areas in and around this ocean are likely to be hit by tsunamis. The Pacific Tsunami Warning Center in Hawaii was established in 1949. The center monitors earthquakes and issues warnings to areas that could be struck by tsunamis. A tsunami warning system is being developed for the Indian Ocean.

Tsunami Travel Time, 2004 Sumatra Earthquake

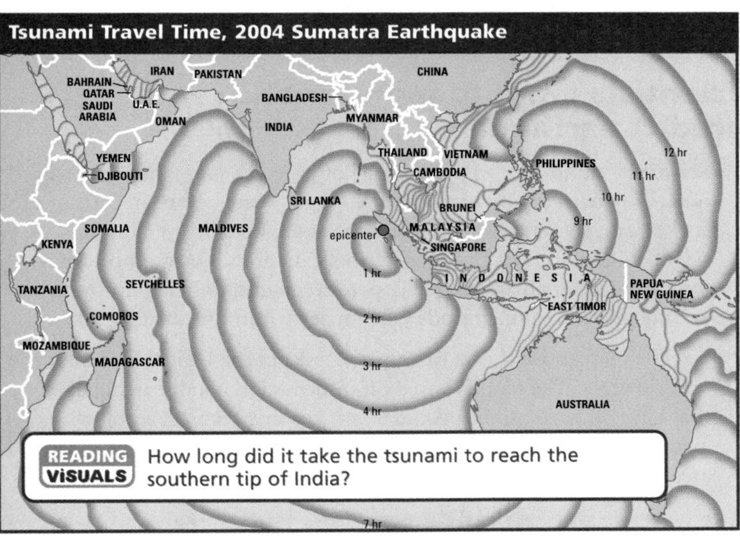

READING VISUALS How long did it take the tsunami to reach the southern tip of India?

DIFFERENTIATE INSTRUCTION

More Reading Support

D How many waves are in a tsunami? *more than one*

E Where are tsunamis most likely to hit? *areas in and around the Pacific Ocean*

Advanced Challenge students to explain why a powerful earthquake along a strike-slip fault under the ocean is unlikely to produce a tsunami, but a powerful earthquake along a reverse fault under the ocean might produce a large, destructive tsunami. *Answer: Only earthquakes that cause the sea floor to move vertically produce large tsunamis.*

R Challenge and Extension, p. 113

Teach from Visuals

To help students interpret the visual showing the speed of a tsunami, ask:

- What does each circle represent? *the position of the tsunami a certain time after the earthquake*
- Where was the epicenter of the earthquake that caused this tsunami? *off the coast of Sumatra*
- Where did people experience this tsunami? *all around the Indian Ocean*

Teaching with Technology

Have students use a search engine and search the Internet to find an animation showing a tsunami in action.

Integrate the Sciences

The waves that are normally seen on a pond, lake, or ocean are generated by winds moving across the water. The water molecules stay in basically the same place, but the energy of the wave moves toward shore. These waves have a short wavelength (distance between wave crests). Tsunamis, by contrast, have a very long wavelength. Even in the deep ocean, their wavelength may be twice as long as the depth of the ocean. The speed at which a tsunami moves depends on the depth of the water—the shallower the water, the slower it moves.

Develop Critical Thinking

INFER Have students infer what a large tsunami looks like when it comes ashore and in what way tsunamis resemble tidal waves, though they are unrelated to tides. *A large tsunami often does not come ashore as a towering wave. Instead, it causes an increase in sea level like a very high and fast-moving high tide. (Students in hurricane-prone areas might compare a tsunami to a storm surge.)* Refer back to p. 306 and discuss why the 1964 tsunami in Valdez Inlet was taller than a 20-story building. *This unusual tsunami was triggered in a narrow inlet, so the water was forced upward.*

Ongoing Assessment

Answer: 4 hours

Teach from Visuals

To help students interpret the visual showing earthquake risk in the United States, ask:

- What are the areas with the greatest risk of earthquakes? *the West Coast, southern Alaska, Hawaii*
- What are the areas with the lowest risk of earthquakes? *mid-United States, southeastern coast*

Mathematics Connection

Discuss probabilities.

Ask: What does it mean when scientists give a percent chance that an area will be hit by an earthquake with a magnitude of 7 or higher within 25 years? *Scientists are giving a long-term prediction of the probability that such an earthquake will occur. The higher the percent given, the more likely that such an earthquake will occur within the time specified.*

Develop Critical Thinking

CONNECT Provide students with an outline map of the United States that shows the states. Have them shade their own state in one color. Have them shade the states with the highest and the lowest risk of earthquakes in two other colors. Then ask them to identify the area of the United States most at risk from earthquakes. What generalizations can they make? *Coastal and mountain regions in the West seem to have the greatest risk; the Great Plains, which are flat, seem to have the lowest.*

Ongoing Assessment

READING VISUALS *Answer: Answers will vary, depending on students' locations.*

Earthquake Risk in the United States

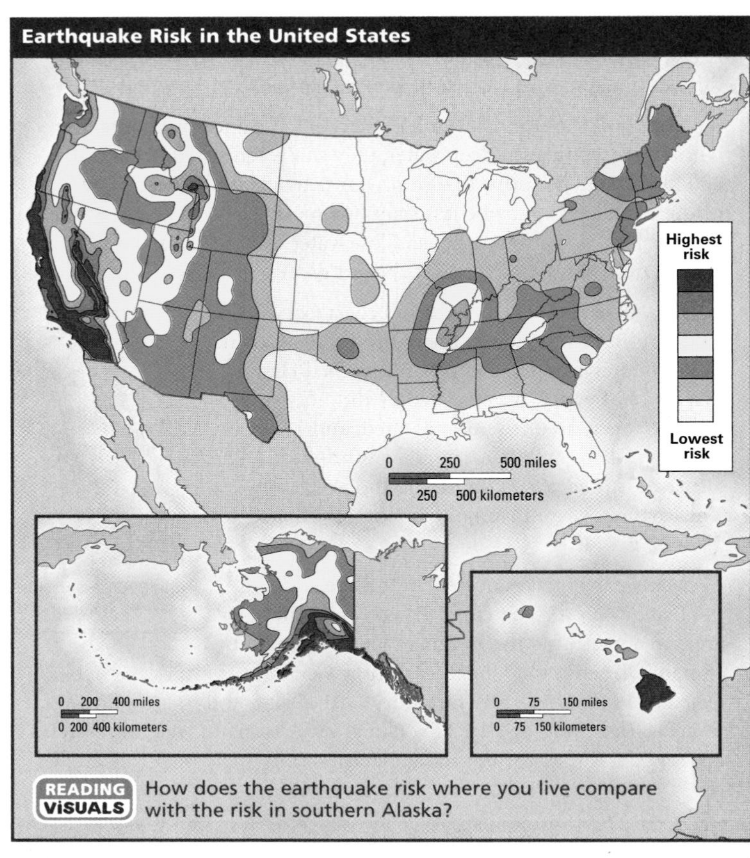

READING VISUALS How does the earthquake risk where you live compare with the risk in southern Alaska?

Scientists work to monitor and predict earthquakes.

READING TIP
A prediction is a statement about an event before it occurs. Scientists use their knowledge to make predictions about when earthquakes might occur.

Scientists cannot yet predict the day or even the year when an earthquake will occur. Sometimes there are signs years before an earthquake strikes, and sometimes there are none at all. Usually the best that scientists can do is to give long-term predictions. For example, they might state that an area has a 60 percent chance of being hit by an earthquake with a magnitude 7 or higher within the next 25 years.

The map above shows earthquake risks in the United States for the next 50 years. The map is based on information about earthquakes that have occurred since people began keeping records, along with evidence of earlier earthquakes preserved in rocks. Note that most areas with the highest earthquake risks are near the Pacific Ocean.

DIFFERENTIATE INSTRUCTION

More Reading Support

F What kind of predictions can scientists make for earthquakes? *long-term predictions*

Inclusion As an auditory strategy for reading the map, read aloud the colors in the key and have students locate regions of the country that have the same color. As a visual aid, display a map of the United States with the state names written in.

320 Unit 3: The Changing Earth

Scientists all over the world study seismic activity along faults to learn more about earthquakes and find ways of predicting them. They monitor whether stress is building up in the rocks along faults. Such signs include

- tilts or changes in the elevation of the ground
- slow movements or stretching in rock
- the development of small cracks in the ground

An increase in small earthquakes can be a sign that stress is building up along a fault and that a large earthquake is likely to occur. But an increase in small earthquakes can also be a sign that a fault is releasing stress bit by bit. This decreases the likelihood of a major earthquake.

Scientists also look for areas where earthquakes have not occurred along an otherwise active fault. They make diagrams in which they plot the locations where earthquakes have started, as shown below. Sometimes such a diagram shows an area of few or no earthquakes that is surrounded by many earthquakes. This area is called a seismic gap. A seismic gap can indicate a location where a fault is stuck. Movement along other parts of the fault can increase stress along the stuck part. This stress could be released by a major earthquake.

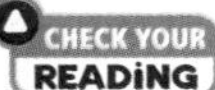

CHECK YOUR READING

Why can a lack of earthquakes in an area near an active fault cause concern?

Seismic Gaps

A seismic gap is a section of a fault with few earthquakes compared with sections of the fault on either side of the gap.

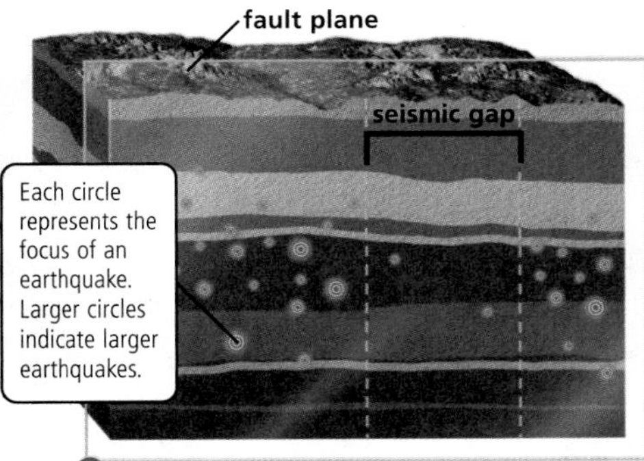

fault plane
seismic gap
Each circle represents the focus of an earthquake. Larger circles indicate larger earthquakes.

1 Over several years many earthquakes have occurred along this fault. However, one section of the fault has had little earthquake activity. Stress is building up along this section.

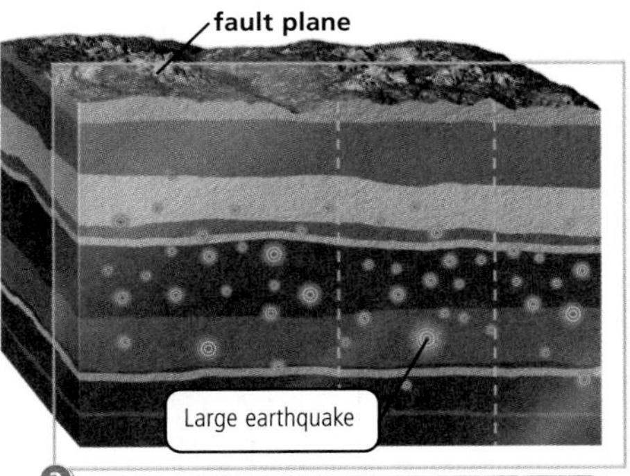

fault plane
Large earthquake

2 A large earthquake and its aftershocks have occurred, releasing built-up stress. Over just a few weeks the seismic gap has been filled in.

Teach from Visuals

To help students interpret the visual showing a seismic gap, ask:

- What does the illustration on the left show? *a fault along which many earthquakes have occurred, except for one section*
- What is important about the section with little earthquake activity? *It might be stuck. A lot of stress may be building up there.*
- What does the illustration on the right show? *A large earthquake and its aftershocks have filled in the gap.*

EXPLORE the BIG idea

Revisit "Internet Activity: Earthquakes" on p. 299. Have students relate their results to how earthquakes are predicted.

Ongoing Assessment

CHECK YOUR READING *Answer: Large amounts of stress could be building up along a fault.*

DIFFERENTIATE INSTRUCTION

More Reading Support

G What do scientists monitor in order to predict earthquakes? *a buildup of stress along a fault*

Alternative Assessment Use a large book as a ramp and put a small box on it. Let pencils roll down and stack up against the box until it slides down the ramp. Have students explain how this relates to earthquakes and seismic gaps. *Each pencil represents an earthquake. The box represents a portion of the fault that is not moving—a seismic gap. When the stress on the box is great enough, it moves, causing a larger "earthquake."*

Address Misconceptions

IDENTIFY Ask: What is the purpose of specially designing and building structures in areas where earthquakes are likely? If students say that the purpose is to have structures that cannot be damaged during earthquakes, they hold the common misconception that people are capable of completely safeguarding themselves against natural disasters such as earthquakes.

CORRECT Tell students that designing structures to resist earthquake damage means that the amount of damage will likely be reduced but not eliminated. Refer back to the graphic on p. 317. Point out that even well-built structures can be damaged or destroyed by powerful earthquakes.

REASSESS Ask: Why is it not possible to make any structure completely earthquake-proof? *A powerful earthquake causes so much shaking of the ground near its epicenter that even well-built structures will be affected.*

Technology Resources

Visit **ClassZone.com** for background on common student misconceptions.

 **MISCONCEPTION DATABASE**

Teaching with Technology

Have students search the Internet for graphics of earthquake-safe building structures and then use presentation software to present their findings to the class.

Real World Example

The Federal Emergency Management Agency (FEMA) provides guidelines for homeowners on making their homes as safe as possible during an earthquake. They also help with disaster relief after an earthquake.

Ongoing Assessment

Understand how scientists estimate the earthquake risk in an area.

Ask: What do scientists make to estimate the earthquake risk in an area? *maps showing locations of fault zones, past earthquakes, and areas prone to flooding, landslides, and liquefaction*

Structures can be designed to resist earthquake damage.

READING TIP

Here, the term *structure* refers to office buildings, homes, bridges, dams, factories—all the things that people build.

It might be best to be outdoors during an earthquake. The safest place would be far from any buildings. But there is no way to tell just when or where an earthquake will occur. For this reason, the best way to reduce deaths, injuries, and damage from earthquakes is to build structures able to withstand strong ground shaking. The first step is to understand what the risks from earthquakes are in an area. The second step is to build structures that are appropriate for the area.

Scientists make maps of areas to show the locations of fault zones, past earthquakes, and areas likely to experience flooding, landslides, or liquefaction. In California, Japan, and other areas that have many earthquakes, planners use these maps to develop rules for building new structures and strengthening older ones. The maps are also used to select building locations that are stable—unlikely to experience landslides or liquefaction.

Earthquake damage to small buildings, such as most houses, often occurs when the buildings are shaken off their foundations. Small buildings are better protected when they are firmly fastened to their foundations. Also, their walls need to be strong. Some houses were built before modern safety rules were in place. The walls of these houses can be made stronger by adding supports. Supports are especially important in brick walls, which can easily collapse in an earthquake. A special type of steel is commonly used for the supports that can bend and then return to its original shape.

SAFETY TIPS

Earthquakes

Before

- Fasten heavy objects, such as bookcases, to floors or walls to keep them from falling.
- Put latches on cabinets to keep dishes from falling out.
- Identify safe spots in every room, such as the space under a strong table.
- Keep an emergency supply of bottled water.

During and After

- If you are inside a building, stay inside until the shaking stops. Objects falling from buildings cause many injuries.
- If you are outdoors, move away from buildings, poles, and trees.
- Make a family plan for contacting a person who lives in another town. As people call to say they are safe, this person can pass on the information.

DIFFERENTIATE INSTRUCTION

More Reading Support

H What might be the safest place to be during an earthquake? *outside, away from buildings*

English Learners The words *should, would,* and *could* are not universal in all languages. Help students understand sentences that contain these words. For example, "What could we do to make our classroom safer during an earthquake?" The word *could* is used in this instance to indicate a hypothetical possibility.

Advanced

 Challenge Reading, pp. 115–116

Many of the methods used to make larger buildings and other structures safer help reduce the amount they shake during an earthquake. One method is to use devices called base isolators, as shown in the illustration. Base isolators are placed between a building and its foundation. The isolators are made of flexible materials that are stacked in layers like pancakes. When an earthquake occurs, the isolators absorb much of the ground motion. Any shaking that does reach the building is slower and smoother.

Earthquake-Resistant Building

A building may also have an open space, or moat, around it. The moat may be covered at the surface with sidewalks and landscaping. It lets the building shake more gently than the ground during an earthquake.

Special walls, called shear walls, add strength to a structure. These walls contain steel supports. Shear walls in the center of a building are often built around a stairwell or an elevator shaft. These walls make up a part of the building known as the shear core.

Walls can also be made stronger by adding braces. Pairs of braces that form an X shape are called cross braces. They help a structure keep its shape while it is being shaken.

 CHECK YOUR READING Describe two methods used to make buildings stronger.

9.3 Review

KEY CONCEPTS

1. How is an earthquake magnitude scale related to the amounts of energy released by earthquakes? (6.1.d)
2. What are the major dangers to people from an earthquake? (6.2.d)
3. Name three methods of improving a building's safety before an earthquake. (6.1.g)

CRITICAL THINKING

4. **Apply** What might people living next to the ocean do to protect themselves if they were given a two-hour warning of an approaching tsunami?
5. **Connect** If you lived in an area where earthquakes were common, what could you do to make your home safer?

CHALLENGE

6. **Analyze** Earthquakes release stress that has built up in rocks. Why do you think aftershocks occur?

ANSWERS

1. *Each whole-number increase represents a release of about 32 times as much energy.*

2. *collapsing structures and fires*

3. *fastening a building to its foundation, adding wall supports; using base isolators, moats, shear walls, shear cores, and/or cross braces during original construction*

4. *go to a higher area*

5. *Fasten bookcases or other heavy furniture to the walls; identify the safest place to be in the room*

6. *Aftershocks occur because stress in the rock is still being released.*

Ongoing Assessment

Describe how structures are built to withstand most earthquakes.

Ask: What is one device used to reduce the shaking experienced by structures? *base isolator*

CHECK YOUR READING *Answer: Students might describe using any two—buildings fastened to their foundations, wall supports, base isolators, moats, shear walls, shear cores, cross braces*

Teach from Visuals

To help students interpret the visual showing an earthquake-resistant building, ask:

- What three special structures add support and strength to a building? *shear walls, shear core, cross braces*
- What is a moat? *an open space around a building*

Reinforce the BIG idea

Have students relate the section to the Big Idea.

 Reinforcing Key Concepts, p. 114

9.3 ASSESS & RETEACH

Assess

 Section 9.3 Quiz, p. 198

Reteach

Write each of these terms on the board: *earthquake damage, magnitude, Richter scale, moment magnitude scale, aftershock, landslide, fires, tsunami, earthquake, prediction, gap, cross braces, shear wall,* and *base isolator.* Have students work together to create a concept map of the terms, explaining them as they work.

Technology Resources

Have students visit **ClassZone.com** for reteaching of Key Concepts.

 **CONTENT REVIEW**

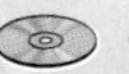 **CONTENT REVIEW CD-ROM**

CHAPTER INVESTIGATION

Focus

PURPOSE To tap into students' creativity as they examine ways to make buildings more earthquake resistant

OVERVIEW Students will explore ways of building earthquake-resistant structures by building a structure from modeling clay, stirrer straws, and cardboard and then observing how long it can withstand shaking. Students will find the following:

- Cross braces make structures sturdier.
- Putting similar materials together in different ways produces structures that react differently to shaking.

Lab Preparation

Construct a shake table.

- Materials: 2 large box lids, 40 marbles, 4 rubber bands, stapler
- Cut the bottom of one lid so that it is 4 cm shorter on all sides than the intact lid. Attach rubber bands to each corner.
- Put the marbles in the intact lid, then put the cut piece on top of them.
- Make small holes in the vertical corners of the intact lid. Pull the rubber bands through the holes. Staple the bands so they are somewhat stretched. The inner cardboard piece should shake when pulled to one side and then released.
- Prior to the investigation, have students read through the investigation, write a hypothesis, and prepare their data tables. Or you may wish to copy and distribute datasheets and rubrics.

UNIT RESOURCE BOOK, pp. 122–130

SCIENCE TOOLKIT, F12

Lab Management

Limit the number of stirrers and amount of clay used to build each structure.

CHAPTER INVESTIGATION

How Structures React in Earthquakes

DESIGN —YOUR OWN—

OVERVIEW AND PURPOSE

In 1989 a magnitude 6.9 earthquake struck the San Francisco Bay area, killing 62 people and leaving 12,000 homeless. In 1988 a magnitude 6.9 earthquake occurred near Spitak, Armenia. There, nearly 25,000 people died and 514,000 lost their homes. The difference in the effects of these two earthquakes was largely due to differences in construction methods. In this investigation you will

- build a structure and measure how long it can withstand shaking on a shake table provided by your teacher
- explore methods of building earthquake-resistant structures

Problem

How can structures be built to withstand most earthquakes?

Hypothesize

Write a hypothesis to explain how structures can be built to withstand shaking. Your hypothesis should take the form of an "If . . . , then . . . , because . . ." statement.

Procedure

1. Make a data table like the one shown on the next page.
2. Use stirrers joined with clay to build a structure at least 20 cm tall on top of the cardboard. Cut the stirrers if necessary.
3. Make a diagram of your structure.

MATERIALS
- modeling clay
- stirrer straws
- piece of thin cardboard 15 cm on each side
- scissors
- ruler
- shake table

6.1.d, 6.2.d, 6.3.a, 6.7.a

INVESTIGATION RESOURCES

CHAPTER INVESTIGATION, How Structures React in Earthquakes
- Level A, pp. 122–125
- Level B, pp. 126–129
- Level C, p. 130

Advanced students should complete Levels B & C.

Writing a Lab Report, D12–13

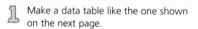

Technology Resources

Customize this student lab as needed or look for an alternative. Print rubrics to assess student lab reports.

Lab Generator CD-ROM

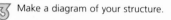

Content Standard
6.2.d Students know earthquakes, volcanic eruptions, landslides, and floods change human and wildlife habitats.

Investigation Standard
6.7.a Develop a hypothesis.

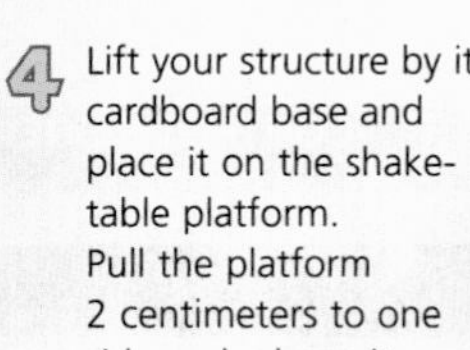

4 Lift your structure by its cardboard base and place it on the shake-table platform. Pull the platform 2 centimeters to one side and release it.

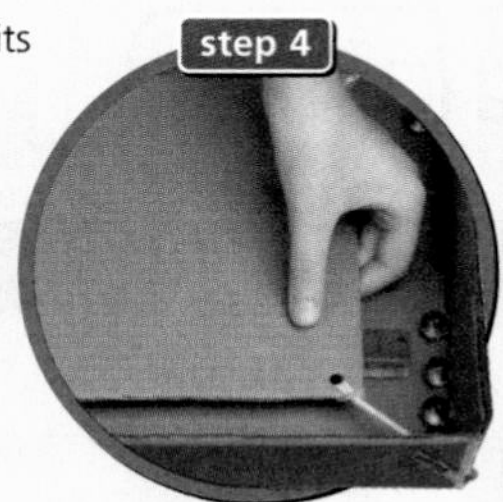

5 Repeat step 4 until the structure begins to collapse.

Observe and Analyze

1. **RECORD** Complete your data table and make notes about the collapse. Include areas of possible weakness in your structure.
2. **INFER** Use your observations to design a structure that will better withstand shaking.

Conclude

1. **INTERPRET** Compare your results with your hypothesis. Do your observations support your hypothesis?
2. **INFER** How would you use the shake table to model earthquakes of different magnitudes?
3. **IDENTIFY VARIABLES** How might your results differ if you always pulled the platform to the same side? if you pulled it to different sides?
4. **IDENTIFY LIMITS** In what ways might a building's behavior during an earthquake differ from the behavior of your structure on the shake table?
5. **COMPARE** Examine the diagrams of the three structures that lasted longest in your class. What characteristics, if any, did they have in common?
6. **APPLY** Based on your results, write a list of recommendations for building earthquake-resistant structures.

INVESTIGATE Further

CHALLENGE Have a contest to see who can build the most earthquake-resistant structure. Design your structure as if you were an earthquake engineer. Make a model of your structure at least 30 centimeters tall, using the types of materials you used in this investigation. Test the structure on the shake table. What design features helped the winning structure to resist shaking the longest?

How Structures React in Earthquakes

Problem How can structures be built to withstand most earthquakes?

Hypothesize

Observe and Analyze

Table 1. Number of Trials Until Collapse of Structure

Trial	Distance Platform Pulled to Side (cm)	Notes
1	2	
2	2	
3	2	
4	2	

Conclude

Observe and Analyze

Sample Data: trial 1, 2 cm, structure tilts to one side after shaking; trial 2, 2 cm, structure completely collapses

1. *See students' data tables.*
2. *Sample answer: The new design will use more cross braces.*

Conclude

1. *Answers will vary, depending on students' results.*
2. *Pull the platform farther to one side before letting go.*
3. *A structure might have more weaknesses in one direction than another and so might collapse faster if shaken in different directions.*
4. *A real building would behave somewhat differently because seismic waves can cause the ground to move up and down as well as back and forth. An earthquake can cause the ground to shake longer than the platform shakes. Real buildings are more sturdy. But these buildings contain potentially dangerous materials such as sheets of glass, electrical wires, and natural gas lines that were not modeled in students' buildings.*
5. *Sample answer: They had more supports and cross braces.*
6. *Answers might include using strong, flexible materials and cross braces.*

INVESTIGATE Further

CHALLENGE Student answers will vary.

Post-Lab Discussion

Ask: What differences did you observe among the buildings students created and their response to shaking? How can you explain these differences? *Answers will vary, depending upon their results.* Ask: How would you modify your design, now that you have seen the results? *Answers will vary depending on students' designs and results, but should suggest new designs that are markedly different and attempt to address limitations of the first design.*

BACK TO

the BIG idea

Ask students to summarize what happened during the 1989 San Francisco earthquake. *Rocks moved suddenly along a fault. Energy was released and spread out from the focus in seismic waves. The seismic waves were in the form of P waves, S waves, and surface waves. The waves made the ground shake, causing destruction of buildings and other structures.*

KEY CONCEPTS SUMMARY

SECTION 9.1
Ask students to explain what is happening in each of the three diagrams. *Blocks of rock are pulling away from each other; blocks of rock are being pushed together; blocks of rock are moving past each other in opposite directions.*

SECTION 9.2
Ask students to describe the relationships among the focus, epicenter, and seismic waves shown in the diagram. *An earthquake begins underground at its focus. Vibrations called seismic waves travel out from the focus. The epicenter is the point on Earth's surface above the focus.*

SECTION 9.3
Have students explain the two ways earthquake damage can be reduced. *Scientists can predict where earthquakes are likely and make maps showing their predictions. Structures can be designed and built to resist earthquake damage.*

Review Concepts

- Big Idea Flow Chart, p. T65
- Chapter Outline, pp. T71–T72

9 Chapter Review

the BIG idea

Earthquakes release stress that has built up in rocks.

KEY CONCEPTS SUMMARY

1 Earthquakes occur along faults.

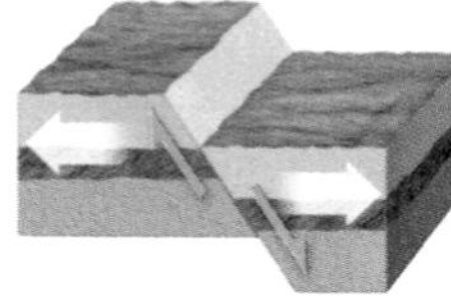
Normal faults form as rocks are pulled apart.

Reverse faults form as rocks are pushed together.

Strike-slip faults form as rocks are pushed horizontally in opposite directions.

VOCABULARY
fault p. 301
stress p. 301
earthquake p. 301

2 Earthquakes release energy.

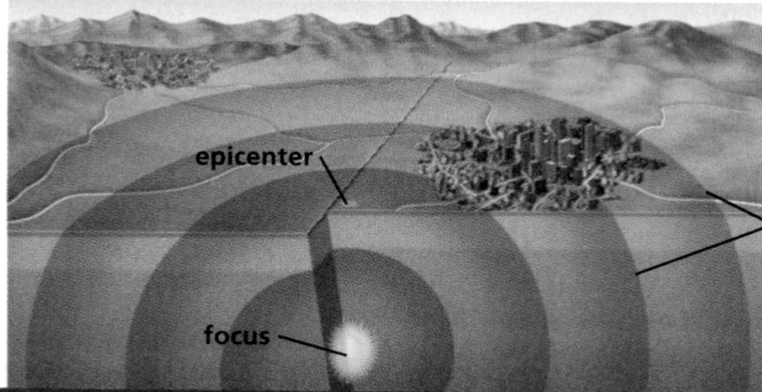

VOCABULARY
seismic wave p. 307
focus p. 308
epicenter p. 308
seismograph p. 312

3 Earthquake damage can be reduced.

A powerful earthquake releases more energy and causes more shaking of the ground than does a weak earthquake.

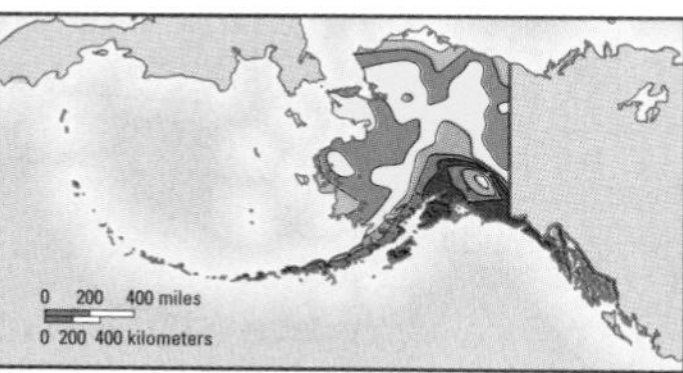

An area's risk of earthquakes can be predicted.

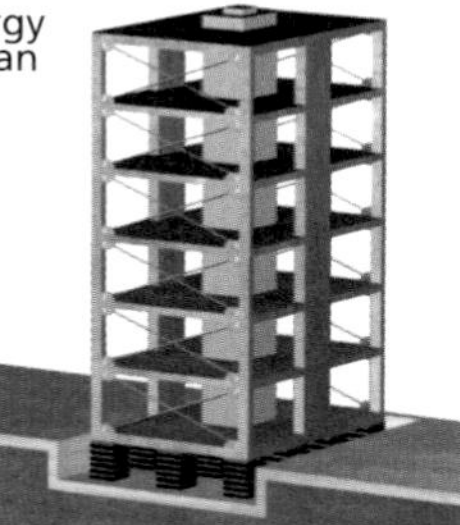
Structures can be designed for greater safety in an earthquake.

VOCABULARY
aftershock p. 318
liquefaction p. 318
tsunami p. 318

326 Unit 3: The Changing Earth

Technology Resources

Have students visit **ClassZone.com** or use the CD-ROM for a cumulative review of concepts.

CONTENT REVIEW

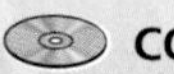
CONTENT REVIEW CD-ROM

Engage students in a whole-class interactive review of Key Concepts. Edit content as you wish.

POWER PRESENTATIONS

Reviewing Vocabulary

On a separate sheet of paper, draw a diagram to show the relationships among each set of words. One set has been done as an example.
seismograph, seismic waves, seismogram

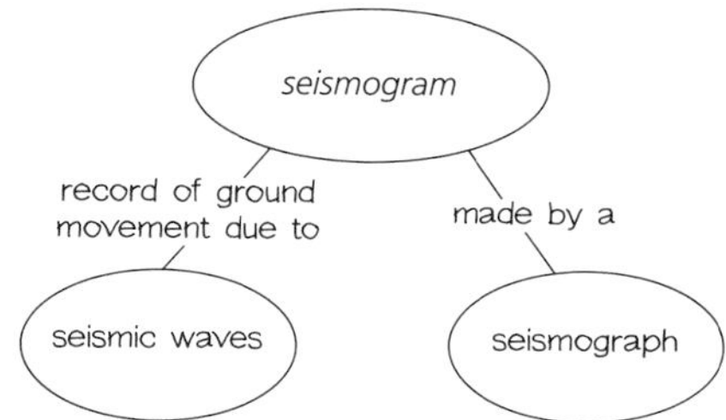

1. earthquake, epicenter, focus
2. earthquake, tsunami, liquefaction
3. fault, stress, earthquake, aftershock
4. tsunami, epicenter, seismogram

Reviewing Key Concepts

Multiple Choice *Choose the letter of the best answer.*

5. What causes an earthquake? (6.1.e)
   a. a rise of magma in the mantle
   b. a sudden movement of blocks of rock
   c. a buildup of seismic waves
   d. a change in Earth's magnetic poles

6. Earthquakes release energy in the form of (6.3.a)
   a. seismic waves
   b. faults
   c. stress lines
   d. seismograms

7. Most damage from an earthquake usually occurs (6.1.g)
   a. below the focus
   b. far from the epicenter
   c. at the focus
   d. near the epicenter

8. To locate the epicenter of an earthquake, scientists need seismograms from at least _____ seismic stations. (6.1.g)
   a. two
   b. three
   c. four
   d. five

9. The seismic waves that usually cause the most damage are (6.3.a)
   a. surface waves
   b. tsunami waves
   c. primary waves
   d. secondary waves

10. Earthquakes release _____ that has built up in rocks. (6.3.a)
    a. water
    b. magnetism
    c. stress
    d. electricity

11. About 80 percent of all earthquakes occur in a belt around the (6.1.a)
    a. Pacific Ocean
    b. San Andreas Fault
    c. North American Plate
    d. African Rift Valley

12. In a strike-slip fault, blocks of rock move _____ along the fault plane. (6.1.d)
    a. up
    b. down
    c. sideways
    d. up and down

13. One method of making a building earthquake resistant is to (6.2.d)
    a. add sand under the foundation
    b. reduce the use of steel
    c. make the walls of brick
    d. use cross braces

Short Answer *Write a short answer to each question.*

14. Why do most earthquakes occur at or near tectonic plate boundaries? (6.1.a)
15. How do data from seismic waves indicate that Earth's outer core is liquid? (6.1.b)
16. What causes most of the injuries and deaths due to earthquakes? (6.2.d)

SSESSMENT RESOURCES

ASSESSMENT BOOK
- Chapter Test A, pp. 199–202
- Chapter Test B, pp. 203–206
- Chapter Test C, pp. 207–210
- Alternative Assessment, pp. 211–212

STANDARDS REVIEW AND PRACTICE, pp. 1–14, 21–24, 57–58

Technology Resources

Edit test items and answer choices.

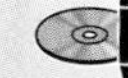
Test Generator CD-ROM

Visit **ClassZone.com** to extend test practice.

Test Practice

Reviewing Vocabulary

Sample answers:

1.
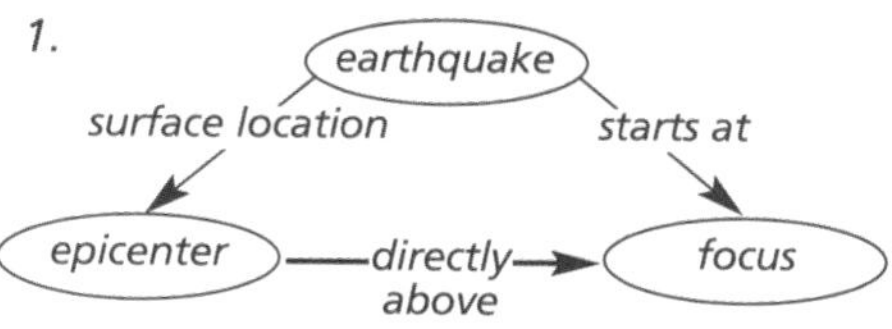

2.
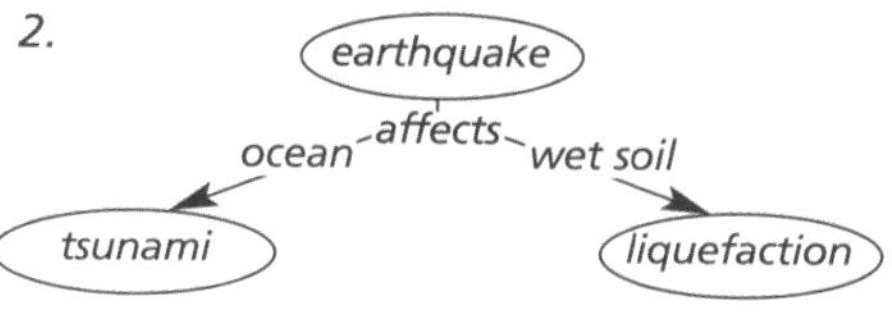

3.
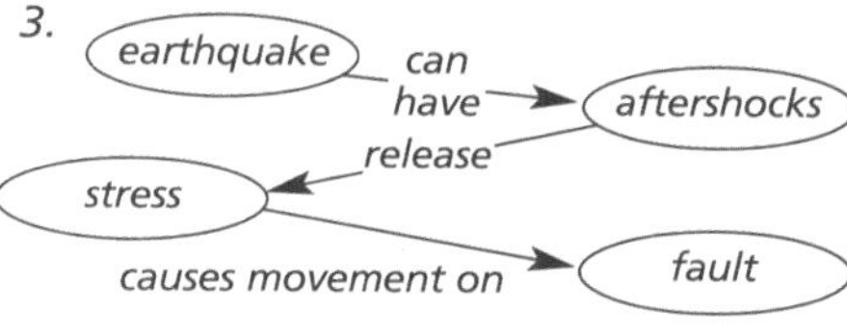

4.
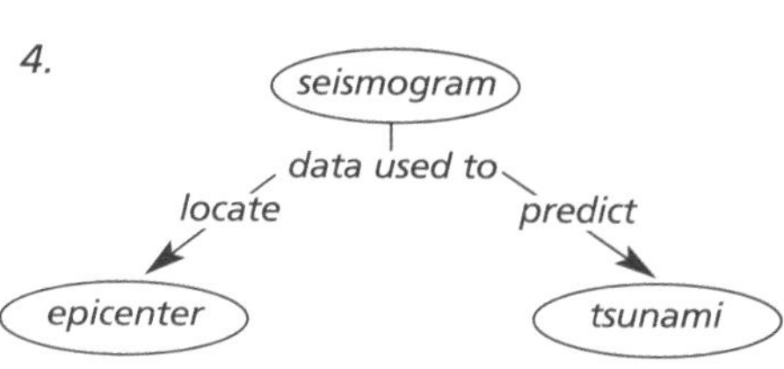

Reviewing Key Concepts

5. b
6. a
7. d
8. b
9. a
10. c
11. a
12. c
13. d
14. Earthquakes occur along faults, and most faults are located at or near tectonic plate boundaries.
15. If the Earth's outer core were solid, secondary waves could pass through it. Since secondary waves cannot pass through the outer core, it must be liquid.
16. Collapsing buildings and outbreaks of fire cause most earthquake injuries and deaths.

Thinking Critically

17. reverse, because one block of rock has moved up the fault plane relative to the other
18. at the epicenter
19. seismic waves moving out from the focus
20. The arrival times will be closer together at A than at B.
21. The block to the right has moved up relative to the block to the left.
22. They are being pushed together.
23. Avoid areas where landslides or liquefaction are likely; use good building practices to make the house resistant to earthquake damage.
24. Students' answers should include two of these: Alaska, Washington, and California. All three states have or are near a plate boundary.
25. a lot of damage to buildings because the epicenter is nearby and the focus is shallow
26. They cause changes as large blocks of rock move up, down, or sideways.
27. 2 minutes and 19 seconds

the BIG idea

28. Seismic waves travel out from an earthquake's focus in all directions. The greater the waves' energy at the surface, the more the ground shakes.
29. Heat inside Earth causes tectonic plates to move, and the movements of tectonic plates cause earthquakes to occur.

UNIT PROJECTS

Check to make sure students are working on their projects. Check schedules and work in progress.

 Unit Projects, pp. 5–10

Thinking Critically

Study the illustration below, showing the epicenter and focus of an earthquake, then answer the following six questions.

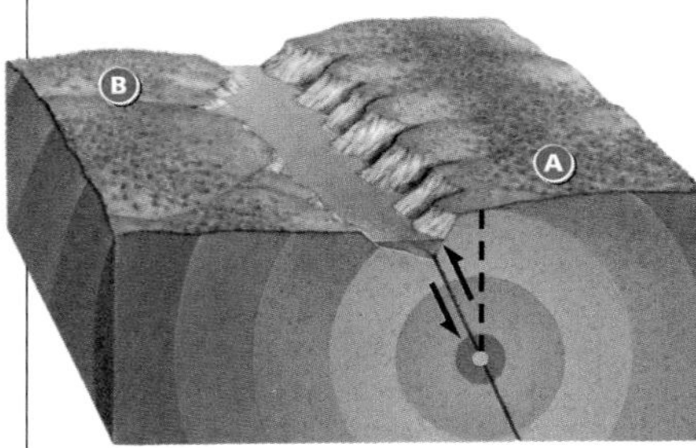

17. **APPLY** What type of fault is shown in the illustration? How do you know? (6.1.d)

18. **APPLY** Where on the surface is the greatest shaking likely to occur? (6.1.g)

19. **INFER** What does the set of circles around the focus represent? (6.3.a)

20. **EXPLAIN** In what ways would the times of arrival of primary and secondary waves be different at points *A* and *B*? (6.3.a)

21. **IDENTIFY EFFECTS** The land surface to the left of the fault is lower than the land surface to the right. How might this be related to movements along the fault? (6.1.d)

22. **ANALYZE** What are the main directions of stress on the blocks of rock on either side of the fault? (6.1.d)

23. **APPLY** A builder is planning to construct a new house near a fault along which earthquakes are common. Write a list of guidelines that the builder might use to decide where and how to build the house. (6.1.g)

24. **ANALYZE** Identify two areas of the United States where earthquakes are most likely to occur. Explain your choices in terms of plate tectonics. (6.1.a)

25. **IDENTIFY EFFECTS** A town has been struck by an earthquake with a magnitude of 5.8. The epicenter was 10 kilometers (6 mi) away, and the focus was shallow. What sort of damage would you expect to find in the town? (6.1.g)

26. **ANALYZE** What role do earthquakes play in shaping Earth's surface? (6.1.f)

27. **CALCULATE** If primary waves travel at a speed of about 5 kilometers per second, how long would it take them to arrive at a seismic station located 695 kilometers from an earthquake's focus? (6.3.a)

the BIG idea

28. **CONNECT** Look again at the photograph of earthquake damage on pages 298–299. Explain how energy released by an earthquake can travel through rock and cause damage at Earth's surface. (6.3.a)

29. **SYNTHESIZE** The illustration below shows convection in Earth's mantle. What are the relationships among the heat inside Earth, the movements of tectonic plates, and the occurrences of earthquakes? (6.1.b)

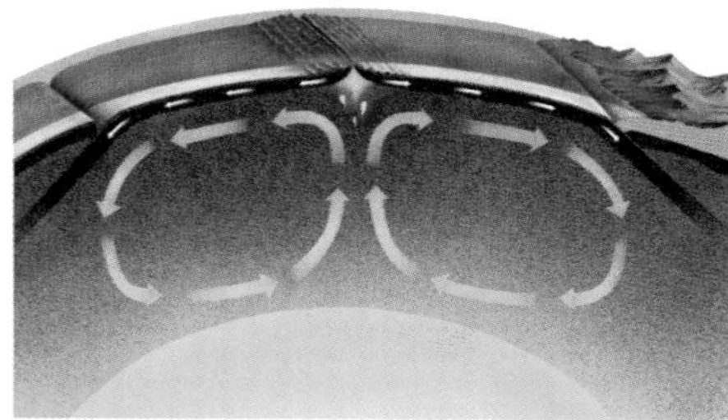

UNIT PROJECTS

If you need to do an experiment for your unit project, gather the materials. Be sure to allow enough time to observe results before the project is due.

MONITOR AND RETEACH

If students have trouble applying the concepts in Chapter Review item 24, have them review the map on p. 302. Have them compare the locations of the plate boundaries and the earthquakes in North America.

Students may benefit from summarizing one or more sections of the chapter.

 Summarizing the Chapter, pp. 140–141

328 Unit 3: **The Changing Earth**

Standards-Based Assessment

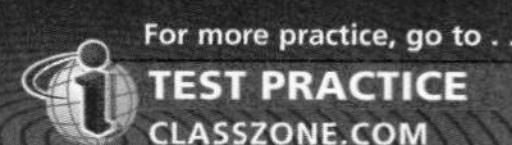

Analyzing Data

The following tables show magnitudes and average numbers of earthquakes in the world per year, and states in which two or more major earthquakes have been recorded. Use the information in the tables to answer the questions below.

Earthquakes in the World per Year

Classification	Magnitude	Average Number per Year
Great	8.0 and higher	1
Major	7.0–7.9	18
Strong	6.0–6.9	120
Moderate	5.0–5.9	800
Light	4.0–4.9	6200
Minor	3.0–3.9	49,000

States That Have Recorded Two or More Major Earthquakes

State	Number of Major Earthquakes
Alaska	74
Arkansas	2
California	16
Hawaii	4
Missouri	2
Nevada	3

1. A major earthquake can have a magnitude of
a. 6.0–6.9 **c.** 7.4
b. 6.0 and higher **d.** 8.2

2. The most major earthquakes have been recorded in which state?
a. Arkansas **c.** Missouri
b. Hawaii **d.** Nevada

3. A magnitude 3.2 earthquake is classified as
a. major **c.** moderate
b. strong **d.** minor

4. The world's most powerful earthquakes occur along reverse faults. In which state are reverse faults most likely to be common?
a. Alaska **c.** Hawaii
b. California **d.** Nevada

5. In which state is a tectonic plate boundary most likely to be located?
a. Arkansas **c.** Hawaii
b. California **d.** Nevada

6. Compared to the number of major earthquakes each year, the number of moderate earthquakes is
a. about 40 times greater **c.** about equal
b. about 4 times greater **d.** smaller

7. Alaska has recorded a total of 82 earthquakes with magnitudes of 7.0 and higher. How many of these earthquakes are classified as "great"?
a. 0 **c.** 56
b. 8 **d.** 74

8. An earthquake of which classification releases the most energy?
a. great **c.** strong
b. major **d.** minor

Extended Response

Answer the two questions below in detail. Include some of the terms shown in the word box. In your answers underline each term you use.

seismic waves	primary	secondary	surface
stress	fault	plate boundary	

9. During an earthquake, Dustin felt a small amount of shaking. About 15 seconds later, he felt some more shaking. Then about 45 seconds later he felt the strongest shaking. Explain what happened.

10. The island of Sumatra is located in an area where the Pacific Plate sinks under the Eurasian Plate. Explain why Sumatra has many earthquakes.

REFLECTING ON THE CHAPTER

Have students answer the following questions in their **Science Notebook:**

1. What did you learn about earthquakes that surprised you?
2. What questions occurred to you that were not answered while you were reading the chapter? How might you seek answers to these questions?
3. What concepts from this chapter apply to your Unit Project?

California Content Standards

6.1.a Students know evidence of plate tectonics is derived from the fit of the continents; the location of earthquakes, volcanoes, and midocean ridges; and the distribution of fossils, rock types, and ancient climatic zones.

6.1.d Students know that earthquakes are sudden motions along breaks in the crust called faults and that volcanoes and fissures are locations where magma reaches the surface.

6.3.a Students know energy can be carried from one place to another by heat flow or by waves, including water, light and sound waves, or by moving objects.

Analyzing Data

1. c *3. d* *5. b* *7. b*
2. b *4. a* *6. a* *8. a*

Extended Response

9. RUBRIC

4 points for a good explanation that uses the following terms accurately: *seismic waves, primary, secondary, surface.*

Sample answer: The first seismic waves Dustin felt were primary waves. They caused a small amount of shaking. Then secondary waves caused a bit more shaking. Finally, surface waves arrived. They caused the strongest shaking.

3 points correctly explains what happened and uses three terms accurately
2 points adequately answers the question and uses two terms accurately
1 point adequately answers the question and uses one term correctly

10. RUBRIC

4 points for a response that correctly answers the question and uses the following terms accurately: *stress, fault, plate boundary.*

Sample answer: Sumatra has many earthquakes because it is along a plate boundary. As the plates push together, stress builds up along the boundary. When that stress is suddenly released, an earthquake occurs.

3 points correctly answers the question and uses two terms accurately
2 points correctly answers the question and uses one term accurately
1 point correctly answers the question, but does not use the terms

TIMELINES in Science

FOCUS

Set Learning Goals

Students will

- Examine the history of the Earth system.
- Compare technologies used to study the Earth system.
- Take and analyze a core sample.

California Content Standards

6.1.a Students know evidence of plate tectonics is derived from the fit of the continents; the location of earthquakes, volcanoes, and midocean ridges; and the distribution of fossils, rock types, and ancient climatic zones.

6.4.a Students know the sun is the major source of energy for phenomena on Earth's surface; it powers winds, ocean currents, and the water cycle.

6.5.e Students know the number and types of organisms an ecosystem can support depends on the resources available and on abiotic factors, such as quantities of light and water, a range of temperatures, and soil composition.

6.6.a Students know the utility of energy sources is determined by factors that are involved in converting these sources to useful forms and the consequences of the conversion process.

INSTRUCT

The top half of the timeline shows major events in the history of the Earth system. The bottom half discusses advances in the technology used to study Earth and its applications. Note that the technology used to study a particular event in Earth's history was often developed billions of years after the event itself took place.

Technology

MEASURING AGE To determine the age of ancient rocks, scientists use radioactive elements with long half-lives, such as uranium-238. Uranium-238 has a half-life of 4.5 billion years. Point out that this element changes too slowly to measure recent events. Ask: What would you use to measure more recent rock ages? ***a radioactive element with a shorter half-life***

TIMELINES in Science

6.1.a, 6.4.a, 6.5.e, 6.6.a

HISTORY OF THE EARTH SYSTEM

Systems of air, water, rocks, and living organisms have developed on Earth during the planet's 4.6 billion years of history. More and more scientists have become curious about how these parts of Earth work together. Today, scientists think of these individual systems as part of one large Earth system.

The timeline shows a few events in the history of the Earth system. Scientists have developed special tools and procedures to study this history. The boxes below the timeline show how technology has led to new knowledge about the Earth system and how that knowledge has been applied.

4.6 BYA

Earth Forms in New Solar System

The Sun and planets form out of a cloud of gas and dust. Earth forms and grows larger as particles collide with it. While Earth is still young, a slightly smaller object smashes into it and sends huge amounts of material flying into space. Some of this material forms a new object—the Moon.

EVENTS

5 BYA

Billion Years Ago

APPLICATIONS AND TECHNOLOGY

TECHNOLOGY

Measuring Age of Solar System

In 1956, Clair C. Patterson published his estimate that the solar system was 4.55 billion years old. Previously, scientists had learned how to use radioactive elements present in rocks to measure their ages. Patterson used this technology to determine the ages of meteorites that were formed along with the solar system and later fell to Earth. Since 1956 scientists have studied more samples and used new technologies. These studies have generally confirmed Patterson's estimate.

This iron meteorite fell in Siberia in 1947. Data from such meteorites are clues to how and when the solar system formed.

DIFFERENTIATE INSTRUCTION

Below Level To help students grasp the broad scope of this timeline, draw it as one continuous line on the chalkboard. Explain that *BYA* and *MYA* mean "billions of years ago" and "millions of years ago." Point out that the first half of the timeline is separated by intervals of one billion years. Ask: How many years separate intervals in the second half of the timeline? ***two hundred million years***

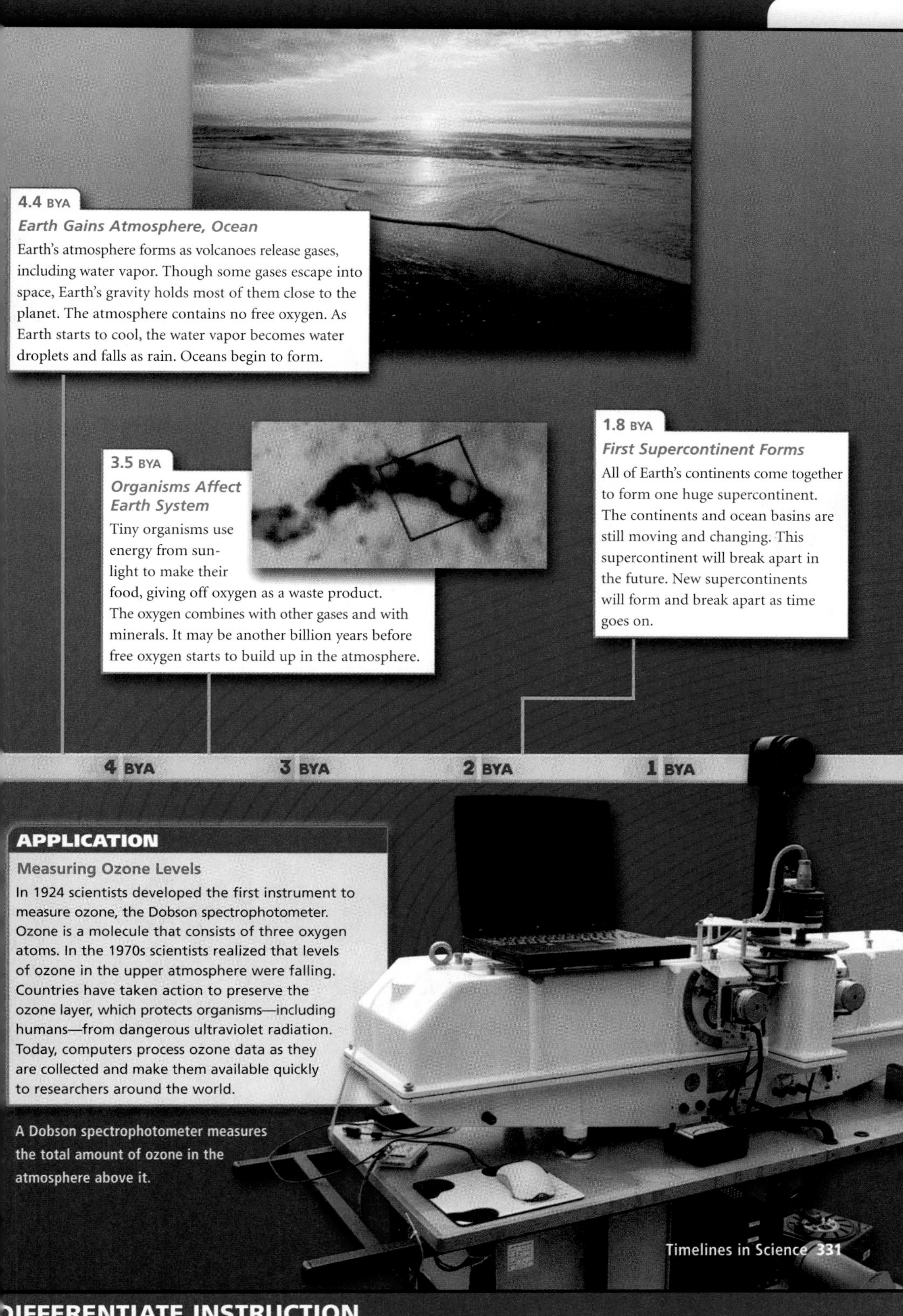

4.4 BYA
Earth Gains Atmosphere, Ocean
Earth's atmosphere forms as volcanoes release gases, including water vapor. Though some gases escape into space, Earth's gravity holds most of them close to the planet. The atmosphere contains no free oxygen. As Earth starts to cool, the water vapor becomes water droplets and falls as rain. Oceans begin to form.
3.5 BYA
Organisms Affect Earth System
Tiny organisms use energy from sunlight to make their food, giving off oxygen as a waste product. The oxygen combines with other gases and with minerals. It may be another billion years before free oxygen starts to build up in the atmosphere.
1.8 BYA
First Supercontinent Forms
All of Earth's continents come together to form one huge supercontinent. The continents and ocean basins are still moving and changing. This supercontinent will break apart in the future. New supercontinents will form and break apart as time goes on.
4 BYA
3 BYA
2 BYA
1 BYA
APPLICATION
Measuring Ozone Levels
In 1924 scientists developed the first instrument to measure ozone, the Dobson spectrophotometer. Ozone is a molecule that consists of three oxygen atoms. In the 1970s scientists realized that levels of ozone in the upper atmosphere were falling. Countries have taken action to preserve the ozone layer, which protects organisms—including humans—from dangerous ultraviolet radiation. Today, computers process ozone data as they are collected and make them available quickly to researchers around the world.
Timelines in Science 331

A Dobson spectrophotometer measures the total amount of ozone in the atmosphere above it.

Integrate the Sciences

The tiny organisms that first began to photosynthesize are called cyanobacteria. Fossils of these blue-green microorganisms (*cyan* stems from the Greek word *kuanos*, meaning "dark blue") have been found in rocks in western Australia. The cells of certain species of modern algae are nearly identical to their ancient counterparts.

Scientific Process

Help students understand that many environmental problems that affect the Earth system require ongoing data collection and analysis. Ask: Why do scientists continue to monitor ozone levels? *The levels can change quickly. A long record of change can aid scientists in identifying patterns and trends.*

DIFFERENTIATE INSTRUCTION

English Learners Encourage students to develop their own science dictionary that lists unfamiliar terms, such as *meteorite*, *ozone*, and *supercontinent*. Students can write definitions next to each new term. They can also draw diagrams to help them remember the terms.

Scientific Process

As students read about when animals first appeared in the fossil record, ask them how scientists might go about testing the hypothesis that some of the animals were attached to the sea floor. *Sample answer: Continue to search for additional, complete fossils; compare the fossils with present-day animals.*

Technology

CORE SAMPLES Ask: How do scientists who are studying Earth's current climate and geology use data gathered from cores? *Sample answer: The data could help scientists identify long-term patterns that explain current climate or geologic events.*

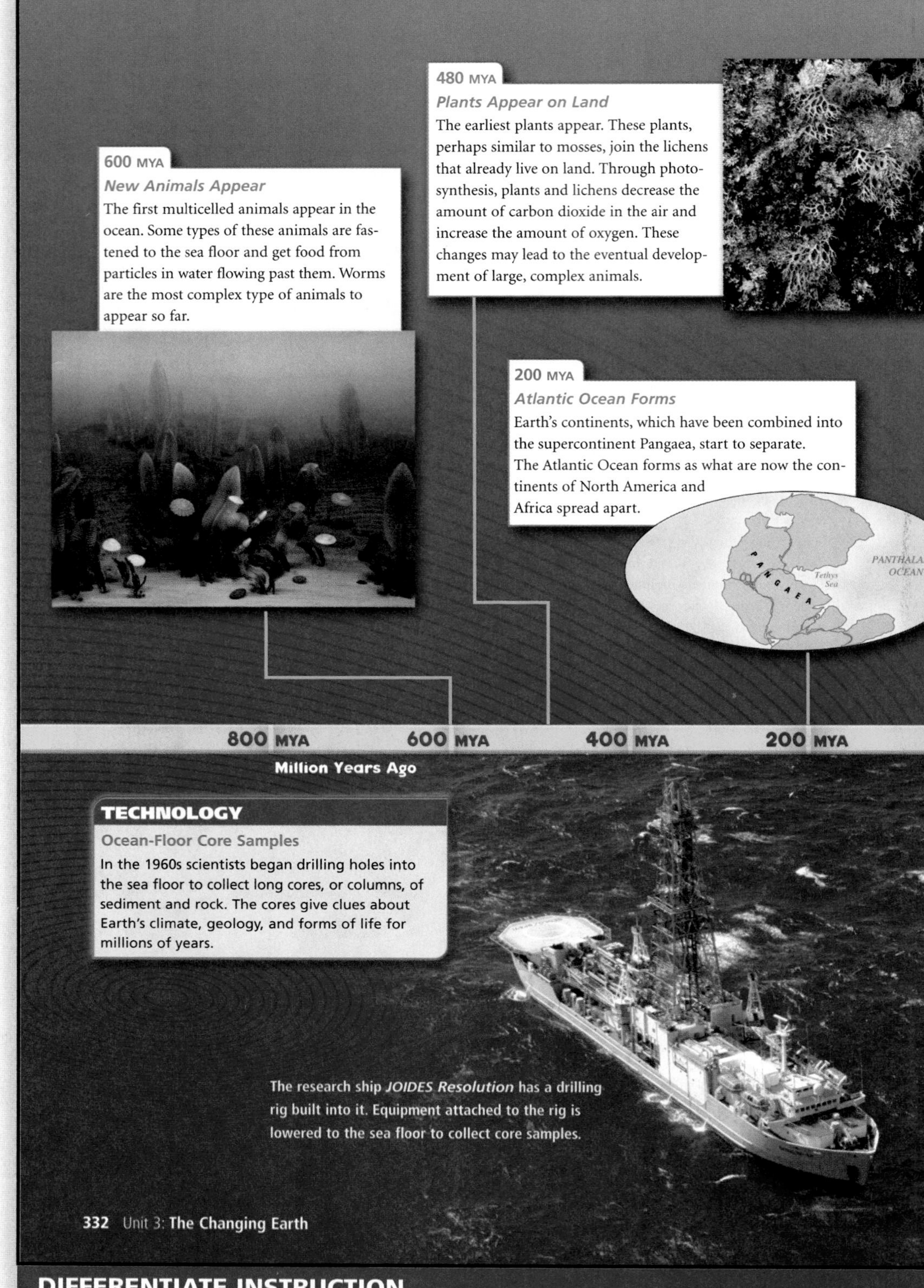

600 MYA
New Animals Appear
The first multicelled animals appear in the ocean. Some types of these animals are fastened to the sea floor and get food from particles in water flowing past them. Worms are the most complex type of animals to appear so far.

480 MYA
Plants Appear on Land
The earliest plants appear. These plants, perhaps similar to mosses, join the lichens that already live on land. Through photosynthesis, plants and lichens decrease the amount of carbon dioxide in the air and increase the amount of oxygen. These changes may lead to the eventual development of large, complex animals.

200 MYA
Atlantic Ocean Forms
Earth's continents, which have been combined into the supercontinent Pangaea, start to separate. The Atlantic Ocean forms as what are now the continents of North America and Africa spread apart.

TECHNOLOGY
Ocean-Floor Core Samples
In the 1960s scientists began drilling holes into the sea floor to collect long cores, or columns, of sediment and rock. The cores give clues about Earth's climate, geology, and forms of life for millions of years.

The research ship *JOIDES Resolution* has a drilling rig built into it. Equipment attached to the rig is lowered to the sea floor to collect core samples.

332 Unit 3: The Changing Earth

DIFFERENTIATE INSTRUCTION

Advanced In terms of geologic time, life has been part of the history of the Earth system for a short time. Ask students to solve the following problem: Plants have existed for what percentage of Earth's total history? *about 10 percent*

$$\left(\frac{4.8 \times 10^8}{4.6 \times 10^9} = \frac{4.8}{46} = 0.104, \text{ or about } 10\%\right)$$

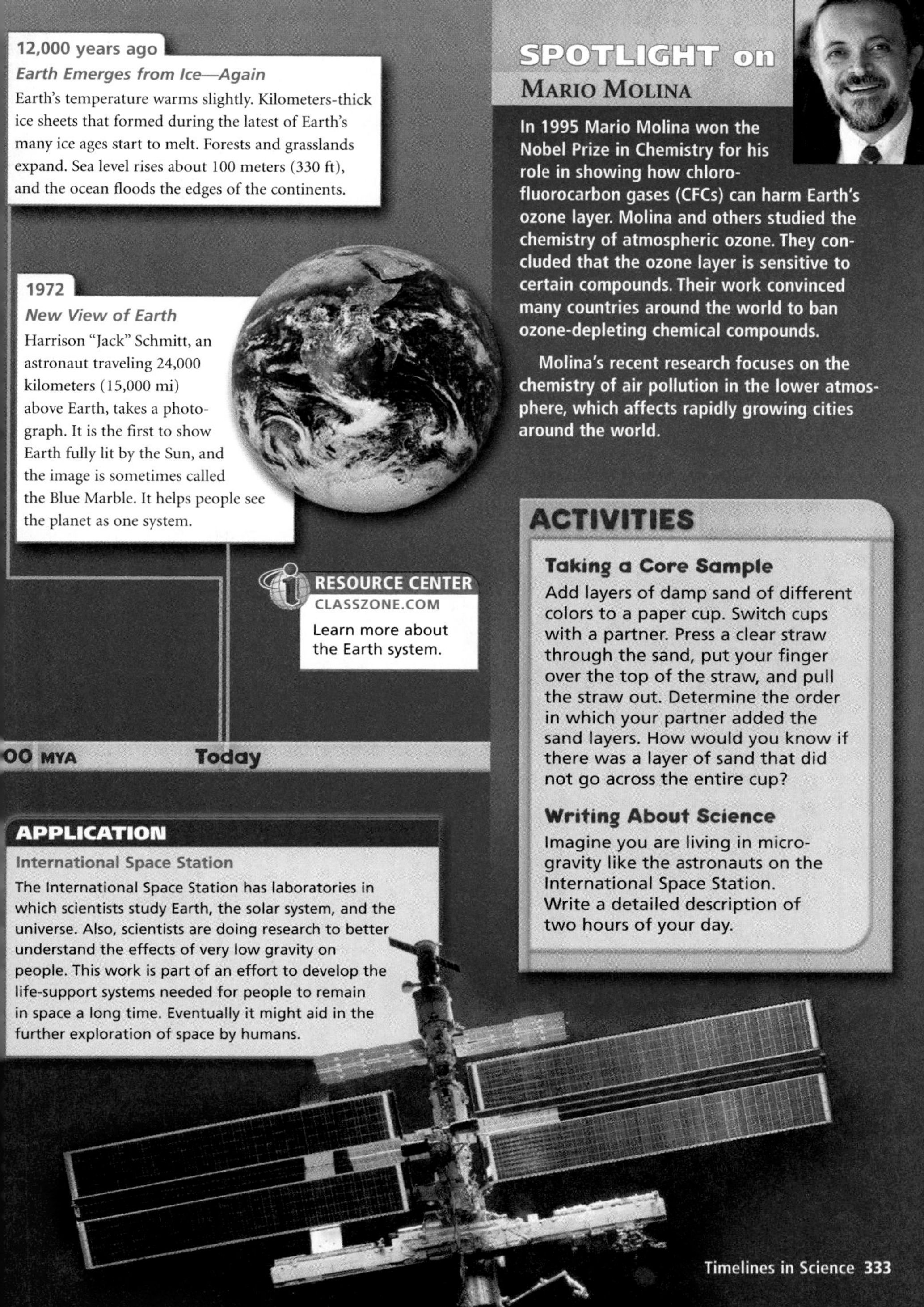

12,000 years ago
Earth Emerges from Ice—Again
Earth's temperature warms slightly. Kilometers-thick ice sheets that formed during the latest of Earth's many ice ages start to melt. Forests and grasslands expand. Sea level rises about 100 meters (330 ft), and the ocean floods the edges of the continents.
1972
New View of Earth
Harrison "Jack" Schmitt, an astronaut traveling 24,000 kilometers (15,000 mi) above Earth, takes a photograph. It is the first to show Earth fully lit by the Sun, and the image is sometimes called the Blue Marble. It helps people see the planet as one system.
RESOURCE CENTER
CLASSZONE.COM
Learn more about the Earth system.
00 MYA
Today
SPOTLIGHT on
MARIO MOLINA
In 1995 Mario Molina won the Nobel Prize in Chemistry for his role in showing how chlorofluorocarbon gases (CFCs) can harm Earth's ozone layer. Molina and others studied the chemistry of atmospheric ozone. They concluded that the ozone layer is sensitive to certain compounds. Their work convinced many countries around the world to ban ozone-depleting chemical compounds.
Molina's recent research focuses on the chemistry of air pollution in the lower atmosphere, which affects rapidly growing cities around the world.
ACTIVITIES
Taking a Core Sample
Add layers of damp sand of different colors to a paper cup. Switch cups with a partner. Press a clear straw through the sand, put your finger over the top of the straw, and pull the straw out. Determine the order in which your partner added the sand layers. How would you know if there was a layer of sand that did not go across the entire cup?
Writing About Science
Imagine you are living in microgravity like the astronauts on the International Space Station. Write a detailed description of two hours of your day.
APPLICATION
International Space Station
The International Space Station has laboratories in which scientists study Earth, the solar system, and the universe. Also, scientists are doing research to better understand the effects of very low gravity on people. This work is part of an effort to develop the life-support systems needed for people to remain in space a long time. Eventually it might aid in the further exploration of space by humans.
Timelines in Science 333

Spotlight on

Mario Molina's experiments on pollutants in the atmosphere were conducted with Sherwood Rowland at the University of California, Irvine. When Molina published their findings in the scientific journal *Nature* in 1974, the theories sparked an international debate on the effects of CFCs on the environment. Your class may want to find out whether CFCs are regulated in your community. One place to start is the Web site of California's Environmental Protection Agency.

Students may also be interested in finding out how other countries are addressing the problem of pollutants in the atmosphere. Discuss how increased global cooperation may be the key to solving many problems that affect the Earth system, such as global climate change, acid rain, deforestation, and depletion of world fisheries.

ACTIVITIES

Taking a Core Sample

Tell students that the sand represents different layers of rock and soil under Earth's surface. Stress that they should keep their finger over the top of the straw as they examine the sand within—otherwise, the sand will spill out. *If a particular color of sand was not in the straw, then that layer did not go across the entire cup.*

Writing About Science

Have students first discuss how the minute amount of gravity physically affects astronauts in space. Remind them about or show them scenes of astronauts floating inside spacecraft. Suggest that students do some research before writing their descriptions, which might take the form of daily journals.

DIFFERENTIATE INSTRUCTION

Advanced Have students extend the "Taking a Core Sample" activity by modeling how erosion removes soil and rock from the geologic record. For example, they could blow across the sand-filled cup to model wind erosion or sprinkle water into the cup to model water erosion.

Alternative Writing Projects Have students imagine that they are astronauts and that the photograph of Earth taken by Harrison Schmitt is a postcard that they are sending home to Earth. Have them write a short note to a friend, describing Earth from the point of view of an observer in space.

Technology Resources

Students can visit **ClassZone.com** for information on the Earth system.

CHAPTER

Mountains and Volcanoes

Earth Science UNIFYING PRINCIPLES

PRINCIPLE 1
Heat energy inside Earth and radiation from the Sun provide energy for Earth's processes.

PRINCIPLE 2
Physical forces, such as gravity, affect the movement of all matter on Earth and throughout the universe.

PRINCIPLE 3
Matter and energy move among Earth's rocks and soil, atmosphere, waters, and living things.

PRINCIPLE 4
Earth has changed over time and continues to change.

Unit: The Changing Earth BIG IDEAS

CHAPTER 8
Plate Tectonics
The movement of tectonic plates causes geologic changes on Earth.

CHAPTER 9
Earthquakes
Earthquakes release stress that has built up in rocks.

CHAPTER 10
Mountains and Volcanoes
Mountains and volcanoes form as tectonic plates move.

CHAPTER 10 KEY CONCEPTS

SECTION 1

Movement of rock builds mountains.

1. Most mountains form along plate boundaries.
2. Mountains can form as rocks fold.
3. Mountains can form as rocks move along faults.

SECTION 2

Volcanoes form as molten rock erupts.

1. Volcanoes erupt many types of material.
2. Most volcanoes form along plate boundaries.
3. Volcanoes can have many shapes and sizes.
4. Scientists monitor volcanoes.

SECTION 3

Volcanoes affect Earth's land, air, and water.

1. Volcanic eruptions affect the land.
2. Volcanic gases and ash affect the air.
3. Volcanic activity affects water.

The Big Idea Flow Chart is available on p. T73 in the **TRANSPARENCY BOOK.**

Previewing Content

SECTION

Movement of rock builds mountains. pp. 337–345

1. Most mountains form along plate boundaries.
The formation of most mountain ranges begins as a collision between tectonic plates and is followed by land being pushed up. In some cases, such as with the Himalayas, the collision continues today. In other cases, such as with the Appalachians, the collision boundary no longer exists.
While some processes push mountains up, other processes wear them down. Running water and wind constantly break rocks into pieces called sediment and carry them away. The sediment may settle in valleys or be carried to the ocean. In this way, tall jagged mountains eventually become low, rounded hills, then flat land.

2. Mountains can form as rocks fold.
Although rock is a hard, brittle material, it bends under certain conditions. When slowly subjected to pressure and high temperatures, rock can fold and crumple like soft modeling clay. **Folded mountains** form as an oceanic plate sinks under a continental plate or as two continental plates collide. The Himalayas are an example of folded mountains. Their development can be divided into different stages:

- 200 million years ago: India moves toward Eurasia, which was separated from India by an ocean. Folded mountains and volcanoes form at the convergent boundary where oceanic crust sinks beneath continental crust.
- 50 million years ago: India collides with Eurasia. Subduction stops. Volcanoes stop erupting. Crust along the edges of both continents continues folding into mountains.
- Today: India and Eurasia continue to collide, and the Himalayas continue to grow.

3. Mountains can form as rocks move along faults.
Whereas folded mountains form where continental crust is being pushed together, **fault-block mountains** form where continental crust is being pulled apart. As the crust is stretched, it breaks into blocks along fault lines. The tilting and dropping of the blocks in various ways creates mountains and valleys.

SECTION

Volcanoes form as molten rock erupts. pp. 346–355

1. Volcanoes erupt many types of material.
A **volcano** is an opening in Earth's crust through which molten rock, rock fragments, and hot gases erupt.

- Molten rock, or magma, that is high in silica resists flowing and can prevent gases from escaping until the pressure builds and the gases blast out.
- Rock fragments can be as big as a house or as tiny as a speck of dust. Fragments form as **lava** cools in the air or as pieces of the volcano walls are ripped loose.
- The main gases from a volcano are water vapor and carbon dioxide. **Pyroclastic flows** are fast-moving mixtures of gases and ash that can sweep up and over hills, then race down a neighboring valley, causing deadly damage within minutes.

2. Most volcanoes form along plate boundaries.
Volcanoes, like earthquakes, are explained by plate tectonics. Volcanoes are commonly found at

- subduction zones where an oceanic plate is sinking beneath another plate
- spreading centers where plates are pulling apart
- hot spots where a plate is moving over an unusually hot area in the mantle

3. Volcanoes can have many shapes and sizes.
The size and shape of a volcano depends on the magma type feeding it. Eruptions form three basic kinds of volcanoes.

- A shield volcano is built from many eruptions of lava that is low in silica and flows easily. It is a broad, flat dome.
- A cinder cone is built of pieces of magma that harden in the air and fall to form a small, steep-sided volcano.
- A composite volcano is built of high-silica magma. The tall cone consists of layers of lava and layers of rock fragments.

4. Scientists monitor volcanoes.
Scientists monitor volcanoes to look for warning signs that an eruption may be coming. Warning signs include earthquakes, changes in the tilt of the ground, rising temperatures of openings, and changes in volcanic gases being released.

Common Misconceptions

MOUNTAIN RANGE Some students might think a mountain range is any expanse of western range land with mountains in the background, as is often seen in a Western movie. Other students may think that a mountain range includes all of the mountains within a large geographic area such as the Rockies or Appalachians. Actually, these mountains represent mountain belts, each made up of many mountain ranges.

This misconception is addressed on p. 338.

MISCONCEPTION DATABASE
CLASSZONE.COM Background on student misconceptions

ORIGIN OF LAVA Many students might think that magma originates in Earth's core. Although the study of seismic, or earthquake, waves indicates that the outer core is liquid, magma originates in the upper portion of the mantle and even in the crust.

This misconception is addressed on p. 347.

Previewing Content

SECTION

Volcanoes affect Earth's land, air, and water. pp. 356–363

1. Volcanic eruptions affect the land.
Volcanic eruptions can be extremely destructive. The damage largely depends on how much and which types of material the volcano ejects.

- Lava flows can knock down and burn trees, fields, roads, and buildings.
- Volcanic ash can suffocate plants, people, and animals. It can collapse buildings and damage machinery.
- Mudflows have buried towns as a mixture of ash, rocks, soil, and water race down a mountain valley.
- Landslides occur when part of a volcano collapses. Landslides can change the landscape and cause tsunamis.
- Steam explosions occur when magma comes near or in contact with water, resulting in an explosion. These are not very common.

Some of the long-term effects of eruptions can be beneficial. Over many years, volcanic rock breaks down to form a rich soil. Highly productive farmland surrounds some volcanoes. Volcanoes can also create beautiful landscapes.

2. Volcanic gases and ash affect the air.
Volcanoes release gases before, during, and after eruptions. Sometimes these gases can be dangerous. Sudden releases of large amounts of carbon dioxide have been deadly. Sulfur dioxide and other gases mix with moisture in the air to form acids that add to **acid rain.** Large amounts of gases and ash from an eruption can travel around the world and affect weather for months or even years.

3. Volcanic activity affects water.
Volcanic activity is responsible for a variety of water-related features.

- Hot springs are pools that form when water moves underground near magma or hot rock. The water gets heated and rises to the surface.
- **Geysers** are similar to hot springs, but rather than flowing out gently, water shoots out into the air. A diagram of a geyser is shown on the right.
- Fumaroles release steam and other gases rather than liquid water.
- Deep-sea vents are hot springs that form at spreading centers in the ocean. Deep-sea vents support unusual life forms that do not exist anywhere else on Earth.

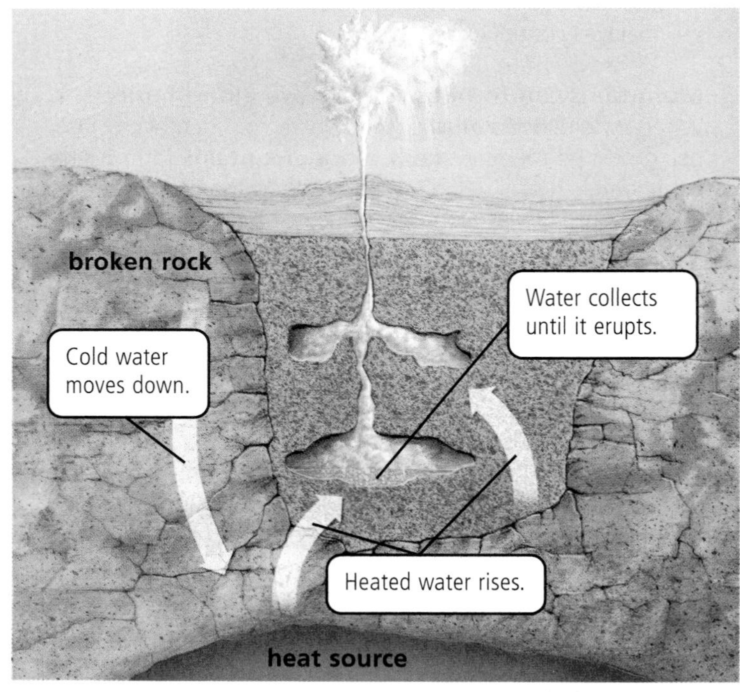
broken rock
Water collects until it erupts.
Cold water moves down.
Heated water rises.
heat source

Previewing Labs

Lab Generator CD-ROM
Edit these Pupil Edition labs and generate alternative labs.

EXPLORE the BIG idea

Making Mountains, p. 335 Students use checkers or coins to model how mountains form from tilted blocks of crust.	**TIME** 5 minutes **MATERIALS** 10 checkers or coins
Internet Activity: Volcanoes, p. 335 Students are introduced to the roles that magma plays in the type of volcanic eruption.	**TIME** 20 minutes **MATERIALS** computer with Internet access

SECTION 

EXPLORE Folding, p. 337 Students use layers of modeling clay to show how solids can bend and fold.	**TIME** 10 minutes **MATERIALS** 2 or 3 colors of modeling clay (1 stick or 1 cup of each color), 2 wooden blocks, newspaper
INVESTIGATE Fault-Block Mountains, p. 342 Students use wooden blocks to model how fault-block mountains form. **ALTERNATIVE:** Teacher Demonstration, URB p. 202	**TIME** 15 minutes **MATERIALS** 3 triangular wooden blocks, 3 rectangular wooden blocks

SECTION 

EXPLORE Eruptions, p. 346 Students use effervescent antacid tablets and film canisters to show how a buildup of pressure can lead to an eruption.	**TIME** 10 minutes **MATERIALS** empty film canister with lid, 1/4 of an antacid tablet, 1/4 c water
CHAPTER INVESTIGATION **Make Your Own Volcanoes,** pp. 354–355 Students build models by using plaster of Paris and gravel to relate volcanic materials to the type of volcano formed. **ALTERNATIVE:** Diagramming Activity, URB p. 202	**TIME** 40 minutes **MATERIALS** 375 mL plaster of Paris, 180 mL water, 500 mL gravel, 3 cardboard pieces (approximately 8 1/2" × 11"), two 250-mL paper cups, stirrer, ruler, protractor

SECTION 

INVESTIGATE Mudflows, p. 359 Students analyze a map to discover how mudflows are affected by land shape. **ALTERNATIVE:** Direct Instruction, URB p. 202  Map of Mount Ranier Mudflows, p. 172	**TIME** 25 minutes **MATERIALS** Map of Mount Rainier Mudflows

R **Additional INVESTIGATION,** Modeling Magma Movement, A, B, & C, pp. 191–199; Teacher Instructions, pp. 202–203

Previewing Chapter Resources

	INTEGRATED TECHNOLOGY	LABS AND ACTIVITIES
CHAPTER 10 **Mountains and Volcanoes**	 CLASSZONE.COM • eEdition Plus • EasyPlanner Plus • Misconception Database • Content Review • Test Practice • Visualization • Resource Centers • Internet Activity: Volcanoes • Math Tutorial  SCILINKS.ORG SCILINKS  **CD-ROMS** • eEdition • EasyPlanner • Power Presentations • Content Review • Lab Generator • Test Generator  **AUDIO CDS** • Audio Readings • Audio Readings in Spanish	 EXPLORE the Big Idea, p. 335 • Making Mountains • Internet Activity: Volcanoes  **UNIT RESOURCE BOOK** Unit Projects, pp. 5–10 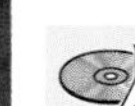 **Lab Generator CD-ROM** Generate customized labs.
SECTION  **Movement of rock builds mountains.** pp. 337–345  Lesson Plan, pp. 142–143	**MATH TUTORIAL**  **TRANSPARENCY BOOK** • Big Idea Flow Chart, p. T73 • Daily Vocabulary Scaffolding, p. T74 • Note-Taking Model, p. T75 • 3-Minute Warm-Up, p. T76 • "Formation of Himalayas" Visual, p. T78	 • EXPLORE Folding p. 337 • INVESTIGATE Fault-Block Mountains, p. 342 • Math in Science, p. 345  **UNIT RESOURCE BOOK** • Datasheet, Fault-Block Mountains, p. 151 • Math Support, p. 180 • Math Practice, p. 181
SECTION  **Volcanoes form as molten rock erupts.** pp. 346–355  Lesson Plan, pp. 153–154	 • **VISUALIZATION,** Erupted Volcanic Material • **RESOURCE CENTER,** Historic/Current Volcanic Eruptions  **TRANSPARENCY BOOK** • Daily Vocabulary Scaffolding, p. T74 • 3-Minute Warm-Up, p. T76	 • EXPLORE Eruptions, p. 346 • CHAPTER INVESTIGATION, Make Your Own Volcanoes, pp. 354–355  **UNIT RESOURCE BOOK** • CHAPTER INVESTIGATION, Make Your Own Volcanoes, A, B, & C, pp. 182–190 • Additional INVESTIGATION, Modeling Magma Movement, A, B, & C, pp. 191–199
SECTION   **Volcanoes affect Earth's land, air, and water.** pp. 356–363  Lesson Plan, pp. 163–164	 **RESOURCE CENTER,** Effects of Volcanic Eruptions  **TRANSPARENCY BOOK** • Big Idea Flow Chart, p. T73 • Daily Vocabulary Scaffolding, p. T74 • 3-Minute Warm-Up, p. T77 • Chapter Outline, pp. T79–T80	 • INVESTIGATE Mudflows, p. 359 • California Close-Up, p. 363  **UNIT RESOURCE BOOK** • Map of Mount Ranier Mudflows, p. 172 • Datasheet, Mudflows, p. 173

KEY TO ICONS 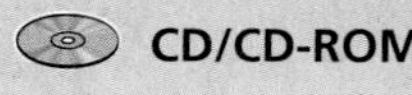 CD/CD-ROM  Teacher Edition  TRANSPARENCY BOOK  STANDARDS REVIEW AND PRACTICE

INTERNET · Pupil Edition · UNIT RESOURCE BOOK · ASSESSMENT BOOK · SCIENCE TOOLKIT

READING AND REINFORCEMENT

ASSESSMENT

STANDARDS

Modified Lesson Plans for English Learners, pp. 38–40

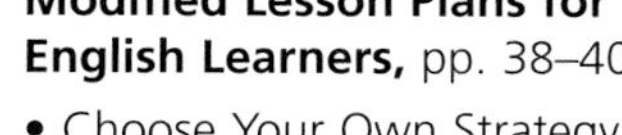

- Choose Your Own Strategy, B20–21, B24–25
- Content Frame, C35
- Daily Vocabulary Scaffolding, H1–8

UNIT RESOURCE BOOK
- Vocabulary Practice, pp. 177–178
- Decoding Support, p. 179
- Summarizing the Chapter, pp. 200–201

Audio Readings CD
Listen to Pupil Edition.

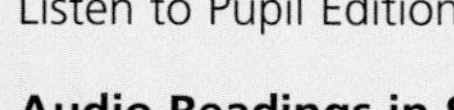

Audio Readings in Spanish CD
Listen to Pupil Edition in Spanish.

- Chapter Review, pp. 365–366
- Standards-Based Assessment, p. 367

ASSESSMENT BOOK
- Diagnostic Test, pp. 213–214
- Chapter Test, A, B, & C, pp. 218–229
- Alternative Assessment, pp. 230–231
- Unit Test A, B, & C, pp. 232–243

STANDARDS REVIEW AND PRACTICE, pp. 3–4, 7–12, 21–22, 35–36, 51–52, 57–58

McDougal Littell Assessment System

Test Generator CD-ROM
Generate customized and Spanish tests.

California Content Standards
6.1.a, 6.1.b, 6.1.c, 6.1.d, 6.1.e, 6.1.f, 6.2.d, 6.4.c, 6.6.a, 6.7.a, 6.7.g

See p. 334 for the standards.

UNIT RESOURCE BOOK
- Reading Study Guide, A & B, pp. 144–147
- Spanish Reading Study Guide, pp. 148–149
- Challenge and Extension, p. 150
- Reinforcing Key Concepts, p. 152

Ongoing Assessment, pp. 339–343

Section 10.1 Review, p. 344

ASSESSMENT BOOK
Section 10.1 Quiz, p. 215

California Content Standards
6.1.a, 6.1.b, 6.1.c, 6.1.e, 6.1.f, 6.7.g

UNIT RESOURCE BOOK
- Reading Study Guide, A & B, pp. 155–158
- Spanish Reading Study Guide, pp. 159–160
- Challenge and Extension, p. 161
- Reinforcing Key Concepts, p. 162
- Challenge Reading, pp. 175–176

Ongoing Assessment, pp. 347–349, 351, 353

Section 10.2 Review, p. 353

ASSESSMENT BOOK
Section 10.2 Quiz, p. 216

California Content Standards
6.1.b, 6.1.d, 6.1.e, 6.7.a

UNIT RESOURCE BOOK
- Reading Study Guide, A & B, pp. 165–168
- Spanish Reading Study Guide, pp. 169–170
- Challenge and Extension, p. 171
- Reinforcing Key Concepts, p. 174

Ongoing Assessment, pp. 358, 360–362

Section 10.3 Review, p. 362

ASSESSMENT BOOK
Section 10.3 Quiz, p. 217

California Content Standards
6.2.d, 6.3.c, 6.4.c, 6.6.a

Previewing Resources for Differentiated Instruction

CHAPTER INVESTIGATION

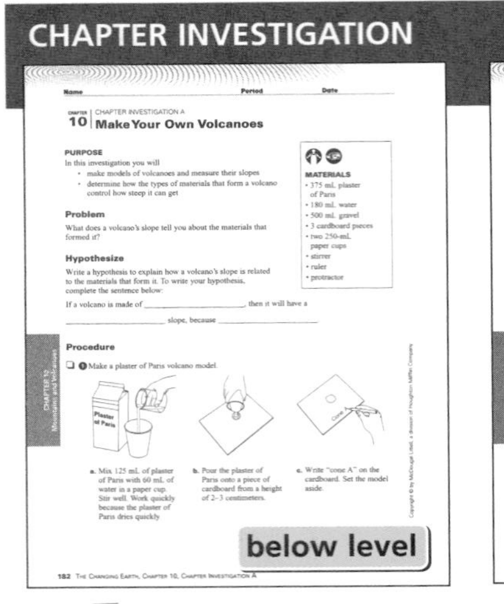

UNIT RESOURCE BOOK, pp. 182–185

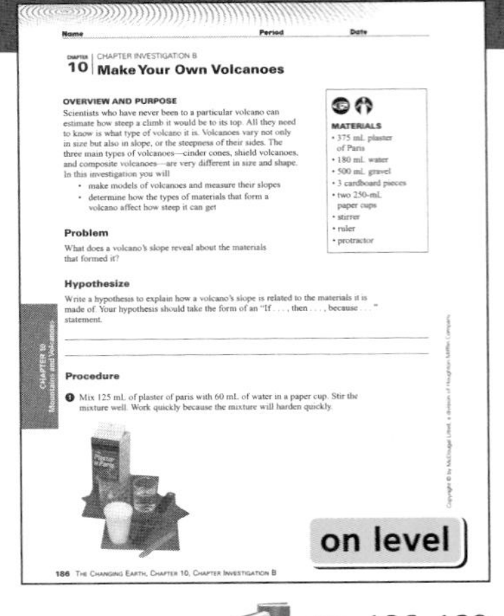

pp. 186–189

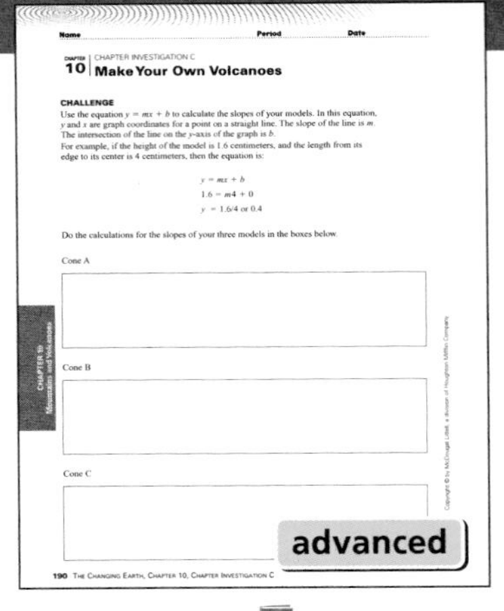

pp. 186–190

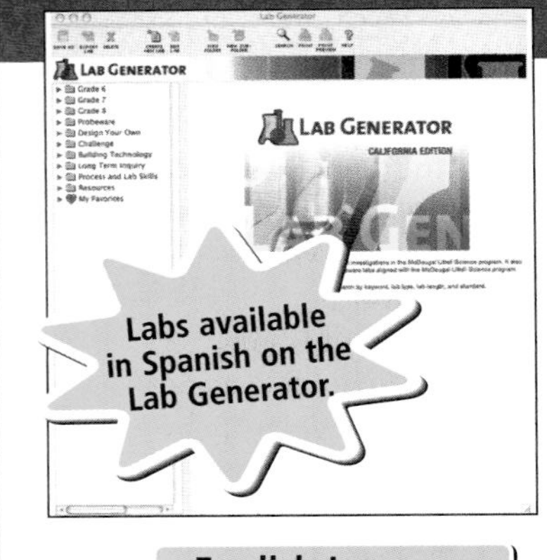

READING STUDY GUIDE

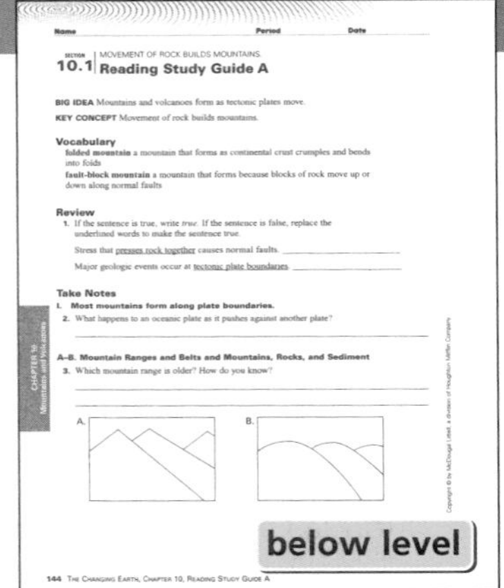

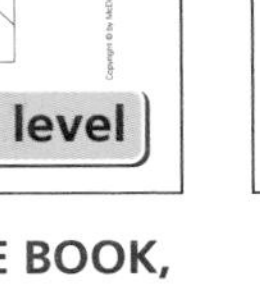

UNIT RESOURCE BOOK, pp. 144–145

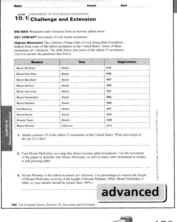

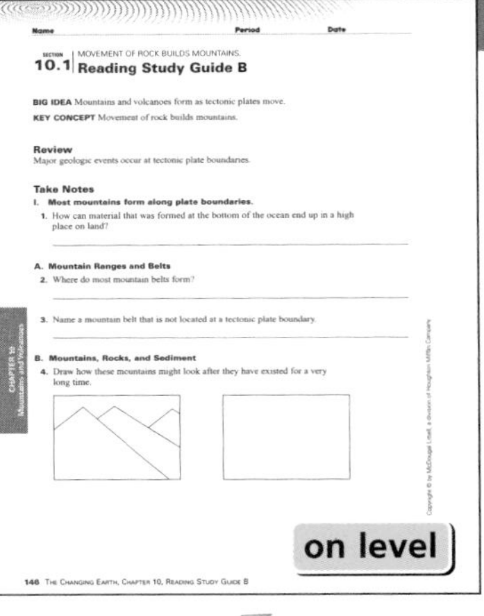

pp. 146–147

p. 150

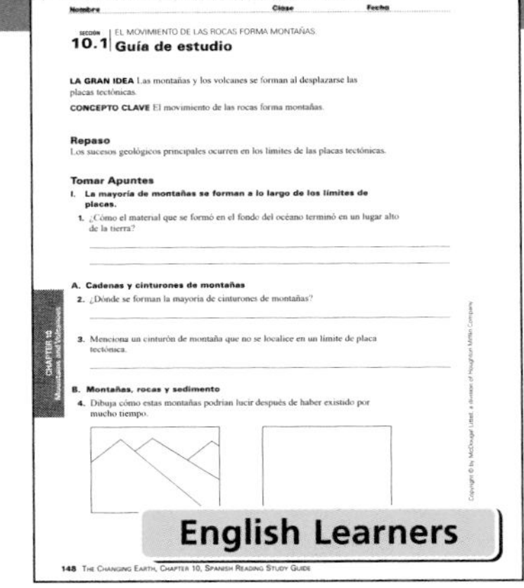

p. 148

CHAPTER TEST

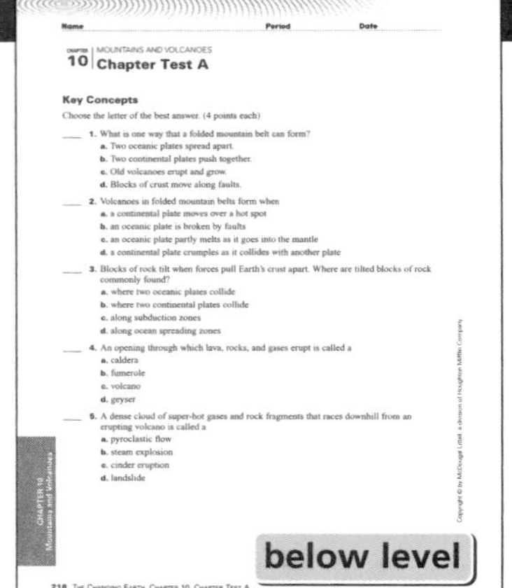

ASSESSMENT BOOK, pp. 218–221

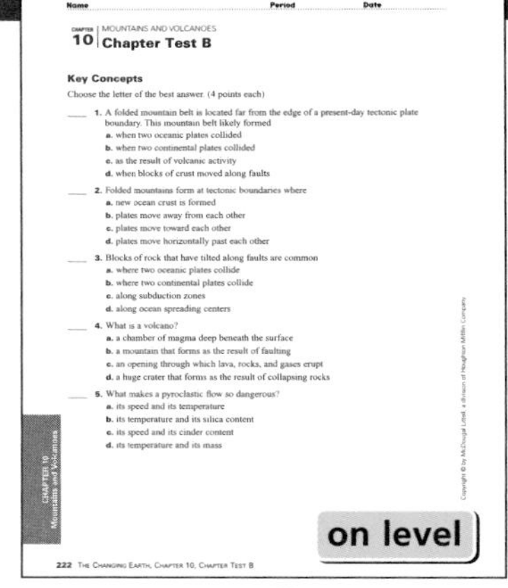

pp. 222–225

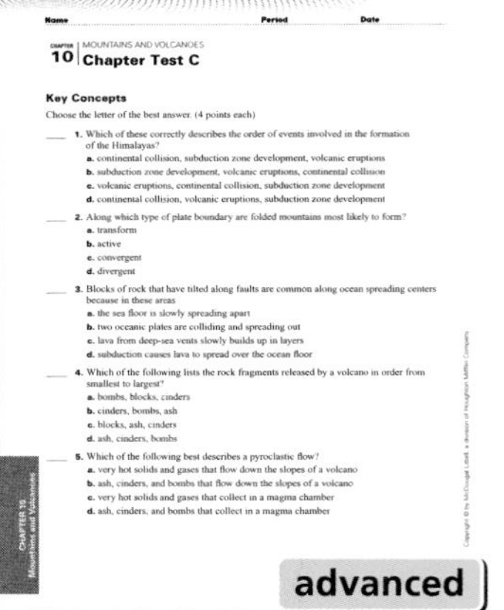

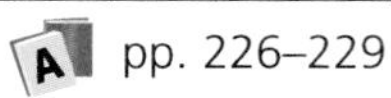

pp. 226–229

TECHNOLOGY

This chapter contains one Simulation, one Visualization, and two Resource Centers.

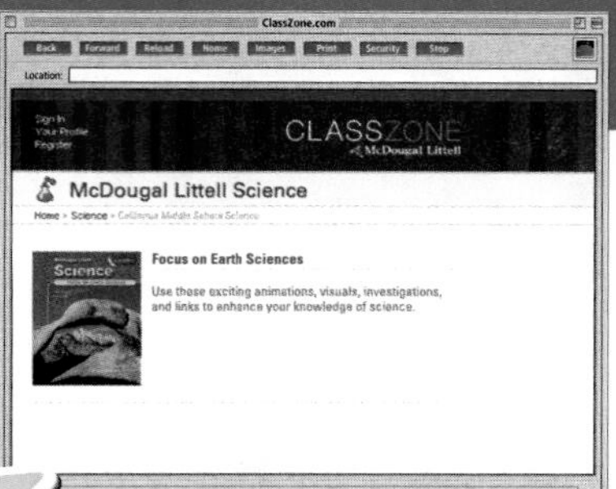

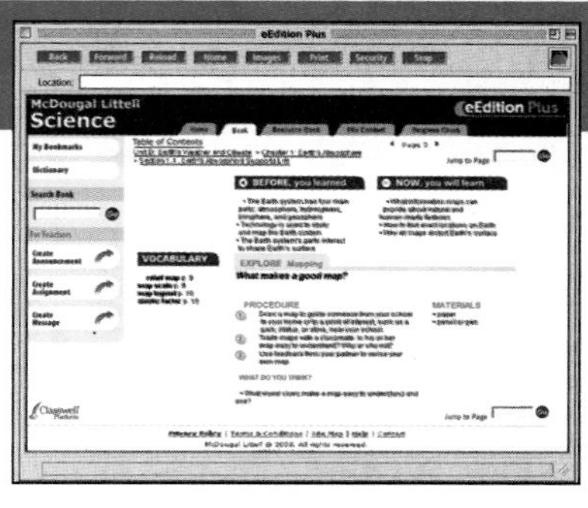

 CLASSZONE.COM

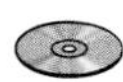 CD/CD-ROMS

VISUAL CONTENT

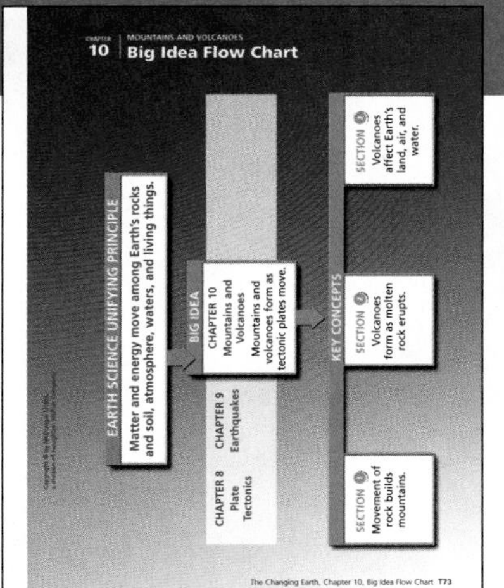

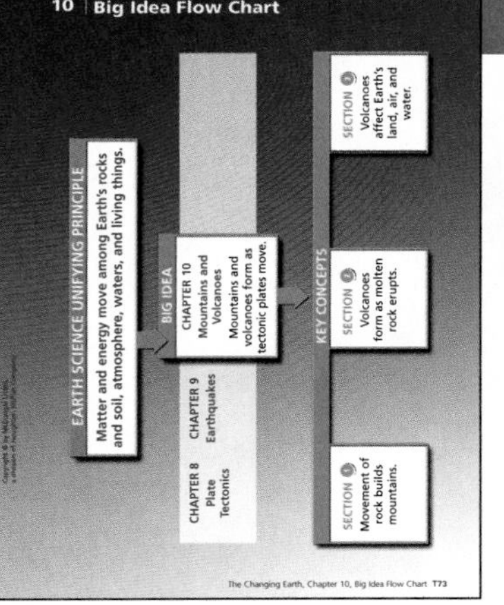

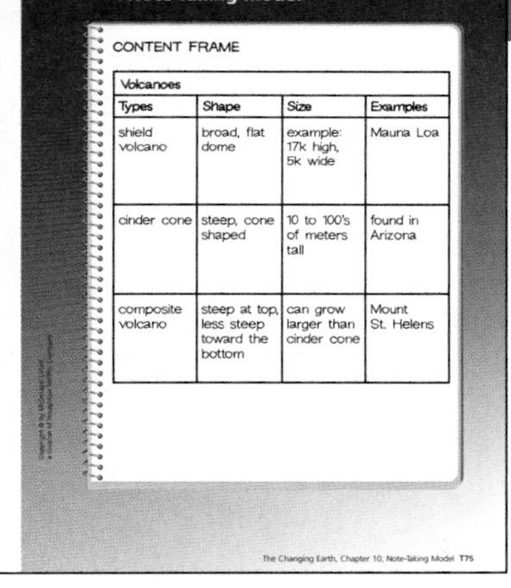

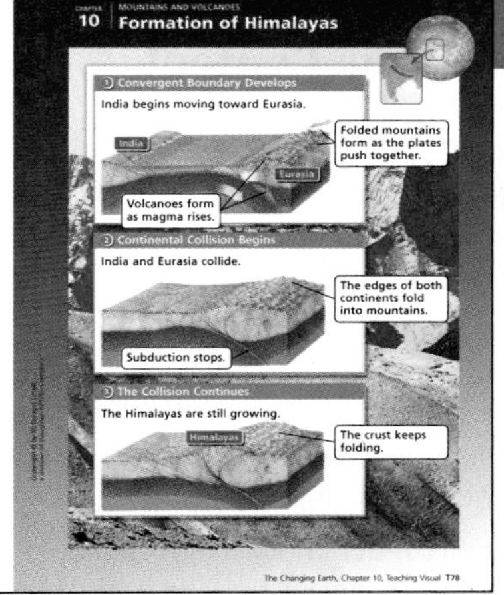

TRANSPARENCY BOOK, p. T73

 p. T75

 p. T78

MORE SUPPORT

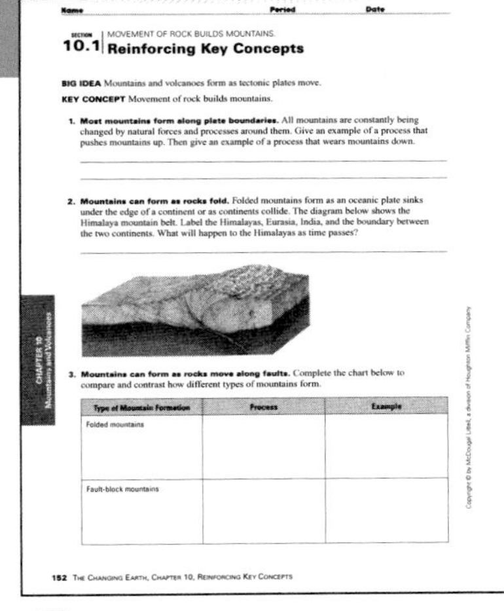

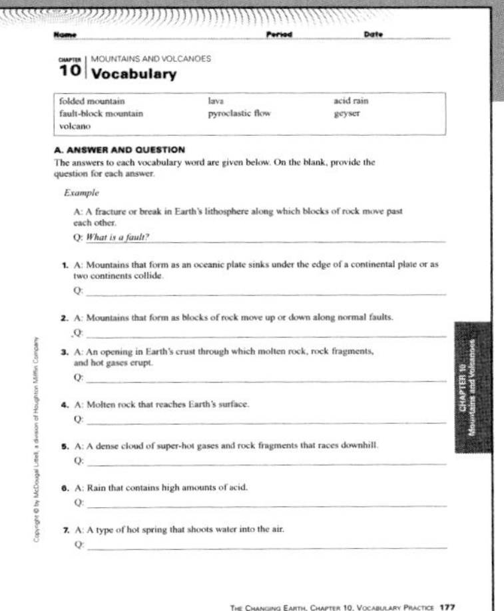

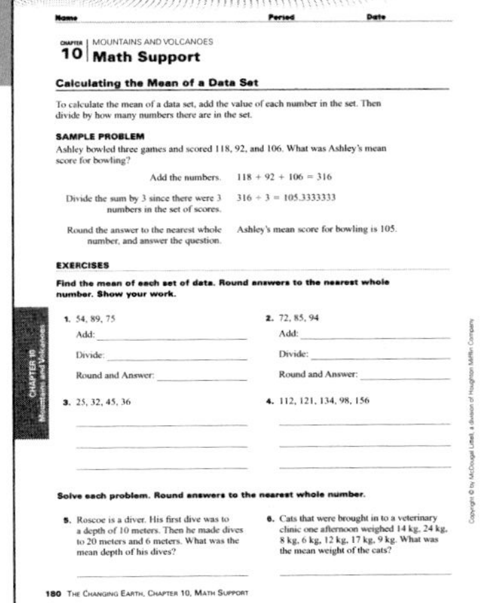

UNIT RESOURCE BOOK, p. 152

pp. 177–178

p. 180

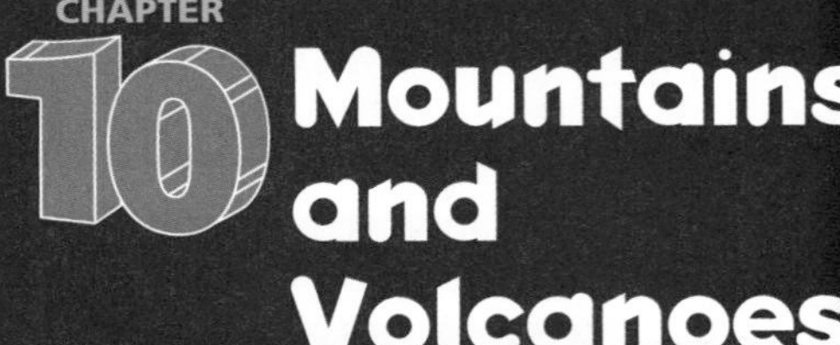

CHAPTER 10 Mountains and Volcanoes

INTRODUCE

the BIG idea

Have students look at the photograph of the erupting volcano and discuss how the question in the box links to the Big Idea:

- What materials are coming from the volcano? What will happen to these materials?
- Where might this volcano be located? Might it be located any place in the world?

California Content Standards

6.1.b Students know Earth is composed of several layers: a cold, brittle lithosphere; a hot, convecting mantle; and a dense, metallic core.

6.1.d Students know that earthquakes are sudden motions along breaks in the crust called faults and that volcanoes and fissures are locations where magma reaches the surface.

6.1.e Students know major geologic events, such as earthquakes, volcanic eruptions, and mountain building, result from plate motions.

6.1.f Students know how to explain major features of California geology (including mountains, faults, volcanoes) in terms of plate tectonics.

6.2.d Students know earthquakes, volcanic eruptions, landslides, and floods change human and wildlife habitats.

6.4.c Students know heat from Earth's interior reaches the surface primarily through convection.

6.6.a Students know the utility of energy sources is determined by factors that are involved in converting these sources to useful forms and the consequences of the conversion process.

6.7.a Develop a hypothesis.

CHAPTER

Mountains and Volcanoes

the BIG idea

Mountains and volcanoes form as tectonic plates move.

How does new land form from molten rock?

Key Concepts

SECTION 1 **Movement of rock builds mountains.** Learn how different types of mountains form.

SECTION 2 **Volcanoes form as molten rock erupts.** Learn why there are different types of volcanoes and volcanic eruptions.

SECTION 3 **Volcanoes affect Earth's land, air, and water.** Learn how volcanic eruptions affect land, air, and water.

California ClassZone

CLASSZONE.COM

Chapter 10 online resources: Content Review, Simulation, Visualization, two Resource Centers, Math Tutorial, Test Practice

INTERNET PREVIEW

CLASSZONE.COM For student use with the following pages:

Review and Practice
- Content Review, pp. 336, 364
- Math Tutorial: Finding the Mean, p. 345
- Test Practice, p. 367

Activities and Resources
- Internet Activity: Volcanoes, p. 335
- Visualization: Erupted Volcanic Material, p. 348
- Resource Centers: Historic/Current Volcanic Eruptions, p. 350; Effects of Volcanic Eruptions, p. 358

Explore Volcanoes
Code: MDL054

EXPLORE the BIG idea

Making Mountains

6.1.e Students know major geologic events, such as earthquakes, volcanic eruptions, and mountain building, result from plate motions.

Line up and hold a row of about ten checkers or coins on a table. Tilt the row, and then let it go.

Observe and Think What happened to the height, length, and shape of the row? How do you think these changes might be similar to the processes by which some mountains and valleys form?

Internet Activity: Volcanoes

6.1.d Students know that earthquakes are sudden motions along breaks in the crust called faults and that volcanoes and fissures are locations where magma reaches the surface.

Go to **ClassZone.com** to make a volcano erupt. As you watch the simulations, notice how different types of volcanoes form based on silica content and pressure.

Observe and Think Why are some volcanic eruptions much more violent than others?

NSTA scilinks.org SCILINKS

Explore Volcanoes **Code: MDL054**

EXPLORE the BIG idea

These inquiry-based activities are appropriate for use at home or as a supplement to classroom instruction.

Making Mountains

PURPOSE To introduce students to how mountains form from tilted blocks of crust.

TIP *5 min.* Suggest that students release the checkers or coins slowly so that the items remain in a fairly straight row.

Answer: The row's height decreases, its length increases, and the top of the row becomes uneven. Blocks of rock might break apart and tilt where the crust is being stretched, causing mountains and valleys to form.

REVISIT after p. 340.

Internet Activity: Volcanoes

PURPOSE To introduce students to the role that the composition of magma plays in the type of volcanic eruption.

TIP *20 min.* Have students predict the answer to the question before they view the Internet page.

Answer: Eruptions of silica-rich magma tend to be much more violent than eruptions of silica-poor magma. Gas bubbles cannot easily escape from silica-rich magma, and as they expand, pressure within the magma increases.

REVISIT after p. 347.

EACHING WITH TECHNOLOGY

nternet Search Engine After reading about the effects of volcanic uptions on p. 357, students can use the Internet to find out about e most recent volcanic eruptions around the world. They can use the formation for a bulletin board display or with presentation software.

PREPARE

CONCEPT REVIEW

Activate Prior Knowledge

- Use two books to represent the basic movements of two adjacent tectonic plates: pulling apart, pushing together, or sliding past.
- Help students identify each kind of boundary as you demonstrate it.
- Discuss which geologic events occur at each of the boundaries.

TAKING NOTES

Content Frame

Content frames are effective tools for comparing and contrasting characteristics of different items. At a glance, students can see, for example, the similarities between different kinds of mountains as well as what distinguishes one kind of mountain from another. Encourage students to use their content frames to organize the topics being described.

Vocabulary Strategy

Have students review these and other strategies found in the Note-Taking Handbook on pp. R45–R51. Each student can then choose the strategy that works best for him or her.

Vocabulary and Note-Taking Resources

- Vocabulary Practice, pp. 177–178
- Decoding Support, p. 179

- Daily Vocabulary Scaffolding, p. T74
- Note-Taking Model, p. T75

- Choose Your Own Strategy, B20–21, B24–25
- Content Frame, C35
- Daily Vocabulary Scaffolding, H1–8

CHAPTER 10

Getting Ready to Learn

CONCEPT REVIEW

- Earthquakes occur as blocks of rock move along faults.
- Tectonic plates pull apart, push together, or scrape past one another along their boundaries.

VOCABULARY REVIEW

magma p. 191
convergent boundary p. 278
subduction p. 286
fault p. 301
earthquake p. 301

Review concepts and vocabulary.

TAKING NOTES

CONTENT FRAME

Organize your notes into a **content frame** for mountains. Make categories at the top that describe their types, features, and how they form. Then fill in the boxes for each type of mountain. Later in the chapter you will make content frames for other topics.

CHOOSE YOUR OWN STRATEGY

Take notes about new vocabulary terms using one or more of the strategies from earlier chapters, such as **description wheel** and **magnet word.** Feel free to mix and match the strategies or use a different strategy.

See the Note-Taking Handbook on pages R45–R51.

SCIENCE NOTEBOOK

TYPE OF MOUNTAINS	CHARACTERISTIC	WHERE THEY FORM	EXAMPLES
folded	rocks bent and folded	at convergent plate boundaries	Appalachians Himalayas
fault-block			

Description Wheel

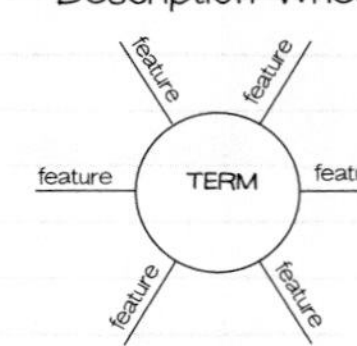

Magnet Word

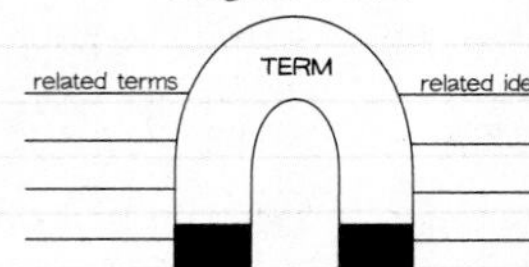

CHECK READINESS

Administer the Diagnostic Test to determine students' readiness for new science content and their mastery of requisite math skills.

 Diagnostic Test, pp. 213–214

Technology Resources

Students needing content and math skills should visit **ClassZone.com.**

- **CONTENT REVIEW**
- **MATH TUTORIAL**

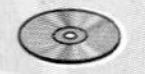 **CONTENT REVIEW CD-ROM**

KEY CONCEPT

Movement of rock builds mountains.

CALIFORNIA Content Standards

6.1.b Students know Earth is composed of several layers: a cold, brittle lithosphere; a hot, convecting mantle; and a dense, metallic core.

6.1.e Students know major geologic events, such as earthquakes, volcanic eruptions, and mountain building, result from plate motions.

6.1.f Students know how to explain major features of California geology (including mountains, faults, volcanoes) in terms of plate tectonics.

BEFORE, you learned

- Major geologic events occur at tectonic plate boundaries
- Most faults are located along plate boundaries

NOW, you will learn

- How the folding of rock can form mountains
- How movement along faults can form mountains

VOCABULARY

olded mountain p. 340
ault-block mountain p. 342

EXPLORE Folding (6.1.e)

How does rock fold?

PROCEDURE

1. Make three flat layers of clay on top of a sheet of newspaper. Put a block at either end of the clay.
2. Hold one block still. Push on the other block slowly to bring the blocks closer together.

MATERIALS

- 2 or 3 colors of modeling clay
- newspaper
- 2 blocks

WHAT DO YOU THINK?

- What happened to the clay when you pushed on the block?
- What shape did the middle layer of clay form?
- If a large block of rock reacted to pressure in a similar way, what kind of landform would result?

Most mountains form along plate boundaries.

A shallow sea once covered the area that is now Mount Everest, Earth's tallest mountain. If you were to climb Mount Everest, you would be standing on rocks containing the remains of ocean animals. Mount Everest also contains rocks that formed far away at a spreading center on the sea floor. How can rocks from the sea floor be on top of a mountain on a continent? Plate tectonics provides the answer.

Recall that an oceanic plate sinks when it collides with a continental plate. Some sea-floor material scrapes off the sinking plate and onto the continent. As continental mountains form, material once at the bottom of an ocean can be pushed many kilometers high.

10.1 FOCUS

Set Learning Goals

Students will

- Describe how the folding of rock can form mountains.
- Recognize how movement along faults can form mountains.
- Model, in an experiment, how fault-block mountains form.

3-Minute Warm-Up

Display Transparency 76 or copy this exercise on the board:

Draw a diagram that shows a convergent plate boundary. Include labels to show the major geologic events that occur at this type of boundary. *Diagrams should show magma, volcanoes and other mountains, and the crust of two colliding plates. If an oceanic plate is colliding with a continental plate, a trench should mark where the oceanic plate is moving beneath the continental plate.*

 3-Minute Warm-Up, p. T76

10.1 MOTIVATE

EXPLORE Folding

PURPOSE To introduce the concept that a solid can bend and fold

TIP *10 min.* Students can work in groups to conserve materials and share ideas, but encourage them to take turns pushing on the block. This will give them a better idea of the amount of stress and the length of time involved.

WHAT DO YOU THINK? *It bent and folded; an arch; a hill or mountain*

ESOURCES FOR DIFFERENTIATED INSTRUCTION

elow Level

NIT RESOURCE BOOK
Reading Study Guide A, pp. 144–145
Decoding Support, p. 179

AUDIO CDS

Advanced

UNIT RESOURCE BOOK
Challenge and Extension, p. 150

English Learners

UNIT RESOURCE BOOK
Spanish Reading Study Guide, pp. 148–149

- Audio Readings in Spanish
- Audio Readings (English)

10.1 INSTRUCT

Teach the Standards

Mountain Building 6.1.e

In this section: Help students understand that mountains result from plates colliding against each other. Point out that plate collisions can either fold or stretch continental crust into mountains.

- **previously taught:** crust, pp. 44, 266–269; plate movement, pp. 278–293
- **future opportunities:** Sierra Nevada, p. 344; Mount Shasta, p. 356

Teach from Visuals

To help students connect the three images, ask:

- In which part of the Never Summer Mountain Range are the mountains in the photograph located? *They appear to be the center of the range.*
- In which part of the Rocky Mountain Belt is the Never Summer Mountain Range located? *southeastern*

Address Misconceptions

IDENTIFY Ask students to name a mountain range or point one out on a map. If they indicate a large mountain belt such as the Rockies or Appalachians or an expanse of range land that includes mountains, they may hold a misconception of what a mountain range is.

CORRECT Tell students that mountain belts are made up of different mountain ranges. Have students look on a map of the Rockies or Appalachians and find the names of various mountain ranges within these belts.

REASSESS Ask students how many mountain ranges they found. Then have them give a definition of a mountain range in their own words.

Technology Resources

Visit **ClassZone.com** for background on common student misconceptions.

Mountain Ranges and Belts

A

A mountain is an area of land that rises steeply from the land around it. A single mountain is rare. Most mountains belong to ranges—long lines of mountains that were formed at about the same time and by the same processes. Ranges that are close together make up mountain belts. For example, the Rocky Mountain belt in western North America contains about 100 ranges.

1 Mountains rise high above the land around them.

2 Most mountains are in groups called mountain ranges.

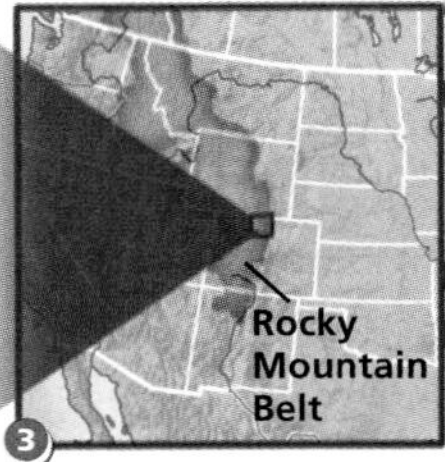

3 Closely spaced mountain ranges make up mountain belts.

B

Most of the world's major mountain belts are located along tectonic plate boundaries. But mountain belts like the Appalachians (AP-uh-LAY-chee-uhnz) in eastern North America are in the interior of plates. Mountains such as these were formed by ancient plate collisions that assembled the present-day continents.

Major Mountain Belts

Major mountain belts mark the locations of present or past plate boundaries.

Caledonian Belt
Urals
Alps
Himalayas
ATLANTIC OCEAN
PACIFIC OCEAN
North American Cordillera
ROCKY MOUNTAIN BELT
Appalachians
Tasman Belt
Andes
ATLANTIC OCEAN
PACIFIC OCEAN
INDIAN OCEAN

DIFFERENTIATE INSTRUCTION

More Reading Support

A What area of land rises steeply from the land around it? *a mountain*

B Where are most major mountain belts located? *along tectonic plate boundaries*

English Learners This section contains some phrasal verb such as *make up* and *break down*. Help English learners understand that these phrases are the verbs of the sentence. Identify the following examples in the text:

1. Ranges that are close together *make up* mountain belts. (p. 33
2. Rocks *break down* into loose pieces that can be carried by water or wind. (p. 339)

Inclusion Have students with visual impairments feel the patterns formed by mountain belts on a relief globe.

Mountains, Rocks, and Sediment

At the same time that some processes push mountains up, other processes wear them down. At Earth's surface, water and wind break rocks apart and move the pieces away. As long as mountains are pushed up faster than they wear down, they grow taller. For this reason, young mountains tend to be tall and steep. But eventually mountain-building processes slow, then end. Water and wind take over. Given enough time, all mountains become rounded hills, and then they are gone. Countless mountains have formed and worn away throughout Earth's long history.

Rocks break down into loose pieces that can be carried by water or wind. These pieces are called sediments. For example, sand on a beach is sediment. Thick layers of sediments can build up in low-lying areas, such as valleys, lakes, or the ocean. Pieces of sediments form sedimentary rock as they are pressed together or joined by natural cement.

The land becomes flatter as mountains wear down and valleys fill with sediments. If tectonic plates were to stop moving, eventually the surfaces of all the continents would be completely flat.

Mountains Wear Down

Mountains wear down as water and wind break their rocks into sediments and carry them away.

Young Mountains

Most young mountains are rugged. But even as they form, their rocks are being broken apart.

Old Mountains

Most old mountains are rounded. Lower areas around them contain thick layers of sediments.

READING VISUALS How do mountains wear away?

Real World Example

The sediment around your school is made up mostly of pieces of rock broken from larger pieces and carried by water or wind to the area.

Develop Critical Thinking

APPLY Ask students to apply what they have read on this page to explain why all the continents eventually would become completely flat if tectonic plates were to stop moving. *The processes that push mountains up would stop, but the processes that wear them down would continue.* Have students predict how long it would take for the continents to become flat. *Answers will vary, but students should recognize that the effects of such processes would take hundreds of millions of years to achieve.*

Teach from Visuals

To help students relate the diagrams of young and old mountains to the photograph, ask:

- In the bottom illustration, what has covered some of the lower peaks? *layers of sediment worn from the mountains*
- Where is the sediment shown in the photograph and how did it get there? *The mound fanning out at the base of the mountain is made of sediment. It moved down the mountain due to gravity.*

Ongoing Assessment

READING VISUALS *Answer: Water and wind break rock apart and carry the pieces away.*

IFFERENTIATE INSTRUCTION

More Reading Support

C What do young mountains look like? *tall and steep*

D Sand on a beach is an example of what? *sediment*

Below Level Ask struggling readers for a definition of *sediment.* If they are having trouble, have them read the second sentence of the second paragraph that includes that word. Then they should read the sentence before and after that sentence as well as the caption for the photograph. Explain how these clues provide a context for the word *sediment* and help explain its meaning.

Teacher Demo

Students may have a difficult time picturing a solid bending under stress. Demonstrate the ability of a candle to bend under stress, over time. Place a long, narrow candle across two piles of books so that it forms a "bridge." To accelerate the bending, hang a piece of string with several washers tied to it over the candle. Discuss other examples, such as a sagging bookshelf.

Develop Critical Thinking

IDENTIFY CAUSE AND EFFECT Ask students to identify cause-and-effect relationships in the development of the Himalayas. Provide students with the following example: cause—India moves northward; effect—oceanic lithosphere sinks under Eurasia.

EXPLORE the BIG idea

Revisit "Making Mountains" on p. 335. Have student discuss their observations.

Ongoing Assessment

Describe how the folding of rock can form mountains.

How is a crumpled rug caught behind an opening door similar to the way folded mountains form? *The opening door provides stress that pushes on the rug and folds it, just as a moving tectonic plate pushes on rock and folds it.*

CHECK YOUR READING *Answer: when stress is applied slowly and rocks are deep in the crust where temperature and pressure are high*

Mountains can form as rocks fold.

Though people usually do not think of rocks as being able to bend and fold, they can. Think of a wax candle. If you bend a candle quickly, it will break. If you leave a candle propped up at an angle, over many days it will bend. If the candle is in a warm area, it will bend more quickly. Rocks can bend when stress is applied slowly. Rocks deep in the crust are at high temperatures and pressures. They are likely to bend rather than break.

CHECK YOUR READING Under what conditions are rocks likely to bend and fold?

VOCABULARY
Remember to add *folded mountain* to your notebook, using the vocabulary strategy of your choice.

E

Remember that tectonic plates move only a few centimeters each year. Stress is applied to the edge of a continent as another plate pushes against it over a long period of time. Some of the continent's rocks break, and others fold. As folding continues, mountains are pushed up. A **folded mountain** is a mountain that forms as continental crust crumples and bends into folds.

F

Folded mountains form as an oceanic plate sinks under the edge of a continent or as continents collide. One example is the Himalaya (HIHM-uh-LAY-uh) belt, which was formed by a collision between India and Eurasia. Its formation is illustrated on page 341.

READING TIP
Eurasia is the landmass consisting of Europe and Asia.

1. **Convergent Boundary Develops** At one time an ocean separated India and Eurasia. As India moved northward, oceanic lithosphere sank in a subduction zone along the Eurasian Plate. Along the edge of Eurasia, folded mountains formed. Volcanoes also formed as magma rose from the subduction zone to the surface.
2. **Continental Collision Begins** Eventually the sea floor was completely destroyed, and India and Eurasia collided. Subduction ended. The volcanoes stopped erupting because they were no longer supplied with magma. Sea-floor material that had been added to the edge of Eurasia became part of the mountains pushed up by the collision.
3. **Collision Continues** India and Eurasia continue to push together. Their collision has formed the Himalayas, the world's tallest mountains. They grow even higher as rock is folded and pushed up for hundreds of kilometers on either side of the boundary.

Earthquakes can also be important to the upward growth of folded mountains. A great deal of rock in the Himalaya belt has been pushed up along reverse faults, which are common at convergent boundaries.

DIFFERENTIATE INSTRUCTION

More Reading Support

E How far do tectonic plates move each year? *a few centimeters*

F What kind of mountains are the Himalayas? *folded mountains*

Inclusion Have students use their fingers to guide their reading on this page. As they read each numbered paragraph, have them point to the corresponding diagram on p. 341.

Formation of Himalayas

The Himalayas are being pushed higher by an ongoing continental collision.

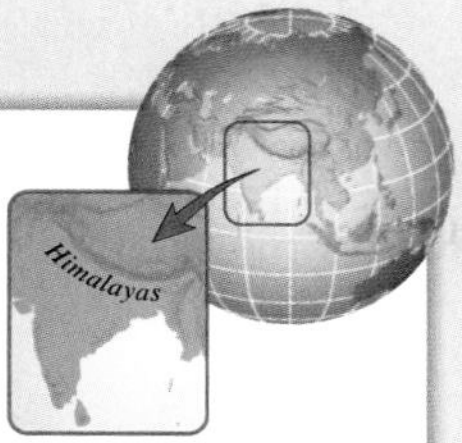

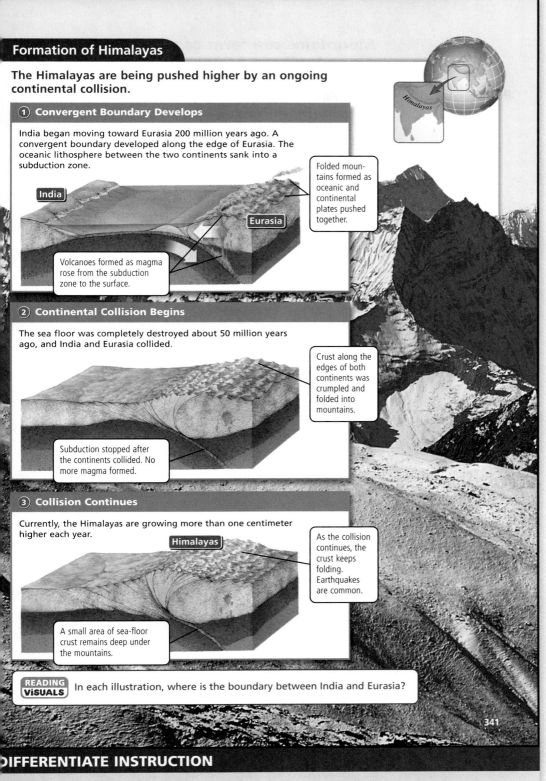

1 Convergent Boundary Develops

India began moving toward Eurasia 200 million years ago. A convergent boundary developed along the edge of Eurasia. The oceanic lithosphere between the two continents sank into a subduction zone.

Himalayas
India
Eurasia
Folded mountains formed as oceanic and continental plates pushed together.
Volcanoes formed as magma rose from the subduction zone to the surface.

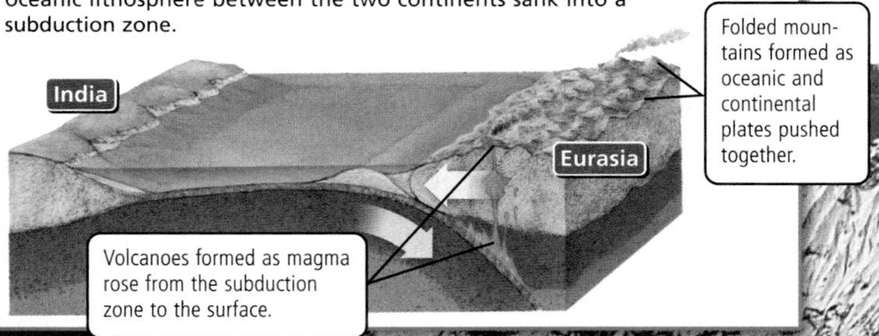

2 Continental Collision Begins

The sea floor was completely destroyed about 50 million years ago, and India and Eurasia collided.

Crust along the edges of both continents was crumpled and folded into mountains.
Subduction stopped after the continents collided. No more magma formed.

3 Collision Continues

Currently, the Himalayas are growing more than one centimeter higher each year.

Himalayas
As the collision continues, the crust keeps folding. Earthquakes are common.
A small area of sea-floor crust remains deep under the mountains.

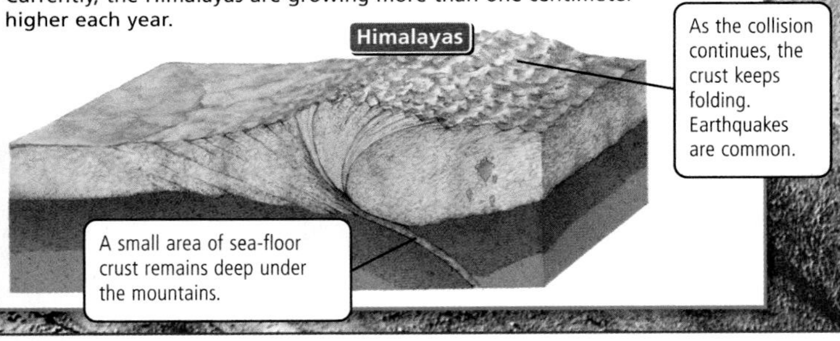

READING VISUALS In each illustration, where is the boundary between India and Eurasia?

341

DIFFERENTIATE INSTRUCTION

Advanced Challenge students to choose a different folded mountain belt and create a poster similar to the one on this page that illustrates the formation of that belt or part of it. They might choose the Appalachians or the Andes.

R Challenge and Extension, p. 150

Teach from Visuals

To help students interpret the diagrams of the formation of the Himalayas, ask:

- Where is the subduction zone in diagram 1? *on the right side where the oceanic plate is shown to be sinking beneath the continental plate*
- Why is there no magma in diagram 2? *Subduction has stopped, so crust is no longer sinking and melting to form magma.*
- What kind of crust is currently colliding under the Himalayas? *continental crust*
- Which diagram shows the most recent activity? *diagram 3*

This visual is also available as T78 in the Transparency Book.

Real World Example

While the Himalayas are, on average, growing more than 1 cm per year, individual mountains differ in their growth rate. Using the Global Positioning System to calculate elevation and movement, scientists measure the growth of Mt. Everest to be 5 to 8 mm (0.5 to 0.8 cm) per year. The Himalayas also are moving toward China. This rate is about 6 cm per year.

Ongoing Assessment

READING VISUALS

Answer: diagram 1: at the subduction zone; diagrams 2 and 3: near the edge of the mountains

INVESTIGATE Fault-Block Mountains

PURPOSE To model how fault-block mountains form

TIPS *15 min.*

- Children's blocks work well for this activity.
- You might want to demonstrate the movements of both the triangular and rectangular blocks before students try it.

WHAT DO YOU THINK? *The edges of the blocks were left sticking up like mountains when the blocks were pulled apart or pulled apart and tilted; divergent, where plates are pulling apart*

CHALLENGE *No vertical movement occurs along strike-slip faults.*

Datasheet, Fault-Block Mountains, p. 151

Technology Resources

Customize this student lab as needed or look for an alternative. Print rubrics to assess student lab reports.

Lab Generator CD-ROM

Ongoing Assessment

CHECK YOUR READING *Answer: As blocks of rock move up or down along normal faults, mountains are formed.*

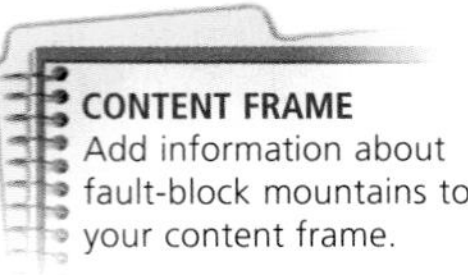

CONTENT FRAME
Add information about fault-block mountains to your content frame.

Mountains can form as rocks move along faults.

In the southwestern United States and northwestern Mexico, hundreds of mountain ranges line up in rows. The ranges and the valleys between them formed along nearly parallel normal faults. Mountains that form as blocks of rock move up or down along normal faults are called **fault-block mountains.**

How can the movement of rocks along faults lead to the formation of mountains?

Fault-block mountains form as the lithosphere is stretched and pulled apart by forces within Earth. The rocks of the crust are cool and hard. As the lithosphere begins to stretch, the crust breaks into large blocks. As stretching continues, the blocks of rock move along the faults that separate them. The illustrations on page 343 show how this process forms fault-block mountains.

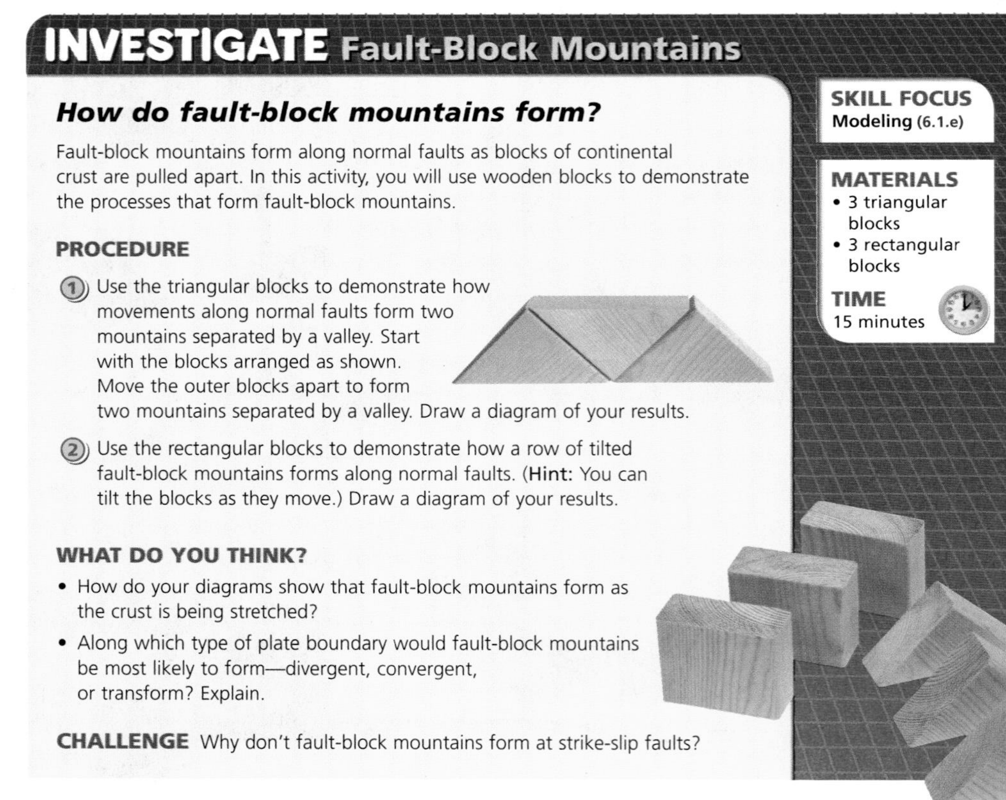

INVESTIGATE Fault-Block Mountains

How do fault-block mountains form?

Fault-block mountains form along normal faults as blocks of continental crust are pulled apart. In this activity, you will use wooden blocks to demonstrate the processes that form fault-block mountains.

SKILL FOCUS
Modeling (6.1.e)

MATERIALS
- 3 triangular blocks
- 3 rectangular blocks

TIME
15 minutes

PROCEDURE

1. Use the triangular blocks to demonstrate how movements along normal faults form two mountains separated by a valley. Start with the blocks arranged as shown. Move the outer blocks apart to form two mountains separated by a valley. Draw a diagram of your results.
2. Use the rectangular blocks to demonstrate how a row of tilted fault-block mountains forms along normal faults. (**Hint:** You can tilt the blocks as they move.) Draw a diagram of your results.

WHAT DO YOU THINK?

- How do your diagrams show that fault-block mountains form as the crust is being stretched?
- Along which type of plate boundary would fault-block mountains be most likely to form—divergent, convergent, or transform? Explain.

CHALLENGE Why don't fault-block mountains form at strike-slip faults?

DIFFERENTIATE INSTRUCTION

More Reading Support

G What do Earth's forces do to the lithosphere while a fault-block mountain is being formed? *stretch and pull it apart*

Alternative Assessment Suggest that students answer the Challenge question in "Investigate Fault-Block Mountains" by demonstrating with their blocks. *Students should demonstrate that strike-slip faults do not involve vertical movements, and therefore, do not cause mountains to form.*

1. An area of the lithosphere can arch upward. For example, it might be heated by material rising in the mantle beneath it. As the crust stretches, it breaks into many blocks separated by faults.
2. As the lithosphere is pulled apart, some blocks tilt. The edges of the blocks that tilt upward form mountains, and the edges that tilt downward form valleys. Other blocks drop down between faults, forming valleys. The edges of the blocks next to blocks that drop down are left standing high above the valleys as mountains.

Fault-block mountains form as stress repeatedly builds up in the crust and then is released during earthquakes. Even the most powerful earthquakes can move blocks of rock only a few meters up or down at one time. Fault-block mountains can be kilometers high. Millions of years and many earthquakes are needed for them to form.

CHECK YOUR READING Describe two ways that blocks of rock can move along faults and form mountains.

Fault-Block Mountains

Fault-block mountains form as the crust stretches and breaks into blocks that move along faults.

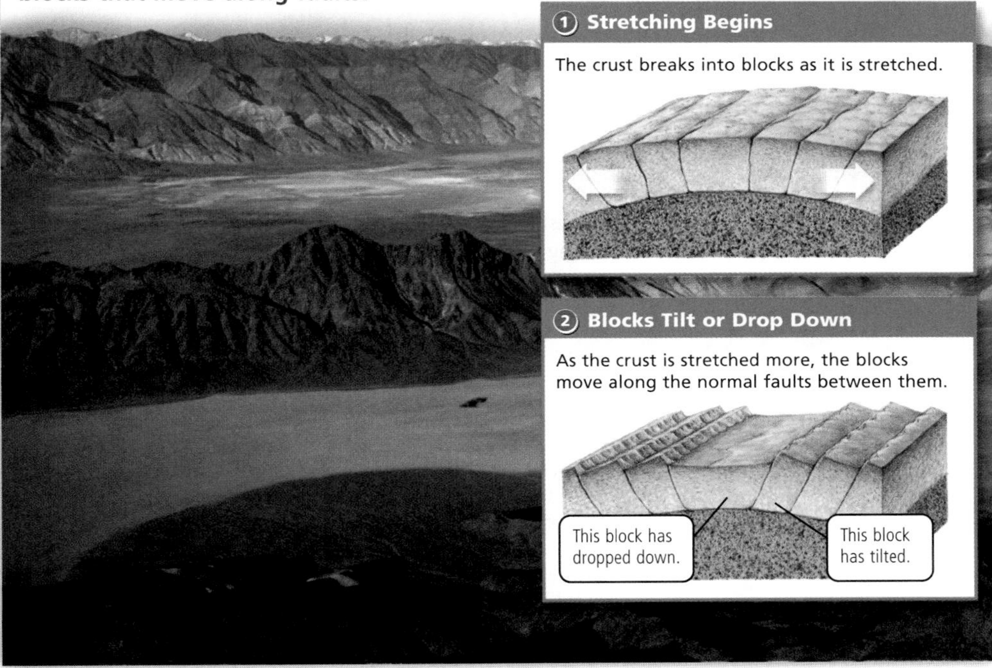

1 Stretching Begins
The crust breaks into blocks as it is stretched.
2 Blocks Tilt or Drop Down
As the crust is stretched more, the blocks move along the normal faults between them.
This block has dropped down.
This block has tilted.

Develop Critical Thinking

COMPARE Ask students to compare folded mountains and fault-block mountains. Have them explain why the Himalayas have many reverse faults, and fault-block mountains are associated with normal faults. *The Himalayas have many reverse faults because two continents are pushing together there; fault-block mountains are associated with normal faults because they form where the crust is being pulled apart.*

Teach from Visuals

To help students interpret the images of fault-block mountains, ask:

- In diagram 1, where are the future faults going to develop? *where the cracks or fractures are forming*
- Which parts of diagram 2 look similar to parts in the photograph? Which parts look different? Why? *The rows of mountains and valleys are similar. The shape of the land, or landscape, looks different because parts of the exposed land in the photograph have been worn away, and sediments have partly filled in the valleys. The diagram just shows the structure of the rock layers without much erosion.*

Ongoing Assessment

Recognize how movement along faults can form mountains.

Which solid makes up mountains? What moves along faults to create fault-block mountains? *rock; large blocks of rock*

CHECK YOUR READING *Answer: A block can drop down, which creates an elevated edge in the block next to it, or a block can tilt upward.*

DIFFERENTIATE INSTRUCTION

More Reading Support

H Which side of a block forms a valley in a fault-block mountain range? *the side that tilts downward*

Below Level Ask students why the term *fault-block* is appropriate for this kind of mountain. If students need help, break the term down into its two parts and show the role that each part plays in describing this kind of mountain.

Reinforce the BIG idea

Have students relate the section to the Big Idea.

 Reinforcing Key Concepts, p. 152

10.1 ASSESS & RETEACH

Assess

 Section 10.1 Quiz, p. 215

Reteach

Point out that a summary, such as the one in the second paragraph, can be done for any kind of passage. Even a single paragraph can be summarized, usually in one sentence. After discussing what a summary is, have students summarize the main ideas, processes, and vocabulary terms that follow each blue heading:

- Most mountains form along plate boundaries.
- Mountains can form as rocks fold.
- Mountains can form as rocks move along faults.

If students need help getting started, ask them to identify or paraphrase a topic sentence in each paragraph.

Technology Resources

Have students visit **ClassZone.com** for reteaching of Key Concepts.

 CONTENT REVIEW

 CONTENT REVIEW CD-ROM

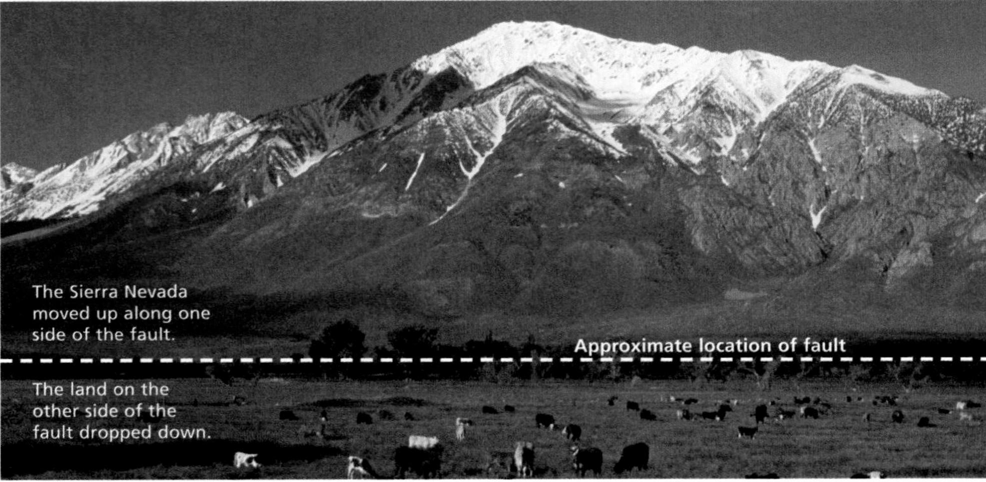
The Sierra Nevada moved up along one side of the fault.
Approximate location of fault
The land on the other side of the fault dropped down.

The Sierra Nevada in California is a fault-block mountain range. The range moved up along a normal fault along its eastern edge. The block on the other side of the fault dropped down. This combination of upward and downward movement formed the steep eastern side of the Sierra Nevada. The western side of the range tilts down gently toward California's Central Valley.

In summary, both folded mountains and fault-block mountains form over millions of years. Folded mountains are pushed up by slow, continual stress that causes rock to bend gradually. Fault-block mountains form, earthquake by earthquake, as stress built up in the crust is released by the movement of rock. Folded mountains form where continental crust is being compressed. Fault-block mountains form where it is being stretched.

10.1 Review

KEY CONCEPTS

1. How is the formation of mountain belts related to tectonic plate boundaries? (6.1.f)
2. How do folded mountains form? (6.1.e)
3. How do fault-block mountains form? (6.1.e)

CRITICAL THINKING

4. **Analyze** The Ural Mountain belt is no longer along the edge of a tectonic plate. Would you expect the Urals to be tall and steep or low and rounded? Why?
5. **Synthesize** How could it be possible for a mountain range to be continually pushed up but not get any higher?

CHALLENGE

6. **Analyze** This graph shows how the heights of two mountains changed as they formed. Which line shows the formation of a folded mountain? a fault-block mountain? Explain.

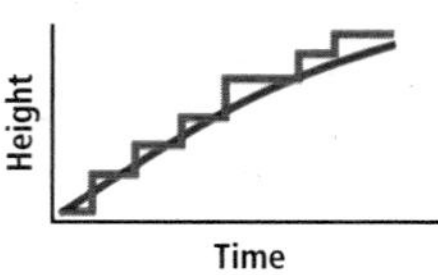
Height
Time

ANSWERS

1. Mountain belts form along convergent plate boundaries.

2. as rocks fold where the crust is being pushed together

3. as blocks of rocks move up or down along normal faults where the crust is being stretched

4. low and rounded; because they are not near a modern plate boundary, they must have formed long ago, and undergone weathering and erosion

5. the rate of growth is equal to the rate of erosion

6. The curved line shows the formation of a folded mountain that was continually pushed up. The stepped line shows the formation of a fault-block mountain that was pushed up by a lot of individual earthquakes.

MATH in SCIENCE

MATH TUTORIAL
CLASSZONE.COM
Click on Math Tutorial for more help finding the mean.

Math 6.SD.1.1, 6.SD.1.4
Science 6.1.e

SKILL: CALCULATING THE MEAN OF A DATA SET

Comparing Mountain Heights

How do the tallest mountains in the United States compare with the tallest mountains in the world? The table shows the heights of the five tallest mountains in the world. All five are in Asia.

Mountain	Height (meters)
Everest	8850
K2	8611
Kanchenjunga	8586
Lhotse	8516
Makalu	8463

To describe data, you can find their average, or mean. The **mean** of a data set is the sum of the values divided by the number of values.

Example

To find the mean height of the five tallest mountains in the world, first add the heights.

$$\begin{array}{r} 8,850 \\ 8,611 \\ 8,586 \\ 8,516 \\ +8,463 \\ \hline 43,026 \end{array}$$

Then divide by 5, the number of mountains.

$$\frac{43,026}{5} = 8605.2$$

Round your result to a whole number.

ANSWER The mean height of the five tallest mountains is 8605 meters.

Answer the following questions.

1. The table to the left shows the heights of the five tallest mountains in the United States. All five are in Alaska. Find the mean of the data.
2. What is the difference between the mean height of the three tallest mountains in the world and the mean height of the three tallest mountains in the United States?
3. Suppose Mount Everest were in the United States. What would the mean of the three tallest mountains in the United States then be?

CHALLENGE **The mean height of all the land in the United States is 763 meters. Does knowing the mean height help you describe the shape of the land in the United States? Explain why or why not.**

Mountain	Height (meters)
McKinley	6194
St. Elias	5489
Foraker	5304
Bona	5029
Blackburn	4996

Mount McKinley, Alaska, is the tallest mountain in North America.

ANSWERS

1. 6194 + 5489 + 5304 + 5029 + 4996 = 27,012
27,012/5 = 5402.4; round to 5402 m

2. world: 8850 + 8611 + 8586 = 26,047; 26,047/3 = 8682
U.S.: 6194 + 5489 + 5304=16,987; 1,698,7/3 = 5662
8682 − 5662 = 3020 m

3. 8850 + 6194 + 5489 = 20,533; 20,533/3 = 6844 m

CHALLENGE *No, you cannot tell the shape of the land. All the land could be at the same height of 763 m.*

MATH IN SCIENCE

Math Skills Practice for Science

Set Learning Goal

To calculate the mean of a data set to compare mountain heights

Math Standards

6.SD.1.1 Compute the range, mean, median, and mode of data sets.

6.SD.1.4 Know why a specific measure of central tendency (mean, median, mode) provides the most useful information in a given context.

Present the Science

Mount Everest's height of 8850 meters was determined by using the Global Positioning System (GPS). This system uses satellites to calculate information about a GPS receiver's exact location, including altitude. In 1999 an expedition placed a receiver on Everest's summit to track Everest's changing height.

Develop Number Sense

As you work through the example with students, point out that the average of this data set (8605 m) is not among the values for the set. Explain that a mean, or average, reduces a data set to one value that represents all values in the set.

DIFFERENTIATION TIP Below-level students may benefit from working through a simpler data set than the one given.

INCLUSION For visual learners, draw triangular mountains to scale on the board in the order given in the table. Ask a volunteer to draw another mountain that would best represent the mean height. The height should be between the lowest and tallest heights.

Close

Ask students to give an example of a height that would lower the mean if added to the data set for the world's five tallest mountains. *any number below the mean of 8605*

- Math Support, p. 180
- Math Practice, p. 181

Technology Resources

Students can visit **ClassZone.com** for more help finding the mean.

MATH TUTORIAL

10.2 FOCUS

Set Learning Goals

Students will

- Identify where most volcanoes are located.
- Explain how volcanoes erupt.
- Recognize different types of volcanoes.

3-Minute Warm-Up

Display Transparency 76 or copy this exercise on the board:

Match each definition with the correct term.

Definitions

1. motion that transfers heat within a material *d*
2. the layer formed by Earth's crust and the very top of the mantle *b*
3. underwater mountain ranges found where the ocean floor is spreading *a*

Terms

a. mid-ocean ridges
b. lithosphere
c. plate tectonics
d. convection current

3-Minute Warm-Up, p. T76

10.2 MOTIVATE

EXPLORE Eruptions

PURPOSE To model how a buildup of pressure due to the formation and expansion of gas bubbles can lead to an eruption

TIP *10 min.* Advise students to wear safety goggles. Have them do the activity with a very small piece of antacid tablet (1/8 of a tablet). They can repeat it while using slightly larger pieces but should not use pieces larger than 1/4 tablet because the lid might pop off too quickly.

WHAT DO YOU THINK? *The water bubbled, and the lid popped off. Pressure from the gas of the bubbles built up inside the canister and pushed the lid off. Pressure from gases can build up inside a volcano until it erupts.*

KEY CONCEPT

10.2 Volcanoes form as molten rock erupts.

CALIFORNIA Content Standards

6.1.b Students know Earth is composed of several layers: a cold, brittle lithosphere; a hot, convecting mantle; and a dense, metallic core.

6.1.d Students know that earthquakes are sudden motions along breaks in the crust called faults and that volcanoes and fissures are locations where magma reaches the surface.

6.1.e Students know major geologic events, such as earthquakes, volcanic eruptions, and mountain building, result from plate motions.

BEFORE, you learned

- Magma is molten rock inside Earth
- Magma forms as a plate sinking in a subduction zone starts to melt
- Volcanoes can form over hot spots far from plate boundaries

NOW, you will learn

- Where most volcanoes are located
- How volcanoes erupt
- What types of volcanoes there are

VOCABULARY

volcano p. 346
lava p. 347
pyroclastic flow p. 348

EXPLORE Eruptions (6.1.d)

What happens when a volcano erupts?

PROCEDURE

1. Add water to the film canister until it is three-fourths full.
2. Drop the antacid tablet in the water and put the lid on the canister. Observe what happens.

WHAT DO YOU THINK?

- What happened to the water and to the canister lid?
- What caused the changes you observed?
- How might the events you observed be similar to the eruption of a volcano?

MATERIALS

- empty film canister
- effervescent antacid tablet
- water

VOCABULARY
Remember to add *volcano* to your notebook, using the vocabulary strategy of your choice.

Volcanoes erupt many types of material.

Earth's thin outer layer is made of cool rock, but most of Earth is made of extremely hot rock and molten metal. Some of the heat inside Earth escapes to the surface through volcanoes. A **volcano** is an opening in Earth's crust through which molten rock, rock fragments, and hot gases erupt. A mountain built up from erupted material is also called a volcano.

A volcano may erupt violently or gently. A violent eruption can cause tremendous destruction even if not much molten rock reaches the surface. For example, a volcano might throw out huge amounts of rock fragments that start fires where they land. Or the fragments might fall in thick layers on roofs, causing them to collapse. A volcano can erupt gently yet pour out rivers of molten rock that flow long distances. The violence of an eruption depends mainly on the type of magma feeding the volcano.

RESOURCES FOR DIFFERENTIATED INSTRUCTION

Below Level

UNIT RESOURCE BOOK

- Reading Study Guide A, pp. 155–156
- Decoding Support, p. 179

AUDIO CDS

Advanced

UNIT RESOURCE BOOK

- Challenge and Extension, p. 161
- Challenge Reading, pp. 175–176

English Learners

UNIT RESOURCE BOOK

Spanish Reading Study Guide, pp. 159–160

AUDIO CDS

- Audio Readings in Spanish
- Audio Readings (English)

Additional INVESTIGATION, Modeling Magma Movement, A, B, & C, pp. 191–199; Teacher Instructions, pp. 202–203

Magma

A major portion of all magma is silica, which is a compound of silicon and oxygen. Magma also contains gases, which expand as the magma rises. Magma that is high in silica resists flowing, so expanding gases are trapped in it. Pressure builds up until the gases blast out in a violent, dangerous explosion. Magma that has less silica flows easily, so gas bubbles move up through it and escape fairly gently. An eruption of silica-poor magma can throw lava high into the air, but visitors can usually watch safely nearby.

Magma rises toward Earth's surface as long as it is less dense than the surrounding rock. Once magma stops rising, it can collect in areas called magma chambers. Sometimes magma remains in a chamber until it cools, forming igneous rock. At other times, it erupts. Volcanic eruptions can occur when a chamber is not large enough to hold additional magma that pushes in. When magma erupts, it is called lava. **Lava** is magma that has reached Earth's surface.

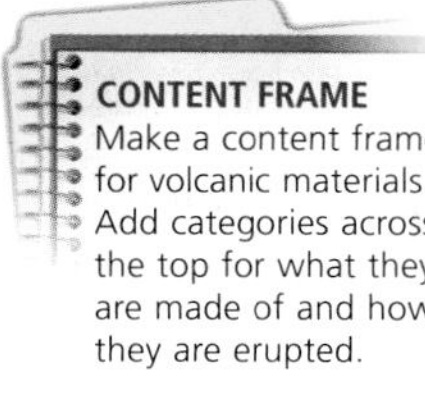

CONTENT FRAME Make a content frame for volcanic materials. Add categories across the top for what they are made of and how they are erupted.

Structure of a Volcano

Magma collects in a magma chamber before erupting through a volcano.

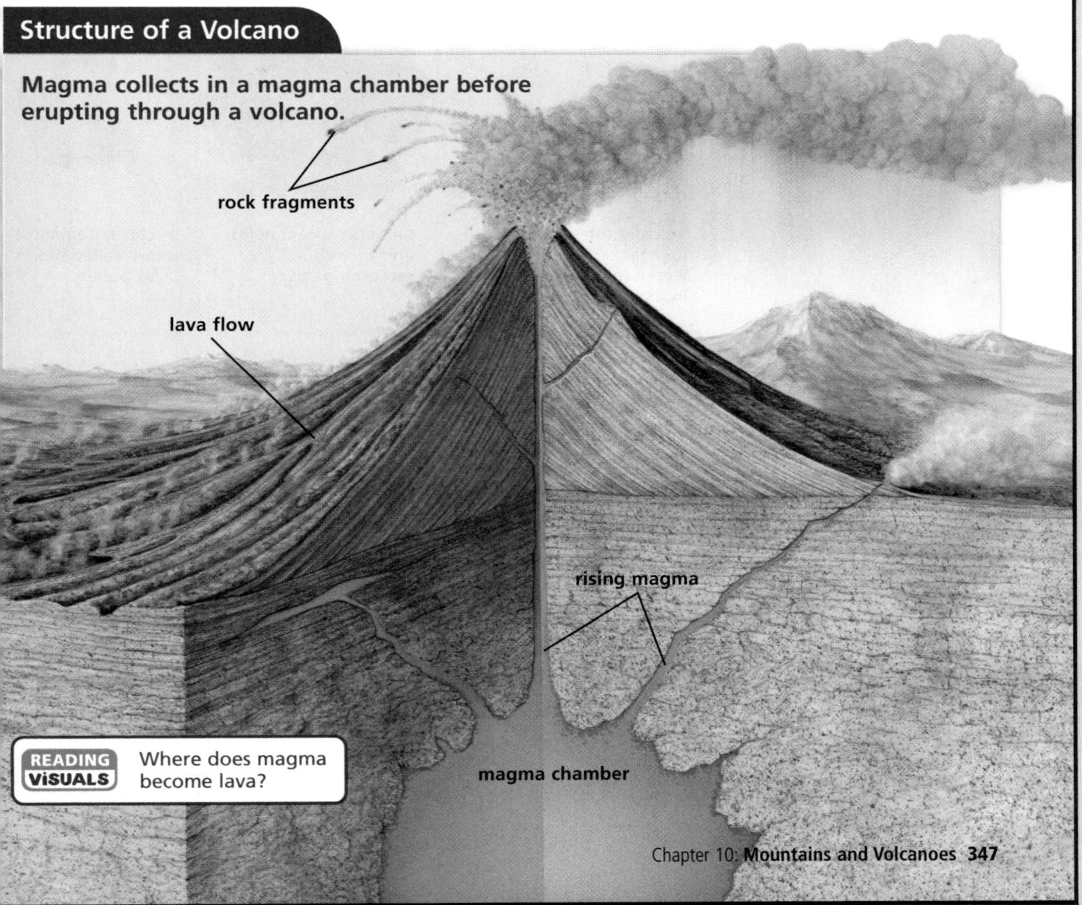

READING VISUALS Where does magma become lava?

DIFFERENTIATE INSTRUCTION

More Reading Support

A Which flows more easily: magma with a lot of silica or magma with a small amount of silica? *small amount*

Additional Investigation

To reinforce Section 10.2 learning goals, use the following full-period investigation:

Additional INVESTIGATION, Modeling Magma Movement, A, B, & C, pp. 191–199, 202–203

English Learners

English learners may not understand that bulleted text can be read as multiple endings to the same sentence. For example, on p. 348, "The fragments form as" is the beginning of a sentence. The clause after each bullet finishes the idea and completes the sentence.

10.2 INSTRUCT

Teach the Standards

Volcanic Eruptions 6.1.d

In this section: Help students understand that during an eruption, magma can explode or pour down the volcano's side. Point out that eruptions release volcanic gases and rock fragments.

- **previously taught:** plate tectonics, pp. 265–293; earthquakes, pp. 301–325
- **future opportunities:** effects of volcanic activity, pp. 356–362

Explore the BIG idea

Revisit "Internet Activity: Volcanoes" on p. 335. Have students discuss their observations.

Address Misconceptions

IDENTIFY Ask students where they think the magma in the diagram comes from. If they say from Earth's core or the center of Earth, they may have misconceptions about the origins of magma.

CORRECT Tell students that magma forms in the lower crust and upper mantle. Minerals can melt in these regions if temperature and pressure conditions are favorable.

REASSESS Draw a cross-sectional diagram of Earth's crust, mantle, and core. Ask students to place an *x* where magma originates.

Technology Resources

Visit **ClassZone.com** for background on common student misconceptions.

MISCONCEPTION DATABASE

Teach Difficult Concepts

Some students may be confused by the names of some of the materials that erupt from a volcano. For example, volcanic ash does not come from the burning of rock, even though the word *ash* typically refers to the remains of burnt material. Explain that volcanic ash refers only to the size of rock fragments.

Ongoing Assessment

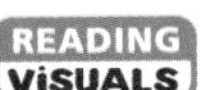

READING VISUALS *Answer: once it reaches the surface*

Teacher Demo

Students may have a difficult time understanding that magma rises only as long as it is less dense than the rock around it. When magma reaches an area of similar density, it stops rising. Demonstrate this concept with a cork, a glass marble, and vegetable oil. Show students the materials and ask them to predict the order of their densities. Place the marble and cork in a plastic container and fill it with vegetable oil. The marble will stay on the bottom, but the cork will rise to the top. Ask students what this shows about the order of their densities. *The most dense item is the marble, then the oil, then the cork.*

Teach from Visuals

To help students interpret the photographs of ash, cinders, and block, ask:

- What do these materials have in common? *They all were erupted from a volcano.*
- Which material has holes and tunnels left by escaping gases? *cinders*

Real World Example

The awesome power and danger of a pyroclastic flow was seen in the 1902 eruption of Mount Pelée on the Caribbean island of Martinique. On the morning of May 8, the volcano erupted, sending a pyroclastic flow of hot ash and gas plunging down the mountain. In one minute the flow reached the town of St. Pierre at the base of the mountain. The hot cloud burned everything in its path, and only two of the town's 29,000 inhabitants survived.

Ongoing Assessment

Explain how volcanoes erupt.

Name three types of materials that erupt from volcanoes. *molten rock, rock fragments, gases*

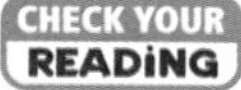

Answer: They are very hot and travel very fast.

Watch clips of erupted volcanic material.

Rock Fragments

A great deal of material erupts from volcanoes as rock fragments. The fragments form as

- escaping gas bubbles pop, tearing magma apart
- larger pieces of lava are thrown into the air, cooling and hardening during their flight
- rocks of all sizes rip loose from volcanoes' walls during eruptions

B Tiny rock fragments form volcanic ash. Ash consists of particles ranging from the size of dust to about the size of rice grains. Volcanic cinders are somewhat larger. The largest fragments are volcanic bombs and blocks. C Bombs are molten when they are thrown out and often have streamlined shapes. Blocks can be the size of houses and erupt as solid pieces of rock. Large rock fragments fall quickly, but ash can be carried long distances by winds—even all the way around Earth.

Volcanic ash is made up of rock fragments less than 2 millimeters in diameter.

Cinders contain holes and tunnels left by escaping gases.

Large fragments are called blocks or bombs.

Volcanic Gases

What looks like smoke rising from a volcano is actually a mixture of ash and gases. The main gases in magma are water vapor and carbon dioxide. Some volcanic gases combine with water in the air to form acids. You will read about these in the next section.

READING TIP

The prefix *pyro-* means "heat," and *clastic* means "made up of rock fragments."

During an eruption, volcanic gases can mix with rock fragments and stay near the ground. The mixture forms a **pyroclastic flow** (PY-roh-KLAS-tihk), which is a dense cloud of superhot gases and rock fragments that races downhill. Such a flow can be as hot as 800°C (1500°F). It can travel faster than 160 kilometers per hour (100 mi/h). Pyroclastic flows are the most dangerous type of volcanic eruption.

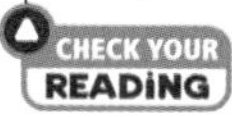

What are two reasons why pyroclastic flows are dangerous?

348 Unit 3: **The Changing Earth**

DIFFERENTIATE INSTRUCTION

More Reading Support

B What are the smallest solid particles erupted from a volcano? *ash*

C Which rock fragments can be the size of a house? *blocks*

Inclusion To help students better understand the differences between rock fragments, obtain samples of volcanic ash, cinders, and blocks from a science supply company. Have students describe the texture of each. Then read the captions to the visual on this page, and ask students to identify each sample.

Most volcanoes form along plate boundaries.

Volcanoes are common along tectonic plate boundaries where oceanic plates sink beneath other plates. As a plate sinks deep into a subduction zone, it heats and begins to melt, forming magma. If the magma reaches the surface, it can build tall volcanic mountains.

Volcanoes are also common along tectonic boundaries where plates pull apart. This allows magma to rise from the mantle. Some of these volcanoes are in Africa's Great Rift Valley. However, much of Earth's volcanic activity takes place underwater. Magma erupts along spreading centers in the ocean and cools to form new lithosphere.

Less often, a volcano forms over a hot spot far from a plate boundary. Heat carried by material rising from deep in the mantle melts some of the rock in the lithosphere above it. Eruptions over a hot spot built the Hawaiian Islands.

More than 400 volcanoes are along subduction zones in the Pacific Ocean. This is about 80 percent of all active volcanoes above sea level. An active volcano is one that is erupting or has erupted in recorded history. The volcanoes around the Pacific Ocean form a belt called the Ring of Fire. Some of these volcanoes are in the western United States.

Ring of Fire

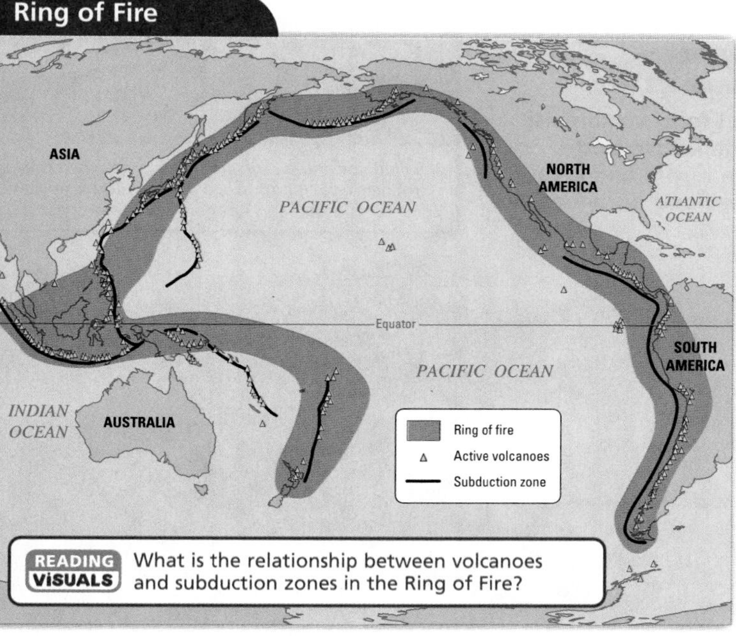

READING VISUALS What is the relationship between volcanoes and subduction zones in the Ring of Fire?

Teach from Visuals

To help students interpret the map, ask:

- What kind of plate boundary occurs most often along the edge of the Pacific Ocean? *convergent boundary*
- What major geologic process is occurring at the trenches? *subduction of an oceanic plate beneath another plate*
- How do you think the islands stretching from the North American mainland in the north Pacific Ocean formed? *from the buildup of underwater volcanoes*
- What does the chain of volcanoes seem to form a ring around? *the Pacific Ocean*

Ongoing Assessment

Identify where most volcanoes are located.

Is a volcanic eruption possible where you live? Why or why not? *If your community is far from a plate boundary or a hot spot, students should recognize that active volcanoes do not exist there.*

READING VISUALS *Answer: The volcanoes are caused by magma that forms because an oceanic plate is sinking beneath another plate. Therefore, volcanoes are near subduction zones.*

IFFERENTIATE INSTRUCTION

More Reading Support

D What is an active volcano? *one that is erupting or has erupted in recorded history*

Advanced Have students use the Internet or other sources to compile a list of at least five recent volcanic eruptions. Have them locate these eruptions on a world map and compare the locations to a map of plate boundaries.

R Challenge and Extension, p. 161

Inclusion Have students with visual impairments feel the raised surfaces on a relief globe to try and find the Ring of Fire. Tell them it is shaped more like a horseshoe than a ring.

Teach from Visuals

To help students summarize the three main types of volcanoes and the processes that form them, tell students that the landscape on pp. 350–351 does not represent a real area. Ask:

- In what way does a shield volcano look like a shield? *It looks like a shield that is lying face-up.*
- Which volcano is not shown near a plate boundary? *the shield volcano*
- Which colors represent magma? *red and yellow*

Develop Critical Thinking

INFER Have students infer answers to the following questions:

- How did the mountains shown to the left of the shield volcano form? *These are also probably volcanoes, built up as the plate moved over a hot spot.*
- Why does some of the magma in the shield volcano take different paths to the surface? *As the magma moves up the central path, it might be forced into cracks or other weakened areas of the rock layers.*

CONTENT FRAME Make a content frame for types of volcanoes. Add categories for shape, size, makeup, and examples.

Volcanoes can have many shapes and sizes.

Mount St. Helens is a cone-shaped volcano in Washington. Its eruption in 1980 killed 57 people. One side of the volcano exploded, blasting out a mixture of hot rock, ash, and gases that destroyed trees tens of kilometers away. Since 1980, this volcano has had many smaller eruptions.

E Volcanoes can have many shapes, including steep cones and nearly flat land. Most volcanoes erupt from openings in bowl-shaped pits called craters. Some volcanoes erupt from long cracks in the ground. The type of magma feeding a volcano determines its shape.

F ① **Shield Volcano** A shield volcano is shaped like a broad, flat dome. It is built up by many eruptions of lava that is low in silica and therefore flows easily and spreads out in thin layers. The largest volcano on Earth, Mauna Loa (MOW-nuh LOH-uh), is a shield volcano. It makes up much of the island of Hawaii. The total height of this volcano is about 17 kilometers (10.5 mi), but only about 4 kilometers (2.5 mi) are above sea level. At the top of Mauna Loa is a crater that is 5 kilometers (3 mi) across at its widest point. Mauna Loa is one of Earth's most active volcanoes.

② **Cinder Cone** A cinder cone is a steep hill formed by the eruption of cinders and other rock fragments that pile up around a crater.

RESOURCE CENTER CLASSZONE.COM

Learn more about historic and current volcanic eruptions.

Three Types of Volcanoes

Two types of material form volcanoes: rock fragments that fall close to the openings they erupted from and lava flows that have cooled and hardened.

① Shield Volcano

A shield volcano is built up of many thin layers of hardened lava. Rangitoto, a shield volcano in New Zealand, is broad and has gently sloping sides.

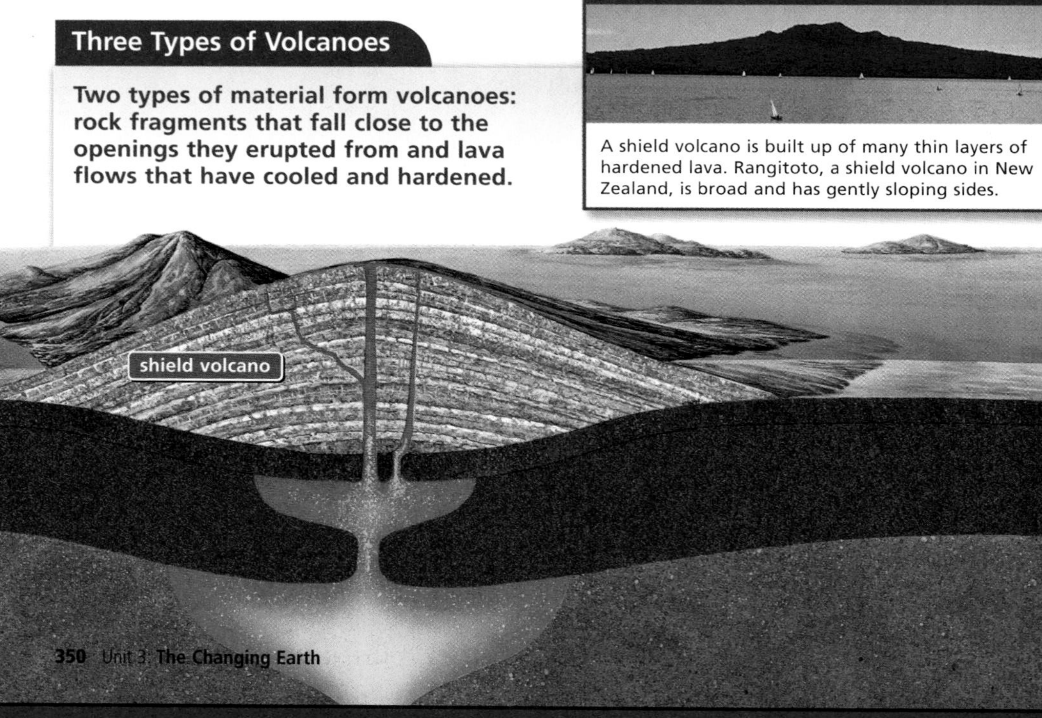

350 Unit 3: The Changing Earth

DIFFERENTIATE INSTRUCTION

More Reading Support

E What determines the shape of a volcano? *the type of magma*

F What is the silica content of lava that builds shield volcanoes? *low*

Advanced Have students research the 1980 eruption of Mount St. Helens and develop a presentation. Presentations should give background on the geology of the area, the sequence of events that led to the 1980 eruption, and the effects of the eruption.

Cinders form as gas-rich magma erupts. Escaping gases throw small chunks of lava into the air, where they harden before landing. Cinder cones are tens to hundreds of meters tall. Many of them form on the sides of other types of volcanoes.

3 Composite Volcano A composite volcano is a cone-shaped volcano built up of layers of lava and layers of rock fragments. Its magma is high in silica, and therefore is pasty. A composite volcano is steep near the top and flattens out toward the bottom. Hardened lava flows add strength to the structure of a composite volcano. As a result, it can grow much larger than a cinder cone.

READING TIP
The word *composite* comes from a Latin word meaning "put together." Something that is composite is made of distinct parts.

Composite volcanoes have violent eruptions for two reasons. First, expanding gases trapped in rising magma tend to cause explosions. Second, hardened lava from earlier eruptions often plugs openings in these volcanoes. This rock must be blown out of the way before any more magma can escape. Mount St. Helens is a composite volcano. Although its 1980 eruption was devastating, many composite volcanoes have exploded with much greater power.

CHECK YOUR READING List the three main types of volcanoes. What questions do you have about how they form?

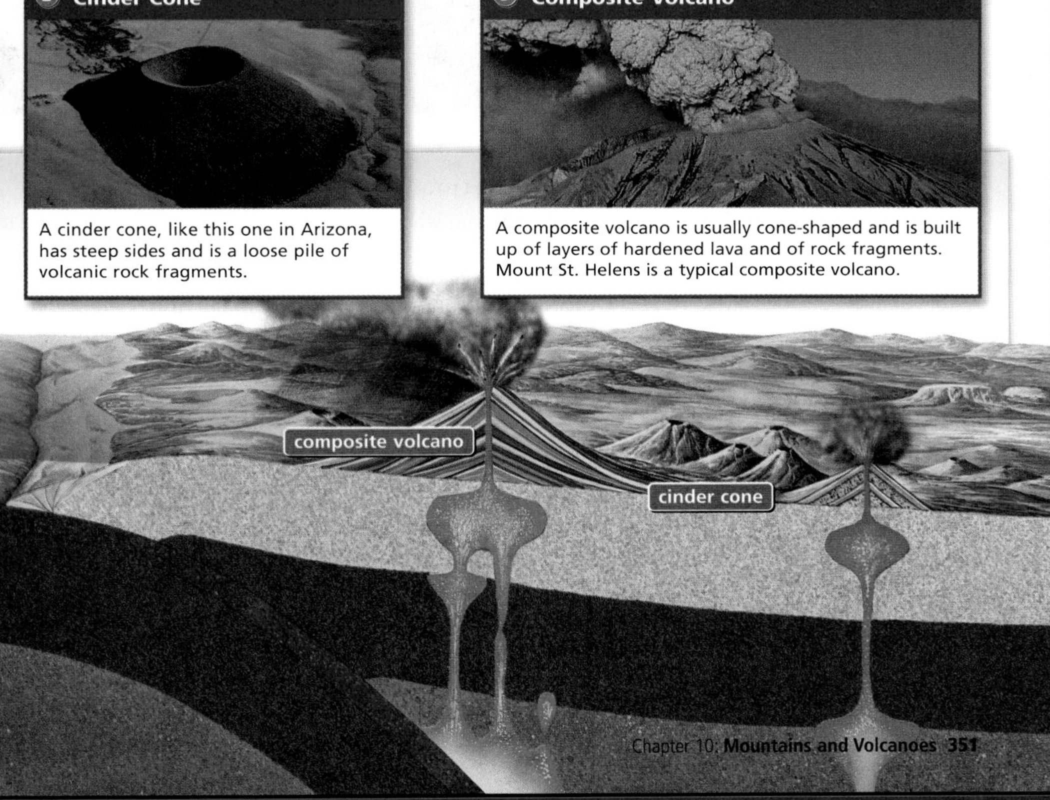

A cinder cone, like this one in Arizona, has steep sides and is a loose pile of volcanic rock fragments.

A composite volcano is usually cone-shaped and is built up of layers of hardened lava and of rock fragments. Mount St. Helens is a typical composite volcano.

Teach from Visuals

To continue helping students interpret the visuals of three volcano types, ask:

- Which underwater feature is shown just off the coast? *trench*
- Which tectonic phenomenon is happening at this feature? *A subduction zone is forming.*
- What is happening at the labeled composite volcano? *Gas, ash, and rock are erupting from the opening; magma is rising from under it.*
- Why are distinct layers shown in the composite volcano? *because it is built of layers of lava and rock fragments*

Develop Critical Thinking

INFER Ask students to infer how the drawing on p. 351 would look if it extended several inches off the bottom of the page. You might want to make a simple reproduction of this drawing on the board or photocopy it at the top half of a piece of paper. Then let students draw how they think it would look. *The edge of the sinking oceanic plate would eventually break up and be incorporated into the mantle as it completely melts.*

Ongoing Assessment

Recognize different types of volcanoes.

What volcano type does not contain layers of hardened lava flows? *cinder cone*

CHECK YOUR READING *Answer: shield, cinder cone, composite; Questions will vary.*

DIFFERENTIATE INSTRUCTION

More Reading Support

G What plugs volcano openings? *hardened lava from earlier eruptions*

Below Level Have students make silhouettes of the three types of volcanoes out of dark construction paper, label them, and place them on a poster. Be sure they make the cinder cone smaller than the composite volcano, even though their shapes are similar. Encourage students to display their completed posters.

Have students who are interested in learning more about how scientists study volcanoes read the following article:

 Challenge Reading, pp. 175–176

Teach from Visuals

To help students interpret the visuals about Crater Lake, ask:

- From what type of volcano did Crater Lake form? *composite*
- Why did the volcano collapse? *After the eruption, there wasn't enough material left in the magma chamber to support the rock above it.*
- Why is the caldera filled with water? *It filled with rain and melting snow.*
- Why is there an island in the caldera? *It is a small volcano built from further eruptions over the years.*

Social Studies Connection

In A.D. 79, Mount Vesuvius, on the southwest coast of Italy, erupted violently. Thousands of people perished in the nearby towns of Pompeii and Herculaneum. They were asphyxiated from the gases or suffocated from the ash and mud that completely buried these towns.

The towns and their inhabitants were forgotten until the mid-18th century when the excavation of Pompeii began. Since then, excavations have given archaeologists unprecedented opportunities to study daily life during the Roman Empire. Plaster casts have been made from many of the molds of victims' bodies preserved in the ash. The casts revealed information about what these individuals were doing at that fateful moment in history. The excavations have also shown that Pompeii's layout was in the form of an oval and that there were theaters and shops and public baths.

Formation of Crater Lake

Crater Lake fills the caldera of a composite volcano.

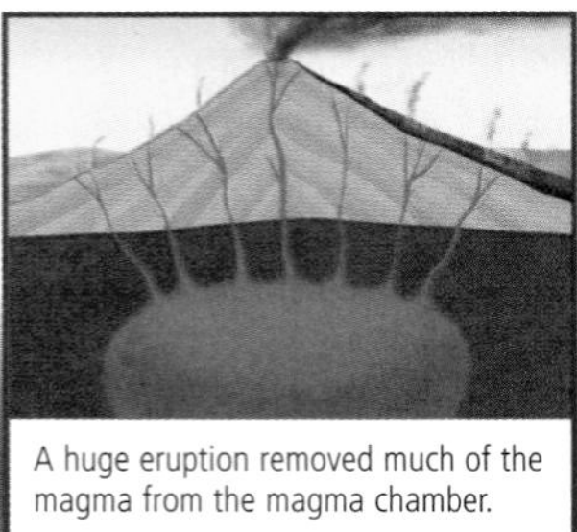

A huge eruption removed much of the magma from the magma chamber.

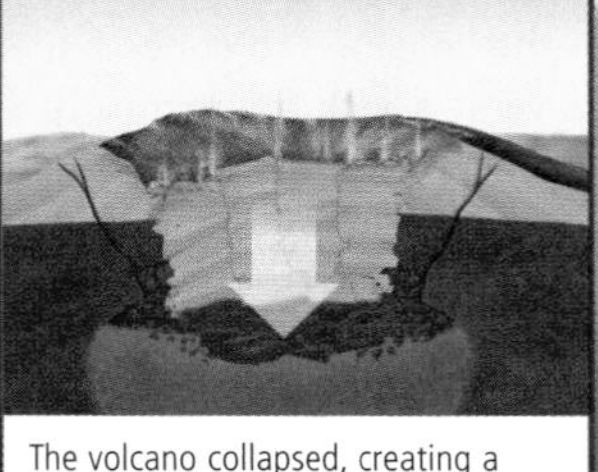

The volcano collapsed, creating a caldera 8 kilometers in diameter and 1.6 kilometers deep.

New eruptions built a small cone in the caldera. The caldera filled with water from rain and snow.

H

Both shield volcanoes and composite volcanoes can form features called calderas (kal-DAIR-uhz). A caldera is a huge crater formed by the collapse of a volcano when magma rapidly erupts from underneath it. The crater at the top of Mauna Loa in Hawaii is a caldera. Crater Lake in Oregon fills a caldera formed by a composite volcano about 7700 years ago. A violent eruption emptied much of its magma chamber, and the top of the volcano collapsed into it. The caldera now holds the deepest lake in the United States.

Scientists monitor volcanoes.

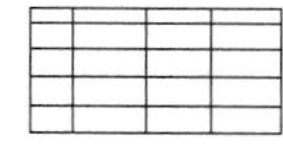

CONTENT FRAME
Make a content frame for types of data used to predict eruptions. Include categories for current activity and history.

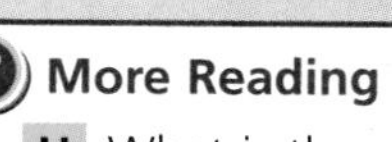

Mount Pinatubo (PIHN-uh-TOO-boh) in the Philippines erupted in 1991. Before that time, most people living in the area did not realize that it was a composite volcano. It had not erupted in about 500 years, and erosion had changed its shape. Fortunately, scientists in the Philippines knew that the volcano was becoming active months before it exploded. They were able to warn the government and ask people to leave the area. Their efforts probably saved tens of thousands of lives.

DIFFERENTIATE INSTRUCTION

More Reading Support

H What is the name of the huge crater formed when a volcano collapses into a partly emptied magma chamber? *caldera*

Alternative Assessment Ask students to design a model of a volcano that forms a caldera by using a balloon, a square box (that a blownup balloon will fit in), and wooden craft sticks. *Students can blow up the balloon, tie it, put it upside down in the box, and arrange craft sticks in a bridge between the sides of the box, resting on top of the balloon. If a small hole is made at the top of the "volcano" (near the tied opening of the balloon), air will slowly escape, and without the support of the balloon, the craft sticks will sink or cave in.*

As the 1991 eruption of Mount Pinatubo shows, volcanoes can go hundreds of years between eruptions. Before Pinatubo's eruption, scientists noticed warning signs. The signs included many small earthquakes followed by explosions of steam near the volcano's top. Researchers brought in equipment to monitor the volcano's activity. Although they could not stop the eruption, they were able to tell when people should leave.

Scientists monitor, or keep an eye on, volcanoes around the world for signs of eruptions. Earthquake activity and changes in the tilt of the ground are signs that magma is moving underneath a volcano. Scientists monitor the temperatures at openings, springs, and lakes on volcanoes. They also note the amounts and types of gases given off by the volcanoes. Rising temperatures and changes in volcanic gases can indicate that fresh magma has moved into a shallow magma chamber.

Scientists study the ages and types of volcanic rocks around a volcano to understand the volcano's history. They can learn how much time has passed between eruptions and how violent the eruptions have been. This information gives clues about possible future eruptions.

The robot Dante II is about to enter the crater of Mt. Spurr, Alaska, where it will collect video data as well as water and gas samples.

Even with close monitoring, most property damage from volcanic eruptions cannot be prevented. But warning people to move away from a volcano that is about to erupt can save lives. Many of the active volcanoes that are closely monitored are located near major cities. One is Mount Rainier (ruh-NEER), which is near Seattle, Washington. Another is Mount Vesuvius (vih-SOO-vee-uhs), which is near Naples, Italy.

CHECK YOUR READING What is the purpose of monitoring volcanoes?

10.2 Review

KEY CONCEPTS

1. Where are most volcanoes located, and why are they located there? (6.1.e)
2. How does the type of material that erupts from a volcano determine the shape of the volcano? (6.1.d)
3. What conditions do scientists examine when they study volcanoes? (6.1.d)

CRITICAL THINKING

4. **Compare and Contrast** How do the three main types of volcanoes differ?
5. **Infer** Volcanic ash can be deposited in areas many kilometers away from the volcano that produced it. What are two ways in which the ash can reach these areas?

CHALLENGE

6. **Analyze** Draw diagrams showing how a composite volcano might change in shape by getting larger or smaller with repeated eruptions.

ANSWERS

1. at divergent and convergent boundaries because magma rises there

2. by whether it flows easily or resists flowing

3. increases in earthquakes, changes in the tilt of the ground, increases in temperatures, and changes in volcanic gases given off

4. shield volcano: largest, flattest, and broadest; cinder cone: steep and small; composite volcano: large and cone-shaped

5. any two: mudflows, pyroclastic flows, carried by winds

6. Drawings should show that the volcano becomes larger as new layers are added with repeated eruptions or smaller due to large, violent eruptions that destroy part of its cone.

Ongoing Assessment

CHECK YOUR READING *Answer: to be able to warn people in time to avoid or escape an eruption*

Teach from Visuals

To help students interpret the photograph of Dante II:

- Ask: Why is a robot being used to collect data? *It may be too dangerous for people to collect data inside the crater of an active volcano.*
- Tell students that Dante II was made by NASA. Then ask: Why do you think that NASA made this machine? *NASA has experience in making machines for exploring areas with extreme conditions.*

Reinforce the BIG idea

Have students relate the section to the Big Idea.

 Reinforcing Key Concepts, p. 162

10.2 ASSESS & RETEACH

Assess

 Section 10.2 Quiz, p. 216

Reteach

As a class, develop content frames to reteach volcanic materials, types of volcanoes, and how volcanoes are monitored. If students have already developed their own content frames, they can compare them with the ones the class develops, or suffice as models for the class.

Technology Resources

Have students visit **ClassZone.com** for reteaching of Key Concepts.

 CONTENT REVIEW

 CONTENT REVIEW CD-ROM

CHAPTER INVESTIGATION

Focus

PURPOSE To find out how the type of materials that form a volcano determines its shape and size

OVERVIEW Students will use different materials to make models of volcanoes and then measure the slopes to find out how the shape relates to the materials that were used. Students will find that a combination of gravel and plaster of Paris builds the tallest volcano with the steepest slopes.

Lab Preparation

- Review with students how to use a protractor to measure angles. Then demonstrate how to measure the steepness of a slope of a model volcano. (Hold the straight edge of the protractor against the cardboard base so that the center point of the protractor is at the spot where the slope meets the base. Read the angle made by the slope in degrees).
- Prior to the investigation, have students read through the investigation and prepare their data tables. Or you may wish to copy and distribute datasheets and rubrics.

 UNIT RESOURCE BOOK, pp. 182–190

 SCIENCE TOOLKIT, F14

Lab Management

Emphasize to students that they should not pour any plaster of Paris down the drain. All cups used to mix the plaster should be thrown away.

INCLUSION Encourage students working together on activities to discuss in advance which tasks each will perform. Help students identify tasks that they can do well or alternative approaches that suit their abilities.

CHAPTER INVESTIGATION

Make Your Own Volcanoes

OVERVIEW AND PURPOSE Scientists who have never been to a particular volcano can estimate how steep a climb it would be to its top. All they need to know is what type of volcano it is. Volcanoes vary not only in size but also in slope, or the steepness of their sides. The three main types of volcanoes—cinder cones, shield volcanoes, and composite volcanoes—are very different in size and shape. In this activity you will

- make models of volcanoes and measure their slopes
- determine how the types of materials that form a volcano affect how steep it can get

Problem

What does a volcano's slope reveal about the materials that formed it?

Hypothesize

Write a hypothesis to explain how a volcano's slope is related to the materials it is made of. Your hypothesis should take the form of an "If . . . , then . . . , because . . ." statement.

MATERIALS
- 375 mL plaster of Paris
- 180 mL water
- 500 mL gravel
- 3 cardboard pieces
- two 250 mL paper cups
- stirrer
- ruler
- protractor

6.1.d, 6.7.a

Procedure

1. Make a data table like the one shown in the sample notebook on page 355.
2. Mix 125 mL of plaster of Paris with 60 mL of water in a paper cup. Stir the mixture well. Work quickly because the mixture will harden quickly.
3. Pour the mixture onto a piece of cardboard from a height of 2–3 cm. Write "cone A" on the cardboard and set it aside.
4. Fill another paper cup with gravel. Slowly pour the gravel onto a second piece of cardboard from a height of about 10 cm. Label this model "cone B" and set it aside.

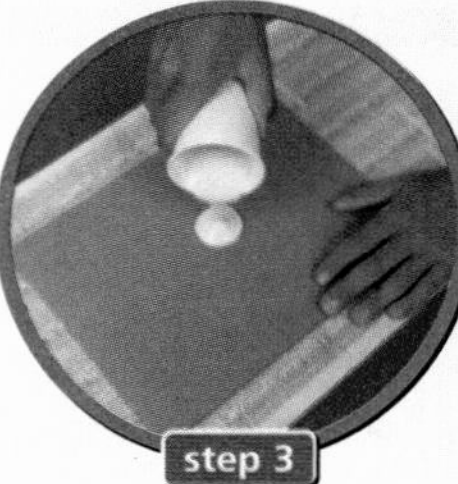

INVESTIGATION RESOURCES

 CHAPTER INVESTIGATION, Make Your Own Volcanoes
- Level A, pp. 182–185
- Level B, pp. 186–189
- Level C, p. 190

Advanced students should complete Levels B & C.

 Writing a Lab Report, D12–13

Technology Resources

Customize this student lab as needed or look for an alternative. Print rubrics to assess student lab reports.

 **Lab Generator CD-ROM**

Content Standard
6.1.d Students know that earthquakes are sudden motions along breaks in the crust called faults and that volcanoes and fissures are locations where magma reaches the surface.

Investigation Standard
6.7.a Develop a hypothesis.

5 In a cup, mix the rest of the plaster of Paris with the rest of the water. Fill the other paper cup with gravel. Pour a small amount of the plaster mixture onto the third piece of cardboard. Then pour some gravel on top. Repeat until all the plaster mixture and gravel have been used. Label this model "cone C" and set it aside until the plaster in both cone A and cone C has hardened (about 20 min).

Observe and Analyze

1. **MEASURE** Use the protractor to measure the approximate slope of each cone.
2. **RECORD** Complete your data table.
3. **OBSERVE** Compare the appearances of the cones. Record your observations in your **Science Notebook.**
4. **COMPARE** How different are the slopes of the cones?

Conclude

1. **CONNECT** Which volcanic materials do the plaster mixture and the gravel represent?
2. **IDENTIFY VARIABLES** What is the relationship between the cones' slopes and the materials they are made of?
3. **ANALYZE** Compare your results with your hypothesis. Do your data support your hypothesis?
4. **INTERPRET** Which type of volcano does each model represent?
5. **DRAW CONCLUSIONS** Which of your models represents a volcano that cannot grow as large as the others? Explain.
6. **APPLY** What factors might cause the slopes of real volcanoes to be different from those of your models?
7. **APPLY** If you were a scientist, what might you need to know besides slope in order to determine a volcano's type?
8. **APPLY** How could the method you used to make a model of a cinder cone be used to show how the slope of a hill or mountain contributes to a landslide?

INVESTIGATE Further

CHALLENGE Calculate the slopes of your models using the formula $y = mx + b$. In this formula, y and x are graph coordinates of a point on a straight line. The slope of the line is m. The intersection of the line with the y-axis of the graph is b. For example, if the height of a model is 1.6 cm, and the distance from its edge to its center is 4 cm, then the equation is $1.6 = m4 + 0$.
The slope is $\frac{1.6}{4}$, or 0.4.

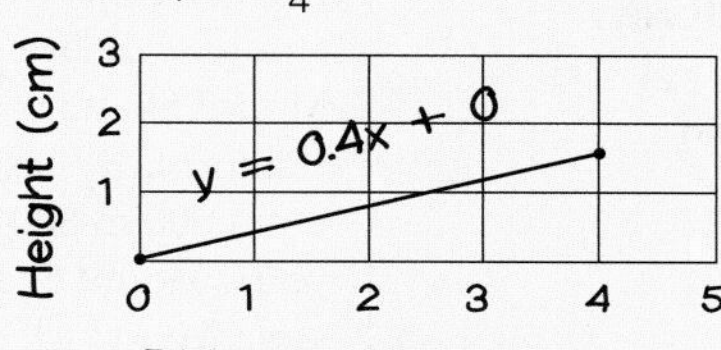

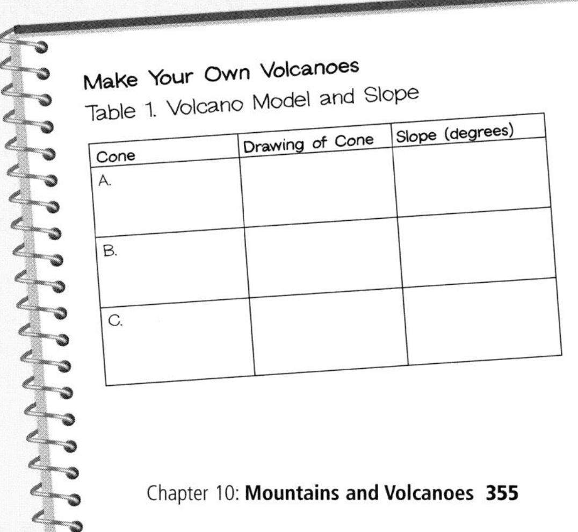
Make Your Own Volcanoes
Table 1. Volcano Model and Slope

Cone	Drawing of Cone	Slope (degrees)
A.		
B.		
C.		

Observe and Analyze

1. *See students' data tables. You may choose to have students measure to the nearest one or two degrees.*
2. *See students' data tables.*
3. *lowest slope—shield volcano; small, steep slope—cinder cone; tall, steep slope—composite volcano*
4. *The slopes are noticeably different.*

Conclude

1. *plaster of Paris—molten rock; gravel—cinders and other cooled volcanic rocks*
2. *plaster of Paris only—low slope; gravel—steeper slopes*
3. *See students' hypotheses.*
4. *plaster of Paris only—shield volcano; gravel only—cinder cone; plaster of Paris and gravel—composite volcano*
5. *cinder cone, because it has no cooled lava flows (plaster of Paris) to help add strength to its structure*
6. *Plaster of Paris and magma have different properties. Material was poured from above rather than erupting from below. Volcanoes form from repeated eruptions rather than just one event.*
7. *the type of magma feeding it*
8. *As gravel is added, the cone gets steep enough that additional gravel falls down the sides rather than adding to the height.*

INVESTIGATE Further

CHALLENGE Answers will vary according to the measurements of students' models.

Post-Lab Discussion

Discuss why it is helpful to measure the angles of the slopes instead of just to observe and describe the slopes. *Descriptions are useful, but they are too subjective to be the only kind of data. Measurements clearly show differences in the slopes.*

10.3 FOCUS

Set Learning Goals

Students will

- Describe how volcanic eruptions affect Earth's surface.
- Explain how volcanic gases affect the atmosphere.
- Describe how volcanic activity affects water.
- Analyze how the shape of land near Mount Rainier affects mudflows.

3-Minute Warm-Up

Display Transparency 77 or copy this exercise on the board:

Decide whether these statements are true. If a statement is not true, correct it.

1. The main gases in volcanic eruptions are water vapor and oxygen. *water vapor and carbon dioxide*
2. Much of Earth's volcanic activity takes place underwater along spreading centers in the oceans. *true*
3. Lava forms as tectonic plates sink into subduction zones. *Magma forms in this process.*
4. Pyroclastic flows are dense and dangerous clouds of superhot gases and rock fragments that race downhill during eruptions. *true*

3-Minute Warm-Up, p. T77

10.3 MOTIVATE

THINK ABOUT

PURPOSE To think about the hazards posed by two different types of volcanoes

DISCUSS Ask students to compare and contrast the threats from ashes, gases, and lava from the two volcanoes.

Sample answer: Mt. Shasta erupts less often than Mauna Loa, but its explosions are much more violent due to built-up pressure. Volcanic gases from Mauna Loa are a constant danger to people with breathing difficulties such as asthma.

KEY CONCEPT

10.3 Volcanoes affect Earth's land, air, and water.

CALIFORNIA Content Standards

6.2.d Students know earthquakes, volcanic eruptions, landslides, and floods change human and wildlife habitats.

6.6.a Students know the utility of energy sources is determined by factors that are involved in converting these sources to useful forms and the consequences of the conversion process.

BEFORE, you learned

- Rock fragments, lava, and gases erupt from volcanoes
- Some volcanoes have explosive eruptions

NOW, you will learn

- How volcanic eruptions affect Earth's surface
- How volcanic gases affect the atmosphere
- How volcanic activity affects water

VOCABULARY

acid rain p. 360
geyser p. 361

THINK ABOUT

Which volcano is more dangerous?

Mauna Loa is a shield volcano that forms a large part of the island of Hawaii. It is one of the most active volcanoes on Earth, frequently producing large amounts of lava that flow long distances. Mount Shasta is a composite volcano in California. It has erupted at least once every 600 to 800 years for the past 10,000 years. Mount Shasta can erupt with great violence. Which volcano do you think it is more dangerous to live near? Why?

CONTENT FRAME Add a content frame for how eruptions affect Earth's land and air. Include categories for what dangers are caused and how long the dangers last.

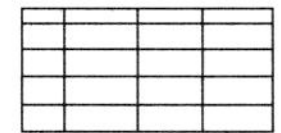

Volcanic eruptions affect the land.

A volcanic eruption can knock down forests and clog rivers with volcanic ash. Damage can occur far from the volcano. But volcanoes build as well as destroy. Material erupted from volcanoes can form new land. Over time, lava flows can form new, rich soil.

Many towns and cities are located close to volcanoes. The people of Goma in the Democratic Republic of the Congo experienced an eruption of a nearby volcano in 2002. A lava flow cut the city in half and destroyed the homes of tens of thousands of people, either by flowing into the homes or by starting fires. Hilo (HEE-loh), the largest city on the island of Hawaii, is built in part on young lava flows. The city is at high risk from future volcanic activity.

RESOURCES FOR DIFFERENTIATED INSTRUCTION

Below Level

UNIT RESOURCE BOOK

- Reading Study Guide A, pp. 165–166
- Decoding Support, p. 179

AUDIO CDS

Advanced

UNIT RESOURCE BOOK

Challenge and Extension, p. 171

English Learners

UNIT RESOURCE BOOK

Spanish Reading Study Guide, pp. 169–170

AUDIO CDS

- Audio Readings in Spanish
- Audio Readings (English)

Immediate Effects

The effects of a volcanic eruption largely depend on how much material and what types of material the volcano ejects. Near a volcano, lava flows can cover the land with new rock. A much larger area can be affected by events such as ash falls, landslides, mudflows, pyroclastic flows, and steam explosions.

Lava Flows Most lava moves slowly enough that people can move away and not be hurt. But even a slow-moving lava flow will knock down, cover, or burn nearly everything in its path.

Volcanic Ash Near a volcanic eruption, the weight of fallen volcanic ash can cause the roofs of buildings to collapse. Volcanic ash is heavy because it is made of tiny pieces of rock. Ash makes roads slippery, and it clogs up machinery, including cars and airplanes. Large amounts of falling ash can suffocate plants, animals, and people.

Mudflows Mudflows are landslides that occur when loose rocks and soil are mixed with water. Heat from an eruption melts any ice and snow on the volcano very quickly. Mudflows form as the water mixes with volcanic ash and other loose particles. Mudflows also form as ash mixes into rivers flowing from a volcano. Fast-moving mudflows have buried entire towns many kilometers from an eruption.

Pyroclastic Flows As a pyroclastic flow rushes downhill, it can knock down or burn everything in its way. Pyroclastic flows tend to follow valleys. However, a fast-moving flow can sweep up and over hills, then race down a neighboring valley. As a flow passes, it can leave a thick layer of volcanic rock fragments. Pyroclastic flows are extremely dangerous. In 1902 a pyroclastic flow from an eruption in the West Indies completely destroyed the city of Saint Pierre. Almost 30,000 people were killed within a few minutes.

Landslides Part of a volcano can collapse and start a landslide—a rapid downhill movement of rock and soil. The collapse may be caused by magma moving underground, an eruption, an earthquake, or even heavy rainfall. A landslide can cause a tsunami if a large amount of material falls into the ocean.

Lava Flow

Trees catch fire as a lava flow moves through a forest in Hawaii in 1999.

Volcanic Ash

Large piles of volcanic ash from the 1991 eruption of Mount Pinatubo line a street in Olongapo, Philippines.

REMINDER

A tsunami is a water wave caused by an earthquake, a volcanic eruption, or a landslide.

DIFFERENTIATE INSTRUCTION

More Reading Support

A What might a landslide into the ocean cause? *tsunami*

English Learners Help English learners recognize phrasal verbs that use prepositions as part of the verbs. Point out cases in which the prepositions should not be taken literally. For example, the phrase *break down* on p. 358 refers to rock weathering and breaking apart but not necessarily moving downhill. Similarly, the phrase *built up* on p. 359 refers to an increasing concentration of carbon dioxide in water, not an upward movement of carbon dioxide.

10.3 INSTRUCT

Teach the Standards

Effects of Volcanoes 6.2.d

In this section: Explain that volcanoes affect humans and wildlife in negative and positive ways: Volcanic eruptions can kill humans and animals or destroy their habitats. Cooled lava and ash eventually form fertile soil.

- **previously taught:** earthquake damage, pp. 316–325; energy conversion, pp. 12–14
- **future opportunities:** natural resources, pp. 471–479

Teach from Visuals

To help students interpret the photographs, ask:

- How might lava cause fires even before the main lava flow reaches the area? *Small amounts of lava ejected from a volcano or splattered from a lava flow can come into contact with trees and other objects.*
- What are some ways to clean the ash off this vehicle? *Push the top layer off with a broom and gently rinse the rest off with water so as not to scrape the paint off.*

Develop Critical Thinking

RANK Ask students to rank the six possible effects of volcanic eruptions that are described from least dangerous to most dangerous. After five minutes, ask them if this is an easy task. Ask what makes it somewhat difficult. Discuss how each event can be dangerous and devastating. *The danger associated with each event depends on factors such as the speed of a lava flow, the distance it covers, and the path it takes; the amount of ash produced by the eruption, wind speed and direction, and amount of water available to contribute to a mudflow; the shape of the land that a pyroclastic flow moves over; and the stability of the volcano's slopes. Only some of these events are likely to occur during a particular eruption.*

Teach from Visuals

To help students interpret the photograph of the bus, ask: About how deep do you think the mudflow is in the photograph? *1–2 m (about 3–6 ft)*

Develop Critical Thinking

HYPOTHESIZE Ask students to hypothesize why people would choose to live near active volcanoes. To help students, have them consider which types of natural disasters are likely to occur in your area. (Examples include hurricanes, tornadoes, wildfires, earthquakes, flooding, and drought.) Then have them apply their knowledge of why these events do or do not cause people to avoid living in your area in order to form their hypotheses. *People get comfortable living near a volcano if the volcano hasn't erupted in many years; large cities—and jobs—happen to be located near some volcanoes; the rich soils near volcanoes provide good agriculture; volcanoes provide a natural beauty to the landscape.*

Ongoing Assessment

Describe how volcanic eruptions affect Earth's surface.

What are four kinds of events that can happen during a volcanic eruption? *any four of the following: lava flows, volcanic ash falls, landslides, mudflows, pyroclastic flows, steam explosions*

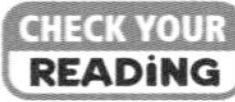

Answer: by causing heavy ash falls or tsunamis

Answer: Ash can mix with other loose materials and rainwater or floodwater to create dangerous mudflows.

Find out more about the effects of volcanic eruptions.

Steam Explosions Steam explosions are rare but can be very destructive. They occur when magma comes near water. A steam explosion may have caused the destruction of a volcanic island in Indonesia. The entire island of Krakatau (KRACK-uh-TOW) exploded in 1883. The explosion caused a tsunami that destroyed hundreds of towns and killed more than 36,000 people.

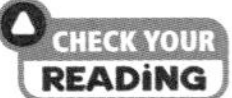

What are two ways a volcanic eruption can result in damage to areas hundreds of kilometers away?

Long-Term Effects

Volcanic eruptions can be very destructive. But even after an eruption ends, a volcano can remain dangerous for many years.

The explosive eruption of Mount Pinatubo in 1991 threw out huge amounts of volcanic ash and rock fragments. The area the volcano is in gets heavy rains each year. Mudflows have formed as large amounts of rainwater mixed with ash and other loose material on the sides of the volcano. Since the eruption, mudflows have destroyed the homes of more than 100,000 people.

This school bus was partly buried by a mudflow from Mount St. Helens. No one was in the bus when the mudflow hit.

Another possible source of water for these mudflows was a lake that began filling the volcano's crater. The upper part of Mount Pinatubo crater is weak, and the lake's level was rising. A collapse of the crater could have emptied the lake of much of its water. In 2001 people dug a channel to lower the level of the lake, greatly decreasing the chance of a collapse.

Why can volcanic ash be dangerous for years after an eruption?

Lava Beds National Monument in northern California features a rugged volcanic landscape formed by eruptions of the giant Medicine Lake shield volcano. Cinder cones, lava flows, and lava tube caves are common. Tourists can explore these caves, which were formed when lava rivers flowing downhill cooled more rapidly on the outside than they did on the inside.

Even though volcanoes are dangerous, over time they can have positive effects. When a lava flow cools, it forms a layer of hard rock on which no plants can grow. However, over many years, this rock can break down to form rich soil. Volcanic ash can smother plants, but the tiny pieces of rock break down quickly and make soil richer. Highly productive farmland surrounds some active volcanoes.

Over time, repeated volcanic eruptions can build a magnificent landscape of mountains and valleys. People may choose to live in a volcanic area in part for its natural beauty. Many other people may visit the area, supporting a tourist industry.

DIFFERENTIATE INSTRUCTION

More Reading Support

B What might happen when magma reaches an ocean? *steam explosion*

C Describe the soil that forms from lava. *rich or fertile*

Advanced Invite students to act as reporters covering a famous past eruption. They can develop a report for a newspaper, radio broadcast, or TV broadcast. Suggest that they include maps and diagrams to accompany their report for a newspaper or TV broadcast. Students should provide background on the geology of the area and information on past eruptions. Other students can act as eyewitnesses and experts. Students also should research the effects of the eruption and provide this information to the eyewitnesses beforehand.

Challenge and Extension, p. 171

INVESTIGATE Mudflows

How does the shape of the land affect mudflows?

SKILL FOCUS
Analyzing (6.2.d)

MATERIAL
Map of Mount Rainier Mudflows

TIME
25 minutes

PROCEDURE

1. Look at the map of Mount Rainier mudflows. Observe the relationship between the paths of rivers and the paths of the mudflows.
2. Write the number of towns shown within the boundaries of mudflow areas.
3. Write the differences in elevation between the following locations: the top of Mount Rainier and the point where the West Fork joins the White River, the point where the rivers join and the town of Buckley, and the towns of Buckley and Auburn. Where is the land steepest?
4. On the back of the paper, explain why in some areas mudflows have followed rivers and in other areas mudflows have spread out.

WHAT DO YOU THINK?

- What three factors are most important in causing mudflows to start near the top of Mount Rainier and flow long distances?
- How likely are future mudflows to follow the same paths as earlier mudflows?

CHALLENGE The largest mudflow starting on Mount Rainier moved at about 22 kilometers per hour (14 mi/h). It covered the land to an average depth of 6 meters (20 ft). Describe the steps you would take to protect people from a similar mudflow in the same area.

Volcanic gases and ash affect the air.

If you visit a volcano, you might notice some unpleasant odors. These odors come from gases released into the air from magma. Some of these gases contain the element sulfur. Hydrogen sulfide gas smells like rotten eggs. Sulfur dioxide gas is what you smell when you strike a match. The volcano might also be releasing carbon dioxide, a gas you would not notice because it has no color or odor. Volcanoes release gases before, during, and after eruptions.

REMINDER
An element is a substance that contains only one type of atom.

Many gases from volcanoes are dangerous. They can make breathing difficult and damage the lungs of people and animals. Carbon dioxide can be fatal. In West Africa, a sudden release of carbon dioxide killed 1700 people in 1986. The gas came from a volcano at the bottom of a lake. Carbon dioxide built up in the water until a large amount escaped at once. Pipes are now being used to release carbon dioxide from the bottom of the lake so that the gas will not build up again.

DIFFERENTIATE INSTRUCTION

More Reading Support

D What are two gases released from a volcano? *any two of the following: carbon dioxide, hydrogen sulfide, sulfur dioxide*

Below Level Have students make flash cards for the different effects of volcanic eruptions. They can write an effect, such as "lava flows" or "volcanic ash," on one side of a card and a brief description of that effect on the opposite side. For "lava flows," students might write "slow-moving" and "burn almost everything." Have students use the phrases as springboards to describe each type of effect to you or to a partner.

INVESTIGATE Mudflows

PURPOSE To analyze how the shape of land near Mount Rainier affects mudflows

TIPS *25 min.*

- Review the features of the map to make sure students are able to do the lab. Point out the rivers, mudflows, and towns.
- Make sure the mudflows show up clearly on the maps. You may have to outline the flows before photocopying the maps.

PROCEDURE *1. Mudflows tend to follow the paths of rivers. 2. Six towns 3. Mount Rainier–West Fork/White River: 3782 m; West Fork/White River–Buckley: 389 m; Buckley–Auburn: 195 m; The land is steepest between the top of Mount Rainier and the point at which the West Fork joins the White River. 4. Mudflows tend to follow the paths of rivers where the land is steep. They tend to spread out where the land is flatter.*

WHAT DO YOU THINK? *Three factors are the presence of ice and snow; heat from an eruption, which can quickly melt the ice and snow; the mountain's steepness. Future mudflows are very likely because mudflows move downhill along the lowest ground.*

CHALLENGE *Answers can include installing warning systems so people can move to higher ground, building barricades to slow or divert mudflows, building ditches to divert mudflows, and relocating towns.*

- Map of Mount Rainier Mudflows, p. 172
- Datasheet, Mudflows, p. 173

Technology Resources

Customize this student lab as needed or look for an alternative. Print rubrics to assess student lab reports.

 **Lab Generator CD-ROM**

Integrate the Sciences

Sulfur dioxide from volcanic eruptions mixes with moisture in the air to form sulfuric acid. This acid mixes with rain or snow to form acid precipitation. The acidity of a substance is measured by its pH on a scale of 0 to 14. Distilled water, with a pH of 7, is neutral. The lower the number, the more acidic the substance. Tomato juice has a pH of 3 and lemon juice has a pH of 2. Normal precipitation is slightly acidic (pH: 5.5) because carbon dioxide dissolves in water in the air to produce a weak carbonic acid. Acid precipitation is defined as precipitation with a pH of less than 5.0, but it has been measured as being as low as 3.

Real World Example

Perhaps the best example of a volcanic weather changer is Mount Tambora, a volcano on Sumbawa Island in Indonesia. On April 5, 1815, Tambora erupted in an explosion that was heard up to 1400 km (870 mi.) away. An even larger eruption occurred less than one week later on April 10–11, 1815. Ash, dust, and gases from these eruptions blasted high into the atmosphere and were carried all around the world. These materials blocked significant amounts of sunlight throughout the rest of that year and the next. Unusual summer frosts, snowfalls, and wildly fluctuating temperatures took their toll on crops, especially during the following year of 1816. An estimated 80,000 people worldwide died of starvation and disease as a result of the crop failures and cold temperatures.

Ongoing Assessment

Explain how volcanic gases affect the atmosphere.

How do volcanic gases aid ash in blocking sunlight? *They lift ash high above an erupting volcano where winds can spread the ash and keep it suspended in the atmosphere, so it blocks sunlight.*

CHECK YOUR READING *Answer: by forming acid rain and by forming a haze that blocks sunlight*

A cloud of hot gases and ash rises high into the atmosphere during an eruption of Mount Etna in Italy.

VOCABULARY
Remember to add *acid rain* to your notebook, using the vocabulary strategy of your choice.

Some gases, such as sulfur dioxide, form acids when they mix with water in the air. These acids fall to Earth's surface in rain, snow, or sleet. Rain that contains large amounts of acid is called **acid rain.** Volcanoes are sources of acid-forming gases, but a bigger source is human activity. For example, the burning of coal in electrical power plants adds acid-forming gases to the air. In some areas, acid rain has damaged forests and killed fish in lakes.

Large amounts of volcanic gases in the atmosphere can change weather worldwide. The 1991 eruption of Mount Pinatubo released enough sulfur dioxide to form a haze high in the atmosphere around the entire planet. The haze decreased the amount of sunlight reaching Earth's surface. It lowered average world temperatures in 1992 and 1993.

Volcanic gases can lift ash high above an erupting volcano. Winds can then carry the ash far away. During the May 1980 eruption of Mount St. Helens, ash fell 400 kilometers (250 mi) away in Spokane, Washington. The ash blocked so much sunlight that Spokane's streetlights were turned on during the day. The smallest ash particles can remain in the air for years, circling Earth many times. These particles also reflect sunlight and can lower Earth's temperature.

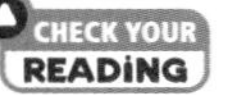

Describe two ways sulfur dioxide can affect the atmosphere.

Volcanic activity affects water.

E

Yellowstone National Park in the western United States is famous for its hot springs. These are places where heated water flows to Earth's surface. Yellowstone is a volcanic region, and its hot springs sit in a huge caldera. The springs' heat comes from a hot spot under the North American Plate.

DIFFERENTIATE INSTRUCTION

More Reading Support

E What causes the heat of the hot springs in Yellowstone National Park? *a hot spot under the North American Plate*

Alternative Assessment Have students use a world map to find the locations of all the places mentioned on p. 360: Mount Etna, Italy; Mount Pinatubo, Philippines; Mount St. Helens, Washington; and Yellowstone National Park, Wyoming. Have students discuss the relationship of these places to tectonic plates. *The first three places are near convergent plate boundaries; Yellowstone is above a hot spot far from plate boundaries.*

Geysers

Rainwater can sink through cracks in rock. If it is heated within Earth, it can rise to form hot springs and geysers.

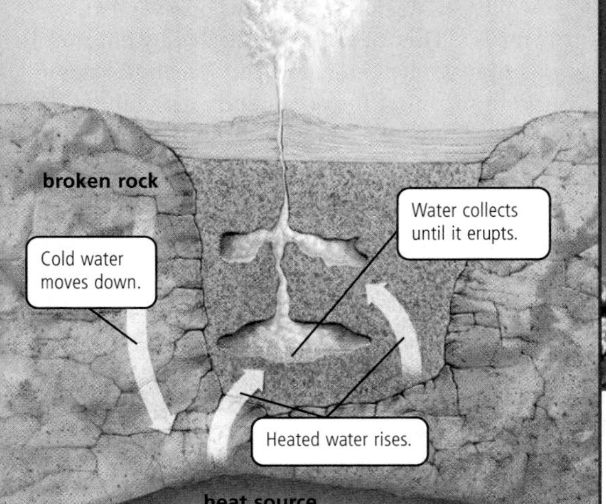

broken rock
Water collects until it erupts.
Cold water moves down.
Heated water rises.
heat source

Old Faithful geyser in Yellowstone National Park erupts more often than any other large geyser. Heated water is forced up into the air through a narrow channel.

Hot Springs, Geysers, and Fumaroles

Most hot springs are in areas where magma or hot rock is near Earth's surface. Water moves down through the ground, gets heated, and rises at a hot spring. At most hot springs, the water flows out into a calm pool. But at a type of hot spring called a **geyser,** water shoots into the air. A geyser forms where water collects in an underground chamber, then erupts through a narrow channel. Old Faithful is a geyser in Yellowstone National Park. It erupts every 35 minutes to 2 hours. Most geysers erupt less regularly.

Countries with many hot springs and geysers include the United States, New Zealand, and Iceland. Iceland sits on an ocean spreading center. Magma rises underneath the country as plates pull apart. People in Iceland use hot underground water as an energy source.

A fumarole (FYOO-muh-ROHL) is similar to a hot spring. Instead of liquid water, a fumarole releases steam and other gases. Changes in hot springs and fumaroles located on the sides of a volcano can show that the volcano is becoming more active. As magma moves close to the surface, water temperatures get higher. As a result, fumaroles can release more or different gases.

CONTENT FRAME
Make a content frame for features formed by heated water. Include categories for how they form and where they form.

CHECK YOUR READING Why might fumaroles and hot springs be monitored?

Teach from Visuals

To help students interpret the visuals of geysers, ask:

- Where does the cold water come from? *groundwater and surface water from rain and melting snow*
- How does the cold water reach the area of heat below ground? *through cracks in the rock*
- Why might Old Faithful be so named? *It erupts relatively regularly.*

Develop Critical Thinking

INFER Ask students to infer what caused the mound of materials around the geyser's opening? *Minerals dissolved in the hot water are deposited when the water cools or evaporates at the surface.*

Ongoing Assessment

Describe how volcanic activity affects water.

How are hot springs, geysers, and fumaroles similar? *They all form from water moving underground near magma or hot rock, then surfacing as a pool, a stream, or a fountain of hot water or steam.*

CHECK YOUR READING *Answer: to see whether a volcano is becoming more active*

DIFFERENTIATE INSTRUCTION

More Reading Support

F What is the name of a hot spring that shoots water into the air? *geyser*

G Why does Iceland have many hot springs? *It is located on an ocean spreading center.*

Advanced Have students further analyze the diagram of a geyser to determine the role of a narrow, underground channel in the eruption of a geyser. *The narrower the channel, the more pressure builds up, and the higher the eruption of water.*

Ongoing Assessment

 CHECK YOUR READING *Answer: The dissolved minerals from the water become solid again and build up very close to the vent as the water cools quickly.*

Integrate the Sciences

Most organisms ultimately depend on energy from the Sun for their food through the process of photosynthesis. At deep-sea vents, however, there is no sunlight. The food-making process in this environment is not photosynthesis but chemosynthesis. Bacteria use sulfur compounds ejected from the vents to make their food. These bacteria become the bottom link on a food chain that supports a community of organisms.

Reinforce the BIG idea

Have students relate the section to the Big Idea.

R Reinforcing Key Concepts, p. 174

10.3 ASSESS & RETEACH

Assess

 Section 10.3 Quiz, p. 217

Reteach

Write the blue and red heads for this section on the board in outline format, leaving space between them for students to fill in subtopics and supporting details. Have students annotate their contributions with page numbers.

Technology Resources

Have students visit **ClassZone.com** for reteaching of Key Concepts.

 **CONTENT REVIEW**

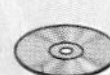 **CONTENT REVIEW CD-ROM**

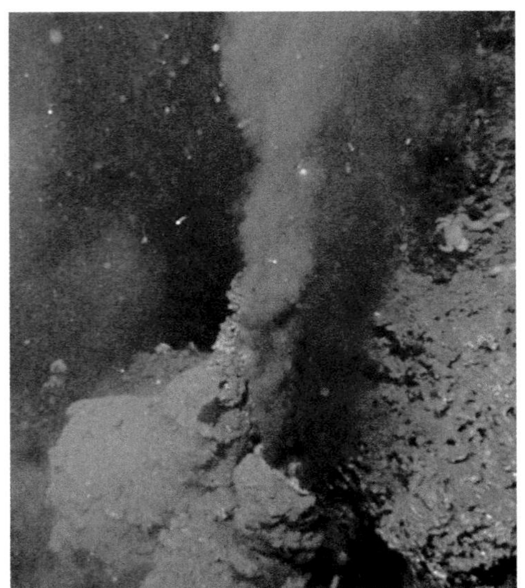

This deep-sea vent is more than 3 kilometers (2 mi) below the surface of the Atlantic Ocean. A black cloud of mineral-rich water rises from the vent.

Deep-Sea Vents

Deep-sea vents are hot springs that form at spreading centers in the ocean. In these places, the ocean floor has many cracks through which cold seawater sinks to depths of several kilometers. The sea water gets heated by hot rock and magma, then rises again. The hot water coming out of the ocean floor is rich in dissolved minerals and gases from the rock and magma.

At some deep-sea vents, warm water flows gently from cracks in the ocean floor. At others, water that can be hotter than 350°C (660°F) shoots out of chimney-like vents. The water looks black because it contains large amounts of dissolved minerals. As the hot water mixes with cold water, dissolved minerals form into solid minerals again. This process builds up the vent chimneys.

Deep-sea vents support unusual life forms such as blind crabs and tubeworms that measure up to 3 meters (10 ft) long. These animals feed on one-celled organisms that get their energy from chemicals in the vent water. Unlike other one-celled organisms, these organisms do not need sunlight to make their food.

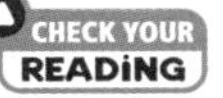 CHECK YOUR READING Why do chimneys form around some deep-sea vents?

10.3 Review

KEY CONCEPTS

1. Describe how a heavy ash fall from a volcanic eruption can affect Earth's surface. (6.2.d)
2. Describe how large amounts of volcanic gases can affect weather around Earth. (6.2.d)
3. Why do hot springs occur in volcanic areas? (6.2.d)

CRITICAL THINKING

4. **Compare and Contrast** What do geysers and deep-sea vents that form chimneys have in common? How are they different?
5. **Evaluate** Which is more dangerous, a pyroclastic flow or a mudflow? Explain.

CHALLENGE

6. **Analyze** Ice in Greenland and Antarctica contains layers of ash from eruptions that occurred many thousands of years ago. How do you think the ash reached the ice, and why is it preserved?

ANSWERS

1. It can cause collapse of roofs, suffocation of plants and animals, clogged machinery, slippery roads, mudflows, and richer soils over time.

2. Volcanic gases can form a haze that blocks sunlight and lowers average temperatures.

3. Magma and hot rock heat groundwater.

4. Very hot water shoots out of both. Geysers form on land, while deep-sea vents form in the ocean.

5. Both can be deadly. Given warning, people can leave the area to avoid pyroclastic flows during an eruption, but mudflows can occur for many years after an eruption.

6. Winds carried the ash to the ice, and new snow covered the ash and trapped it.

Lassen Peak hasn't erupted since 1917, but the hydrothermal system at Lassen Volcanic National Park shows there is a heat source under the volcano. The heat causes convection currents that reach the surface at hydrothermal features.

GEOTHERMAL FEATURES

In Hot Water!

6.4.c Students know heat from Earth's interior reaches the surface primarily through convection.

Roaring fumaroles. Steaming hot springs. Thumping mud pots. No, these are not names of California theme-park rides. They are descriptions of geothermal features at Lassen Volcanic National Park in northeastern California. And they are all clues that Lassen Peak is likely to erupt again.

Lassen Volcanic National Park is located at the foot of the Cascade Mountains. Its hydrothermal system heats and recycles groundwater. *Hydro-* refers to "water," and *thermal* refers to "heat," so the word *hydrothermal* means "of or relating to hot water."

Lassen Peak last erupted in 1917. Even without a volcanic eruption, Lassen Park is an active place. Steam and gas escape through fumaroles, or vents in the ground. Since the steam and hot water have only a small opening through which to escape, they shoot up into the air. In some places, you can see the chemicals that were once dissolved in the boiling water. Hot water bubbles up, and when it evaporates, colorful metals are left behind on the rocks. What about thumping mud pots? Well, just imagine the sound made by thick mud when boiling water rises under it.

Steam rises from a hot pool in Lassen Park. Mud pots (inset) form where steam and water bubble up through mud at the surface.

WRITING ABOUT SCIENCE

Make an information pamphlet for Lassen Volcanic National Park. Include a diagram of your favorite geothermal feature. Use the Internet to find more information and photos.

CALIFORNIA CLOSE-UP

Science in action in California

Set Learning Goal

To understand features caused by geothermal activity

Present the Science

The geothermal features in Lassen Volcanic National Park are caused by conduction and convection. The heat source for the geothermal features is deep underground. It is either a body of magma or very hot rock that has cooled from magma. As cool water that seeps into the ground reaches the hot rock near the heat source, it is heated by conduction. It then becomes less dense and rises in convection currents. The heated groundwater eventually reaches Earth's surface at fumaroles, geysers, hot springs, or mud pots.

Discussion Questions

Have students share their knowledge of and experience with California's geography.

- Ask: What is the heat source for geothermal features? *magma or hot rock*
- Ask: Why must a geyser have a small opening in the ground through which steam and hot water shoot into the air? *It allows pressure to build before the steam and hot water escape.*
- Ask: What is a thumping mud pot? *thick mud that bubbles from boiling water rising beneath it*

Close

Ask students to name any of the volcanic parks in California they have visited or geothermal features they have seen. Point out that although volcanoes can be dangerous, the geothermal activity related to them can be used to generate geothermal energy and conserve fossil fuels.

WRITING ABOUT SCIENCE

Writing Applications 6.4.c This assignment will give students practice in researching and writing an informational pamphlet. Suggest that pairs of students read each other's pamphlets and evaluate them in terms of how informative and readable they are.

The best descriptions will

- present accurate information
- provide an understandable diagram and helpful photos

BACK TO

the BIG idea

Have students choose a type of mountain (folded, fault-block, or different types of volcanoes) and demonstrate how that mountain forms. They should relate the mountain formation to plate tectonics. Students can choose to use sheets of paper, clay, wooden blocks, coins, their hands, or other items for their demonstration.

KEY CONCEPTS SUMMARY

SECTION 10.1

Ask: Which rock movements occur to form each of the types of mountains shown? *Folded mountains: An oceanic plate pushes against and sinks beneath a continental plate or two continental plates collide. The pressure folds the continental crust and raises mountains. Fault-block mountains: The lithosphere is stretched and pulls apart, forming faults. Blocks of rock tilt and move along the faults, making parts of the blocks rise.*

SECTION 10.2

Ask: Why are the three types of volcanoes different shapes and sizes? *because each type erupts different kinds of materials such as low-silica lava, high-silica lava, cinders, and different amounts of gases*

SECTION 10.3

Ask students to write a sentence that relates each bulleted item to volcanic activity. Instead of separate sentences, students might write a brief paragraph for the set of items in each box. *During an eruption, part of a volcano can collapse and start a landslide. Large amounts of volcanic gases can produce a worldwide haze that decreases global temperatures. Hot springs form where water is heated near Earth's surface.*

Review Concepts

- Big Idea Flow Chart, p. T73
- Chapter Outline, pp. T79–T80

10 Chapter Review

the BIG idea

Mountains and volcanoes form as tectonic plates move.

KEY CONCEPTS SUMMARY

Movement of rock builds mountains.

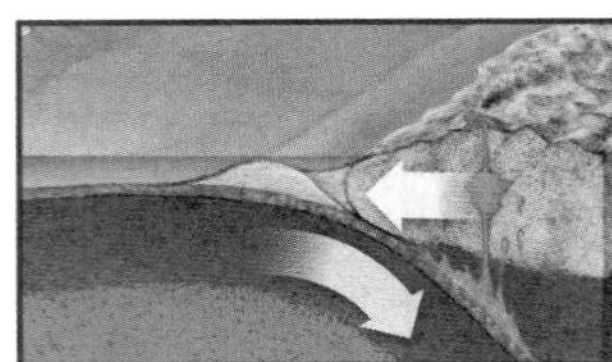

Folded mountains form as plates push together.

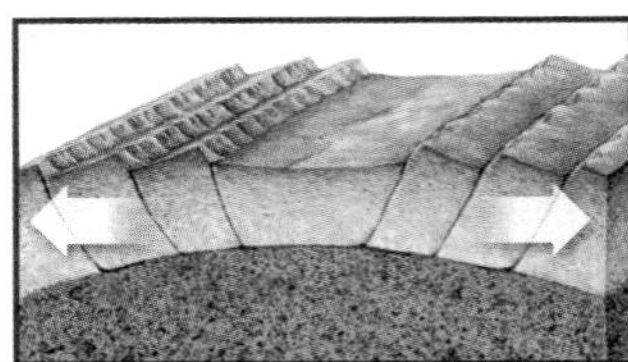

Fault-block mountains form as the lithosphere is stretched.

VOCABULARY
folded mountain p. 340
fault-block mountain p. 342

Volcanoes form as molten rock erupts.

Volcanoes erupt molten rock, rock fragments, and gases. Different types of erupted materials build up different types of volcanoes.

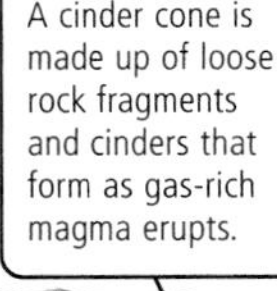

A cinder cone is made up of loose rock fragments and cinders that form as gas-rich magma erupts.

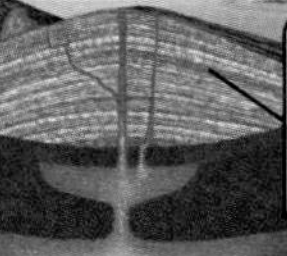

A shield volcano is made up of many layers of low-silica lava.

A composite volcano consists of layers of erupted rock fragments and cooled flows of high-silica lava.

VOCABULARY
volcano p. 346
lava p. 347
pyroclastic flow p. 348

Volcanoes affect Earth's land, air, and water.

Materials erupted from volcanoes, as well as heat from molten rock underground, affect Earth's surface.

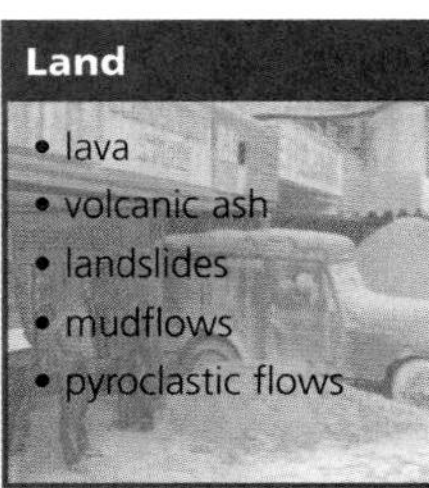

Land
- lava
- volcanic ash
- landslides
- mudflows
- pyroclastic flows

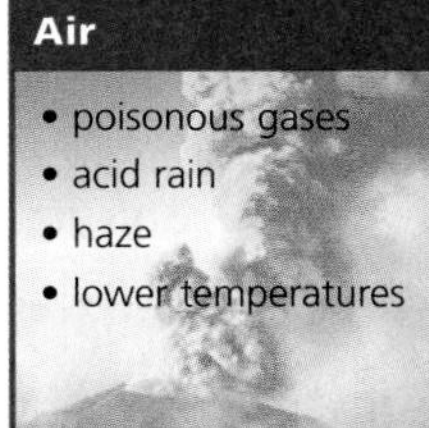

Air
- poisonous gases
- acid rain
- haze
- lower temperatures

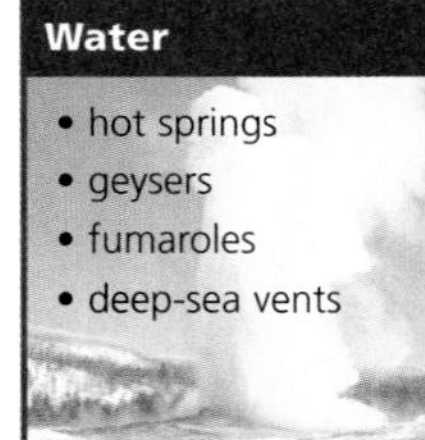

Water
- hot springs
- geysers
- fumaroles
- deep-sea vents

VOCABULARY
acid rain p. 360
geyser p. 361

Technology Resources

Have students visit **ClassZone.com** or use the CD-ROM for a cumulative review of concepts.

CONTENT REVIEW

CONTENT REVIEW CD-ROM

Engage students in a whole-class interactive review of Key Concepts. Edit content as you wish.

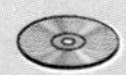

POWER PRESENTATIONS

Reviewing Vocabulary

Draw a Venn diagram to compare and contrast each pair of features. Example:

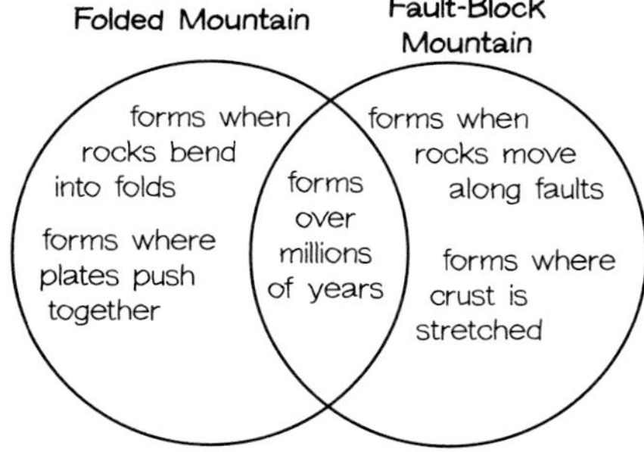

1. folded mountain, volcano
2. lava, pyroclastic flow
3. volcano, geyser

Reviewing Key Concepts

Multiple Choice *Choose the letter of the best answer.*

4. In areas where the lithosphere is being pulled apart, the crust **(6.1.b)**
   - **a.** folds and crumples into mountains
   - **b.** breaks into blocks separated by faults
   - **c.** slides down into the mantle
   - **d.** develops a subduction zone
5. When two plates carrying continental crust collide, the rock of the continents **(6.1.e)**
   - **a.** folds
   - **b.** melts
   - **c.** expands
   - **d.** stretches
6. The movement of huge blocks of rock along a fault can produce **(6.1.e)**
   - **a.** lava plugs
   - **b.** volcanoes
   - **c.** fault-block mountains
   - **d.** folded mountains
7. Volcanoes in the Ring of Fire are supplied with magma rising from **(6.1.d)**
   - **a.** spreading centers
   - **b.** hot spots
   - **c.** rift valleys
   - **d.** subduction zones
8. Before magma erupts it collects under a volcano in a **(6.1.d)**
   - **a.** chamber
   - **b.** caldera
   - **c.** crater
   - **d.** vent
9. The explosiveness of a volcanic eruption depends mostly on what quality of the magma? **(6.1.d)**
   - **a.** gas content
   - **b.** silica content
   - **c.** amount
   - **d.** temperature
10. The type of magma erupting from a volcano determines the volcano's **(6.1.d)**
    - **a.** size
    - **b.** age
    - **c.** shape
    - **d.** location
11. Volcanic ash can be carried thousands of kilometers from an eruption by **(6.2.d)**
    - **a.** lava flows
    - **b.** pyroclastic flows
    - **c.** landslides
    - **d.** winds
12. What happens at a geyser? **(6.1.d)**
    - **a.** Water erupts through a narrow channel.
    - **b.** Warm water flows into a calm pool.
    - **c.** Lava erupts out of a volcano.
    - **d.** Lava flows gently down the side of a volcano.

Short Answer *Write a short answer to each question.*

13. Describe how an old mountain belt located in the center of a continent most likely formed. **(6.1.e)**
14. How are the locations of volcanoes related to tectonic plate boundaries? **(6.1.f)**
15. What causes a shield volcano to be shaped like a broad dome? **(6.1.d)**
16. By what processes can a volcanic eruption affect temperatures around the world? **(6.2.d)**

ASSESSMENT RESOURCES

ASSESSMENT BOOK
- Chapter Test A, pp. 218–221
- Chapter Test B, pp. 222–225
- Chapter Test C, pp. 226–229
- Alternative Assessment, pp. 230–231
- Unit Test, A, B, C, pp. 232–243
- Unit Alternative Assessment, pp. 244–245

STANDARDS REVIEW AND PRACTICE, pp. 3–4, 7–12, 21–22, 35–36, 51–52, 57–58

Technology Resources

Edit test items and answer choices.

 **Test Generator CD-ROM**

Visit **ClassZone.com** to extend test practice.

 **Test Practice**

Reviewing Vocabulary

1. folded mountain: forms when rocks bend into folds, forms where plates collide; both: forms where an oceanic plate sinks under a continent; volcano: is built up of molten rock and rock fragments, forms where magma reaches the surface

2. lava: is molten rock at Earth's surface; both: erupts from a volcano, has very high temperatures, is dangerous; pyroclastic flow: is dense cloud of superhot volcanic gases and rock fragments

3. volcano: is built up of molten rock and rock fragments, forms where magma reaches the surface; both: erupts, has source of heat underneath it; geyser: is a hot spring that shoots water into the air

Reviewing Key Concepts

4. b

5. a

6. c

7. d

8. a

9 b

10. c

11. d

12. a

13. It most likely formed as different parts of the continent pushed together along a collision boundary.

14. Volcanoes commonly occur at divergent boundaries and subduction boundaries.

15. many layers of lava that was low in silica, so it flowed easily and spread out in thin layers

16. A volcanic eruption can release enough sulfur dioxide to form a haze around the planet as well as volcanic ash that stays in the air for a long time. The haze and/or ash can decrease the amount of sunlight reaching Earth's surface and cause average temperatures to drop.

Thinking Critically

17. shield volcano, because the lava flows easily for long distances

18. no, because the eruptions of shield volcanoes are usually gentle and do not produce large amounts of ash

19. They might make breathing difficult and cause lung damage.

20. a steam explosion

21. It could cover farmland with lava. Over time, the lava could break down into rich soil.

22. increases in earthquakes, changes in the tilt of the ground, increases in temperatures on the volcano, changes in volcanic gases

23. folded mountains: stress is pushing the crust together; fault-block mountains: stress is pulling the crust apart

24. Diagrams should show a magma chamber beneath a shield volcano with a main conduit to the center and a side conduit to a small cinder cone on the side of the shield volcano.

25. composite volcanoes, because they are the most likely to erupt violently

26. The hot springs and geysers would cool over time and stop erupting.

27. The oceanic plate sinks, and magma forms and rises. Where two continents push together, neither plate sinks and no magma forms.

28. Different types and amounts of magma feed each volcano, causing various shapes to form as eruptions occur.

the BIG idea

29. An oceanic plate is sinking beneath a plate carrying continental crust.

30. A continental collision will occur. Folded mountains along the coast will be pushed up.

UNIT PROJECTS

Have students present their projects. Use the appropriate rubrics from the URB.

Unit Projects, pp. 5–10

Thinking Critically

This photograph shows a volcanic eruption. The volcano produces rivers of lava that flow long distances. Use the photograph to answer the next six questions.

17. **INFER** What kind of volcano is shown in the photograph? How do you know? **(6.1.d)**

18. **APPLY** Is this eruption likely to produce large amounts of ash that could lead to dangerous mudflows for many years afterward? Why or why not? **(6.2.d)**

19. **IDENTIFY EFFECTS** How might volcanic gases affect the health of people and animals living near the volcano? **(6.2.d)**

20. **ANALYZE** What would be likely to happen if a large amount of water reached the volcano's magma chamber? **(6.1.d)**

21. **COMPARE AND CONTRAST** How could this volcano affect nearby farmland during the eruption? many years after the eruption? **(6.2.d)**

22. **SYNTHESIZE** What types of changes would let scientists monitoring the volcano know that an eruption was likely to occur? **(6.1.e)**

23. **COMPARE AND CONTRAST** How does the stress on continental crust in areas where folded mountains form differ from that in areas where fault-block mountains form? **(6.1.e)**

24. **APPLY** Draw a diagram showing how one magma chamber can supply magma to a shield volcano and to a cinder cone on the side of the shield volcano. **(6.1.d)**

25. **INFER** Many of the volcanoes in the Ring of Fire erupt explosively. Would you expect these volcanoes to be cinder cones, shield volcanoes, or composite volcanoes? Explain your answer **(6.1.d)**.

26. **PREDICT** How might an area with many hot springs and geysers be affected as magma and hot rock near the surface cooled? **(6.1.d)**

27. **ANALYZE** Why do volcanoes form along boundaries where oceanic plates are pushing into other plates but not along boundaries where continents are pushing together? **(6.1.e)**

28. **APPLY** Explain why shield volcanoes, composite volcanoes, and cinder cones have different sizes and shapes. **(6.1.d)**

the BIG idea

29. **INFER** How would you expect tectonic plates to be moving at a plate boundary where folded mountains are being pushed up and volcanoes are erupting? **(6.1.e)**

30. **PREDICT** If tectonic plates continue to move as they are moving today, the continents of Australia and Antarctica will collide in the far future. What will happen after the sea floor that is now between the continents is destroyed? **(6.1.e)**

UNIT PROJECTS

Evaluate all of the data, results, and information from your project folder. Prepare to present your project to the class. Be ready to answer questions posed by your classmates about your results.

MONITOR AND RETEACH

If students have trouble applying the concepts in items 15, 24, and 28, suggest that they review the visuals on pp. 350–351. Have them orally explain how each type of volcano forms. Then they can answer the questions by using the diagram.

Students may benefit from summarizing one or more sections of the chapter.

Summarizing the Chapter, pp. 200–201

Standards-Based Assessment

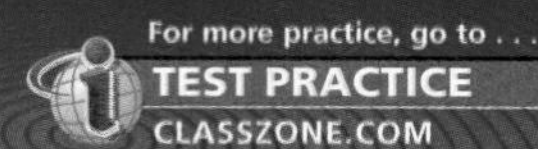

Analyzing Data

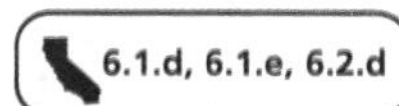

The graph below shows the amounts of lava, rock, and other materials released in four large volcanic eruptions. Study the graph, then answer the questions below.

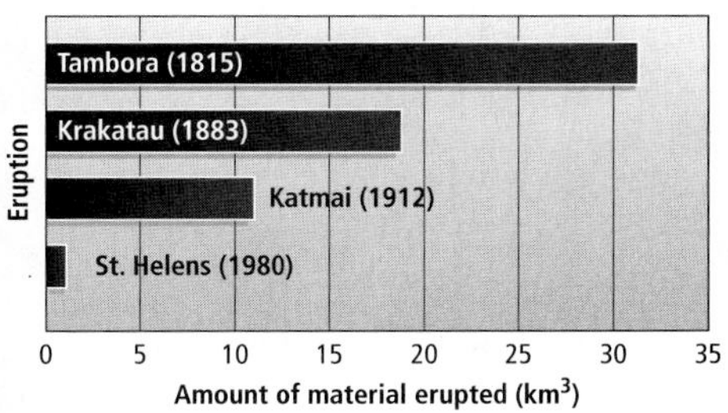

1. About how much material did the eruption of Katmai release in 1912?
   a. 12 km^3
   b. 17 km^3
   c. 29 km^3
   d. 41 km^3

2. After 1850, which of these eruptions released the greatest amount of material?
   a. Krakatau
   b. Tambora
   c. Katmai
   d. St. Helens

3. About how much more material erupted from Krakatau in 1883 than from Katmai in 1912?
   a. 28 km^3
   b. 12 km^3
   c. 6 km^3
   d. 2 km^3

4. Katmai, a large mountain built of layers of hardened lava flows and of rock fragments, is a
   a. cinder cone
   b. shield volcano
   c. pyroclastic cone
   d. composite volcano

5. How much material did the 1815 eruption of Tambora produce compared with the 1883 eruption of Krakatau?
   a. less than one-half the amount
   b. a nearly equal amount
   c. almost two times the amount
   d. almost four times the amount

6. All of the eruptions shown in the graph created calderas—craters formed by the collapse of volcanoes—because the eruptions were large enough to
   a. mostly empty the volcanoes' magma chambers
   b. produce lava that flowed long distances
   c. produce lava that had a low silica content
   d. form dangerous pyroclastic flows and mudflows

7. The average temperature of Earth can decrease for several years when a huge volcanic eruption adds to the atmosphere large amounts of
   a. acid rain
   b. energy
   c. volcanic cinders
   d. volcanic gases

8. A thick layer of volcanic ash can be heavy enough to collapse the roofs of buildings because ash
   a. is produced as rocks burn
   b. is made up of tiny pieces of rock
   c. becomes heavier as it cools
   d. can hold large amounts of water

Extended Response

Answer the two questions below in detail. Include some of the terms shown in the word box. In your answers, underline each term you use.

boundaries	hot spots	rising
subduction	magma	heat
spreading centers		

9. Petra is marking the locations of active volcanoes on a map of the world. Explain how the locations of the volcanoes are related to the locations of tectonic plates.

10. Scientists regularly check the temperature of a lake on a volcano. Explain how this information might help them learn whether the volcano is becoming more active.

REFLECTING ON THE CHAPTER

Have students answer the following questions in their **Science Notebook:**

1. What did you find most difficult to understand about mountains and volcanoes?
2. What ideas did you have that you learned were incorrect?
3. How do the concepts of this chapter apply to your Unit Project?

California Content Standards

6.1.d Students know that earthquakes are sudden motions along breaks in the crust called faults and that volcanoes and fissures are locations where magma reaches the surface.

6.1.e Students know major geologic events, such as earthquakes, volcanic eruptions, and mountain building, result from plate motions.

6.2.d Students know earthquakes, volcanic eruptions, landslides, and floods change human and wildlife habitats.

Analyzing Data

1. a *3. c* *5. c* *7. d*

2. a *4. d* *6. a* *8. b*

Extended Response

9. RUBRIC

4 points for a response that correctly explains the relationship between volcanoes and tectonic plates and uses the underlined terms accurately.

Sample: Volcanoes are common at subduction zones along plate boundaries where an oceanic plate sinks beneath another plate. As the oceanic plate sinks, it partially melts into magma, which rises to form volcanoes. Volcanoes are also common at spreading centers where plates pull apart, allowing magma to rise from the mantle. Volcanoes can also form over hot spots far from plate boundaries as material rises from the mantle and melts the crust above it.

3 points correctly explains the relationship and uses three terms accurately
2 points correctly answers with two terms
1 point correctly answers with no terms

10. RUBRIC

4 points for a response that correctly explains the relationship between rising lake temperatures and increased volcanic activity and uses the underlined terms accurately.

Sample: Increased temperatures might mean that magma is rising under the volcano and heating lakes, springs, and other openings on the volcano.

3 points correctly explains the relationship and uses two terms accurately
2 points correctly explains answers with one term
1 point correctly answers with no terms

UNIT 4

Ecology and Resources

symbiosis

Tickbird
(Buphagus erythrorhynchus)

Impala
(Aepyceros melampus)

Contents Overview

Unit 4 Scientific Background

Below is an in-depth look at some subtopics of the concepts presented in this unit.

ECOSYSTEMS AND BIOMES: Primary Producers and Consumers

The oceans cover more than 70 percent of Earth's surface and have a variety of ecosystems, just as the landmasses do. In comparing marine and terrestrial ecosystems, some key differences are apparent among primary producers and consumers on land, in the ocean's upper layer, and in the ocean's deep-sea vents.

On Land The majority of primary producers on land are trees and other plants, which produce food for themselves and for animals through photosynthesis. Trees and other plants on land are comparatively large and anchored in place by roots. The primary consumers of terrestrial plants are varied and include insects, snails, seed-eating birds, and grazing mammals.

In the Ocean's Photic Zone Most of the primary production in the ocean occurs in the upper layer called the *photic zone,* where enough sunlight penetrates for photosynthesis to occur. The primary marine producers are *phytoplankton*, which are organisms that photosynthesize and drift with the ocean currents. The phytoplankton consists mostly of microscopic algae. Unlike the primary producers on land, these organisms are small and are not anchored to one site. The primary consumers of the phytoplankton are the *zooplankton*, small animals that also drift with the ocean currents. Krill and small crustaceans called copepods are typical zooplankton.

In Deep-Sea Vents Sunlight never reaches the deep-sea hydrothermal vents, which occur along spreading centers on the ocean floor. In these areas, seawater seeps into the hot crust, dissolves minerals, and spews back up. The primary producers in these hot, dark regions are archaea, bacteria-like organisms that produce food through a process called chemosynthesis. Unlike terrestrial plants and marine phytoplankton, archaea do not require sunlight to produce food. Archaea produce food for themselves and other organisms by oxidizing hydrogen sulfide. Some archaea are symbionts that live inside and provide food for giant tubeworms, which grow up to 3 meters (10 feet) long. Other primary consumers of archaea are yellow mussels, giant white clams, and pink sea urchins.

INTERACTIONS WITHIN ECOSYSTEMS: Redwood Forests

The redwood forests of northern California are a unique and endangered ecosystem. Groves of Coast Redwood *(Sequoia sempervirens)* grow along the Pacific Coast from central California to southern Oregon in the moist environments produced by coastal fogs in the summer and Pacific storms in the winter. The redwoods are among the largest and oldest trees in the world, growing more than 60 meters (200 feet) tall and living for more than 2,000 years. Redwood forests have a higher biomass than any other ecosystem on land.

Thriving in the area called the fog belt, redwoods depend on California's summer fog for water. The leaves of the trees absorb some of the water from fog directly. Water that condenses on the leaves also drips to the ground, supplying water not only to the trees' roots but also to other plants. Up to two-thirds of the water used by understory plants in the summer comes from this source.

Large redwood trees have a complex structure, with multiple trunks growing from other trunks. Some trees have hundreds of trunks, leading ecologists to call the crown of a redwood tree a forest in itself.

Redwoods shed their leaves annually. Some of the shed foliage falls on the large branches, where it decomposes to form "canopy soil." Plants and fungi grow in this soil, forming the base of a canopy community. Plants that grow on other plants are called *epiphytes*. Several types of ferns grow on redwood trees, forming mats that can weigh hundreds of kilograms. Because redwoods are so large, even shrubs and other trees grow as epiphytes on them.

The redwood canopy also supports an animal community that includes beetles, earthworms, mollusks, arthropods, amphibians, and birds. The clouded salamander lives in the redwood canopy and is the only species of canopy-living salamander outside the tropics of the Western Hemisphere. Many species of birds, including peregrine falcons, bald eagles, northern spotted owls, great white egrets, great blue herons, and endangered marbled murrelets nest in redwood trees.

NATURAL RESOURCES: Energy Efficiency

Energy efficiency refers to the percentage of useful energy produced in an energy-conversion process. When energy is converted and transmitted, much of the original energy from the source is lost, typically as wasted heat. For example, more than 98 percent of the original energy in coal may be lost during all the steps involved in converting it to electricity, transmitting the electricity to a home, and changing the electricity into light in an incandescent light bulb. That means the overall energy efficiency of the process is less than 2 percent.

Improved Technologies A great deal of research has been devoted to developing more energy-efficient technologies for generating, storing, transmitting, and using energy. The goal of this research is to increase the usable energy obtained from a fuel or other energy source. New technologies already in use have increased the energy efficiency of some power plants. Newer power plants may be 50 percent more efficient than older ones.

Newer consumer products also have improved in energy efficiency. Fluorescent light bulbs are four times as efficient as incandescent light bulbs. New refrigerators, washers, driers, and other home appliances are much more energy-efficient than older ones, and hybrid electric cars have much higher fuel efficiencies than standard gasoline-engine cars.

Renewable Resources The further development of certain renewable energy sources could also contribute to energy efficiency. Hydrogen fuel cells, for example, can be highly efficient and could be used to power cars, to heat and cool buildings, and to provide electricity. Some fuel cell systems that produce heat and generate power have energy efficiencies of more than 80 percent, and hydrogen fuel cells can double or triple the energy efficiency of cars.

HUMAN IMPACT ON ECOSYSTEMS: Pollution Control

Power plant emissions are one of the main sources of air pollution. These emissions include sulfur dioxide, nitrogen oxides, carbon monoxide, lead, mercury, and particulate matter. These air pollutants adversely affect human health and contribute to smog and acid rain.

To help power plants meet federal regulations for reducing these emissions, the U.S. Department of Energy (DOE) has promoted the development of more effective pollution-control technologies, with an emphasis on the gas emissions of coal-fired plants. The focus on coal-fired power plants reflects the fact that they generate about 50 percent of the electricity used in the United States.

The technologies being developed for controlling the emissions of nitrogen oxides are an example of the multiple approaches being taken to pollution control. One approach focuses on burning coal in stages because nitrogen oxides only form in large amounts at very high temperatures. Staged combustion reduces the amount of nitrogen oxides that form. Burners that use staged combustion are called *low-NOx burners*. These burners are already in use and have been successful in reducing NOx emissions, but the DOE is working to develop advanced low-NOx burners to meet more stringent standards.

Reburning is another approach to reducing NOx emissions. In this process, a portion of the fuel is reburned under conditions of low oxygen, which breaks down nitrogen oxides formed during the original combustion.

Still another approach is to increase the amount of oxygen supplied during combustion. This increases the efficiency of the combustion, which means less fuel is used and so the amount of nitrogen is reduced. This method has reduced NOx emissions at glass melting furnaces by 80 to 90 percent.

FRONTIERS in Science

VIDEO SUMMARY

SCIENTIFIC AMERICAN FRONTIERS

"Prairie Comeback" is a segment of the Scientific American Frontiers series that aired on PBS stations. In this video, host Alan Alda visits the Tallgrass Prairie Preserve in northeastern Oklahoma. This is the location of an attempt to reconstruct an ecosystem that once covered more than a quarter of the continental United States. The Great Plains was once the largest grassland on Earth. Cultivation and the disappearance of wildlife, including buffalo herds, resulted in the prairie's disappearance. In 1989, the Nature Conservancy identified a large ranch that had never been farmed and therefore still had all the plants that grew on the original prairie. On 50 square miles of land, they have attempted to create a model of the prairie. They introduced a herd of buffalo to graze on the prairie plants. Today, a system based on controlled fires and grazing buffalo reproduces the life cycles of the original prairie.

California Content Standards

6.5.b Students know matter is transferred over time from one organism to others in the food web and between organisms and the physical environment.

6.5.e Students know the number and types of organisms an ecosystem can support depends on the resources available and on abiotic factors, such as quantities of light and water, a range of temperatures, and soil composition.

FRONTIERS in Science

ECOSYSTEMS ON FIRE

It may seem strange to set fire to a wilderness preserve, but fire brings health to some ecosystems.

California Content Standards

6.5.b Students know matter is transferred over time from one organism to others in the food web and between organisms and the physical environment.

6.5.e Students know the number and types of organisms an ecosystem can support depends on the resources available and on abiotic factors, such as quantities of light and water, a range of temperatures, and soil composition.

SCIENTIFIC AMERICAN FRONTIERS

View the video "Prairie Comeback" to learn about the restoration of a prairie ecosystem.

370 Unit 4: Ecology and Resources

ADDITIONAL RESOURCES

Technology Resources

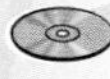
Scientific American Frontiers Video: *Ecosystems on Fire:* 8-minute video segment that introduces the unit.

ClassZone.com
CAREER LINK, Ecologist

Guide student viewing and comprehension of the video:

Video Teaching Guide, pp. 1–2; Video Viewing Guide, p. 3; Video Wrap-Up, p. 4

Scientific American Frontiers Video Guide, pp. 13–16

Unit projects procedures and rubrics:

Unit Projects, pp. 5–10

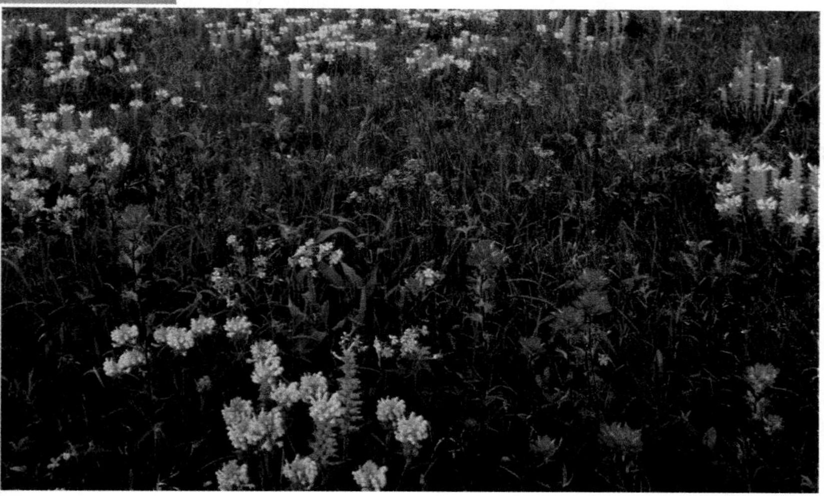
An astonishing variety of plants blooms in this prairie in Missouri.

Fire and Life

Intense heat, smoke, the crackling of burning grasses, the crashing of flaming trees—all these characteristics of fire seem threatening. In recent years, forest fires have burned huge areas of forest and have endangered people and property. But even though fire can be destructive, it can also bring forth life. In fact, scientists are actively using fire to manage ecosystems. Ecosystems are areas that contain specific groups of living and nonliving things. Prairies, forests, and woodlands are examples of ecosystems. **? A**

The fear of fire has led people to limit fires that are a natural part of some ecosystems. Preventing or putting out smaller fires in a forest ecosystem can mean trouble. Occasional small fires burn small amounts of material and cause only limited damage. Without these smaller fires, burnable materials may build up and lead to the outbreak of a terrible fire.

Species of living things in some ecosystems have adaptations that allow them to thrive after a fire. **? B** In western forests in North America, trees such as lodgepole pine and jack pine depend upon heat from a fire to release seeds from their cones. Cape lilies on the forest floor bloom almost immediately after a forest fire. On prairies, flowers such as the prairie fringed orchid in Illinois benefit from prairie fires.

DIFFERENTIATE INSTRUCTION

More Reading Support

A What are scientists using fire to do? *manage ecosystems*

B Why do some species survive and even thrive in fires? *because they have adaptations*

Advanced Have students determine the locations of major forests, woodlands, and prairies in the United States. Ask them to indicate these locations on a blank map. Students may wish to look up statistics on occurrences of wildfires in the United States and draw a conclusion about the conditions of these forests and prairies.

FOCUS

Set Learning Goals

Students will

- Observe positive and negative effects of prairie fires.
- Examine unanswered questions concerning ecosystem restoration.
- Explore the parts of an ecosystem.

Remind students that frontiers are undeveloped fields for discovery or research, and that the "Ecosystems on Fire" video shows real scientists gathering and analyzing data to find answers or solve problems. Have students look at the photographs and title on pp. 370–371 and predict what questions the scientists are trying to answer.

INSTRUCT

Scientific Process

Emphasize to students that understanding the effects of fires on ecosystems requires that scientists learn as much as they can about the plants and animals that live in the ecosystem. Have students review the parts of the scientific process on pages CA20–CA23 and ask what part this step falls under. *Determine what is known*.

Integrate the Sciences

Executing a controlled burn in an ecosystem requires attention to many details. Besides knowing how plants and animals will react to the effects of the fire, what other knowledge, skills, or personnel should scientists have before attempting a controlled burn? *They should know how to start fires and how fires spread.*

Teach from Visuals

Have students look at the photos of the forest after the controlled burn and seven months after the burn. Ask students why the second photo shows a healthier ecosystem. *There is new, green vegetation and the trees have leaves in the second photo.*

Scientific Process

Ask students to identify the skill scientists use most in studying ecosystems. *observing*

Sharing Results

Ask students why it is even more crucial that scientists share what they learn from their observations of different ecosystems with other scientists. *The lives of people and animals depend upon the ecosystem. The better scientists understand an ecosystem, the better they help preserve the lives that depend on it.*

Social Studies Connection

The American bison, or buffalo, has had a troubled existence in the United States. Once it was a major source of food and clothing for many Native American tribes. However, increased settlement on the prairie brought increased hunting and near extinction for the buffalo as well as for the Native Americans that depended on them.

Seven months after a controlled burn, light shines on a new patch of wild hyacinth growing at the base of an oak tree.

Observing Patterns

C

Ecosystems include living things, such as plants and animals. They also include nonliving things, such as water and soil. Fires affect both the living and the nonliving. The photographs above show part of an oak woodland ecosystem. The photograph on the left shows a burn—a fire set on purpose by humans. The photograph on the right shows the same area seven months later.

Ashes left from fires add nutrients to the soil. Fire also opens space on the forest floor. Areas that were shaded by small trees, shrubs, and dead branches receive light. Over time, wild hyacinth and other new plants grow around the oak, and new insects and animals move into the area.

View the "Prairie Comeback" segment of your Scientific American Frontiers video to see how understanding ecosystems can help bring a prairie into bloom.

IN THIS SCENE FROM THE VIDEO a bison grazes on new growth that appears after the prairie is burned.

BRINGING BACK THE PRAIRIE At one time natural events and human activity caused regular patterns of fire on the prairie. Bison grazed on tender young plants that grew up after fires, and the plants that weren't eaten by the bison had room to grow. In 1989 an organization called The Nature Conservancy turned the Chapman-Barnard Cattle Ranch in Northeast Oklahoma into the Tall Grass Prairie Restoration Preserve.

Scientists at the preserve are using controlled fire and reintroducing bison to the area. Today, there are more than 750 species of plants and animals growing in the preserve.

DIFFERENTIATE INSTRUCTION

More Reading Support

C What do ecosystems include? *living and nonliving things*

D Name two benefits of fires. *addition of nutrients, increased light*

Below Level Have students identify all of the words on this page that refer to protecting or safeguarding: *conservatory, restoration,* and *preserve.* Point out to students how the words *conservatory* and *preserve* share a stem, *–serve.* Have students think of another word that has this stem, like *reserve,* and ask if it has a similar meaning. *Yes. When you reserve something, you are protecting it in a way.*

In tall-grass prairie ecosystems, fire provides similar benefits. Fire burns away overgrown plants, enriches the soil, and clears the way for the growth of new plants. Bison prefer to graze on these new plants that appear after a fire.

A New Understanding

Some of the benefits provided by ecosystems can't be measured. But researchers are starting to measure the financial contributions of ecosystems. Ecosystems help clean our water, balance gases in the atmosphere, and maintain temperature ranges.

E

Researchers today are studying these benefits. A new frontier in ecology, called ecosystem services, is emerging. This new study is gaining the attention of both scientists and economists.

F

Given our growing awareness of the importance of ecosystems, should humans deliberately set fire to areas in forests or prairies? The answer to this question requires an understanding of interactions among living and nonliving parts of ecosystems. Forest and prairie fires can be dangerous. However, if properly managed, they can provide important benefits to society as well as to the natural world.

UNANSWERED Questions

Understanding the connections within ecosystems raises more questions. In the coming years, people will need to analyze the costs and benefits of ecosystem restoration.

- How will humans balance the need to feed the human population with the cost of destroying ecosystems such as the prairie?
- How can scientists and wildlife managers protect people and property near forests while maintaining forest ecosystems?
- How do ecosystems protect natural resources, such as soil and water?

UNIT PROJECTS

As you study this unit, work alone or with a group on one of the projects listed below. Use the bulleted steps to guide your project.

Build an Ecosystem (6.5.e)

Use an aquarium or other container to build an ecosystem.

- Set up your ecosystem. Observe it daily, and record your observations.
- Bring your ecosystem into your classroom, or take photographs and make diagrams of it. Present the record of your observations along with the visual displays.

Conservation Campaign (6.6.b)

Find out how much water, paper, and energy are used in a month at your school.

- Describe a plan for conserving resources.
- Present your plan. You might make posters, write announcements, or perform a short skit.

Design a Park (6.7.d, 6.7.h)

You are part of a group that is planning a park near your school. Your group wants the park to include plants that lived in the area twenty-five years ago.

- Collect information from local museums, park districts, or botanic gardens. You can also visit Web sites sponsored by those organizations.
- Prepare a report and drawing of your park design.

Learn more about careers in ecology.

UNANSWERED Questions

Have students read the questions and think of some of their own. Remind them that scientists always end up with more questions—that inquiry is the driving force of science.

- With the class, generate on the board a list of new questions.
- Students can add to the list after they watch the *Scientific American Frontiers* Video.
- Students can use the list as a springboard for choosing their Unit Projects.

UNIT PROJECTS

Encourage students to pick the project that most appeals to them. Point out that each is long-term and will take several weeks to complete. You might group or pair students to work on projects and in some cases guide student choice. Each project has two worksheet pages, in–cluding a rubric to guide students through criteria, process, and schedule.

 Unit Projects, pp. 5–10

REVISIT concepts introduced in this article:

Chapter 11
- Ecosystems support life, pp. 377–383
- Living things depend on the environment, pp. 377–378
- All ecosystems need certain materials, p. 384

Chapter 12
- Groups of living things interact within ecosystems, pp. 413–419
- Ecosystems are always changing, pp. 431–437

Chapter 14
- Human activities affect the environment, pp. 497–505
- People are working to protect ecosystems, pp. 506–515

DIFFERENTIATE INSTRUCTION

More Reading Support

E Name one way ecosystems help us. *clean water, balance gases in the atmosphere*

F Who is interested in ecosystem services? *scientists and economists*

Differentiate Unit Projects Projects are appropriate for varying abilities. Allow students to choose the ones that interest them most and let them vary their product. Encourage below level students to give visual or oral presentations or to record audio presentations about their topic.

Below Level Encourage students to try "Build an Ecosystem."

Advanced Challenge students to complete "Design a Park."

CHAPTER

Ecosystems and Biomes

Life Science
UNIFYING PRINCIPLES

PRINCIPLE 1
All living things share common characteristics.

PRINCIPLE 2
All living things share common needs.

PRINCIPLE 3
Living things meet their needs through interactions with the environment.

PRINCIPLE 4
The types and numbers of living things change over time.

Unit: Ecology and Resources
BIG IDEAS

CHAPTER 11
Ecosystems and Biomes
Matter and energy together support life within an environment.

CHAPTER 12
Interactions Within Ecosystems
Living things within an ecosystem interact with each other and the environment.

CHAPTER 13
Natural Resources
Society depends on natural resources for energy and materials.

CHAPTER 14
Human Impact on Ecosystems
Humans and human population growth affect the environment.

CHAPTER 11
KEY CONCEPTS

SECTION 1

Ecosystems support life.
1. Living things depend on the environment.
2. Biotic factors interact with an ecosystem.
3. Many abiotic factors affect ecosystems.

SECTION 2

Matter cycles through ecosystems.
1. All ecosystems need certain materials.
2. Water cycles through ecosystems.
3. Carbon cycles through ecosystems.
4. Nitrogen cycles through ecosystems.

SECTION 3

Energy flows through ecosystems.
1. Living things capture and release energy.
2. Models help explain feeding relationships.
3. Available energy decreases as it moves through an ecosystem.

SECTION 4

Biomes contain many ecosystems.
1. Regions of Earth are classified into biomes.
2. Water covers most of Earth's surface.

The Big Idea Flow Chart is available on p. T81 in the **TRANSPARENCY BOOK.**

Previewing Content

SECTION

1 Ecosystems support life. pp. 377–383

1. Living things depend on the environment.
An **ecosystem** comprises organisms and their physical environment. **Ecology** is the scientific study of how organisms interact with their environment and with other organisms.
- Natural ecosystems include water, air, and sunlight, as well as microorganisms, plants, and animals.
- **Biotic factors** are the living parts of an ecosystem.
- **Abiotic factors** are the nonliving parts.

2. Biotic factors interact with an ecosystem.
Every organism affects, and is affected by, other organisms in its ecosystem. Moles are a good example of this interrelatedness. They eat insects, worms, and grubs. They can severely damage plants, but moles help keep insect populations in check. Mole tunnels aerate soil, which is necessary for the growth of soil organisms and plant roots.

3. Many abiotic factors affect ecosystems.
Abiotic factors include any nonliving features of the environment, from soil fertility to climate characteristics—precipitation, temperature, air currents, and humidity. Here is a short list of the most influential factors.
- available water
- temperature
- available light
- soil content

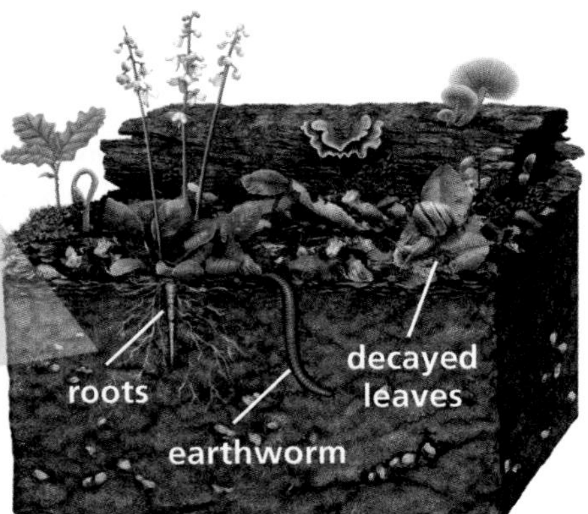

The size of soil particles affects how much air and water the soil can hold.

SECTION

2 Matter cycles through ecosystems. pp. 384–389

1. All ecosystems need certain materials.
Living things need certain materials, or matter, to meet their needs. This matter remains in the ecosystem, moving through it in continuous **cycles,** in which the matter changes form, but is never created or destroyed.

2. Water cycles through ecosystems.
All substances on Earth, including water, are repeatedly recycled. Five processes make up the water cycle.
- Condensation: water vapor condenses to liquid in the atmosphere.
- Precipitation: water falls back to Earth.
- Transpiration: plants take up water in their roots and release it from their leaves.
- Respiration: animals release water vapor as they exhale.
- Evaporation: heat changes liquid water to gaseous water vapor, which rises into the atmosphere.

3. Carbon cycles through ecosystems.
Life on Earth is based on carbon compounds. The **carbon cycle** includes several different processes.
- Photosynthesis removes carbon from the air.
- Animals obtain carbon by eating plants.
- Plants and animals release carbon dioxide during respiration.
- Carbon contained in fossil fuels and wood is released as carbon dioxide during combustion.

4. Nitrogen cycles through ecosystems.
Nitrogen is required for all life. Almost 78 percent of the air is nitrogen, but organisms cannot use nitrogen in gaseous form. In the **nitrogen cycle**, bacteria in soil and roots fix nitrogen by changing it from a gas to nitrate compounds that can be taken up by plants.

Common Misconceptions

MISCONCEPTION DATABASE
CLASSZONE.COM Background on student misconceptions

PHOTOSYNTHESIS Students generally think that plants absorb food from the soil rather than manufacturing it. Through photosynthesis, plants make food—sugars—from sunlight, carbon dioxide, and water from the environment.

 This misconception is addressed on p. 380.

WATER CYCLE Though students may be familiar with the water cycle, they often think that water gets added to the system from somewhere. Earth has a finite amount of water that cycles through living things and the environment continuously.

 This misconception is addressed on p. 385.

Previewing Content

SECTION

Energy flows through ecosystems.
pp. 390–397

1. Living things capture and release energy.
Energy and matter can move through an ecosystem as food.

- **Producers** capture energy from sunlight or, in a few cases, from chemicals in the deep sea.
- **Consumers** obtain food by eating producers or other consumers.
- **Decomposers** break down dead plant and animal matter into simpler compounds, returning them to the water or soil so that the matter may be used again.

2. Models help explain feeding relationships.
Food chains and food webs are models that show how energy and matter move through the organisms of an ecosystem.

- A **food chain** shows one path of energy movement through an ecosystem, from producer (e.g., grass) to herbivore or primary consumer (grasshopper), to a secondary consumer (robin), to a tertiary consumer (hawk).
- A **food web** shows many paths of energy movement through an ecosystem. It indicates that each organism eats and is eaten by several organisms.

3. Available energy decreases as it moves through an ecosystem.
An **energy pyramid** models the amount of energy available to producers and consumers in an ecosystem. At the bottom of the pyramid are the producers, which use the Sun's abundant energy to manufacture sugars. At the top of the pyramid are the tertiary consumers.
This model shows that the amount of available energy decreases with each succeeding layer.

SECTION

Biomes contain many ecosystems.
pp. 398–405

1. Regions of Earth are classified into biomes.
Earth's six terrestrial **biomes** are regions made up of ecosystems with similar plant life and climate.

- Tundra has little precipitation and lowest temperatures of all land biomes. Typical vegetation is lichens and mosses.
- Taiga has cold winters and short, cool summers. It supports **coniferous** trees with needlelike leaves.
- Desert has little precipitation and can be hot or cold. Typical vegetation is cacti and small plants.
- Grassland has rich soil but supports few shrubs and trees.
- Temperate forest includes mostly **deciduous** trees.
- Tropical rain forest is consistently warm and wet. Typical vegetation is broadleaf evergreen trees, with a huge number of species.

2. Water covers most of Earth's surface.
Freshwater biomes include

- rivers and streams, with high oxygen levels; plants are limited to shorelines and slow-moving shallows.
- lakes and ponds, with middling to very low oxygen levels; plants grow along the shoreline or float in upper layers.
- wetlands, such as swamps and bogs, that are wet most or all of the year; waterlogged soils limit plant species.
- **estuaries,** which are mixed fresh and salt water, where river meets ocean; fertile ecosystems act as nurseries for fish and other sea animals.

Marine biomes include

- coastal ocean, or seashore areas; many ecosystems, from sandy beaches to mud flats to rocky shores.
- open ocean to depths where sunlight stops penetrating; the plankton here serve as the basis of the ocean food web.
- deep ocean, where sunlight does not reach.

Common Misconceptions

MISCONCEPTION DATABASE
CLASSZONE.COM Background on student misconceptions

FOOD CHAINS AND WEBS Students often think of feeding relationships as linear. They may misunderstand the food chain model in several ways: 1. They think arrows represent who eats whom rather than flow of energy; 2. They think organisms high up the chain eat everything that is lower on the chain; 3. They see only linear food chains as unconnected to a food web.

 This misconception is addressed on p. 394.

PYRAMID OF ENERGY Students commonly think that energy accumulates as it moves up a food chain or web. In reality, significant amounts of available energy are lost moving up a food chain or web. The least amount of energy is available and the fewest number of organisms are present at the top of an energy pyramid.

 This misconception is addressed in the Teach from Visuals on p. 396.

Previewing Labs

Lab Generator CD-ROM
Edit these Pupil Edition labs and generate alternative labs.

EXPLORE the BIG idea

How Do Plants React to Sunlight? p. 375 Students observe a plant's response to light.	**TIME** 10 minutes **MATERIALS** potted plant
Internet Activity: A Prairie Ecosystem, p. 375 Students simulate a prairie ecosystem.	**TIME** 20 minutes **MATERIALS** computer with Internet access

SECTION 

EXPLORE Your Environment, p. 377 Students measure the temperature in different places to discover variations in warmth.	**TIME** 10 minutes **MATERIALS** thermometer, stopwatch
CHAPTER INVESTIGATION Testing Soil, pp. 382–383 Students investigate soil properties. **ALTERNATIVE:** Reading Activity, URB p. 273	**TIME** 40 minutes, plus time for materials to settle overnight **MATERIALS** dried soil sample, 250 mL graduated cylinder, 1 qt jar with lid, water, 2 L plastic bottle, scissors, window screening, rubber band, pH test strips, clock with second hand; *for Challenge*: Texture Flow Chart

SECTION 

EXPLORE The Water Cycle, p. 384 Students cover part of a plant and discover that plants give off water vapor.	**TIME** 10 minutes **MATERIALS** 1 small potted plant, 1 clear plastic bag, tape, water
INVESTIGATE Carbon, p. 387 Students observe how carbon is released in the ocean by adding vinegar to broken sea shells. **ALTERNATIVE:** Teacher Demonstration, URB p. 273	**TIME** 15 minutes **MATERIALS** whole seashell or fragments, mortar and pestle, white vinegar, small beaker

SECTION 

EXPLORE Energy, p. 390 Students observe that all objects have energy, even when they are stationary.	**TIME** 10 minutes **MATERIALS** large plastic bowl, sand, pebble, rock
INVESTIGATE Decomposers, p. 393 Students observe the effect of decomposers on plant matter. **ALTERNATIVE:** Teacher Demonstration, URB p. 273	**TIME** 30 minutes **MATERIALS** clear plastic bottle with cap, scissors, stones, garden soil, leaves, slices of fruit, masking tape, marker, water

SECTION 

INVESTIGATE Climate, p. 403 Students collect and graph climate data for their area. **ALTERNATIVE:** Reading Activity, URB p. 273 Climate Graph, p. 52	**TIME** 20 minutes **MATERIALS** graph data, 2 colored pencils, Climate Graph

 **Additional INVESTIGATION,** The Water Cycle, A, B, & C, pp. 72–80; Teacher Instructions, pp. 273–275

Previewing Chapter Resources

CHAPTER 11 Ecosystems and Biomes

INTEGRATED TECHNOLOGY

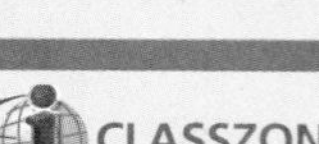
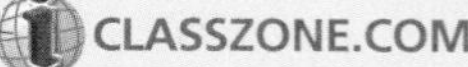

CLASSZONE.COM
- eEdition Plus
- EasyPlanner Plus
- Misconception Database
- Content Review
- Test Practice
- Visualizations
- Resource Centers
- Internet Activity: A Prairie Ecosystem
- Math Tutorial

SCILINKS.ORG

SCILINKS

CD-ROMS
- eEdition
- EasyPlanner
- Power Presentations
- Content Review
- Lab Generator
- Test Generator

AUDIO CDS
- Audio Readings
- Audio Readings in Spanish

LABS AND ACTIVITIES

EXPLORE the Big Idea, p. 375
- How Do Plants React to Sunlight?
- Internet Activity: A Prairie Ecosystem

UNIT RESOURCE BOOK
- Family Letter, p. ix
- Spanish Family Letter, p. x
- Unit Projects, pp. 5–10

Lab Generator CD-ROM
Generate customized labs.

SECTION

1 Ecosystems support life.
pp. 377–383

Lesson Plan, pp. 11–12

RESOURCE CENTER, Ecosystems

TRANSPARENCY BOOK
- Big Idea Flow Chart, p. T81
- Daily Vocabulary Scaffolding, p. T82
- Note-Taking Model, p. T83
- 3-Minute Warm-Up, p. T84

- EXPLORE Your Environment, p. 377
- CHAPTER INVESTIGATION Testing Soil, pp. 382–383

UNIT RESOURCE BOOK
- Texture Flow Charts, p. 62
- CHAPTER INVESTIGATION, Testing Soil, A, B, & C, pp. 63–71

SECTION

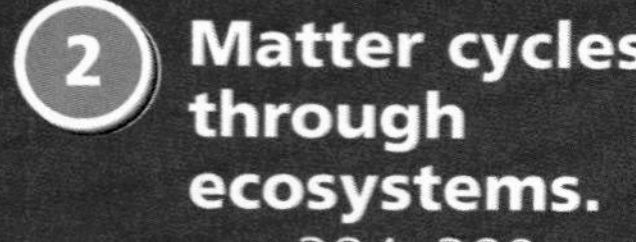

2 Matter cycles through ecosystems.
pp. 384–389

Lesson Plan, pp. 21–22

- **RESOURCE CENTER,** Cycles in Nature
- **VISUALIZATION,** Nitrogen Cycle
- **MATH TUTORIAL**

TRANSPARENCY BOOK
- Daily Vocabulary Scaffolding, p. T82
- 3-Minute Warm-Up, p. T84

- EXPLORE The Water Cycle, p. 384
- INVESTIGATE Carbon, p. 387
- Math in Science, p. 389

UNIT RESOURCE BOOK
- Datasheet, Carbon, p. 30
- Math Support and Practice, pp. 60–61
- Additional INVESTIGATION, The Water Cycle, A, B, & C, pp. 72–80

SECTION

3 Energy flows through ecosystems.
pp. 390–397

Lesson Plan, pp. 32–33

TRANSPARENCY BOOK
- Daily Vocabulary Scaffolding, p. T82
- 3-Minute Warm-Up, p. T85
- "Energy Flows Through Ecosystems" Visual, p. T86

- EXPLORE Energy, p. 390
- INVESTIGATE Decomposers, p. 393
- Connecting Sciences, p. 397

UNIT RESOURCE BOOK
Datasheet, Decomposers, p. 41

SECTION

4 Biomes contain many ecosystems.
pp. 398–405

Lesson Plan, pp. 43–44

RESOURCE CENTER, Land and Aquatic Biomes

TRANSPARENCY BOOK
- Big Idea Flow Chart, p. T81
- Daily Vocabulary Scaffolding, p. T82
- 3-Minute Warm-Up, p. T85
- Chapter Outline, pp. T87–T88

INVESTIGATE Climate, p. 403

UNIT RESOURCE BOOK
- Climate Graph, p. 52
- Datasheet, Climate, p. 53

KEY TO ICONS: CD/CD-ROM · Teacher Edition · TRANSPARENCY BOOK · STANDARDS REVIEW AND PRACTICE · INTERNET · Pupil Edition · UNIT RESOURCE BOOK · ASSESSMENT BOOK · SCIENCE TOOLKIT

READING AND REINFORCEMENT	ASSESSMENT	STANDARDS
Modified Lesson Plans for English Learners, pp. 40–43 • Frame Game, B26–27 • Combination Notes, C36 • Daily Vocabulary Scaffolding, H1–8 **UNIT RESOURCE BOOK** • Vocabulary Practice, pp. 57–58 • Decoding Support, p. 59 • Summarizing the Chapter, pp. 81–82 **Audio Readings CD** Listen to Pupil Edition. **Audio Readings in Spanish CD** Listen to Pupil Edition in Spanish.	• Chapter Review, pp. 407–408 • Standards-Based Assessment, p. 409 **ASSESSMENT BOOK** • Diagnostic Test, pp. 248–249 • Chapter Test, A, B, & C, pp. 254–265 • Alternative Assessment, pp. 266–267 **STANDARDS REVIEW AND PRACTICE,** pp. 15–16, 27–28, 41–44, 47–50, 59–60 **McDougal Littell Assessment System** **Test Generator CD-ROM** Generate customized and Spanish tests.	California Content Standards 6.2.a, 6.3.c, 6.5.a, 6.5.b, 6.5.d, 6.5.e, 6.7.b, 6.7.c, 6.7.h See p. 374 for the standards.
UNIT RESOURCE BOOK • Reading Study Guide, A & B, pp. 13–16 • Spanish Reading Study Guide, pp. 17–18 • Challenge and Extension, p. 19 • Reinforcing Key Concepts, p. 20	Ongoing Assessment, pp. 378–381 Section 11.1 Review, p. 381 **ASSESSMENT BOOK** Section 11.1 Quiz, p. 250	California Content Standards 6.5.a, 6.5.e, 6.7.b
UNIT RESOURCE BOOK • Reading Study Guide, A & B, pp. 23–26 • Spanish Reading Study Guide, pp. 27–28 • Challenge and Extension, p. 29 • Reinforcing Key Concepts, p. 31	Ongoing Assessment, pp. 385–388 Section 11.2 Review, p. 388 **ASSESSMENT BOOK** Section 11.2 Quiz, p. 251	California Content Standards 6.2.a, 6.3.c, 6.5.b
UNIT RESOURCE BOOK • Reading Study Guide, A & B, pp. 34–37 • Spanish Reading Study Guide, pp. 38–39 • Challenge and Extension, p. 40 • Reinforcing Key Concepts, p. 42 • Challenge Reading, pp. 55–56	Ongoing Assessment, pp. 391–395 Section 11.3 Review, p. 396 **ASSESSMENT BOOK** Section 11.3 Quiz, p. 252	California Content Standards 6.5.a, 6.5.b
**UNIT RESOURCE BOOK** • Reading Study Guide, A & B, pp. 45–48 • Spanish Reading Study Guide, pp. 49–50 • Challenge and Extension, p. 51 • Reinforcing Key Concepts, p. 54	Ongoing Assessment, pp. 400, 402, 404–405 Section 11.4 Review, p. 405 **ASSESSMENT BOOK** Section 11.4 Quiz, p. 253	California Content Standards 6.5.d, 6.7.c, 6.7.h

Previewing Resources for Differentiated Instruction

CHAPTER INVESTIGATION

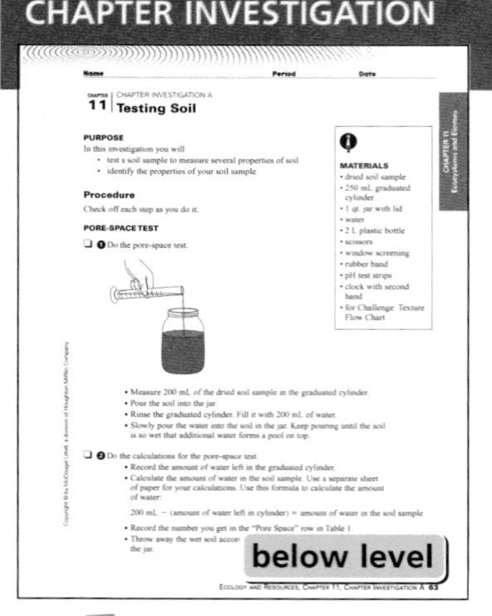

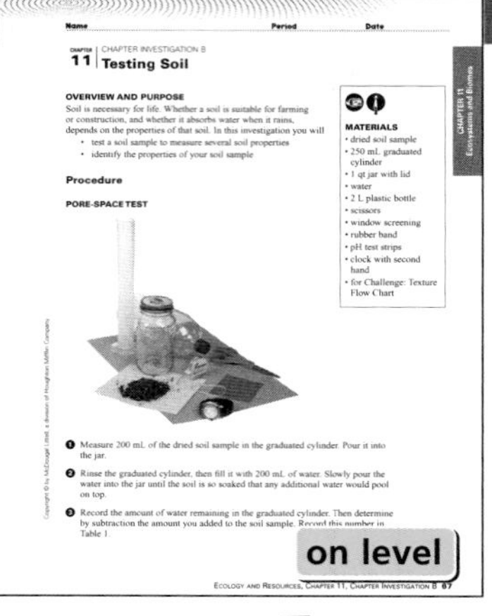

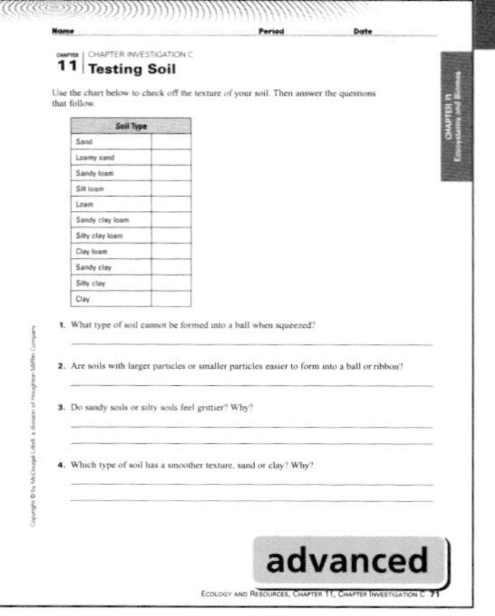

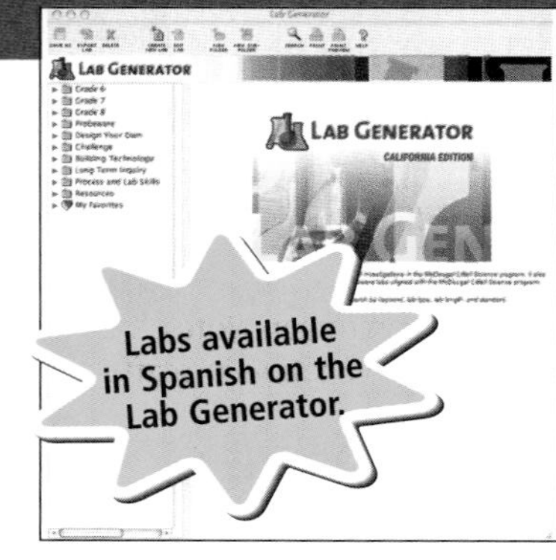

R UNIT RESOURCE BOOK, pp. 63–66

R pp. 67–70

R pp. 67–71

READING STUDY GUIDE

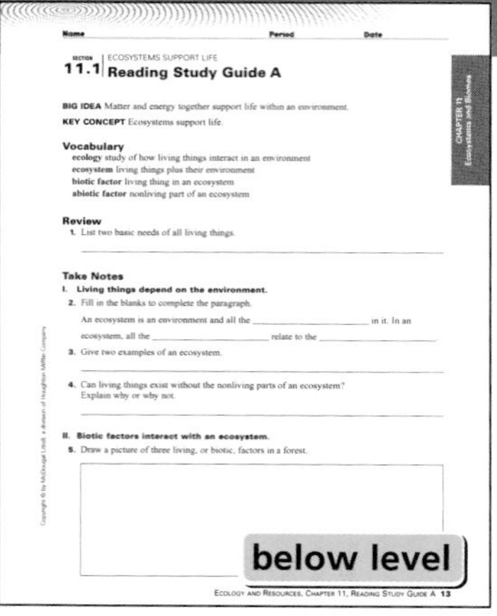

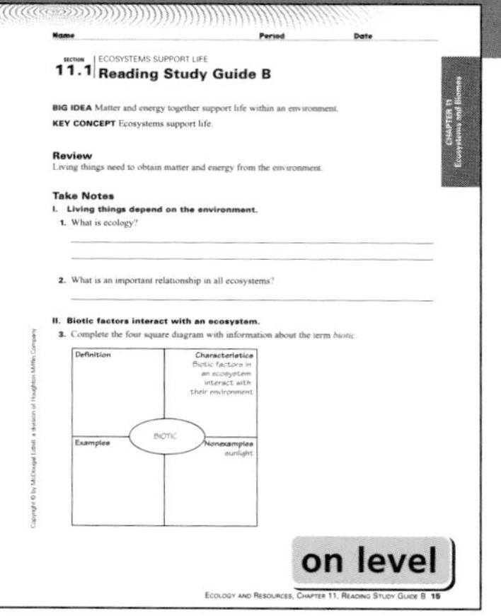

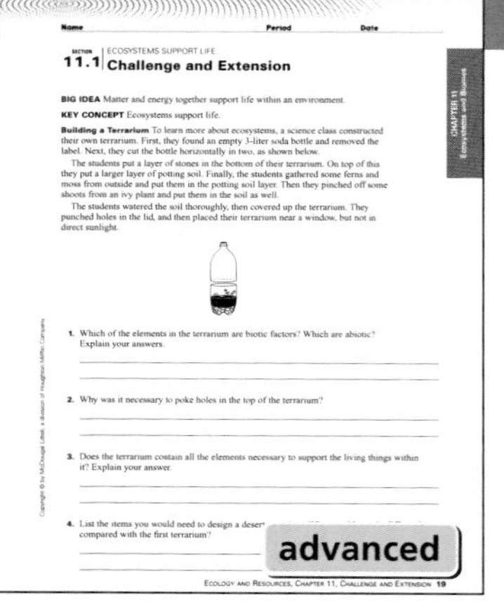

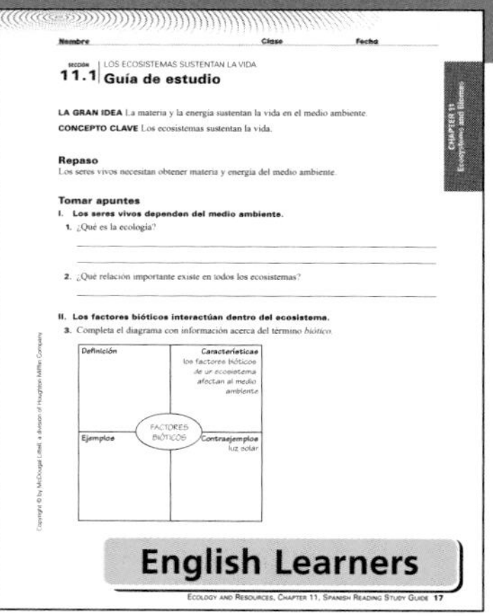

R UNIT RESOURCE BOOK, pp. 13–14

R pp. 15–16

R p. 19

R p. 17

CHAPTER TEST

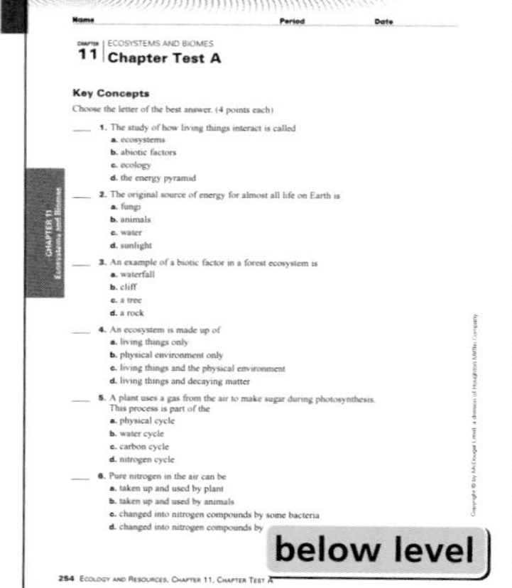

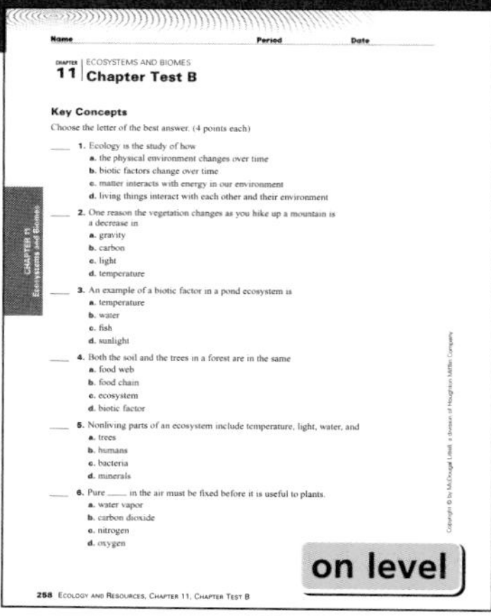

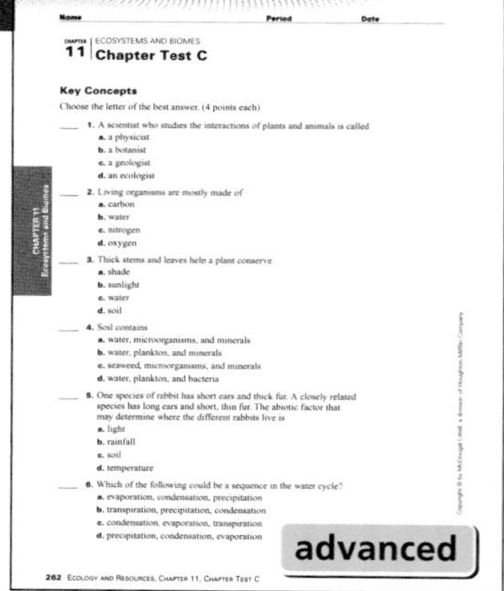

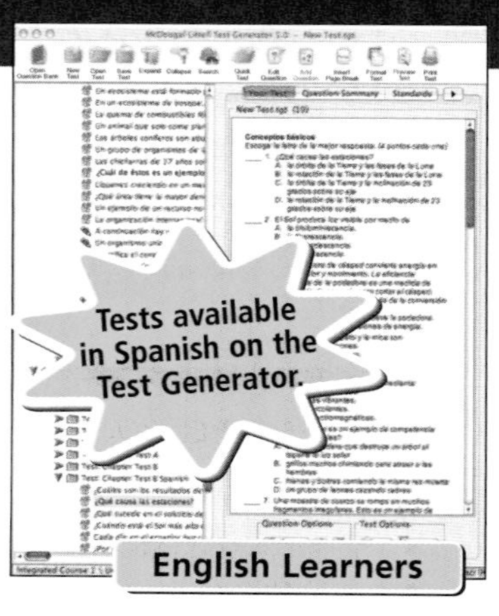

A ASSESSMENT BOOK, pp. 254–257

A pp. 258–261

A pp. 262–265

TECHNOLOGY

This chapter has four Resource Centers and one Visualization.

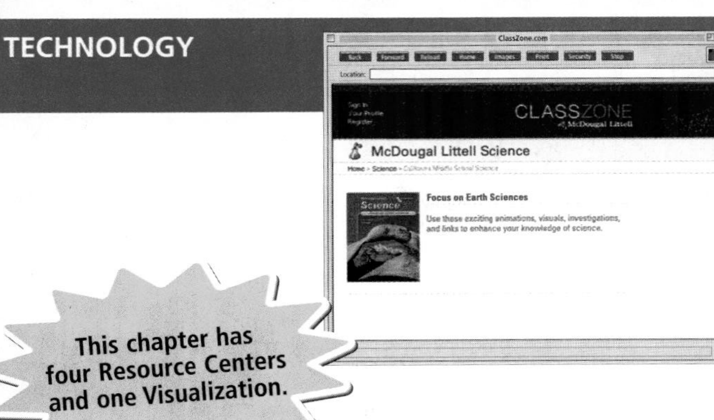

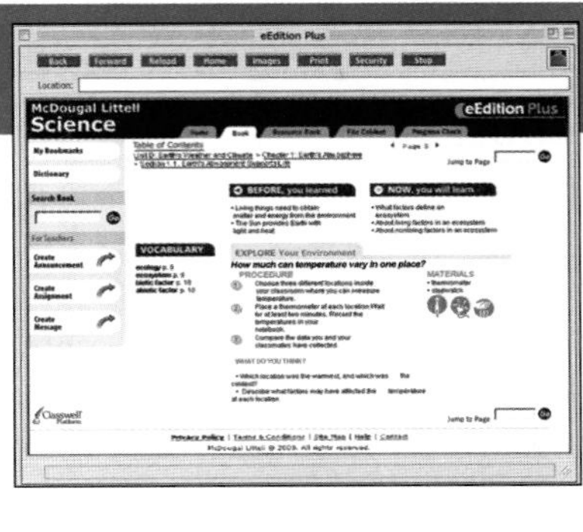

VISUAL CONTENT

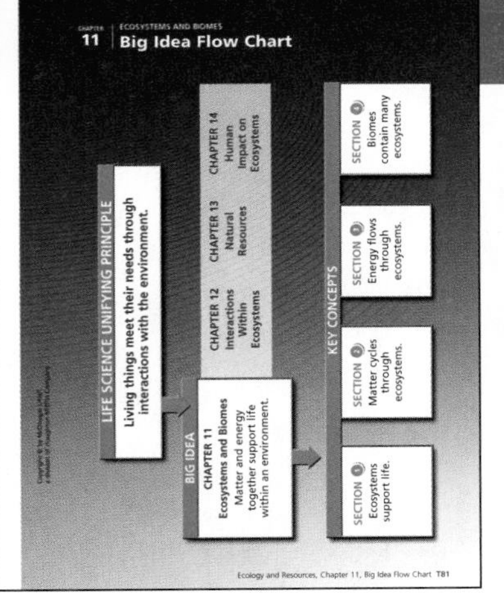

TRANSPARENCY BOOK, p. T81

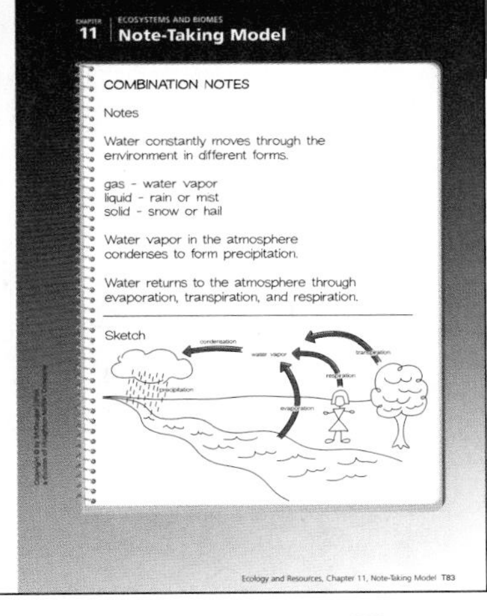

p. T83

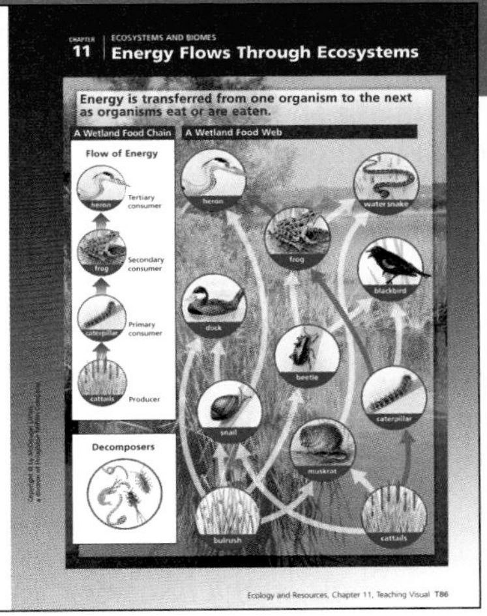

p. T86

MORE SUPPORT

Reinforcing Key Concepts for each section

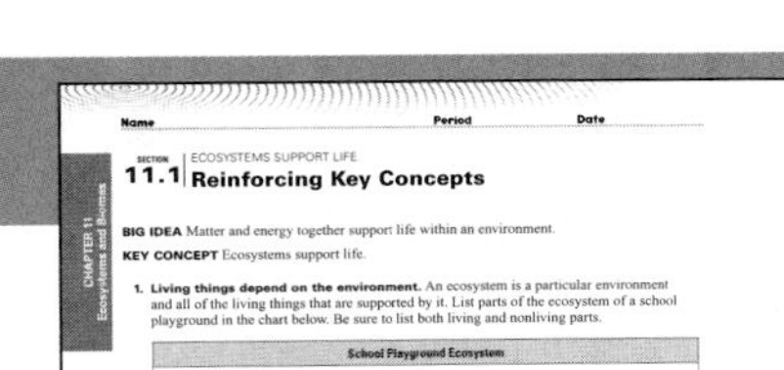

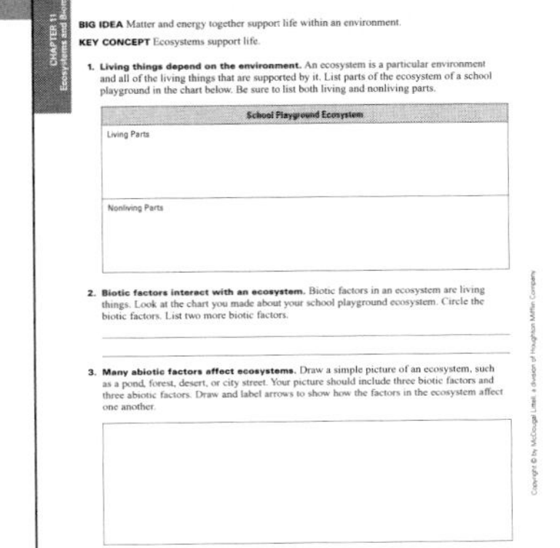

UNIT RESOURCE BOOK, p. 20

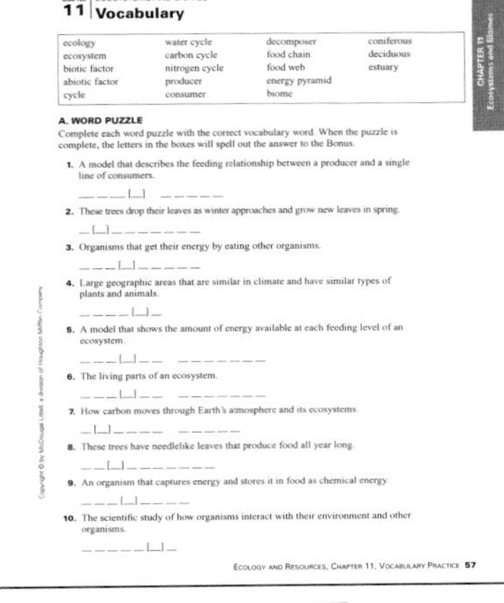

pp. 57–58

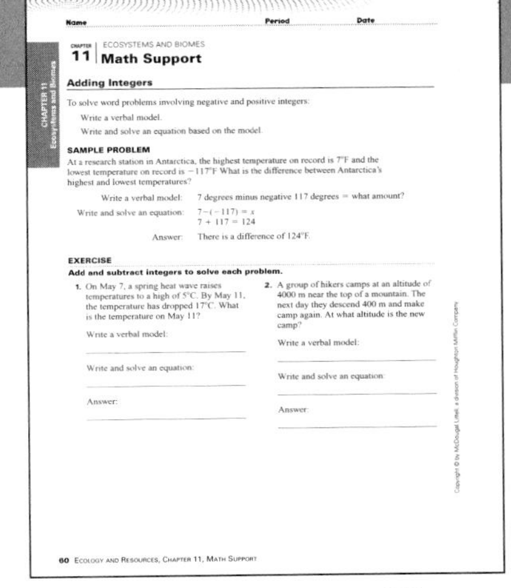

p. 60

Ecosystems and Biomes

INTRODUCE

the BIG idea

Have students look at the photograph of Lake Tahoe. Discuss how the question in the box relates to the Big Idea:

- What plants and animals are in the photograph?
- What might be keeping them alive?

California Content Standards

6.5.a Students know energy entering ecosystems as sunlight is transferred by producers into chemical energy through photosynthesis and then from organism to organism through food webs.

6.5.b Students know matter is transferred over time from one organism to others in the food web and between organisms and the physical environment.

6.5.d Students know different kinds of organisms may play similar ecological roles in similar biomes.

6.5.e Students know the number and types of organisms an ecosystem can support depends on the resources available and on abiotic factors, such as quantities of light and water, a range of temperatures, and soil composition.

6.7.b Select and use appropriate tools and technology (including calculators, computers, balances, spring scales, microscopes, and binoculars) to perform tests, collect data, and display data.

CHAPTER

Ecosystems and Biomes

the BIG idea

Matter and energy together support life within an environment.

How many living and nonliving things can you identify in this photograph of Lake Tahoe?

Key Concepts

SECTION 1 **Ecosystems support life.**
Learn about different factors that make up an ecosystem.

SECTION 2 **Matter cycles through ecosystems.**
Learn about the water, carbon, and nitrogen cycles.

SECTION 3 **Energy flows through ecosystems.**
Learn how energy moves through living things.

SECTION 4 **Biomes contain many ecosystems.**
Learn about different land and water biomes.

California ClassZone

CLASSZONE.COM

Chapter 11 online resources: Content Review, Visualization, four Resource Centers, Math Tutorial, Test Practice

INTERNET PREVIEW

CLASSZONE.COM For student use with the following pages:

Review and Practice
- Content Review, pp. 376, 406
- Math Tutorial: Adding Integers, p. 389
- Test Practice, p. 409

Activities and Resources
- Internet Activity: A Prairie Ecosystem, p. 375
- Resource Centers: Ecosystems, p. 379; Cycles in Nature, p. 384; Land and Aquatic Biomes, p. 404
- Visualization: Nitrogen Cycle, p. 387

Food Chains and Food Webs
Code: MDL001

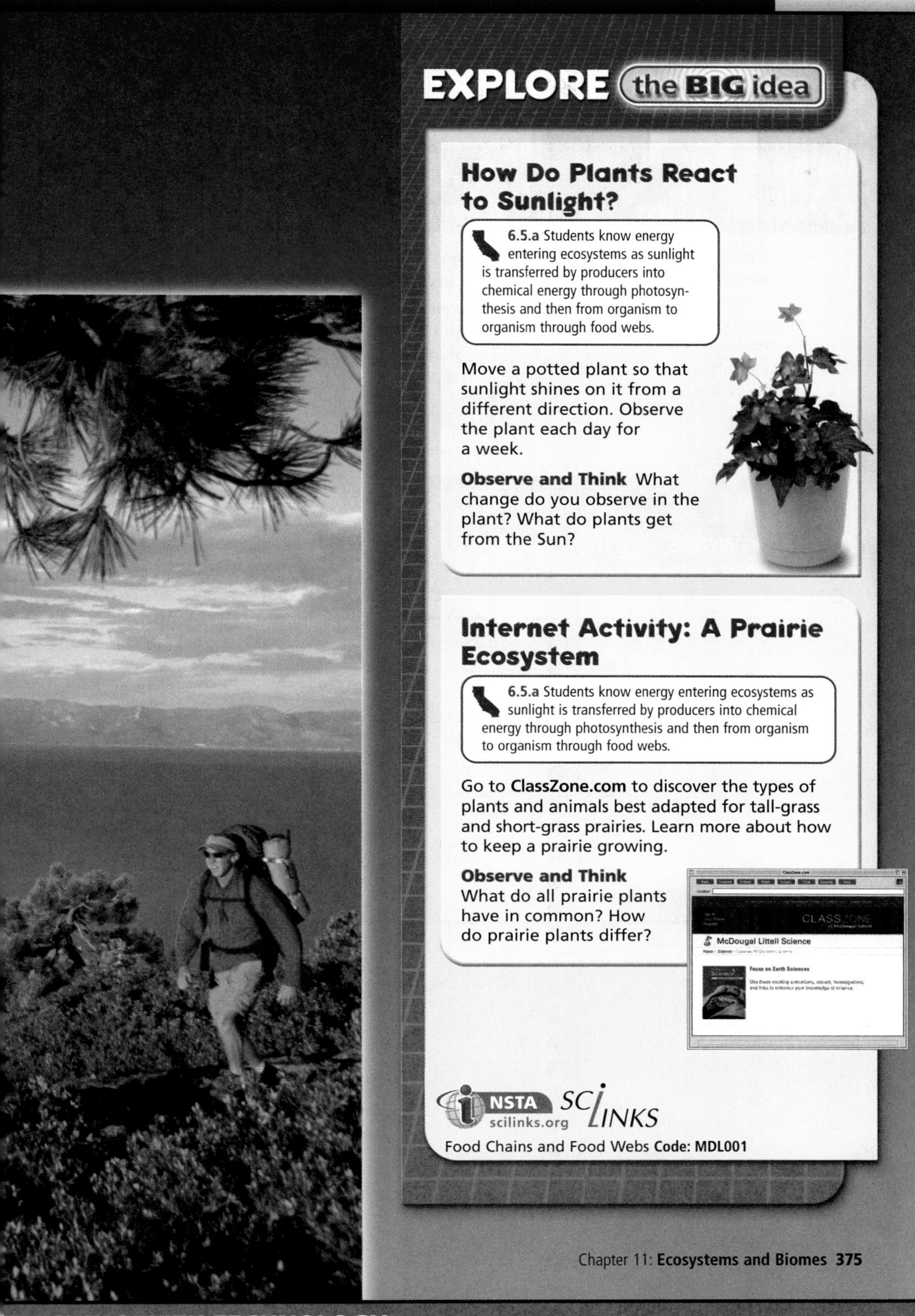

EXPLORE the BIG idea

How Do Plants React to Sunlight?

6.5.a Students know energy entering ecosystems as sunlight is transferred by producers into chemical energy through photosynthesis and then from organism to organism through food webs.

Move a potted plant so that sunlight shines on it from a different direction. Observe the plant each day for a week.

Observe and Think What change do you observe in the plant? What do plants get from the Sun?

Internet Activity: A Prairie Ecosystem

6.5.a Students know energy entering ecosystems as sunlight is transferred by producers into chemical energy through photosynthesis and then from organism to organism through food webs.

Go to **ClassZone.com** to discover the types of plants and animals best adapted for tall-grass and short-grass prairies. Learn more about how to keep a prairie growing.

Observe and Think What do all prairie plants have in common? How do prairie plants differ?

NSTA scilinks.org SCILINKS

Food Chains and Food Webs **Code: MDL001**

EXPLORE the BIG idea

These inquiry-based activities are appropriate for use at home or as a supplement to classroom instruction.

How Do Plants React to Sunlight?

PURPOSE To demonstrate that plants respond to the presence of sunlight.

TIP *10 min.* Use plants with flexible, leafy stems. Bean, radish, or other seedlings will move toward light in a short time period.

Answer: Leaves and stems moved toward the sunlight; energy.

REVISIT after p. 380.

Internet Activity: A Prairie Ecosystem

PURPOSE To introduce students to factors that cause changes in an ecosystem.

TIP *20 min.* You might bring real samples of grasses into the classroom and compare them with the varieties on screen.

Answer: They are all grasses; some are low to ground, others tall.

REVISIT after p. 394.

TEACHING WITH TECHNOLOGY

Digital Camera If a digital camera is available, students can photograph their potted plants (pp. 375, 384) each day. They can then assemble a series of still shots as a digital movie and dub sound over the image or add text screens to create a presentation.

Computer Microscope Have students use a computer microscope to examine particles in the Chapter Investigation on p. 382.

Spreadsheet Software Students can use graphing calculators or spreadsheet software to present their climate data on p. 403.

PREPARE

CONCEPT REVIEW

Activate Prior Knowledge

- Ask students to come to the board and draw familiar plants and animals in their natural environment.
- Ask students to name the living organisms shown in the environment and to suggest ways in which the organisms might interact with one another.
- Ask students to suggest possible ways in which each organism finds water, energy, and living space.

TAKING NOTES

Combination Notes

Combining pictures with notes will help students connect abstract concepts with concrete examples. Later, students can fold over their two-column combination notes and quiz themselves based on their pictures.

Vocabulary Strategy

Surrounding each term with a context helps students develop meaning. Students can opt to use their frame game notes to create a guessing game with a partner. Partners fill in frames, but leave the "picture," or center word, blank. Then they trade with each other to "complete the picture."

Vocabulary and Note-Taking Resources

- Vocabulary Practice, pp. 57–58
- Decoding Support, p. 59

- Daily Vocabulary Scaffolding, p. T82
- Note-Taking Model, p. T83

- Frame Game, B26–27
- Combination Notes, C36
- Daily Vocabulary Scaffolding, H1–8

CHAPTER 11

Getting Ready to Learn

CONCEPT REVIEW

- The natural world that surrounds all living things is called the environment.
- Most living things need water, air, food, and living space.
- All living things need a source of energy to stay alive and grow.

VOCABULARY REVIEW

system p. 41

See Glossary for definitions.

environment
nutrient
photosynthesis
respiration

CONTENT REVIEW
CLASSZONE.COM

Review concepts and vocabulary.

TAKING NOTES

COMBINATION NOTES

To take notes about a new concept, first make an informal outline of the information. Then make a sketch of the concept and label it so you can study it later.

VOCABULARY STRATEGY

Write each new vocabulary term in the center of a **frame game** diagram. Decide what information to frame the term with. Use examples, descriptions, sentences that use the term in context, or pictures. You can change the frame to fit each item.

See the Note-Taking Handbook on pages R45–R51.

SCIENCE NOTEBOOK

CHECK READINESS

Administer the Diagnostic Test to determine students' readiness for new science content and their mastery of requisite math skills.

 Diagnostic Test, pp. 248–249

Technology Resources

Students needing content and math skills should visit **ClassZone.com.**

- **CONTENT REVIEW**
- **MATH TUTORIAL**

 **CONTENT REVIEW CD-ROM**

KEY CONCEPT

Ecosystems support life.

CALIFORNIA Content Standards

6.5.a Students know energy entering ecosystems as sunlight is transferred by producers into chemical energy through photosynthesis and then from organism to organism through food webs.

6.5.e Students know the number and types of organisms an ecosystem can support depends on the resources available and on abiotic factors, such as quantities of light and water, a range of temperatures, and soil composition.

BEFORE, you learned

- Living things need to obtain matter and energy from the environment
- The Sun provides Earth with light and heat

NOW, you will learn

- What factors define an ecosystem
- About living factors in an ecosystem
- About nonliving factors in an ecosystem

EXPLORE Your Environment (6.5.e)

How much can temperature vary in one place?

PROCEDURE

1. Choose three locations inside your classroom where you can measure temperature.
2. Place a thermometer at each location. Wait for at least two minutes. Record the temperatures in your notebook.
3. Compare the data you and your classmates have collected.

MATERIALS

- thermometer
- stopwatch

WHAT DO YOU THINK?

- Which location was the warmest? Which was the coldest?
- Describe what factors may have affected the temperature at each location.

VOCABULARY

ecology p. 377
ecosystem p. 377
biotic factor p. 378
abiotic factor p. 378

Living things depend on the environment.

You wouldn't find a kangaroo in the Arctic or a polar bear in Australia. Each animal is suited to a certain environment. The kangaroo and the polar bear are able to survive despite the harsh conditions of their surroundings. **Ecology** is the scientific study of how organisms interact with their environment and all the other organisms that live in that environment.

Scientists use the word **ecosystem** to describe a particular environment and all the living things that are supported by it. An ecosystem can be as small as a rotting log or as large as a desert. What is important in an ecosystem is how the living parts of the ecosystem relate to the nonliving parts.

VOCABULARY
Add frame game diagrams for *ecology* and *ecosystem* to your notebook.

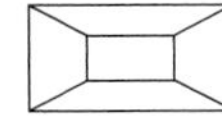

RESOURCES FOR DIFFERENTIATED INSTRUCTION

Below Level

UNIT RESOURCE BOOK

- Reading Study Guide A, pp. 13–14
- Decoding Support, p. 59

 **AUDIO CDS**

Advanced

UNIT RESOURCE BOOK

Challenge and Extension, p. 19

English Learners

UNIT RESOURCE BOOK

Spanish Reading Study Guide, pp. 17–18

 **AUDIO CDS**

- Audio Readings in Spanish
- Audio Readings (English)

11.1 FOCUS

Set Learning Goals

Students will

- Explain what factors define an ecosystem.
- Describe the living factors in an ecosystem.
- Describe the nonliving factors in an ecosystem.

3-Minute Warm-Up

Display Transparency 84 or copy this exercise on the board:

Match the definitions to the correct terms.

Definitions

1. It is an organized group of parts that work together to form a whole. *d*
2. All living organisms need it. *b*
3. It gives Earth most of its energy. *e*

Terms

a. organism
b. energy
c. the ocean
d. system
e. the Sun

 3-Minute Warm-Up, p. T84

11.1 MOTIVATE

EXPLORE Your Environment

PURPOSE To demonstrate that microclimates with different characteristics differ in temperature

TIP *10 min.* Students should select three locations that receive different amounts of sunlight, air exchange with the outdoors, or heat or air conditioning from indoor sources.

WHAT DO YOU THINK? *Sample answer: The location with the most sunlight was warmest; proximity to windows, doors, heat sources, air conditioning vents, number of people in the area, open windows or doors.*

11.1 INSTRUCT

Teach the Standards

Resources and abiotic factors 6.5.e

In this section: Help students understand that both biotic and abiotic factors interact in an ecosystem. Make sure students understand how temperature, light, soil, and water affect an ecosystem.

previously taught: energy from sunlight, pp. 9–11; water cycle, pp. 60–61

future opportunities: habitats, pp. 414–415; changing ecosystems, pp. 434–436

Teach from Visuals

To help students interpret the photograph of the pond ecosystem, ask:

- How do nonliving factors affect the living factors in this ecosystem? *They provide nutrients and energy.*
- Are there factors in this ecosystem that are not visible in the photograph? *living factors: fish, insects, microorganisms; nonliving factors: nutrients, oxygen, rocks*

History of Science

Biosphere 2 was built in the late 1980s with the goal of creating a closed, self-sustaining system similar to Earth. The initial two-year experiment yielded valuable data, but the system was not self-sustaining.

A project in Japan called Mini Earth is picking up where Biosphere 2 left off. Intended to be a self-sustaining environment, the project involves scientists sealed inside along with plants and animals. Developers hope that the technologies used in Mini Earth will help future space exploration.

Ongoing Assessment

Explain what factors define an ecosystem.

Ask: What is the definition of an ecosystem? *living things and the physical environment around them*

PHOTO CAPTION Sample answer: living—turtles, grass, trees; non-living—soil, water, sunlight

READING TIP
A microorganism is an organism that is so tiny it can be seen only through a microscope.

READING TIP
The word *biotic* means "living." The prefix *a-* in *abiotic* means "not," so *abiotic* means "not living."

A

Think about a pond. A pond ecosystem is more than just water and fish. Plants grow in and around the water, and animals feed on these plants. Microorganisms in the water are food for fish and for each other. These are just a few of the living parts, or **biotic factors** (by-AHT-ihk), of a pond ecosystem. The nonliving parts, or **abiotic factors** (AY-by-AHT-ihk), include the air that supplies oxygen and carbon dioxide, the soil that provides nutrients, the water in the pond, and the sunlight that plants need to grow.

CLASSIFY Name three living and three nonliving factors that are part of this pond ecosystem.

Biotic factors interact with an ecosystem.

B

Living things depend upon an ecosystem for food, air, and water, as well as other things they need for survival. In turn, living things affect the ecosystem in which they live. Plants are biotic factors in land ecosystems. They affect other biotic and abiotic parts of ecosystems. For example, plants are an important source of food. As a result, the types of plants found in an ecosystem determine the types of animals that can live there. Plants can affect temperature by blocking sunlight. Plant roots hold soil in place. Even the atmosphere is affected by plants as they take in carbon dioxide and release oxygen.

Animals are also biotic factors that affect an ecosystem. A beaver that builds a dam changes the flow of a river and so affects the surrounding landscape. Large herds of cattle can overgraze a grassland ecosystem and cause the soil to erode. In an ocean ecosystem, corals form giant reefs that provide food and shelter for marine organisms.

378 Unit 4: Ecology and Resources

DIFFERENTIATE INSTRUCTION

More Reading Support

A What two kinds of factors are in an ecosystem? *biotic and abiotic*

B Are plants abiotic or biotic factors? *biotic*

English Learners Have English learners write the definitions of *ecology* and *ecosystem* in their Science Word Dictionaries. Encourage students to look up *eco-* in the dictionary. Be certain that English learners understand the difference between *biotic factors* and *abiotic factors*. Ask them to list the different biotic and abiotic factors they see around them. Some biotic factors might be classmates, teachers, class pets, and plants in the classroom or visible through a window. Abiotic factors might be desks, books, board, and lights.

Many abiotic factors affect ecosystems.

Abiotic factors include both the physical and chemical parts of an ecosystem. Physical factors are factors that you can see or feel, such as the temperature, water, and sunlight. Chemical factors include the minerals and compounds found in the soil and whether the ecosystem's water is fresh or salty. The combination of different abiotic factors determines the types of organisms that an ecosystem can support.

REMINDER

Compounds were discussed in Chapter 6.

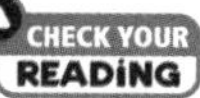

CHECK YOUR READING List four different abiotic factors that can affect an ecosystem.

Temperature

Temperature is an important abiotic factor in any ecosystem. In a land ecosystem, temperature affects the types of plants that grow well there. The types of plants available for food and shelter determine the types of animals that can live there. For example, a tropical rain forest has a lot of rain and consistently warm temperatures. The wide variety of plants in a tropical rain forest supports a wide variety of monkeys, birds, and other organisms.

Animals are as sensitive to temperature as plants are. Musk oxen have a thick coat of fur, so they can survive in very cold environments. Water buffalo have a light coat, so they are better suited to warm temperatures. Wild water buffalo live in tropical climates.

RESOURCE CENTER
CLASSZONE.COM

Learn more about ecosystems.

This musk ox's thick fur keeps it warm in the cold temperatures of northern Canada.

A water buffalo cools itself in a shallow stream during a hot day in India.

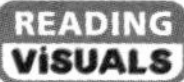

READING VISUALS COMPARE AND CONTRAST How are these animals alike? How are they different?

Teach from Visuals

Using the photographs, have students compare abiotic factors of the ecosystems in which musk oxen and water buffalo live. Ask:

- How does temperature affect the availability of water in each ecosystem? ***Liquid water is present in the water buffalo's ecosystem, but water is often frozen in the musk ox's ecosystem.***
- How do temperature and water affect soil and plant life in each ecosystem? ***Musk ox: Soil is often frozen, and vegetation is short and sparse. Water buffalo: Soil is often moist or muddy, and plant life is plentiful.***

Language Arts Connection

Help students understand the terms *ecology* and *ecosystem* by explaining the origin of the word root *ecos,* which means "house" or "place to live." Ecology then can be thought of as the study of places where organisms *live*; an ecosystem as the *system* of relationships among organisms and their *home* or surroundings.

Ongoing Assessment

Describe the living factors in an ecosystem.

Ask: Give some examples of the biotic factors in an ecosystem. ***Sample answer: bacteria, insects, plants, algae, animals***

CHECK YOUR READING *Answer: light, temperature, soil, water, air*

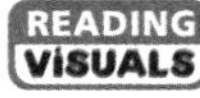

READING VISUALS *Answer: They both have similar sizes, similar bodies, and horns. In a warm climate, the musk ox's fur would make the animal too hot. The water buffalo has no protection from the cold.*

DIFFERENTIATE INSTRUCTION

More Reading Support

C What are physical abiotic factors? ***light, temperature, amount of water***

D What determines the types of animals in an ecosystem? ***plants***

Advanced Give students examples of three ecosystems of different sizes, such as an anthill, a one-acre meadow, and a continent. Have them describe the features that make each of these an ecosystem.

Address Misconceptions

IDENTIFY Ask: Where do green plants get their food? If students answer "from the soil," they might hold the misconception that plants obtain food from the environment rather than capturing energy from sunlight, and combining it with the chemicals in air.

CORRECT On the board, write an equation for photosynthesis: water + carbon dioxide + light = sugar + oxygen. Remind students that photosynthesis takes place in leaf cells and that sugar is food for the plant.

REASSESS Ask students where each item in the equation comes from. *water from soil, carbon dioxide from air, light from the Sun, sugar from all three combined, oxygen is left over*

Technology Resources

Visit **ClassZone.com** for background on common student misconceptions.

 **MISCONCEPTION DATABASE**

EXPLORE the BIG idea

Revisit "How Do Plants React to Sunlight?" on p. 375. Have students explain their results.

Teach from Visuals

To help students interpret the soil visuals, explain the following interactions:

- Plant roots interact with soil. Roots take water from soil. Bacteria and fungi on plant roots help the roots absorb nutrients. Roots help hold soil in place.
- Air interacts with soil. Most soil organisms need air to survive. Their activity loosens soil, allowing air to circulate.
- Earthworms interact with soil. Worms digest organic matter, pass waste back into soil, and mix and aerate soil.

Ongoing Assessment

Describe the nonliving factors in an ecosystem.

Ask: What are some examples of abiotic factors in an ecosystem? *Sample answer: light, soil, water, temperature, minerals*

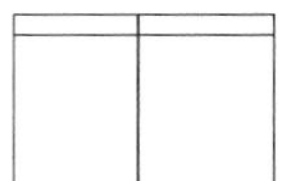

COMBINATION NOTES Remember to make notes and diagrams to show how abiotic factors affect biotic factors in an ecosystem.

Light

You can understand how abiotic factors work together when you think about sunlight and temperature. Sunlight warms Earth's surface and atmosphere. In addition, energy from sunlight supports all life on Earth. The Sun provides the energy that plants capture and use to produce food in a process called photosynthesis. The food produced by plants and other photosynthetic organisms feeds almost all the other living things found on Earth.

The strength of sunlight and the amount of sunlight available in a land ecosystem determine the types of plants in that ecosystem. A desert ecosystem has plants such as cacti, which can survive where sunlight is very strong. In a forest, much of the sunlight is blocked by trees. Mosses and ferns grow well on the shaded ground.

Light is a factor in ocean ecosystems as well. The deeper the water is, the less light there is available. In shallow water near the shore, photosynthetic organisms can survive at the surface and on the ocean floor. In the deep ocean, light is available for photosynthetic organisms only in the first hundred meters below the surface.

READING TIP Soil is a mixture of mineral and rock particles, organic matter, water, and air.

Soil

Soil is an important abiotic factor in land ecosystems. Organisms in the soil break down the remains of dead plants and animals. These decaying remains become part of the soil. This process of decay provides important raw materials to the living plants and animals of an ecosystem.

The size of soil particles affects how much air and water the soil can hold.

DIFFERENTIATE INSTRUCTION

More Reading Support

E Ecosystems need energy to function. Where does this energy come from? *the Sun*

F How do plants get energy? *by photosynthesis*

Advanced Invite students to observe small soil samples using a hand lens or a dissecting microscope. Have them draw and identify the organisms they see, and use their research skills to find out more about them.

 Challenge and Extension, p. 19

Different ecosystems have different types of soil. The characteristics of the soil in an ecosystem affect plant growth. Soils that have a lot of organic matter hold water well and allow air to reach the plant roots. Sandy soils usually do not hold water well because the water flows through too easily. Clay soil, which has small, tightly packed particles, does not allow water to move through easily. Minerals in the soil also affect plant growth.

READING TIP Organic matter is made up of carbon compounds from living or once-living organisms.

 Explain how soil can affect plant life in an ecosystem.

Water

Another important abiotic factor in land ecosystems is the amount of water available to support life. All living things need water to carry out life processes. Plants need water as well as sunlight for photosynthesis. Animals need water to digest food and release the energy stored in the food. Look at the photograph to see the effect that an underground water source has on an otherwise dry, desert ecosystem. Trees could not survive there without a plentiful supply of water.

Ecosystems that have a lot of water can support a large number of different types of plants. These plants can then support a large number of different types of animals. Tropical rain forests are the wettest of all ecosystems on land and have the most types of plants and animals. Desert ecosystems are the driest land ecosystems and have far fewer types of plants and animals. The types and number of living things in a land ecosystem are always related to the amount of fresh water available for its inhabitants.

INFER An oasis forms in the desert when underground water comes to the surface. How can you identify the boundary of this oasis?

11.1 Review

KEY CONCEPTS

1. Draw a diagram of an ecosystem near where you live. Label the factors "biotic" or "abiotic." **(6.5.e)**
2. Give two examples of how plants and animals affect their environment. **(6.5.e)**
3. Describe how temperature, light, and soil affect an ecosystem. **(6.5.e)**

CRITICAL THINKING

4. **Predict** Think of a forest ecosystem. Now imagine that a large volcanic eruption throws large amounts of dust and ash into the air, blocking out sunlight. How might the forest ecosystem be affected if the sunlight is blocked for a day? for a year?

CHALLENGE

5. **Apply** Think of how you fit into your local environment. List ways in which you interact with biotic and abiotic factors in your ecosystem.

ANSWERS

. Diagrams should show wareness that biotic factors re organisms and abiotic actors are nonliving.

. Sample answer: Plants pro-luce oxygen and food. Coral eefs provide shelter.

3. They determine the types and abundance of plant life.

4. For a day: would have little effect on the ecosystem; for a year: much of the plant life and the animal life that depends on it would disappear

5. Sample answer: biotic factors: eating plants and animals, being stung by an insect, feeding birds; abiotic factors: breathing air, drinking water, building with stone

Ongoing Assessment

 *Answer: The amount of water and nutrients in the soil affects what types of plants can survive.*

PHOTO CAPTION Answer: The boundary of this oasis would be represented by the outside edge of the trees; they need water to sustain life, and no other plant life appears in the photograph

Reinforce the BIG idea

Have students relate the section to the Big Idea.

 Reinforcing Key Concepts, p. 20

11.1 ASSESS & RETEACH

Assess

 Section 11.1 Quiz, p. 250

Reteach

Choose one of these ecosystems: an artificial ecosystem such as a classroom aquarium or terrarium; an ecosystem shown in photographs from books or magazines; or a backyard, a park, or a schoolyard ecosystem. Have students identify as many biotic and abiotic factors as they can. Ask them to write a paragraph describing how the abiotic factors influence the biotic factors in the chosen ecosystem.

Technology Resources

Have students visit **ClassZone.com** for reteaching of Key Concepts.

 **CONTENT REVIEW**

 **CONTENT REVIEW CD-ROM**

CHAPTER INVESTIGATION

Focus

PURPOSE To measure and identify soil properties

OVERVIEW Students will use appropriate technology to test a soil sample for pore space, pH, and particle size. Students will find the following:

- Pore space affects soil's ability to absorb water.
- Different soils have different pH levels.
- Different soils contain different amounts of sand, silt, and clay.

Lab Preparation

On the day before conducting this experiment, have students bring in samples of soil. To ensure a variety of soil samples, suggest that each group obtain soil from a different area, such as topsoil from a garden, compacted soil from a park, and subsoil with gravel from a playground.

Prior to the investigation have students read through the investigation and prepare their data tables. Or you may wish to copy and distribute datasheets and rubrics.

 UNIT RESOURCE BOOK, pp. 63–71

 SCIENCE TOOLKIT, F15

Lab Management

- If the screen over the bottle clogs, have students add about 2 cm of sand above the screen before adding the soil.
- Draw bar graphs on the chalkboard so groups can compare their data. Graphs should show the porosity, permeability, pH, and particle size of the samples.

SAFETY Tell students to be careful when using scissors.

Teaching with Technology

Have students use a computer microscope to examine soil particles.

CHAPTER INVESTIGATION

Testing Soil

OVERVIEW AND PURPOSE Soil is necessary for life. Whether a soil is suitable for farming or construction, and whether it absorbs water when it rains, depends on the properties of that soil. In this investigation you will

- test a soil sample to measure several soil properties
- identify the properties of your soil sample

MATERIALS

- dried soil sample
- 250 mL graduated cylinder
- 1 qt jar with lid
- water
- 2 L plastic bottle
- scissors
- window screening
- rubber band
- pH test strips
- clock with second hand
- *for Challenge:* Texture Flow Chart

6.5.e, 6.7.b

Procedure

PORE-SPACE TEST

1. Measure 200 mL of the dried soil sample in the graduated cylinder. Pour it into the jar.
2. Rinse the graduated cylinder, then fill it with 200 mL of water. Slowly pour the water into the jar until the soil is so soaked that any additional water would pool on top.
3. Record the amount of water remaining in the graduated cylinder. Then determine by subtraction the amount you added to the soil sample. Make a soil properties chart in your **Science Notebook** and record this number in it.
4. Discard the wet soil according to your teacher's instructions, and rinse the jar.

pH TEST AND DRAINAGE TEST

5. Cut off the top of a plastic bottle and use a rubber band to attach a piece of window screening over its mouth. Place the bottle top, mouth down, into the jar.
6. Use the graduated cylinder to measure 200 mL of soil. Pour the soil into the inverted bottle top.
7. Rinse the graduated cylinder, and fill it with 100 mL of water. Use a pH test strip to test the water's pH. Record the result in the "before" space in your soil properties chart.
8. Pour the water into the soil. Measure the amount of time it takes for the first drips to fall into the jar. Record the result in your chart.

top of plastic bottle

jar

step 5

window screening

382 Unit 4: Ecology and Resources

INVESTIGATION RESOURCES

 CHAPTER INVESTIGATION, Testing Soil
- Texture Flow Chart, p. 62
- Level A, pp. 63–66
- Level B, pp. 67–70
- Level C, p. 71

Advanced students should complete Levels B & C.

 Writing a Lab Report, D12–13

Technology Resources

Customize this student lab as needed or look for an alternative. Print rubrics to assess student lab reports.

 **Lab Generator CD-ROM**

Content Standard
6.5.e Students know the number and types of organisms an ecosystem can support depends on the resources available and on abiotic factors, such as quantities of light and water, a range of temperatures, and soil composition.

Investigation Standard
6.7.b Select and use appropriate tools and technology (including calculators, computers, balances, spring scales, microscopes, and binoculars) to perform tests, collect data, and display data.

9 When the water stops dripping, remove the bottle top. Use a new pH strip to measure the pH of the water in the jar. Record this measurement in the "after" space in your chart. Note any differences in the appearance of the water before and after it was filtered through the soil.

10 Discard the wet soil according to your teacher's instructions, and rinse the jar.

PARTICLE-TYPE TEST

11 Add water to the jar until it is two-thirds full. Pour in soil until the water level rises to the top of the jar, then replace the lid. Shake the jar, and set it to rest on a countertop overnight.

12 The next day, observe the different soil layers. The sample should have separated into sand (on the bottom), silt (in the middle), and clay (on the top). Measure the height of each layer and the total height of the three layers. Record your measurements in your chart.

13 Use the following formula to calculate the percentage of each kind of particle in the sample:

$$\frac{\text{height of layer}}{\text{total height of all layers}} \times 100$$

Record your results and all calculations in your chart.

Observe and Analyze

Write It Up

1. **RECORD** Complete your soil properties chart.
2. **IDENTIFY** How did steps 1–3 test your soil sample's pore space?
3. **IDENTIFY** How did steps 5–9 test your soil sample's drainage rate?

Conclude

1. **EVALUATE** In step 3 you measured the amount of space between the soil particles in your sample. In step 8 you measured how quickly water passed through your sample. Are these two properties related? Explain your answer.
2. **EVALUATE** Would packing down or loosening up your soil sample change any of the properties you tested? Explain your answer.
3. **INTERPRET** What happened to the pH of the water that passed through the soil? Why do you think that happened?
4. **ANALYZE** Look at the percentages of sand, silt, and clay in your sample. How do the percentages help explain the properties you observed and measured?

INVESTIGATE Further

CHALLENGE Soil texture depends on the size of the weathered rock particles the soil contains. Use the Texture Flow Chart to determine the texture of your soil sample.

Testing Soil
Observe and Analyze
Table 1. Soil Properties Chart

Property	Result	Notes and Calculations
Pore space	_ mL water added	
pH	before: pH = _ after: pH = _	
Drainage	_ seconds	
Particle type	height of sand = _ cm height of silt = _ cm height of clay = _ cm total height = _ cm	

Conclude

Observe and Analyze

SAMPLE DATA Sample 1: pore space, 17%; pH before: 6, pH after: 6; drainage, 3.6 seconds; composition: sand 75%, silt 9.1%, clay 15.2%. Sample 2: pore space, 13%, pH before: 6, pH after: 5; drainage, 9.8 seconds; composition: sand 71.4%, silt 21%, clay 7.1%

1. *Make sure students' charts are complete.*
2. *by measuring the amount of water the soil absorbed*
3. *by measuring the time that passed before the first drop of water fell*

Conclude

1. *Yes, the two properties are related. When there is more space between the soil particles, the water drains more quickly.*
2. *Packing down the soil would decrease pore space and the rate of drainage. Loosening the soil would increase the rate of drainage.*
3. *It became more acidic. The water dissolved chemicals as it passed through the soil.*
4. *Sample answer: The soil was mostly sandy so water moved through it quickly.*

INVESTIGATE Further

CHALLENGE Answers will vary depending on the samples that were used.

Post-Lab Discussion

To reinforce the idea that soil is an essential resource, have students provide examples of ways to recycle the soil samples used in this experiment. *The soil could be used to pot plants for the classroom or placed in a garden.*

Discuss possible sources of error for this investigation, such as inaccurately measuring the water in the pore space test or miscalculating particle size. Ask: How could these errors have been avoided? *by repeating trials, rechecking calculations*

11.2 FOCUS

Set Learning Goals

Students will

- Explain how matter is exchanged between organisms and their environment.
- Describe the water, carbon, and nitrogen cycles.
- Observe carbon gas released from crushed seashells.

3-Minute Warm-Up

Display Transparency 84 or copy this exercise on the board:

Decide whether these statements are true. If not true, correct them.

1. Organisms in soil are an example of abiotic factors. *Organisms in soil are an example of biotic factors.*
2. The amount of light available in an ecosystem affects the types and amount of plant life that will grow there. *true*
3. Plants use energy to make sugars through photosynthesis. *true*

 3-Minute Warm-Up, p. T84

11.2 MOTIVATE

EXPLORE The Water Cycle

PURPOSE To introduce the concept that plants release water vapor (transpiration)

TIPS *10 min.* Put bags on a single stem to make them easier to seal. If possible, move the activity outdoors. Any lamp will work for this exploration.

SAFETY Have students place the lamp at a safe distance from the plant to avoid burning the leaves or melting the plastic bag.

WHAT DO YOU THINK? *Water condenses inside each bag. The plastic bag traps water vapor.*

Teaching with Technology

Students can use a digital camera as described on p. 375 to photograph plants.

KEY CONCEPT

11.2 Matter cycles through ecosystems.

CALIFORNIA Content Standard

6.5.b Students know matter is transferred over time from one organism to others in the food web and between organisms and the physical environment.

BEFORE, you learned

- Ecosystems support life
- Living and nonliving factors interact in an ecosystem
- Temperature, light, soil, and water are important nonliving factors in ecosystems

NOW, you will learn

- How matter is exchanged between organisms and their environment
- About the water, carbon, and nitrogen cycles

VOCABULARY

cycle p. 384
carbon cycle p. 386
nitrogen cycle p. 387

EXPLORE The Water Cycle (6.5.b)

Do plants release water?

PROCEDURE

1. Cover a branch of the plant with a plastic bag. Tape the bag firmly around the stem.
2. Water the plant and place it in a sunny window or under a lamp. Wash your hands.
3. Check the plant after ten minutes, at the end of class, and again the next day.

WHAT DO YOU THINK?

- What did you see inside the plastic bag?
- What purpose did the plastic bag serve?

MATERIALS

- 1 small potted plant
- 1 clear plastic bag
- tape
- water

Explore cycles in nature.

All ecosystems need certain materials.

Living things depend on their environment to meet their needs. You can think of those needs in terms of the material, or matter, required by all living things. For example, all organisms take in water and food in order to survive. All of the materials an organism takes in are returned to the ecosystem during the organism's life or after it dies.

The movement of matter through the living and nonliving parts of an ecosystem is a cycle. A **cycle** is a series of events that happens over and over again. Matter in an ecosystem may change form, but it never leaves the ecosystem. Therefore, the matter is said to cycle through the ecosystem. Three of the most important cycles in ecosystems involve water, carbon, and nitrogen.

RESOURCES FOR DIFFERENTIATED INSTRUCTION

Below Level

UNIT RESOURCE BOOK

- Reading Study Guide A, pp. 23–24
- Decoding Support, p. 59

 **AUDIO CDS**

Additional INVESTIGATION, The Water Cycle, A, B, & C, pp. 72–80; Teacher Instructions, pp. 273–275

Advanced

UNIT RESOURCE BOOK

Challenge and Extension, p. 29

English Learners

UNIT RESOURCE BOOK

Spanish Reading Study Guide, pp. 27–28

 **AUDIO CDS**

- Audio Readings in Spanish
- Audio Readings (English)

Water Cycle

Different processes combine to move water through the environment.

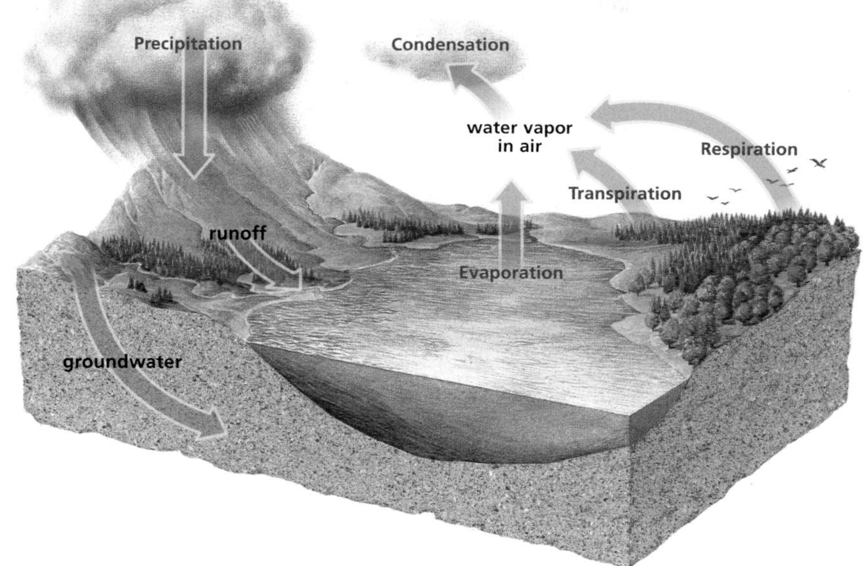

Water cycles through ecosystems.

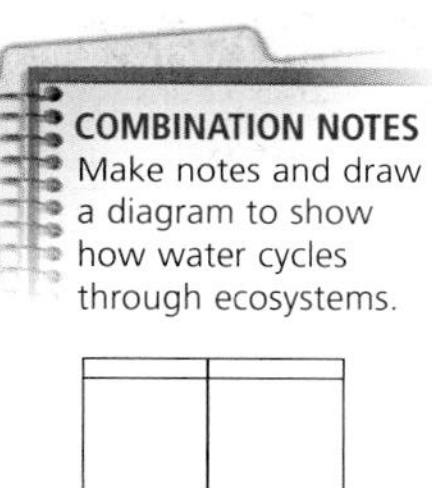

COMBINATION NOTES
Make notes and draw a diagram to show how water cycles through ecosystems.

Water is stored on Earth's surface in lakes, rivers, and oceans. Water is found underground, filling the spaces between soil particles and cracks in rocks. Large amounts of water are stored in glaciers and polar ice sheets. Water is also part of the bodies of living things. But water is not just stored. It is also constantly moving. As you read in Chapter 1, the movement of water through the environment is called the water cycle.

As water moves through an ecosystem, it changes in physical form. Water moves back and forth between gas, liquid, and solid forms. Water in the atmosphere is usually in the form of a gas—water vapor. Water that falls to Earth's surface is precipitation. For precipitation to occur, water vapor must cool and condense—it must change into a liquid or solid. This water can fall as rain, snow, sleet, mist, or hail.

What are the three physical forms of water in the water cycle?

Water returns to the atmosphere by changing back into vapor when heated. As you learned, this process is called evaporation. Living things also release water vapor. Animals release water vapor when they breathe. Plants release water vapor through a process called transpiration.

11.2 INSTRUCT

Teach the Standards

Transfer of matter 6.5.b

In this section: Help students see how matter, in the form of water, carbon, and nitrogen, changes form as it cycles through an ecosystem.

- **previously taught:** Sun as energy resource, pp. 9–11, 24; Earth system, pp. 41–46; water cycle, pp. 60–61
- **future opportunities:** symbiosis, pp. 426–429; fossil fuels, pp. 452–456

Teach from Visuals

Remind students that the arrows in the diagram of the water cycle represent the movement of water molecules. Ask:

- What happens during condensation? *Water vapor becomes liquid water.*
- What happens during transpiration? *Water vapor is released from tiny openings in plant leaves.*

Address Misconceptions

IDENTIFY Ask: Where does the water in Earth's water cycle come from? If students answer "oceans" or "atmosphere," they may think that water is added to or created within the water cycle.

CORRECT Create a demonstration using two beakers; fill one with water. Stopper the beakers, and connect them with a rubber hose. Boil the water, and have students observe as the water leaves one beaker and reappears in the other.

REASSESS Ask: Where did the water that appeared in the second beaker come from? *from the first beaker*
How did it move? *Heating caused the water to change from liquid form into water vapor, which traveled through the hose. As water vapor cooled, it changed back into a liquid and collected in the second beaker.*

Technology Resources

Visit **ClassZone.com** for background on common student misconceptions.

MISCONCEPTION DATABASE

Ongoing Assessment

Answer: gas, liquid, and solid

DIFFERENTIATE INSTRUCTION

More Reading Support

A What is an example of precipitation? *rain, snow, sleet*

B What process turns water to water vapor? *evaporation*

Additional Investigation To reinforce Section 11.2 learning goals, use the following full-period investigation:

R **Additional INVESTIGATION,** The Water Cycle, A, B, & C, pp. 72–80, 273–275 (Advanced students should complete Levels B and C.)

Advanced Have students study plants' role in the water cycle by completing this activity.

R Challenge and Extension, p. 29

Teach from Visuals

To help students interpret the diagram of the carbon cycle, ask:

- How does carbon move from the air into plants and animals? ***Carbon moves into plants by photosynthesis, and into animals by eating plants or other animals.***
- How does carbon move into the air from plants and animals? ***The cells of plants and animals use oxygen to release the energy stored in food molecules. This process is called respiration. Carbon dioxide is released as a by-product of respiration.***
- How does carbon move into the air from fossil fuels? ***Carbon is released as carbon dioxide when fossil fuels burn.***

History of Science

Recently, groups of college graduates in science were asked where a plant's mass comes from. Almost all of them answered sunlight, water, or soil. Few understood that carbon in the air was responsible.

In the 1640s, Jan Baptista van Helmont conducted an experiment that proved most of a plant's mass does not come from soil. Setting out to bolster his theory that everything is made of water, he placed 200 pounds of soil in a pot in which he planted a 5-pound willow tree. He watered the tree regularly and protected it from dust, but added no soil.

In five years, the tree gained 164 pounds, but the soil weighed 199 pounds.

The experiment showed that little of the tree's weight came from soil. Van Helmont thought the increase of weight was from water; in fact, it came from carbon dioxide.

Ongoing Assessment

CHECK YOUR READING *Answers should include three of the following: plants take in CO_2, animals release CO_2, carbon is deposited on seafloor when an organism dies, decaying matter releases CO_2, carbon in dead plants and animals becomes fossil fuel.*

Carbon cycles through ecosystems.

C

Carbon is an element found in all living things. Carbon moves through Earth's ecosystems in a cycle referred to as the **carbon cycle.** It is through carbon dioxide gas found in Earth's atmosphere that carbon enters the living parts of an ecosystem.

READING TIP
Note that photosynthesis is a process that brings carbon into living matter. Respiration is a process that releases carbon.

Plants use carbon dioxide to produce sugars in a process called photosynthesis. Sugars are carbon compounds that are important building blocks in food and all living matter. Food supplies the energy and materials living things need to live and grow. To release the energy in food, organisms break down the carbon compounds in a process called respiration. Carbon is released and cycled back into the atmosphere as carbon dioxide. When living things die and decay, the rest of the carbon that makes up living matter is released.

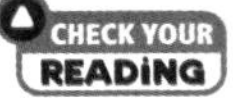

CHECK YOUR READING Name three ways that living things are part of the carbon cycle.

Earth's oceans contain far more carbon than the air does. In water ecosystems—lakes, rivers, and oceans—carbon dioxide is dissolved in water. Algae and certain types of bacteria are the photosynthetic organisms that produce food in these ecosystems. Marine organisms also release carbon dioxide during respiration. Carbon is deposited on the ocean floor when organisms die.

Carbon Cycle

Different processes combine to move carbon through the environment.

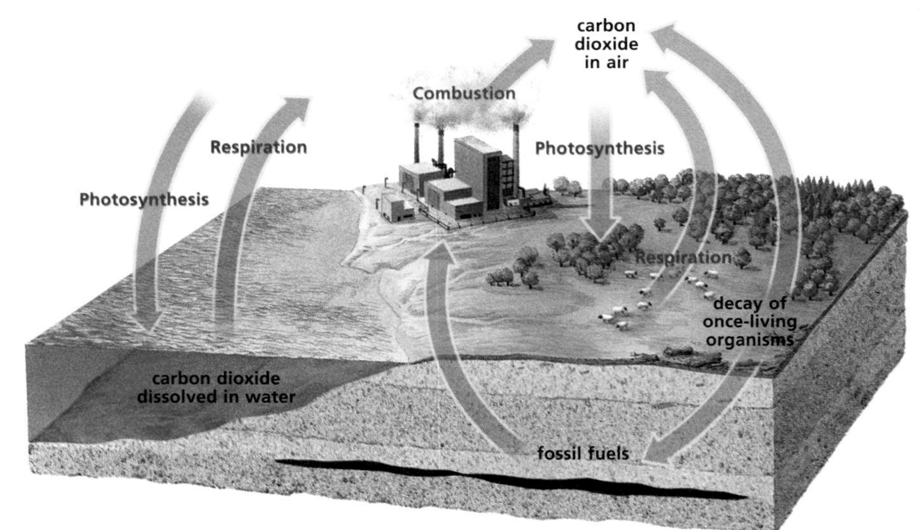

DIFFERENTIATE INSTRUCTION

More Reading Support

C All living things contain what chemical element? *carbon*

Below Level Encourage students to create their own colorcoded diagrams of the carbon cycle. Have them use one color to represent carbon dioxide gas and another for solid carbon. Ask: Where is carbon dioxide gas found? *in the air and dissolved in oceans, lakes, streams* Ask: Where is solid carbon found? *in the bodies of plants and animals*

386 Unit 4: Ecology and Resources

INVESTIGATE Carbon

What is one form in which carbon is stored on the ocean floor?

SKILL FOCUS
Observing (6.5.b)

PROCEDURE

1. Use the mortar and pestle to crush the seashell into a powder.
2. Pour the powder into the beaker.
3. Add enough white vinegar to cover the powder.

MATERIALS
- mortar and pestle
- whole seashell or pieces
- small beaker
- white vinegar

TIME
15 minutes

WHAT DO YOU THINK?
- What happened when white vinegar was added to the crushed shell?
- What material was produced in the reaction? Where did it come from originally?

CHALLENGE What type of reaction did you observe?

Large amounts of carbon are stored underground. The remains of plants and animals buried for millions of years decay slowly and change into fossil fuels, such as coal and oil. As humans burn fossil fuels to release energy, dust particles and gases containing carbon are released into the environment.

Nitrogen cycles through ecosystems.

Watch the nitrogen cycle in action.

Nitrogen is another element that is important to life. Nitrogen cycles through Earth's ecosystems in the **nitrogen cycle.** Almost four-fifths of the air you breathe is clear, colorless nitrogen gas. But you cannot get the nitrogen you need to live from air. All animals must get nitrogen from plants.

Plants cannot use pure nitrogen gas either. Instead, plants can absorb certain compounds of nitrogen. Plants take in these nitrogen compounds through their roots, along with water and other nutrients. So how does the nitrogen from the atmosphere get into the soil? One source is lightning. Every lightning strike fixes pure nitrogen, or changes it into a form that plants can use. This form of nitrogen falls to the ground in rain.

DIFFERENTIATE INSTRUCTION

More Reading Support

D Where do animals get nitrogen? *from plants*

E Where do plants get the nitrogen they need? *from the soil*

English Learners Place the terms *water cycle, carbon cycle,* and *nitrogen cycle* on the Science Word Wall with abbreviated definitions. It may be helpful for English learners to discuss each cycle with other English learners in their first language. Working out difficult concepts together in their first language can be beneficial to students. Encourage them to repeat or write down what they have learned in English afterwards.

INVESTIGATE Carbon

PURPOSE To observe the release of carbon in water

TIPS *15 min.* Students should wear safety goggles or protective eyewear throughout the experiment. Calcium carbonate is also in the shells of birds' eggs. A similar test with an egg will have good results.

WHAT DO YOU THINK? *Answers: Gas bubbles form. CO_2 is produced; it originally came from the shells*

CHALLENGE *chemical*

R Datasheet, Carbon, p. 30

Technology Resources

Customize this student lab as needed or look for an alternative. Print rubrics to assess student lab reports.

Lab Generator CD-ROM

Real World Example

All living things contain carbon. People get carbon compounds from food. In the oceans, living things get carbon from carbon dioxide dissolved in water. Clams and oysters, for example, use carbon to make the hard calcium carbonate in their shells. To find out if an element, such as carbon, is present, scientists use chemical tests. In the case of carbon, an acid, such as vinegar, reacts with calcium carbonate to produce carbon dioxide gas.

Integrate the Sciences

Living organisms are made up of chemical compounds: carbohydrates, fats, and proteins. All of these compounds contain carbon, hydrogen, and oxygen. Proteins contain nitrogen as well.

Ongoing Assessment

Explain how matter is exchanged between organisms and their environment.

Ask: How does matter cycle between organisms and their environment? *Organisms take in water, carbon, and nitrogen; use them for life processes; and release them.*

Ongoing Assessment

Describe the water, carbon, and nitrogen cycles.

Ask: How are the water, carbon, and nitrogen cycles alike? *Sample answer: All three pass into and out of the atmosphere, soil, and living organisms.*

Reinforce the BIG idea

Have students relate the section to the Big Idea.

 Reinforcing Key Concepts, p. 31

11.2 ASSESS & RETEACH

Assess

 Section 11.2 Quiz, p. 251

Reteach

Draw or have volunteers draw simple versions of the three cycle diagrams in Section 11.2 on the board. Next, have students describe similarities and differences in the water, carbon, and nitrogen cycles. Ask:

- How does water enter the atmosphere? Carbon? Nitrogen? *Water evaporates, is transpired by plants, and is exhaled by animals during respiration. Carbon is released during respiration and decay. Nitrogen is converted into gas by bacteria.*
- How does water leave the atmosphere? Carbon? Nitrogen? *Water vapor condenses and falls to the ground as precipitation. Carbon is fixed by plants during photosynthesis. Nitrogen is fixed by bacteria or by lightning.*
- Where is water stored? Carbon? Nitrogen? *water: oceans, lakes, groundwater; carbon: plant and animal bodies, ocean floor; nitrogen: plant and animal bodies*

Technology Resources

Have students visit **ClassZone.com** for reteaching of Key Concepts.

 CONTENT REVIEW

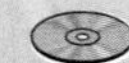 CONTENT REVIEW CD-ROM

Nitrogen Cycle

Different processes combine to move nitrogen through the environment.

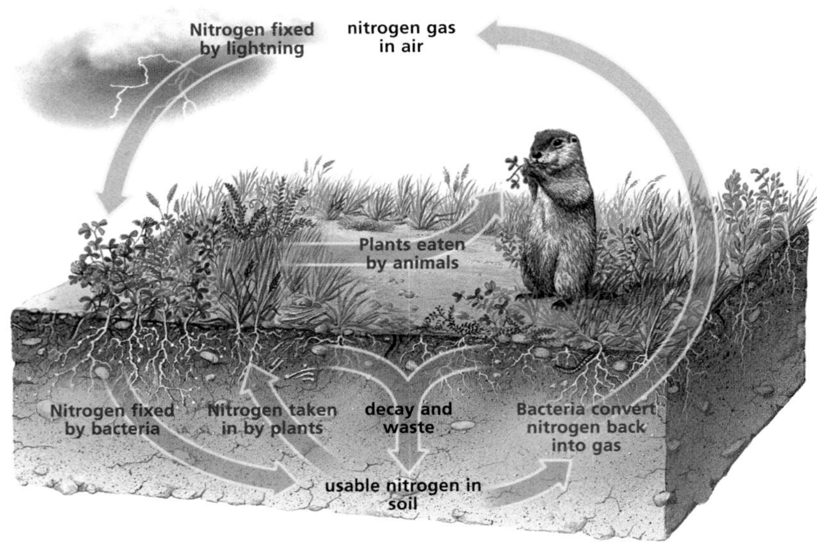

READING TIP
Bacteria are microscopic single-celled organisms.

A far greater source of nitrogen is nitrogen-fixing bacteria. These bacteria live in oceans as well as in soil. Some attach themselves to the roots of plants such as alfalfa and soybeans. When organisms die, decomposers in the ocean or soil break them down. Nitrogen in the soil or water is used again by living things. A small amount is returned to the atmosphere by bacteria that can break down nitrogen compounds into nitrogen gas.

11.2 Review

KEY CONCEPTS

1. Draw a diagram of the water cycle. Show three ways in which water moves through the cycle. (6.5.b)
2. Summarize the main parts of the carbon cycle. (6.5.b)
3. Explain two ways that nitrogen gas in the atmosphere is changed into nitrogen compounds that plants can use. (6.5.b)

CRITICAL THINKING

4. **Predict** When people burn fossil fuels, carbon dioxide gas is added to the atmosphere. How might increased carbon dioxide affect plant growth?
5. **Compare and Contrast** Review the nitrogen and carbon cycles. How are these two cycles similar and different?

CHALLENGE

6. **Apply** Draw a cycle diagram that shows how water is used in your household. Include activities that use water, sources of water, and ways that water leaves your house.

ANSWERS

1. Diagrams should include precipitation, evaporation, and condensation.

2. Green plants and algae remove CO_2 from air. Animals get carbon from food and release carbon as CO_2. The burning of fossil fuels, wood, or other organisms and decay release carbon.

3. Bacteria break down nitrogen compounds into nitrogen gas. Lightning breaks apart pure nitrogen in the atmosphere.

4. Plants might grow larger or increase in numbers.

5. Both have a gaseous form. Plants make both elements available to animals. Decay returns both elements to the atmosphere.

6. Diagrams should include activity, source, and exit route

MATH TUTORIAL
CLASSZONE.COM
Click on Math Tutorial for more help with adding integers.

Math 6.NS.2.3
Science 6.2.a, 6.3.c

This iceberg is made up of fresh water, which freezes at 0°C. The surrounding ocean is salt water, which doesn't freeze at 0°C.

SKILL: ADDING INTEGERS

Temperature and the Water Cycle

Changes in temperature help water move through the environment. At freezing temperatures—below 32°F or 0°C for sea-level environments—water can begin to become solid ice. Ice starts to melt when the temperature rises above freezing, causing the water to become liquid again. Temperature change also causes water to become vapor, or gas, within the air.

Example

Suppose you are waiting for winter to come so you can skate on a small pond near your house. The weather turns cold. One day the temperature is 5°C. The next day the air temperature drops by 8°C. What temperature is the air? If the air stays below 0°C, some of the water will begin to freeze.

(1) Write a verbal model:
5 degrees + an 8-degree drop = what temperature?

(2) Write an equation. Use negative and positive integers:
$5 + (-8) = ?$

(3) Solve the equation:
$5 - 8 = -3$

ANSWER −3°C.

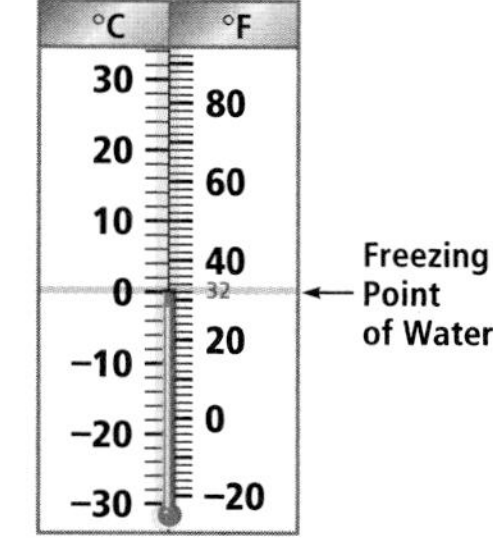

Answer the following questions.

1. A container of water is left out overnight, when the temperature is −18°C. In the morning, the air temperature rises by 8°C. What temperature is the air? What will happen to the water?

2. An ice block sits in a field where the air is 0°C. The air temperature rises by 16°C. Then it drops by 8°C. What temperature is the air in the field now? What will happen to the ice?

3. What happens to a block of ice after the temperature in the air follows this pattern: −6°C + 4°C + 3°C + 1°C + (−5°C)? What temperature has the air reached?

CHALLENGE **Use a thermometer to measure the temperature of the air outside and indoors in degrees Celsius. Write two addition equations that show the temperature change between the two locations. One equation should show a rise, and one should show a drop.**

ANSWERS

1. $-18 + 8 = -10$°C; the water will freeze.

2. $0 + 16 - 8 = 8$°C; the ice block will melt.

3. some of the ice block will melt and then re-freeze; −3°C

CHALLENGE Temperature figures should be recorded in degrees Celsius. The equations should show lower temperature + difference = higher temperature, and higher temperature + (− difference) = lower temperature.

MATH IN SCIENCE

Math Skills Practice for Science

Set Learning Goal

To add positive and negative integers in situations involving temperature

Math Standard

6.NS.2.3 Solve addition, subtraction, multiplication, and division problems, including those arising in concrete situations, that use positive and negative integers and combinations of these operations.

Present the Science

Read the explanation with students. Make sure they understand the freezing point and boiling point of fresh water, and that a temperature below zero is preceded by a minus sign. Remind students that saltwater freezes at a lower temperature. The term "water" in this exercise refers to fresh water only.

Develop Algebra Skills

Go through the sample question with students. Ask:

- Why is a negative number (−8) used for the equation in step 2? *The temperature decreases so a negative number is used.*
- How do you subtract a larger number from a smaller number? *You can subtract the smaller number from the larger one, and then add a negative sign: $8 - 5 = 3$; $5 - 8 = -3$*

DIFFERENTIATION TIP Suggest that students use a number line. Demonstrate how to use the number line to figure rise and fall in temperatures.

Close

Ask: Name another example in the sciences where adding positive and negative integers is used. *elevations below sea level, dates B.C. and A.D.*

- Math Support, p. 60
- Math Practice, p. 61

Technology Resources

Students can visit **ClassZone.com** for practice in adding integers.

MATH TUTORIAL

11.3 FOCUS

Set Learning Goals

Students will

- Explain how living organisms move energy through an ecosystem.
- Explain how feeding relationships are important in an ecosystem.
- Observe plants decomposing with the help of microorganisms.

3-Minute Warm-Up

Display Transparency 85 or copy this exercise on the board:

Serena puts a small amount of water in a saucer and leaves it on a sunny windowsill for several hours. What happens to the water? Why? *The water evaporates. Heat from the Sun changes liquid water into vapor, which escapes into the air. After several hours, the saucer may be completely dry.*

3-Minute Warm-Up, p. T85

11.3 MOTIVATE

EXPLORE Energy

PURPOSE To observe that all objects have energy, even when they are stationary

TIPS *10 min.*

- Bowls with wide openings work best.
- Packing peanuts may be used instead of sand.

WHAT DO YOU THINK? *The pebble made a small dent in the sand; the rock made a much larger dent in the sand. The rock contains more (mechanical) energy due to the force of gravity.*

KEY CONCEPT

11.3 Energy flows through ecosystems.

CALIFORNIA Content Standards

6.5.a Students know energy entering ecosystems as sunlight is transferred by producers into chemical energy through photosynthesis and then from organism to organism through food webs.

6.5.b Students know matter is transferred over time from one organism to others in the food web and between organisms and the physical environment.

BEFORE, you learned

- Matter cycles continuously through an ecosystem
- Living things are part of the water, carbon, and nitrogen cycles

NOW, you will learn

- How living things move energy through an ecosystem
- How feeding relationships are important in ecosystems
- How the amount of energy changes as it flows through an ecosystem

VOCABULARY

EXPLORE Energy (6.5.a)

How can you demonstrate energy?

PROCEDURE

1. Fill the bowl halfway with sand and place it on the floor. Be sure the sand is level.
2. Place the pebble and rock near the edge of a table above the bowl of sand.
3. Gently push the pebble off the table into the sand. Record your observations.
4. Remove the pebble and make sure the sand is level. Gently push the rock off the table into the sand. Record your observations.

MATERIALS

- large plastic bowl
- sand
- pebble
- rock

WHAT DO YOU THINK?

- What happened to the sand when you dropped the pebble? when you dropped the rock?
- How can you explain any differences you observed?

Living things capture and release energy.

Everything you do—such as running, reading, and working—requires energy. The energy you use is chemical energy, which comes from the food you eat. When you run, you use up energy. As you sweat, some of that energy is released to the environment as heat. Eventually, you will need to replace the energy you've used.

Energy is important to all living things. Most of that energy comes directly or indirectly from sunlight. To use the energy, living things must first capture it and store it in a form they can use. Because energy is continuously used by the activities of living things, it must be continuously replaced in the ecosystem.

RESOURCES FOR DIFFERENTIATED INSTRUCTION

Below Level

UNIT RESOURCE BOOK

- Reading Study Guide A, pp. 34–35
- Decoding Support, p. 59

AUDIO CDS

Advanced

UNIT RESOURCE BOOK

- Challenge and Extension, p. 40
- Challenge Reading, pp. 55–56

English Learners

UNIT RESOURCE BOOK

Spanish Reading Study Guide, pp. 38–39

AUDIO CDS

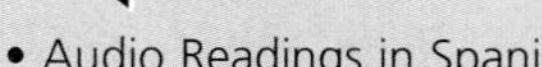

- Audio Readings in Spanish
- Audio Readings (English)

Producers

All of these producers capture energy from sunlight.

Plants

This tomato plant uses energy from the Sun to produce food.
The food is used as a source of energy and material for the plant and all the organisms that eat the plant.

Seaweed

Seaweed is a producer found in Earth's oceans and coastal zones.

Phytoplankton

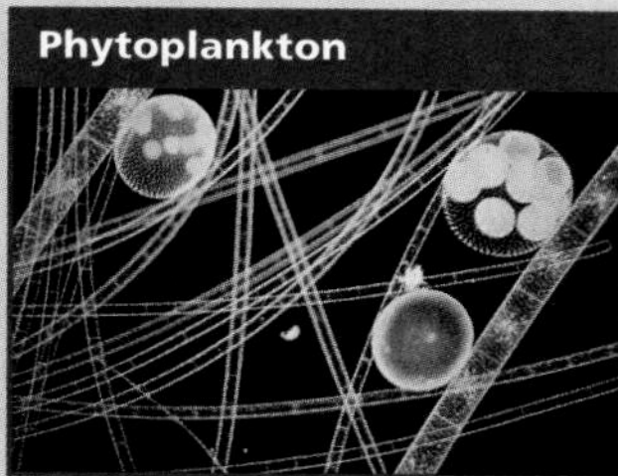

The most numerous producers are tiny organisms that live in water called phytoplankton.

READING VISUALS What process do all of these producers have in common?

Producers

A **producer** is an organism that takes in energy and stores it in food as chemical energy. The producers in an ecosystem make energy available to all the other living parts of the ecosystem. Most energy enters ecosystems through photosynthesis. Plants and other photosynthetic organisms take water and carbon dioxide from their environment and use energy from sunlight to produce sugars. The chemical energy stored in sugars can be released when sugars are broken down.

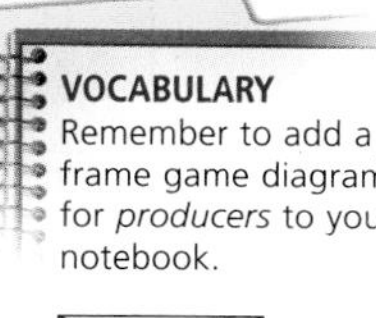

VOCABULARY Remember to add a frame game diagram for *producers* to your notebook.

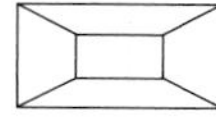

CHECK YOUR READING How does energy enter into the living parts of an ecosystem?

Plants are the most common producers found in land ecosystems. In water ecosystems, most food is produced by photosynthetic bacteria and algae. Examples of producers that use photosynthesis are shown in the photographs above.

READING TIP Algae are photosynthetic, plantlike organisms that live in water.

Sunlight provides most of the energy that is stored in food. One exception is a type of bacteria that lives in the deep ocean, where there is no sunlight. These bacteria produce food using chemicals released from underwater vents. You read about deep-sea vents in Chapter 10.

DIFFERENTIATE INSTRUCTION

More Reading Support

A In an ecosystem, what do producers do? *make energy available*

B How does a producer use energy from the Sun? *It uses energy to produce sugars.*

English Learners Providing models is an effective way to help English learners produce work that is representative of their abilities. If a student is asked to write an explanatory paragraph, provide an appropriate model of one. For example, on p. 396 students are asked to draw a food chain and a food web. Refer students back to the examples on p. 395 for a model of each.

11.3 INSTRUCT

Teach the Standards

Food webs 6.5.a, 6.5.b

In this section: Make sure students understand the roles of producers, consumers, and decomposers in an ecosystem. Point out that usable energy decreases as it moves through a food web.

previously taught: energy from sunlight, pp. 9–11; biotic factors, p. 378

future opportunities: biomes, pp. 398–405; symbiosis, pp. 426–429

Teach from Visuals

To help students interpret the "Producers" Visual:

- Tell students the photographs show three types of producers. One type is green plants. Ask: What are the other two? *seaweed and phytoplankton*
- Ask: Which of these producers do humans use for food? *green plants and seaweed*
- Ask: What form of energy do the producers use, and what form of energy do they produce? *Producers change light energy into chemical energy.*

Develop Critical Thinking

CLASSIFY Ask students to apply the concept of *producers* to the following ecosystems by identifying the producers in each list:

- forest: pine trees, birds, ferns, decaying logs, termites, earthworms, squirrels *trees, ferns*
- ocean: jellyfish, corals, phytoplankton, fish, crabs, seaweed *seaweed, phytoplankton*

Ongoing Assessment

READING VISUALS *Answer: They perform photosynthesis.*

CHECK YOUR READING *Answer: through photosynthesis and chemical energy*

Teach from Visuals

To help students interpret the visual of consumers, ask:

- Why is the plant identified as the producer? *It is where photosynthesis takes place.*
- Why is the caterpillar identified as the primary consumer? *It eats the leaves of the plant (the producer).*
- Why is the bird identified as the secondary consumer? *The bird is second in the line of consumers—it eats a primary consumer.*

Develop Critical Thinking

CONNECT Have students discuss the transfer of energy and matter in the food chain represented in the illustration. Ask:

- Once the bird has eaten the caterpillar, what happens to the matter that made up the caterpillar and the energy that was stored in the caterpillar's cells? *It transfers to the body of the bird.*
- What kind of energy conversion is involved when a bird flies? *Chemical energy converts to mechanical energy.*

Integrate the Sciences

All matter on Earth is reused. Your body might contain carbon atoms that once were part of a dinosaur.

Energy cannot be recycled, but it is constantly converted from one form to another and transferred from place to place. For example, the Sun's radiation changes to heat energy as it shines on Earth. Chemical energy stored in wood changes to heat energy as it ignites and burns.

Ongoing Assessment

READING VISUALS *Answer: The bird eats the caterpillar, which ate the leaf. Energy and matter transfer from leaf to caterpillar to bird.*

CHECK YOUR READING *Answer: Producers transform the Sun's energy into sugars. Consumers take in this stored energy when they eat the producers.*

Consumers

A consumer is an organism that gets energy by eating producers or other consumers.

Primary consumer: caterpillar

Producer: tree

Secondary consumer: bird

READING VISUALS How does the energy inside the leaf get transferred to the bird?

Consumers

Organisms that cannot produce their own food must get their food from other sources. **Consumers** are organisms that get their energy by eating, or consuming, other organisms. To understand how energy flows through an ecosystem, you have to study feeding relationships. A feeding relationship starts with a producer, followed by one and often many more consumers.

Describe the producer-consumer relationship in terms of energy.

Consumers are classified by their position in a feeding relationship. In a meadow ecosystem, animals such as antelopes and grasshoppers feed on grasses. They are primary consumers because they are the first link between the producers and the rest of the consumers in the ecosystem. The wolves that eat the antelopes are secondary consumers. So are the meadowlarks that eat the grasshoppers. The prairie falcon that eats the meadowlark is a tertiary consumer. Ecosystems also have special consumers called scavengers. A vulture is a scavenger because it feeds on dead animals.

READING TIP *Primary* means "first in order." *Secondary* means "second in order." *Tertiary* means "third in order."

In the photograph above, energy enters the ecosystem through the tree, which is the producer. The caterpillar that gets its energy by feeding on the tree's leaves is the primary consumer. The bird that gets its energy by feeding on the caterpillar is a secondary consumer.

DIFFERENTIATE INSTRUCTION

More Reading Support

C What organisms get energy by eating other organisms? *consumers*

D What feeds on dead animals? *scavengers*

Below Level Have students draw the organisms in the "Consumers" diagram as a food chain. Then have them draw a tertiary consumer, such as a fox or a hawk, in its appropriate place in the food chain.

Decomposers

If you've hiked through a forest or walked through a park, you have seen the interaction of producers and consumers. Tall trees and leafy shrubs are home to many insects and the birds that eat them. Also important to an ecosystem are decomposers, a group of organisms that often go unseen. **Decomposers** are organisms that break down dead plant and animal matter into simpler compounds.

Fungi, such as these mushrooms, are decomposers.

You can think of decomposers as the cleanup crew of an ecosystem. In a forest, consumers such as deer and insects do not eat all of the leaves on trees and shrubs. Many leaves are left on the forest floor, along with dead roots and branches. These materials are eventually digested by fungi and bacteria living in the soil. Decomposers also break down animal remains, including waste materials. A pinch of soil may contain almost half a million fungi and millions of bacteria.

The energy within an ecosystem is used up as it flows from organism to organism. Decomposers are the organisms that release the last bit of energy from once-living matter. Decomposers also return matter to soil or water, where it may be used again and again.

READING TIP
Fungi are organisms that are similar to plants, but they have no leaves or flowers. The singular form of *fungi* is *fungus*.

INVESTIGATE Decomposers

Where do decomposers come from?

SKILL FOCUS
Observing (6.5.b)

PROCEDURE

1. Carefully use scissors to cut an opening across the middle of the bottle.
2. Place a handful of stones in the bottom of the bottle for drainage, and add enough soil to make a layer 10 cm deep.
3. Place some leaves and fruit slices on top of the soil.
4. Seal the cut you made with tape. Mark the date on the tape.
5. Add water through the top of the bottle to moisten the soil, and then put the cap on the bottle. Wash your hands.
6. Observe the fruit slices each day for two weeks. Record your observations. Keep the soil moist.

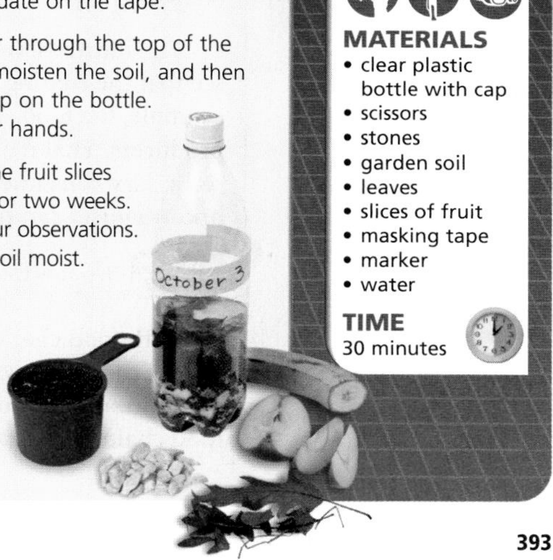

WHAT DO YOU THINK?

- What did you observe happening to the fruit slices?
- Where did the decomposers in your bottle come from?

CHALLENGE Predict what would happen if you used potting soil instead of soil from outdoors.

MATERIALS
- clear plastic bottle with cap
- scissors
- stones
- garden soil
- leaves
- slices of fruit
- masking tape
- marker
- water

TIME
30 minutes

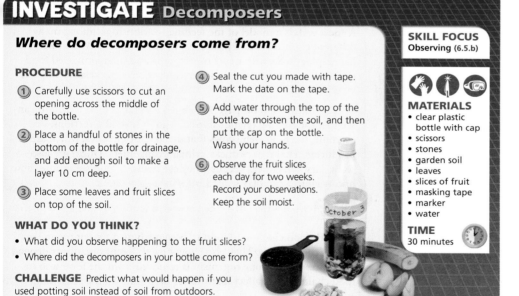

INVESTIGATE Decomposers

PURPOSE To observe the effect of decomposers on plant matter

TIP *30 min.* You might want to start with rotting fruit rather than fresh fruit in this activity. It will speed the process, and you will avoid wasting food.

WHAT DO YOU THINK? *Answers: The fruit slices turned brown and rotted; the decomposers came from the garden soil.*

CHALLENGE *The fruit would take longer to decay and not break down as well because potting soil does not have as many decomposers as garden soil.*

 Datasheet, Decomposers, p. 41

Technology Resources

Customize this student lab as needed or look for an alternative. Print rubrics to assess student lab reports.

 **Lab Generator CD-ROM**

Ongoing Assessment

Explain how living organisms move energy through an ecosystem.

Ask: How does the Sun's energy end up in the milk you drink at lunch? *Grasses (producers) convert the Sun's energy into food. Cows use matter and energy from grass to produce milk.*

DIFFERENTIATE INSTRUCTION

More Reading Support

E What kind of organism breaks down the bodies of dead plants and animals into simpler compounds? *decomposer*

Advanced Decomposers such as fungi and bacteria are continuously at work in ecosystems breaking down plant and animal wastes. Have students list and describe some specific processes of decomposition that benefit human beings.

Have students who are interested in ecosystem processes that benefit humans read the following article:

 Challenge Reading, pp. 55–56

Address Misconceptions

IDENTIFY Ask: What do the arrows in the food web on p. 395 mean? If students answer that the arrows point from the eater to the eaten, they may hold the misconception that a food web is a linear model showing only which organism eats which.

CORRECT Create a food web bulletin board for an ecosystem in your area, using pictures of producers and consumers linked by arrows. Explain that the arrows show the flow of energy from one organism to another. Therefore, the arrows point from the eaten to the eater. Arrange the arrows so that they point in the opposite direction from the way they should. Have students explain the error.

REASSESS Ask: In a food web, what does an arrow pointing from a frog to a stork mean? *It means that energy flows from the frog to the stork when the stork eats the frog.*

Technology Resources

Visit **ClassZone.com** for background on common student misconceptions.

 **MISCONCEPTION DATABASE**

EXPLORE the BIG idea

Revisit "Internet Activity: A Prairie Ecosystem" on p. 375. Have students explain the feeding relationships and other factors moving energy and water through that ecosystem.

Ongoing Assessment

CHECK YOUR READING *Answer: A food chain shows only one set of feeding relationships in an ecosystem; a food web shows many different feeding relationships.*

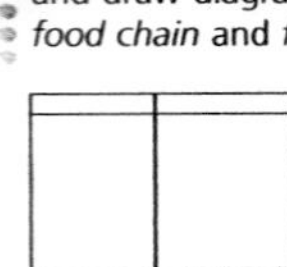

COMBINATION NOTES Remember to take notes and draw diagrams for *food chain* and *food web.*

Models help explain feeding relationships.

You have learned how energy is captured by producers and moved through ecosystems by consumers and decomposers. Scientists use two different models to show the feeding relationships that transfer energy from organism to organism. These models are food chains and food webs.

Food Chain

A chain is made of links that are connected one by one. Scientists use the idea of links in a chain to show simple feeding relationships. A **food chain** describes the feeding relationship between a producer and a single chain of consumers in an ecosystem.

The illustration in the white box on page 395 shows a wetland food chain. The first link in the chain is a cattail, a producer that captures energy from sunlight and stores it. The second link is a caterpillar, a primary consumer of the cattail. A frog is a secondary consumer that eats the caterpillar. The final link is a heron, a tertiary consumer that eats the frog. Energy is taken in and released at each link in the chain. The arrows represent the flow of energy from organism to organism. You can see that some of the energy captured by the cattail makes its way through a whole chain of other organisms in the ecosystem.

Food Web

A **food web** is a model of the feeding relationships among many different consumers and producers in an ecosystem. A food web is like a spider web, with many overlapping and interconnected food chains. It is a better model for the complex feeding relationships in an ecosystem.

READING TIP Notice that the food chain described above is also a part of the food web described here. Follow the blue arrows in the diagram on page 395.

The illustration on page 395 shows a wetland food web. You can see that the feeding relationships can go in several directions. For example, the food web shows that ducks eat bulrushes, which are producers. That makes ducks primary consumers. Ducks are also secondary consumers because they eat snails. A food web shows how one organism can play several roles in an ecosystem.

CHECK YOUR READING What is the difference between a food chain and a food web?

Both food chains and food webs show how different organisms receive their energy. They also show how different organisms depend on one another. If one organism is removed from the food web or food chain, it may affect many other organisms in the ecosystem.

DIFFERENTIATE INSTRUCTION

More Reading Support

F What are the links in a food chain or food web? *organisms and their feeding relationships*

G Which shows complex feeding relationships? *food web*

Below Level Have students create a simple food web with four to six organisms. Have them remove one of the organisms and explain some likely results for the rest of the organisms.

Inclusion Let students with cognitive disabilities use their bodies to represent the links in a food chain or food web. Have each student make and wear the name or picture of the organism he or she represents. Use yarn or string to show the links in the food web they are modeling.

Energy Flows Through Ecosystems

Energy is transferred from one organism to the next as organisms eat or are eaten.

A Wetland Food Chain

Flow of Energy
Energy flow starts at the bottom. Arrows represent energy moving from an organism that is eaten to the organism that eats it.

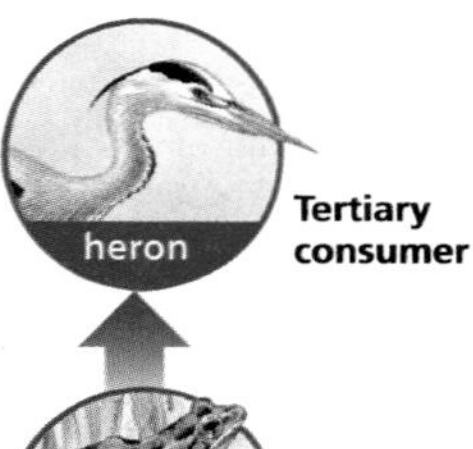

Tertiary consumer

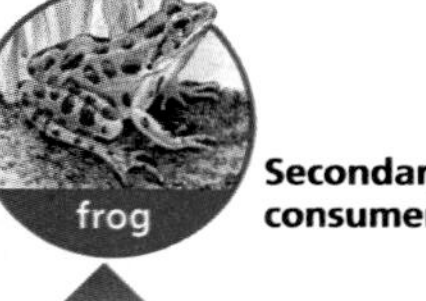

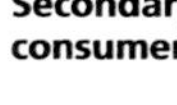

Secondary consumer

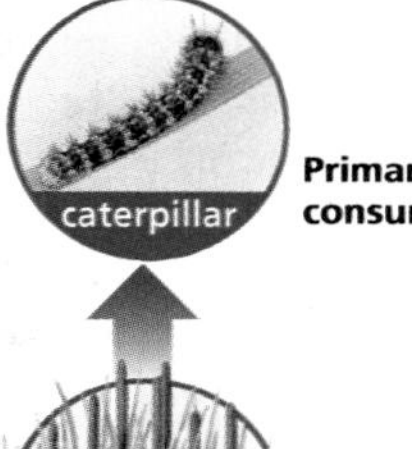

Primary consumer

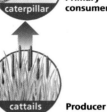

Producer

Decomposers
These tiny organisms recycle dead and decayed material.

A Wetland Food Web

Chapter 11: Ecosystems and Biomes 395

DIFFERENTIATE INSTRUCTION

Below Level Have students work in pairs to identify the different food chains in the food web in the illustration. Assign each pair of students one of the organisms, and have them draw all of the food chains associated with that organism.

Advanced Have students draw food chains for foods they eat everyday.

 Challenge and Extension, p. 40

Teach from Visuals

To help students interpret the visual of energy flowing through an ecosystem:

- Ask: Why are there no arrows pointing away from the heron or the water snake? *Answer: because they are the tertiary consumers and they are not eaten by any organism shown in this food web*
- Have students list three different food chains that you can find in the food web shown here. *bulrush, beetle, blackbird; cattails, snail, duck; bulrush, snail, heron; bullrush, beetle, frog, watersnake*

 The visual "Energy Flows Through Ecosystems" is available as T86 in the Transparency Book.

Develop Critical Thinking

CONNECT Have students apply their knowledge of a food web by asking them to create a food web for familiar organisms they observe in a local ecosystem, such as a park, garden, backyard, vacant lot, or urban neighborhood. *Sample answer: Aphids, crickets, and other insects feed on leaves of plants. Pigeons and sparrows eat insects. Falcons and hawks eat sparrows and pigeons.*

Ongoing Assessment

Explain how feeding relationships are important in an ecosystem.

Ask: What would happen to secondary consumers, such as cats, if primary consumers were eliminated from a food web? *Secondary consumers would starve unless they could eat and use producers or find another primary consumer on which to feed.*

Teach from Visuals

To help students interpret the energy pyramid, ask:

- Which layer of the pyramid contains the most energy? *producers*
- Which layer of the pyramid contains the least energy? *tertiary consumers*
- Why is there less energy in the primary consumers than there is in the producers? *The life processes of the producers use up some of the energy before primary consumers eat the producers.*

Reinforce the BIG idea

Have students relate the section to the Big Idea.

 Reinforcing Key Concepts, p. 42

11.3 ASSESS & RETEACH

Assess

 Section 11.3 Quiz, p. 252

Reteach

Have students draw a food chain for one or more foods they've eaten. Ask them to indicate how energy travels in the chain and how much there is at each step. Ask:

- Did all of the Sun's energy absorbed by the producer in your food chain end up in your body? Why or why not? *No; some of the energy was used by the plant before it was eaten.*
- Describe your place in the food chain. *Answer should be a primary or higher consumer.*
- What other animals might take your place in this food chain? *other high-level consumers*

Technology Resources

Have students visit **ClassZone.com** for reteaching of Key Concepts.

 CONTENT REVIEW

 CONTENT REVIEW CD-ROM

Available energy decreases as it moves through an ecosystem.

Another way to picture the flow of energy in an ecosystem is to use an energy pyramid. An **energy pyramid** shows the amount of energy available at each feeding level of an ecosystem. The first level includes the producers, the second level the primary consumers, and so on. Because usable energy decreases as it moves from producers to consumers, the bottom level is the largest. The available energy gets smaller and smaller the farther up the pyramid you go.

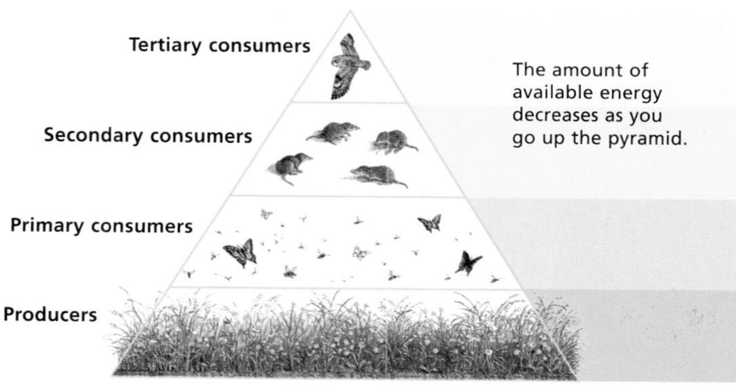

READING TIP

Refer to the diagram above as you read the text. The diagram takes the shape of a pyramid because available energy decreases at each level.

In the pyramid shown here, plants are the producers. They capture energy from sunlight, use some of it, then store the rest as food. The plants are eaten by insects, which also use some of the energy before being eaten by small mammals called shrews. The shrews use energy before being eaten by the owl. You can see that it takes a lot of sunlight to support the producers and consumers in a food web that feeds an owl.

11.3 Review

KEY CONCEPTS

1. Describe the role of producers, consumers, and decomposers in an ecosystem. (6.5.b)
2. Explain why a food web provides a better model of an ecosystem than a food chain does. (6.5.a)
3. Explain how the amount of available energy changes as energy moves up a food chain. (6.5.a)

CRITICAL THINKING

4. **Apply** Draw a food chain and a food web for an ecosystem near your home.
5. **Predict** Imagine that muskrats are removed from a wetland ecosystem. Predict what would happen to producers and secondary consumers.

CHALLENGE

6. **Synthesize** Explain how the carbon cycle is related to a food web. Describe how energy and matter move through the food web and the carbon cycle.

ANSWERS

1. Producers make sugars using sunlight. Consumers eat other consumers and producers. Decomposers break down dead producers and consumers.

2. Food webs show that one organism can have more than one role in an ecosystem.

3. Available energy decreases.

4. Food chains should show one energy path. Webs should show multiple paths.

5. Producers would increase without the muskrats. Other primary consumers and the secondary consumers that eat those other primary consumers would also increase.

6. A food web shows movement of energy, but it also shows movement of matter. As consumers eat, carbon in plants and animals is transferred through the food web

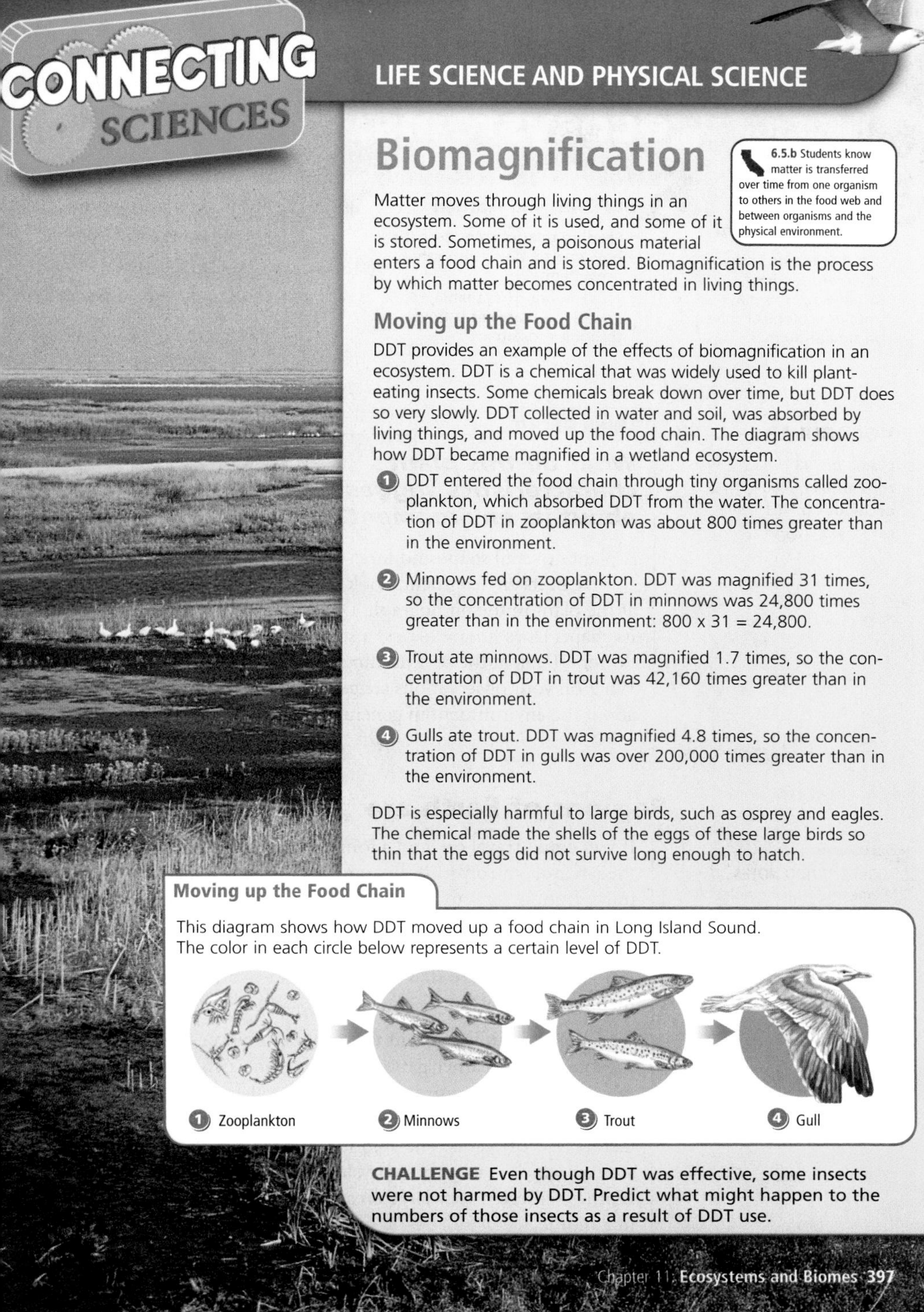

CONNECTING SCIENCES

LIFE SCIENCE AND PHYSICAL SCIENCE

Biomagnification

6.5.b Students know matter is transferred over time from one organism to others in the food web and between organisms and the physical environment.

Matter moves through living things in an ecosystem. Some of it is used, and some of it is stored. Sometimes, a poisonous material enters a food chain and is stored. Biomagnification is the process by which matter becomes concentrated in living things.

Moving up the Food Chain

DDT provides an example of the effects of biomagnification in an ecosystem. DDT is a chemical that was widely used to kill plant-eating insects. Some chemicals break down over time, but DDT does so very slowly. DDT collected in water and soil, was absorbed by living things, and moved up the food chain. The diagram shows how DDT became magnified in a wetland ecosystem.

1. DDT entered the food chain through tiny organisms called zooplankton, which absorbed DDT from the water. The concentration of DDT in zooplankton was about 800 times greater than in the environment.
2. Minnows fed on zooplankton. DDT was magnified 31 times, so the concentration of DDT in minnows was 24,800 times greater than in the environment: 800 x 31 = 24,800.
3. Trout ate minnows. DDT was magnified 1.7 times, so the concentration of DDT in trout was 42,160 times greater than in the environment.
4. Gulls ate trout. DDT was magnified 4.8 times, so the concentration of DDT in gulls was over 200,000 times greater than in the environment.

DDT is especially harmful to large birds, such as osprey and eagles. The chemical made the shells of the eggs of these large birds so thin that the eggs did not survive long enough to hatch.

Moving up the Food Chain

This diagram shows how DDT moved up a food chain in Long Island Sound. The color in each circle below represents a certain level of DDT.

CHALLENGE Even though DDT was effective, some insects were not harmed by DDT. Predict what might happen to the numbers of those insects as a result of DDT use.

Chapter 11: Ecosystems and Biomes 397

EXPLORE

CHALLENGE *Insects not affected by DDT might increase in numbers as living things that consume those insects might decrease in population.*

CONNECTING SCIENCES

Connecting Life and Physical Sciences

Set Learning Goal

To understand how chemicals in the environment can accumulate in organisms that feed high on the food chain

Present the Science

DDT is stored in fatty tissues. Accumulations of DDT in the body may not lead to death, but its gradual buildup can affect an animal's health and ability to reproduce. Although DDT was banned in the United States in 1972, it lingers in the environment. It is still used in some countries, especially to control malaria-carrying mosquitoes.

Discussion Questions

Go through the steps of the biomagnification food chain. Ask:

- How does DDT get into the bodies of zooplankton? *Runoff washes DDT into waterways, where zooplankton absorb it from the water.*
- How does an organism's place on the food chain relate to the concentration of DDT in its body? *Organisms higher on the food chain have higher concentrations of DDT.*
- How does the biomagnification of DDT affect reproduction in birds of prey? *It causes thin eggshells that break before young birds have a chance to hatch.*

Close

Ask: How does the biomagnification of nonbiodegradable chemicals show that matter moves through a food chain? *DDT is not broken down or used at each step in the food chain, so increasing amounts accumulate in the bodies of organisms that are higher on the chain.*

11.4 FOCUS

Set Learning Goals

Students will

- Describe how biomes vary by region and how they are classified by the plant life they support.
- Explain that different ecosystems make up a biome.
- Describe different land and water biomes on Earth.
- Gather and graph local climate data.

3-Minute Warm-Up

Display Transparency 85 or copy the exercise on the board:

The organisms in a certain grassland ecosystem include grasses, insects, meadowlarks, mice, and owls. Draw a diagram that shows how these organisms depend on one another for food. Label each organism, and use an arrow to show which organism(s) it feeds on. *Students should produce a simple food web with arrows from grasses to insects, insects to meadowlarks and mice, and mice to owls.*

 3-Minute Warm-Up, p. T85

11.4 MOTIVATE

THINK ABOUT

PURPOSE To understand how a plant's characteristics are important for survival

DISCUSS What adaptations do cacti have? *thick green stems and spines* What do they do for the plants? *reduce water loss, perform photosynthesis, protect plant from herbivores.*

Answers: tubular stems and oval-shaped growth off stems; it has spines instead of leaves; its pads are stems; it flowers; it must conserve water; the environment is dry.

KEY CONCEPT

11.4 Biomes contain many ecosystems.

CALIFORNIA Content Standard

6.5.d Students know different kinds of organisms may play similar ecological roles in similar biomes.

BEFORE, you learned

- Feeding relationships describe how energy flows through ecosystems
- The amount of available energy decreases as it flows through ecosystems

NOW, you will learn

- How biomes vary by region and by the plant life they support
- How different ecosystems make up a biome
- About the different land and water biomes on Earth

VOCABULARY

biome p. 398
coniferous p. 400
deciduous p. 401
estuary p. 404

THINK ABOUT

What do this plant's characteristics suggest about its environment?

A plant's overall shape and form help it survive in its environment. Look closely at the plant in the photograph. Describe its shape. Does it have leaves? a stem? flowers? Look at the surrounding area. What do your observations suggest about the environment in general?

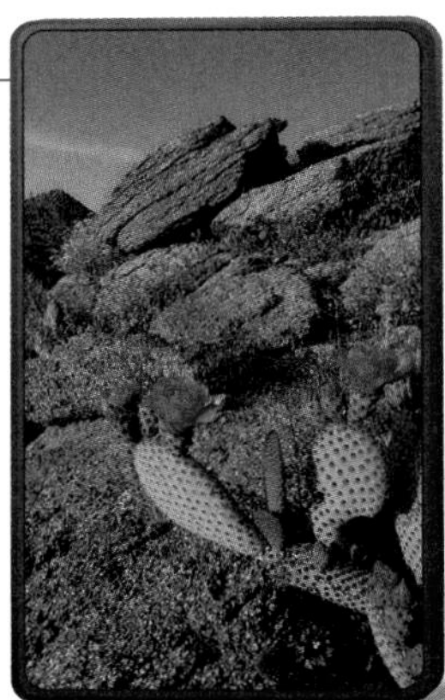

COMBINATION NOTES
Remember to take notes and draw a diagram for each of the six land biomes described in the text.

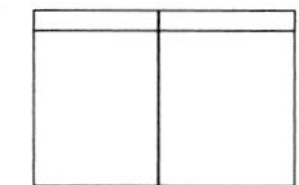

Regions of Earth are classified into biomes.

If you could travel on land a long distance, either north or south of the equator, you'd probably notice an interesting pattern. You would move from deserts to grasslands to forests. Across Earth, there are large geographic regions that have similar climates and similar types of plants and animals. Each of these regions is called a **biome** (BY-OHM). There are six major land biomes on Earth, as shown on the map on page 399.

Climate is an important factor in land biomes. Climate describes the long-term weather patterns of a region, such as average yearly rainfall and temperature ranges. Climate also affects soil type. You know that available water, temperature, and soil are important abiotic factors in ecosystems. The abiotic factors of a particular biome are similar, which is why the ecosystems found in that biome are similar. Biomes represent very large areas, so there are many ecosystems within a biome.

RESOURCES FOR DIFFERENTIATED INSTRUCTION

Below Level

UNIT RESOURCE BOOK

- Reading Study Guide A, pp. 45–46
- Decoding Support, p. 59

Advanced

UNIT RESOURCE BOOK

Challenge and Extension, p. 51

English Learners

UNIT RESOURCE BOOK

Spanish Reading Study Guide, pp. 49–50

- Audio Readings in Spanish
- Audio Readings (English)

Land Biomes

Each land biome is characterized by a particular climate, the quality of the soil, and the plant life found there.

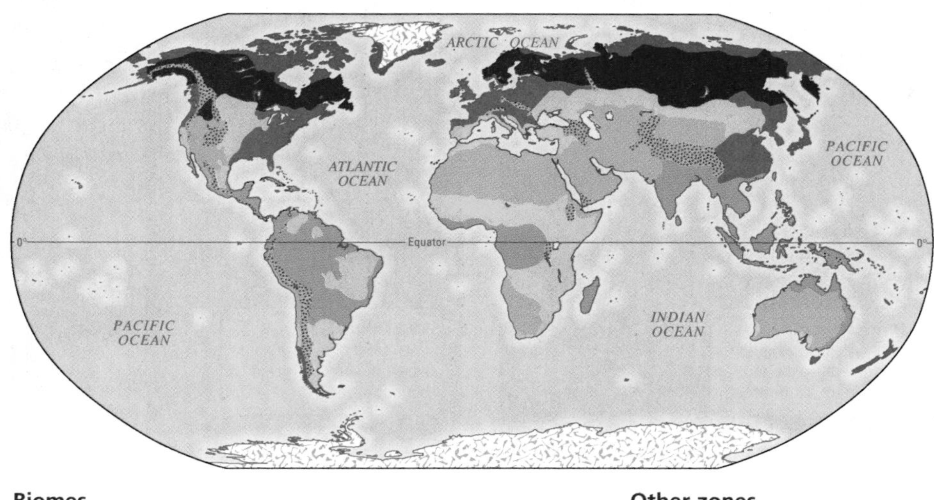

Biomes
- Tundra
- Taiga
- Desert
- Grassland
- Temperate Forest
- Tropical Forest

Other zones
- Mountain Zones
- Polar Ice

Taiga and Tundra

If you go to the most northern regions of Earth, you will find two biomes, tundra and taiga. Both are characterized by long, cold winters and short, cool summers. In the Arctic tundra, temperatures can be as low as –45°C, with a high of about 16°C.

Tundra doesn't get much precipitation—less than 25 centimeters each year. Yet the area is wet because cold temperatures keep the water from evaporating. One of the important characteristics of tundra is permafrost, a deep layer of permanently frozen soil that lies just below the surface soil. Permafrost prevents trees from taking root in tundra regions. Tundra plants are small and include mosses, grasses, and woody shrubs. Organisms called lichens also do well in tundra.

snowy owl

The producers of tundra ecosystems support rodents, caribou, and musk oxen. Grizzly bears, Arctic foxes, and snowy owls are predators found there. Migrating birds come to nest in tundra, feeding on insects that mature in summer.

11.4 INSTRUCT

Teach the Standards

Biomes 6.5.d

In this section: Help students see the similarities between the following pairs of biomes: tundra and taiga, desert and grassland, temperate forest and tropical forest, and freshwater and marine. Explain the roles that producers and consumers play in these biome pairs.

previously taught: Earth system, pp. 41–46; ecosystems, pp. 377–381, 384–388, 390–396

future opportunities: changing ecosystems, pp. 431–436

Teach from Visuals

To help students interpret the map of land biomes, ask:

- How many of the six land biomes occur in North America? *all six*
- Which biomes occur in South America? *all except taiga and tundra*
- Which biome dominates Europe? *temperate forest*
- How do the biomes of Australia and southern Africa compare? *Both include desert and grassland and some tropical forest.*

Geography Connection

Remind students that latitude lines mark distance above and below the equator. Point out the location of the equator and the Arctic Circle on a world map or globe. Ask:

- In what latitudes does tundra occur? *around the Arctic Circle; in the Northern Hemisphere only*
- Why is there no tundra or taiga in the Southern Hemisphere? *No landmasses, other than the polar ice of Antarctica are close to the south pole.*
- Where do tropical forests occur on Earth? *near the equator, and spreading north and south*

DIFFERENTIATE INSTRUCTION

More Reading Support

A What two biomes are found in Earth's northernmost regions? *tundra and taiga*

B Which biome is drier than and nearly as cold as the taiga? *tundra*

English Learners Ask English learners to describe the climate, soil quality, and plant life found in their home country. Help them determine which type of biome they have described. Be certain that students understand that a country or region may have more than one type of biome. Have students write the definitions of *biome, coniferous, deciduous,* and *estuary* in their Science Word Dictionaries.

Teach from Visuals

To help students compare and contrast the photographs of tundra and taiga, ask:

- What differences do you notice between the taiga and tundra? *Taiga has tall trees and bushes; tundra has only low-growing plants.*
- What is a primary reason for these differences? *Permafrost prevents the growth of the large, deep root systems of large plants in the tundra.*

Teach Difficult Concepts

Students may have difficulty remembering differences between taiga and tundra. Point out that tundra can be considered a kind of cold desert because it is cold, windy, and dry. The taiga, by contrast, is thickly forested with tall trees. Taiga receives more precipitation than tundra (30 to 60 cm compared to less than 25 cm) and has trees and no permafrost.

Teacher Demo

Show students what permafrost is like. Use a sharp spade or trowel to collect a block of turf or other soil that measures about 15 cm square. Keep the block intact and place it in a shallow container in the freezer for several hours. Remove the container from the freezer a few minutes before class so that the upper portion will begin to thaw. Let students use disposable chopsticks or other probes to explore the texture of the frozen soil. Students may find it helpful to know that *permafrost* is short for "permanent frost."

Ongoing Assessment

Describe how biomes vary by region and are classified by the plant life they support.

Ask: Where do you find taiga and how do you recognize it? *It is in northern latitudes, has long winters and short summers, and is often dominated by coniferous trees.*

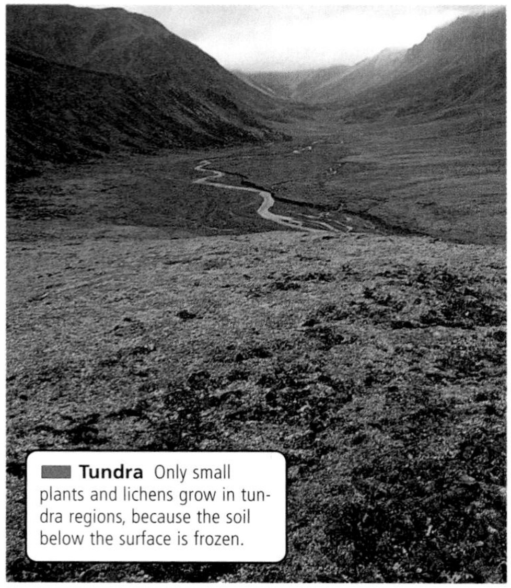

Tundra Only small plants and lichens grow in tundra regions, because the soil below the surface is frozen.

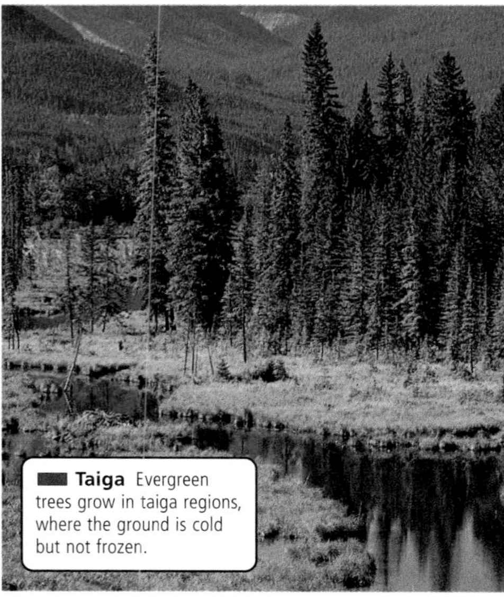

Taiga Evergreen trees grow in taiga regions, where the ground is cold but not frozen.

Even though the temperatures of taiga (TY-guh) regions are similar to those of tundra regions, taiga has more precipitation—40 to 100 centimeters a year. As a result, there is more snow on the ground. This insulates the soil below, keeping it from freezing permanently.

In taiga ecosystems, you will find evergreen trees called **coniferous** (koh-NIHF-uhr-uhs) trees. These trees have needlelike leaves that produce food all year long. This is an advantage in taiga ecosystems. Decomposers work slowly in the cold, so the soil is low in nutrients. Insects eat the wood and leaves of these trees, and birds and squirrels eat their seeds. Taiga ecosystems support deer, elk, snowshoe hares, and beavers. Predators include lynx, owls, bears, and wolves.

Desert and Grassland

collared lizard

Deserts and grasslands are biomes found near or in the middle latitudes. You can see from the map on page 399 that a desert biome often leads into a grassland biome. Deserts and some grasslands do not get enough precipitation to support trees.

D

Some deserts are cold and some deserts are hot, but all deserts have dry soil. Less than 25 centimeters of rain falls each year in a desert. Desert plants and animals can get by on very little water. Small burrowing animals, such as kangaroo rats and ground squirrels, are part of desert ecosystems. Desert predators include snakes, owls, and foxes.

DIFFERENTIATE INSTRUCTION

More Reading Support

C What are evergreens in taiga ecosystems called? *coniferous*

D Which biome is defined by dry soil? *desert*

Inclusion For students who are still at a concrete stage of learning, model the rainfall amounts in this section either by filling a clear beaker or by displaying vertical strips of varying lengths. Explain how each amount represents the water that would collect in a rain gauge from falling precipitation.

Grassland ecosystems develop in areas of moderate rainfall, generally from 50 to 90 centimeters each year. There is enough rain to support grasses, but too little rain to support forests. Regular wildfires and droughts keep smaller shrubs and tree seedlings from growing. Summers in grassland ecosystems can be hot—more than 30°C—but winters are cold.

Grasses do well in large open areas. The more rain a grassland ecosystem gets, the higher the grasses grow. These ecosystems support seed-eating rodents that make their burrows in the grassland soil. There are also large grazing animals, such as bison, wild horses, gazelles, and zebras. Predators include wolves, tigers, and lions.

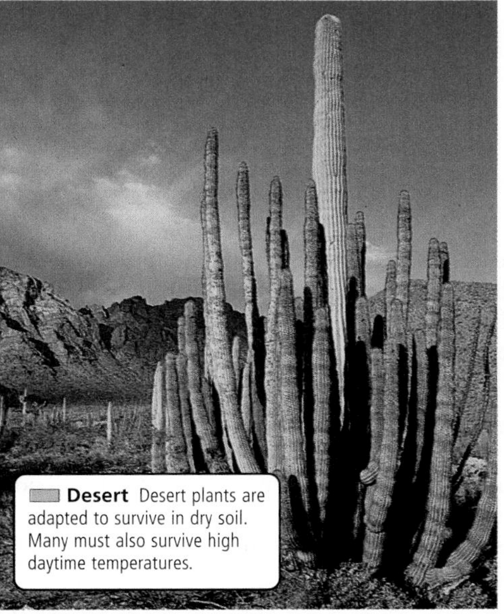

Desert Desert plants are adapted to survive in dry soil. Many must also survive high daytime temperatures.

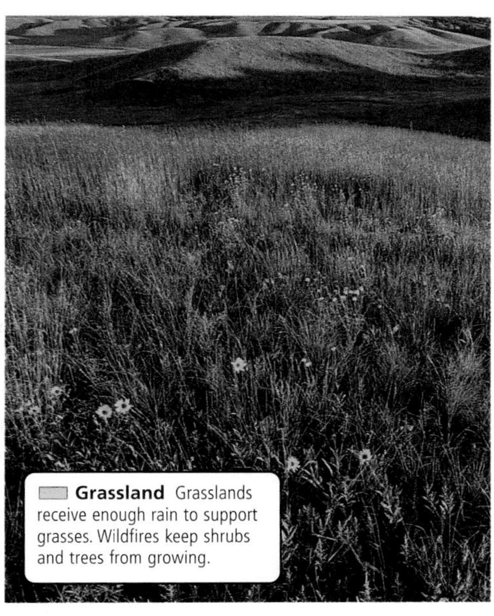

Grassland Grasslands receive enough rain to support grasses. Wildfires keep shrubs and trees from growing.

Temperate Forest and Tropical Forest

Trees need more water than smaller plants, shrubs, and grasses. Therefore, forest biomes are usually located in regions where more water is available. The taiga is a forest biome. There, coniferous trees survive on smaller amounts of precipitation because the cold weather limits evaporation. Across the middle latitudes, temperate forests grow where winters are moderate and 75 to 150 centimeters of precipitation fall each year. Near the equator, there are no winters. There, tropical forests grow where more than 200 centimeters of rain fall each year.

Most temperate forests are made up of deciduous trees, sometimes referred to as broadleaf trees. **Deciduous** (dih-SIHJ-oo-uhs) trees drop their leaves as winter approaches and then grow new leaves in the spring.

Teach from Visuals

To help students compare and contrast the photographs of deserts and grasslands, ask:

- What differences do you notice between the desert and grassland? *Desert has bare soil with rocks and cacti; grassland soil is covered with grasses and wildflowers.*
- What are some primary reasons for these differences? *Grasslands receive more rain and have richer soil than deserts do.*

Teacher Demo

Compare features of grasses and broad-leaved plants for students. Carefully wash the soil from the roots of a sample of lawn grass and an uprooted broad-leaved plant. Show students the intact plants, including root system. Ask: Why can grass plants survive grazing and fire? *New leaves grow from an underground part of the plant that usually escapes damage from grazing or fire.*

Develop Critical Thinking

SYNTHESIZE Have students choose one animal from the taiga and suggest adaptations that animal would need to survive in the tundra. Students might choose other animals from other biomes as well. For example, what would make it hard for a snowy owl to survive in a grassland? What adaptations could increase its survival?

DIFFERENTIATE INSTRUCTION

More Reading Support

E What kind of plant does well in large open areas? *grass*

F Which biome has trees that are bare of leaves in winter? *temperate forest*

Below Level Help students remember the differences among biomes by having them make flash cards. On one side of a card, have them write a biome name, and on the other side, one feature of that biome. Give students time to study their flash cards with the help of a partner.

Teach from Visuals

To help students compare and contrast the photographs of temperate and tropical forests, ask:

- What differences do you notice between the temperate and tropical forests? *Sample answer: more vines, greater number and variety of trees in the tropics*
- What do you notice about the variety of types of leaves in temperate and tropical forests? *A tropical forest has a greater variety of leaf types and sizes.*

Real World Example

The Alaskan forest contains cedar and spruce trees, salmon in rivers, sea lions, otters, and belugas in coastal waters. In 1989, the need to protect this bounty was magnified when the *Exxon Valdez* accidentally dumped 11 million gallons of oil on 15,000 miles of coastline. Wildlife like the otter, harbor seal, and harlequin duck still haven't recovered. Now the forest faces a greater threat: logging. Humans are leveling trees at a record rate. Some environmental groups are trying to preserve the rainforest. Oil-spill funds from the *Exxon Valdez* have added 66,000 acres of forest to the state-park system.

Ongoing Assessment

Explain that different ecosystems make up a biome.

Ask: What are some of the ecosystems in our biome? *Sample answer for temperate forest: deciduous forest, shrubland, marsh; grassland: meadow, field, banks of a stream*

CHECK YOUR READING *Answer: the greater the plant variety in a biome, the greater the variety of animals*

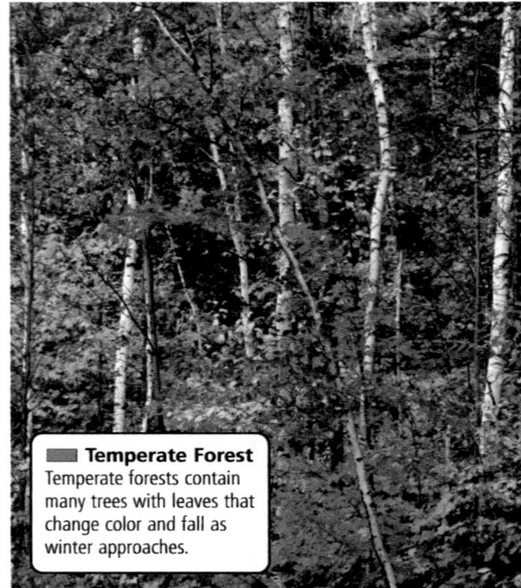

Temperate Forest Temperate forests contain many trees with leaves that change color and fall as winter approaches.

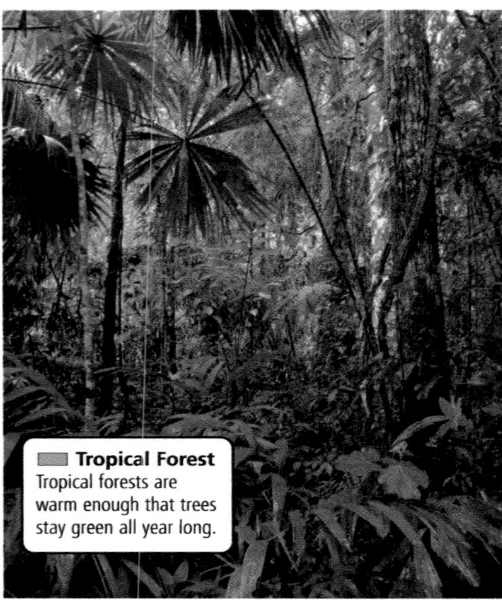

Tropical Forest Tropical forests are warm enough that trees stay green all year long.

The most common broadleaf trees in North American deciduous forests are oak, birch, beech, and maple. Temperate forests support a wide variety of animals. Animals such as mice, chipmunks, squirrels, raccoons, and deer live off seeds, fruit, and insects. Predators include wolves, bobcats, foxes, and mountain lions.

CALIFORNIA Focus

California is home to some of the world's oldest and tallest trees, the giant sequoias. They thrive along the western Sierra Nevada range. Although these trees were once logged for many uses, they are now protected. Trees over 3000 years old can be found in Sequoia and Kings Canyon National Parks in central California.

G Most temperate forests in North America are deciduous. However, the wet winters and drier summers in the Pacific Northwest support forests made up mostly of coniferous trees. These include redwood, spruce, and fir trees. These forests are also called temperate rain forests. The largest trees in the United States are found in these temperate rain forests.

H Tropical forests are located near the equator where the weather is warm all year—around 25°C. The tropical forest is the wettest land biome, with a rainfall of 200 to 400 centimeters each year. Therefore, it is also called the tropical rain forest. Most trees have leaves year round. This is an advantage because the soil has few nutrients. High temperatures cause materials to break down quickly, but there are so many plants the nutrients are used up quickly.

More types of animals, plants, and other organisms live in tropical rain forests than anywhere else on Earth. The trees grow close together and support many tree-dwelling animals, such as monkeys, birds, insects, and snakes. Some plants, such as orchids and vines, grow in the tops of the trees.

CHECK YOUR READING How does the variety of plants in a biome affect the variety of animals in that biome?

DIFFERENTIATE INSTRUCTION

More Reading Support

G Which biome includes forests that are deciduous? *temperate forest*

H What is the wettest biome on Earth? *tropical forest*

Advanced Tropical rain forests are rapidly disappearing. Challenge students to brainstorm products that come from the rain forest. Ask them to infer why use of each product would either help or harm rain forest conservation.

Have students compare yearly precipitation for each biome in the following activity.

 Challenge and Extension, p. 51

INVESTIGATE Climate

How can you graph climate data for your area?

SKILL FOCUS
Graphing data (6.5.e)

MATERIALS
- graph paper
- 2 colored pencils

TIME
20 minutes

PROCEDURE

1. Find data about the average monthly precipitation and average monthly temperature for a 12-month period in your area.
2. On graph paper, mark off 12 months along the *x*-axis. Make a *y*-axis for each side of the graph. Label one "Temperature (°C)" and the other "Precipitation (mm)."
3. Make a bar graph that shows the average precipitation for each month.
4. Use a different color to make another bar graph that shows the average temperature for each month.

WHAT DO YOU THINK?
- How much precipitation did your area receive overall?
- What was the temperature range for the area?

CHALLENGE Find data for the same location from a different year. Graph the data. Compare your graphs. How different are the data for the two years? How might changes in climate affect the plant and animal life in your area?

Water covers most of Earth's surface.

Almost three-fourths of Earth's surface is covered by water. Water biomes are also called aquatic biomes. They can be divided into two broad categories: freshwater biomes and salt-water biomes. Plants have a role as producers in water biomes that are closely surrounded by land—in ponds and streams and wetlands, and in coastal areas. The food webs of deep-water ecosystems depend on tiny photosynthetic microorganisms called phytoplankton.

leopard frog

Freshwater Biomes

The ecosystems of freshwater biomes are affected by the qualities of the landscape in which they are found. For example, differences in elevation affect how water flows in streams and rivers. In shallow rivers, algae and plants provide food for insects and snails. These in turn are eaten by fish, salamanders, turtles, and frogs. Plants in a freshwater biome may take root in the soil under the water if the water is not too deep or moving too fast. Phytoplankton are not part of river ecosystems because of the flowing water.

INVESTIGATE Climate

PURPOSE To understand differences in precipitation and temperature over a 12-month period

TIP *20 min.* You may wish to have students work in pairs to create their graphs.

WHAT DO YOU THINK? *Sample answers should match climate in your region.*

CHALLENGE *Sample answers should match climatic change in your region. One example of severe climatic change is drought, which affects plant growth.*

- Climate Graph, p. 52
- Datasheet, Climate, p. 53

Technology Resources

Customize this student lab as needed or look for an alternative. Print rubrics to assess student lab reports.

 **Lab Generator CD-ROM**

Teaching with Technology

Students may use spreadsheets or graphing software to organize data and create their graphs.

DIFFERENTIATE INSTRUCTION

More Reading Support

I What covers almost three-quarters of Earth's surface? *water*

Alternative Assessment Rather than asking students to write a formal report on the investigation, have student pairs explain the story that the data tell. Ask students to write a paragraph explaining how the lines on the graph describe the data.

Teach from Visuals

To help students understand the illustration and photographs of aquatic biomes, ask:

- What differences do you notice between the river and the lake or pond? *A river has flowing water that travels a long way through the countryside. Ponds and lakes have still water that does not travel.*
- What differences do you notice between the estuary and the lake or pond? *There are no trees around the estuary. There is flowing water in the estuary. The pond is farther from the ocean.*

Integrating the Sciences

The biosphere is the part of Earth that supports life. It includes air, soil, and water. It extends from the bottom of the deepest ocean to high in the atmosphere, miles above Earth's surface. Just as biomes are made up of ecosystems, the biosphere is made up of biomes. In turn, the Earth as a system is made up of spheres. The spheres include the geosphere, the hydrosphere, the atmosphere, and the biosphere.

Ongoing Assessment

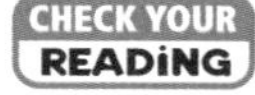

CHECK YOUR READING

Answer: any two: lakes, ponds, estuaries, and rivers

Aquatic Biomes
Freshwater biomes include the still water of lakes, the running water of rivers, and estuaries where fresh water and salt water mix.
Lakes and Ponds
Estuaries
Rivers and Streams

Ponds and lakes have still water. Ponds are shallow and support many plants as producers. Organisms in deeper lakes depend much more on phytoplankton for food. Ponds and lakes support many different insects, shellfish, snakes, fish, and the land animals that eat them.

CHECK YOUR READING Name two types of freshwater biomes.

Estuaries are water ecosystems that mark a transition between freshwater and saltwater biomes. An **estuary** is a shoreline area where fresh water from a river mixes with salt water from the ocean. Estuaries are sometimes referred to as the nurseries of the sea because so many marine animals travel into the calm waters to reproduce. Seaweed, marsh grasses, shellfish, and birds all thrive in estuaries.

Marine Biomes

Marine biomes are saltwater biomes. The three main types of marine biomes are the coastal ocean, the surface zone of the open ocean, and the deep ocean. Beaches are part of the coastal ocean biome. Tidal pools form along the coast as the tide comes in and goes out and the conditions constantly change. Organisms such as crabs and clams thrive in the ever-changing conditions in coastal areas.

The open ocean has two main parts—the surface zone and the deep zone. The surface zone is, on average, about 100 meters deep.

RESOURCE CENTER
CLASSZONE.COM

Find out more about land and aquatic biomes.

DIFFERENTIATE INSTRUCTION

More Reading Support

J Which biome combines fresh and saltwater? *estuary*

K Which biomes are in the ocean? *coastal ocean, open ocean, deep ocean*

Advanced Have students select freshwater or marine ecosystems and draw or paint an ecosystem in that biome. If possible, use a technique called "crayon resist." Students draw organisms with oil pastels or crayons, then paint the watery surrounding using water-color paint. Ask them to use their drawings to create a classroom display that shows how the ecosystems combine to form different aquatic biomes.

Coastal Ocean

Marine biomes include rocky and sandy shores as well as the surface zone of the open ocean and the deep waters below, where no light can reach.

Open Ocean

Deep Ocean

Phytoplankton use the sunlight to make food. They are the main producers in the ocean food web. Many types of fish, other marine animals, and floating seaweed live in the upper ocean.

The dark and cold deep zone of the open ocean lies under the surface zone. Because sunlight does not reach the deep zone, no phytoplankton can live there. Therefore, deep-sea animals must either eat other animals or eat food that drifts down from the surface zone.

11.4 Review

KEY CONCEPTS

1. In biomes located on land, abiotic factors are used to classify the different biome types. What are these abiotic factors? **(6.5.d)**
2. Name a type of plant found in each of the six land biomes. **(6.5.d)**
3. Name six different aquatic biomes. **(6.5.d)**

CRITICAL THINKING

4. **Predict** If an ecosystem in the grassland biome started to receive less and less rainfall every year, what new biome would be established?
5. **Infer** Name some abiotic factors that affect aquatic biomes and ecosystems.

CHALLENGE

6. **Apply** Use the map on page 399 to list the following four biomes in the order you would find them moving from the equator to the poles.
   - desert
   - taiga
   - tropical forest
   - tundra

ANSWERS

1. available water, temperature, soil

2. tundra: mosses, lichens; taiga: coniferous trees; desert: cacti; grassland: grasses; temperate forest: deciduous trees; tropical forest: plants grow on top of each other

3. rivers and streams, lakes and ponds, estuaries, coastal ocean, open ocean, deep ocean

4. desert

5. sunlight, water depth, temperature, nutrients

6. tropical forest, desert, taiga, tundra

Teach from Visuals

To help students understand marine biomes, ask:

- How are the coastal ocean and open ocean similar? *Both receive sunlight.*
- How does the deep ocean differ from the coastal and open ocean? *It is dark and cold.*

Ongoing Assessment

Describe diferent land and water biomes on Earth.

Ask: Do land biomes or water biomes make up the majority of Earth? *water biomes*

Reinforce the BIG idea

Have students relate the section to the Big Idea.

 Reinforcing Key Concepts, p. 54

11.4 ASSESS & RETEACH

Assess

 Section 11.4 Quiz, p. 253

Reteach

Start by listing the six land biomes on the board. Then list aquatic biomes.

Next, show pictures of landscapes and ask students to identify what biome they could be from. Have students point to details that support their identification. Discuss any landscapes that are difficult to categorize.

Technology Resources

Have students visit **ClassZone.com** for reteaching of Key Concepts.

 **CONTENT REVIEW**

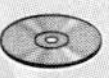 **CONTENT REVIEW CD-ROM**

BACK TO

the BIG idea

Have students draw and label a diagram showing how matter and energy are both needed to support life in an ecosystem. *Drawings should show the movement of matter through an ecosystem and the movement of energy and matter through its food web.*

KEY CONCEPTS SUMMARY

SECTION 11.1

Ask: What abiotic features are pictured? *temperature, sunlight, soil, water*

Ask: What biotic features are pictured? *tree, horse*

SECTION 11.2

Ask: What are the three important processes that take place in the water cycle? *evaporation, condensation, precipitation*

Ask: How does carbon move from air to plants to animals? *Plants absorb carbon dioxide from air, and animals eat plants.*

Ask: How does nitrogen move from air to plants to animals in an ecosystem? *Bacteria fix nitrogen gas into a compound that is taken up by plants. Animals eat plants.*

SECTION 11.3

Ask: Name one path that matter and energy take as they move through the food web shown in the picture on p. 395. *Sample answer: bulrush, snail, heron*

Ask: Which organisms are at the top of this ecosystem's energy pyramid? *heron, water snake*

SECTION 11.4

Ask: What are the chief factors that define a biome? *plant life and climate*

Review Concepts

- Big Idea Flow Chart, p. T81
- Chapter Outline, pp. T87–T88

11 Chapter Review

the BIG idea

Matter and energy together support life within an environment.

KEY CONCEPTS SUMMARY

Ecosystems support life.

Ecosystems are made up of living things (biotic) and nonliving things (abiotic).

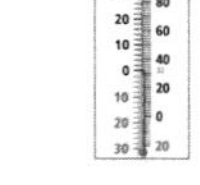

plants animals — **Biotic Factors**

temperature Sun soil water — **Abiotic Factors**

VOCABULARY
ecology p. 377
ecosystem p. 377
biotic factor p. 378
abiotic factor p. 378

Matter cycles through ecosystems.

Water, carbon, and nitrogen are materials that are necessary for life. They move through ecosystems in continuous cycles.

VOCABULARY
cycle p. 384
carbon cycle p. 386
nitrogen cycle p. 387

Energy flows through ecosystems.

Producers are the basis of feeding relationships in ecosystems.

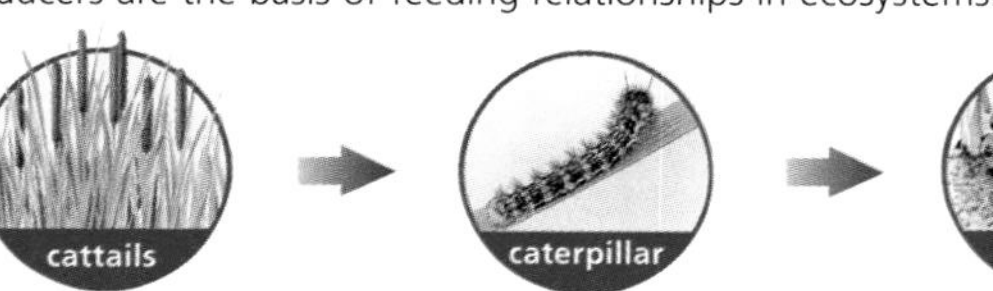

Food chains and food webs help show how energy moves through living things.

VOCABULARY
producer p. 391
consumer p. 392
decomposer p. 393
food chain p. 394
food web p. 394
energy pyramid p. 396

4 **Biomes contain many ecosystems.**

Ecosystems of land biomes
- are affected by climate
- are affected by conditions of the soil
- are characterized by types of plants

Ecosystems of water biomes
- can be freshwater or saltwater
- are affected by landscape if freshwater
- are affected by ocean depth

VOCABULARY
biome p. 398
coniferous p. 400
deciduous p. 401
estuary p. 404

406 Unit 4: **Ecology and Resources**

Technology Resources

Have students visit **ClassZone.com** or use the CD-ROM for a cumulative review of concepts.

CONTENT REVIEW

CONTENT REVIEW CD-ROM

Engage students in a whole-class interactive review of Key Concepts. Edit content as you wish.

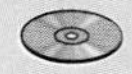

POWER PRESENTATIONS

Reviewing Vocabulary

Write a statement describing how the terms in each pair are similar and different.

1. biotic, abiotic
2. producer, consumer
3. food chain, food web

The table shows the meanings of word roots that are used in many science terms.

Root	Meaning
bio-	life
oikos (eco)	house
-logy	study of

Use the information in the table to write definitions for the following terms.

4. ecology
5. biome
6. ecosystem

Reviewing Key Concepts

Multiple Choice *Choose the letter of the best answer.*

7. Which best describes the parts of an ecosystem? **(6.5.e)**
   - **a.** light, water, soil, and temperature
   - **b.** plants and animals
   - **c.** biotic factors and abiotic factors
   - **d.** producers, consumers, and decomposers
8. What is the main source of energy for most ecosystems? **(6.5.a)**
   - **a.** water
   - **b.** nitrogen
   - **c.** soil
   - **d.** sunlight
9. What is the process by which the water in rivers, lakes, and oceans becomes a gas and moves into the atmosphere? **(6.5.b)**
   - **a.** precipitation
   - **b.** evaporation
   - **c.** condensation
   - **d.** transpiration
10. The process called nitrogen fixation is essential for life on Earth. Which of the following is an example of nitrogen fixation? **(6.5.b)**
    - **a.** Plants take in nitrogen gas from the atmosphere.
    - **b.** Animals take in nitrogen gas from the atmosphere.
    - **c.** Water absorbs nitrogen.
    - **d.** Bacteria convert nitrogen gas into a form that plants can use.
11. Which organism is a decomposer? **(6.5.d)**
    - **a.** vulture
    - **b.** sunflower
    - **c.** musk ox
    - **d.** fungus
12. How are decomposers important in an ecosystem? **(6.5.d)**
    - **a.** They make atmospheric nitrogen available to plants in a usable form.
    - **b.** They convert organic matter into more complex compounds.
    - **c.** They are an important source of food for scavengers.
    - **d.** They break down organic matter into simpler compounds.
13. What factor is least important in determining the plant life in a biome? **(6.5.e)**
    - **a.** average annual rainfall
    - **b.** average annual temperature
    - **c.** the type of soil
    - **d.** the type of animals living there

Short Answer *Write a short answer to each question.*

14. Write a paragraph to describe how carbon dioxide gas in the atmosphere can become part of the carbon compounds found inside animals. **(6.5.b)**
15. Write a paragraph to explain how the amount of available energy changes as you move from producers to consumers in a food web. **(6.5.a)**
16. Write a paragraph to describe one important way in which the flow of energy through ecosystems is different from the cycling of matter. **(6.5.a)**

ASSESSMENT RESOURCES

ASSESSMENT BOOK
- Chapter Test A, pp. 254–257
- Chapter Test B, pp. 258–261
- Chapter Test C, pp. 262–265
- Alternative Assessment, pp. 266–267

STANDARDS REVIEW AND PRACTICE, pp. 15–16, 27–28, 41–44, 47–50, 59–60

Technology Resources

Edit test items and answer choices.

 **Test Generator CD-ROM**

Visit **ClassZone.com** to extend test practice.

 **Test Practice**

Reviewing Vocabulary

1. Both are parts of the ecosystem. Biotic are the living parts, and abiotic are the nonliving parts.

2. Producers and consumers are parts of the ecosystem. Consumers get their food from producers directly by eating them, or indirectly by eating other consumers that eat producers.

3. Both are feeding relationships. A food chain is a single relationship; food webs have many interconnected food chains in the same ecosystem.

4. ecology: from oikos (eco) meaning "house" and –ology meaning "study of"—the scientific study of how organisms interact with their environment and all the other organisms in that environment.

5. biome: from bio– meaning "life"—a region on Earth with similar types of plants and animals.

6. ecosystem: from oikos (eco) meaning "house" and system, parts that work together—a particular environment and all the living things supported by it.

Reviewing Key Concepts

7. c	*11. d*
8. d	*12 d*
9. b	*13. d*
10. d	

14. Plants use carbon dioxide in the air to produce sugars in a process called photosynthesis. Then animals eat the plants. The compounds in the plants become part of the animals.

15. Available energy decreases as you move from the bottom to the top of the energy pyramid. Each time energy moves from one level to the next, it changes form, and some energy is lost in that process. Some of the energy is also used by the organisms at each level.

16. Sample answers: Cycles involve movement of matter through the environment. A cycle happens over and over again. The flow of energy involves food webs in which energy and matter are transferred from one organism to the next as organisms eat and are eaten.

Thinking Critically

17. *a food web; a model of the feeding relationships in an ecosystem*
18. *producer: cattails; primary: mosquito, slug; secondary: frog, salamander; tertiary: water snake*
19. *shrew next to salamander, arrow from slug to shrew, arrow from salamander to shrew, arrow from shrew to water snake*
20. *about one-thousandth*
21. *Decomposers do not produce food. They break down dead plant and animal matter for food.*
22. *desert, taiga, grassland, deciduous forest, tropical rain forest*
23. *Climate, temperature, rainfall, and available water determine type of plants that will grow. Some animals migrate to different biomes during the year. In theory, this makes plants a more reliable indicator of difference.*
24. *Diagrams should show correct relationships among various aquatic biomes; saltiness of water and amount of oxygen available in water differ among these biomes.*
25. *Answers might include a description of the living and nonliving things in a home, home climate, and that a home environment is a controlled environment.*
26. *Sample answer: a summer drought killed grasses and plant life, which were food for small animals.*

the BIG idea

27. *Sample answer: I would add organisms you can't see such as decomposers and plankton. I would mention soil, air, and sunlight as well.*
28. *Student answers should use the eight listed terms correctly in a paragraph(s).*

UNIT PROJECTS

Give students the appropriate Unit Project worksheets from the Unit Resource Book for their projects. Both directions and rubrics can be used as a guide.

R Unit Projects, pp. 5–10

Thinking Critically

Use the diagram to answer the next four questions.

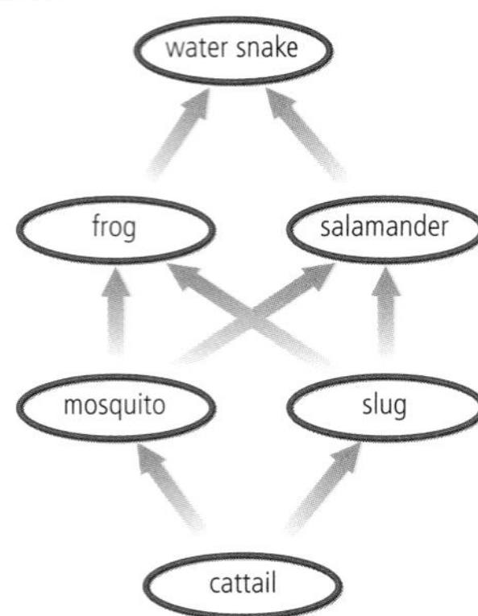

17. **CONNECT** What does the diagram above represent and how does it relate to energy in an ecosystem? **(6.5.a)**
18. **CLASSIFY** Identify each of the animals in the diagram above as a producer, primary consumer, secondary consumer, or tertiary consumer. **(6.5.d)**
19. **APPLY** An animal that is found in many wetland ecosystems is the shrew. The shrew eats salamanders and slugs and is eaten by water snakes. Copy the diagram above and show how you would add the shrew to the diagram. **(6.5.d)**
20. **CONNECT** Use the diagram above to make an energy pyramid. If only one-tenth of the energy available at each level is passed on to the next higher level, how much of the energy in a cattail is transferred to a salamander? **(6.5.a)**
21. **SYNTHESIZE** Why would it be difficult to show a decomposer as part of an energy pyramid? **(6.5.d)**
22. **RANK** Arrange the following list of biomes according to the relative amounts of precipitation in each, going from the least amount to the most: grassland, desert, deciduous forest, taiga, tropical rain forest. **(6.5.e)**
23. **SYNTHESIZE** Why are plants but not animals considered important factors in classifying a land biome? **(6.5.d)**
24. **SUMMARIZE** Draw a diagram that illustrates aquatic biomes. On your diagram label the following: freshwater river, freshwater lake, estuary, coastal zone, open ocean zone. How do abiotic factors differ among these biomes? **(6.5.e)**
25. **COMPARE AND CONTRAST** In what ways is your home like an ecosystem? In what ways is it different? **(6.5.e)**
26. **APPLY** Describe a change in an abiotic factor that affected living factors in an ecosystem near you. **(6.5.e)**

the BIG idea

27. **CLASSIFY** Look again at the photograph on pages 374–375. Now that you have finished the chapter, how would you change or add details to your answer to the question on the photograph? **(6.5.e)**
28. **SYNTHESIZE** Write one or more paragraphs describing how matter and energy together support life in an ecosystem. You may use examples from one specific ecosystem if you wish. In your description, use each of the following terms. Underline each term in your answer. **(6.5.b)**

ecosystem	decomposer
food web	nitrogen cycle
producer	carbon cycle
primary consumer	secondary consumer

UNIT PROJECTS

If you are doing a unit project, make a folder for your project. Include in your folder a list of the resources you will need, the date on which the project is due, and a schedule to track your progress. Begin gathering data.

MONITOR AND RETEACH

If students have trouble with concepts in items 17–21, have them review the energy pyramid on p. 396, then make pie graphs with captions to show relative amount of energy available. Tell students the pie graphs are a visual memory device and the data is estimated.

Students may benefit from summarizing one or more sections of the chapter.

 Summarizing the Chapter, pp. 81–82

Standards-Based Assessment

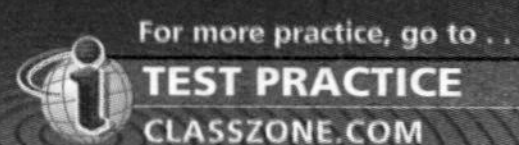

Interpreting Graphs

6.5.b, 6.5.d, 6.5.e

Choose the letter of the best response.

The graphs below show average monthly temperature and precipitation for one year in Staunton, Virginia, an area located in a temperate deciduous forest biome.

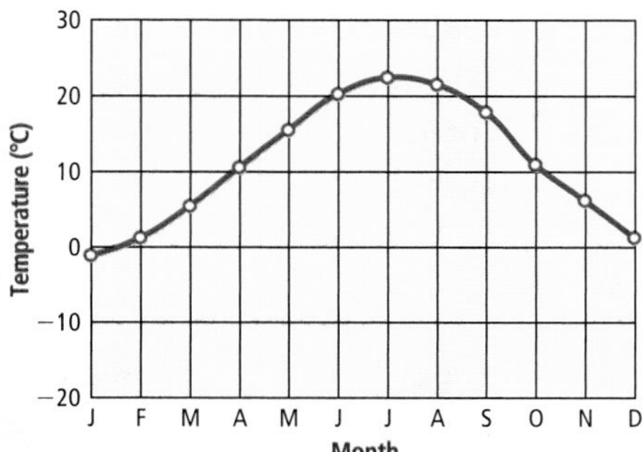

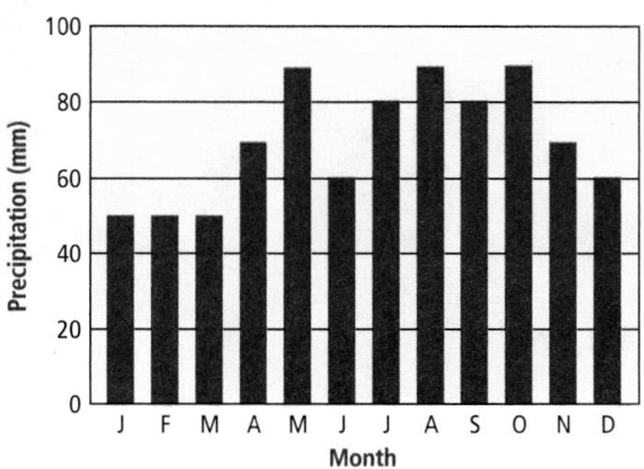

SOURCE: NASA

1. What was the average temperature during July?
   - **a.** 20°
   - **b.** 10°
   - **c.** 23°
   - **d.** 0°
2. Which months had the most precipitation?
   - **a.** January, February, March
   - **b.** May, August, October
   - **c.** July, August, September
   - **d.** December, January, February
3. What were conditions during May?
   - **a.** warm and moist
   - **b.** warm and dry
   - **c.** cool and moist
   - **d.** cool and dry
4. Which temperature is closest to the average temperature for the year shown?
   - **a.** about 16°
   - **b.** about 0°
   - **c.** about 20°
   - **d.** about 10°
5. How much precipitation would you estimate fell as snow in the year shown?
   - **a.** less than 10 mm
   - **b.** between 50 and 100 mm
   - **c.** between 200 and 300 mm
   - **d.** more than 400 mm

Extended Response

6. Much of the United States is part of a temperate deciduous forest biome. The deciduous forest biome has seasonal changes. Trees in this biome lose their leaves yearly. Use this information, as well as the information in the graphs, to describe the seasons in the temperate deciduous forest biome.

7. Write a paragraph in which you describe a typical ecosystem in your city or town. In your answer include biotic factors such as plants, animals, and other organisms. Also include abiotic factors such as light, temperature, soil, and water. Finish your description by saying how you and other humans affect the ecosystem.

REFLECTING ON THE CHAPTER

Have students answer the following questions in their **Science Notebook:**

1. What ecosystems and biomes were you already familiar with? What new things have you learned about those places?
2. How do you see yourself taking part in an ecosystem?
3. What goals have you set for your Unit Project? What is the next step you will complete?

California Content Standards

6.5.b Students know matter is transferred over time from one organism to others in the food web and between organisms and the physical environment.

6.5.d Students know different kinds of organisms may play similar ecological roles in similar biomes.

6.5.e Students know the number and types of organisms an ecosystem can support depends on the resources available and on abiotic factors, such as quantities of light and water, a range of temperatures, and soil composition.

Interpreting Graphs

1. c *3. a* *5. b*
2. b *4. d*

Extended Response

6. RUBRIC

4 points for a correct response that includes temperature and precipitation and refers to the graphs:

Sample: This biome has trees that lose their leaves yearly. There are four seasons. Average precipitation is lowest in the winter months, when trees do not have their leaves. Average temperatures range from about 20°C in summer to around 0°C in winter.

3 points gives a mostly complete response and refers to information in the graphs
2 points gives a partly complete response
1 point gives a mostly incorrect response

7. RUBRIC

4 points for a correct response that includes a description of biotic and abiotic factors, as well as human effects on the ecosystem:

Sample: The town park has ponds with fish, frogs, insects, and ducks. There are shrubs, grass, and trees. Humans walk on the grass and sometimes litter. Walking on the grass can kill it. Litter can block sunlight from a small plant.

3 points gives a mostly complete response about biotic and abiotic factors and human effects on the ecosystem
2 points gives a partly complete response
1 point gives a mostly incorrect response

CHAPTER

Interactions Within Ecosystems

Life Science

UNIFYING PRINCIPLES

PRINCIPLE 1
All living things share common characteristics.

PRINCIPLE 2
All living things share common needs.

PRINCIPLE 3
Living things meet their needs through interactions with the environment.

PRINCIPLE 4
The types and numbers of living things change over time.

Unit: Ecology and Resources

BIG IDEAS

CHAPTER 11
Ecosystems and Biomes
Matter and energy together support life within an environment.

CHAPTER 12
Interactions Within Ecosystems
Living things within an ecosystem interact with each other and the environment.

CHAPTER 13
Natural Resources
Society depends on natural resources for energy and materials.

CHAPTER 14
Human Impact on Ecosystems
Humans and human population growth affect the environment.

CHAPTER 12

KEY CONCEPTS

SECTION 1

Groups of living things interact within ecosystems.

1. Organisms occupy specific living areas.
2. The environment can be organized into five levels.
3. Patterns exist in populations.

SECTION 2

Organisms can interact in different ways.

1. Organisms interact in different ways.
2. The survival of one species might depend on another species.
3. Interactions in an ecosystem are complex.

SECTION 3

Ecosystems are always changing.

1. Populations change over time.
2. Ecosystems change over time.

The Big Idea Flow Chart is available on p. T89 in the **TRANSPARENCY BOOK**.

Previewing Content

SECTION

Groups of living things interact within ecosystems. pp. 413–421

1. Organisms occupy specific living areas.
Organisms are members of the same **species** if they are similar to each other and produce offspring that can breed. Members of the same species who live in a particular **habitat** constitute a **population.** The habitat provides everything the population needs to survive.

Organisms perform roles, called **niches,** in the habitat. For instance, grasses on a prairie anchor the topsoil and provide food for grazing animals. Populations that live together and interact form a **community.**

2. The environment can be organized into five levels.
Beyond the community are higher levels of organization.

- Organisms and their local environments constitute an **ecosystem.**
- Places that are similar in terms of climate and vegetation are called **biomes.** These are broadly defined and have world-wide distribution.

The diagram shows the levels of organization at a glance.

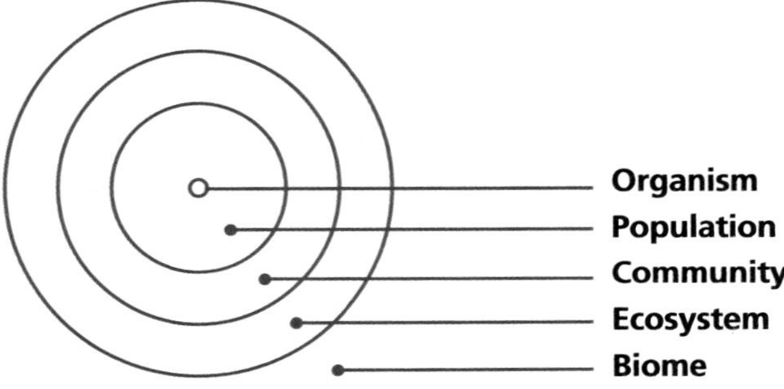

3. Patterns exist in populations.
The size of a population may change over time as a result of factors such as the change of seasons or interaction with another species. Spatial patterns of population distribution may result from the way organisms gather resources or from their need for mutual protection.

SECTION

Organisms can interact in different ways. pp. 422–430

1. Organisms interact in different ways.
A food chain is made up of producers and consumers, although the distinction between the two groups is not always clear-cut. An animal, for example, could be predator, prey, or both.

When more than one organism, whether of the same species or not, needs the same resources, the organisms will **compete.** Some organisms, such as ants or packs of hunters, **cooperate** to improve their survival.

2. The survival of one species might depend on another species.
Individuals of two species may have a close relationship called **symbiosis.** Three kinds of symbiosis are commonly recognized.

- **Mutualism** occurs when both species in the symbiosis benefit from the interaction.
- **Commensalism** occurs if one species benefits while the other is unharmed and unaffected.
- **Parasitism** occurs when one species is harmed while the other benefits.

The table shows how the three symbiotic relationships can be beneficial (+), neutral (**0**), or harmful (–).

Symbiosis		
Relationship Between Species	**One Species**	**Other Species**
mutualism	+	+
commensalism	0	+
parasitism	–	+

3. Interactions in an ecosystem are complex.
Relationships and interactions do not exist in isolation. Any one species can have a range of symbiotic or predatory relationships with many other species.

Common Misconceptions

MISCONCEPTION DATABASE
CLASSZONE.COM Background on student misconceptions

HUMANS IN AN ECOSYSTEM Students commonly think that they themselves are not part of ecosystems. Many children view the lives of humans as separate and different from those of plants, animals, and microorganisms. Each species of living thing is unique, yet all share common needs and characteristics. All species—including humans—live and interact in ecosystems.

This misconception is addressed on p. 417.

Previewing Content

SECTION

Ecosystems are always changing.

pp. 431–437

1. **Populations change over time.**
   Population size changes in response to food supply, predation, the seasons, and birth rates. A **limiting factor,** such as water, light, or food, can affect population survival and growth. The **carrying capacity** of an environment is the maximum population it can support. At carrying capacity a population stops growing.

2. **Ecosystems change over time.**
   Succession is a gradual series of changes that take place in an ecosystem after a disturbance.
   - **Primary succession** starts from an environment that is mostly empty of life. After the retreat of a glacier, for example, or on new rock produced by a volcano, life can begin to return. **Pioneer species** move into the barren environment and begin the task of creating soil.
   - **Secondary succession** occurs in areas that have soil with roots and seeds below the surface. In such cases, life already survives. Living things produce new generations and attract the return of diverse species. Secondary succession may begin after a fire or flood disturbs the ecosystem.

   The pictures on the right show the difference at the start of two successional sequences. In both types of natural succession, plants may facilitate the establishment of other plants by creating a hospitable habitat. Some species, however, create conditions that prevent competitors from moving in.

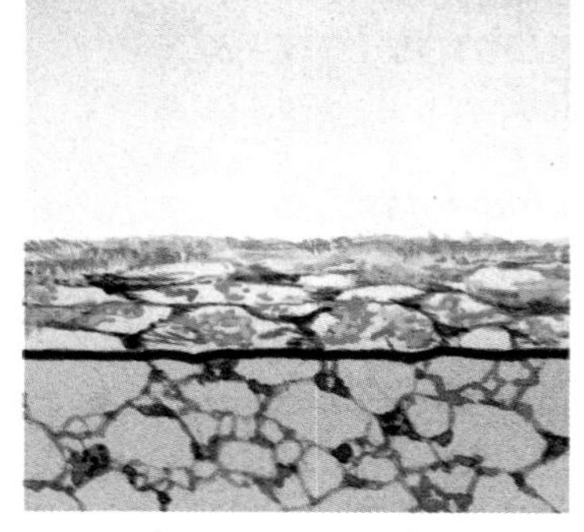

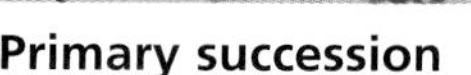

Primary succession

Secondary succession

A key difference between primary and secondary succession is the presence of soil in the environment at the start of the series of changes.

Common Misconceptions

MATTER CHANGES FORM Most students think that matter can be destroyed. They often think that dead or decaying matter rots away to nothing. In fact, living and decaying matter is constantly transforming, changing from one form into another.

This misconception is addressed on p. 434.

MISCONCEPTION DATABASE

CLASSZONE.COM Background on student misconceptions

Previewing Labs

Lab Generator CD-ROM
Edit these Pupil Edition labs and generate alternative labs.

EXPLORE the BIG idea

How Do Living Things Interact Where You Live? p. 411 Students observe how plants and animals interact in an environment.	**TIME** 10 minutes **MATERIALS** notebook, outdoor area, hand lens (optional)
How Many Roles Can a Living Thing Have in an Ecosystem? p. 411 Students analyze how an organism fits with an environment.	**TIME** 10 minutes **MATERIALS** notebook, outdoor area, hand lens (optional)
SECTION 1 **CHAPTER INVESTIGATION** Environmental Conditions, pp. 420–421 **ALTERNATIVE:** Teacher Demonstration, URB p. 273	**TIME** 15 minutes **MATERIALS** shoebox lid, marker, 6 pill bugs, watch or clock with secondhand, paper towel, water, black construction paper, incandescent lamp, thermometer
SECTION 2 **INVESTIGATE** Species Interactions, p. 425 Students use cardboard and paper pieces to analyze the effects of predators on prey and vice versa over 15 generations. **ALTERNATIVE:** Reading Activity, URB p. 273	**TIME** 30 minutes **MATERIALS** 20 10-cm squares of cardboard, 200 3-cm squares of paper, masking tape, graph paper, 2 colored pencils
SECTION 3 **EXPLORE** Population Growth, p. 431 Students observe the effects of different sugar concentrations on the growth of yeast.	**TIME** 20 minutes **MATERIALS** 3 clear plastic cups, warm water, sugar, dry yeast, measuring spoons, measuring cup, stirring rod, marker, ruler
INVESTIGATE Limiting Factors, p. 433 Students design an experiment to test whether space is a limiting factor for the growth of radishes. **ALTERNATIVE:** Direct Instruction, URB p. 274	**TIME** 20 minutes **MATERIALS** paper cups, potting soil, radish seeds, water, pencil, ruler

R **Additional INVESTIGATION,** Prey Survival, A, B, & C, pp. 131–139; Teacher Instructions, pp. 273–274

Previewing Chapter Resources

INTEGRATED TECHNOLOGY | **LABS AND ACTIVITIES**

CHAPTER 12
Interactions Within Ecosystems

Integrated Technology

CLASSZONE.COM
- eEdition Plus
- EasyPlanner Plus
- Misconception Database
- Content Review
- Test Practice
- Resource Centers
- Math Tutorial

SCILINKS.ORG

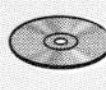

CD-ROMS
- eEdition
- EasyPlanner
- Power Presentations
- Content Review
- Lab Generator
- Test Generator

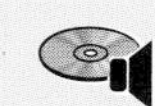

AUDIO CDS
- Audio Readings
- Audio Readings in Spanish

Labs and Activities

EXPLORE the Big Idea, p. 411
- How Do Living Things Interact Where You Live?
- How Many Roles Can a Living Thing Have in an Ecosystem?

UNIT RESOURCE BOOK
Unit Projects, pp. 5–10

Lab Generator CD-ROM
Generate customized labs.

SECTION

Groups of living things interact within ecosystems.
pp. 413–421

Lesson Plan, pp. 83–84

Integrated Technology

TRANSPARENCY BOOK
- Big Idea Flow Chart, p. T89
- Daily Vocabulary Scaffolding, p. T90
- Note-Taking Model, p. T91
- 3-Minute Warm-Up, p. T92
- "Levels in the Environment" Visual, p. T94

Labs and Activities

CHAPTER INVESTIGATION, Environmental Conditions pp. 420–421

UNIT RESOURCE BOOK
CHAPTER INVESTIGATION, Environmental Conditions, A, B, & C, pp. 122–130

SECTION

Organisms can interact in different ways.
pp. 422–430

Lesson Plan, pp. 93–94

Integrated Technology

RESOURCE CENTER, Symbiotic Relationships

TRANSPARENCY BOOK
- Daily Vocabulary Scaffolding, p. T90
- 3-Minute Warm-Up, p. T92

Labs and Activities

- INVESTIGATE Species Interactions, p. 425
- Think Science, p. 430

UNIT RESOURCE BOOK
- Datasheet, Species Interactions, p. 102
- Additional INVESTIGATION, Prey Survival, A, B, & C, pp. 131–139

SECTION

Ecosystems are always changing.
pp. 431–437

Lesson Plan, pp. 104–105

Integrated Technology

- **RESOURCE CENTER,** Succession
- **MATH TUTORIAL**

TRANSPARENCY BOOK
- Big Idea Flow Chart, p. T89
- Daily Vocabulary Scaffolding, p. T90
- 3-Minute Warm-Up, p. T93
- Chapter Outline, pp. T95–T96

Labs and Activities

- EXPLORE Population Growth, p. 431
- INVESTIGATE Limiting Factors, p. 433
- Math in Science, p. 437

UNIT RESOURCE BOOK
- Datasheet, Limiting Factors, p. 113
- Math Support, p. 120
- Math Practice, p. 121

KEY TO ICONS 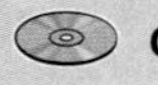 CD/CD-ROM 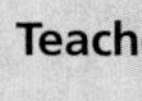 Teacher Edition  TRANSPARENCY BOOK  STANDARDS REVIEW AND PRACTICE

 INTERNET  Pupil Edition  UNIT RESOURCE BOOK  ASSESSMENT BOOK  SCIENCE TOOLKIT

READING AND REINFORCEMENT	ASSESSMENT	STANDARDS
 **Modified Lesson Plans for English Learners,** pp. 44–46  • Four Square, B22–23 • Outline, C43 • Daily Vocabulary Scaffolding, H1–8  **UNIT RESOURCE BOOK** • Vocabulary Practice, pp. 117–118 • Decoding Support, p. 119 • Summarizing the Chapter, pp. 140–141  **Audio Readings CD** Listen to Pupil Edition. 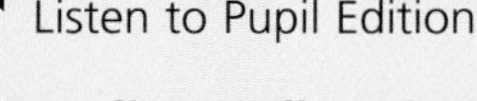  **Audio Readings in Spanish CD** Listen to Pupil Edition in Spanish.	 • Chapter Review, pp. 439–440 • Standards-Based Assessment, p. 441  **ASSESSMENT BOOK** • Diagnostic Test, pp. 268–269 • Chapter Test, A, B, & C, pp. 273–284 • Alternative Assessment, pp. 285–286  **STANDARDS REVIEW AND PRACTICE,** pp. 41–50, 59–62, 71–72  **McDougal Littell Assessment System** 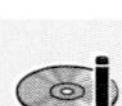 **Test Generator CD-ROM** Generate customized and Spanish tests.	California Content Standards 6.5.a, 6.5.c, 6.5.d, 6.5.e, 6.7.b, 6.7.c, 6.7.d, 6.7.h See p. 410 for the standards.
 **UNIT RESOURCE BOOK** • Reading Study Guide, A & B, pp. 85–88 • Spanish Reading Study Guide, pp. 89–90 • Challenge and Extension, p. 91 • Reinforcing Key Concepts, p. 92	 Ongoing Assessment, pp. 414–418  Section 12.1 Review, p. 419  **ASSESSMENT BOOK** Section 12.1 Quiz, p. 270	California Content Standards 6.5.c, 6.5.e, 6.7.b, 6.7.c, 6.7.d
 **UNIT RESOURCE BOOK** • Reading Study Guide, A & B, pp. 95–98 • Spanish Reading Study Guide, pp. 99–100 • Challenge and Extension, p. 101 • Reinforcing Key Concepts, p. 103 • Challenge Reading, pp. 115–116	 Ongoing Assessment, pp. 422–424, 426–429  Section 12.2 Review, p. 429 **ASSESSMENT BOOK** Section 12.2 Quiz, p. 271	California Content Standards 6.5.c, 6.5.e, 6.7.c
UNIT RESOURCE BOOK • Reading Study Guide, A & B, pp. 106–109 • Spanish Reading Study Guide, pp. 110–111 • Challenge and Extension, p. 112 • Reinforcing Key Concepts, p. 114	 Ongoing Assessment, pp. 433, 435  Section 12.3 Review, p. 436 **ASSESSMENT BOOK** Section 12.3 Quiz, p. 272	California Content Standards 6.5.e, 6.7.h

Previewing Resources for Differentiated Instruction

CHAPTER INVESTIGATION

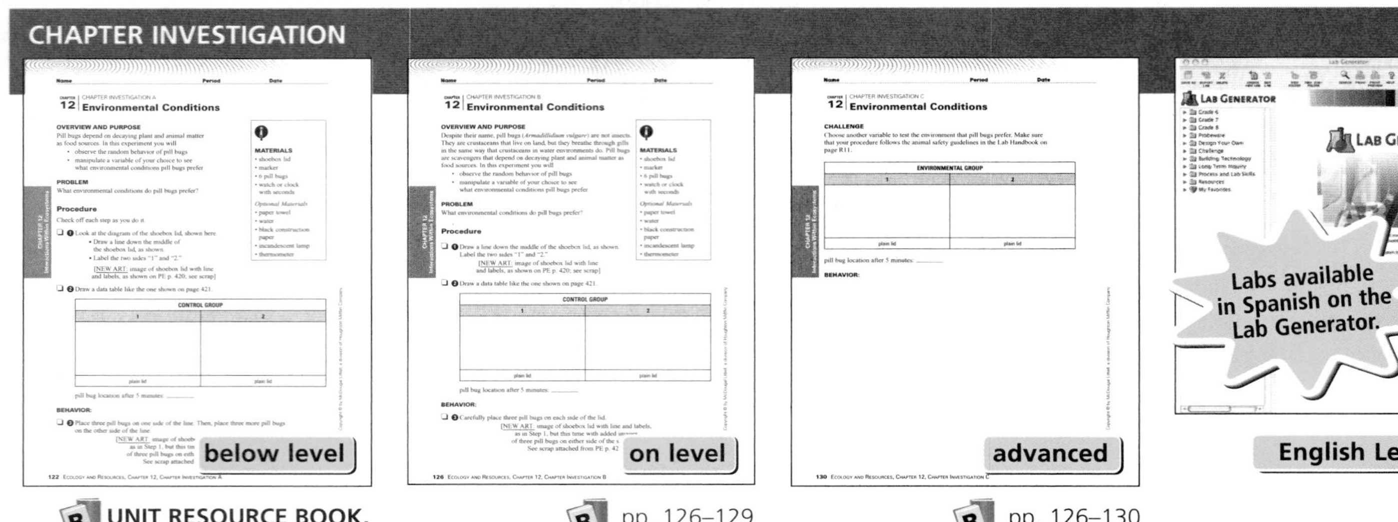

UNIT RESOURCE BOOK, pp. 122–125

pp. 126–129

pp. 126–130

READING STUDY GUIDE

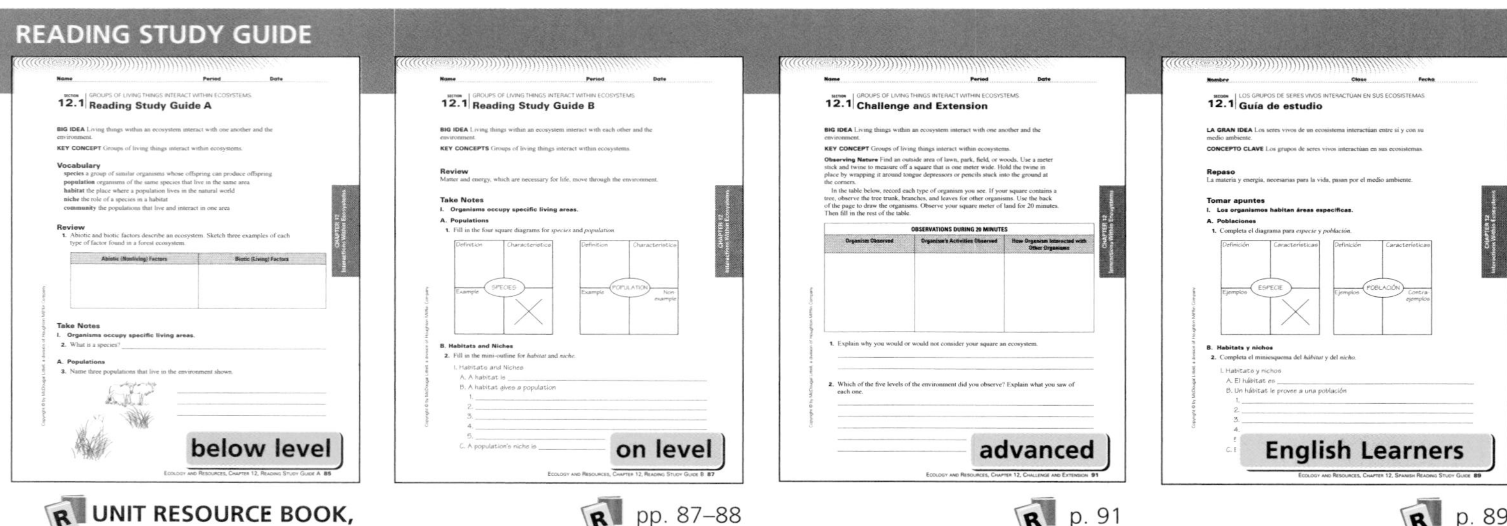

UNIT RESOURCE BOOK, pp. 85–86

pp. 87–88

p. 91

p. 89

CHAPTER TEST

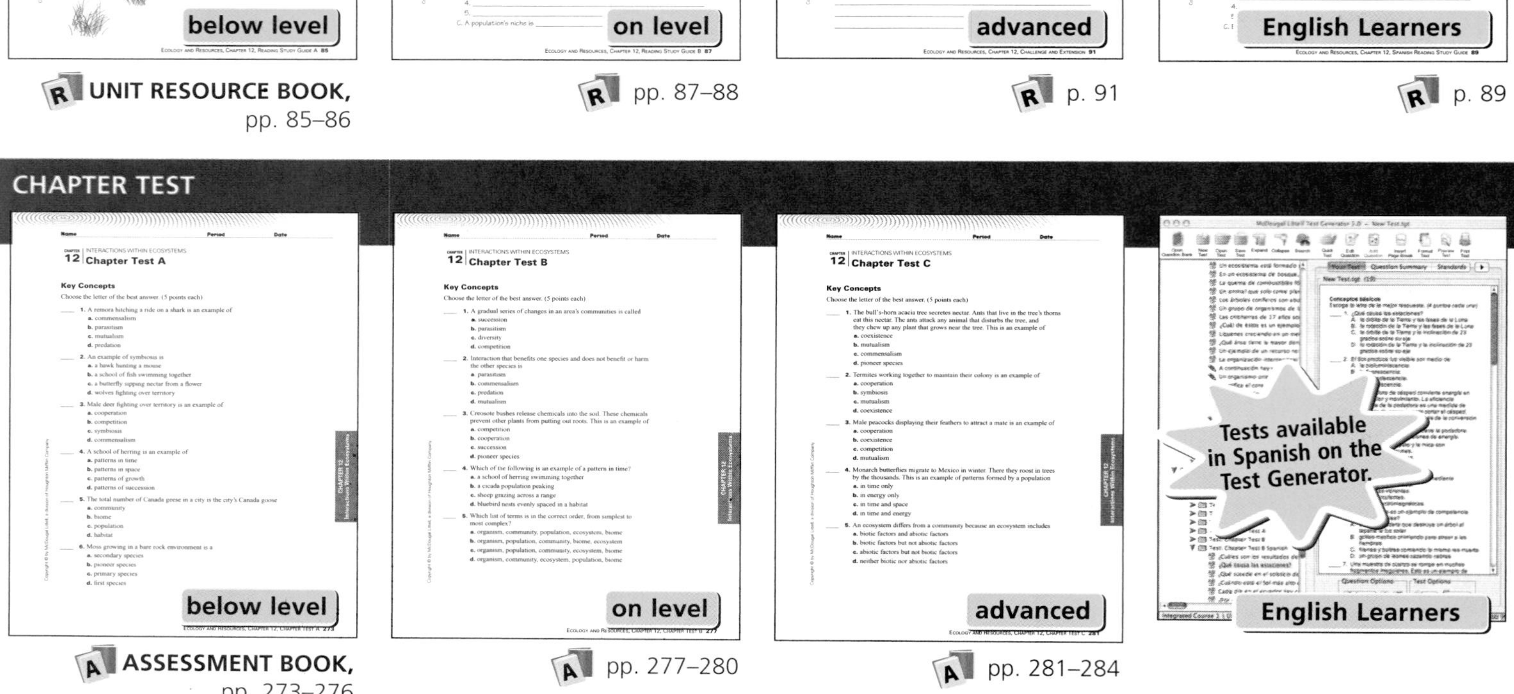

ASSESSMENT BOOK, pp. 273–276

pp. 277–280

pp. 281–284

TECHNOLOGY

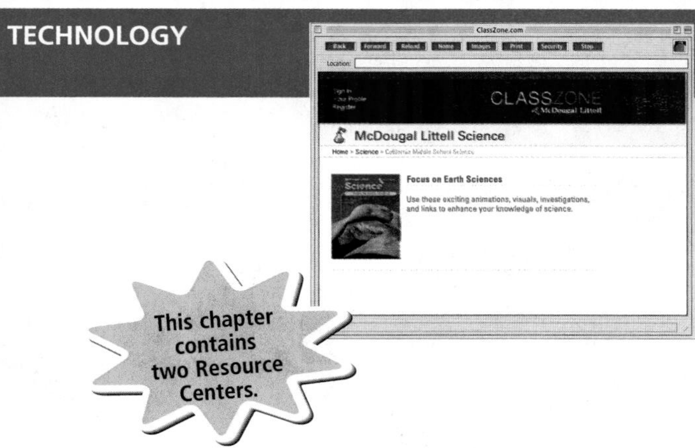

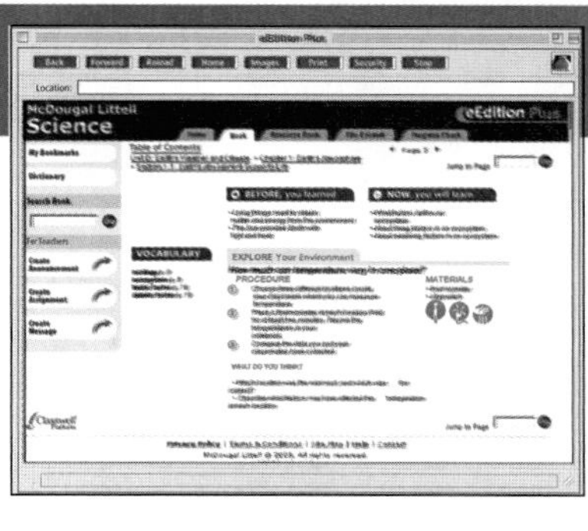

CLASSZONE.COM

CD/CD-ROMS

CLASSZONE.COM

VISUAL CONTENT

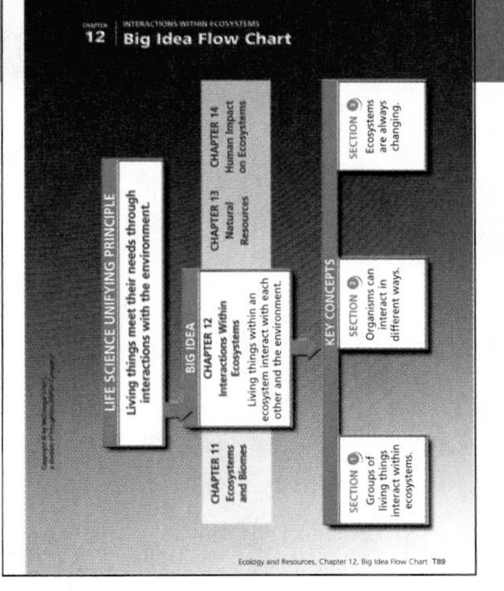

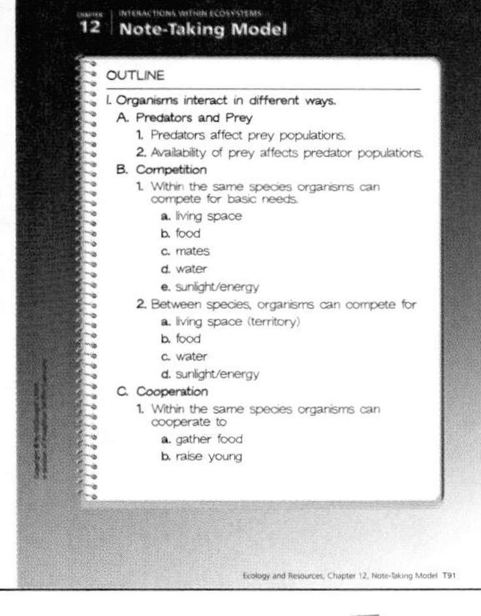

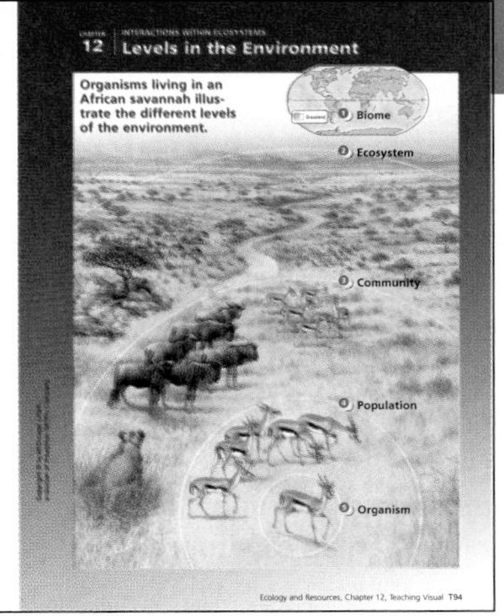

TRANSPARENCY BOOK, p. T89

p. T91

p. T94

MORE SUPPORT

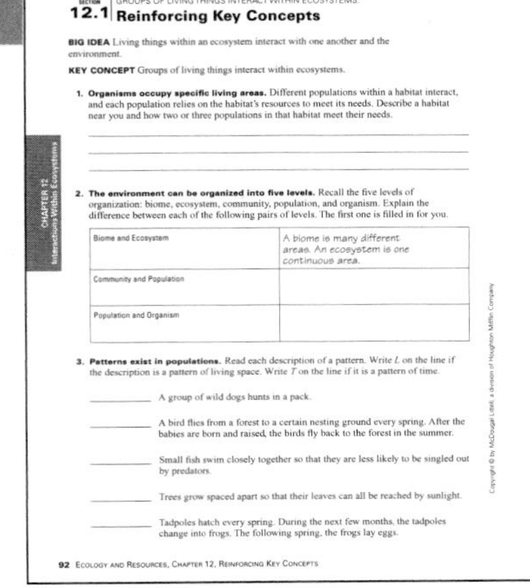

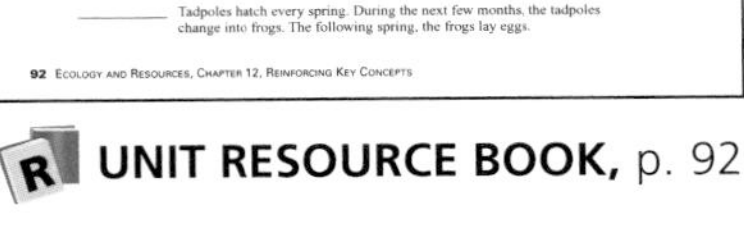

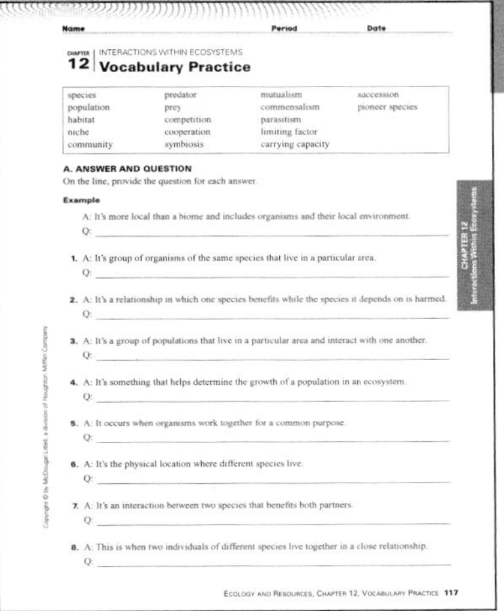

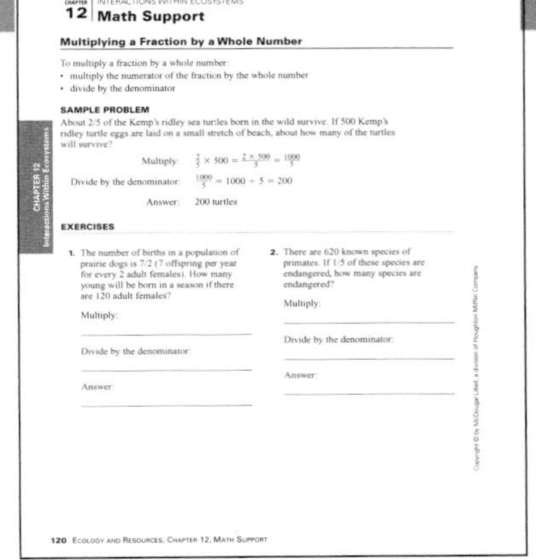

UNIT RESOURCE BOOK, p. 92

pp. 117–118

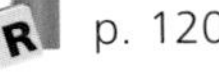
p. 120

CHAPTER

12 Interactions Within Ecosystems

INTRODUCE

the BIG idea

Have students look at the photograph of the reef lizardfish with the goby inside its mouth. Discuss how the question in the box links to the Big Idea:

- Ask: How does the reef lizardfish seem to be interacting with the goby?
- Have students brainstorm a quick class list of ways living things interact.

California Content Standards

6.5.a Students know energy entering ecosystems as sunlight is transferred by producers into chemical energy through photosynthesis and then from organism to organism through food webs.

6.5.b Students know matter is transferred over time from one organism to others in the food web and between organisms and the physical environment.

6.5.c Students know populations of organisms can be categorized by the functions they serve in an ecosystem.

6.5.d Students know different kinds of organisms may play similar ecological roles in similar biomes.

6.5.e Students know the number and types of organisms an ecosystem can support depends on the resources available and on abiotic factors, such as quantities of light and water, a range of temperatures, and soil composition.

6.7.b Select and use appropriate tools and technology (including calculators, computers, balances, spring scales, microscopes, and binoculars) to perform tests, collect data, and display data.

6.7.h Identify changes in natural phenomena over time without manipulating the phenomena (e.g., a tree limb, a grove of trees, a stream, a hillslope).

CHAPTER

Interactions Within Ecosystems

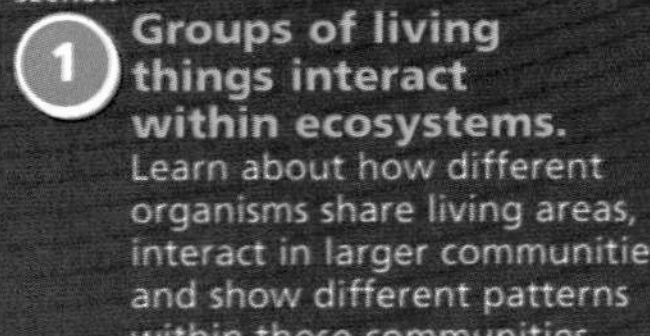

the BIG idea

Living things within an ecosystem interact with each other and the environment.

How do living things interact?

Key Concepts

SECTION

1 Groups of living things interact within ecosystems.
Learn about how different organisms share living areas, interact in larger communities, and show different patterns within those communities.

SECTION

2 Organisms can interact in different ways.
Learn about the different types of interactions in an ecosystem, including competition, cooperation, and symbiosis.

SECTION

3 Ecosystems are always changing.
Learn about the limits and boundaries of organisms within an ecosystem and how ecosystems may change over time.

California ClassZone

CLASSZONE.COM

Chapter 12 online resources: Content Review, two Resource Centers, Math Tutorial, Test Practice

INTERNET PREVIEW

CLASSZONE.COM For student use with the following pages:

Review and Practice
- Content Review, pp. 412, 438
- Math Tutorial: Multiplying Fractions and Whole Numbers, p. 437
- Test Practice, p. 441

Activities and Resources
- Resource Centers: Symbiotic Relationships, p. 427; Succession, p. 435

Populations and Communities
Code: MDL002

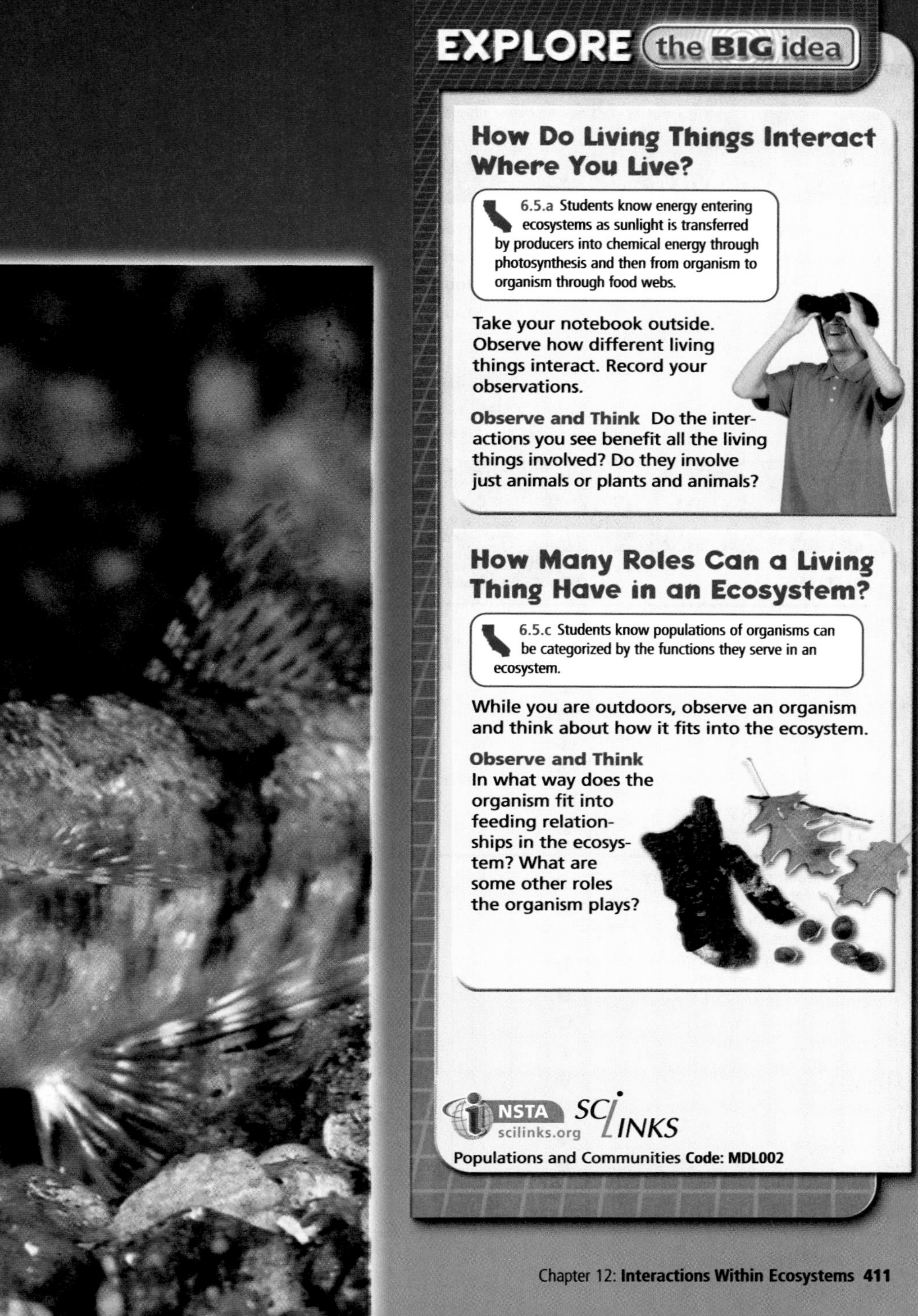

EXPLORE the BIG idea

How Do Living Things Interact Where You Live?

6.5.a Students know energy entering ecosystems as sunlight is transferred by producers into chemical energy through photosynthesis and then from organism to organism through food webs.

Take your notebook outside. Observe how different living things interact. Record your observations.

Observe and Think Do the interactions you see benefit all the living things involved? Do they involve just animals or plants and animals?

How Many Roles Can a Living Thing Have in an Ecosystem?

6.5.c Students know populations of organisms can be categorized by the functions they serve in an ecosystem.

While you are outdoors, observe an organism and think about how it fits into the ecosystem.

Observe and Think
In what way does the organism fit into feeding relationships in the ecosystem? What are some other roles the organism plays?

NSTA scilinks.org SCILINKS
Populations and Communities **Code: MDL002**

EXPLORE the BIG idea

These inquiry-based activities are appropriate for use at home or as a supplement to classroom instruction.

How Do Living Things Interact Where You Live?

PURPOSE To demonstrate to students how plants and animals interact, and to have students recognize that they are part of the environment

TIP *10 min.* If you need to do the activity indoors, students could observe interactions in a fish tank.

Answers should mention plants, animals, and resources, and should describe various behaviors.

REVISIT after p. 425.

How Many Roles Can a Living Thing Have in an Ecosystem?

PURPOSE To introduce students to the concept of roles in an ecosystem

TIP *10 min.* If you cannot go outdoors, photographs or videotapes might help students examine one organism with many roles. It is important to view the organism in context.

Answers should mention feeding other organisms, and the various ways that the organism meets its own needs.

REVISIT after p. 415.

EACHING WITH TECHNOLOGY

preadsheets and Visual Displays Students ould use a spreadsheet for recording data vhile investigating predator-prey relationships, . 425. They could also enter and plot the data n a graphing calculator.

Digital Camera You might want to take daily photographs of the radish plants, p. 433. Students could use the photographs to construct a presentation of the experiment. They could create a time-lapse slideshow with fades.

PREPARE

CONCEPT REVIEW

Activate Prior Knowledge

- Ask students to name some living and nonliving factors that make it possible to live in your town.
- Discuss how these factors affect different species in varying ways.
- Help students identify what biome they live in.

TAKING NOTES

Outline

Students can rely on the blue and red headings in the textbook to form the basic structure of their outlines. In an outline, one idea hangs off another, which helps link the ideas in a student's memory. Encourage students to discuss how ideas in the outline are related. Encourage them to use their outlines to study.

Vocabulary Strategy

The four square diagram organizes all aspects of a word into a coherent pattern. By filling in their own words, students personalize their understanding. Be sure students know they can leave a square blank in the diagram. Many words, such as *species* and *habitat*, have no clear "Nonexamples."

Vocabulary and Note-Taking Resources

- Vocabulary Practice, pp. 117–118
- Decoding Support, p. 119

- Daily Vocabulary Scaffolding, p. T90
- Note-Taking Model, p. T91

- Four Square, B22–23
- Outline, C43
- Daily Vocabulary Scaffolding, H1–8

CHAPTER 12

Getting Ready to Learn

CONCEPT REVIEW

- Ecosystems support life.
- Different ecosystems make up a biome.

VOCABULARY REVIEW

producer p. 391
consumer p. 392
food chain p. 394
food web p. 394
See Glossary. **interaction, lichen**

Review concepts and vocabulary.

TAKING NOTES

OUTLINE

As you read, copy the headings on your paper in the form of an outline. Then add notes in your own words that summarize what you read.

VOCABULARY STRATEGY

Write each new vocabulary term in the center of a **four square** diagram. Write notes in the squares around each term. Include a definition, some characteristics, and some examples of the term. If possible, write some things that are not examples of the terms.

See the Note-Taking Handbook on pages R45–R51.

SCIENCE NOTEBOOK

I. Groups of living things interact within ecosystems.
  A. Organisms occupy specific living areas.
    1. populations: same species in one area
    2. habitat and niche: place where organisms live; role of organisms
    3. community: several populations living together

Definition where something lives	Characteristics supplies shelter and food
HABITAT	
Examples a tree is a habitat for a bird	Nonexamples

CHECK READINESS

Administer the Diagnostic Test to determine students' readiness for new science content and their mastery of requisite math skills.

 Diagnostic Test, pp. 268–269

Technology Resources

Students needing content and math skills should visit **ClassZone.com.**

- **CONTENT REVIEW**
- **MATH TUTORIAL**

 **CONTENT REVIEW CD-ROM**

KEY CONCEPT

12.1 Groups of living things interact within ecosystems.

CALIFORNIA Content Standard

6.5.c Students know populations of organisms can be categorized by the functions they serve in an ecosystem.

BEFORE, you learned

- Abiotic and biotic factors interact in an ecosystem
- Matter and energy necessary for life move through ecosystems

NOW, you will learn

- How groups of organisms interact in an ecosystem
- About levels of organization in an ecosystem
- About living patterns of different groups of organisms

VOCABULARY

species p. 413
population p. 414
habitat p. 414
niche p. 415
community p. 416

THINK ABOUT

How do California sea lions get the resources they need?

California sea lions are ocean mammals. Their name comes in part from the loud, roaring noises they make. California sea lions live in large groups along the coasts of California, the Galápagos Islands, and Japan. They are skillful underwater swimmers, and they hunt in the ocean for food. In what ways do California sea lions depend on their environment for survival?

Organisms occupy specific living areas.

On a walk through the woods, you may see many different plants and animals. These organisms, like all living things, depend on their environment to meet their needs. The particular types of living things you see will depend on the characteristics of the area you are visiting.

Scientists group living things according to their shared characteristics. The smallest grouping is the species. Scientists consider organisms to be members of the same **species** (SPEE-sheez) if the organisms are so similar that they can produce offspring that can also produce offspring. Members of a species can successfully reproduce.

READING TIP

The terms *species, specific,* and *special* come from the same Latin root meaning "kind." A species is a kind, or type, of organism.

12.1 FOCUS

Set Learning Goals

Students will

- Describe how groups of organisms interact in an ecosystem.
- Analyze levels of organization in the environment.
- Recognize living patterns of different groups of organisms.

3-Minute Warm-Up

Display Transparency 92 or copy this exercise on the board:

Imagine that a pond in the park is a thriving ecosystem. A brick wall is built to separate the pond from a new playground. The wall is high enough to keep stray kickballs and other toys from falling into the pond. What might be the effect of the wall on the ecosystem of the pond? *Sample answer: The wall will reduce sunlight reaching the pond. Some organisms may die from lack of light; organisms that like shade may increase. The wall may also affect water runoff.*

 3-Minute Warm-Up, p. T92

12.1 MOTIVATE

THINK ABOUT

PURPOSE To introduce the concept of the interaction between organisms and their environment

DISCUSS Have students brainstorm for answers to the question in the text. *They rely on food in the ocean; their pups are born on land.*

RESOURCES FOR DIFFERENTIATED INSTRUCTION

Below Level

UNIT RESOURCE BOOK
Reading Study Guide A, pp. 85–86
Decoding Support, p. 119

AUDIO CDS

Advanced

UNIT RESOURCE BOOK
Challenge and Extension, p. 91

English Learners

UNIT RESOURCE BOOK
Spanish Reading Study Guide, pp. 89–90

- Audio Readings in Spanish
- Audio Readings (English)

12.1 INSTRUCT

Teach the Standards

Populations of organisms 6.5.c

In this section: Make sure students understand that the term *population* refers to members of the same species that live in an area. Point out that members of the same species that live in different areas belong to different populations.

- **previously taught:** biotic factors in ecosystems, p. 378; producers and consumers, pp. 391–392; food chains and food webs, pp. 394–395
- **future opportunities:** human population growth, pp. 489–495

Teach from Visuals

To help students connect the three photographs, remind them of what they learned in Chapter 11: matter cycles through ecosystems, and energy flows through ecosystems. Ask:

- What are some activities of the three species in the photographs? *growing, breathing, photosynthesis, getting water, eating, moving*
- How might the activities move and transform matter in the ecosystem? *Sample: drinking or absorbing water moves it inside an organism. The water can become part of that organism's structure.*
- What effect do you think these species might have on one another? *All use water; cacti release oxygen, which the crabs and the iguana breathe; iguana wastes fertilize the cacti; the crabs clean the beach.*

Ongoing Assessment

CHECK YOUR READING *Answer: A population exists within a certain boundary. A species may exist in many places worldwide.*

Galápagos Island Populations

A population is a group of organisms of the same species that live in an area.

Cacti

Crabs

Iguanas

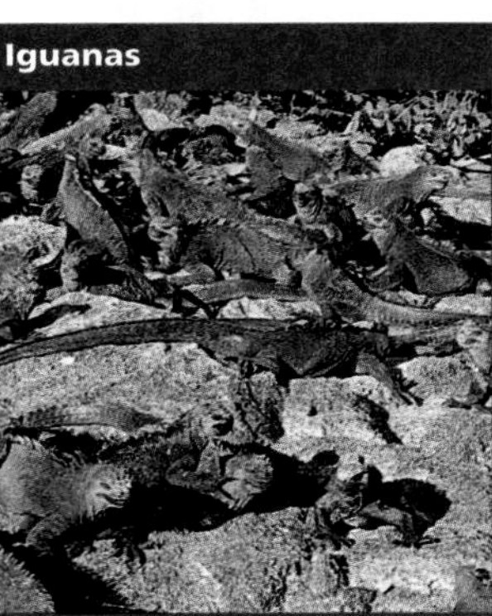

Populations

Scientists use the term **population** to mean a group of organisms of the same species that live in a particular area. This is similar to the population of people who live in a particular city or town. You can then think of people who live in different cities or towns as belonging to different populations. It is the boundary of an area that defines a population. In the study of ecology, members of the same species that live in different areas belong to different populations.

A

READING TIP Ecology is the study of relationships between organisms and their environment.

A biological population can be a group of animals or a group of plants. It can be a group of bacteria or fungi or any other living thing. Populations of many different species may live in the same area. For example, the photographs above show different populations of organisms that all live in the same place—on one of the Galápagos Islands. The island has a population of cacti, a population of crabs, and a population of iguanas.

CHECK YOUR READING What is the difference between a species and a population?

Habitats and Niches

VOCABULARY Add four square diagrams for *population* and *habitat* to your notebook.

B

The Galápagos Islands are a small group of volcanic islands off the western coast of South America. The islands are famous for their unusual plant and animal life. They are the **habitat**—the physical location—where these plants and animals live. Island habitats have certain physical characteristics that describe them. These characteristics include the amount of precipitation, the range of temperatures, and the quality of the soil. Different habitats have different characteristics.

DIFFERENTIATE INSTRUCTION

More Reading Support

A How does a boundary define a population? *Members are within the boundary.*

B What is a habitat? *the physical location of a population*

English Learners Students new to English may find the following science words challenging: *environment, characteristics, offspring, reproduce, boundary (-ies), precipitation, vegetation, fertilize, toxin.* Preview vocabulary by adding these words and their definitions to a Science Word Wall.

Students who are from South or Central America, Mexico, or the Southwest may be familiar with iguanas and cacti. They can share observations or knowledge.

Galápagos Island Habitat

This island habitat is home to many different populations.

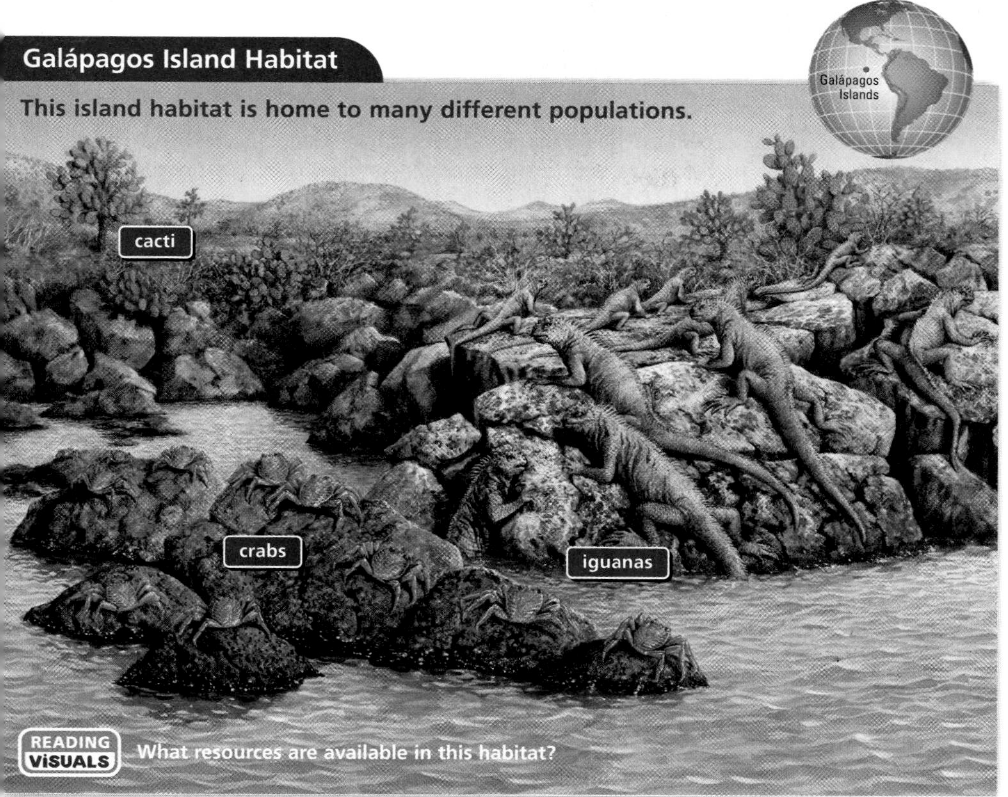

READING VISUALS What resources are available in this habitat?

A habitat is filled with different species. Each species depends on the habitat's resources to meet its needs. The characteristics of a habitat determine the species of plants that can grow there. The species of plants that grow determine the species of animals and other organisms that will do well there.

Different populations interact within a habitat. They are part of the flow of energy and matter through an ecosystem. For example, in the Galápagos Island scene above, the cacti capture energy from sunlight and store fresh water. They also provide food for the iguanas, which eat cactus. The cactus is a producer, and the iguana is a primary consumer. The crabs of the Galápagos are secondary consumers that feed on other shellfish. Each of these organisms has a role to play in the habitat. Each organism's role is referred to as its **niche** (nihch).

The niche an organism fills in a habitat is not limited to its place in a food web. Plants provide nesting sites as well as food. The droppings left behind by animals fertilize soil and often spread seeds. Generally, no two species fill the same niche in a habitat.

DIFFERENTIATE INSTRUCTION

More Reading Support

C What is a niche? *a species' role in a habitat*

D What things about an animal show us its niche? *what it eats or uses, what it is eaten by, what it provides other organisms*

Advanced Have students name habitats other than those already listed—for example, rainforest or swamp. Challenge them to find plants, animals, or insects that live in these habitats and to describe the niches of the organisms.

R Challenge and Extension, p. 91

Teach from Visuals

To help students interpret the relationships shown in the illustration, ask:

- What niche do the crabs fill? *They pass matter and energy up the food chain to gulls and large fish. Some crabs clean the beach as they feed.*
- Which living thing in the picture might be a primary consumer? *iguanas* Why? *because they eat plants*
- What animals or plants that are not in the picture would you expect to find in this habitat? *Sample answer: insects, birds, grasses, seaweed, fish*

Teach Difficult Concepts

Students may not fully understand the relationship between a specie's habitat and its niche. *Habitat* is a location. *Niche* is a role. Different species may share a habitat, but each species fills a particular niche within that habitat. Using a familiar local habitat as an example, have students list elements of several species' niches.

EXPLORE the BIG idea

Revisit the activity and observations from "How Many Roles Can a Living Thing Have in an Ecosystem?" on p. 411. How have students' understandings changed?

Ongoing Assessment

Describe how groups of organisms interact in an ecosystem.

Give an example of a population of organisms interacting with its habitat. *Sample answer: The cacti population stores fresh water and energy from sunlight.*

READING VISUALS *Answer: The cacti are green plants, so they are producers for this ecosystem. They are food and shelter for animals.*

Develop Critical Thinking

APPLY Have students discuss these examples of habitats: grassy field, pond, park. For each example, ask students to name some of the species that live in the habitat and to describe the niches they fill. *Sample answer: The meadow might contain grasses, worms, flowers, and insects. Insects feed on flowers and pollinate them. Worms loosen and fertilize the soil. Grasses anchor the soil and provide oxygen.*

Ongoing Assessment

Analyze levels of organization in the environment.

Ask: Starting from an individual organism, describe the different levels into which scientists organize the environment. *An organism is a single living thing. Groups of individuals of the same species that live in the same area are a population. All living things within one ecosystem are a community. An ecosystem includes the living and nonliving factors in a local environment. A biome consists of similar places that have the same type of climate and vegetation.*

CHECK YOUR READING *Answer: A school community has many people that share the same space and use the same resources. A biological community has many organisms that share the same habitat and natural resources.*

Communities

Take a mental tour of your school. Note that you share space with people who do many different things—students, teachers, custodians, librarians, counselors, and many others. They all work together and help each other. We often say that a school is a community.

E

Scientists use the term *community* in a similar way. A biological **community** is a group of populations that live in a particular area and interact with one another. Cacti, iguanas, and crabs are part of the Galápagos Island community. This community also includes populations of tortoises, finches, flies, bacteria, and many other species.

CHECK YOUR READING How is a school community similar to a community of living things in nature?

The environment can be organized into five levels.

OUTLINE
Add the different levels of the environment to your outline. Make sure to explain each term in the supporting details.

I. Main idea
  A. Supporting idea
    1. Detail
    2. Detail
  B. Supporting idea

F

Five terms—biome, ecosystem, community, population, and organism—describe the environment at different levels.

1. **Biome** A biome describes in very general terms the climate and types of plants that are found in similar places around the world.
2. **Ecosystem** Within each biome are many ecosystems. Inside an ecosystem, living and nonliving factors interact to form a stable system. An ecosystem is smaller than a biome and includes only organisms and their local environment.
3. **Community** A community is made up of the living components of the ecosystem. In a community, plants, animals, and other organisms interact with one another.
4. **Population** A population is a group of organisms of the same species that live in the same ecosystem.
5. **Organism** An organism is a single animal, plant, fungus, or other living thing. As the illustration on page 417 shows, an organism plays a part in each level of the environment.

Patterns exist in populations.

Members of a population settle themselves into the available living space in different ways, forming a pattern. Populations may be crowded together or spread far apart, or they may live in small groups. A population may also show a pattern over time. The number of individuals in the population may rise and fall, depending on the season or other conditions. Numbers may also change as a result of interactions with other organisms.

DIFFERENTIATE INSTRUCTION

More Reading Support

E What is a community? *many populations that interact in one area*

F Name 5 levels in the environment. *organism, population, community, ecosystem, biome*

English Learners Students will find the visual on p. 417 especially helpful. They can take notes in a step diagram, adding definitions in their own words.

biome
ecosystem
community
population
organism

Levels in the Environment

Organisms living in an African savannah illustrate the different levels of the environment.

1 Biome
The African savannah is part of a grassland biome.

2 Ecosystem
The community of organisms, along with water, soil, and other abiotic factors, make up an ecosystem.

3 Community
Populations of wildebeests, gazelles, lions, and grasses share the same living areas and resources. These and other populations form a savannah community.

4 Population
Gazelles travel together in herds, looking for grazing areas. The total number of gazelles in an ecosystem is called a population of gazelles.

5 Organism
The gazelle lives in various grassland habitats in eastern Africa and fills a particular niche.

READING VISUALS Describe the gazelle's role in each level of the environment.

417

DIFFERENTIATE INSTRUCTION

Advanced Challenge advanced students to choose a different biome and create a poster or illustration similar to the one on this page, showing the relationship of one organism to its population, community, and larger environment.

For a further challenge, students could add more specific levels of organization within the organism, down to the cellular level.

Teach from Visuals

To help students interpret the levels in the environment illustration, ask:

- What is the most specific level pictured? *organism*
- What level of organization do we have in this classroom? *population*
- Is the water in the picture a part of the ecosystem, the population, or the community? *ecosystem*

The visual "Levels in the Environment" is available as T94 in the Transparency Book.

Address Misconceptions

IDENTIFY Ask students to list the factors in a familiar local ecosystem. If they do not include human beings in their list, they may hold the common misconception that humans are not part of an ecosystem.

CORRECT Have students list the effects that human beings have had on the local ecosystem.

REASSESS Ask students to describe what the local ecosystem might be like if human beings were not part of it. *Descriptions may include the following: more animals; different types of plants; no pollution; no buildings, roads, or other structures; no cats, dogs, or other domestic animals; and so on.*

Technology Resources

Visit **ClassZone.com** for background on common student misconceptions.

MISCONCEPTION DATABASE

Ongoing Assessment

READING VISUALS *Answer: One gazelle is a single organism. A group of gazelles that live in one area is a population. All of the organisms that live in the same place as the gazelle population make up a community. These gazelles live within one African savannah ecosystem, made up of the community and its environment. Finally, gazelles are one kind of animal that lives in the grassland biome.*

Teach Difficult Concepts

To help students visualize population patterns in time and space, give a very dramatic example: Wildebeests show three unique patterns in populations:

- At night wildebeests sleep on the ground in rows, so they have the security of the large group and the space to run if necessary.
- Most calves are born within two to three weeks at the start of the rainy season. The huge number of calves increases an individual's chance of surviving, because predators can kill only so many prey at once.
- Wildebeest herds may grow to a million animals when they migrate in search of pasture.

Teacher Demo

Try using a game of jacks to demonstrate population patterns. It is easier to "pick off" individuals when they are spread out. It is easier to "wipe out" a group when it is closer together.

Ongoing Assessment

Recognize living patterns of different groups of organisms.

Tell students about the three unique patterns shown by wildebeests, described above. Ask: Which are patterns in time, and which in space? *space, time, time and space*

CHECK YOUR READING *Answer: Different organisms meet their needs in different ways, so they need different amounts of space.*

READING VISUALS *Answer: binoculars*

Patterns in Living Space

The patterns formed by a population often show how the population meets its needs. For example, in California's Mojave desert, the pale soil is dotted with dark green shrubs called creosote bushes. A surprising thing about the bushes is their even spacing. No human shaped this habitat, however. The bushes are the same distance from one another because the root systems of mature plants absorb so much water that nearby seeds cannot germinate. This results in a "dead zone" around each plant.

The distribution of animals in a habitat is often related to the availability of resources. Animals must be able to reach their food supply and have places to raise their young. If you put up birdhouses for bluebirds, they should be spaced at least a hundred meters apart. Bluebirds need a large area of their own around their nest in order to collect enough insects to feed their young.

READING TIP
As you read this paragraph, note the pattern of wildebeests and elephants in the photograph.

Sometimes, the particular pattern of individuals in a living space helps a population survive. Herring swim in schools, with the individual fish spaced close together. Wildebeests roam African grasslands in closely packed herds. These animals rely on the group for their safety. If one member of the group is attacked, many more will survive.

CHECK YOUR READING What are some reasons for the spacing patterns observed in different populations?

READING VISUALS What tool might a person use to observe these animals from a distance?

DIFFERENTIATE INSTRUCTION

More Reading Support

G How does living in large herds meet animals' needs? *protects them from predators*

Below Level When geese migrate or fly south for the winter, they travel in a "V" formation. This example contains within it both a pattern in time and a pattern in space. Ask students to tell how the example shows both patterns. *time: seasonal movement, southward in winter; space: flying in formation*

Cicada Population

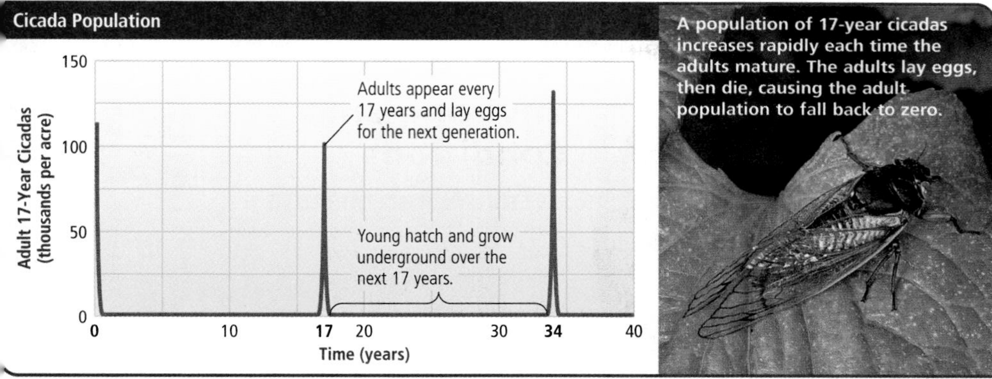

A population of 17-year cicadas increases rapidly each time the adults mature. The adults lay eggs, then die, causing the adult population to fall back to zero.

Patterns in Time

The graph above shows an unusual pattern of population growth. Certain species of cicadas appear only every 17 years. No other species can rely on these insects as their main source of food, so the cicadas survive long enough to lay eggs when they do appear.

Many birds that nest in North America in the summer fly south to Central and South America in the winter. There, they find enough food and good nesting sites. In North America, this seasonal pattern leads to small bird populations in winter and large ones in summer. You might use binoculars to observe changes in bird populations throughout the year.

Yellow jacket wasps provide another example of a population whose size changes over time. In the spring, the queen wasp lays eggs and new wasps hatch. She continues to lay eggs all summer, and the population grows. When winter comes, all the wasps except the queen die. The population decreases.

12.1 Review

KEY CONCEPTS

1. What are two characteristics of a population? (6.5.c)
2. Order these terms from the simplest to the most complex: biome, community, ecosystem, organism, population. (6.5.c)
3. How do the terms *habitat* and *niche* relate to each other? (6.5.c)

CRITICAL THINKING

4. **Apply** Choose a biological community in your region. Describe some of the populations that make up that community.
5. **Infer** How might the seasonal patterns of insect populations relate to the seasonal patterns of bird populations?

CHALLENGE

6. **Synthesize** In some years, California sea lions have trouble finding the types of ocean animals they most like to eat. How is this likely to affect populations of other ocean animals?

ANSWERS

1. organisms of same species; living in same area

2. organism, population, community, ecosystem, biome

3. Habitat refers to the physical setting an organism lives in; niche is the role any one organism fills in that habitat.

4. Sample answer: Pond will have fish, insects, frogs, birds, and surrounding plants.

5. Population booms for insects would allow bird populations to thrive.

6. The sea lions may eat other ocean animals, causing a decline in the populations of these animals.

Teach from Visuals

To help students interpret the cicada population graph, ask:

- What is represented on the vertical axis? *thousands of adult cicadas in a given area*
- What is represented on the horizontal axis? *time in years*
- How many complete population cycles are shown on the graph? *two*

Reinforce the BIG idea

Have students relate the section to the Big Idea.

 Reinforcing Key Concepts, p. 92

12.1 ASSESS & RETEACH

Assess

 Section 12.1 Quiz, p. 270

Reteach

Have students identify an animal in their neighborhood. Ask for volunteers to explain

- the animal's niche. *Answers should include what the animal eats and whether another animal eats it.* (Point out that a niche is the animal's role in the transfer of matter and energy though the entire system.)
- any patterns in space or in time that it fits. Does it migrate? Does it flock? Are groups spaced closely together or far apart? *Answers will vary.*
- how it fits into scientific organization of the environment. *Answers should show levels of organism, population, community, ecosystem, and biome.*

Technology Resources

Have students visit **ClassZone.com** for reteaching of Key Concepts.

 **CONTENT REVIEW**

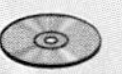 **CONTENT REVIEW CD-ROM**

CHAPTER INVESTIGATION

Focus

PURPOSE Students will design an experiment to observe how pill bugs behave under different environmental conditions.

OVERVIEW Students will prepare a shoebox lid and place three pill bugs on each side. They will record observations of behavior and then change a variable to alter the environment. Students will record the pill bugs' behavior and any changes due to changing the variable.

Lab Preparation

- Prior to the investigation, have students read the investigation and prepare their data tables, or you may wish to copy and distribute datasheets and rubrics.
- A few days before the investigation, have students do some research on pill bugs. The research will help students determine which variables to choose for the investigation.

 UNIT RESOURCE BOOK, pp. 122–130

 SCIENCE TOOLKIT, F14

Lab Management

- Some students may be leery or afraid of the pill bugs. Explain that pill bugs are harmless to humans.
- Instruct students to pick up the pill bugs carefully. Remind them of the importance of humane treatment of animals in experiments.
- Some pill bugs can move quickly. Make sure that students handle them carefully.
- Be sure students wash their hands after touching the pill bugs.

Cooperative Learning

ACTIVITY After students complete step four, elicit examples of pill-bug behavior from students. Then ask students to brainstorm for variables that would affect pill bugs.

CHAPTER INVESTIGATION

Environmental Conditions

DESIGN —YOUR OWN— EXPERIMENT

OVERVIEW AND PURPOSE

Despite their name, pill bugs *(Armadillidium vulgare)* are not insects. They are crustaceans that live on land, but they breathe through gills in the same way that crustaceans in water environments do. Pill bugs are scavengers that depend on decaying plant and animal matter as food sources. In this experiment you will

- observe the behavior of pill bugs
- manipulate a variable of your choice to see which of two environmental conditions pill bugs prefer

Problem

Write It Up

What environmental conditions do pill bugs prefer?

MATERIALS
- shoebox lid
- marker
- 6 pill bugs
- watch or clock with second hand

Optional Materials
- paper towel
- water
- black construction paper
- incandescent lamp
- thermometer

6.5.e, 6.7.b, 6.7.c

Procedure

1. Draw a line down the middle of the shoebox lid, as shown. Label the two sides "1" and "2."
2. Draw a data table like the one shown on page 421.
3. Carefully place three pill bugs on each side of the lid.
4. Observe the behavior of the pill bugs. Count and record the number on each side of the lid after five minutes.
5. Use available materials to alter a condition of your choice on one side of the lid. For example, you could make one side light and the other dark, one dry and the other wet, or one warm and the other cold. The condition you choose is your variable.
6. Repeat step 4.

step 1

INVESTIGATION RESOURCES

 CHAPTER INVESTIGATION, Environmental Conditions
- Level A, pp. 122–125
- Level B, pp.126–129
- Level C, p. 130

Advanced students should complete Levels B & C.

 Writing a Lab Report, D12–D13

Technology Resources

Customize this student lab as needed or look for an alternative. Print rubrics to assess student lab reports.

 **Lab Generator CD-ROM**

Content Standard
6.5.e Students know the number and types of organisms an ecosystem can support depends on the resources available and on abiotic factors, such as quantities of light and water, a range of temperatures, and soil composition.

Investigation Standard
6.7.c Construct appropriate graphs from data and develop qualitative statements about the relationships between variables.

Observe and Analyze

1. **RECORD** Write a narrative about what happened during five minutes of observing. Describe how the pill bugs moved. Use the terms *control group* and *experimental group* in your narrative.
2. **DIAGRAM** Draw your pill-bug environment setup with the altered condition. Make a series of drawings showing the positions of the pill bugs over time. Be sure to label the variables.
3. **IDENTIFY** What was your variable?
4. **IDENTIFY** What did you keep constant in the control group and experimental group?
5. **PRESENT DATA** Look at your drawings. What effect, if any, did the condition you changed have on the movements of the pill bugs?

Conclude

1. **DRAW CONCLUSIONS** Based on your data, which condition do pill bugs prefer?
2. **COMPARE AND CONTRAST** In what ways is your setup like an environment in nature? In what ways is your setup different?
3. **PRESENT DATA** Combine your data with those of groups who changed other variables. Decide which type of graph would be best for showing your results, how to label each axis, and what units you will use.
4. **PREDICT** Based on your class data, what do you think would happen to pill bugs during a drought?
5. **PREDICT** When would you expect to see pill bugs more active, during the day or at night?

INVESTIGATE Further

CHALLENGE Choose another variable to test the environment that pill bugs prefer. Make sure that your procedure follows the animal safety guidelines in the Lab Handbook on page R11.

Environmental Conditions
Problem What type of environment do pill bugs prefer?
Observe and Analyze

Control Group

1	2
plain lid	plain lid

pill bug location after 5 minutes
Behavior:

Experimental Group

1	2
plain lid	variable:_____

pill bug location after 5 minutes
Behavior:

421

Observe and Analyze

1. *Students' answers will vary.*
2. *Students' diagrams will vary depending on the variables they chose.*
3. *Students' answers will vary. Sample answer: My variable was color. I put dark paper in one side of the box.*
4. *Students' answers will vary. Sample answer: I kept the color of the lid constant for the control group and in half the lid for the experimental group.*
5. *Students' answers will vary.*

Conclude

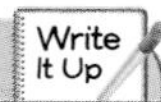

1. *Students' answers will vary.*
2. *Sample answer: The setup is similar to an environment in nature because the setup allows for light and heat. The setup is different because the materials are manufactured. In addition, pill bugs usually live under logs or bricks in a dark, damp soil environment.*
3. *Students' answers will vary.*
4. *They would die. Pill bugs require moisture to live.*
5. *In a hot climate, pill bugs would probably be more active at night. In a cooler climate, they might be more active during the day.*

INVESTIGATE Further

CHALLENGE: Answers will vary depending on the variables chosen.

Post-Lab Discussion

What strengths did your design have? *Students' answers will vary.*

In what ways could you improve your design? *Students' answers will vary.*

Based on class data, what environmental conditions do pill bugs prefer? *Sample answer: Pill bugs prefer moist, shaded areas.*

12.2 FOCUS

Set Learning Goals

Students will

- Describe the different types of interactions in an ecosystem.
- Describe symbiotic relationships in which one or more species benefit.
- Describe symbiotic relationships in which one species is harmed.
- Analyze data to learn how predator-prey populations interact.

3-Minute Warm-Up

Display Transparency 92 or copy this exercise on the board:

Decide whether these statements are true. If not true, correct them.

1. An ecosystem is composed of biotic factors. *An ecosystem is composed of both biotic and abiotic factors.*
2. In a species, the organisms' offspring must be able to breed. *true*
3. The same niche in a habitat may be occupied by more than one species. *Different species never occupy exactly the same niche.*

3-Minute Warm-Up, p. T92

12.2 MOTIVATE

THINK ABOUT

PURPOSE To understand ways people interact

DISCUSS Brainstorm for situations in which two or more people interact. Begin with a game, a group project, or a purchase. Discuss whether the interaction is competitive or cooperative.

Sample answer: Players on opposite teams compete to score points. Players on the same team cooperate by passing the ball to one another and by dividing the field to defend it. Fans give energy by cheering.

Ongoing Assessment

Sample answer: sharing food, a water source, living in the same place

KEY CONCEPT

12.2 Organisms can interact in different ways.

CALIFORNIA Content Standards

6.5.c Students know populations of organisms can be categorized by the functions they serve in an ecosystem.

6.5.e Students know the number and types of organisms an ecosystem can support depends on the resources available and on abiotic factors, such as quantities of light and water, a range of temperatures, and soil composition.

BEFORE, you learned

- Different populations live together in a habitat
- Different species fill different niches in a habitat
- There are patterns in the ways organisms interact with each other and their environment

NOW, you will learn

- About different types of interactions in an ecosystem
- How some species benefit from interactions
- How some species are harmed by interactions

VOCABULARY

predator p. 423
prey p. 423
competition p. 423
cooperation p. 425
symbiosis p. 426
mutualism p. 426
commensalism p. 427
parasitism p. 427

THINK ABOUT

What are some of the ways people interact?

People in a community interact with one another in many ways. An interaction is the way a person behaves toward or responds to another person. This photograph shows groups of people at a soccer game. There are players from two teams and fans who are watching the game. How would you describe the interactions among the people in this photograph?

Organisms interact in different ways.

The photograph above shows how members of a human community both compete and cooperate. Different members of the populations of a biological community also compete and cooperate. They not only share a habitat, but they also share the resources in that habitat. How different organisms interact depends on their relationships with one another.

A robin in a meadow finds a caterpillar and swallows it. This is one obvious way organisms in an ecosystem interact—one eats, and the other is eaten. Organisms also compete. The robin may have to compete with a flicker to get the caterpillar. And, just like people, organisms can cooperate. Ants work together to build a nest, collect food, and defend their colony.

Name three ways organisms may interact with each other in an ecosystem.

RESOURCES FOR DIFFERENTIATED INSTRUCTION

Below Level

UNIT RESOURCE BOOK

- Reading Study Guide A, pp. 95–96
- Decoding Support, p. 119

AUDIO CDS

Additional INVESTIGATION, Prey Survival, A, B, & C, pp. 131–139; Teacher Instructions, pp. 273–274

Advanced

UNIT RESOURCE BOOK

- Challenge and Extension, p. 101
- Challenge Reading, pp. 115–116

English Learners

UNIT RESOURCE BOOK

Spanish Reading Study Guide, pp. 99–100

AUDIO CDS

- Audio Readings in Spanish
- Audio Readings (English)

Predator and Prey

Many interactions among organisms in an ecosystem involve food. A food chain shows the feeding relationships among different species. Some are producers, and others are consumers. Another way to look at a food chain is through the interactions of predators and prey. A **predator** is an animal that eats another animal. A **prey** is an animal that is eaten by a predator. In a food chain, an organism can be both predator and prey. A meadowlark that eats a grasshopper may, in turn, be eaten by a prairie falcon.

REMINDER
A producer is an organism that makes its own food. A consumer is an organism that eats another organism for food.

Predators can affect how members of their prey populations are distributed. For example, herring move together in a school, and wildebeests travel in a herd, to protect themselves. Sick or older members of the population tend to move more slowly. They are the ones that are most likely to be eaten by predators.

Prey populations affect the location and number of predator populations. For example, some birds are predators that feed on insects. One factor that may affect the movement of these birds from one location to another is the availability of insects.

Competition

In a team game, two teams compete against each other with the same goal in mind—to win the game. In a biological community, competition is for resources. **Competition** is the struggle between individuals or different populations for a limited resource.

In an ecosystem, competition may occur within the same species. Individual plants compete with each other for light, space, and nutrients. For example, creosote bushes compete with other creosote bushes for the same water supply.

Competition also occurs between members of different species. In the tropical rain forests of Indonesia, vines called strangler figs compete with trees for water, light, and nutrients. The vine attaches itself to a host tree. As it grows, the vine surrounds and eventually kills the tree by blocking out sunlight and using up available water and nutrients.

INFER Do you think a strangler fig could survive on its own?

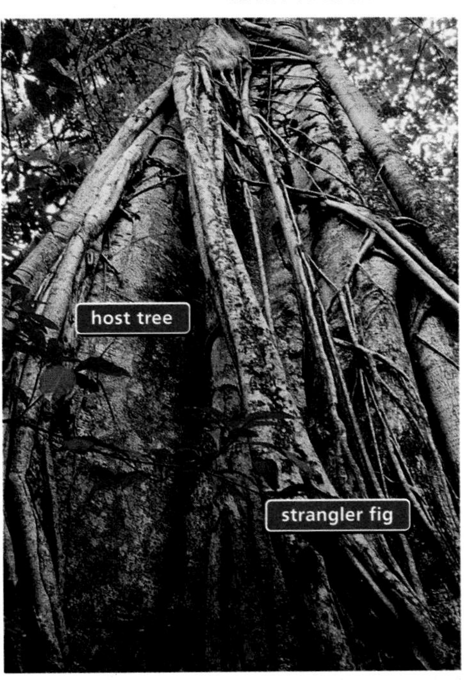

12.2 INSTRUCT

Teach the Standards

Functions of organisms 6.5.c

In this section: Help students understand that organisms within an ecosystem work either with or against members of the same or different species for food and resources. Point out the differences among these sets of terms: *competition* and *cooperation; predator* and *prey; symbiosis, mutualism, commensalism,* and *parasitism.*

previously taught: interactions of biotic and abiotic factors, pp. 378–381; organisms in biomes, pp. 399–405

future opportunities: conserving resources, pp. 466–467; difficulties of sharing resources, pp. 492–495

Teach from Visuals

To help students interpret the photograph of the strangler fig and the host tree, ask:

- What is it like on the floor of the rain forest? *deep shade, damp, moist*
- What is at the top of the rainforest? *lots of sunlight, leafy*
- What does the tree give to the fig vine? *support so it can grow up towards the sunlight*

Teach Difficult Concepts

Predator-prey relationships are not the only sort of feeding relationships in ecosystems. Point out that predators and prey are both always animal species. Foraging is another type of interaction. It takes place when an organism eats a producer, such as a plant, protist, bacteria, or fungus.

DIFFERENTIATE INSTRUCTION

More Reading Support

A Is a robin a predator? If so, what is its prey? *yes; earthworms*

B What do plants compete for? *light, space, nutrients, water*

English Learners Have students write the definitions for *symbiosis, mutualism, commensalism,* and *parasitism* in their Science Word Dictionaries. Ask students to think of predator-prey relationships between animals found in their home countries.

Ongoing Assessment

PHOTO CAPTION Answer: No; the strangler fig needs something to attach itself to.

Teach from Visuals

To help students interpret the photographs of interspecies and intraspecies competition, ask:

- In what ways do organisms of the same or different species compete? *for food, space, water, other resources*
- What groups of organisms compete for mates? *males or females of the same species*

Develop Critical Thinking

INFER Ask students to decide whether they think competing for mates or competing for food is more common within a species and which is more common between species.

Ongoing Assessment

Describe the different types of interactions in an ecosystem.

Ask: When animals mark their territory, how are they relating to other members of their species? *They are competing.* How are they relating when they hunt in packs? *They are cooperating within their species, and they are preying on another species.*

Answer: space, light, water, nutrients

Competition

Competition between species Two different species, hyenas and vultures, compete for the remains of a dead animal.

Competition within species Two male deer lock horns as they battle over territory.

C

Competition occurs between species and within species. For example, vultures and hyenas compete over the food left in the remains of a dead animal. Wolves compete with one another over territory. A wolf marks its territory by urinating on trees. In this way, it warns off other wolves. Animals also compete over territory by fighting or making threatening sounds and displays.

Competition within species often occurs during the mating season. Male birds use special songs and displays of feathers to compete for the attention of females. Male wart hogs fight to attract female wart hogs. Male crickets chirp to attract female crickets.

What types of resources do plants and animals compete for?

READING TIP
Compare and contrast the meanings of *competition* and *coexistence*.

Competition does not occur between all populations that share the same resources. Different species can live together in a habitat without causing harm to one another. For example, many different populations of plants coexist in a forest. Maple trees, beech trees, and birch trees can live side by side and still have enough water, nutrients, and sunlight to meet their needs.

DIFFERENTIATE INSTRUCTION

More Reading Support

C What are examples of competition among animals? *marking territory, fighting for mates*

Advanced Have students search news sources for stories about interactions between species. Encourage them to generate new questions about species interactions that might be appropriate for current science research.

Have students who are interested in interactions between species read the following article:

Challenge Reading, pp. 115–116

INVESTIGATE Species Interactions

How do predator-prey populations interact?

Use these rules for predator-prey interaction for each round. If a predator card touches three or more prey cards, remove the prey cards that were touched. If the predator card does not touch at least three prey cards, remove the predator card and leave the prey cards.

SKILL FOCUS
Analyzing data (6.5.b)

MATERIALS
- 20 10 × 10 cm cardboard squares (predators)
- 200 3 × 3 cm paper squares (prey)
- masking tape

for Challenge:
- graph paper
- 2 colored pencils

TIME
30 minutes

PROCEDURE

1. Use masking tape to mark a boundary on a tabletop.
2. Scatter five prey cards into the area. Take a predator card and toss it, trying to get it to land on the prey.
3. According to the rules above, remove the predators and prey that have "died." Record the number of predators and prey that have "survived." This represents one generation.
4. Double the populations of predators and prey—they have "reproduced."
5. Scatter the prey cards into the area and then toss the predator cards as before. Repeat steps 3 and 4 for a total of 15 rounds, or "generations."

WHAT DO YOU THINK?

- How did the size of the prey population affect the predator population?
- How might the size of a habitat affect the interaction of predators and prey?

CHALLENGE Use graph paper and colored pencils to make a graph of your results. Or use a spreadsheet program if one is available to you.

Cooperation

Not all interactions in an ecosystem involve competition. **Cooperation** is an interaction in which organisms work in a way that benefits them all. Some predators cooperate when they hunt. Although individual lions may hunt on their own, they also hunt in groups to kill large prey.

Killer whales cooperate when they hunt. The whales swim in groups called pods. The pod members swim in circles around a school of fish, forcing the fish close together so they are easier to catch. Pod members may also take turns chasing a seal until it gets tired and is easily killed. The pod may even work together to attack larger species of whales.

Ants, bees, and termites are social insects. Members of a colony belong to different groups, which have different responsibilities. Some groups gather food while others defend the colony. Other animals, such as apes and monkeys, live in family groups. Members of the family cooperate to care for their young.

Cooperation
Driver ants work together to bring food to their nest.

INVESTIGATE Species Interactions

PURPOSE Simulate predator-prey relationships to generate and analyze data

TIPS *30 min.* Limit area to two feet by two feet, perhaps by using tape to mark boundaries. You might use sticky notepads and cut off the sticky side of the pad instead of cutting squares individually.

WHAT DO YOU THINK? *Results should show a cycle, with the number of prey increasing for several generations, then predators increasing, then prey decreasing, and repeating. A larger habitat may mean that prey would be spread farther apart; this could lead to less interaction between predator and prey, yielding a longer survival rate for prey.*

CHALLENGE Student graphs will vary but should show the trends described above.

R Datasheet, Species Interactions, p. 102

Technology Resources

Customize this student lab as needed or look for an alternative. Print rubrics to assess student lab reports.

Lab Generator CD-ROM

Teaching with Technology

If spreadsheet software is available, have students use it to record data for the investigation. They can also use a graphing calculator to show the data visually.

EXPLORE the BIG idea

Revisit "How Do Living Things Interact Where You Live?" on p. 411. Now that students have studied the basic types of interactions between and within species, have them explain their observations.

DIFFERENTIATE INSTRUCTION

More Reading Support

D Besides competition, what is another way for animals to interact? *cooperation*

Additional Investigation To reinforce Section 12.2 learning goals, use the following full-period investigation:

R **Additional INVESTIGATION,** Prey Survival, A, B, & C, pp. 131–139; 273–274
(Advanced students should complete Levels B and C.)

Teach from Visuals

To help students interpret the photograph of the hummingbird, ask:

- Which structures and behaviors of the hummingbird enable it to get nectar from the flower? *It has a long thin beak and can hover.*
- How is the structure of the flower suited to its interaction with the hummingbird? *Its blooms are deep; it is colorful, bright, and produces sweet food.*
- Why is this a good example of mutualism? *Two different species interact. The interaction benefits both.*

Ongoing Assessment

Describe symbiotic relationships in which one or more species benefit.

Ask: What is the difference between a mutualistic relationship and a commensal relationship between species? *In a mutualistic relationship, both species get something they need. In a commensal relationship, only one species benefits, but the other is unaffected.*

The survival of one species might depend on another species.

OUTLINE
Add a sentence about *symbiosis* to your outline and define the three types of symbiosis in the supporting details.

I. Main idea
  A. Supporting idea
    1. Detail
    2. Detail
  B. Supporting idea

You have learned that many different organisms live together in a habitat. Because organisms live together, they must interact in different ways. You have read that an organism might prey upon another for food. Or it might compete or cooperate for resources such as food, water, and territory.

The actions of different organisms can be so closely related that the survival of one species depends on the actions or presence of another. In such a relationship, at least one of the species is getting a resource that it needs to survive. Benefits of the relationship may include food, reproductive help, or protection.

READING TIP
Symbiosis comes from a Greek word that means "living together."

E

The relationship between individuals of two different species who live together in a close relationship is called **symbiosis** (SIHM-bee-OH-sihs). A symbiotic relationship may affect the partners in different ways.

- Both species benefit from the relationship.
- One species benefits while the other is not affected.
- One species benefits while the other is harmed.

Here are some examples of each of the three types of symbiosis.

Both Species Benefit

Stroll through a garden on a sunny day and notice the bees buzzing from flower to flower. Look closely at a single bee and you may see yellow pollen grains sticking to its hairy body. The bee carries these grains of pollen as it goes from flower to flower. The relationship between the flower and the bee is an example of **mutualism** (MYOO-choo-uh-LIHZ-uhm)—an interaction between two species that benefits both. The bee gets food in the form of nectar. The flower gets pollen, which it needs to make seeds.

Mutualism The interaction between the hummingbird and the flower benefits both.

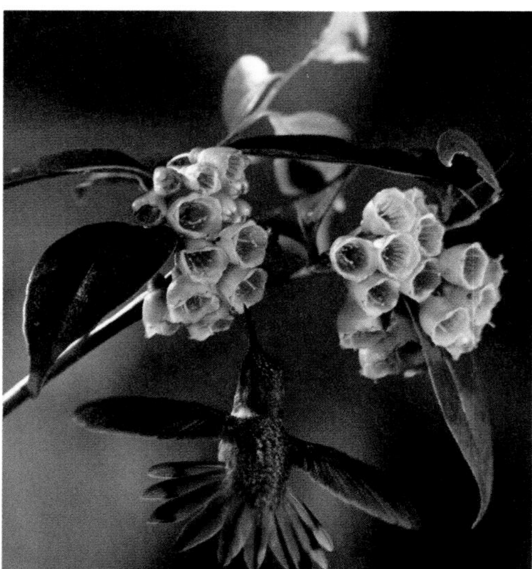

Many plants rely on mutualism to reproduce. The pollen needed to make seeds must be spread from flower to flower. Birds and insects that feed on the nectar in these flowers transfer pollen from one flower to the next. The seeds produced are then moved to other places by animals that eat the seeds or the fruits that hold the seeds. This form of mutualism doesn't benefit the individual flower, but it does ensure the survival of the species.

DIFFERENTIATE INSTRUCTION

More Reading Support

E What does *symbiosis* mean? *living together*

F What happens when two species act in mutualism? *They interact in a way that benefits each other.*

Below Level Struggling readers may not know the words *benefit* and *mutual*. Both words are key to understanding the material on pp. 426–429. Define these words for students (*benefit* = have some need met, have some help; *mutual* = shared, equally taking part in). Then have them make their own word webs, in which *mutual* is the central word and *benefit* is one of the many related words.

In some cases, mutualism is necessary for the survival of the organisms themselves. For example, termites are able to eat a food that most animals cannot digest: wood. Termites can't digest wood either, but they have tiny single-celled organisms in their bodies that can break the wood down into digestible parts. The tiny organisms get a safe place to live, and the termites can take advantage of a plentiful food source.

Explore symbiotic relationships.

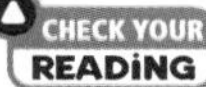

Describe how a bee and a flower benefit from a symbiotic relationship.

One Species Benefits

Commensalism (kuh-MEHN-suh-LIHZ-uhm) is a relationship between two species in which one species benefits while the other is not affected. Orchids and mosses are plants that can have a commensal relationship with trees. The plants grow on the trunks or branches of trees. They get the light they need as well as nutrients from rainwater. As long as these plants do not grow too heavy, the tree is not affected.

READING TIP

Commensal means "sharing a meal" in Middle English. Its root is the Latin word *mēnsa*, meaning "table."

Commensal relationships are very common in ocean ecosystems. Small fish called remoras use a type of built-in suction cup to stick to a shark's skin and hitch a ride. When the shark makes a kill, the remora eats the scraps. The shark makes no attempt to attack the remora. The remora benefits greatly from this commensal relationship. The shark is not affected.

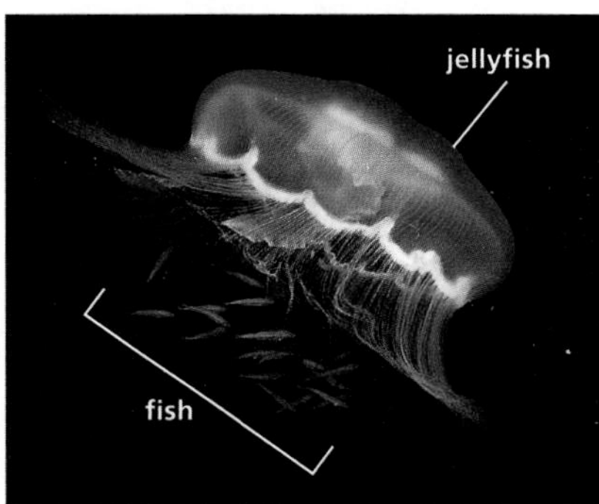

Commensalism The interaction between the jellyfish and the fish benefits only the fish.

Not all commensal relationships involve food. Some fish protect themselves by swimming among the stinging tentacles of a moon jellyfish. The fish benefit from the relationship because the tentacles keep them safe from predators. The jellyfish is not helped or hurt by the presence of the fish. As in this example, it is common in commensal relationships for the species that benefits to be smaller than the species that does not.

One Species Is Harmed

There is one symbiotic relationship in which a smaller organism can harm a much larger organism. **Parasitism** (PAR-uh-suh-TIHZ-uhm) is a relationship between two species in which one species benefits while the species it depends on, the host, is harmed. Parasites are organisms that feed off and weaken their hosts. Ticks, lice, and mites are external parasites that live on or attach to their host's skin. Tapeworms and roundworms are internal parasites that live inside their host.

Real World Example

All humans have resident populations of bacteria, fungi, and protozoans. These are called the "normal flora" of the body, and an average body has more of them than it has cells. Normal flora live on the skin, in the eyes, nose, mouth, upper throat, urethra, and small intestine, and in especially high numbers in the large intestine. The relationships of these species to humans are mainly commensal. In some cases they are mutualistic. Some flora compete with disease-causing microorganisms.

Teach from Visuals

To help students interpret the photograph of the moon jellyfish, ask:

Why is the size of the fish a factor in this method of protection? *The fish must be small enough to swim among the tentacles. If the fish were larger, they might not need this type of protection.*

Teach Difficult Concepts

The three types of relationships can be hard to remember, especially mutualism and commensalism. Ask the class to bring in pictures of examples for display on a bulletin board that you have started.

Ongoing Assessment

CHECK YOUR READING *Answer: A bee gets food from a flower, and the flower's pollen is carried by the bee to other flowers.*

DIFFERENTIATE INSTRUCTION

More Reading Support

G How are species affected in commensalism? *one species gains; one is not affected*

H How are species affected in parasitism? *one gains; one is harmed*

Below Level Have students make a two-column chart with the types of relationships in one column. In the other column, have them draw a picture or paste a photograph of animals and plants that illustrate each relationship.

Teach from Visuals

To help students interpret the illustration of symbiotic relationships, ask:

- What are the parasites shown in the image? *mistletoe and ticks*
- In the commensal relationships shown, which species benefit? Which species are unaffected? *Lichens and mice benefit; trees and humans are unaffected.*
- What might be another example of mutualism that you would find in this environment? *Sample answer: Bees feed on nectar and help flowers pollinate.*

Ongoing Assessment

Describe symbiotic relationships in which one species is harmed.

Ask: What are some ways that one plant can be a parasite of another plant? *Sample answer: A vine might climb a taller or stronger plant to get light and choke or shade the stronger plant; one plant might take nutrients from another plant.*

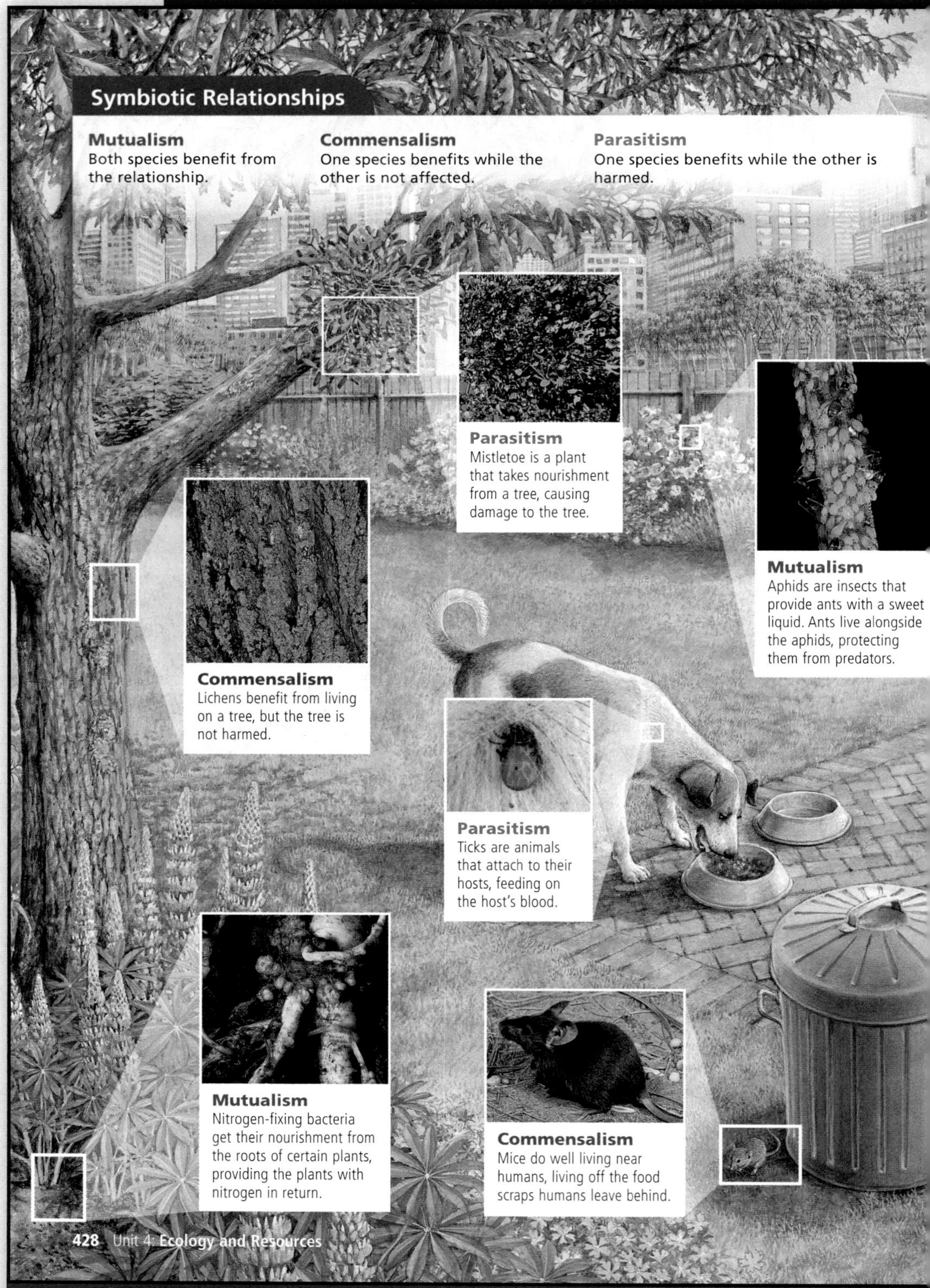

Symbiotic Relationships

Mutualism
Both species benefit from the relationship.

Commensalism
One species benefits while the other is not affected.

Parasitism
One species benefits while the other is harmed.

Parasitism
Mistletoe is a plant that takes nourishment from a tree, causing damage to the tree.

Mutualism
Aphids are insects that provide ants with a sweet liquid. Ants live alongside the aphids, protecting them from predators.

Commensalism
Lichens benefit from living on a tree, but the tree is not harmed.

Parasitism
Ticks are animals that attach to their hosts, feeding on the host's blood.

Mutualism
Nitrogen-fixing bacteria get their nourishment from the roots of certain plants, providing the plants with nitrogen in return.

Commensalism
Mice do well living near humans, living off the food scraps humans leave behind.

428 Unit 4: Ecology and Resources

DIFFERENTIATE INSTRUCTION

Advanced Have students choose one of the relationships in the Symbiotic Relationships illustration, p. 428, and find out more about it. Ask them to consider just one of these three issues:

- Do organisms shown on p. 428 participate in a parasitic relationship?
- Where do disruptions of a mutualistic relationship occur?
- How could a commensal relationship become parasitic?

 Challenge and Extension, p. 101

Cowbirds and warblers have an unusual relationship called nest or brood parasitism. Female cowbirds never build their own nests or raise their own young. Instead, they lay their eggs in warbler nests. Although nest parasitism does not harm the host warbler, it may harm the warbler species. Cowbirds push most warbler eggs from the nest in order to make room for their own eggs. Once the cowbird chicks hatch, they compete with the warbler chicks for food. Because cowbird chicks are larger, the warbler chicks may starve.

 How is parasitism different from commensalism?

Parasitism The larger cowbird chick is cared for by a warbler at the expense of the smaller warbler chick.

Interactions in an ecosystem are complex.

Different types of symbiosis occur throughout an ecosystem and often overlap. They may occur in the same locations, and the same species might be involved in more than one symbiotic relationship. The illustration on page 428 shows different symbiotic relationships that may occur in a backyard.

Symbiosis is just one of many interactions that take place in an ecosystem. For example, a garden in the yard may have individual tomato plants that compete for water and nutrients. It may have ants that cooperate to maintain a successful colony. An ecosystem is more than just a collection of biotic and abiotic factors. Interactions within an ecosystem help explain how resources are shared and used up and how energy flows through the system.

12.2 Review

KEY CONCEPTS

1. Name two ways in which members of the same species interact. (6.5.c)
2. In what ways do members of different species interact? (6.5.c)
3. Give an example of each type of symbiotic relationship: mutualism, commensalism, and parasitism. (6.5.c)

CRITICAL THINKING

4. **Apply** Think of a biological community near you, and give an example of how one population has affected another.
5. **Compare and Contrast** Explain how symbiotic relationships are similar to and different from predator-prey interactions.

CHALLENGE

6. **Synthesize** Mutualism is more common in tropical ecosystems, such as rain forests and coral reefs, than in other ecosystems. Why do you think this is so?

ANSWERS

1. compete for mates, cooperate for resources

2. compete, cooperate, or form symbiotic relationships

3. Sample answer: mutualism—bee and flower; commensalism—fish and jellyfish; parasitism—tapeworms in humans

4. Sample answer: Bittersweet competes with trees for space and sunlight, and has stunted their growth.

5. In a predator-prey relationship, one species benefits and the other is harmed. Parasitism is similar, but the effect is more dramatic because the parasite relies on its host for survival.

6. Sample answer: Tropical rainforests and coral reefs have many more species than other ecosystems; there are more opportunities for mutualism.

Ongoing Assessment

CHECK YOUR READING *Answer: In parasitism, one organism is harmed by another. In commensalism, neither organism is harmed.*

Reinforce the BIG idea

Have students relate the section to the Big Idea.

 Reinforcing Key Concepts, p. 103

12.2 ASSESS & RETEACH

Assess

 Section 12.2 Quiz, p. 271

Reteach

Explain each concept. Have students name examples from the text or elsewhere.

- Organisms interact.
- Organisms may be predators or prey—some animals are both.
- Organisms compete for light, space, nutrients, territory, or mates. Members of the same species may compete, or different species may compete.
- Some organisms cooperate. They accomplish things together that they couldn't do as individuals.
- *Symbiosis* means "living in a close relationship". If all the organisms benefit, it is called *mutualism*.
- If one organism benefits at the expense of another, it is called *parasitism*.
- If one organism benefits while the other is unaffected, it is called *commensalism*.

Technology Resources

Have students visit **ClassZone.com** for reteaching of Key Concepts.

 **CONTENT REVIEW**

 **CONTENT REVIEW CD-ROM**

THINK SCIENCE
Scientific Methods of Thinking

Set Learning Goal
To make inferences by combining new knowledge with past knowledge

Present the Science
Salamanders absorb water through their skin. These amphibians generally live in freshwater wetlands and damp woods. They range from 5 cm to 1.5 m long, and are bright orange or yellow with stripes or spots. They feed on insects, worms, snails, and other small animals.

Guide the Activity
- Remind students that an inference is a statement that is probably true, based on other information. It must be supported by prior knowledge, observations, or data.
- The first notebook contains evidence. Ask: Which statements are qualitative observations—those that must be described? *(b, e)* Which are quantitative—those that can be counted, measured, or calculated? *(a, c, d)*
- The second notebook shows inferences that may or may not be supported. They have not been directly observed or measured. Explain that students must decide which ones are reasonable.

COOPERATIVE LEARNING STRATEGY
Divide the class into groups of five. Have each group brainstorm inferences. A time keeper can keep track of 10 minutes, while a recorder quickly writes all suggestions. Group members suggest which inferences to keep, and which to cross out. They must support their choices.

Close
Ask: Why is it important to study what killed the salamanders? *Sample answer: All organisms have a niche, and their disappearance can affect the entire community. It may be possible to prevent spread of the disease to other populations.*

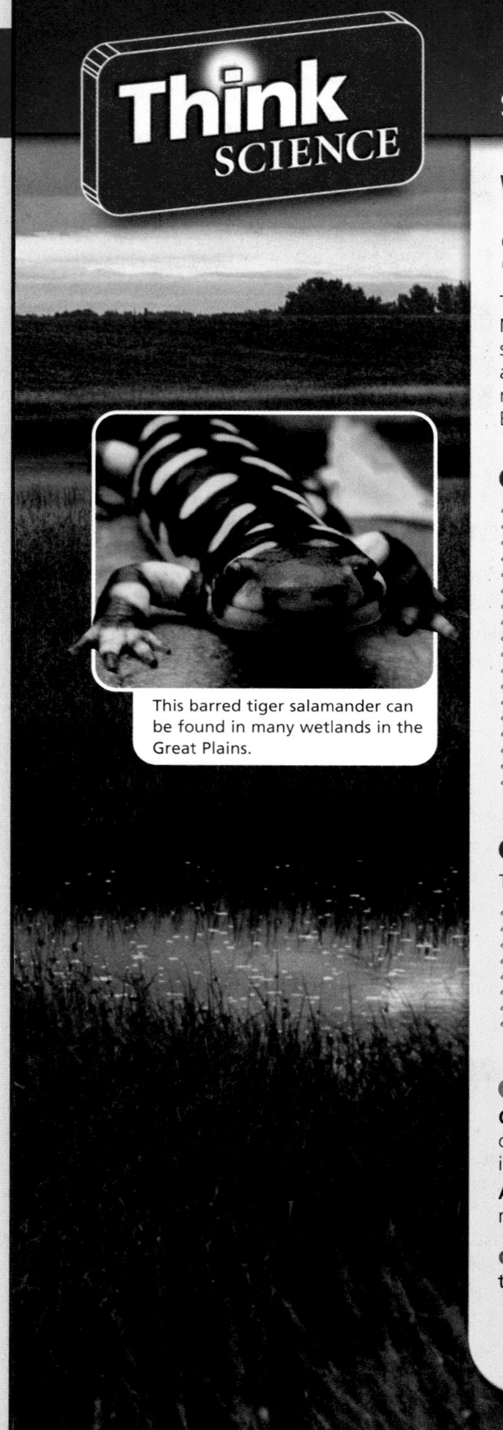

This barred tiger salamander can be found in many wetlands in the Great Plains.

SKILL: INFERRING

Where Are the Salamanders?

6.7.e Recognize whether evidence is consistent with a proposed explanation.

The Cottonwood Lake Study Area is in rural Stutsman County, North Dakota. U.S. Fish and Wildlife Service biologists have been studying wetland ecosystems there for more than 30 years. There are many salamanders in these wetlands. But in May 2000, the researchers started noticing sick salamanders in one wetland. By July, most salamanders had died. What killed them?

Observations
a. In the past, cold winter weather and food shortages have killed salamanders at Cottonwood Lake.
b. The sick salamanders had discolored skin and enlarged livers.
c. The previous year, leopard frogs in a nearby wetland were found dying from a contagious fungal infection.
d. A viral disease has killed tiger salamanders elsewhere in the western United States.
e. Both large, well-fed salamanders and small, poorly nourished salamanders died.

Inferences
The following statements are possible inferences.

a. A food shortage caused salamanders to starve.
b. The fungal disease that killed leopard frogs also killed the salamanders.
c. Salamanders were killed by a viral disease.

Evaluate Inferences
On Your Own Which of the inferences are supported by the observations? Write the observations that support each of the inferences you identify.

As a Group Discuss your decisions. Come up with a list of reasonable inferences.

CHALLENGE What further observations would you make to test any of these inferences?

430 Unit 4: Ecology and Resources

ANSWERS
***Inference a** is not supported. Large well-fed salamanders died off. This does not support the inference that the animals starved to death.*

***Inference b** is partly supported. Frogs and salamanders share many traits. It is reasonable to think that they could be killed by the same infection. But, they also have differing traits. The frogs may be unharmed by it.*

***Inference c** is supported. The exact same species of salamanders died in both locations. Viral diseases can spread over large areas.*

***CHALLENGE** Study other tiger salamanders for symptoms of the virus, and study other leopard frogs for symptoms of the fungal infection. Dissect dead salamanders for clues.*

KEY CONCEPT

Ecosystems are always changing.

CALIFORNIA Content Standards

6.5.e Students know the number and types of organisms an ecosystem can support depends on the resources available and on abiotic factors, such as quantities of light and water, a range of temperatures, and soil composition.

6.7.h Identify changes in natural phenomena over time without manipulating the phenomena (e.g., a tree limb, a grove of trees, a stream, a hillslope).

BEFORE, you learned
- Populations in an ecosystem interact in different ways
- Organisms can benefit from interactions in an ecosystem
- Organisms can be harmed by interactions in an ecosystem

NOW, you will learn
- How different factors affect the size of a population
- How biological communities get established
- How biological communities change over time

VOCABULARY

limiting factor p. 432
carrying capacity p. 433
succession p. 434
pioneer species p. 434

EXPLORE Population Growth (6.5.b, 6.5.e)

How does sugar affect the growth of yeast?

PROCEDURE

1. Use a marker to label the cups A, B, and C. Pour 150 mL of warm water into each cup. Mark the water level with the marker.
2. Add 1/2 teaspoon of dry yeast to each cup and stir.
3. Add 1/4 teaspoon of sugar to cup B. Add 1 teaspoon of sugar to cup C. Stir.
4. Wait 15 minutes. Measure the height of the foam layer that forms in each cup.

WHAT DO YOU THINK?
- Which cup had the most foam? Which cup had the least?
- Describe the effect of sugar on a population of yeast.

MATERIALS
- 3 clear plastic cups
- warm water
- sugar
- dry yeast
- measuring spoons
- measuring cup
- stirring rod
- marker
- ruler

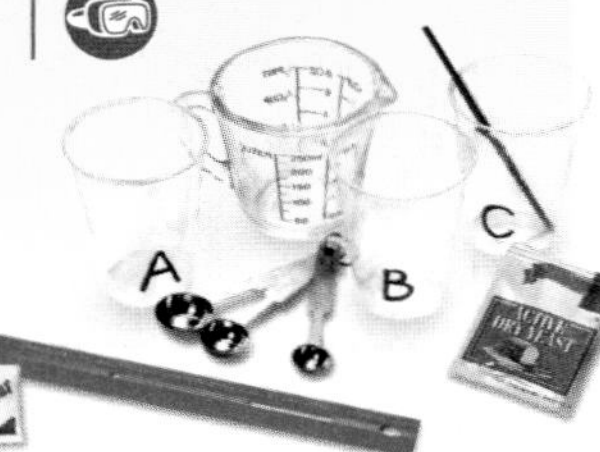

Populations change over time.

REMINDER
A population is a group of organisms of the same species that live together in the same habitat.

You may have a strong memory of a park you visited as a little child. You might remember collecting pine cones, listening to woodpeckers, and catching frogs. Then you visit again, years later, and the park has changed. Maybe more land has been added, and there are more birds and trees. Or maybe the area around the park has been developed. There seem to be fewer woodpeckers, and you can't find any frogs. The community has changed. There are a lot of factors that affect the populations within a biological community. Some have to do with the organisms themselves. Others relate to the habitat.

RESOURCES FOR DIFFERENTIATED INSTRUCTION

Below Level
UNIT RESOURCE BOOK
- Reading Study Guide A, pp. 106–107
- Decoding Support, p. 119

 **AUDIO CDS**

Advanced
UNIT RESOURCE BOOK
Challenge and Extension, p. 112

English Learners
UNIT RESOURCE BOOK
Spanish Reading Study Guide, pp. 110–111

AUDIO CDS
- Audio Readings in Spanish
- Audio Readings (English)

12.3 FOCUS

Set Learning Goals
Students will
- Explain how different factors affect the size of a population.
- Explore ways that biological communities are established.
- Describe how biological communities change over time.
- Design an experiment that explores the effect spacing has on plant population.

3-Minute Warm-Up
Display Transparency 93 or copy this exercise on the board:

Match the definitions to the words.

Definitions
1. a relationship in which two organisms both try to get the same thing *d*
2. a relationship in which both of the organisms benefit *e*
3. the role a species fills in a habitat *b*

Terms
a. parasitism
b. niche
c. habitat
d. competition
e. mutualism

 3-Minute Warm-Up, p. T93

12.3 MOTIVATE

EXPLORE Population Growth

PURPOSE To introduce students to limiting factors affecting growth of a population of yeast

TIP *20 min.* Check the yeast before the lab to make sure it's alive.

WHAT DO YOU THINK? *Cup C had the most foam; cup A had the least; yeast feeds on sugar, so the more food, the more foam.*

12.3 INSTRUCT

Teach the Standards

Resources and change 6.5.e

In this section: Help students understand that a significant increase or decrease in biotic or abiotic factors will cause an ecosystem to change. Explain that populations will grow until available resources cannot support the needs of larger populations.

previously taught: biotic and abiotic factors in ecosystems, pp. 378–381; food webs and food chains, pp. 394–395

future opportunities: effects of population growth, pp. 489–495; effects of habitat loss on biodiversity, pp. 502–504

Teach from Visuals

To help students interpret the graphs, ask:

- What was the moose population in 1970? *about 1300* The wolf population in 1970? *20*
- How did the moose population change between 1970 and 1975? How did the wolf population change in the same period? *The moose population peaked. The wolf population grew.*
- What time period did the wolf population decrease as the moose population decreased? *1980–1982*

Real World Example

In the United States, many animal populations are endangered as a result of human use of their habitat. Whooping cranes are endangered because their wetland habitat has been drained for farmland. The endangered sawback turtle's food (snails and insects) has been reduced by flood controls, siltation, and pollution.

CALIFORNIA Focus

The tule elk is a type of elk that lives only in California. In 1800, large herds of tule elk roamed open grasslands. By 1870, hunting and the development of farms had led to the near extinction of the tule elk. Conservation efforts have increased the population to more than 3000 today.

A

Population Growth and Decline

One obvious factor that affects population size is how often organisms reproduce. Birth rate is a measure of the number of births in an animal population. It can also be a measure of changes in an ecosystem. For example, black bears reproduce once every two years. If there is not enough food available, reproduction is delayed. As a result, the bear population does not grow.

Predator-prey interactions also affect population size. Wolves are predators that prey on moose in Isle Royale National Park in Michigan. The graphs show how an increase in the moose population was followed by an increase in the wolf population. The wolves preyed upon the moose, the moose population decreased, and then the wolf population decreased.

Moose and Wolf Populations, Isle Royale National Park

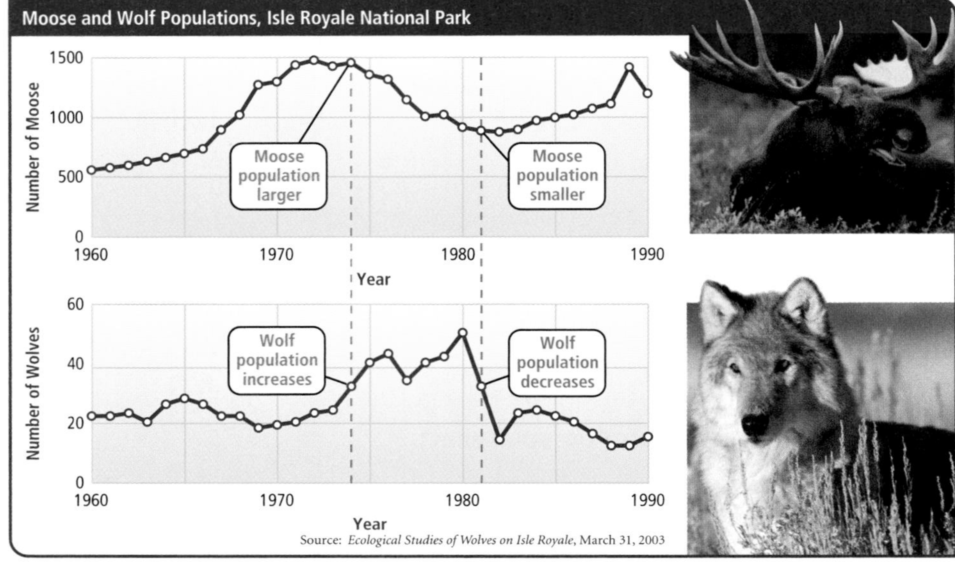

Source: *Ecological Studies of Wolves on Isle Royale*, March 31, 2003

READING TIP

Note in the graphs above that it can take some time for the size of one population to affect the size of another.

B

Any factor or condition that limits the growth of a population in an ecosystem is called a **limiting factor.** A large population of predators will limit the population of prey. A small population of prey will limit the population of predators. Too much or too little of any biotic or abiotic factor—such as food, water, or light—makes an ecosystem unstable and brings about change.

A lack of nutrients in the soil is a limiting factor for plants. That is why farmers fertilize their crops. However, if the fertilizer runs off into a lake, it can increase the population of algae. A large population of algae can cover a lake and use up oxygen needed by fish. This then limits the fish population.

DIFFERENTIATE INSTRUCTION

More Reading Support

A What can cause a population to grow? *fewer predators*

B What does a limiting factor do? *limits the growth of a population*

English Learners There are many different kinds of charts and graphs. English learners may be unfamiliar with some uncommon types. Help students understand how to read the population chart on the page above.

Advanced Have students study another population graph and answer questions in the following worksheet.

Challenge and Extension, p. 112

INVESTIGATE Limiting Factors

What effect does spacing have on a population of plants?

DESIGN — YOUR OWN — EXPERIMENT

Using the materials listed, design an experiment to test this hypothesis: "If plants grow too close together, the health of the population will be affected, because the individual plants do not get enough of the nutrients and water that they need."

SKILL FOCUS
Designing experiments (6.5.e)

MATERIALS
- paper cups
- potting soil
- radish seeds
- water
- pencil
- ruler

TIME
20 minutes

PROCEDURE

1. Decide how to use the seeds, cups, and soil to test the hypothesis.
2. Write up your experimental procedure. Include safety tips.

WHAT DO YOU THINK?

- What are the variables in your experiment?
- What types of evidence would support your hypothesis?

CHALLENGE Conduct your experiment. Note that seeds must be planted near the top of the soil. A good measure for this is the tip of a pencil. Measure and record the growth of the seedlings. Allow the seedlings to grow for two weeks before making your conclusions.

Maintaining a Balance

Living things have certain minimum requirements for food, water, and living space. When a population reaches a state where it can no longer grow, the population has reached its **carrying capacity,** the maximum number of individuals that an ecosystem can support. You can see on page 432 that the graph for the moose population appears to peak around 1500. Even if there were no wolves on Isle Royale, the population of moose would still be limited because there is only so much food and space available.

VOCABULARY
Remember to make a four square diagram for *carrying capacity* in your notebook. Try to use *limiting factor* in your diagram.

CHECK YOUR READING Explain the term *carrying capacity.*

An ecosystem's carrying capacity is different for each population. For example, a meadow ecosystem supports many more bees and ants than bluebirds. Isle Royale supports many more moose than wolves. The moose is a primary consumer of plants. It is at a lower level of the energy pyramid than the wolf, a secondary consumer.

Biotic factors can be limiting factors. These factors include the interactions between populations such as competition, predation, and parasitism. Abiotic factors are also limiting. These include temperature, availability of water or minerals, and exposure to wind.

DIFFERENTIATE INSTRUCTION

More Reading Support

C What's the name for the largest population that an environment can support? *carrying capacity*

Below Level Students may have trouble with the concept of *carrying capacity*. Use the analogy of a group of people on a boat. Ask: What are the factors that limit the number of people that can safely board the boat? *buoyancy of the boat relative to weight of passengers and supplies; space available to fit people without hurting one another; also could be food and water available for a trip* What are factors that limit the number of organisms that can survive in a population? *food, water, space, light*

INVESTIGATE Limiting Factors

PURPOSE To observe how space can be a limiting factor for plants

TIPS *20 min.*

- Do not plant seeds any deeper than twice their length.
- To accentuate the effects of limited space, crowd the 20 seeds closely together. Using 3-oz. cups for this experiment will dramatize the results.

WHAT DO YOU THINK?

- *The space given to the radish seeds should be the only variable.*
- *Radish seeds given less space would grow less successfully. There would be fewer and/or smaller plants.*

 Datasheet, Limiting Factors, p. 113

Technology Resources

Customize this student lab as needed or look for an alternative. Print rubrics to assess student lab reports.

 **Lab Generator CD-ROM**

Teaching with Technology

Use a digital camera to take daily photos of the plants. Students can use the photos in a presentation of the experiment.

Ongoing Assessment

Explain how different factors affect the size of a population.

Ask: What factors affect the carrying capacity of a population of trees? *nutrients, space, light, and water; disease, competition, predation*

CHECK YOUR READING *Answer:* Carrying capacity *is the maximum population that an environment can support.*

Address Misconceptions

IDENTIFY Ask: What happens to organic material as it decays? If students answer that it "disappears" or "is destroyed," they may hold the misconception that decay causes matter to break down into nothing.

CORRECT Direct students to the primary succession diagram on p. 434. Explain that the broken-down rocks contribute to the mineral content of soil. As the first plants that grow on the thin, rocky soil die and decay, the materials that made up their living tissues become the soil's organic content. As this process continues, the soil layer eventually becomes deep enough to support trees.

REASSESS Ask: What else besides plants and rock particles contributes to soil content? *dead and decaying animal matter* What happens to the decaying organic matter after it becomes part of the soil? *Living organisms eat or absorb the nutrients it contains to carry on their life processes; organic matter becomes part of the life cycle in an altered form.*

Technology Resources

Visit **ClassZone.com** for background on common student misconceptions.

 **MISCONCEPTION DATABASE**

Integrate the Sciences

In 1980 Mount St. Helens in Washington erupted, causing a blast of hot gas and debris that reached 300°C. The surface was new rock or scorched ash. Soon after the eruption, the Forest Service reported seeing long earth cores on top of the ash layer. The northern pocket gopher had made tunnels in the snow and filled them with fertile soil from underground burrows. The soil mixture became a seed bed for new plant life.

Teach from Visuals

To help students interpret the sequence of illustrations, ask:

- How is the underground different in the three pictures? *It is rock; then partly rock, partly soil; then soil.*
- What caused this difference? *Pioneering species broke down rock and contributed organic material.*

Ecosystems change over time.

If you take a walk in a New Hampshire woods, you may see the remains of old stone walls. Once this land was mostly farmland. Then the farms were abandoned. Now, new trees have grown where farm animals once grazed.

Succession (suhk-SEHSH-uhn) is the gradual change in an ecosystem in which one biological community is replaced by another. The change from field to forest is an example of succession. Over time the grasses of open farmland are slowly replaced by small plants and shrubs and then by trees.

Primary Succession

READING TIP
Succeed and *succession* come from the same Latin word, *succedere,* meaning "to go up" or "to follow after."

Very few places on Earth are without some form of life. Even when a lava flow covers an area or a glacier melts and leaves behind an empty and barren environment, plants will move into the area and bring it back to life. These are examples of primary succession, the establishment of a new biological community.

Pioneer species are the first living things to move into a barren environment. In the illustration below, mosses and lichens move in after a glacier retreats. There is little or no topsoil. Lichens are common pioneers because they can grow on bare rock. They hold moisture and add organic matter.

Primary Succession

Primary succession can occur after a glacier retreats, when little topsoil is present.

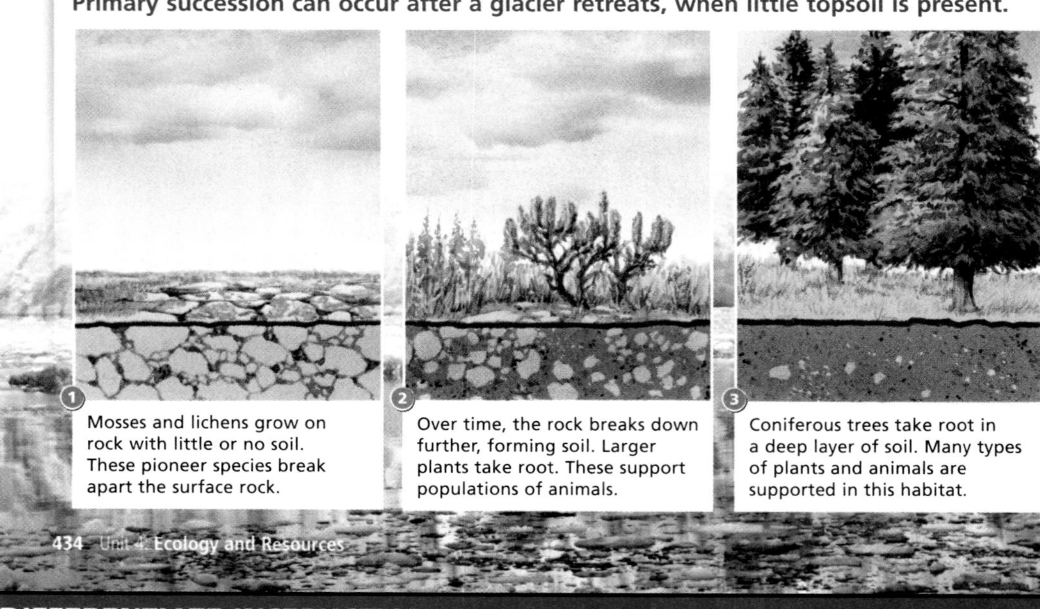

1. Mosses and lichens grow on rock with little or no soil. These pioneer species break apart the surface rock.
2. Over time, the rock breaks down further, forming soil. Larger plants take root. These support populations of animals.
3. Coniferous trees take root in a deep layer of soil. Many types of plants and animals are supported in this habitat.

434 Unit 4: Ecology and Resources

DIFFERENTIATE INSTRUCTION

More Reading Support

D What is succession? *a gradual change in an ecosystem when one community replaces another*

E Give an example of a pioneer species. *moss, lichen*

Advanced Challenge students to come up with examples of how secondary succession could be followed by primary succession in a particular environment.

Mosses and other plants join the lichens in the newly forming soil. As these pioneers grow, they gradually weaken the rock surface. The rock breaks down and weathers over time. Decaying plant matter adds nutrients, forming more soil. Now a variety of small plants and shrubs can take root. These plants support insects, birds, and small rodents. Eventually there is enough soil to support coniferous trees. Forests grow, providing a habitat for larger animals.

Learn more about succession.

Secondary Succession

Secondary succession takes place after a major disturbance to the biological community in a stable ecosystem. Despite the disturbance, the soil remains. A community can be disturbed by a natural event, such as fire or flood, or it can be disturbed by human activity. A cleared forest or abandoned farmland can lead to secondary succession.

The illustration below shows secondary succession following a forest fire. The damage is bad, but it is surface damage. Below the surface, seeds and plant roots survive. After a time, grasses and small shrubs grow up among the decaying remains of the original plants. Birds, insects, and rodents return. Alder trees take root and put nutrients into the soil. Over time, many types of trees and plants grow, providing food for a variety of animals.

What is the difference between primary and secondary succession?

Secondary Succession

Secondary succession occurs if soil remains after a disturbance, such as a forest fire.

1 Plants at the surface are burned. However, below the surface, seeds and some roots survive.

2 Grasses and small shrubs sprout among the charred trees and vegetation. Small animals return.

3 Deciduous trees, such as elms and maples, grow and mature. A forest habitat is restored. More animals are supported.

DIFFERENTIATE INSTRUCTION

More Reading Support

F What is secondary succession? *regrowth after a disturbance when the soil remains*

G What can trigger secondary succession? *floods, fires, or human activity*

Below Level Use a table to help students understand the different ways ecosystems change over time.

Type of change	Soil	Cause	Pioneer species
primary succession	no	lava flow, glacier movement, landslide	need to move in via seeds and spores
secondary succession	yes	fire, flooding, land-use change	survive in soil

Teach from Visuals

To help students interpret the sequence of illustrations, ask:

- What kind of soil is still on the surface in the first image? *topsoil*
- Why are some plants able to grow back quickly? *because some roots and seeds survive below the surface*
- What lures animals and insects back to the area? *new plant life*

Teach Difficult Concepts

Give more extreme examples to help students distinguish between primary and secondary succession. Primary succession examples: the surface of new construction such as a building or wall, a sterilized canning jar. Secondary succession examples: ice-scoured riverbank, scrubbed footstep, a rinsed-out cup. To help students understand, try the following demonstration.

Teacher Demo

Collect a newly broken rock and a moss- or lichen-covered stone from an old wall, or a new brick and a mossy one. Show them to the class and point out the totally bare sharp surface of the new rock. Describe the succession that could lead to the lichen-covered rock: Pioneer species trap dirt and litter and provide hiding places for small organisms and rooting material for plants.

Ongoing Assessment

Describe how biological communities change over time.

Ask: When a glacier retreats or a forest burns, how does the ecosystem recover? *After a glacier retreats, primary succession occurs. Pioneer species add soil, small plants and animals move in, then large plants and animals arrive. After a fire, secondary succession occurs. Small plants and shrubs grow from roots and seeds that survived underground. Large plants and animals return.*

CHECK YOUR READING *Answer: Primary succession occurs when life moves to a barren, soilless area. In secondary succession, the ecosystem changes after a disturbance, when there is still soil for life to gain a foothold.*

Ongoing Assessment

Explore ways that biological communities are established.

Describe the pattern of formation for biological communities. *First, a community of producers is established, followed by decomposers and consumers. Then more of each are added, and over time, a biological community is established.*

Reinforce the BIG idea

Have students relate the section to the Big Idea.

 Reinforcing Key Concepts, p. 114

12.3 ASSESS & RETEACH

Assess

 Section 12.3 Quiz, p. 272

Reteach

Write the following terms on the board:

- carrying capacity
- limiting factors
- pioneer species
- predator-prey interaction
- primary succession
- secondary succession

Have students tell whether each term relates more closely to the concept of "population change" or the concept of "ecosystem change." Encourage them to explain their answers. Then discuss how population changes cause overall ecosystem changes and vice versa. Point out that the ecosystem includes all the populations within it.

Technology Resources

Have students visit **ClassZone.com** for reteaching of Key Concepts.

 CONTENT REVIEW

 CONTENT REVIEW CD-ROM

Patterns of Change

All types of ecosystems go through succession. Succession can establish a forest community, a wetland community, a coastal community, or even an ocean community. Succession can happen over tens or hundreds of years. The pattern is the same, however. First a community of producers is established. These are followed by decomposers and consumers, then more producers, and then more decomposers and consumers. Over time, a stable biological community develops.

In a way, establishing a biological community is like planting a garden. To start a garden, you first prepare the soil. Perhaps you add compost. This adds organic matter and nutrients to the soil, which helps the soil hold water. With the right preparation, your vegetables and flowers should grow well.

Pioneer species can function in one of two ways in an ecological succession. They can help other species grow or they can prevent species from getting established.

READING TIP

As you read about the two ways plant species function in succession, think in terms of cooperation and competition.

- Some plant species are like gardeners. Trees such as alders have nitrogen-fixing bacteria on their roots that improve the nutrient content of the soil. This allows other tree seedlings to grow. Pioneering species may also stabilize the soil, shade the soil surface, or add nutrients to the soil when they die and decay.
- Some plant species produce conditions that keep out other plants. The plants may release chemicals that keep other plants from taking root. Or a new species may outcompete other species by using up resources or better resisting a disease.

Such interactions between living things help determine the type and rate of succession in an ecosystem.

12.3 Review

KEY CONCEPTS

1. Describe three factors that could limit the size of a population in a habitat. **(6.5.e)**
2. List two natural disturbances and two human-made disturbances that can lead to succession. **(6.7.h)**
3. What role do pioneer species play in succession? **(6.5.e)**

CRITICAL THINKING

4. **Infer** How and why would secondary succession in a tundra habitat differ from secondary succession in a rainforest habitat?
5. **Predict** Suppose you are clearing an area in your yard to make a small pond. Sketch the stages of succession that would follow this disturbance.

CHALLENGE

6. **Synthesize** Imagine you are the wildlife manager for a forest preserve that supports both moose and wolves. What types of information should you collect to determine the carrying capacity for each species?

ANSWERS

1. predators, parasites, food, space, nutrients, disease, etc.

2. volcanic eruptions, glacier retreat, fire, flooding, abandoned fields, development, logging

3. Mosses, lichens, and plants can move into a barren area on the wind. Over time they help break rock into soil, die into the soil, and attract insects and other animals.

4. Succession occurs more slowly in the tundra because of cold temperatures and a short growing season.

5. Sketches could include pioneering seeds, insects, and small lifeforms in the pond. Vegetation and larger animals might be shown around an older pond.

6. Sample answer: a census of animals, including their sex; plants; food sources; breeding sites; human factors that may affect population

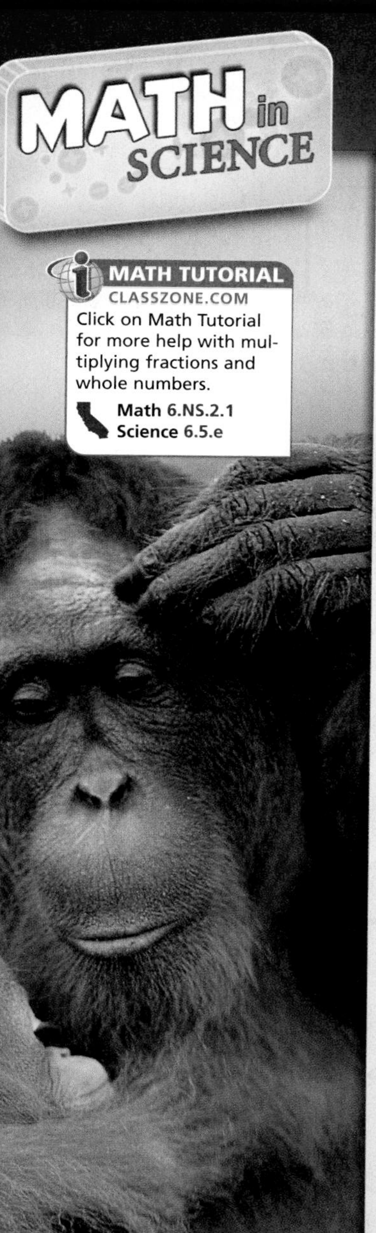

MATH in SCIENCE
MATH TUTORIAL
CLASSZONE.COM
Click on Math Tutorial for more help with multiplying fractions and whole numbers.
Math 6.NS.2.1
Science 6.5.e

SKILL: MULTIPLYING A FRACTION BY A WHOLE NUMBER

Number of Births and Populations

Ecologists pay careful attention to the number of offspring born to endangered species. When the number of births is divided by the number of adult females, the result is a fraction. If there are two births for every five adult females in a population, then the fraction is $\frac{2}{5}$.

Example

Suppose that over time at a national park in Borneo, 2 offspring have been born for every 5 adult female orangutans. There are 150 adult females in the park. Estimate how many young will be born this year. To find out, multiply $\frac{2}{5}$ by the number of adult females.

(1) Multiply the numerator of the fraction by the whole number.

$$150 \text{ females} \times \frac{2 \text{ births}}{5 \text{ females}} = \frac{150 \times 2}{5} = \frac{300}{5}$$

(2) Divide by the denominator.

$$\frac{300}{5} = 300 \div 5 = 60$$

ANSWER 60 young

Answer the following questions.

1. In 2001 there were about 72 adult female right whales. Scientists observing the whales reported one birth for every 3 females. About how many right whales were born in 2001?
2. Giant pandas are endangered. Currently only about 140 giant pandas live in captivity in zoos and in parks. About $\frac{3}{5}$ of these were born in captivity. How many is that?
3. The orangutan population of the world has decreased sharply. At one time there were over 100,000 ranging across Asia. Now there may be 25,000, of which $\frac{2}{3}$ live in Borneo. About how many orangutans live in Borneo?

CHALLENGE Suppose 1 birth per year for every 2 adult females is necessary to save an endangered population. There are now 5 births per 20 adult females per year. By what factor does the number of births need to increase?

NSWERS

$\frac{72}{3}$ = *24 calves*

$\frac{140 \times 3}{5} = \frac{420}{5}$ = *84 pandas*

$\frac{25{,}000 \times 2}{3} = \frac{50{,}000}{3}$ = *16,667 orangutans*

IALLENGE The rate is $\frac{5}{20}$, or $\frac{1}{4}$, of what is desired. The desired rate $\frac{1}{2}$. Therefore, the current rate needs to increase by a factor of 2 $\times 2 = \frac{1}{2}$).

MATH IN SCIENCE

Math Skills Practice for Science

Set Learning Goal

To calculate birth rates and populations by multiplying fractions and whole numbers

Math Standard

6.NS.2.1 Solve problems involving addition, subtraction, multiplication, and division of positive fractions and explain why a particular operation was used for a given situation.

Present the Science

Animals become endangered for various reasons. Right whales were hunted to near extinction, not only because they had thick blubber and valuable baleen, but also because they swam slowly and floated when killed.

Develop Calculation Skills

Remind students that the numerator of the fraction is above the line, and the denominator is below.

To help them remember which part of the fraction to multiply, emphasize that they can think of "below the line" as "division." If you multiply "below the line," you are really dividing, making the total decrease: $\frac{1}{16}$ is less than $\frac{1}{2}$.

DIFFERENTIATION TIP Use grid paper or graph paper to model some simple problems multiplying friendly fractions such as $\frac{1}{2}$, $\frac{3}{4}$, $\frac{2}{3}$ by small whole numbers, such as 4, 5, 6. In each case, shade squares that show the fraction as a portion of a larger square. Students will see that repeated addition gets the same result as multiplying.

Close

Ask students to brainstorm for how scientists can increase the population of an endangered species. *Raise birth rates by encouraging captive breeding, restoring habitats, protecting animals from hunting.*

- Math Support, p. 120
- Math Practice, p. 121

Technology Resources

Students can visit **ClassZone.com** to practice multiplying fractions and whole numbers.

MATH TUTORIAL

BACK TO

the BIG idea

Have students choose one of the habitats discussed in the chapter and give examples of the different types of relationships found there. Ask them to propose a natural disaster that could occur in that habitat and to explain how the habitat will recover.

KEY CONCEPTS SUMMARY

SECTION 12.1

Ask students to describe the habitat in which the crabs live, as shown in the picture on the right. *The crabs live in a rocky, beach habitat, next to the ocean.* Based on the crabs' habitat, what niche do you think the crabs fill? *Crabs gather food from the beach and the ocean. They use the beach and the ocean for reproduction and shelter. The crabs are also food for other animals in the habitat.*

SECTION 12.2

Ask students to explain how the faces represent the different symbiotic relationships. *For mutualism, both faces are smiles, meaning both benefit. For commensalism, one face is smiling and one is blank, meaning one benefits and the other is not affected. For parasitism, one face is smiling and the other is frowning, meaning one benefits and the other is harmed.*

SECTION 12.3

Ask: What types of succession are shown? *primary and secondary* What is the main difference between them? *In secondary succession, soil remains.*

Review Concepts

- Big Idea Flow Chart, p. T89
- Chapter Outline, pp. T95–T96

12 Chapter Review

the BIG idea

Living things within an ecosystem interact with each other and the environment.

 KEY CONCEPTS SUMMARY

1 Groups of living things interact within ecosystems.

- Members of the same species form a population within a habitat.
- Each species has a distinct role within a habitat. This is its niche.

Population of Crabs

Island Habitat for Crabs

VOCABULARY
species p. 413
population p. 414
habitat p. 414
niche p. 415
community p. 416

2 Organisms can interact in different ways.

Some organisms within a community are predators, and some are prey. Some compete with one another, and some cooperate. Some species form symbiotic relationships with other species:

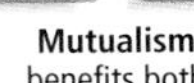

Mutualism
benefits both

Commensalism
benefits one, other unaffected

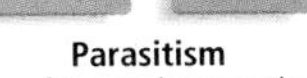

Parasitism
benefits one, harms other

VOCABULARY
predator p. 423
prey p. 423
competition p. 423
cooperation p. 425
symbiosis p. 426
mutualism p. 426
commensalism p. 427
parasitism p. 427

3 Ecosystems are always changing.

Primary Succession

In a barren area, a new community is established with pioneer species, such as mosses, that do well with little or no soil. Mosses eventually give way to coniferous trees.

Secondary Succession

When a disturbance damages a community but soil remains, the community gets reestablished from seeds and roots left behind. Grasses grow, then small shrubs, and eventually trees.

VOCABULARY
limiting factor p. 432
carrying capacity p. 433
succession p. 434
pioneer species p. 434

438 Unit 4: **Ecology and Resources**

Technology Resources

Have students visit **ClassZone.com** or use the CD-ROM for a cumulative review of concepts.

CONTENT REVIEW

CONTENT REVIEW CD-ROM

Engage students in a whole-class interactive review of Key Concepts. Edit content as you wish.

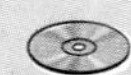

POWER PRESENTATIONS

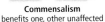

Reviewing Vocabulary

Draw a Venn diagram for each pair of terms. Put shared characteristics in the overlap area, put differences to the outside. A sample diagram is provided.

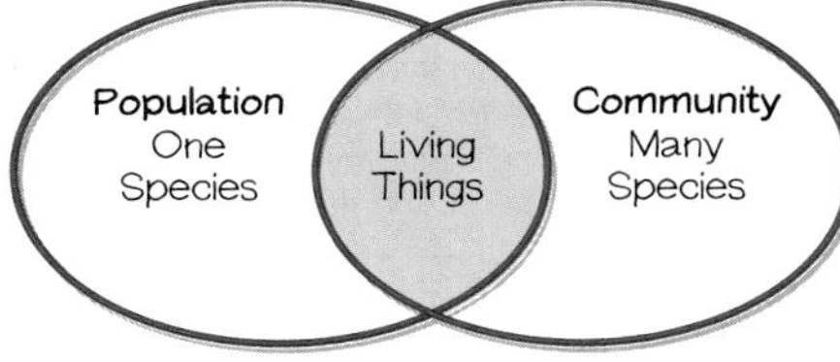

1. habitat, niche
2. mutualism, commensalism
3. mutualism, parasitism
4. competition, cooperation
5. primary succession, secondary succession

Reviewing Key Concepts

Multiple Choice *Choose the letter of the best answer.*

6. What is carrying capacity? (6.5.e)
   a. the largest population an ecosystem can support
   b. the smallest population an ecosystem can support
   c. the number of species an ecosystem can support
   d. the number of habitats in an ecosystem
7. A new species of bird moves into a habitat. The birds feed on a particular caterpillar, so that the resulting population of butterflies is small. What can be said of the relationship between the birds and the butterflies? (6.5.c)
   a. The birds and the butterflies have a commensal relationship.
   b. The birds and butterflies compete.
   c. The birds are a limiting factor for the butterflies.
   d. The birds and butterflies cooperate.
8. Certain types of worms live in the mud at the bottom of lakes. What does the mud represent for the worm? (6.5.e)
   a. an ecosystem
   b. a niche
   c. a community
   d. a habitat
9. What is a pioneer species? (6.5.c)
   a. a species that travels within an ecosystem
   b. a species that is among the first to move into an area after a natural disaster
   c. a species that depends upon animal life
   d. a species that cannot return after a natural disaster
10. The spacing of creosote bushes in a dry area is an example of (6.5.c)
   a. commensalism
   b. parasitism
   c. competition
   d. mutualism
11. Which is an example of parasitism? (6.5.c)
   a. dog and tick
   b. termite and protozoans
   c. shark and remora
   d. flower and hummingbird
12. Which is an example of secondary succession? (6.5.e)
   a. succession after a forest fire
   b. succession after a large volcanic lava flow devastates an area
   c. succession after a glacier retreats, leaving bare rock
   d. succession after a hurricane washes away all the sand from a beach

Short Answer *Write a short answer to each question.*

13. Put the terms in order, starting with the term that includes the largest number of individuals and ending with the group containing the fewest individuals: community, population, ecosystem, biome. (6.5.c)
14. List four ways in which members of the same species can cooperate with each other. (6.5.c)
15. Describe three different types of symbiosis. (6.5.c)

ASSESSMENT RESOURCES

ASSESSMENT BOOK
- Chapter Test A, pp. 273–276
- Chapter Test B, pp. 277–280
- Chapter Test C, pp. 281–284
- Alternative Assessment, pp. 285–286

STANDARDS REVIEW AND PRACTICE, pp. 41–50, 59–62, 71–72

Technology Resources

Edit test items and answer choices.

 **Test Generator CD-ROM**

Visit **ClassZone.com** to extend test practice.

 **Test Practice**

Reviewing Vocabulary

1. habitat: environment surrounding a living thing; both: within a boundary; relate to matter and energy; niche: role of one type of living thing in moving matter and energy

2. mutualism: two species benefit by interactions; both: symbiotic relationships; benefit at least one species; neither is harmed; commensalism: one species benefits from an interaction, the other remains neutral.

3. mutualism: two species benefit by an interaction; both: symbiotic relationships, benefit at least one species; parasitism: one species benefits from an interaction, the other is harmed.

4. competition: two living things are in conflict or oppose each other; both: types of interactions; can be between or within species; cooperation: two living things work together or help each other.

5. primary succession: takes place in a barren landscape; both: series of changes in an ecosystem; take place after disaster or erosion; secondary succession: takes place after most living things have died; soil remains

Reviewing Key Concepts

6. a	*10. c*
7. c	*11. a*
8. d	*12. a*
9. b	

13. biome, ecosystem, community, population

14. hunt together (whales), move together for protection (wildebeest, herring), share different tasks (ants), care for young (primates)

15. benefits to both species (mutualism), benefits one, but harms another (parasitism), benefits one while other is unaffected (commensalism)

Thinking Critically

16. *Years 1–5: steady increase in both; Years 6–10: a decline in both.*
17. *It is reasonable to infer that the larger a population of lynx or hare, the more pelts traders would sell. The data given is not for populations, but it does suggest increase and decrease in the populations.*
18. *limiting factors for hares: other predators, food, weather, and area of habitat*
19. *No. Trees function in similar ways, but each species has its niche. Birds, insects, and mammals feed on different trees; shade and nutrients vary plants and fungi around trees.*
20. *All plants need sunlight. In early stages of succession, small plants grow fastest. Eventually, shrubs, then trees grow, blocking light for smaller plants. Large trees limit growth of small trees.*
21. *any three: clearing land for development, abandoning farmland, logging, fires, flooding from dams*
22. *Creosotes are part of a desert community in which populations compete for limited resources. They spread widely and evenly. The roots release a toxin that is a limiting factor for other bushes. Thus, each creosote gets the resources it needs.*
23. *It would cause populations that rely on those trees for food or shelter to decrease; however, open space might increase low bushes, grasses, and animals that feed on them.*

the BIG idea

24. *One fish eating another is a predator-prey interaction. Fish may clean, protect, or attract food to one another.*
25. *Answers should use correct terms in ecology and should address interactions and carrying capacity.*

UNIT PROJECTS

Collect schedules, materials lists, and questions. Be sure dates and materials are obtainable and questions are focused.

 Unit Projects, pp. 5–10

Thinking Critically

The data in the table below come from the records of a Canadian trading company that, in the late 1800s, bought lynx and hare pelts from hunters and trappers. The Canadian lynx and hare share the same habitat. The lynx relies on the hare as a food source. Use the table to answer the next three questions.

Year	Lynx	Hare
1	2	30
2	15	55
3	65	90
4	75	160
5	100	200
6	95	140
7	75	80
8	40	35
9	20	3
10	3	4
11	30	40
12	55	95

16. **ANALYZE** How would you describe the pattern that emerges between the two populations in years 1–7? How does the pattern change in years 8–10? (6.5.d)
17. **EVALUATE** The data on the lynx and hare pelts have been used to suggest the sizes of the lynx and hare populations. Is this a reasonable approach to take? Why or why not? (6.5.d)
18. **ANALYZE** Scientists have observed that hare populations will go through cycles of increasing and decreasing populations even when the lynx is not part of the habitat. How would you explain this observation? (6.5.e)
19. **APPLY** A forest has pine trees, along with oak trees and birch trees. All of the trees provide shelter and food for different animals in the habitat. Do these trees occupy the same niche? Explain. (6.5.c)
20. **INFER** Explain why low-growing plants such as mosses are eventually replaced by shrubs, and shrubs are then replaced by trees, in both primary and secondary successions. (6.5.e)
21. **PROVIDE EXAMPLES** List three human activities that could lead to secondary succession.
22. **ANALYZE** Creosote bushes in the Mojave desert are spread out so that each plant is about an equal distance from another. Write a short paragraph to describe the interaction of the creosote bushes, using the terms below. (6.5.c)

competition	population pattern
limiting factor	community

23. **APPLY** How might building homes in a wooded area affect carrying capacities of different populations in the area?

the BIG idea

24. **SUMMARIZE** Look again at the photograph on pages 410–411. How would you change or add details to your answer to the question on the photograph? (6.5.c)
25. **APPLY** Imagine that you are an ecologist from another galaxy who arrives on Earth. Describe a human community using the terms that an Earth ecologist would use to describe a natural community. Your description should include at least three examples of interactions between individuals (whether the same or a different species). Identify the biotic or abiotic factors that serve as limiting factors to human population growth. Also state whether you think the human population is at or below its carrying capacity—and why. (6.5.e)

UNIT PROJECTS

By now you should have completed the following items for your unit project:

- questions that you have asked about the topic
- schedule showing when you will complete each step of your project
- list of resources including Web sites, print resources, and materials

MONITOR AND RETEACH

If students are having trouble using the concepts in Chapter Review items 2, 3, 15, and 24, suggest that they review the visual on p. 428. Have them answer the questions using the illustration of the backyard habitat and the organisms that are pictured.

Students may benefit from summarizing one or more sections of the chapter.

 Summarizing the Chapter, pp. 140–141

Standards-Based Assessment

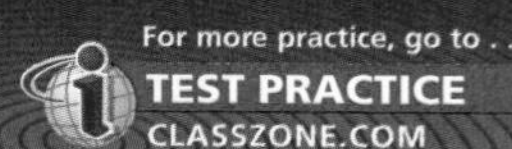

Understanding Symbiosis

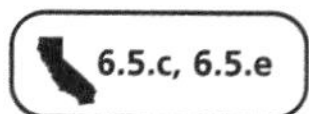

Read the following description of the strangler fig and the relationship it has with other species in a rain forest. Then answer the questions that follow.

Strangler figs are part of many symbiotic relationships in a rain-forest ecosystem. In some cases, the symbiotic relationship benefits both the fig and an animal. Fig wasps lay their eggs in the fruit of the strangler fig. In turn, the wasps pollinate the fig. Many birds feed on the fruit of the strangler fig. In doing so, they spread the seeds of the plant. The fig does not benefit from its interactions with all species. For example, certain butterflies feed on juice from the fruit without affecting the tree in any way.

The symbiotic relationship that gives the strangler fig its name is between the strangler fig and its host tree. Birds drop seeds onto the top of a tree, and vines of the fig grow downward. Eventually, the vines of the strangler fig touch the ground and join with the roots of the host tree. The host tree is harmed because the leaves of the strangler fig block sunlight. Also, its roots use up nutrients the host tree needs.

1. Which feeding relationship is a form of mutualism in which both species benefit?
- **a.** the strangler fig and its host tree
- **b.** the strangler fig and the butterflies
- **c.** the strangler fig and the birds
- **d.** the strangler fig and the fig wasp

2. Which symbiotic relationship is a form of parasitism in which one species benefits and the other is harmed?
- **a.** the strangler fig and its host tree
- **b.** the strangler fig and the butterflies
- **c.** the strangler fig and the birds
- **d.** the strangler fig and the fig wasp

3. Which symbiotic relationship is a commensal relationship in which one species benefits without affecting the other?
- **a.** the strangler fig and its host tree
- **b.** the strangler fig and the butterflies
- **c.** the strangler fig and the birds
- **d.** the strangler fig and the fig wasp

4. Which word best describes the interaction between the strangler fig and its host?
- **a.** coexistence
- **b.** cooperation
- **c.** competition
- **d.** community

Extended Response

5. Strangler figs attach to trees that are sometimes cut for lumber. Write a paragraph that describes how removal of the host trees would affect these populations.
- butterflies
- birds
- wasps
- strangler figs

6. Write a paragraph describing some of the different roles played by a strangler fig in a rain forest. Use the terms below in your answer.

habitat	niche	populations
community	ecosystem	

REFLECTING ON THE CHAPTER

Have students answer the following questions in their **Science Notebook:**
1. What did you find the most surprising about interactions in ecosystems?
2. What questions do you still have about interactions in ecosystems?
3. What are the strongest pieces right now in your Unit Project?

California Content Standards

6.5.c Students know populations of organisms can be categorized by the functions they serve in an ecosystem.

6.5.e Students know the number and types of organisms an ecosystem can support depends on the resources available and on abiotic factors, such as quantities of light and water, a range of temperatures, and soil composition.

Understanding Symbiosis

1. c *2. a* *3. b* *4. c*

Extended Response

5. RUBRIC
4 points for a response that correctly identifies these effects: on butterflies, food lost; birds, food lost; wasps, nesting area lost; strangler fig, access to sunlight lost.

Sample answer: The populations of birds and butterflies would be affected, since the strangler fig provides them with food. The population of wasps would decrease in the next generation because wasps need the fig to reproduce. The figs would get cut down with the host trees.

3 points correctly identifies how three populations would be affected
2 points correctly identifies how two populations would be affected
1 point correctly identifies how one population would be affected

6. RUBRIC
4 points for a response that correctly describes the role and uses four of the terms accurately.

Sample answer: The strangler fig fills an important niche in a rainforest habitat. Populations of birds and butterflies depend on it for food. The fig wasp uses the fruit as part of its reproductive cycle. Figs are part of a diverse community in a rainforest ecosytem.

3 points describes role adequately and uses three terms accurately
2 points describes role partially and uses two terms accurately
1 point describes role partially and uses 1 term accurately

FOCUS

Set Learning Goals

Students will

- Examine historical steps people have taken to protect ecosystems.
- Learn about some of the tools people have used to study and preserve ecosystems.
- Write a proposal for protecting the ecosystem.

California Content Standards

6.5.c Students know populations of organisms can be categorized by the functions they serve in an ecosystem.

6.5.d Students know different kinds of organisms may play similar ecological roles in similar biomes.

6.5.e Students know the number and types of organisms an ecosystem can support depends on the resources available and on abiotic factors, such as quantities of light and water, a range of temperatures, and soil composition.

INSTRUCT

History Connection

Point out to students that the top half of the timeline shows major events in wilderness conservation in the United States starting in the1870s. The bottom half of the timeline illustrates advances in technology and the application of wilderness conservation. The gap between 1910 and 1950 represents a block of time that has been omitted.

Technology

PHOTOGRAPHY First sold in 1888, the Kodak Camera was simple: press a button to expose the film, then turn a key to advance the film. Ask students how this new camera influenced the way conservationists were able to work. *Both conservationists and wildlife photographers could move freely with a lightweight camera to capture images in the environment.*

TIMELINES in Science

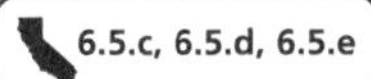

WILDERNESS CONSERVATION

The idea of wilderness conservation would have seemed strange to anyone living before the 1800s. The wilderness was vast, and much of the wildlife in it dangerous to humans.

In the late 1800s, smoke from railroads and factories rose in American skies. Scientists, artists, and even presidents began the work of setting aside land as parks and reservations to protect natural landscapes. Forestry, new to the U.S. in the 1890s, became a priority of the federal government. Industries learned to harvest and nurture forests rather than clear them. Next came the protection of animal species and a call to control the pollution and depletion caused by human activity.

1872

National Parks Protect Resources

On March 1, 1872, President Ulysses S. Grant signs a law declaring Yellowstone's 2 million acres in northwest Wyoming as the country's first national park. The law states that the land will forever be "set apart . . . for the benefit and enjoyment of the people."

EVENTS

1870

APPLICATIONS and TECHNOLOGY

TECHNOLOGY

Seeing the Wilderness

Developments in photography in 1839, and its spread during the Civil War, led to adventurous mobile photographers in the late 1800s. In the early 1860s, Mathew Brady and other photographers took mobile studios to the battlefields to bring war news to the public. By the late 1860s and early 1870s, cameras were much smaller. In 1871 William Henry Jackson used a tripod in Yellowstone as the official photographer of the region's first U.S. Geological Survey.

DIFFERENTIATE INSTRUCTION

Below Level For those students who may have difficulty understanding how information is organized on a timeline, call their attention to the dates on the yellow center line.

Point out how the dates become more recent as they move from left to right. Call attention also to the lines connecting the event boxes to specific dates in the timeline. Emphasize how timelines are a good way of showing quickly a brief or selected history of any subject.

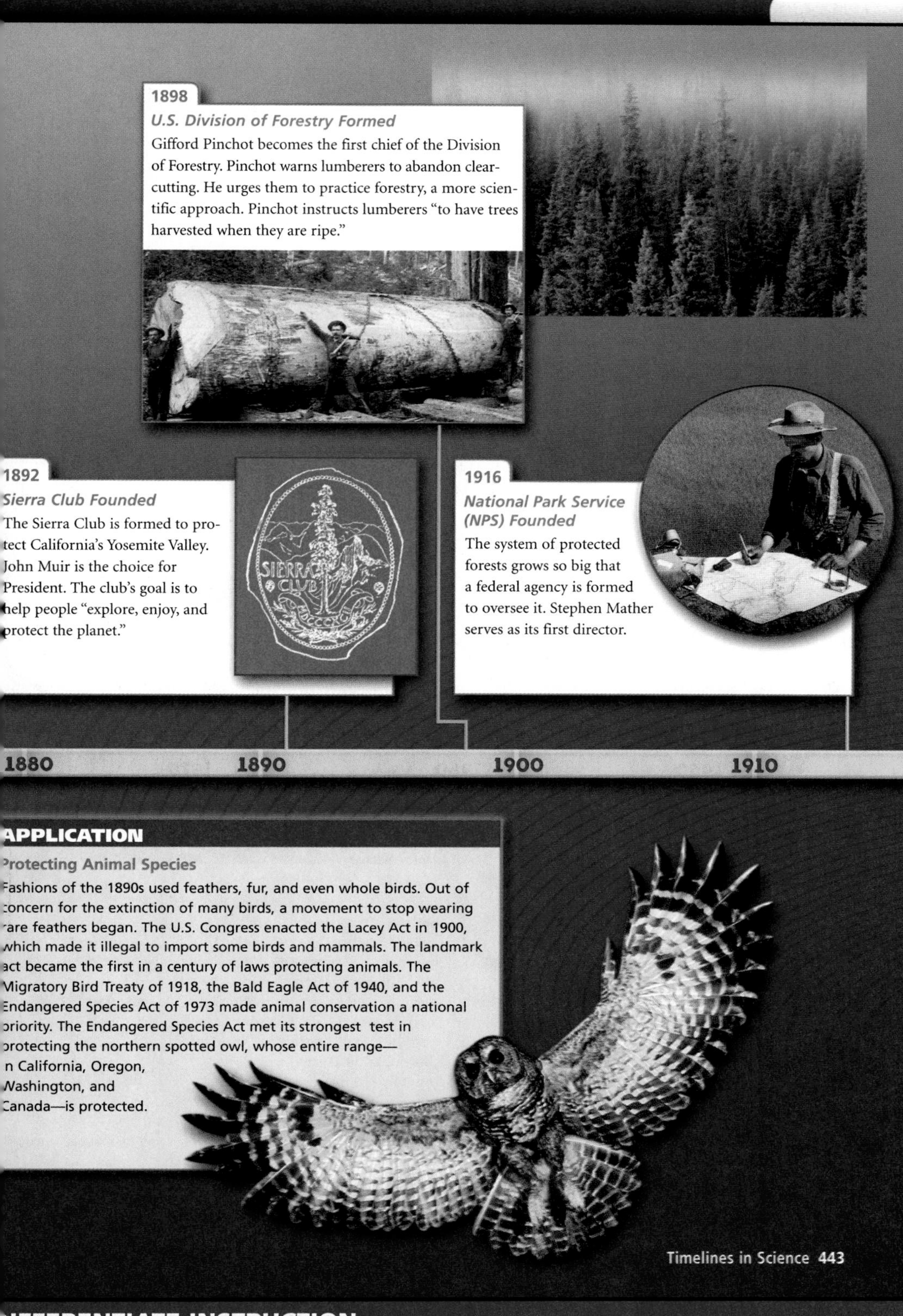

1898

U.S. Division of Forestry Formed

Gifford Pinchot becomes the first chief of the Division of Forestry. Pinchot warns lumberers to abandon clear-cutting. He urges them to practice forestry, a more scientific approach. Pinchot instructs lumberers "to have trees harvested when they are ripe."

1892

Sierra Club Founded

The Sierra Club is formed to protect California's Yosemite Valley. John Muir is the choice for President. The club's goal is to help people "explore, enjoy, and protect the planet."

1916

National Park Service (NPS) Founded

The system of protected forests grows so big that a federal agency is formed to oversee it. Stephen Mather serves as its first director.

APPLICATION

Protecting Animal Species

Fashions of the 1890s used feathers, fur, and even whole birds. Out of concern for the extinction of many birds, a movement to stop wearing rare feathers began. The U.S. Congress enacted the Lacey Act in 1900, which made it illegal to import some birds and mammals. The landmark act became the first in a century of laws protecting animals. The Migratory Bird Treaty of 1918, the Bald Eagle Act of 1940, and the Endangered Species Act of 1973 made animal conservation a national priority. The Endangered Species Act met its strongest test in protecting the northern spotted owl, whose entire range—in California, Oregon, Washington, and Canada—is protected.

Timelines in Science 443

DIFFERENTIATE INSTRUCTION

Advanced Students can visit the website of the U.S. Fish and Wildlife Service and learn about other endangered and threatened species. They can also find out which species have been taken off the endangered list—the success stories.

Students might then select one species and report on what actions are recommended for that species' future. Encourage students to suggest things anyone could do to help ensure the species is protected in a balanced or ecological way.

Scientific Process

Testing hypotheses in ecology takes a long time. A conservationist has no way to be certain about the long-term results of the actions he or she supports. Ecosystems are always larger and more complex than laboratories. When a conservationist takes an action to preserve the environment, he or she must often wait years to fully understand the results. Similarly, the environmental impacts of other human activity, such as industry and agriculture, often take years to truly be felt. As scientists, ecologists have to balance the two.

Art Connection

1892 The Sierra Club has had several logos in its history. The current logo features a giant sequoia tree and the peak of Yosemite's Half Dome mountain. Although the Sierra Club is now a nationwide organization, these symbols were chosen then to symbolize the distinctive beauty of the Sierra Nevada Mountain range. Students may wish to design their own conservation logo. Tell students to think about which natural resources of their region (trees, water, etc.) are most important to preserve and incorporate these into their logos.

Application

PROTECTING ANIMAL SPECIES

The Lacey Act eventually led to the Endangered Species Act, which set up two classes of protected species: *threatened* and *endangered.* The act covers all species of plants and animals. Species classified as threatened are not as in danger of dying out as species classified as endangered. The Fish and Wildlife Service monitors the populations of threatened and endangered species as steps are taken to preserve their habitats. Ask students why they think certain species of plants and animals are threatened. *loss of food and habitat due to human beings' actions on the environment*

Social Studies Connection

1960s The1960s was both an exciting and troubling time in American history. The decade saw the assassinations of President John F. Kennedy in 1963 and civil rights leader Dr. Martin Luther King, Jr. in 1968. College students in the '60s held peaceful protests against American foreign and domestic policies and succeeded in getting much legislation passed by Congress. Some of this legislation eventually led to significant environmental initiatives like the Endangered Species Act and establishment of the Environmental Protection Agency. Ask: Why do you think environmental issues would have concerned people at this time? *Sample answer: People were concerned about their country and wanted to protect it from threats;* or *People were disappointed by human activities and wanted to focus on nature and wildlife.*

Language Arts Connection

1962 Many people consider the publication of *Silent Spring* to be the start of the environmentalist movement. More than simply calling for a stop to the use of pesticides, Carson urged that people needed to adopt a different view of their place in the world. People needed to see themselves as part of nature, not as masters of nature. Ask students why they think this change in view would give people a greater respect for nature. *Sample answer: If people are part of nature, they will want to protect it.*

Social Studies Connection

1968 The Grand Canyon has been considered a sacred site by the Hopi of the southwestern United States. Hopi mythology holds that the first people emerged from inside the Earth through the Grand Canyon.

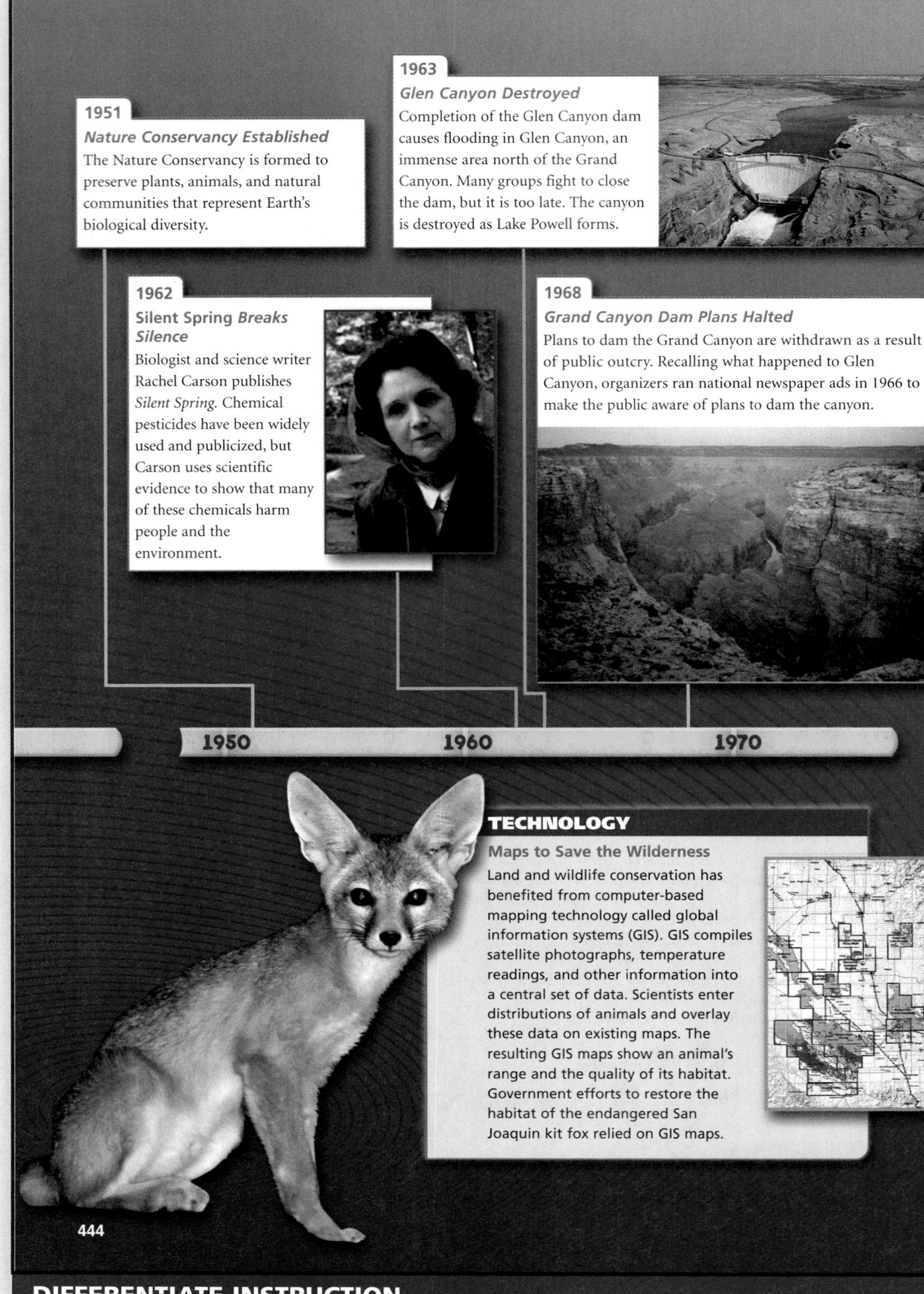

1951
Nature Conservancy Established
The Nature Conservancy is formed to preserve plants, animals, and natural communities that represent Earth's biological diversity.
1963
Glen Canyon Destroyed
Completion of the Glen Canyon dam causes flooding in Glen Canyon, an immense area north of the Grand Canyon. Many groups fight to close the dam, but it is too late. The canyon is destroyed as Lake Powell forms.
1962
Silent Spring Breaks Silence
Biologist and science writer Rachel Carson publishes Silent Spring. Chemical pesticides have been widely used and publicized, but Carson uses scientific evidence to show that many of these chemicals harm people and the environment.
1968
Grand Canyon Dam Plans Halted
Plans to dam the Grand Canyon are withdrawn as a result of public outcry. Recalling what happened to Glen Canyon, organizers ran national newspaper ads in 1966 to make the public aware of plans to dam the canyon.
1950
1960
1970
TECHNOLOGY
Maps to Save the Wilderness
Land and wildlife conservation has benefited from computer-based mapping technology called global information systems (GIS). GIS compiles satellite photographs, temperature readings, and other information into a central set of data. Scientists enter distributions of animals and overlay these data on existing maps. The resulting GIS maps show an animal's range and the quality of its habitat. Government efforts to restore the habitat of the endangered San Joaquin kit fox relied on GIS maps.
444

DIFFERENTIATE INSTRUCTION

English Learners English learners may not know the expression *public outcry* (1968). Students may also need help with words such as *pesticides, publishes,* and *evidence* (1962). You might point out the connection between the terms: *publishes, publicized,* and *public.* Write such terms on the board and put reminder sketches beside them.

Encourage students with limited English to focus mainly on understanding the red headings in the event boxes.

2001

Reservation vs. Resource

In 1980, Congress expanded the Arctic National Wildlife Refuge (ANWR) to more than twice its size in 1960. In 2001 President George W. Bush proposes limited oil drilling within the range. Debate continues over how to manage its resources and wildlife.

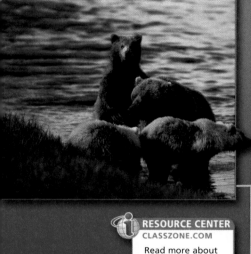

RESOURCE CENTER
CLASSZONE.COM

Read more about current conservation efforts.

1990 2000

APPLICATION

Selling a Service

In 1996 the New York City water department spent $1.5 billion to protect natural watersheds rather than build a $6 billion water treatment plant. In 2001 a group of scientists met to promote the value that ecosystems bring to society—benefits that include pest control, air purification, and water treatment. For example, dragonflies can eat 300 mosquitoes in a single day. Toads and bats can eat a thousand or more mosquitoes in a single day or night.

SPOTLIGHT on MARIA MIRITI

Ecologist Maria Miriti studies the interactions of plant populations within a plant community. Her findings have been important for the rapidly growing field of landscape ecology. Knowing how plants interact helps people plan land use, evaluate vegetation changes, and control invasive species.

In 2004 Miriti led a group of researchers in taking a census of desert plants in the Colorado Desert of California's Joshua Tree National Park. They studied the impact of dominant species on plant diversity.

A desert is a harsh environment for plants. Many plants benefit from being close to another plant. Some plants are entirely dependent on other plants for germination, growth, and survival. Miriti thinks deserts are a good model for such studies because all members of the community depend on a scarce water supply.

ACTIVITIES

Ecosystem Services Proposal

What services does your local ecosystem provide to the human population? Choose one service and describe how natural processes and interactions within the ecosystem provide the benefits you've identified.

Write a proposal for protecting the ecosystem. Compare the estimated cost of protecting the ecosystem with the cost of human services that provide a similar benefit.

Writing Project: The Story Behind the News

Research one of the events described on the timeline. Then write the story behind that event.

DIFFERENTIATE INSTRUCTION

Advanced Encourage motivated students to submit their proposals to their local town or neighborhood board. Tell students that the reports do not need to be comprehensive and numbers exact, but that they should be able to justify how they arrived at the values.

Spotlight on

Maria Miriti's research addresses the spatial patterns of plants in communities. Remind students how much of science is research. Research for ecology is usually field research, not laboratory research, and can take a long time. Miriti's field research involves counting plants, measuring distances, and watching slow changes in growth.

Health Connection

Ask students how the health of our environment and wildlife population affects the health of the human population. Have them to give examples of this interconnectedness. *Sample answer: Fish living in polluted water become contaminated; human beings eat the contaminated fish.*

ACTIVITIES

Ecosystem Services Proposal

Students could get help with this project by contacting their local 4-H, Sierra Club, or chapter of the Forestry Service. Remind students that they need to write persuasively and present their cost estimates clearly when writing their proposals.

Writing Project: The Story Behind the News

Suggest to students that they write their stories from the point of view of one of the participants. If reporting on the founding of the Sierra Club, for example, students could write from the perspective of John Muir, as if he were telling it to a newspaper reporter.

Technology Resources

Students can visit **ClassZone.com** for current news about conservation.

CHAPTER

Natural Resources

Earth Science UNIFYING PRINCIPLES

PRINCIPLE 1
Heat energy inside Earth and radiation from the Sun provide energy for Earth's processes.

PRINCIPLE 2
Physical forces, such as gravity, affect the movement of all matter on Earth and throughout the universe.

PRINCIPLE 3
Matter and energy move among Earth's rocks and soil, atmosphere, waters, and living things.

PRINCIPLE 4
Earth has changed over time and continues to change.

Unit: Ecology and Resources BIG IDEAS

CHAPTER 11 Ecosystems and Biomes
Matter and energy together support life within an environment.

CHAPTER 12 Interactions Within Ecosystems
Living things within an ecosystem interact with each other and the environment.

CHAPTER 13 Natural Resources
Society depends on natural resources for energy and materials.

CHAPTER 14 Human Impact on Ecosystems
Humans and human population growth affect the environment.

CHAPTER 13 KEY CONCEPTS

SECTION 1

Natural resources support human activity.
1. Natural resources provide materials and energy.
2. Fossil fuels supply most of society's energy.
3. Fossil fuels, minerals, and plants supply materials for modern products.

SECTION 2

Minerals and rocks are nonrenewable resources.
1. Minerals have many uses in industry.
2. Minerals have many uses in the arts.
3. Minerals form in several ways.
4. Many minerals are mined.

SECTION 3

Resources can be conserved and recycled.
1. Conservation involves reducing waste and reusing natural resources.
2. Recycling involves recovering and extending natural resources.

SECTION 4

Resources can be converted to useful forms.
1. Renewable resources are used to produce electricity and as fuel.
2. Nuclear power is used to produce electricity.

The Big Idea Flow Chart is available on p. T97 in the **TRANSPARENCY BOOK**.

Previewing Content

SECTION

Natural resources support human activity. pp. 449–457

1. Natural resources provide materials and energy.
A **natural resource** is any energy source, organism, or substance found in nature that people use. A **renewable resource** is a natural resource that can be replaced in nature at about the same rate that it is used. Examples of renewable resources are

- sunlight
- wind
- water
- trees and other plants
- animal waste

A **nonrenewable resource** is a natural resource that exists in a fixed amount or that is used up faster than it can be replaced. Examples of nonrenewable resources are

- coal
- oil
- natural gas
- uranium
- minerals and rocks

2. Fossil fuels supply most of society's energy.
A **fossil fuel,** such as coal, oil, or natural gas, is a nonrenewable resource made from once-living plants and animals that were buried in Earth's crust for millions of years. In the United States, 86 percent of the energy used comes from burning fossil fuels. Fossil fuels burn easily and give off a lot of heat. However, there are disadvantages to their use. In addition to being nonrenewable, fossil fuels produce pollution when they are burned and can harm the environment in other ways, such as through oil spills.

3. Fossil fuels, minerals, and plants supply materials for modern products.
Most products today, such as plastics, are made from fossil fuels. Other resources used to make products are minerals, rocks, and plants.

SECTION

Minerals and rocks are nonrenewable resources. pp. 458–465

1. Minerals have many uses in industry.
Modern society depends on minerals in making machines and everyday products. Some examples include:

- chromite, a source of chromium used in cars
- bauxite, a source of aluminum used in soda cans
- hematite, a source of iron used in cooking pots

2. Minerals have many uses in the arts.
Gems and such metals as gold and silver are used in jewelry making and other decorative arts. Minerals are also used as pigments in dyes and paints.

3. Minerals form in several ways.
Minerals form when the atoms of one or more elements join together and crystals begin to grow. This can occur when

- water at Earth's surface evaporates
- hot water within Earth's crust cools
- magma or lava cools and becomes solid
- heat or pressure deep within Earth causes minerals to change
- organisms produce minerals to form shells or bones

4. Many minerals are mined.
A rock that contains enough of a mineral to be mined for a profit is called an **ore.** When minerals lie at or near Earth's surface, they may be recovered by surface-mining methods, including

- separation from other materials in a stream, either by hand or by machine
- strip mining, which involves stripping away the surface vegetation, soil, and rock to dig out an ore
- open-pit mining, which involves digging a deep pit to mine an ore

Deep-mining methods are used when ores lie far below Earth's surface.

Common Misconceptions

MISCONCEPTION DATABASE
CLASSZONE.COM Background on student misconceptions

RENEWABLE RESOURCES Students may hold the misconception that renewable resources are unlimited and can be used anywhere. In fact, some resources, such as trees, can be considered nonrenewable in certain cases—for example, if trees are cut down faster than they are replaced.

 This misconception is addressed on p. 450..

FORMATION IN NATURE Students may have difficulty identifying materials that are formed by natural processes. For example, they might consider a brick to be natural because it contains minerals, or they might consider a mineral sample to have been manufactured once it has been cut or polished.

 This misconception is addressed on p. 460.

Previewing Content

SECTION

Resources can be conserved and recycled. pp. 466–470

1. Conservation involves reducing waste and reusing natural resources.

In the United States, people produce almost 180 million tons of trash annually. The term *waste stream* is used to refer to the amount of trash generated. More than half of the waste stream in the United States is dumped in landfills.

Conservation means protecting, restoring, and managing natural resources so they last as long as possible. Conserving resources by consuming less energy and fewer products can also reduce pollution problems. Ways to conserve include

- reducing waste
- reusing products.

2. Recycling involves recovering and extending natural resources.

Recycling means recovering materials that people usually throw away. Items that can be recycled include glass, aluminum cans, certain plastics, paper, scrap iron, and certain other metals. It takes time, money, and energy to recycle products. These costs must be weighed against the benefits of extending natural resources and protecting the environment and human health.

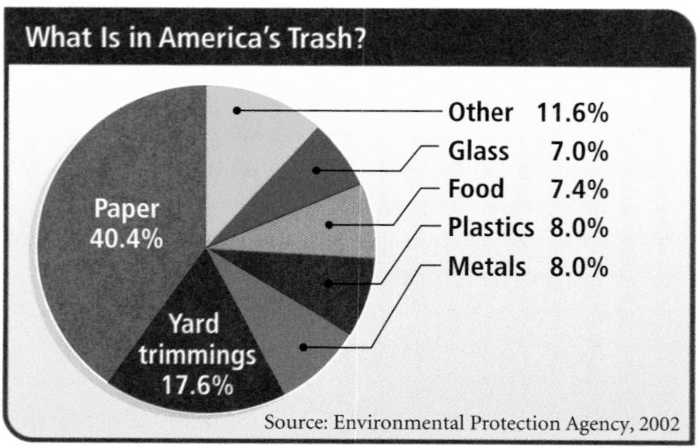

SECTION

Resources can be converted to useful forms. pp. 471–481

1. Renewable resources are used to produce electricity and as fuel.

Today, people are exploring alternatives to using fossil fuels, including such energy sources as sunlight, moving water, wind, Earth's heat, organic matter, and hydrogen. As with fossil fuels, each source has both advantages and disadvantages.

Currently, renewable resources make up only a small percentage of the energy sources used globally. Most are nonpolluting. However, there are costs associated with each source.

- **Hydroelectric energy** is electricity produced by using moving water. Disadvantages include flooding and the destruction of wildlife habitats.
- **Solar cells** are specially constructed of silicon and other materials to convert light energy to electricty.
- **Geothermal energy** is energy produced by using heat within Earth's crust. Disadvantages include geographic limitations.
- Wind energy produces electricity by using the force of moving air. Disadvantages include geographic limitations.
- **Biomass** is organic matter that can be used as fuel. Disadvantages include economic limitations, and use of land that could grow food crops.
- **Hydrogen fuel cells** are devices that produce electricity by separating hydrogen atoms into protons and electrons. The electrons form an electric current. Disadvantages include economic limitations.

2. Nuclear power is used to produce electricity.

Nuclear energy is an energy source that comes from splitting atoms. In the process known as fission, the nuclei of radioactive atoms are split and energy is released in the form of heat and light. The energy released is used to create steam, which turns turbines. The turbines drive generators that produce electricity. Nuclear energy produces heat more efficiently than do fossil fuels, but the dangers of working with and storing radioactive waste materials are drawbacks to using this source of energy. Radioactive waste must be stored securely for thousands of years.

Common Misconceptions

MISCONCEPTION DATABASE
CLASSZONE.COM Background on student misconceptions

COST OF RESOURCES Students may hold the misconception that renewable resources provide inexpensive energy. Currently, electrical energy produced by using renewable resources costs much more than electricity produced by using fossil fuels.

This misconception is addressed on p. 477.

Previewing Labs

Lab Generator CD-ROM
Edit these Pupil Edition labs and generate alternative labs.

EXPLORE the BIG idea

Sunlight as an Energy Source, p. 447 Students are introduced to the concept of solar energy.	**TIME** 35 minutes **MATERIALS** black paper, two plastic cups, water, plastic wrap, two rubber bands, thermometer,
Internet Activity: Resources, p. 447 Students learn about local natural resources.	**TIME** 20 minutes **MATERIALS** computer with Internet access

SECTION 1

INVESTIGATE Fossil Fuels Distribution, p. 455 Students analyze data of nonrenewable energy resources. **ALTERNATIVE:** Direct Instruction, URB p. 273	**TIME** 15 minutes **MATERIALS** Map of Fossil Fuels Distribution

SECTION 2

EXPLORE Minerals at Your Fingertips, p. 458 Students examine pencils to identify how minerals in the pencils are useful.	**TIME** 10 minutes **MATERIALS** No. 2 and No. 4 wooden pencils, paper
INVESTIGATE Mining, p. 463 Students sort seeds and beads to draw conclusions about the benefits and costs of mining ores. **ALTERNATIVE:** Reading Activity, URB p. 273	**TIME** 25 minutes **MATERIALS** 1 pound wild-bird seed mixed with sunflower seeds, shallow pan, 2 small red beads, 4 small green beads, 8 small blue beads, 3 medium yellow beads

SECTION 3

EXPLORE Energy Use, p. 466 Students calculate their energy quotients to help them recognize how much energy they use every day.	**TIME** 20 minutes **MATERIALS** calculator, paper, pen or pencil
INVESTIGATE Conservation, p. 468 Students design an experiment to test the energy efficiency of fluorescent versus incandescent light bulbs. **ALTERNATIVE:** Teacher Demonstration, URB p. 273	**TIME** 10 minutes **MATERIALS** two table lamps, 60-watt incandescent light bulb, 60-watt fluorescent light bulb, two thermometers, pen or pencil

SECTION 4

CHAPTER INVESTIGATION Wind Power, pp. 480–481 Students construct a model windmill and use appropriate technology to improve its performance. **ALTERNATIVE:** Diagramming Activity, URB p. 273	**TIME** 40 minutes **MATERIALS** file folder, metric ruler, a quarter, scissors, brass paper fastener, straw, pushpin, masking tape, pint carton, 30 cm string, hole puncher, small paper clips, clock or stopwatch, small desktop fan with speed settings

R **Additional INVESTIGATION,** Stalagmites and Stalactites, or A, B, & C, pp. 202–210; Teacher Instructions, pp. 273–274

Previewing Chapter Resources

	INTEGRATED TECHNOLOGY	LABS AND ACTIVITIES
CHAPTER 13 **Natural Resources**	 CLASSZONE.COM • eEdition Plus • EasyPlanner Plus • Misconception Database • Content Review • Test Practice • Visualization • Simulation • Resource Centers • Internet Activity: Resources • Math Tutorial SCILINKS.ORG SCILINKS **CD-ROMS** • eEdition • EasyPlanner • Power Presentations • Content Review • Lab Generator • Test Generator 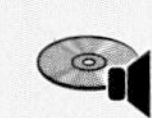 **AUDIO CDS** • Audio Readings • Audio Readings in Spanish	 EXPLORE the Big Idea, p. 447 • Sunlight as an Energy Source • Internet Activity: Resources  **UNIT RESOURCE BOOK** Unit Projects, pp. 5–10    **Lab Generator CD-ROM** Generate customized labs.
SECTION  **1 Natural resources support human activity.** pp. 449–457  Lesson Plan, pp. 142–143	 **TRANSPARENCY BOOK** • Big Idea Flow Chart, p. T97 • Daily Vocabulary Scaffolding, p. T98 • Note-Taking Model, p. T99 • 3-Minute Warm-Up, p. T100 • "Natural Resources" Visual, p. T102	 • INVESTIGATE Fossil Fuels Distribution, p. 455 • California Close-Up, p. 457 **UNIT RESOURCE BOOK** • Map of Fossil Fuels Distribution, p. 151 • Datasheet, Fossil Fuels Distribution, p. 152
SECTION  **2 Minerals and rocks are nonrenewable resources.** pp. 458–465  Lesson Plan, pp. 154–155	 **RESOURCE CENTER,** Gemstones  **TRANSPARENCY BOOK** • Daily Vocabulary Scaffolding, p. T98 • 3-Minute Warm-Up, p. T100 • "Mineral Formation" Visual, p. T102	 • EXPLORE MInerals at Your Fingertips, p. 458 • INVESTIGATE Mining, p. 463 • Science on the Job, p. 465  **UNIT RESOURCE BOOK** Datasheet, Mining, p. 163
SECTION  **3 Resources can be conserved and recycled.** pp. 466–470   Lesson Plan, pp. 165–166	 **MATH TUTORIAL**  **TRANSPARENCY BOOK** • Daily Vocabulary Scaffolding, p. T98 • 3-Minute Warm-Up, p. T101	 • EXPLORE Energy Use, p. 466 • INVESTIGATE Conservation, p. 468 • Math in Science, p. 470  **UNIT RESOURCE BOOK** • Datasheet, Conservation, p. 174 • Math Support, p. 191 • Math Practice, p. 192
SECTION **4 Resources can be converted to useful forms.** pp. 471–481   Lesson Plan, pp. 176–177	 • **RESOURCE CENTER,** Renewable Energy Resources • **SIMULATION,** Nuclear Power Plant • **VISUALIZATION,** Hydrogen Fuel Cell  **TRANSPARENCY BOOK** • Big Idea Flow Chart, p. T97 • Daily Vocabulary Scaffolding, p. T98 • 3-Minute Warm-Up, p. T101 • Chapter Outline, pp. T103–T104	 CHAPTER INVESTIGATION, Wind Power, pp. 480–481   **UNIT RESOURCE BOOK** • CHAPTER INVESTIGATION, Wind Power, A, B, & C, pp. 193–201 • Additional INVESTIGATION, Solar Houses, A, B, & C, pp. 202–210

 **KEY TO ICONS**

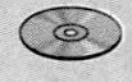 CD/CD-ROM
 Teacher Edition
 TRANSPARENCY BOOK
 STANDARDS REVIEW AND PRACTICE
INTERNET
 Pupil Edition
 UNIT RESOURCE BOOK
 ASSESSMENT BOOK
 SCIENCE TOOLKIT

READING AND REINFORCEMENT	ASSESSMENT	STANDARDS
  **Modified Lesson Plans for English Learners,** pp. 47–50  • Word Triangle, B18–19 • Supporting Main Ideas, C42 • Daily Vocabulary Scaffolding, H1–8 **UNIT RESOURCE BOOK** • Vocabulary Practice, pp. 188–189 • Decoding Support, p. 190 • Summarizing the Chapter, pp. 211–212  **Audio Readings CD** Listen to Pupil Edition.  **Audio Readings in Spanish CD** Listen to Pupil Edition in Spanish.	 • Chapter Review, pp. 483–484 • Standards-Based Assessment, p. 485  **ASSESSMENT BOOK** • Diagnostic Test, pp. 287–288 • Chapter Test, A, B, & C, pp. 293–304 • Alternative Assessment, pp. 305–306  **STANDARDS REVIEW AND PRACTICE,** pp. 23–24, 51–58, 61–62  **McDougal Littell Assessment System** 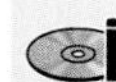 **Test Generator CD-ROM** Generate customized and Spanish tests.	California Content Standards 6.3.a, 6.6.a, 6.6.b, 6.6.c, 6.7.a, 6.7.c, 6.7.d See p. 446 for the standards.
UNIT RESOURCE BOOK • Reading Study Guide, A & B, pp. 144–147 • Spanish Reading Study Guide, pp. 148–149 • Challenge and Extension, p. 150 • Reinforcing Key Concepts, p. 153	 Ongoing Assessment, pp. 450–455  Section 13.1 Review, p. 456  **ASSESSMENT BOOK** Section 13.1 Quiz, p. 289	California Content Standards 6.6.a, 6.6.b, 6.6.c
UNIT RESOURCE BOOK • Reading Study Guide, A & B, pp. 156–159 • Spanish Reading Study Guide, pp. 160–161 • Challenge and Extension, p. 162 • Reinforcing Key Concepts, p. 164	 Ongoing Assessment, pp. 458–464  Section 13.2 Review, p. 464  **ASSESSMENT BOOK** Section 13.2 Quiz, p. 290	California Content Standards 6.6.a, 6.6.b, 6.6.c
UNIT RESOURCE BOOK • Reading Study Guide, A & B, pp. 167–170 • Spanish Reading Study Guide, pp. 171–172 • Challenge and Extension, p. 173 • Reinforcing Key Concepts, p. 175	Ongoing Assessment, pp. 467, 469  Section 13.3 Review, p. 469  **ASSESSMENT BOOK** Section 13.3 Quiz, p. 291	California Content Standards 6.6.a, 6.6.b, 6.6.c, 6.7.c
 **UNIT RESOURCE BOOK** • Reading Study Guide, A & B, pp. 178–181 • Spanish Reading Study Guide, pp. 182–183 • Challenge and Extension, p. 184 • Reinforcing Key Concepts, p. 185 • Challenge Reading, pp. 186–187	 Ongoing Assessment, pp. 472–479  Section 13.4 Review, p. 479  **ASSESSMENT BOOK** Section 13.4 Quiz, p. 292	California Content Standards 6.3.a, 6.6.a, 6.6.b, 6.7.a, 6.7.b, 6.7.c, 6.7.d

Previewing Resources for Differentiated Instruction

CHAPTER INVESTIGATION

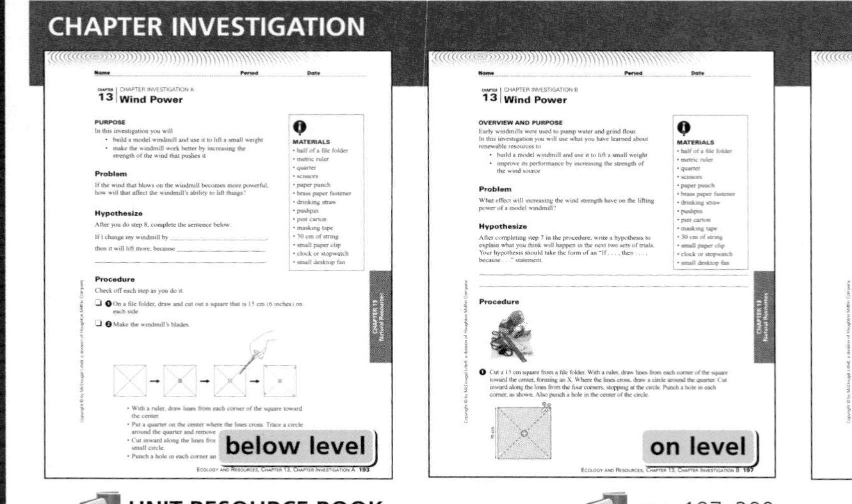

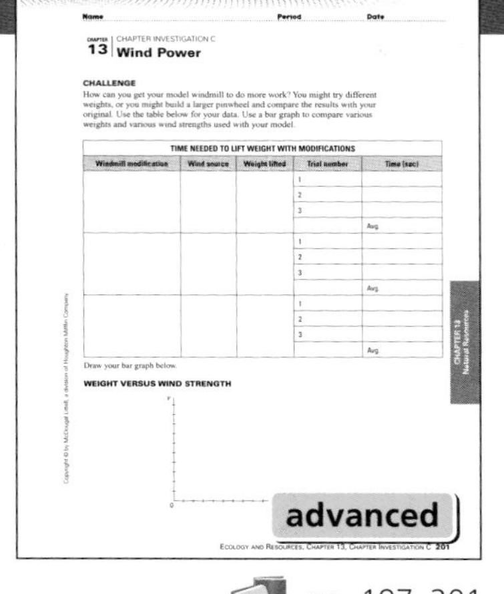

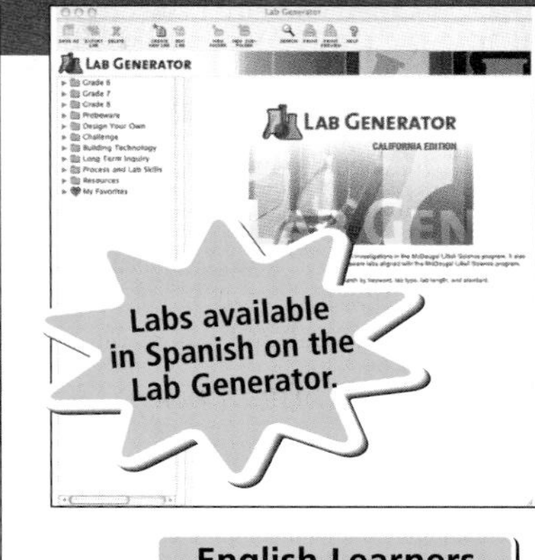

R UNIT RESOURCE BOOK, pp. 193–196

R pp. 197–200

R pp. 197–201

READING STUDY GUIDE

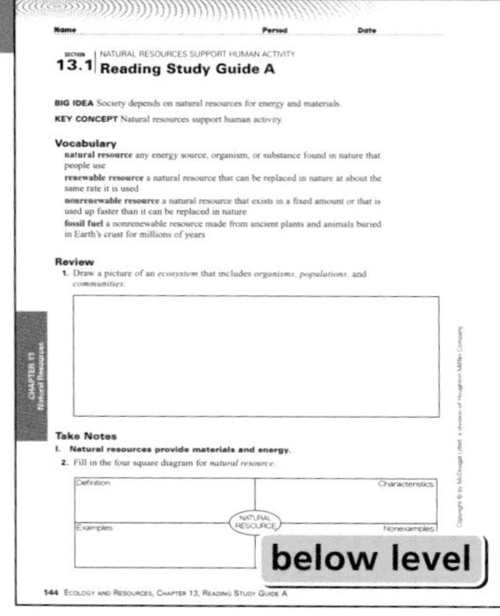

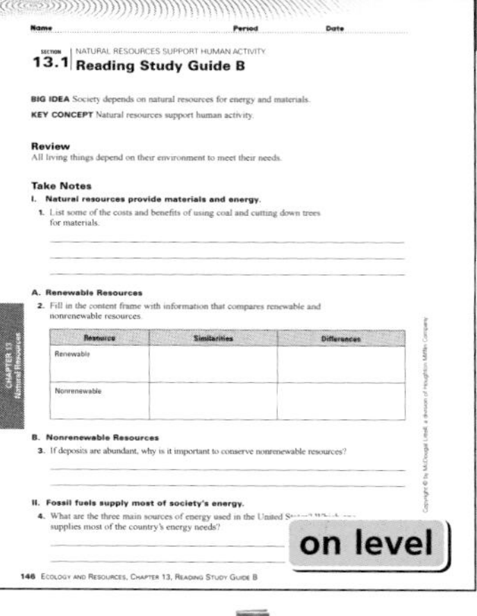

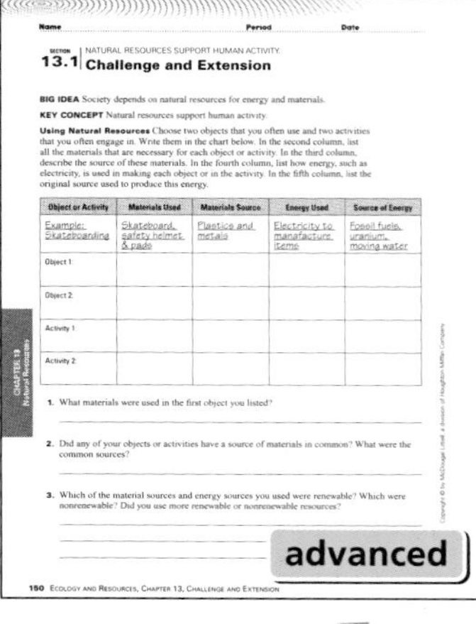

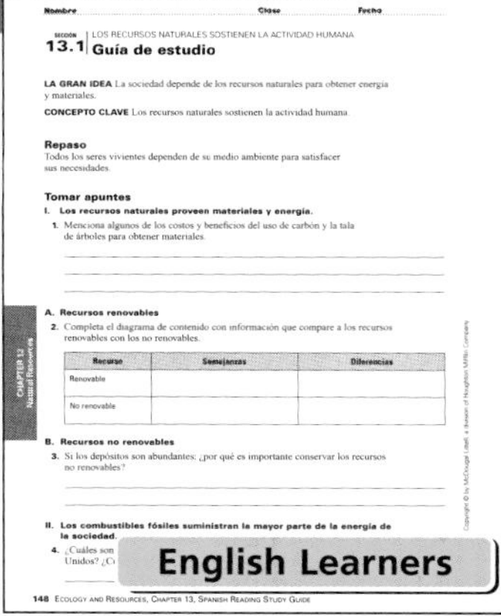

R UNIT RESOURCE BOOK, pp. 144–145

R pp. 146–147

R p. 150

R p. 148

CHAPTER TEST

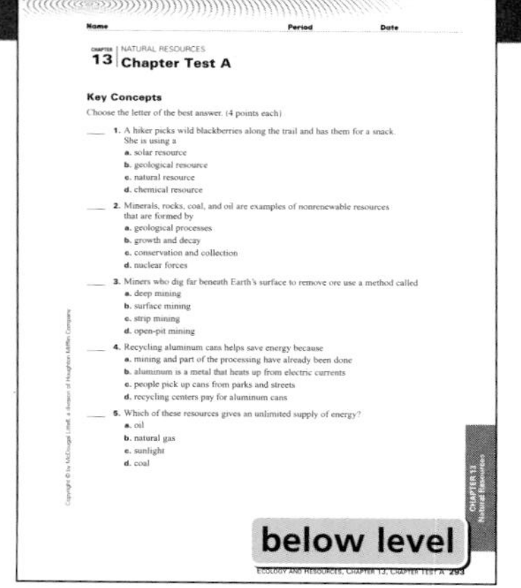

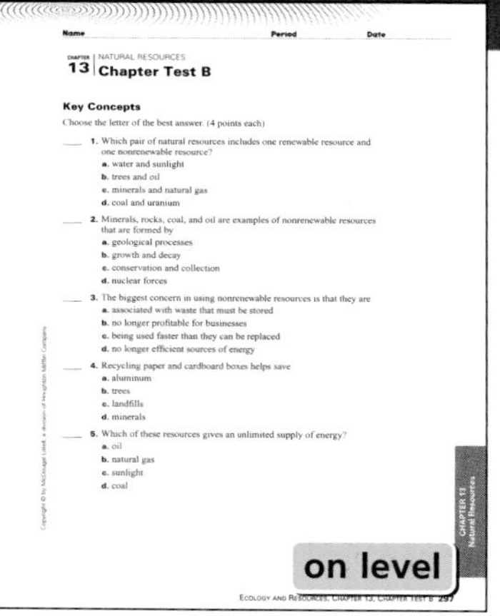

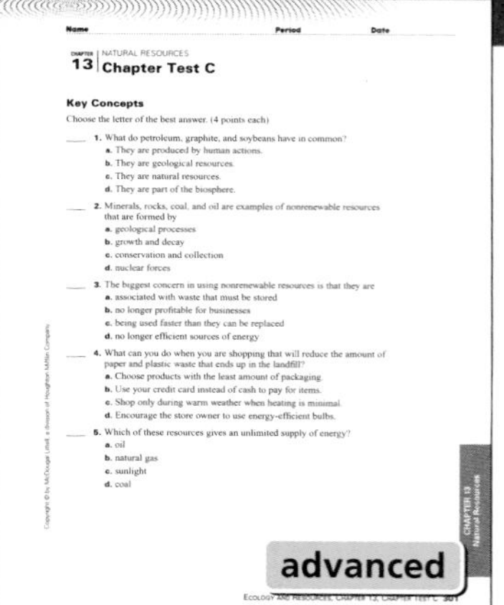

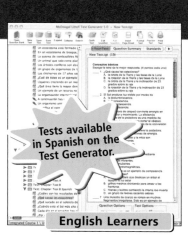

Tests available in Spanish on the Test Generator.

English Learners

A ASSESSMENT BOOK, pp. 293–296

A pp. 297–300

A pp. 301–304

TECHNOLOGY

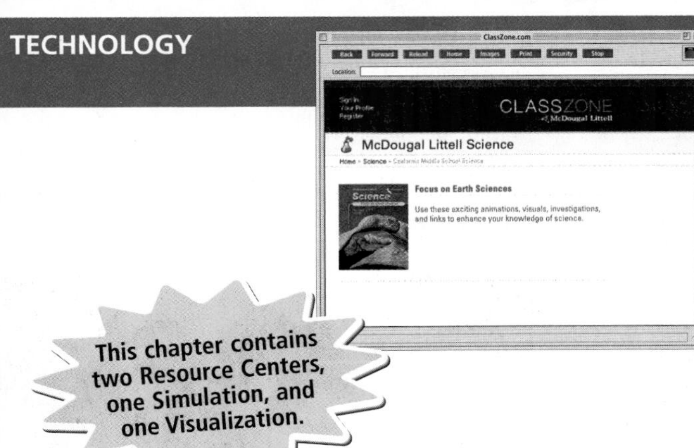

ClassZone.com
CLASSZONE
McDougal Littell Science
Focus on Earth Sciences
Use these exciting animations, visuals, investigations, and links to enhance your knowledge of science.
This chapter contains two Resource Centers, one Simulation, and one Visualization.

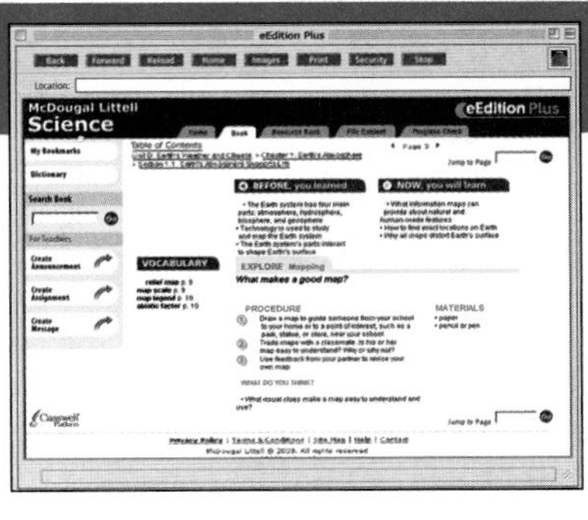

VISUAL CONTENT

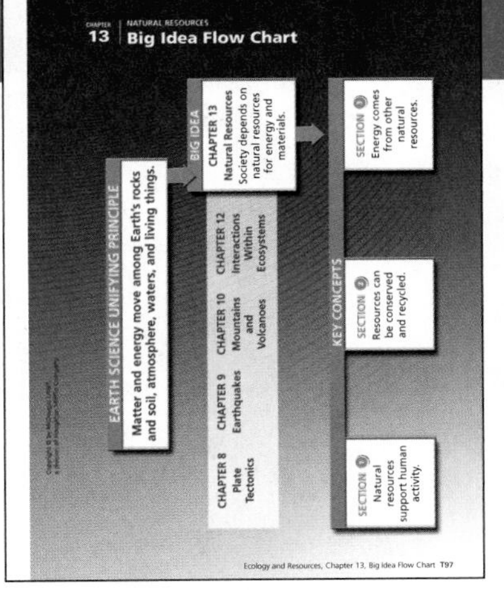

TRANSPARENCY BOOK, p. T97

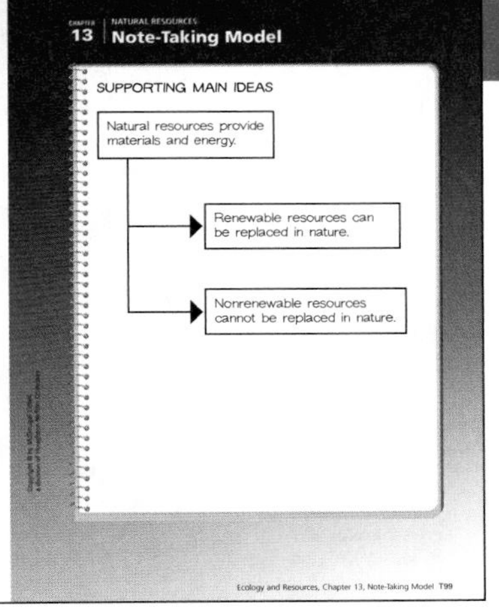

p. T99

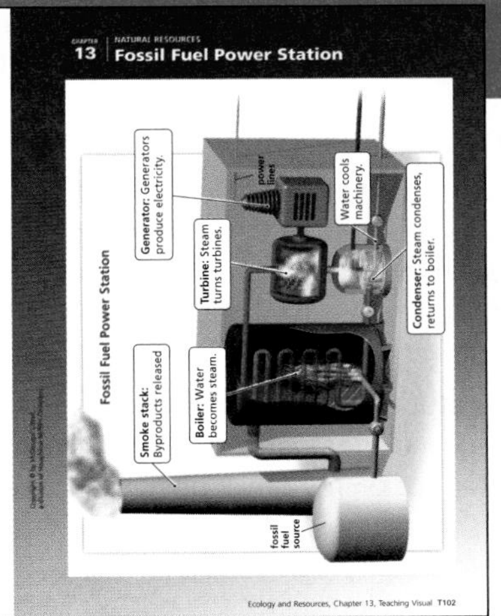

p. T102

MORE SUPPORT

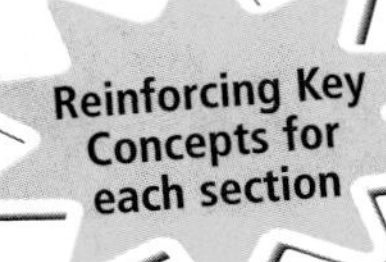

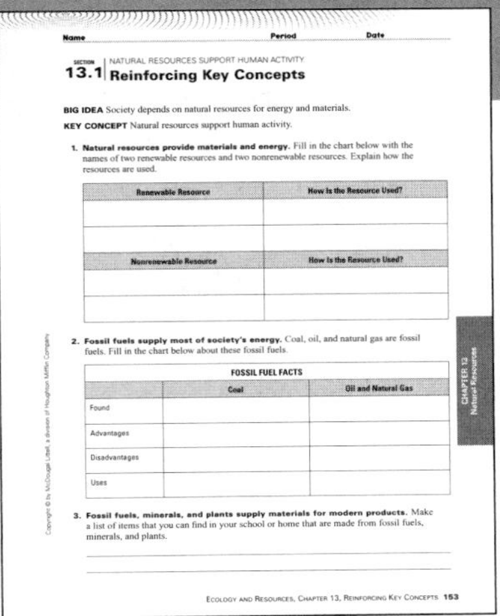
13.1 Reinforcing Key Concepts

BIG IDEA Society depends on natural resources for energy and materials.

KEY CONCEPT Natural resources support human activity.

1. Natural resources provide materials and energy. Fill in the chart below with the names of two renewable resources and two nonrenewable resources. Explain how the resources are used.

Renewable Resource	How Is the Resource Used?

Nonrenewable Resource	How Is the Resource Used?

2. Fossil fuels supply most of society's energy. Coal, oil, and natural gas are fossil fuels. Fill in the chart below about these fossil fuels.

FOSSIL FUEL FACTS	Coal	Oil and Natural Gas
Found		
Advantages		
Disadvantages		
Uses		

3. Fossil fuels, minerals, and plants supply materials for modern products. Make a list of items that you can find in your school or home that are made from fossil fuels, minerals, and plants.

Ecology and Resources, Chapter 13, Reinforcing Key Concepts 153

UNIT RESOURCE BOOK, p. 153

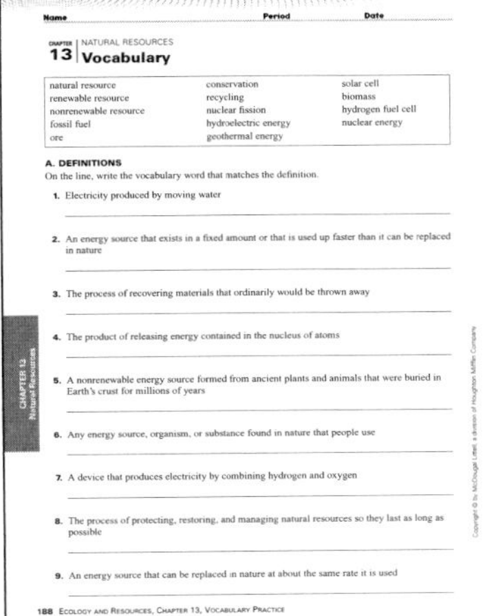
13 Vocabulary

natural resource	conservation	solar cell
renewable resource	recycling	biomass
nonrenewable resource	nuclear fission	hydrogen fuel cell
fossil fuel	hydroelectric energy	nuclear energy
ore	geothermal energy	

A. DEFINITIONS

On the line, write the vocabulary word that matches the definition.

1. Electricity produced by moving water
2. An energy source that exists in a fixed amount or that is used up faster than it can be replaced in nature
3. The process of recovering materials that ordinarily would be thrown away
4. The product of releasing energy contained in the nucleus of atoms
5. A nonrenewable energy source formed from ancient plants and animals that were buried in Earth's crust for millions of years
6. Any energy source, organism, or substance found in nature that people use
7. A device that produces electricity by combining hydrogen and oxygen
8. The process of protecting, restoring, and managing natural resources so they last as long as possible
9. An energy source that can be replaced in nature at about the same rate it is used

188 Ecology and Resources, Chapter 13, Vocabulary Practice

pp. 188–189

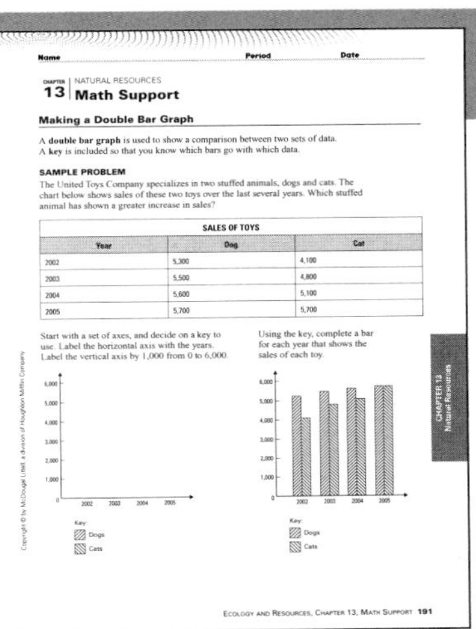
13 Math Support

Making a Double Bar Graph

A double bar graph is used to show a comparison between two sets of data. A key is included so that you know which bars go with which data.

SAMPLE PROBLEM

The United Toys Company specializes in two stuffed animals, dogs and cats. The chart below shows sales of these two toys over the last several years. Which stuffed animal has shown a greater increase in sales?

Year	Dog	Cat
2002	5,300	4,100
2003	5,500	4,800
2004	5,600	5,100
2005	5,700	5,700

Ecology and Resources, Chapter 13, Math Support 191

p. 191

INTRODUCE

the BIG idea

Have students look at the photograph of the offshore oil rig and discuss how the question in the box links to the Big Idea. For further discussion:

- What makes electric lights burn?
- What makes cars run?
- What other things depend on natural resources?

California Content Standards

6.3.a Students know energy can be carried from one place to another by heat flow or by waves, including water, light and sound waves, or by moving objects.

6.6.a Students know the utility of energy sources is determined by factors that are involved in converting these sources to useful forms and the consequences of the conversion process.

6.6.b Students know different natural energy and material resources, including air, soil, rocks, minerals, petroleum, fresh water, wildlife, and forests, and know how to classify them as renewable or nonrenewable.

6.6.c Students know the natural origin of the materials used to make common objects.

6.7.a Develop a hypothesis.

6.7.c Construct appropriate graphs from data and develop qualitative statements about the relationships between variables.

CHAPTER

Natural Resources

the BIG idea

Society depends on natural resources for energy and materials.

Key Concepts

SECTION 1
Natural resources support human activity.
Learn about the costs and benefits of using natural resources to obtain energy and to make products.

SECTION 2
Minerals and rocks are nonrenewable resources.
Learn how minerals form, how they are mined, and how they are used.

SECTION 3
Resources can be conserved and recycled.
Learn about efforts to conserve and recycle natural resources.

SECTION 4
Resources can be converted to useful forms.
Learn how nuclear power and renewable resources can provide energy to the world.

California ClassZone

CLASSZONE.COM

Chapter 13 online resources: Content Review, Simulation, Visualization, three Resource Centers, Math Tutorial, Test Practice

How do people obtain energy from Earth's resources?

INTERNET PREVIEW

CLASSZONE.COM For student use with the following pages:

Review and Practice

- Content Review, pp. 448, 482
- Math Tutorial: Bar Graphs, p. 470
- Test Practice, p. 485

Activities and Resources

- Internet Activity: Resources, p. 447
- Resource Centers: Gemstones, p. 459; Renewable Energy Resources, p. 472
- Simulation, p. 479
- Visualization: Hydrogen Fuel Cell, p. 476

Nonrenewable Resources
Code: MDL056

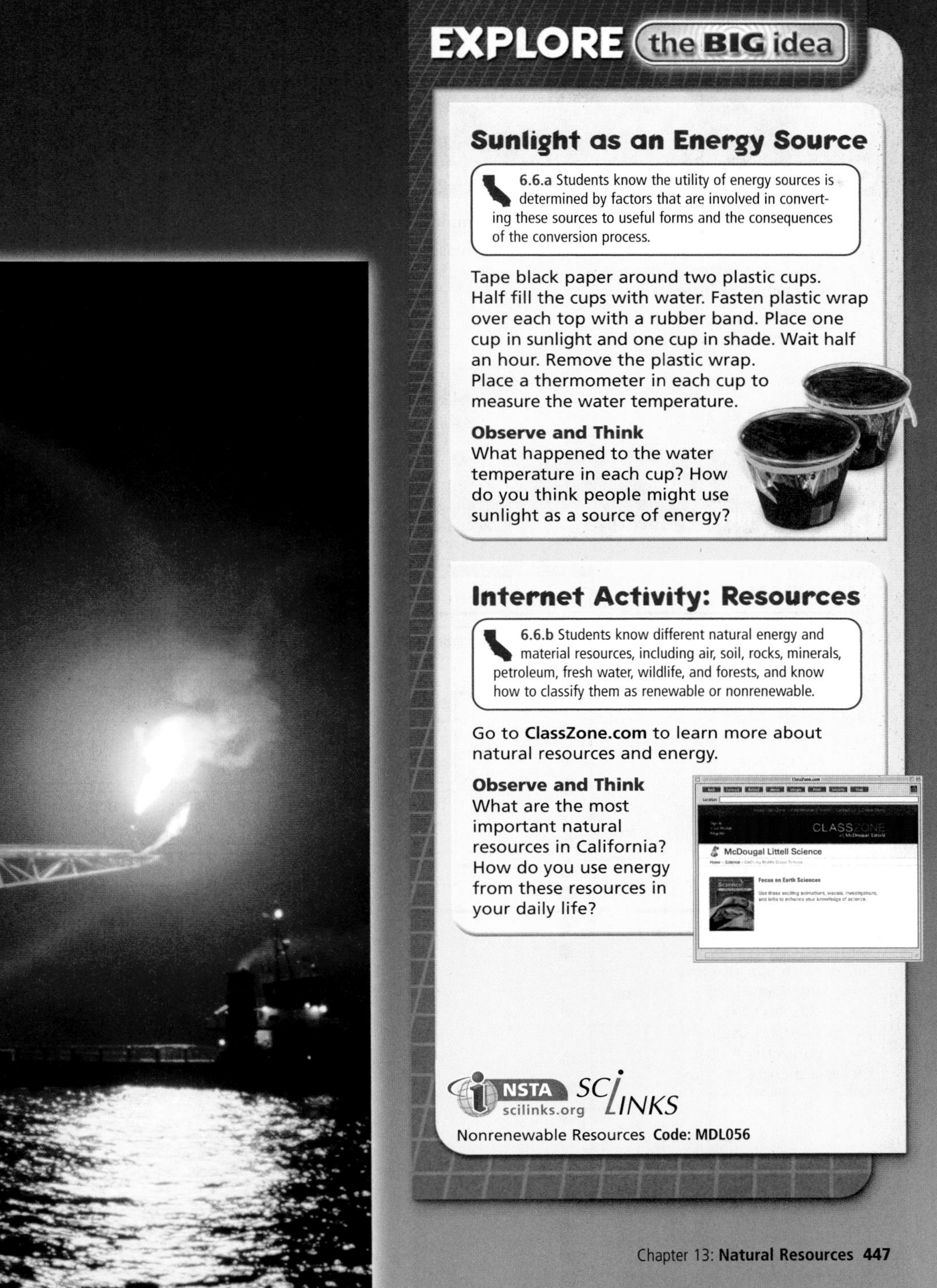

EXPLORE the BIG idea

Sunlight as an Energy Source

6.6.a Students know the utility of energy sources is determined by factors that are involved in converting these sources to useful forms and the consequences of the conversion process.

Tape black paper around two plastic cups. Half fill the cups with water. Fasten plastic wrap over each top with a rubber band. Place one cup in sunlight and one cup in shade. Wait half an hour. Remove the plastic wrap. Place a thermometer in each cup to measure the water temperature.

Observe and Think
What happened to the water temperature in each cup? How do you think people might use sunlight as a source of energy?

Internet Activity: Resources

6.6.b Students know different natural energy and material resources, including air, soil, rocks, minerals, petroleum, fresh water, wildlife, and forests, and know how to classify them as renewable or nonrenewable.

Go to **ClassZone.com** to learn more about natural resources and energy.

Observe and Think
What are the most important natural resources in California? How do you use energy from these resources in your daily life?

NSTA scilinks.org SCILINKS
Nonrenewable Resources **Code: MDL056**

TEACHING WITH TECHNOLOGY

CBL and Probeware In this chapter, students can use the temperature probe and graphing calculator in "INVESTIGATE Conservation" on p. 468.

EXPLORE the BIG idea

These inquiry-based activities are appropriate for use at home or as a supplement to classroom instruction.

Sunlight as an Energy Source

PURPOSE To introduce students to the concept of solar energy. By observing how sunlight warms a cup of water, they will recognize that sunlight can be used as a source of energy to do work.

TIPS *35 min.* At the beginning of the activity, water in both cups should be at room temperature. Make sure the thermometers have the same starting temperature.

Answer: The water exposed to sunlight became warmer than the water placed in the shade. Sunlight could be used to heat water for homes and businesses and to produce electricity.

REVISIT after p. 475.

Internet Activity: Resources

PURPOSE To have students learn about local natural resources.

TIP *20 min.*

Answer: Students should name resources found only in California.

REVISIT after p. 451.

PREPARE

CONCEPT REVIEW

Activate Prior Knowledge

- Show students several examples of natural resources, such as a piece of wood, a chunk of coal, and a sample of copper.
- Ask students to identify items in the classroom that may have been made using these resources.
- Challenge students to think of an item that is NOT made with natural resources. The goal of the discussion should be to help students recognize their dependence on natural resources.

TAKING NOTES

Supporting Main Ideas

Identifying main ideas and supporting details is a basic reading comprehension skill students will need to master if they are to perform well on standards-based tests. If students have a hard time remembering the information they put in their charts, they may be including too much information with the supporting details they identify.

Vocabulary Strategy

Tell students that they can make one larger drawing of a single renewable resource, or several small drawings of multiple renewable resources. Suggest that students make the boundary lines of the triangle as they complete each section to ensure that they have enough space for their writing and drawings.

Vocabulary and Note-Taking Resources

- Vocabulary Practice, pp. 188–189
- Decoding Support, p. 190

- Daily Vocabulary Scaffolding, p. T98
- Note-Taking Model, p. T99

- Word Triangle, B18–19
- Supporting Main Ideas, C42
- Daily Vocabulary Scaffolding, H1–8

CHAPTER 13

Getting Ready to Learn

CONCEPT REVIEW

- When fuel is burned, energy is released.
- The Earth system is made up of parts that interact.
- Most rocks are made of minerals.

VOCABULARY REVIEW

mineral p. 184

fossil, geosphere *See Glossary.*

Review concepts and vocabulary.

TAKING NOTES

SUPPORTING MAIN IDEAS

Make a chart to show each main idea and the information that supports it. Copy each blue heading. Below each heading, add supporting information, such as reasons, explanations, and examples.

VOCABULARY STRATEGY

Draw a **word triangle** diagram for each new vocabulary term. On the bottom line, write and define the term. Above that, write a sentence that uses the term correctly. At the top, draw a picture to show what the term looks like.

See the Note-Taking Handbook on pages R45–R51.

SCIENCE NOTEBOOK

Natural resources provide materials and energy.

- A natural resource is any energy source, organism, or substance found in nature that people use.
- Four parts of the Earth system provide all the materials needed to support human life.
- There are costs as well as benefits to using natural resources.

Sun

Sunlight and water are renewable resources.

renewable resource: a natural resource that can be replaced in nature at about the same rate it is used

CHECK READINESS

Administer the Diagnostic Test to determine students' readiness for new science content and their mastery of requisite math skills.

 Diagnostic Test, pp. 287–288

Technology Resources

Students needing content and math skills should visit **ClassZone.com.**

- **CONTENT REVIEW**
- **MATH TUTORIAL**

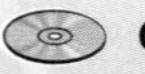 **CONTENT REVIEW CD-ROM**

KEY CONCEPT

Natural resources support human activity.

CALIFORNIA Content Standards

6.6.a Students know the utility of energy sources is determined by factors that are involved in converting these sources to useful forms and the consequences of the conversion process.

6.6.b Students know different natural energy and material resources, including air, soil, rocks, minerals, petroleum, fresh water, wildlife, and forests, and know how to classify them as renewable or nonrenewable.

BEFORE, you learned

- Heat flow transfers energy
- Energy from the Sun heats Earth's surface
- Ecosystems change over time

NOW, you will learn

- What makes a natural resource renewable or nonrenewable
- About benefits and costs of using fossil fuels
- How people use natural resources in modern life

VOCABULARY

natural resource p. 449
renewable resource p. 450
nonrenewable resource p. 450
fossil fuel p. 452

THINK ABOUT

What resources do you need the most?

Think about all the products you use at school and at home—clothing, books, video games, CDs, backpacks, and other items.

Which ones do you use the most often? What materials are these products made of? Plastic? Cloth? Metal? What would you lose if one of these materials, such as plastic, vanished from Earth overnight?

Natural resources provide materials and energy.

VOCABULARY
Make a word triangle diagram in your notebook for *natural resource.*

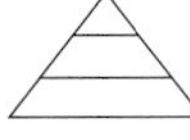

For thousands of years, people have used natural resources to make tools, build cities, heat their homes, and make their lives more comfortable. A **natural resource** is any energy source, organism, or substance found in nature that people use.

The four parts of the Earth system—atmosphere, hydrosphere, biosphere, and geosphere—provide all the materials needed to support human life. The atmosphere provides the air you breathe and the rain that helps living things grow. The hydrosphere contains all of Earth's waters in rivers, lakes, oceans, and underground. The biosphere and the geosphere are sources of food, fuel, clothing, and shelter.

RESOURCES FOR DIFFERENTIATED INSTRUCTION

Below Level

UNIT RESOURCE BOOK
Reading Study Guide A, pp. 144–145
Decoding Support, p. 190

AUDIO CDS

Advanced

UNIT RESOURCE BOOK
Challenge and Extension, p. 150

English Learners

UNIT RESOURCE BOOK
Spanish Reading Study Guide, pp. 148–149

- Audio Readings in Spanish
- Audio Readings (English)

13.1 FOCUS

Set Learning Goals

Students will

- Recognize what makes a natural resource renewable or nonrenewable.
- Determine the benefits and costs of using fossil fuels.
- Explain how people use natural resources in modern life.
- Analyze data of nonrenewable energy resources across the United States.

3-Minute Warm-Up

Display Transparency 100 or copy this exercise on the board:

Answer the following questions:

1. What is the major source of energy for the earth system? *sun*
2. Name three forms of energy. *mechanical, sound, chemical, heat, electromagnetic*
3. Describe one way energy is transferred. *through radiation, conduction, or convection, for example*

 3-Minute Warm-Up, p. T100

13.1 MOTIVATE

THINK ABOUT

PURPOSE To determine what resources students need the most

DISCUSS To help students answer the questions, have them list in a column on the board the products they use throughout a typical day. In a separate column, students should list what the products are made of.

13.1 INSTRUCT

Teach the Standards

Natural Resources 6.6.b

In this section: Make sure students can classify natural resources as renewable or nonrenewable. Help students understand the process used to convert fossil fuels into useful energy.

- **previously taught:** solar energy, pp. 48–49; energy transfers within Earth system, pp. 58–59
- **future opportunities:** human impact on environment, p. 503

Address Misconceptions

IDENTIFY Ask: Do renewable resources ever run out? If students answer no, they may hold the misconception that a "renewable" resource is unlimited.

CORRECT Emphasize that a renewable resource can be replaced in nature at about the same rate it is used. For example, windmills generate energy that is used instantly or is stored. Windless days require the use of stored energy. Sometimes, though, energy is used at a faster rate than it is replaced.

REASSESS Say to students, A community wants to use only wind for its energy production. What are some limitations they should consider? *It might take many windmills for energy production to match consumption; it might not be windy enough for wind to be the sole method of energy production.*

Technology Resources

Visit **ClassZone.com** for background on common student misconceptions.

MISCONCEPTION DATABASE

Ongoing Assessment

CHECK YOUR READING *Answer: Benefit: supplies for all our needs; costs: pollution, soil loss, and depletion of some resources*

CHECK YOUR READING *Answer: A renewable resource can be replaced at about the same rate it is used. A nonrenewable resource cannot be replaced or can be replaced only over millions of years.*

People know that there are costs as well as benefits in using natural resources. For example, burning coal produces heat but also releases smoke that pollutes the air. When forests are cut down, the soil beneath is exposed to the air. Wind and rain can strip away valuable topsoil. This makes it harder for new trees to grow. The soil can choke streams and rivers and kill fish and other animals living in the waters. As you can see, using resources from one part of Earth's system affects all the other parts.

People are also concerned about saving natural resources. Some resources, such as the water in a river or the wind used to turn a windmill, are constantly being replaced. But others, such as oil, take millions of years to form. If these resources are used faster than they are replaced, they will run out. Today, people are more aware of which resources can be renewed and which cannot.

Summarize the costs and benefits of using natural resources.

Renewable Resources

The charts on page 451 list some of the most common resources people use in modern life. As you might have guessed, sunlight, wind, water, and trees and other plants are renewable. A **renewable resource** is a natural resource that can be replaced in nature at about the same rate it is used.

For example, a lumber company might plant a new tree for each mature tree it cuts down. Over time, the forest will continue to have the same number of trees. However, if the trees are cut down faster than they can be replaced, even a renewable resource will run out.

Nonrenewable Resources

A **nonrenewable resource** is a natural resource that exists in a fixed amount or that is used up faster than it can be replaced in nature. This means the supply of any nonrenewable resource is limited. In general, all resources produced by geologic forces are nonrenewable. Examples are coal, natural gas, oil, and uranium. These resources form over millions of years.

Today, people are using coal, oil, and natural gas much faster than these resources are forming in nature. As a result, they are becoming more scarce and expensive. Many countries realize that they must conserve their nonrenewable resources. Some, like the United States, are developing alternative energy sources, such as solar and wind energy.

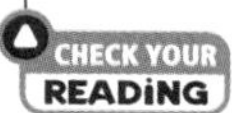
Compare and contrast renewable and nonrenewable resources.

DIFFERENTIATE INSTRUCTION

More Reading Support

A What kind of resource is sunlight? *renewable*

B What kind of resource is coal? *nonrenewable*

English Learners Make sure students understand abstract meanings of words such as *harder,* as in the sentence, "Wind and rain can strip away valuable topsoil. This makes it harder for new trees to grow" (p. 450). Tell them *harder* refers to a degree of difficulty, not to the hardness of the topsoil. Also, help them understand words associated with positive and negative effects, such as *byproducts* (p. 453), and *costs* and *dollars* (p. 454).

Natural Resources

Natural resources can be classified as renewable and nonrenewable.

Renewable Resources	
Resource	**Common Uses**
Sunlight	power for solar cells and batteries, heating of homes and businesses, and generating electricity
Wind	power for moving windmills that pump water, grind grain, and generate electricity
Water	power for generating electricity, transportation by boats and ships, drinking and washing
Trees and other plants	materials for furniture, clothing, fuel, dyes, medicines, paper, and cardboard
Animal waste	material for fuels

Nonrenewable Resources	
Resource	**Common Uses**
Coal	fuel for generating **electricity**, chemicals for medicines and consumer products
Oil	fuel for cars, airplanes, and trucks; fuel for heating and generating electricity; chemicals for plastics, synthetic fabrics, medicines, grease, and wax
Natural gas	fuel for heating, cooking, and generating electricity
Uranium	fuel for generating electricity
Minerals and rocks	materials for coins, jewelry, buildings, computer chips, lasers, household products, paint, and dyes

READING VISUALS Read the common uses of each resource. Which of these resources are used to generate electricity?

DIFFERENTIATE INSTRUCTION

Below Level Clarify for students the meaning of any difficult terms in the visual. For example, define *solar cells* and tell students they will learn more about these devices later in the chapter. Other terms to clarify are *synthetic fabrics, computer chips,* and *lasers.*

Advanced Challenge students to name other natural resources that are not listed. For example, soil is an important natural resource, as is land itself.

 Challenge and Extension, p. 150

Teach from Visuals

To help students interpret the visual about natural resources, ask:

- What natural resource is used to make paper? *trees and other plants*
- What natural resource is used to make plastics? *oil*
- What natural resources in the table may have contributed to the food you ate at breakfast this morning? *Sunlight, water, and plants were part of the growing process for the food. Water and oil may have been involved in transporting the food. Coal or natural gas may have been the fuels used to cook the food.*

History of Science

The first energy source used by early humans was probably fire. In fact, scientists have discovered evidence of fire use in one-million-year-old archeological sites. Around 10,000 years ago, humans began domesticating animals and quickly learned to harness their brute strength. Shortly thereafter, humans may have begun using wind and water power. Coal did not become a widely used energy source until the 19th century. Its rise coincided with the invention of the steam engine and with diminishing supplies of wood in some countries. Oil use surpassed coal use in the 20th century, largely because oil is easier to transport and store.

EXPLORE the BIG idea

Revisit "Internet Activity: Resources" on p. 447. Have students explain why these resources are the most important ones for their state.

Ongoing Assessment

Recognize what makes a natural resource renewable or nonrenewable.

Ask: Why are trees and other plants classified as renewable resources? *Trees and plants can be replaced after use by planting a new tree or plant.*

READING VISUALS *Answers: Resources used to produce electricity: sunlight, wind, water, coal, oil, natural gas, and uranium*

Integrate the Sciences

The law of conservation of energy states that energy cannot be created or destroyed; however, it can change form. The visual of the fossil fuel power station serves as an excellent illustration of this law. Fossil fuels contain stored chemical energy. When they are burned, the chemical energy is released and changes into thermal energy, or heat. The thermal energy is transferred to the water, producing steam. The steam reaches the turbine, which has blades or gears that turn. The steam turns the turbine, and produces mechanical energy. The turbine drives the generator, which changes the mechanical energy into electricity.

Teach from Visuals

To help students interpret the fossil fuel power station visual, ask:

- What is the function of the fossil fuel source? *to provide heat (to the boiler)*
- What does the boiler produce? *steam*
- What does the steam do? *turns the turbine*
- What does the turbine do? *drives the generator*
- Which part of the plant actually produces the electricity? *the generator*

 This visual is also available as T102 in the Transparency Book.

Ongoing Assessment

CHECK YOUR READING *Answer: Fossil fuels come from once-living plants and animals that were buried in Earth's crust for millions of years. Over time, intense heat and pressure changed the decayed remains into oil, coal, and natural gas.*

READING VISUALS *Answer: Fossil fuels are used to heat water, which produces steam that turns a turbine. The turbine drives a generator, which produces the electricity.*

Fossil fuels supply most of society's energy.

When you turn on an air conditioner, a computer, or a microwave oven, you may use energy from fossil fuels. Billions of people depend on coal, oil, and natural gas for electricity, heat, and fuel.

A **fossil fuel** is a nonrenewable energy resource formed from ancient plants and animals buried in Earth's crust for millions of years. The energy in such a fuel represents a form of stored sunlight, because ancient organisms depended on sunlight. The buried organisms form layers at the bottom of oceans and swamps. Over a long time, this material is compressed and pushed deeper into Earth's crust. High heat and pressure change it chemically into coal, oil, and natural gas.

 Explain how fossil fuels are formed from ancient organisms.

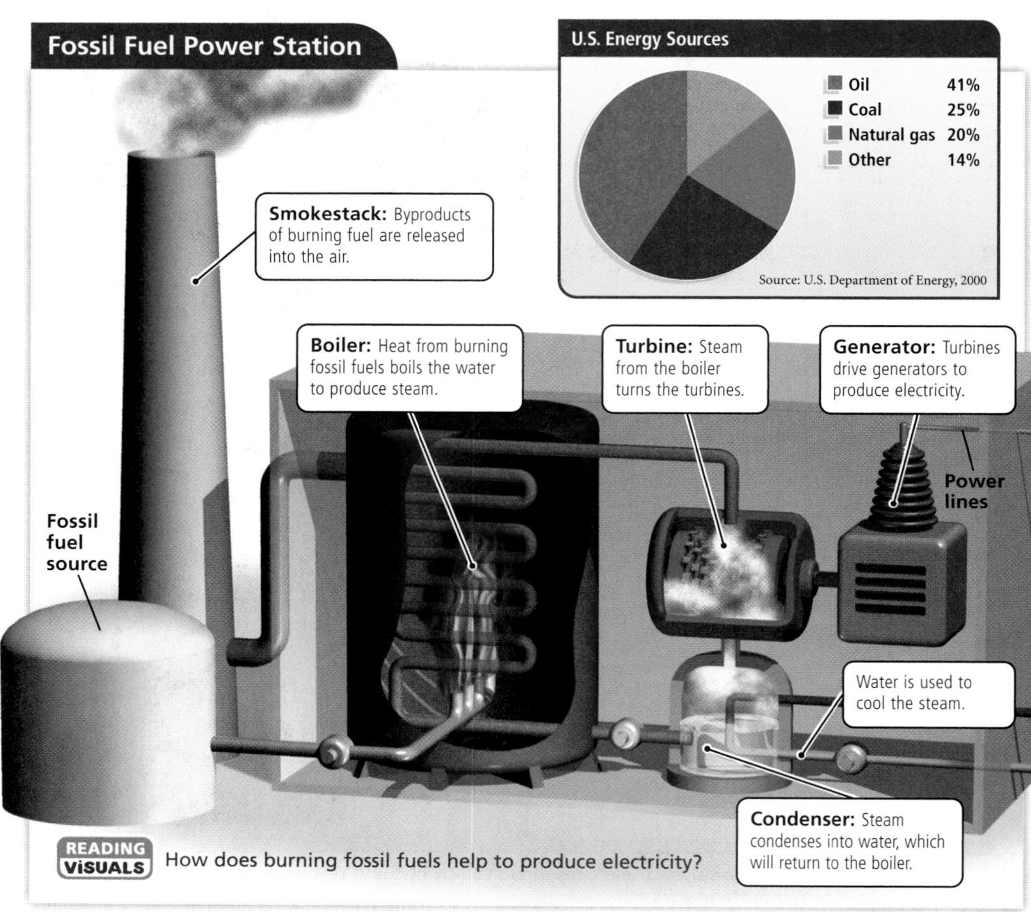
Fossil Fuel Power Station
U.S. Energy Sources
Oil 41%
Coal 25%
Natural gas 20%
Other 14%
Source: U.S. Department of Energy, 2000
Smokestack: Byproducts of burning fuel are released into the air.
Boiler: Heat from burning fossil fuels boils the water to produce steam.
Turbine: Steam from the boiler turns the turbines.
Generator: Turbines drive generators to produce electricity.
Power lines
Fossil fuel source
Water is used to cool the steam.
Condenser: Steam condenses into water, which will return to the boiler.

READING VISUALS How does burning fossil fuels help to produce electricity?

DIFFERENTIATE INSTRUCTION

 **More Reading Support**

C Name three fossil fuels. *coal, oil, and natural gas*

Alternative Assessment The U.S. Environmental Protection Agency (EPA) has projected that by the year 2050, energy in this country will come from the following sources: oil, 6%; nuclear fission, 6%; coal 7%; natural gas, 24%; and renewable resources, 57%. Have students make a circle graph using the data and compare it with the circle graph above. Discuss what lifestyle changes may have to be made to conform to the EPA projections. For example, the projections assume a substantial reduction in the use of fossil fuels and nuclear energy.

Fossil fuels burn easily and produce a lot of heat. They are used to run most of the power plants that generate electricity in the United States. As shown in the diagram on page 452, heat from a burning fuel is used to change water into steam. The steam turns a turbine. The turbine drives a generator to produce electricity, which is carried through power lines to towns and cities. Electricity is used in many parts of modern life, from running giant factories to the smallest light in your home.

READING TIP

Turbine is based on the Latin *turbo,* which means "spinning top." *Generator* is based on the Latin *generāre,* which means "to produce."

But these resources also harm the environment. Burning fossil fuels produces excess carbon dioxide, harmful acids, and other forms of pollution. Most of this pollution comes from power plants and fossil fuels burned by cars and other vehicles.

Coal

Coal is a solid fossil fuel formed underground from buried and decayed plant material. As shown below, heat and pressure determine the type of coal formed. The hardest coal makes the best energy source. It burns hotter and much cleaner than softer coals. At one time, coal was the main source of energy in the United States.

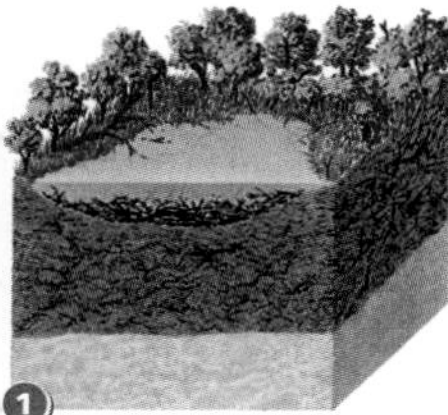

1 Swamp plants decay and are compressed to form peat.

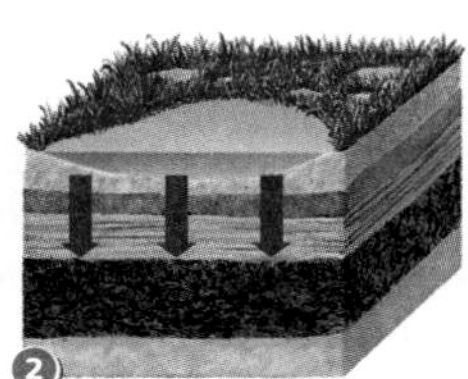

2 Sediments bury the peat. Rising pressure and heat change it into soft coal.

3 Over millions of years, increasing pressure and heat form harder coal.

4 It takes the longest time and the greatest heat and pressure to form the hardest coal.

The United States, Russia, and China are major producers of coal. People use surface mining and deep mining to obtain coal. In surface mines, overlying rock is stripped away to expose the coal. In deep mines, miners must go underground to dig out the coal. Most of the world's coal is used to fuel power plants and to run factories.

When coal is burned as a fuel, it releases byproducts that pollute air and water. Also, surface mining can destroy entire landscapes. Coal dust in mines damages miners' lungs. Yet, reducing pollution, restoring landscapes, and protecting miners cost millions of dollars. Society faces a difficult choice: keep the cost of energy low or raise the price to protect the environment and human health.

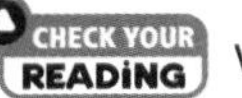

CHECK YOUR READING What is the main use of coal?

DIFFERENTIATE INSTRUCTION

More Reading Support

D Why are fossil fuels good sources of energy? *They burn easily and produce a lot of heat.*

E The type of coal that forms depends on heat and what? *pressure*

Alternative Assessment Place students in small groups, and have them role-play various participants in the following scenario: A coal company has applied for a license to mine an area on the outskirts of your town. Local officials have called a town meeting to discuss the proposal. Discuss the advantages and disadvantages of the proposed coal mine. (Potential roles include coal company officials, government officials, environmentalists, coal miners, and landowners.)

Real World Example

Pollutants in the air, primarily those from industries and utilities, can mix with moisture and other particles to create sulfuric acid and nitric acid. These acids may eventually fall to Earth in precipitation known as acid rain. Acid rain causes billions of dollars of damage annually to buildings in the United States alone. Acid rain has also damaged well-known historical structures around the world, including the Parthenon in Greece and the Colosseum in Italy. Eastern Europe, in particular, is plagued by air pollution problems. In one German town, acid rain has eroded exterior doorknobs and nameplates.

Teach from Visuals

To help students interpret the visual about coal formation, ask:

Why do the rock layers in the fourth visual appear wavy? Relate your answer to the formation of the hardest type of coal. *Forces inside Earth acted on the rock layers. The intense pressure caused the rock layers to bend. This same pressure helped form the hardest type of coal.*

Ongoing Assessment

Determine the benefits and costs of using fossil fuels.

Give three reasons why you think your school should or should not rely on fossil fuels for heating and cooling. *should: fossil fuels burn easily, give off a lot of heat, and are cost efficient; should not: fossil fuels produce pollution, can impair human health, and obtaining them can result in damaged landscapes.*

CHECK YOUR READING *Answer: Coal is used in industry to make heat for generating electricity and to provide power to manufacture steel and cement.*

Teach Difficult Concepts

Students may have a difficult time understanding how oil and natural gas collect underground. Tell them that layers of nonporous rock act as "lids" that keep oil and natural gas sealed within porous rock layers. To help students understand, you might try the following demonstration.

Teacher Demo

Obtain a large sponge and a plastic sheet or lid. Wet the sponge. Place a sheet of paper over the sponge. Tell students that the paper represents a porous rock layer, and that the water in the sponge represents oil trapped in a rock layer. Have students observe how the "oil" seeps upward to the paper. Then place the plastic on top of the sponge. Ask: What does the plastic represent? *a hard, nonporous rock layer*

Ongoing Assessment

CHECK YOUR READING *Answer: Wells are drilled through rock layers, and oil is brought to the surface.*

CHECK YOUR READING *Answer: Benefits: These fuels can be easily transported and used. Oil is used to produce many different products. Costs: Using fuels made from oil produces byproducts that pollute air and water. Oil spills endanger wildlife and ecosystems.*

Oil and Natural Gas

READING TIP

Non- is a Latin prefix meaning "not." Porous rock is full of tiny cracks or holes. Therefore, *nonporous* rock is rock that does not have tiny cracks or holes.

F

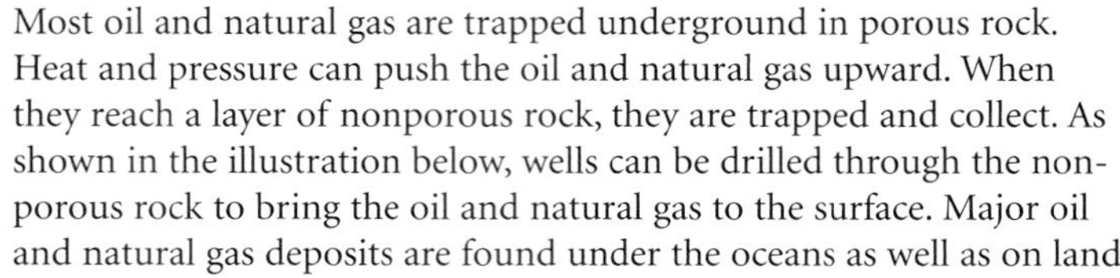

Most oil and natural gas are trapped underground in porous rock. Heat and pressure can push the oil and natural gas upward. When they reach a layer of nonporous rock, they are trapped and collect. As shown in the illustration below, wells can be drilled through the nonporous rock to bring the oil and natural gas to the surface. Major oil and natural gas deposits are found under the oceans as well as on land.

CHECK YOUR READING How is oil removed from layers of rock?

CALIFORNIA Focus

The two main sources of energy in California's energy system are petroleum and natural gas. Second only to Texas, California uses the most natural gas and petroleum per person of the 50 states.

California is also a leader in developing renewable resources, such as solar energy and wind power. It has plans to produce a large amount of its electricity from renewable energy sources.

Recovered oil is transported by ships, trucks, and pipelines from the wells to refineries. Refineries use heat to break down the oil into its different parts. Each part is used to make different products. These include gasoline, jet fuel, cleaning supplies, and plastics. Oil and natural gas burn at high temperatures, releasing energy. They are easily transported, which makes them ideal fuels to heat homes and to power vehicles.

There are costs in using oil. When ships that transport oil are damaged, they can spill millions of gallons into the environment. These spills pollute coastlines and waterways, killing many plants and animals. Cleaning up these spills costs governments millions of dollars each year. Even after the cleanup, some of the oil will remain in the environment for years.

G

Air pollution is another problem. Waste products from the burning of gasoline, jet fuels, and diesel fuels react with sunlight to produce smog—a foglike layer of air pollution. Some countries have passed clean air laws to reduce this pollution. Yet smog continues to be a problem in most large cities.

CHECK YOUR READING What are the benefits and costs of using oil?

Oil and Natural Gas Wells

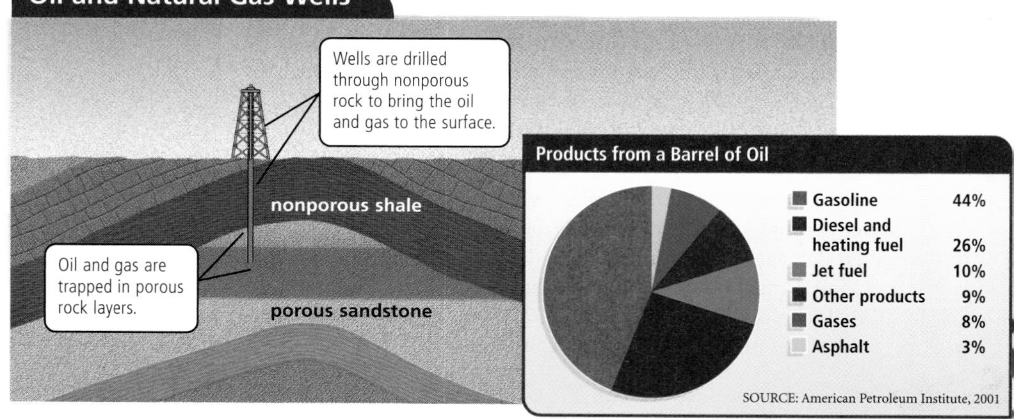

DIFFERENTIATE INSTRUCTION

More Reading Support

F Oil and natural gas are usually found where? *in underground porous rock*

G What is smog? *a foglike layer of air pollution*

Advanced Have students make a list of manufactured items in the classroom made from wood, glass, minerals, plants (such as cotton clothing), plastics, and other synthetic materials. Ask them to calculate the percentage of the total items that each category of manufactured items represents and make a circle graph of their data.

INVESTIGATE Fossil Fuels Distribution

Which fossil fuels are found in California?

SKILL FOCUS
Analyzing data (6.6.b)

MATERIALS
- Map of Fossil Fuels Distribution

TIME
15 minutes

PROCEDURE

1. Study the map of U.S. nonrenewable energy resources. Identify the symbols that represent deposits of coal, uranium, natural gas, and oil.
2. Find the state of California on the map. Identify the deposits of nonrenewable resources found in the state of California.
3. Compare the nonrenewable energy resource deposits found in other regions of the United States with those found in California.

WHAT DO YOU THINK?

- What types of nonrenewable energy sources shown on the map are found in California?
- How do the types of nonrenewable energy resources in California compare with the types of resources found in the Appalachian region of the United States?

CHALLENGE Why do you think the state of California is trying to use more renewable energy resources even though the state is rich in natural gas and oil deposits?

Fossil fuels, minerals, and plants supply materials for modern products.

Many of the products you use come from fossil fuels. For example, oil is broken down into different chemicals used to make plastics. Plastic materials can be easily shaped, colored, and formed. They are used in electronic and computer equipment, in packaging, in cars and airplanes, and in such personal items as your shoes, toothbrush, and comb.

Minerals are found in cars, airplanes, tools, wires, computer chips, and probably your chair. Minerals such as calcite and gypsum are used to make building materials and cement. In the United States, it takes 9720 kilograms (20,000 lbs) of minerals every year to make the products used by just one person.

Plants are used to make another large group of products. For thousands of years, people have used wood to build homes and to make furniture, household utensils, and different types of paper. Plants are also rich sources of dyes, fibers, and medicines. The plant indigo, for example, has been used to dye fabrics for about 4000 years.

These products benefit people's lives in many important ways, but they also have drawbacks. Fossil fuels must be burned to generate power for the factories and businesses that produce these products.

INVESTIGATE Fossil Fuels Distribution

PURPOSE To analyze data of nonrenewable sources of energy in California and around the United States

TIPS *15 min.*

- Use a projection screen to enable visually impaired students to read the map.
- Make sure students understand the resource that each symbol stands for before they study the map.

WHAT DO YOU THINK? *oil and gas; the Appalachian region has extensive coal deposits as well as oil and gas*

CHALLENGE *Sample answer: By using renewable energy resources, Californians can reduce pollution from fossil fuels and conserve natural resources.*

- Map of Fossil Fuels Distribution, p. 151
- Datasheet, Fossil Fuels Distribution, p. 152

Technology Resources

Customize this student lab as needed or look for an alternative. Print rubrics to assess student lab reports.

 **Lab Generator CD-ROM**

Ongoing Assessment

Explain how people use natural resources in modern life.

Ask: What products are made from plants? *homes, furniture, household utensils, paper, dyes, fabrics, and medicines*

DIFFERENTIATE INSTRUCTION

More Reading Support

H Many of the products you use come from what? *fossil fuels*

I What other natural resources are used to make products? *minerals and plants*

Reinforce  the BIG idea

Have students relate the section to the Big Idea.

 Reinforcing Key Concepts, p. 153

13.1 ASSESS & RETEACH

Assess

 Section 13.1 Quiz, p. 289

Reteach

Hold up a common item in the classroom, such as a book. Have students list all the natural resources that went into making the item. Stress that students should not focus on the manufacturing process alone. Rather, they should consider what the original materials were, how they were obtained, how they were transported to the factory, how they were made into the item, and how the item itself ended up at the school.

Technology Resources

Have students visit **ClassZone.com** for reteaching of Key Concepts.

 CONTENT REVIEW

CONTENT REVIEW CD-ROM

Consumer Products

Thousands of everyday products are made from natural resources.

Fossil Fuels

Fossil fuels are used to make thousands of products, from aspirin to zippers. For example, oil-based plastics were used to make this motocross rider's safety helmet, suit, gloves, and boots. Gasoline powers the motorbike.

Minerals and Rocks

The U.S. Treasury uses zinc, copper, and nickel to mint billions of coins each year. Gold and silver are used in special coins.

Trees and Other Plants

Each year, the United States produces billions of square meters of corrugated cardboard used to make boxes of all sizes.

Factory waste can pollute air, water, and soil. Even making computer chips can be a problem. A large amount of water is needed to clean the chips during manufacture, which can add to water pollution problems.

To maintain modern life and to protect the planet, people must use natural resources wisely. In the next section, you will read about ways for every person to conserve resources and reduce pollution.

13.1 Review

KEY CONCEPTS

1. Define *renewable resource* and *nonrenewable resource*. Give four examples of each type of resource. (6.6.b)
2. List three advantages and three disadvantages of using fossil fuels. (6.6.a)
3. In what ways are natural resources used to make people's lives more comfortable? (6.6.c)

CRITICAL THINKING

4. **Infer** Why do you think people are willing to accept the costs as well as the benefits of using fossil fuels?
5. **Predict** If supplies of coal, oil, and natural gas ran out tomorrow, what are some of the ways your life would change?

CHALLENGE

6. **Apply** Suppose you are lost in the woods, miles from any city or town. You have some dried food and matches but no other supplies. What natural resources might you use to survive until you are found?

ANSWERS

1. renewable: can be replaced as fast as it's used—sunlight, wind, water, trees; nonrenewable: used up faster than it can be replaced—coal, natural gas, oil, uranium

2. advantages: easy to transport, easy to use, easily burned; disadvantages: pollution, environmental damage, nonrenewable

3. provide housing, food, transportation, medicines, energy, and consumer products

4. Fossil fuels provide most of society's energy products.

5. Less electricity would be available; less fuel for transportation; no plastic products; no heat for many homes, schools, and businesses

6. wood for fuel, plant materials for shelter and food, water for drinking, and food

California Close-Up

WATER CONSERVATION

Feeling Thirsty?

6.6.b Students know different natural energy and material resources, including air, soil, rocks, minerals, petroleum, fresh water, wildlife, and forests, and know how to classify them as renewable or nonrenewable.

Imagine drinking a glass of water. Now imagine millions of people drinking with you. Every day in California more than 35 million people drink water. They also wash, swim, boil pasta, and water their lawns.

Northern California gets plenty of rain and snow. But most Californians live in Southern California, where the climate is dry and hot. The Great Central Valley also gets very little rain. There, huge farms use more than 40 percent of the state's fresh water. All of these numbers add up to one thing: a water problem in California.

Lake Hollywood is a reservoir that was built in 1924 to provide water for the Los Angeles area.

Every winter a lot of snow falls in the Sierra Nevada. When the snow melts, water rushes down the mountainsides. This fresh water is collected in reservoirs. Much of the water used in California is from reservoirs.

California's dry regions get their water from aqueducts. An aqueduct is a human-made pipe or canal that carries water a long way. Aqueducts carry water from the mountains to farms. They bring huge amounts of water from the north to the south. They also bring in more water from Colorado, Oregon, and Mexico.

Fresh water is a renewable resource as long as there is rain. But because there are so many people in California, fresh water can run out. Therefore, Californians are working to conserve water. Many cities water trees with recycled water. They help people pay for showerheads and toilets that use less water. Other methods for saving water include turning off the tap when brushing teeth and planting gardens that need less water.

The California Aqueduct starts at the Sacramento River Delta, east of San Francisco, and continues south a distance of 440 kilometers (273 mi).

Owens Lake was once as large as 280 square kilometers. The city of Los Angeles started using the lake's water in 1913. By 1926 Owens Lake was dry.

WRITING ABOUT SCIENCE

Write a problem-and-solution essay. Explain some of the water problems in California. Then describe some solutions. Include tips for saving water in daily activities.

CALIFORNIA CLOSE-UP

Science in action in California

Set Learning Goal

To understand the problem of fresh-water shortage in California and solutions to the problem

Present the Science

The California State Water Project began in 1960 and has since been constructing an aqueduct and reservoir system designed to deliver over 4 million acre-feet of water per year to residents throughout much of California. The water supply is fed from snowfall, rainfall, and water from the Sacramento-San Joaquin Delta. The system uses electric, coal, and hydroelectric power and gravity to channel water from northern to southern California through a series of aboveground and belowground aqueducts, reservoirs, and pumping stations.

Discussion Questions

Have students share their knowledge of and experience with water conservation.

- Ask: What steps do you take at home or at school to conserve water? *Possible answers: I turn off the faucet when brushing my teeth; I limit time in the shower or take baths rather than showers.*
- Ask: Aqueducts use electrical pumps to deliver water from northern to southern California. Gravity is also used. How would the aqueducts have to be built to take advantage of gravity? *The aqueduct pipes must be built higher in one place and lower in another so gravity can move water from the northern to the southern part of the state.*

Close

Summarize the process that occurs from the time that water falls as precipitation to the point at which it is taken from reservoirs and made available to consumers. *Sample answer: Snow or rain falls in high elevations such as mountains. When the snow melts, water travels down the mountains as streams and empties into reservoirs. Water from these reservoirs is made available to consumers.*

WRITING ABOUT SCIENCE

Writing Applications 6.1.f This assignment will give students practice in writing problem-and-solution essays. Suggest that pairs of students read each other's solutions and evaluate them in terms of effectiveness and practicality.

The best descriptions will

- completely describe the main problems
- offer realistic solutions

13.2 FOCUS

Set Learning Goals

Students will

- Identify ways minerals are used in industry and art.
- Explain how minerals form.
- Explain how minerals are mined.
- Draw conclusions, from an experiment, about the benefits and costs of mining.

3-Minute Warm-Up

Display Transparency 100 or copy this exercise on the board:

Decide if these statements are true. If not, correct them.

1. Renewable resources are replaced over the course of millions of years. *Renewable resources are replaced at about the same rate they are used.*
2. Nonrenewable resources include sunlight, water, and wind. *Nonrenewable resources include coal, oil, natural gas, and uranium.*
3. Most of the electricity in the United States comes from fossil fuels. *true*

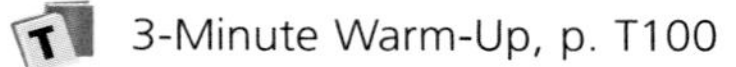

3-Minute Warm-Up, p. T100

13.2 MOTIVATE

EXPLORE Minerals at Your Fingertips

PURPOSE To introduce the concept that minerals have many everyday uses

TIP *10 min.* To expand, you might discuss other items containing minerals.

WHAT DO YOU THINK? *The different proportions allow manufacturers to vary the hardness of the writing core. A No. 4 pencil is more useful than a No. 2 pencil when a goal is to reduce smearing or smudging.*

Ongoing Assessment

Sample answer: quartz in glass, fluorite in toothpaste, mica in paint

KEY CONCEPT

13.2 Minerals and rocks are nonrenewable resources.

CALIFORNIA Content Standards

6.6.a Students know the utility of energy sources is determined by factors that are involved in converting these sources to useful forms and the consequences of the conversion process.

6.6.b Students know different natural energy and material resources, including air, soil, rocks, minerals, petroleum, fresh water, wildlife, and forests, and know how to classify them as renewable or nonrenewable.

6.6.c Students know the natural origin of the materials used to make common objects.

BEFORE, you learned

- Minerals are classified according to their compositions and crystal structures
- A mineral can be identified by its properties
- Most rocks are made of minerals

NOW, you will learn

- How minerals are used in industry and art
- How minerals form
- How minerals are mined

VOCABULARY

ore p. 462

EXPLORE Minerals at Your Fingertips (6.6.c)

What is an everyday use of minerals?

PROCEDURE

1. Observe the core of a wooden pencil. Even though it is called lead, it is made of a mixture of minerals—clay and graphite. A No. 4 pencil has more clay in its lead.
2. Use each pencil to draw something. Notice how each marks the page.

WHAT DO YOU THINK?

- Why do pencils have different proportions of clay and graphite?
- When would a No. 4 pencil be more useful than a No. 2 pencil?

MATERIALS

- No. 2 wooden pencil
- No. 4 wooden pencil
- paper

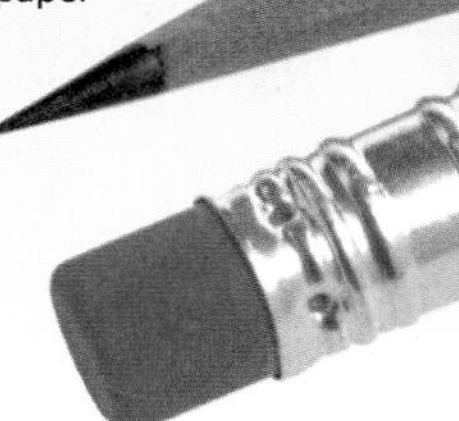

Minerals have many uses in industry.

Minerals are necessary to our modern way of life. Mineral deposits are sources of

- metals for cars and airplanes
- quartz and feldspar for glass
- fluorite and calcite for toothpaste
- silver compounds for photographic film
- mica and talc for paint

These examples illustrate just a few of the many ways we depend on minerals.

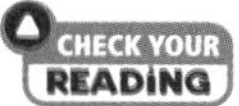

Give three examples of the use of minerals in familiar products.

RESOURCES FOR DIFFERENTIATED INSTRUCTION

Below Level

UNIT RESOURCE BOOK

- Reading Study Guide A, pp. 156–157
- Decoding Support, p. 190

AUDIO CDS

Advanced

UNIT RESOURCE BOOK

Challenge and Extension, p. 162

English Learners

UNIT RESOURCE BOOK

Spanish Reading Study Guide, pp. 160–161

AUDIO CDS

- Audio Readings in Spanish
- Audio Readings (English)

Minerals have many uses in the arts.

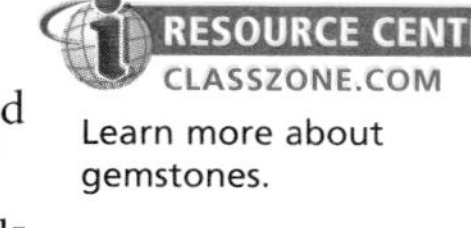

Learn more about gemstones.

No matter what month you were born in, there is a mineral associated with it—your birthstone. The tradition of birthstones is hundreds of years old. It is one example of the value that people place on the beautiful minerals known as gemstones. In fact, the ancient Egyptians used gems in necklaces and other jewelry at least 4000 years ago.

When gemstones are found, they are usually rough and irregularly shaped. Before a gemstone is used in jewelry, a gem cutter grinds it into the desired shape and polishes it. This process increases the gemstone's beauty and sparkle. The material used to shape and polish a gemstone must be at least as hard as the gemstone itself. Metals, such as gold and silver, also are used in jewelry making and other decorative arts. Both gold and silver are usually combined with copper to increase their hardness.

CHECK YOUR READING How are minerals prepared for use in jewelry? What other questions do you have about how minerals are used?

Uses of Minerals

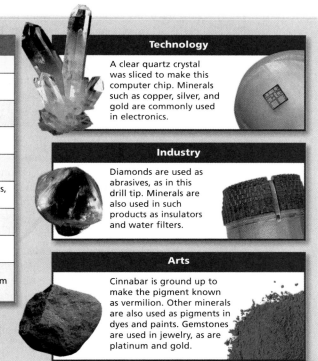

Common Uses of Minerals

Mineral	Products
Quartz (source of silicon)	optics, glass, abrasives, gems
Hematite (source of iron)	machines, nails, cooking utensils
Bauxite (source of aluminum)	soda cans, shopping carts
Dolomite (source of magnesium)	insulators, medicines
Chromite (source of chromium)	automobile parts, stainless steel
Galena (source of lead)	batteries, fiber optics, weights
Kaolinite (found in clay)	ceramics, paper, cosmetics
Beryl (source of beryllium)	computer parts, gems (green form is emerald)

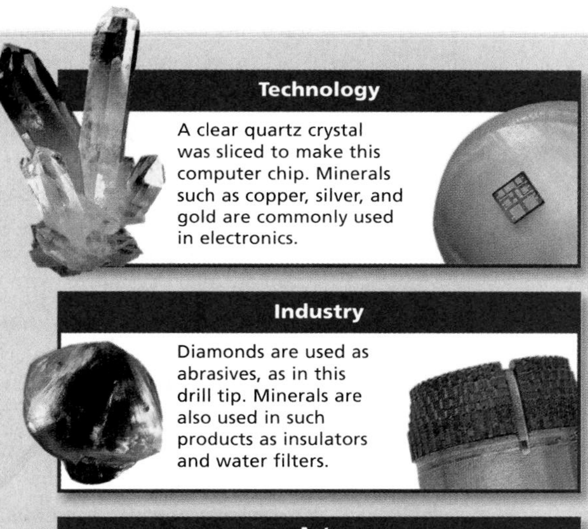

Technology

A clear quartz crystal was sliced to make this computer chip. Minerals such as copper, silver, and gold are commonly used in electronics.

Industry

Diamonds are used as abrasives, as in this drill tip. Minerals are also used in such products as insulators and water filters.

Arts

Cinnabar is ground up to make the pigment known as vermilion. Other minerals are also used as pigments in dyes and paints. Gemstones are used in jewelry, as are platinum and gold.

DIFFERENTIATE INSTRUCTION

More Reading Support

A What are gemstones? *beautiful minerals used in jewelry*

B What are gemstones like when they are found? *rough and irregularly shaped*

English Learners English learners may be unfamiliar with the tradition of birthstones mentioned on this page. Tell them a birthstone is a gem that symbolizes the month of birth. Throughout history and in different cultures, many different sets of birthstones have been used.

13.2 INSTRUCT

Teach the Standards

Minerals and Rocks 6.6.b

In this section: Help students understand that most minerals are formed by pressure and temperature changes in water, molten rock, and Earth. Point out that minerals are used to make numerous common products, from airplanes to medicine.

previously taught: natural origin of minerals, pp. 183–188; rocks, pp. 190–197

Teach from Visuals

Explain that some minerals are combined with other minerals to make products, while other minerals are refined to extract useful elements from them.

To help students interpret the chart of mineral uses, ask:

- What mineral does the aluminum for soda cans come from? *bauxite*
- Where does the lead used in batteries and weights come from? *galena*
- What is a mineral used to make abrasives? *quartz*

Real World Example

Diamonds are used both in jewelry making and in industry. Diamonds that are not gem quality are used in industry because of their hardness. Manufacturers of automobiles, airplanes, and other machinery use diamonds to cut, grind, bore, and shape hard metal. The demand for industrial diamonds is so great that synthetic diamonds are often used.

Ongoing Assessment

Identify ways minerals are used in industry and art.

Ask: How are minerals used in industry and art? *Students might list any of the examples given in the visual on this page.*

CHECK YOUR READING *Answer: Gemstones are shaped and polished for use in jewelry. Gold and silver are usually combined with copper to make them harder. Students' questions about how minerals are used will vary.*

Address Misconceptions

IDENTIFY Hold up a sample of a polished mineral, an unaltered mineral, and a brick. Ask: Which of these is a material that formed by natural processes? Students who do not select the polished mineral may hold the misconception that after people cut or polish a mineral, it is no longer a natural material. Students who select the brick may think that it is natural because it contains some minerals.

CORRECT Tell students that people make bricks by shaping a mixture of minerals and other substances into rectangular blocks that are then baked. Unlike minerals, bricks do not form in nature.

REASSESS Ask: Why is the polished mineral considered to be a natural material and the brick is not? *The mineral, despite being polished, formed in nature, but the brick was manufactured by people.*

Technology Resources

Visit **ClassZone.com** for background on common student misconceptions.

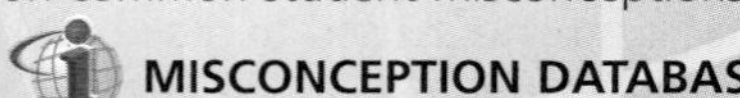

Teach Difficult Concepts

To help students grasp how a material can be formed or changed by changes in temperature, mention some examples that students are familiar with, such as these:

- Flour and other ingredients change into bread when they are baked in an oven.
- Water vapor in the air condenses and falls as rain when the temperature drops.

Ask students to think of other examples.

Ongoing Assessment

CHECK YOUR READING *Answer: These two processes of mineral formation are similar because both involve atoms that join together to form mineral crystals.*

Minerals form in several ways.

REMINDER
An element is a substance that contains only one type of atom. For instance, oxygen is an element. Pure oxygen contains only oxygen atoms.

C

Minerals form within Earth or on Earth's surface as a result of natural processes. Minerals develop when atoms of one or more elements join together and crystals begin to grow. Recall that each type of mineral has its own chemical makeup. Therefore, what types of minerals form in an area depends in part on which elements are present there. Temperature and pressure also affect which minerals form.

SUPPORTING MAIN IDEAS
Enter each blue heading in a chart and record supporting information.

Water evaporates. Water usually contains many dissolved substances. Minerals can form when such water evaporates. When salt water evaporates, the atoms that make up halite join to form crystals. Halite is used as table salt. Other minerals form from evaporation too, depending on the substances dissolved in the water. The mineral gypsum often forms as water evaporates.

Hot water cools. As hot water within Earth's crust moves through rocks, it can dissolve minerals. When the water cools, the dissolved minerals separate from the water and become solid again. In some cases, minerals are moved from one place to another. Gold can dissolve in hot water that moves through the crust. As the water cools and the gold becomes solid again, it can fill cracks in rocks. In other cases, the minerals that form are different from the ones that dissolved. Lead from the mineral galena can later become part of the mineral wulfenite as atoms join together into new minerals.

D

Molten rock cools. Many minerals grow from magma. Magma—molten rock inside Earth—contains all the types of atoms that are found in minerals. As magma cools, the atoms join together to form different minerals. Minerals also form as lava cools. Lava is molten rock that has reached Earth's surface. Quartz is one of the many minerals that crystallize from magma and lava.

Heat and pressure cause changes. Heat and pressure within Earth cause new minerals to form as bonds between atoms break and join again. The mineral garnet can grow and replace the minerals chlorite and quartz as their atoms combine in new ways. The element carbon is present in some rocks. At high temperatures and at high pressure, carbon forms the mineral graphite, which is used in pencils.

Organisms produce minerals. A few minerals are produced by living things. For example, ocean animals such as oysters and clams produce calcite and other carbonate minerals to form their shells. Even you produce minerals. Your body produces one of the main minerals in your bones and teeth—apatite.

CHECK YOUR READING How is the formation of minerals as molten rock cools similar to the formation of minerals as water evaporates?

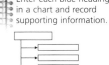

DIFFERENTIATE INSTRUCTION

More Reading Support

C Where do minerals form? *within Earth or on Earth's surface*

D What substance contains all the types of atoms that are found in minerals? *magma*

Mineral Formation

Minerals form at Earth's surface and within Earth.

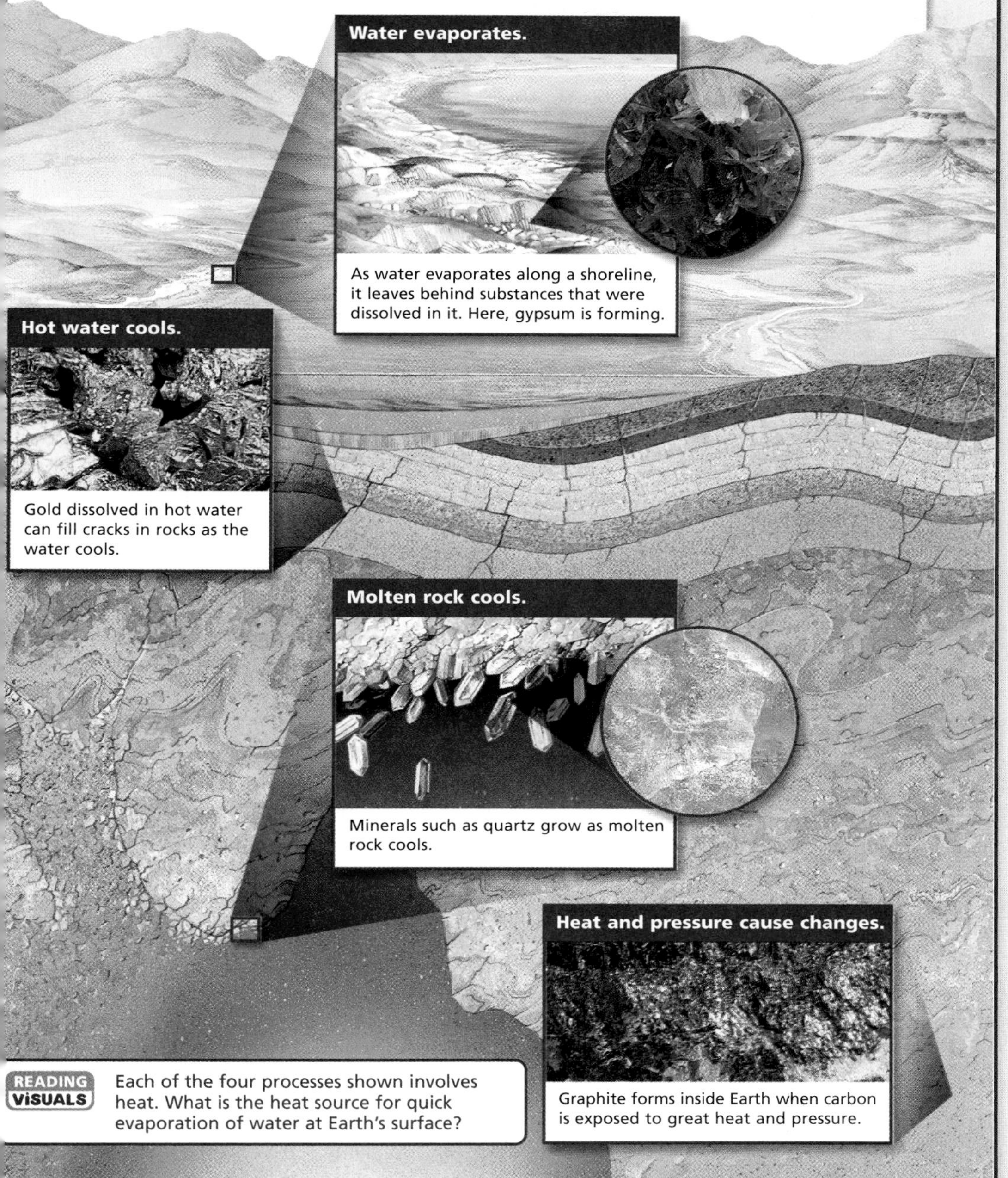

Water evaporates.

As water evaporates along a shoreline, it leaves behind substances that were dissolved in it. Here, gypsum is forming.

Hot water cools.

Gold dissolved in hot water can fill cracks in rocks as the water cools.

Molten rock cools.

Minerals such as quartz grow as molten rock cools.

Heat and pressure cause changes.

Graphite forms inside Earth when carbon is exposed to great heat and pressure.

READING VISUALS Each of the four processes shown involves heat. What is the heat source for quick evaporation of water at Earth's surface?

DIFFERENTIATE INSTRUCTION

Below Level Have students copy the headings in this visual and draw their own pictures of each process. Advise students to keep in mind the main idea—that minerals form through natural processes. You can also ask students to create a two-column chart. In one column, labeled "Mineral Formation," have them write the different types of mineral formation listed on p. 460. Students should label the other column "Minerals" and list examples that go along with each type of formation.

Teach from Visuals

To help students interpret the illustration of mineral formation, ask:

- In this visual, how do the locations of the examples of mineral formation change from the top of the picture to the bottom? *They go from the surface of Earth to deeper and deeper within Earth.*
- Where does the evaporation of water to form gypsum take place? *on Earth's surface, along a shoreline*
- Where and how can gold crystallize? *underground, in cracks in rocks, as hot water cools*
- What might be a source of heat for underground water? *magma*
- Where does magma cool and form minerals first? *around the edges of the body of magma*
- How does graphite form? *by the exposure of carbon to high heat within Earth*

The visual "Mineral Formation" is available as T102 in the Transparency Book.

Ongoing Assessment

Explain how minerals form.

Ask: In general, what causes minerals to form? *changes in the temperature or state of a liquid, or high heat or pressure*

Answer: the Sun

Teach from Visuals

To help students interpret the map of minerals and ores around the world, ask:

- Which mineral resources might the United States need to import? *aluminum, diamond, gold*
- From what continents could the United States import aluminum? *South America, Africa, Asia, Australia*
- What symbol is used to identify copper? *a circle*

Social Studies Connection

The sorting action of currents often results in the settling of heavy minerals at certain locations in rivers. Mineral deposits that develop in this way are called *placers*. The California gold rush of 1848 occurred as a result of the discovery of such placers. By following the deposits upstream, people located the source rocks of the deposits in the Sierra Nevada.

Ongoing Assessment

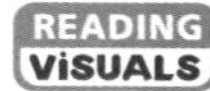

Answer: Copper is most common.

Minerals and Ores Around the World

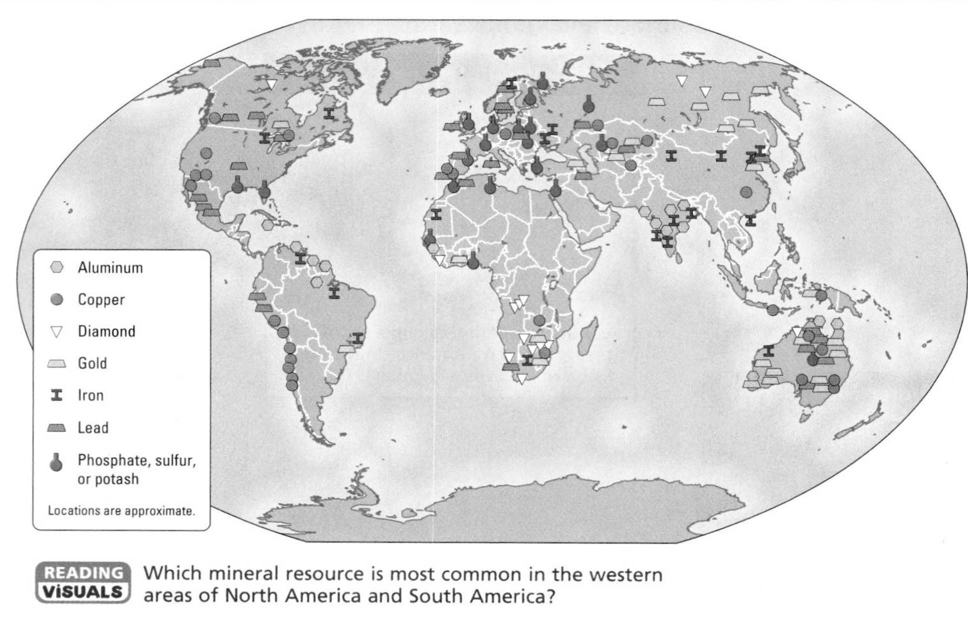

READING VISUALS Which mineral resource is most common in the western areas of North America and South America?

Many minerals are mined.

Before minerals can be used to make products, they must be removed from the ground. Some minerals are found near Earth's surface, while others lie deep underground. Some minerals are found at a wide range of depths, from the surface to deep within Earth.

READING TIP To make a profit, mine owners must be able to sell ores for more than it cost them to dig the ores out.

Most minerals are combined with other minerals in rocks. For any mineral to be worth mining, there must be a fairly large amount of the mineral present in a rock. Rocks that contain enough of a mineral to be mined for a profit are called **ores.**

Surface Mining

Minerals at or near Earth's surface are recovered by surface mining. Some minerals, such as gold, are very dense. These minerals can build up in riverbeds as less dense minerals are carried away by the water. In a method called panning, a miner uses a pan to wash away unwanted minerals that are less dense. The gold and other dense minerals stay in the bottom of the pan and can then be further separated. In bigger riverbed mining operations, miners use machines to dig out and separate the valuable minerals.

? F

DIFFERENTIATE INSTRUCTION

E What is an ore? *a rock that contains enough of a mineral to be mined for a profit*

F What is panning? *using a pan to sort out heavier minerals*

Advanced Students will need to look closely to match the minerals on the map key to the minerals' sources on the chart. Have students consult reference sources to find the uses for any minerals or ores on the map key that don't appear in the chart.

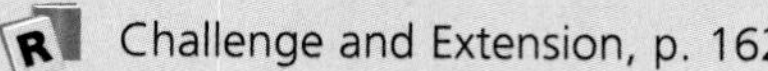

Another method of surface mining is strip mining. Miners strip away plants, soil, and unwanted rocks from Earth's surface. Then they use machines to dig out an ore.

Like strip mining, open-pit mining involves removing the surface layer of soil. Miners then use explosives to break up the underlying rock and recover the ore. As they dig a deep hole, or pit, to mine the ore, they build roads up the sides of the pit. Trucks carry the ore to the surface. Ores of copper and of iron are obtained by open-pit mining.

This open-pit copper mine in Utah is about 4 km wide and 0.8 km deep. For every kilogram of ore removed from the mine, about 5 g of copper is obtained.

CHECK YOUR READING How are strip mining and open-pit mining similar? How are they different?

INVESTIGATE Mining

What are the benefits and costs of mining ores?

PROCEDURE

1. Put the birdseed into a pan. Add the beads to the birdseed and mix well.
2. Search through the seeds and separate out the beads and sunflower seeds, placing each kind in a different pile. Take no more than 3 minutes.
3. Assign a value to each of the beads and seeds: red bead, $5; green bead, $4; blue bead, $3; sunflower seed, $2. Count up the value of your beads and seeds. For every yellow bead, subtract $100, which represents the cost of restoring the land after mining.

WHAT DO YOU THINK?

- How does the difficulty of finding the red beads relate to the difficulty of finding the most valuable ores?
- How does the total value of the blue beads and the sunflower seeds compare to the total value of the red and green beads? What can you conclude about deciding which materials to mine?

CHALLENGE The sunflower seeds and the red, green, and blue beads could represent minerals that contain copper, gold, iron, and silver. Which bead or seed is most likely to represent each mineral? Explain your choices.

SKILL FOCUS
Drawing conclusions (6.6.a)

MATERIALS
- 1 pound wild-birdseed mix with sunflower seeds
- shallow pan
- 2 small red beads
- 4 small green beads
- 8 small blue beads
- 3 medium yellow beads

TIME
25 minutes

DIFFERENTIATE INSTRUCTION

More Reading Support

G Where do you think strip mining gets its name? *Miners strip away the plants, soil, and unwanted rock from Earth's surface to get to an ore.*

Below Level Have students draw simple sketches of the three methods of surface mining: panning, strip mining, and open-pit mining. Tell students to label their sketches.

INVESTIGATE Mining

PURPOSE To model the mining of ores in order to draw conclusions about the benefits and costs of mining

TIP *25 min.* Have students work in teams of two for this activity.

WHAT DO YOU THINK? *Answers may vary, but students should say that the smaller, rarer beads were hardest to find. The most valuable ores are usually the hardest to find, too. The total value of the more common beads and seeds may be greater than the value of the rarer beads. It can be more profitable to mine a large amount of a less valuable mineral than to mine a small amount of a more valuable mineral.*

CHALLENGE *On the basis of the values given for the beads and seeds, the red beads might represent gold, the yellow beads silver, the green beads copper, and the sunflower seeds iron.*

 Datasheet, Mining, p. 163

Technology Resources

Customize this student lab as needed or look for an alternative. Print rubrics to assess student lab reports.

 **Lab Generator CD-ROM**

Ongoing Assessment

CHECK YOUR READING *Answer: They are similar because they are both types of surface mining. They differ in their depth. In strip mining, a layer of soil and rocks is removed to get to an ore. In open-pit mining, a much deeper hole is made.*

Ongoing Assessment

Explain how minerals are mined.

Ask: What do strip mining, open-pit mining, and deep mining have in common? *They all involve digging into Earth to recover ores.*

Reinforce the BIG idea

Have students relate the section to the Big Idea.

Reinforcing Key Concepts, p. 164

13.2 ASSESS & RETEACH

Assess

Section 13.2 Quiz, p. 290

Reteach

Help students review this section's concepts by writing the heading "Uses of Minerals" on the board, with these three headings under it: "Technology," "Industry," and "Arts." Have students list examples of mineral uses and products under each heading. *Sample answers: Technology: computer chips, electronics, photographic film, fiber optics; Industry: machines (including cars and aircraft), batteries, abrasives, drill tips, insulators, water filters; Arts: gemstones and metals for jewelry, paints, dyes, glass, ceramics*

Technology Resources

Have students visit **ClassZone.com** for reteaching of Key Concepts.

CONTENT REVIEW

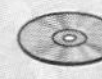
CONTENT REVIEW CD-ROM

Deep Mining

Deep-mining methods are needed when an ore lies far below Earth's surface. These methods are used to obtain many minerals. Miners dig an opening to reach a deep ore. When the ore is inside a mountain or hill, miners can cut a level passage to reach the mineral they want. Miners dig a vertical passage to reach an ore that lies underground in a flat area or under a mountain.

From the main passage, miners blast, drill, cut, or dig the ore. If the body of ore is horizontal, miners dig farther and farther into the hill or mountain. If it is vertical, they remove the ore in layers.

These gold miners are working underground near Carlin, Nevada. The world's deepest gold mine is in South Africa and extends almost 4 km (2.5 mi) underground.

13.2 Review

KEY CONCEPTS

1. Give two examples of the use of minerals in industry and two examples of the use of minerals in the arts. (6.6.c)
2. What are the five ways in which minerals form? (6.6.c)
3. What is required for rocks to be considered ores? (6.6.c)

CRITICAL THINKING

4. **Infer** Would an ore at Earth's surface or an ore deep underground be more expensive to mine? Explain.
5. **Apply** Why do gem cutters usually shape and polish gemstones before using them in jewelry?

CHALLENGE

6. **Analyze** Both strip mining and open-pit mining are types of surface mining. When might miners choose to use open-pit mining rather than strip mining to obtain an ore?

ANSWERS

1. Answers will vary but may include examples from the chart on p. 459.

2. as water evaporates, as hot water cools, as molten rock cools, as heat and pressure change existing minerals, and as organisms produce minerals for shells or bones

3. The rocks must be rich in minerals that people want. The minerals must be worth more than it costs to mine the ores.

4. the ore deep underground since it is harder to reach

5. to increase the gemstone's beauty and sparkle

6. Open-pit mining would be used when the ore extends too deep within Earth to be recovered by strip mining.

GEM CUTTER

Geometry for Gems

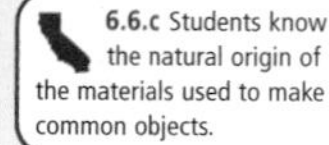

6.6.c Students know the natural origin of the materials used to make common objects.

If you found a gemstone in nature, it would probably look dull and rough. You might want to take it to a gem cutter, who would use a grinding wheel to shape and polish your rough stone into a beautiful gem. You would also discover that a lot of the rough gemstone is ground away into powder.

Gem cutters use geometry to help them choose the best final shapes of gems. Geometry also helps them to shape gems with many small, flat surfaces at specific angles. These surfaces are called facets, and they make the gems sparkle.

Starred Gems

Some gems—such as certain rubies, sapphires, and forms of quartz—show a six-pointed star when cut in a rounded shape instead of facets. These gems contain tiny flaws aligned at 120-degree angles. When light hits the flaws, it scatters in a star-shaped pattern. The star ruby shown here is a good example of these beautiful gems.

Deeply Colored Gems

Some gems are shaped to show off their rich colors rather than their sparkle. These gems have fewer and larger facets. Also, many brightly colored gems contain lighter and darker areas of color. The gems are shaped so that the richest color is toward the bottom. Light entering one of these gems strikes the bottom and reflects the rich color to the viewer's eye.

Sparkling Gems

How much a gem sparkles depends on the geometric angles at which it is cut. If the overall angle of the bottom part of a gem is too shallow **(A)** or too steep **(C)**, light will go through the gem.

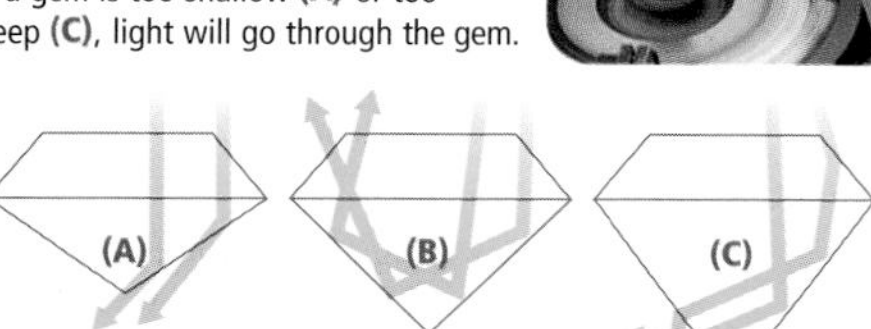

However, if the angles are correct **(B)**, light will bounce around inside the gem as it is reflected to the viewer's eye. The more facets a gem has, the more the light will bounce, and the more the gem will sparkle.

EXPLORE

1. **COMPARE** Table salt, which is the mineral halite, sparkles as light is reflected from its crystal faces. Snow, which is the mineral ice, also sparkles in sunlight. How are the crystal faces of salt and snow similar to facets? How are they different?
2. **CHALLENGE** When would it be best for a gem cutter to split an irregularly shaped crystal into two or more smaller stones before grinding them into finished gems? Remember, one larger stone is usually more valuable than two smaller ones.

SCIENCE ON THE JOB

Relevance of Science to Non-science Jobs

Set Learning Goal

To appreciate why gem cutters need to understand geometry

Present the Science

- Remind students that the colors they see in objects come from reflected light. People see different wavelengths of light as different colors. For example, the shortest wavelengths appear to us as violet, and the longest appear as deep red. Different objects reflect different wavelengths, so the objects appear to us as differently colored.
- The shapes into which gems are cut do not resemble natural crystals. Facets are not the same as crystal faces.
- Many gemstones have common names that differ from their mineral names. For example, gem forms of the mineral corundum are called rubies or sapphires, depending on their color. Small amounts of foreign substances give corundum a variety of colors.

DIFFERENTIATION TIP If possible, allow students with visual impairments to feel the facets on a gemstone.

Close

Ask: In what other fields might a knowledge of angles and reflected light be important? *Answers may vary but might include such fields as art, photography, and optometry.*

EXPLORE

1. ***COMPARE*** *Crystal faces and facets are both flat surfaces. Crystal faces form naturally; facets do not.*
2. ***CHALLENGE*** *If the rough gem has a very irregular shape, it would be best to split it before grinding it. It would be better to end up with two smaller stones than with one stone that had an excessive amount of it ground away into powder.*

13.3 FOCUS

Set Learning Goals

Students will

- Describe how conservation can help people to reduce waste and reuse natural resources.
- Explain how recycling can help people to recover and extend natural resources.
- Design an experiment to test the energy efficiency of light bulbs.

3-Minute Warm-Up

Display Transparency 101 or copy this exercise on the board:

Decide whether these statements are true. If they are not true, correct them.

1. Minerals can form when molten rock cools. *true*
2. Minerals form within Earth but not on Earth's surface. *Minerals form both within Earth and on its surface.*
3. *Ores* are the rarest and most expensive of the known minerals. *Ores are rocks that contain enough of a mineral to be mined for profit.*

13.3 MOTIVATE

EXPLORE Energy Use

PURPOSE To help students recognize how much energy they use every day

TIP *20 min.* To save time, make copies of the usage chart and hand them out to students.

WHAT DO YOU THINK? *The television or computer is probably used the most, but much of the time, they are left on when no one is watching or using them. Turning off appliances when they aren't in use will conserve energy.*

KEY CONCEPT

13.3 Resources can be conserved and recycled.

CALIFORNIA Content Standards

6.6.a Students know the utility of energy sources is determined by factors that are involved in converting these sources to useful forms and the consequences of the conversion process.

6.6.b Students know different natural energy and material resources, including air, soil, rocks, minerals, petroleum, fresh water, wildlife, and forests, and know how to classify them as renewable or nonrenewable.

6.6.c Students know the natural origin of the materials used to make common objects.

BEFORE, you learned

- Natural resources are either renewable or nonrenewable
- Fossil fuels are used to supply most of society's energy and products, but at a cost to the environment

NOW, you will learn

- How conservation can help people to reduce waste and reuse natural resources
- How recycling can help people to recover and extend natural resources

VOCABULARY

conservation p. 467
recycling p. 468

EXPLORE Energy Use (6.6.b)

What is your EQ (energy quotient)?

PROCEDURE

1. Think about the electrical appliances you use every day (TV, computer, room lights, microwave, hair dryer). Draw a usage chart like the one in the photo.
2. Estimate the number of hours you use each item every day. Add up all the hours in each column.
3. Multiply the total of each column by 2.5 kilowatts. This is your energy quotient.

WHAT DO YOU THINK?

- Which item(s) do you use the most? How much of the use is necessary?
- What ways can you think of to conserve electricity each day?

MATERIALS

- paper
- pen or pencil
- calculator

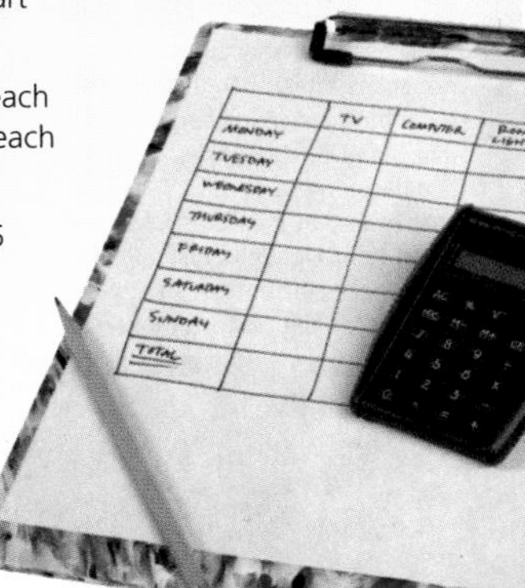

SUPPORTING MAIN IDEAS
Enter this blue heading in a chart and record supporting information.

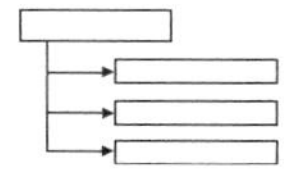

Conservation involves reducing waste and reusing natural resources.

In the 1960s, each person in the United States produced 1.2 kilograms (2.7 lb) of trash a day. Today, that number has more than doubled. All together, the nation's households produce about 236 million tons of trash each year! Over half of this amount is buried in landfills.

Conservation programs can be used to extend natural resources, to protect human health, and to slow the growing mountain of trash. Read on to find out how much your efforts count.

466 Unit 4: Ecology and Resources

RESOURCES FOR DIFFERENTIATED INSTRUCTION

Below Level

UNIT RESOURCE BOOK
- Reading Study Guide A, pp. 167–168
- Decoding Support, p. 190

AUDIO CDS

Advanced

UNIT RESOURCE BOOK
Challenge and Extension, p. 173

English Learners

UNIT RESOURCE BOOK
Spanish Reading Study Guide, pp. 171–172

AUDIO CDS
- Audio Readings in Spanish
- Audio Readings (English)

Conservation means protecting, restoring, and managing natural resources so that they last as long as possible. Conserving resources can also reduce the amount of pollution released into the air, water, and soil. There are two ways every person can help: reducing and reusing.

VOCABULARY
Add a word triangle diagram for *conservation* to your notebook.

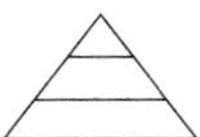

Reduce You can reduce waste at the source, whether the source is a local store or your own home. Here are a few suggestions:

- When choosing between two similar products, choose the one with less packaging. Product packaging is a major source of paper and plastic waste.
- When brushing your teeth or washing your face, turn the water off until you are ready to rinse. You can save 8 to 23 liters (2 to 6 gal.) of water a day, or 2920 to 8395 liters (730 to 2190 gal.) per year.
- When eating in a restaurant or cafeteria, use only the napkins and ketchup and mustard packets that you really need. The less you throw away, the less garbage will be buried in a landfill.
- Where possible, use energy-efficient light bulbs in your home. Turn off lights and appliances when you are not using them.

Reuse Many products can be used more than once. Reusable products and containers conserve materials and resources. Here are some things that you can do:

- Refill plastic water bottles instead of buying new bottles.
- Donate old clothes and other items instead of throwing them away.
- Rinse and reuse plastic sandwich and storage bags.
- Cut the top off a half-gallon container to make a watering can.

Reducing Waste

You can reduce paper and plastic waste by choosing products with the least packaging.

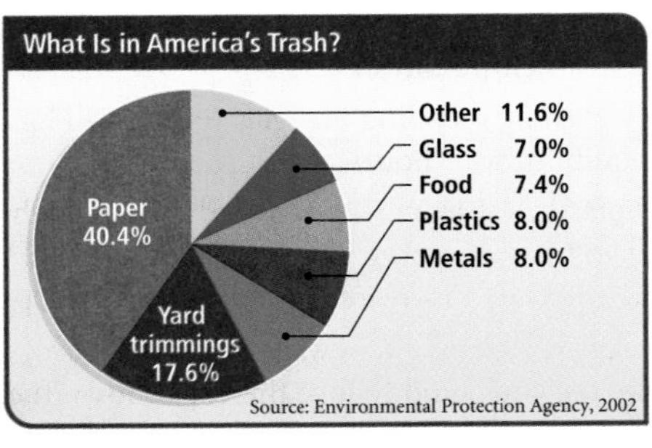

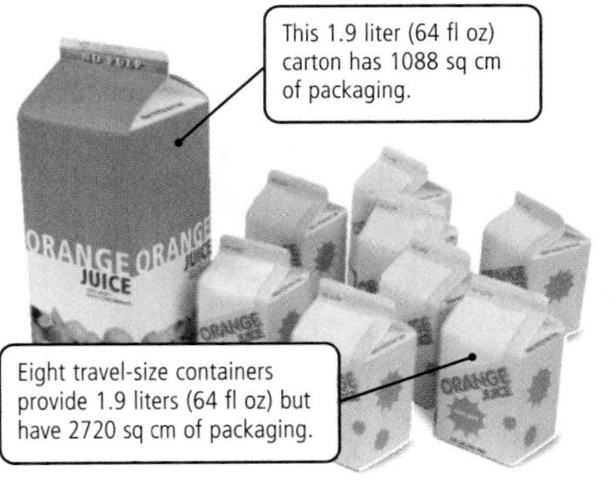

This 1.9 liter (64 fl oz) carton has 1088 sq cm of packaging.
ORANGE JUICE
Eight travel-size containers provide 1.9 liters (64 fl oz) but have 2720 sq cm of packaging.

DIFFERENTIATE INSTRUCTION

More Reading Support

A What are two ways to conserve? *reduce and reuse*

English Learners Have students write the definitions for *conservation* and *recycling* in their Science Word Dictionaries. English learners may not have prior knowledge of the terms *variables* and *ski jacket* on p. 468.

13.3 INSTRUCT

Teach the Standards

Resource conservation 6.6.c

In this section: Help students understand that recycled products are converted into new products; recycling reduces the amount of natural resources that are used. Explain that processing recycled materials requires less time, energy, and money than is required to process natural resources.

future opportunities: human impact on ecosystems, pp. 490–495; conservation, pp. 510–515

Real World Example

In the United States, only about 40 percent of all newspapers are recycled. In other developed countries, however, recycling is a way of life. Japan's program, in particular, is hailed as an outstanding success—about 95 percent of newspapers are recycled there. Japanese residents separate their garbage into several categories. Each type of garbage is picked up on a different day. In some towns, recycling trucks hand out free goods in exchange for recycled materials.

Teach from Visuals

To help students interpret the visual about reducing waste, ask:

- How much more paper is thrown away than plastics? *about five times more*
- How much waste would be reduced if all food scraps and yard trimmings were composted? *Food (7.4%) + yard trimmings (17.6%) = 25%*

Ongoing Assessment

Describe how conservation can help people to reduce waste and reuse natural resources.

Ask: What are some ways that you can reduce waste and reuse natural resources? *Answer: Turn off the water when brushing your teeth, and donate old clothes instead of throwing them away.*

INVESTIGATE Conservation

PURPOSE To design an experiment that tests which type of light bulb wastes less energy

TIPS *10 min.* The light bulbs will get hot; caution students not to touch the bulbs. Then, suggest the following:

- In order to control variables, place both lamps in the same area rather than placing one on a sunny ledge and the other in a shady corner.
- Keep in mind that the more heat a bulb generates, the more energy it wastes.

WHAT DO YOU THINK? *temperature and type of light bulb; the incandescent bulb gives off more heat than the fluorescent bulb; the fluorescent bulb wastes less energy because it gives off less heat. Therefore, it uses less energy to produce the same amount of light.*

 Datasheet, Conservation, p. 174

Technology Resources

Customize this student lab as needed or look for an alternative. Print rubrics to assess student lab reports.

 **Lab Generator CD-ROM**

Teaching with Technology

If students have probeware, they can use a temperature probe for this Investigate.

Develop Critical Thinking

APPLY Have students apply their results from the investigation to a realistic scenario. Suppose that the energy-efficient light bulb costs more than the other bulb. Ask: What would you say to convince someone to buy the more efficient bulb? *You may pay more for the bulb up front, but you will save more in the long run by conserving energy.*

INVESTIGATE Conservation

How can you tell which bulb wastes less energy?

DESIGN — YOUR OWN — EXPERIMENT

The more heat a light bulb gives off, the more energy it wastes. Use what you know about how to measure the temperature of an object to design an experiment that tests which type of light bulb wastes less energy.

PROCEDURE

1. Figure out how you are going to test which light bulb—incandescent or fluorescent—wastes less energy.
2. Write up your procedure.
3. Conduct your experiment and record your results.

WHAT DO YOU THINK?

- What were the variables in your experiment?
- What were the results of your experiment?
- How does your experiment demonstrate which light bulb is less wasteful?

SKILL FOCUS
Designing experiments (6.6.a)

MATERIALS
- 2 table lamps
- incandescent light bulb and fluorescent light bulb of same wattage
- 2 thermometers
- pen or pencil

TIME
20 minutes

Recycling involves recovering and extending natural resources.

Did you know that recycling one aluminum can saves enough energy to run a television set for three hours? **Recycling** involves recovering materials that people usually throw away. Some common materials you can recycle are glass, aluminum cans, certain plastics, paper, scrap iron, and such metals as gold, copper, and silver. Here are a few statistics that might encourage you to recycle:

With every item you recycle, you help to recover and extend limited resources.

- Recycling 90 percent of the newspapers printed in the United States on just one Sunday would save 500,000 trees, equal to an entire forest.
- The energy saved by recycling one glass bottle will light a 100-watt bulb for four hours.
- Five 2-liter plastic bottles can be recycled into enough plastic fiber to fill a ski jacket. Thirty-six bottles will make enough fiber for a square yard of synthetic carpet.
- If you recycled all household newspapers, cardboard, glass, and metal, you could reduce the use of fossil fuels. It takes less energy to make products from recycled materials than to make new products.

DIFFERENTIATE INSTRUCTION

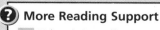

More Reading Support

B What is recycling? *recovering materials that would usually be thrown away*

Advanced Have students organize a recycling drive at your school. Students will need to interview local health department officials for information on what materials can be collected and how they should be sorted. Have students keep count and record the numbers of recycled materials gathered; they can then compare their data with the statistics on p. 467 in order to estimate how many resources they saved.

 Challenge and Extension, p. 173

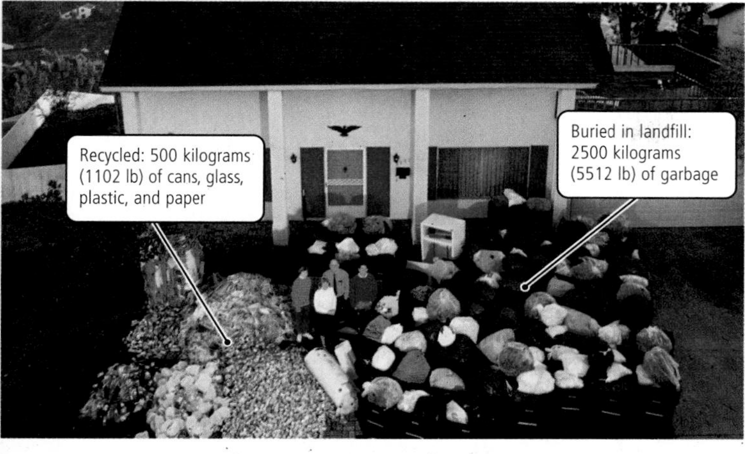

The average family of four generates about 3000 kilograms (6614 lb) of trash per year. Recycling is catching on, but there is still a long way to go.

It is important to remember that not every item can be recycled or reused. In the photograph above, for instance, only about one-sixth of the family's trash is being recycled. Even some types of plastic and glass items must be thrown away because they cannot be recovered. All the trash in the family's plastic bags will be buried in landfills. You can see why it is important to recycle the items you can and to avoid using items that cannot be recycled.

Recycling is only part of the solution to our resource problems. It takes time, energy, and money to collect waste materials, sort them, remove what can be used, and form new objects. Even with these limitations, recycling can help extend available resources and protect human health and the environment.

 **CHECK YOUR READING** What are some of the benefits and drawbacks of recycling?

13.3 Review

KEY CONCEPTS

1. Give examples of ways people can reduce waste and conserve natural resources. **(6.6.b)**
2. Explain how recycling can help people recover and extend natural resources. **(6.6.b)**
3. What are some of the limitations of conservation and recycling programs? **(6.6.b)**

CRITICAL THINKING

4. **Evaluate** How can conserving or recycling materials help protect the environment?
5. **Calculate** Your city pays $115 per ton to bury an average of 13 tons of garbage a month in a landfill. A recycling program could reduce that number to 8 tons a month. How much would the city save in landfill fees per month? per year?

CHALLENGE

6. **Synthesize** Work with a group of classmates to list some of the ways in which you could conserve and recycle resources in your home and at school. Create a poster or advertisement to present your ideas to the rest of the class.

ANSWERS

1. buy and use fewer products; reuse items

2. Fewer resources are used, so resources will last longer.

3. time, energy, and money

4. Less waste in landfills; less fossil fuel burned; so less pollution; fewer resources used to make new products

5. $115/ton × 13 tons/month = $1495/month; $115/ton × 8 tons/month = $920/month; $1495/month − $920/month = $575/month in savings; $575/month × 12 months/year = $6900/year in savings.

6. sponsor a paper drive, urge parents to car-pool, buy products made of recycled materials, use fewer products, reuse products

Ongoing Assessment

Explain how recycling can help people to recover and extend natural resources.

Ask: How can recycling newspapers save trees? *The paper will be used again, and fewer trees will be cut down.*

CHECK YOUR READING *Answer: benefits: less fossil fuels burned, fewer resources used; drawbacks: time, energy, money needed to recycle*

Reinforce the BIG idea

Have students relate the section to the Big Idea.

 Reinforcing Key Concepts, p. 175

13.3 ASSESS & RETEACH

Assess

 Section 13.3 Quiz, p. 291

Reteach

Show students an example of a product with a lot of packaging, such as a multipack of snack foods. Have students describe how they could reuse or recycle the product. For example, they might use the empty cardboard container to hold something else—this is an example of reuse. They could recycle the packaging, if feasible. Some students might refuse to buy the product because of the amount of packaging—this is an example of reducing waste.

Technology Resources

Have students visit **ClassZone.com** for reteaching of Key Concepts.

 **CONTENT REVIEW**

 **CONTENT REVIEW CD-ROM**

MATH IN SCIENCE
Math Skills Practice for Science

Set Learning Goal

To make double bar graphs showing patterns of pollution over time

Math Standard

6.MR.2.4 Use a variety of methods, such as words, numbers, symbols, charts, graphs, tables, diagrams, and models, to explain mathematical reasoning.

Present the Science

Lead and arsenic are poisons that attack the nervous system. Lead can destroy nerve cells, cause brain damage, and induce seizures and comas. Exposure to arsenic can cause memory impairment, inability to concentrate, irritability, and death. Sources of lead pollution include dust and fumes from factories that make car batteries, rubber, and electronic products. Arsenic is used in much electrical equipment, rat poisons, and insecticides.

Develop Graphing Skills

Remind students that colors in the key should explain colors used in the graph.

DIFFERENTIATION TIP Students with physical impairments may have trouble drawing the graphs. Enlarge graph paper, and encourage them to use rulers to align numbers and bars. Or allow them to make graphs on a computer.

Close

Ask: What might account for the large increase in levels of lead between 1880 and 1960? ***Sample answer: increased use of cars and leaded gasoline***

- Math Support, p. 191
- Math Practice, p. 192

Technology Resources

Students can visit **ClassZone.com** for practice with comparing decimals.

MATH TUTORIAL

MATH in SCIENCE
MATH TUTORIAL
CLASSZONE.COM
Click on Math Tutorial for more help with bar graphs.
Math 6.MR.2.4
Science 6.7.c

Machines mounted on boats drill down into the ocean floor to collect sediment cores.

This tube contains a sediment core.

SKILL: MAKING A DOUBLE BAR GRAPH

Tracking Contaminants

The layered sediments at the bottom of the ocean have formed over time. The particles in the deeper layers settled to the floor long ago, while those in the top layers settled out of the water more recently. By studying the amounts of pollutants in different layers of sediment, scientists can see how the water quality has changed over time. In 1991 scientists collected sediment cores north of Dash Point in Puget Sound. The table below shows levels of two pollutants, lead and arsenic, in the sediment layers for 1880, 1960, and 1990. The levels are measured in milligrams per kilogram dry weight (mg/kg d.w.).

Levels of Lead and Arsenic in Sediments

Year	Lead (mg/kg d.w.)	Arsenic (mg/kg d.w.)
1880	10	6
1960	62	22
1990	45	17

You can use a double bar graph to analyze the data. A double bar graph shows two sets of data on the same graph. The first two bars of the graph are drawn for you below.

Example

(1) Copy the axes and labels.

(2) Draw bars for the lead data. Use the scale to determine the height of each bar, as shown.

(3) Draw the arsenic bars next to the lead bars.

(4) Shade the bars in different colors. Include a key.

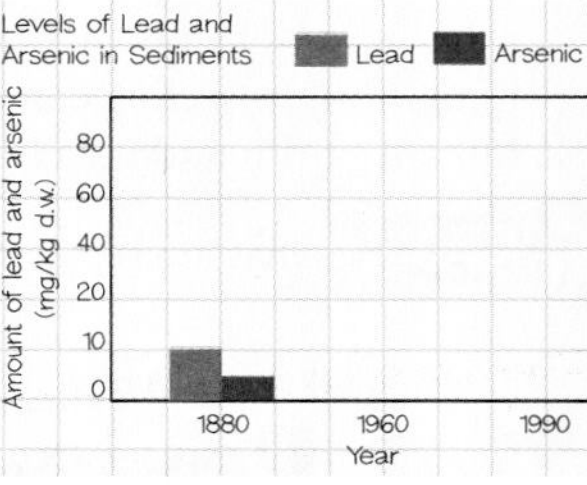

Make a double bar graph of the data by following the steps above. Use your graph to answer the following questions.

1. What happened to the levels of lead and arsenic between 1880 and 1960?

2. What happened to the levels of lead and arsenic between 1960 and 1990?

CHALLENGE Because lead can be harmful to humans, all new cars were designed to run on unleaded gasoline starting in 1975. The use of lead-based paint in homes was banned in 1978. How might these bans have affected the amount of lead in Puget Sound? Use evidence from your graph to support your answer.

ANSWERS

1. The levels of both contaminants increased.

2. The levels of both contaminants decreased.

CHALLENGE *Before lead was banned, lead levels in Puget Sound were rising, as shown in the graph. By 1990, more than a decade after the ban, lead levels in Puget Sound decreased significantly. Thus, the ban may have prevented more lead from entering Puget Sound.*

KEY CONCEPT

Resources can be converted to useful forms.

CALIFORNIA Content Standards

6.3.a Students know energy can be carried from one place to another by heat flow or by waves, including water, light and sound waves, or by moving objects.

6.6.a Students know the utility of energy sources is determined by factors that are involved in converting these sources to useful forms and the consequences of the conversion process.

BEFORE, you learned

- Conservation helps people reduce waste and reuse natural resources
- Recycling helps people recover and extend natural resources

NOW, you will learn

- How renewable resources are used to generate energy
- About the benefits and costs of nuclear power

VOCABULARY

hydroelectric energy p. 472
geothermal energy p. 473
solar cell p. 475
biomass p. 476
hydrogen fuel cell p. 476
nuclear energy p. 477

THINK ABOUT

What can the energy of moving water do?

The flow of water over the upper edge of Yosemite Falls is the greatest in the spring. About 9000 liters (2400 gallons) of water go over the cliff's edge every second. The water flows through a V-shaped cut in the cliff. Where did the energy come from to cut the rock of the cliff?

Renewable resources are used to produce electricity and as fuel.

Sources of renewable energy include moving water, sunlight, and wind. Unlike fossil fuels, many renewable sources of energy are unlimited in supply. These sources can be converted to useful forms such as electricity. The conversion produces little or no air pollution. Using these clean energy sources helps preserve the environment and protect human health.

However, so far these resources cannot produce enough energy to pay for the cost of developing them on a large scale. As a result, only about 6 percent of the total energy used in the United States comes from these resources. Scientists and engineers must improve the necessary technologies before renewable resources can supply more clean energy.

SUPPORTING MAIN IDEAS
Enter this blue heading in a chart and record supporting information.

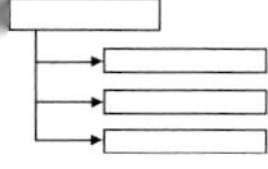

CHECK YOUR READING What makes renewable resources attractive as energy sources?

13.4 FOCUS

Set Learning Goals

Students will

- Describe the benefits and costs of nuclear power.
- Explain how renewable resources are used to generate energy.

3-Minute Warm-Up

Display Transparency 101 or copy this exercise on the board:

Match each definition to the correct term.

Definitions

1. nonrenewable resource made from once-living plants and animals *c*
2. any energy source, organism, or substance found in nature that people use *a*
3. the protection, restoration, and management of natural resources *b*

Terms

a. natural resource
b. conservation
c. fossil fuel
d. sunlight

 3-Minute Warm-Up, p. T101

13.4 MOTIVATE

THINK ABOUT

PURPOSE To introduce the idea that renewable resources can produce useful forms of energy

DISCUSS Ask students to describe examples of what moving water can do to Earth or to things in the water. *Sample answers: Moving water can move ships, erode hills, and carry silt.*

Answer: Over a very long time, the mechanical energy of the moving water cut the rock.

RESOURCES FOR DIFFERENTIATED INSTRUCTION

Below Level

UNIT RESOURCE BOOK
Reading Study Guide A, pp. 178–179
Decoding Support, p. 190

 **AUDIO CDS**

Additional INVESTIGATION, Solar Houses A, B, & C, pp. 202–210; Teacher Instructions, pp. 273–274

Advanced

UNIT RESOURCE BOOK
- Challenge and Extension, p. 184
- Challenge Reading, pp. 186–187

English Learners

UNIT RESOURCE BOOK
Spanish Reading Study Guide, pp. 182–183

 **AUDIO CDS**

- Audio Readings in Spanish
- Audio Readings (English)

13.4 INSTRUCT

Teach the Standards

Alternative energy sources 6.6.a

In this section: Explain to students that renewable sources of energy, such as hydrogen, have few harmful consequences, but they currently are too costly to produce widely. Other sources, such as nuclear energy, yield much energy, but they produce dangerous waste products.

previously taught: movement of energy, pp. 11–14, 19–20, 26–27

Teach Difficult Concepts

As students read about alternative energy sources, they'll discover that each source has its advantages and disadvantages. It might be helpful to stress that energy sources are evaluated from both a scientific and an economic point of view. The following factors are usually weighed: energy output, energy efficiency, pollution output, and cost. The best energy source would produce the most energy at the most efficient rate and lowest cost, with the least amount of pollution.

Teach from Visuals

To help students interpret the visual of the dam, ask:

- The reservoir was once what? *part of the river*
- Why is the reservoir higher than the river? *the blocked water created an artificial lake, deeper than the river*
- How could you affect water flow and stop the production of electrical energy in the power plant? *close the intake gate or lower the level of the reservoir to below the intake gate*

Real World Example

Hydroelectric power can be produced on a small scale. Small turbines can be placed directly underwater to run microhydroelectric generators. Even a relatively slow-moving current can produce enough electricity for a single house.

Ongoing Assessment

READING VISUALS *Answer: No water would flow down the tunnel to turn the turbines; therefore, no electricity would be produced.*

A

Learn more about the benefits and costs of renewable energy resources.

Hydroelectric Energy

Hydroelectric energy is electricity produced by moving water. If you have ever stood near a waterfall or even just turned on a faucet, you have felt the force of moving water. People can use flowing water to generate electricity.

In most cases, a dam is built across a large river. It blocks the river's flow and creates an artificial lake, or reservoir. As the illustration below shows, water from the reservoir enters the dam through intake gates and flows down a tunnel. The fast-flowing water turns turbines that drive generators, which produce electricity. Because hydroelectric power does not burn any fuel, it produces no air pollution. Dams in the United States generate enough electricity to save 500 million barrels of oil a year.

However, building dams poses problems for the environment. By flooding land to create reservoirs, dams destroy wildlife habitats. In some rivers, such as the Snake and Columbia rivers in the United States, dams interfere with the annual migration of salmon and other fish. Areas near the end of the river may receive less water than before, making it harder to raise crops and livestock.

Areas with large rivers can use their power to produce electricity. The dam in the photo was built on the Yukon River in Alaska.

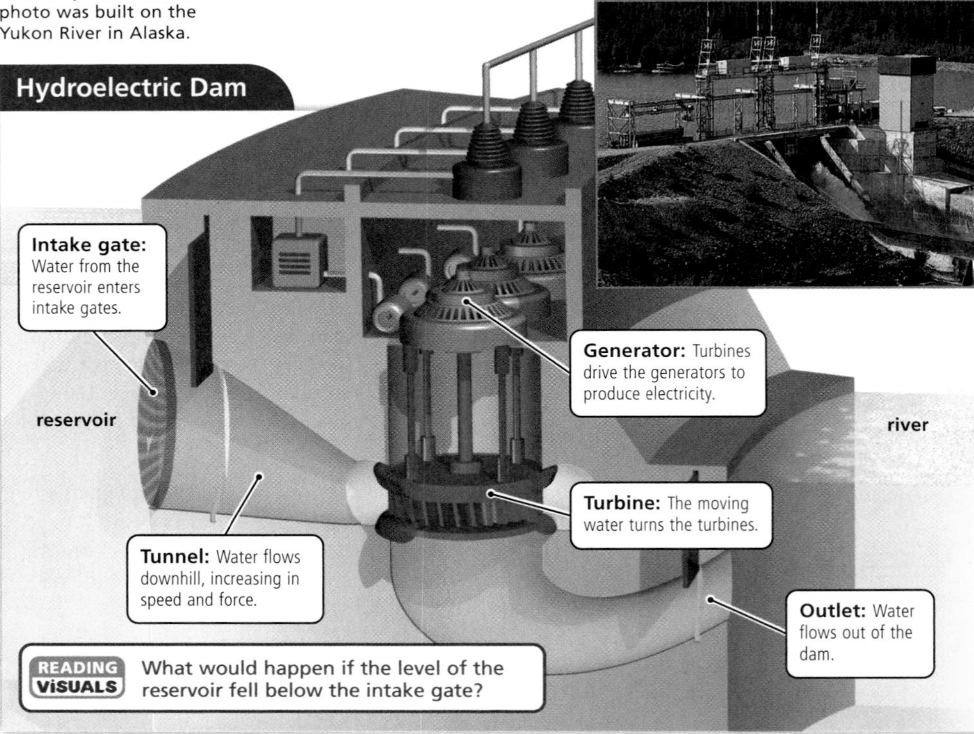

Hydroelectric Dam
Intake gate: Water from the reservoir enters intake gates.
reservoir
Generator: Turbines drive the generators to produce electricity.
river
Turbine: The moving water turns the turbines.
Tunnel: Water flows downhill, increasing in speed and force.
Outlet: Water flows out of the dam.

READING VISUALS What would happen if the level of the reservoir fell below the intake gate?

DIFFERENTIATE INSTRUCTION

More Reading Support

A What resource produces hydroelectric energy? *moving water*

Advanced Have students compare the different power plant diagrams in sections 1 and 4. Ask them whether they can see any consistent patterns among the different methods of electric energy production. *Students should observe that in each diagram, an energy source, such as steam or moving water, turns a turbine which drives a generator to produce electricity.*

R Challenge and Extension, p. 184

Have students who are interested in a new potential energy source read the following article:

R Challenge Reading, pp. 186–187

Geothermal Energy

Imagine tapping into Earth's heat to obtain electricity for your home. In some places, that is exactly what people do. They use **geothermal energy,** or energy produced by heat within Earth's crust.

Geothermal energy comes from underground water that is heated by hot rock. The illustration below shows how hot water is piped from a well into a power plant. This superheated water enters a flash tank and produces enough steam to run turbines, which power generators. Excess water is then pumped back into the ground. Some plants also pipe hot water into homes and businesses for heating.

In the United States, geothermal energy provides electricity for more than 3.5 million people. Other major geothermal power plants are in New Zealand and Iceland.

Geothermal energy is clean and renewable. So far, its use is limited to areas where hot water is fairly close to the surface. However, some companies are experimenting with pumping cold water into underground areas of hot rock in Earth's crust. The rock heats the water, which is then pumped back to the surface and used to generate electricity. This new technique may allow more countries to make use of geothermal energy.

READING TIP *Geothermal* combines the Greek prefix *geo-*, meaning "earth," and the Greek word *thermē*, meaning "heat."

CHECK YOUR READING What is the source of geothermal energy?

In Iceland, geothermal power plants like the one in the photograph supply nearly all of the country's electricity.

Geothermal Power Plant

Production well: Hot water is piped from the ground into the plant.
Flash tank: Water is changed into steam.
Turbine and generator: Steam turns turbines, which drive generators to produce electricity.
Cooling tower: Water from the tower cools steam in the condenser.
Condenser: Steam condenses into water.
Injection well: Excess water is pumped back into the ground.

READING VISUALS How is this plant similar to a nuclear power plant? How is it different?

473

DIFFERENTIATE INSTRUCTION

More Reading Support

B Geothermal energy use is currently limited to where? *where hot water and steam are fairly close to the surface*

Below Level Students have read about several different types of power plants that use turbines and generators. They might recognize the steps used in generating electricity more easily if they can actually see the technology in use. Arrange a field trip to the nearest power plant. Have students come up with questions beforehand to ask your guide. If a field trip is not possible, have students search the Internet for virtual tours of power plants.

Develop Critical Thinking

HYPOTHESIZE You can often find volcanoes near places that use geothermal energy. Have students hypothesize why this is so. *Very hot rock is close to the surface in those places, so magma or molten rock must be close to the surface, too.*

Also ask students to identify the similar components of geothermal plants and the other plants they've seen so far. *heat source + steam + turbine + generator = electrical energy.*

Teach from Visuals

To help students interpret the visual, have them number the steps in the production of geothermal energy in proper order. Then ask: Which step comes first: water enters the flash tank or water enters the condenser? *Water enters the flash tank.*

Integrate the Sciences

Geothermal power plants are useful for more than just generating electricity. The outflow of hot water from these plants may also contain bacteria that can live in temperatures near that of boiling water (100°C or 212°F). One bacteria in particular, named *Thermus aquaticus,* has proved to be extremely useful to science and business.

The enzymes in *T. aquaticus* work in high temperatures, where chemical reactions occur more quickly. As a result, *T. aquaticus* can be used to speed up chemical changes in commercial products, such as converting millions of pounds of corn into sugar to sweeten soft drinks.

CHECK YOUR READING *Answer: heat within Earth's crust*

Ongoing Assessment

Have students compare this visual with that on page 478.

READING VISUALS *Answer: Similar: Both plants use heated water changed into steam to turn a turbine, which drives a generator; water from a cooling tower helps condense steam back into water. Different: a geothermal plant has a renewable supply of energy and produces no pollution or radioactive waste.*

Teach from Visuals

To help students interpret the visual about windmills, ask:

- What part of the windmill head is similar to a turbine in a hydroelectric plant? *the gear*
- Why must the windmill head be pointed toward the wind at all times? *The windmill blades would not turn as fast if they were not facing the force of moving air.*

Ongoing Assessment

CHECK YOUR READING *Answer: wind speed and angle of the wind across the blades; the faster the blades turn, the more electricity the windmill produces*

C

Wind Energy

For thousands of years, people have captured the tremendous energy of wind to move ships, grind grain, and pump water from underground. Today, people also use wind energy—from the force of moving air—to generate electricity.

REMINDER

The generator is the part that produces the electric current, whether it is driven by turbines or gears.

A modern windmill can stand as tall as a 40-story building. The blades act as a turbine, turning a set of gears that drives the generator. The amount of electricity a windmill produces depends on the speed and angle of the wind across its blades. The faster the blades turn, the more power the windmill produces.

To supply electricity to an area, hundreds of windmills are built on a "wind farm." Wind farms are already producing electricity in California, Hawaii, Texas, and other states. Other countries, such as Denmark and Germany, also use wind farms to supply electricity to some of their cities.

Although wind energy is clean and renewable, it has certain drawbacks. It depends on steady, strong winds blowing most of the time, which are found only in a few places. Wind farms take up a great deal of land, and the turning blades can be noisy. There is also a limit to how much power each windmill can produce. However, in the future, wind farms may become more productive and more widely used.

CHECK YOUR READING What factor determines how much electricity a windmill produces?

D

The blades turn the gears, which drive the generator to produce electricity. The controller causes the windmill to operate when wind speeds are about 15 to 100 km/hr.

DIFFERENTIATE INSTRUCTION

More Reading Support

C The force of moving air produces what kind of energy? *wind energy*

D What do we call an area with hundreds of windmills? *a wind farm*

Advanced Challenge students to come up with a way to model solar power, wind power, or hydroelectric power. For example, students can show how the energy of water from a running faucet spins a toy wheel. Have students explain how their models relate to the concepts learned in this section.

Solar Energy

Only a tiny amount of the Sun's energy falls on Earth. Yet even this amount is huge. Enough solar energy strikes the United States each day to supply the country's energy needs for a year and a half. The problem is how to use this abundant resource to produce electricity.

In an effort to solve the problem, scientists developed solar cells. A **solar cell** is a specially constructed sandwich of silicon and other materials that converts light energy to electricity. A single solar cell produces a small amount of electricity. It could be used to power small appliances, such as calculators and watches.

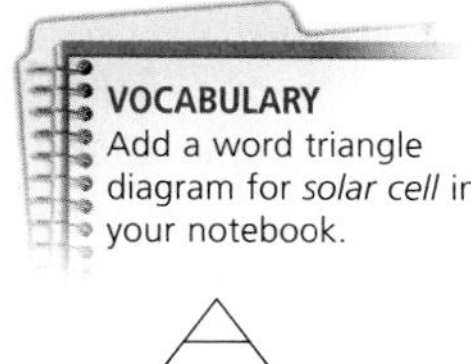

VOCABULARY
Add a word triangle diagram for *solar cell* in your notebook.

The diagram below shows that many solar cells can be used together. They can be put into solar panels, which provide heat and electricity for homes and businesses. Solar panels are also used to power some spacecraft and space stations once they are in orbit. To meet the energy needs of some cities, hundreds or even thousands of solar panels are built into large structures called arrays. Many cities in the western United States receive part of their electricity from solar arrays.

READING TIP
An array is an arrangement of objects in rows and columns.

Sunlight is an unlimited source of clean energy. But current methods of collecting sunlight are expensive and somewhat inefficient. As solar technology improves, sunlight is likely to become an important energy source for the world.

CHECK YOUR READING How can people use sunlight to produce electricity?

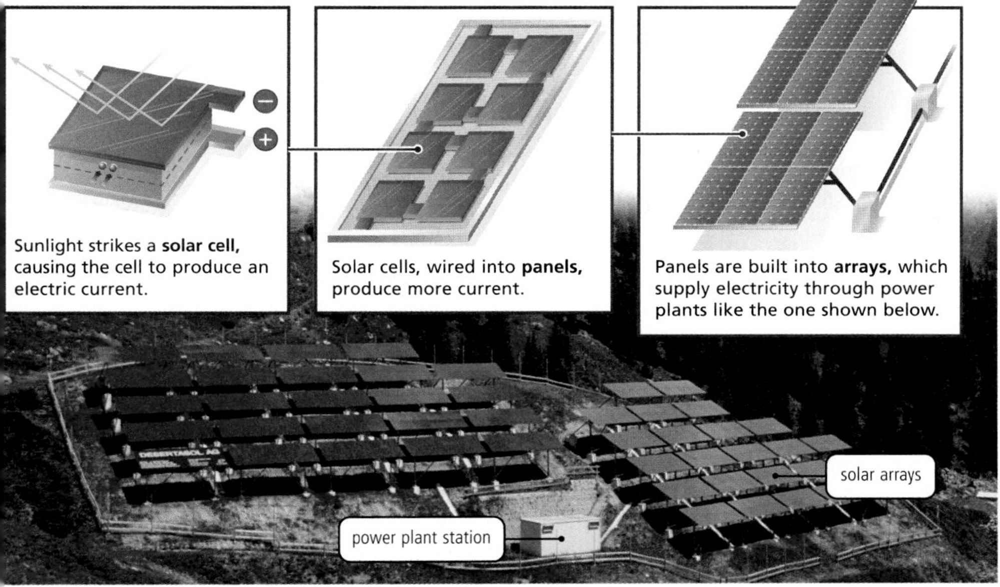
Sunlight strikes a **solar cell,** causing the cell to produce an electric current.
Solar cells, wired into **panels,** produce more current.
Panels are built into **arrays,** which supply electricity through power plants like the one shown below.
solar arrays
power plant station

History of Science

In the early 1950s, the modern solar cell was developed by scientists working on electrical devices called *transistors.* They found that a specially built transistor could be powered by sunlight. Some of the first solar cells were used in the U.S. space program. The cost was high—around $2,000 per watt. These early solar cells converted only 1 to 2 percent of sunlight energy into electrical energy. Today, solar cells are still used in space, powering the International Space Station and hundreds of satellites. The cost is now around $20 per watt, and the cells convert anywhere from 7 to 17 percent of sunlight energy. The latest revolution in the solar cell industry is a dye-sensitized solar cell. This cell can use indoor light and UV light on cloudy days. It works similar to the way that plant leaves absorb energy from the Sun. This new technology will allow solar power to be used in areas with fewer sunny days.

Teacher Demo

Obtain a solar-powered watch or calculator and use a small screwdriver to open it up. Allow students to examine its components. Have them compare the solar cell to the one shown in the visual on this page.

Teach from Visuals

To help students interpret the visual of solar cells and panels, ask: What do the positive and negative signs represent? *electrical charges*

EXPLORE the BIG idea

Revisit "Sunlight as an Energy Source" on p. 447. Have students explain their results.

DIFFERENTIATE INSTRUCTION

More Reading Support

E What solar-energy device is made of silicon and other materials? *solar cell*

Additional Investigation To reinforce Section 13.4 learning goals, use the following full-period investigation:

Additional INVESTIGATION, Solar Houses, A, B, & C, pp. 202–210, 273–274
(Advanced students should complete Levels B and C.)

Alternative Assessment Tell students that some materials are better than others at absorbing sunlight. Have them design experiments to test the absorption rates of construction materials, such as tile, concrete, gravel, and brick.

Ongoing Assessment

CHECK YOUR READING *Answer: Sunlight strikes a solar cell, which causes electrons to move and produce an electric current. The cells can be wired together in panels and arrays to produce enough electricity to power homes and businesses.*

Real World Example

Like the other energy sources, biomass can be used to produce electricity. Biomass power plants usually burn wood chips, sawdust, and other plant materials to produce the thermal energy needed to turn turbines, which then drive generators. Although burning wood can contribute to air pollution, wood is a more environmentally friendly choice than fossil fuels. Wood contains much less sulfur than coal, so acid rain is reduced.

Integrate the Sciences

The properties of hydrogen pose some safety issues. Hydrogen is an odorless, tasteless, invisible gas that is lighter than air and highly flammable. Its tiny molecules can pass right through most construction materials. Scientists can make hydrogen safer to use by adding an odor to the gas and by storing it in containers that will hold in the molecules. To make fuel cell cars safer, they can install sensors to shut off the motors if a hydrogen leak occurs.

Ongoing Assessment

Explain how renewable resources are used to generate energy.

Ask: How do hydrogen fuel cells produce electricity? *A fuel cell separates hydrogen into electrons and protons. The electrons form an electric current.*

CHECK YOUR READING *Answer: Biomass fuels can be cheaper than fossil fuels. However, they release carbon dioxide into the air, take up crop land, and some types of biomass are too expensive to produce on a large scale.*

Biomass Energy

Biomass is organic matter, such as plant and animal waste, that can be used as fuel. The U.S. Department of Energy works with state and local groups to find ways of converting biomass materials into energy sources.

F

This wood-burning biomass plant sends electrical energy at a rate of 21 million watts to the San Francisco Bay area. Wood waste products are collected from farms and industries as fuel for the plant.

Each year biomass power stations in the United States burn about 60 million tons of wood and other plant material to generate 40 billion kilowatt hours of electricity. That is similar to the amount of electricity the state of Colorado uses per year. Small biomass stations are used in rural areas to supply power to farms and towns. Fast-growing trees, grasses, and other crops can be planted to supply a renewable energy source that is cheaper than fossil fuels.

Some plant and animal waste can be converted into liquid fuels. For example, the sugar and starch in corn and potatoes are made into a liquid fuel called ethanol. Ethanol can be added to gasoline to form gasohol. This fuel can power cars, farm machinery, and buses. A liquid fuel made from animal waste is used for heating and cooking in many rural areas around the world.

Although biomass is a renewable resource, certain problems limit its use. Burning wood and crops can release as much carbon dioxide into the air as burning fossil fuels does. Biomass crops take up land that could be used to raise food. Also, plant fuels such as ethanol are expensive to produce on a large scale. For now, biomass materials provide only a small part of the world's energy.

What are the advantages and disadvantages of biomass fuels?

Hydrogen Fuel Cells

Watch a hydrogen fuel cell in action.

Scientists are also exploring the use of hydrogen gas as a renewable energy source. They have found ways to generate hydrogen from water and from fossil fuels. Hydrogen gas can be set on fire easily and must be handled with care.

Hydrogen is used in a **hydrogen fuel cell,** a device that produces electricity by a chemical reaction between hydrogen and oxygen. Hydrogen enters one side of the cell while oxygen from the air enters the other side. As the reaction happens, electricity flows out of the cell through wires and powers the motor. Water forms as a byproduct of the reaction.

Hydrogen fuel cells are used to supply electrical energy on spacecraft and space stations. Fuel-cell buses are being tested in several countries. Some fuel-cell cars are now available to the public. Storage tanks in these vehicles carry hydrogen fuel for the cells.

DIFFERENTIATE INSTRUCTION

More Reading Support

F What is organic matter that can be used as fuel called? *biomass*

G How do hydrogen fuel cells produce electricity? *by combining hydrogen and oxygen*

Advanced Write the following statement on the board: Most energy on Earth comes from the Sun. Have students relate the statement to the various energy sources that they have studied in this chapter. For example, fossil fuels and biomass contain the sun's stored energy. Wind is powered by the Sun's uneven heating of Earth's surface.

A storage tank in the back of this SUV holds hydrogen fuel. Electrical energy from fuel cells powers the motor and a backup battery.

Fuel-cell technology holds great promise for the future. Hydrogen is a clean source of energy, producing only water and heat as byproducts. If every vehicle in the world were powered by hydrogen, the level of air pollution would drop sharply.

However, hydrogen fuel cells are still too expensive to produce in large numbers. Separating hydrogen from water or from fossil fuels takes a great deal of energy, time, and money. Also, there are only a few fueling stations to supply cars and other vehicles that run on hydrogen. The U.S. Department of Energy is working with the automotive industry and other industries to solve these problems.

CHECK YOUR READING Why is hydrogen considered a promising alternative energy source?

Nuclear power is used to produce electricity.

Nuclear energy power plants generate about 20 percent of the total energy used in the United States. **Nuclear energy** is produced by releasing energy contained in the nucleus, or center part, of atoms.

The source of energy in a nuclear power plant is uranium, which is an element. You read in Chapter 6 that an element is a substance that contains only one type of atom. Some elements, such as uranium, are unstable. They change into other elements over time.

An atom of an unstable element has an unstable nucleus. The nucleus gives off particles and energy in a process known as radioactivity. Radioactivity continues until enough particles and energy have been given off to create a new, stable nucleus. In this process, atoms of the original, unstable element can change into atoms of a completely different element.

READING TIP *Unstable* means "having a strong tendency to change."

DIFFERENTIATE INSTRUCTION

More Reading Support

H What are the byproducts of hydrogen? *water and heat*

I What is the process in which a nucleus gives off particles and energy? *radioactivity*

Below Level Have students work cooperatively to develop a poster that distinguishes the advantages and disadvantages between energy sources. Encourage students to draw upon their strengths. Visual learners, for example, can draw sketches that illustrate the captions on the poster.

Address Misconceptions

IDENTIFY Have students look at the fossil fuel plant on p. 452 and the solar plant on p. 475. Ask them to guess which plant produces electricity at a cheaper cost. If students answer that solar energy is cheaper to produce, they may hold the misconception that renewable resources are less expensive as an energy source because they are plentiful.

CORRECT Put the following information about the cost of electricity on the board:

Nuclear = 2.3 cents per kilowatt-hour
Oil = 3.9 cents per kilowatt-hour
Coal = 4.2 cents per kilowatt-hour
Natural gas = 7.2 cents per kilowatt-hour
Solar = 22 cents per kilowatt-hour

Explain that, at present, methods of using such renewable resources as sunlight are more costly than using fossil fuels.

REASSESS Ask students to compare the disadvantages of fossil fuels with the disadvantages of renewable resources. *Fossil fuels: They cause pollution; they will eventually run out. Renewable resources: Current methods produce electricity at a higher cost.*

Technology Resources

Visit **ClassZone.com** for background on common student misconceptions.

MISCONCEPTION DATABASE

Integrate the Sciences

Nuclear energy produced by fusion is a potential future energy source. Fusion is the bringing together of atoms. Fusion reactions on Earth have taken place only in laboratories, but in space, stars get their energy from fusion. In main-sequence stars, such as the Sun, four hydrogen nuclei combine to make one helium nucleus. In the process, a small amount of mass is lost. The lost mass is converted into a tremendous amount of energy.

Ongoing Assessment

CHECK YOUR READING *Answer: Hydrogen is an abundant element that burns cleanly and produces only heat and water as a byproduct.*

Teach from Visuals

To help students interpret the visual of the nuclear power plant, ask:

- What is released when uranium atoms split? *energy in the form of light and heat*
- What parts of a nuclear power plant are similar to parts of a fossil fuel power plant, which is shown on p. 452? *steam, turbine, generator, condenser, cooling water, power lines*

Real World Example

Nuclear power plants must be kept secure, or hazardous radiation can endanger people and the environment. In 1979, a nuclear power plant on Three-Mile Island, near Harrisburg, PA, experienced a failure of the cooling system of one of its reactors. As a result, some radioactive water and gases escaped. People were evacuated, and no one was hurt. The government recommended changes to improve reactor safety.

The worst nuclear accident in history occurred in 1986 in Chernobyl, Ukraine. Engineers at the facility shut down emergency backup systems and then ran an unauthorized test. The next day, the uncontrolled chain reaction exploded the roof from one of the buildings, and a total of eight tons of radioactive material was sent into the atmosphere, causing the deaths of approximately 8,000 people and severely damaging the surrounding environment. The facility was eventually closed and the town has since been abandoned.

Ongoing Assessment

READING VISUALS *Answer: The energy released by splitting atoms is used to heat water, which produces steam to run turbines. The turbines run the generators that produce electricity.*

READING TIP

The plural form of the word *nucleus* is *nuclei*.

J

A nuclear power plant uses uranium atoms as fuel. The atoms' nuclei are made to split, which releases a huge amount of energy. When each atom splits, it produces two smaller atoms. It also releases several tiny particles. The tiny particles hit other uranium nuclei, causing them to split.

A chain reaction happens as particles from each split atom cause other atoms to split. You can think of this process as being similar to shooting one marble into a group of marbles. Every marble that is hit will strike other, nearby marbles.

The power-plant diagram below shows a reactor vessel, which is where the chain reaction takes place. Control rods are used to limit the reaction to provide a safe amount of energy. The chain reaction creates enough heat to produce steam in the reactor vessel. The steam heats a coiled pipe, which is used to boil water in the heat exchanger.

Steam from the exchanger turns the turbines, which drive the generators that produce electricity. The steam condenses into water and is pumped back into the heat exchanger. Water from the cooling tower keeps the equipment from overheating. As you can see, nuclear power plants require a large water supply to produce steam and to stay cool.

Nuclear Power Plant

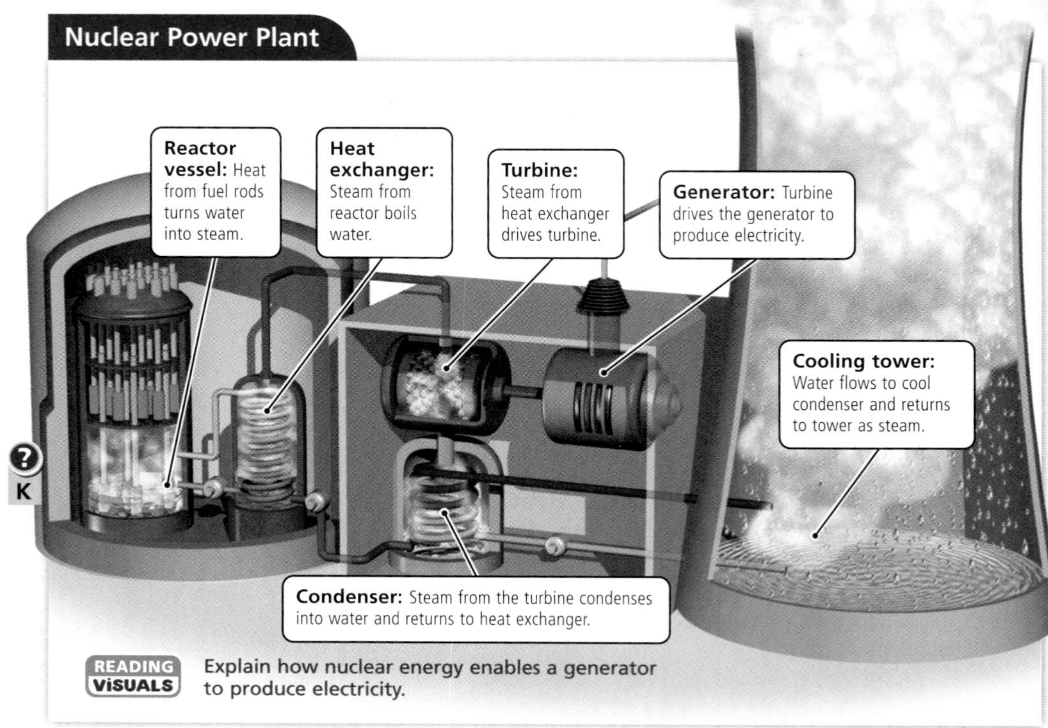

Reactor vessel: Heat from fuel rods turns water into steam.
Heat exchanger: Steam from reactor boils water.
Turbine: Steam from heat exchanger drives turbine.
Generator: Turbine drives the generator to produce electricity.
Cooling tower: Water flows to cool condenser and returns to tower as steam.
Condenser: Steam from the turbine condenses into water and returns to heat exchanger.
K

READING VISUALS Explain how nuclear energy enables a generator to produce electricity.

DIFFERENTIATE INSTRUCTION

More Reading Support

J What element is used to produce nuclear energy? *uranium*

K The process of particles splitting other atoms is called what? *chain reaction*

English Learners Point out to students that *which* is a signal for more information about a word or phrase that precedes it. Examples include "arrays, which supply electricity. . . ." in the photograph caption on p. 475 and "reactor vessel, which is where the chain reaction. . . ." on this page.

A nuclear power plant usually has three main sections: reactor buildings, turbine buildings, and cooling towers.

Splitting just one atom of uranium releases millions of times more energy than burning one molecule of natural gas does. However, nuclear power plants also produce radioactive waste. Radioactivity can cause death and disease if living things are exposed to it long enough. Nuclear waste from a power plant will remain radioactive for thousands of years. Countries that use nuclear energy face the challenge of storing this waste safely. The storage sites must keep any radioactivity from escaping until the waste material becomes harmless.

SIMULATION CLASSZONE.COM

Explore how a nuclear power plant produces energy.

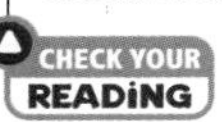
CHECK YOUR READING Explain how nuclear energy is used to generate electricity.

13.4 Review

KEY CONCEPTS

1. Describe the advantages of using sunlight, water, and Earth's heat energy to produce electrical power. (6.3.a)
2. What are some factors that limit the use of biomass, wind, and hydrogen as energy sources? (6.6.a)
3. List the main advantages and disadvantages of nuclear energy as a power source. (6.6.a)

CRITICAL THINKING

4. **Evaluate** Do you think people would use a clean, renewable fuel that cost twice as much as gasoline? Explain.
5. **Calculate** One acre of corn yields 20 gallons of ethanol. A bus gets 20 miles per gallon and travels 9000 miles in one year. How many acres of corn are needed to fuel the bus for a year?

CHALLENGE

6. **Synthesize** Review the energy sources discussed in this section. Then think of ways in which one or more of them could be used to supply electricity to a house in Florida and a house in Alaska. Which energy sources would be best in each environment? Describe your ideas in writing, or make sketches of the houses.

ANSWERS

1. renewable energy sources, nonpolluting, reduce dependence on fossil fuels

2. Biomass and hydrogen are too expensive to mass produce. Wind farms require a lot of land and windy locations.

3. It releases a lot of energy and helps to conserve fossil fuels but produces radioactive waste.

4. Yes, people may be willing to sacrifice for the environment. No, people's main concern is about price.

5. 9000 / 20 = 450 gallons
450 / 20 = 22.5 acres

6. Answers may include solar, biomass, and wind energy in Florida; wind, hydroelectric, geothermal, some solar, and biomass energy in Alaska.

Ongoing Assessment

Describe the benefits and costs of nuclear power.

Ask: Explain one benefit and one cost of using nuclear power. *Using nuclear power could result in less use of fossil fuels, but it produces nuclear waste, which poses serious dangers to people, animals, and Earth.*

CHECK YOUR READING *Answer: When a uranium atom is split, it releases neutrons and a large amount of energy in the form of light and heat. The neutrons split other atoms, creating a chain reaction.*

Reinforce the BIG idea

Have students relate the section to the Big Idea.

 Reinforcing Key Concepts, p. 185

13.4 ASSESS & RETEACH

Assess

 Section 13.4 Quiz, p. 292

Reteach

Have students design an energy plan for their town or city, based on the use of energy sources appropriate for their geographic area. For example, if they live in a sunny area near a large river, solar and hydroelectric energy may be good sources. Remind students that their plans should reflect current technology. For example, it would not be feasible to design a plan that relied on hydrogen fuel cells alone. In their designs, students should include pie charts, showing how much energy would come from each source. They should also explain the reasoning behind their decisions.

Technology Resources

Have students visit **ClassZone.com** for reteaching of Key Concepts.

 CONTENT REVIEW

 CONTENT REVIEW CD-ROM

CHAPTER INVESTIGATION

Focus

PURPOSE Students will construct a model windmill and use appropriate technology to improve its performance.

OVERVIEW Students will use cardboard, a brass paper fastener, a straw, a length of string, a large paper clip, and a pint carton to construct a model windmill. They will conduct several trials to test the lifting power of the windmill. Students will find that:

- the energy of wind can lift a small weight
- they can increase the lifting power of the windmill by increasing the speed of the turning blades

Lab Preparation

- Before beginning the investigation, construct a pinwheel (steps 1–4) using the listed materials. Place the pinwheel on your desk so students can refer to it as a guide when they build their own models.
- Prior to the investigation, have students read through the investigation and prepare their data tables. Or you may wish to copy and distribute datasheets and rubrics.

 UNIT RESOURCE BOOK, pp. 193–201

 SCIENCE TOOLKIT, F14

Lab Management

- Place students into small groups of three or four.
- There are a lot of materials for this investigation. It may be helpful to place the items in separate piles on a long table, forming a sort of "buffet table." Students can put the materials they need on cafeteria trays, so that no items are dropped or misplaced.

SAFETY Caution students to take care when using the fans. They should not stick any objects into the turning blades of the fans.

CHAPTER INVESTIGATION

Wind Power

OVERVIEW AND PURPOSE Early windmills were used to pump water and grind flour. In this lab, you will use what you have learned about renewable resources to

- build a model windmill and use it to lift a small weight
- improve its performance by increasing the strength of the wind source

Problem

What effect will increasing the wind strength have on the lifting power of a model windmill?

Hypothesize

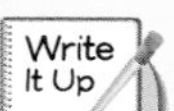

After completing step 8 of the procedure, write a hypothesis to explain what you think will happen in the next two sets of trials. Your hypothesis should take the form of an "If . . . , then . . . , because . . ." statement.

Procedure

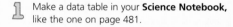

1. Make a data table in your **Science Notebook,** like the one on page 481.

2. Cut a 15 cm square from a file folder. With a ruler, draw lines from the corners toward the center, forming an X. Where the lines cross, draw a circle around the quarter. Cut inward along the lines from the four corners, stopping at the circle. Punch a hole in each corner, as shown. Also punch a hole in the center of the circle.

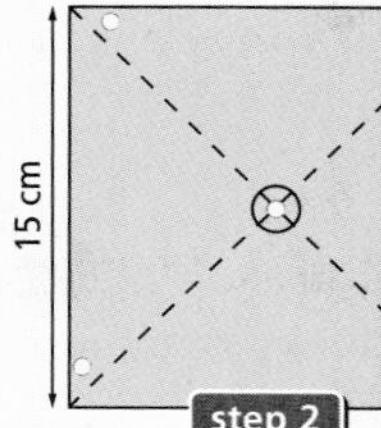

3. Bend the cardboard to align the holes and form a pinwheel. Push a paper fastener through the holes toward the back of the pinwheel. Do not flatten the metal strips of the fastener.

4. Use a pushpin to poke a hole through a straw, about 4 cm from the end. Then push the metal strips through the hole and flatten them at right angles to the straw. Fold the tip of the straw over and tape it to the rest of the straw.

MATERIALS
- half of a file folder
- metric ruler
- quarter
- scissors
- paper punch
- brass paper fastener
- drinking straw
- pushpin
- masking tape
- small paper clip
- pint carton
- 30 cm of string
- clock or stopwatch
- small desktop fan

6.6.a, 6.7.a, 6.7.c

INVESTIGATION RESOURCES

 CHAPTER INVESTIGATION, Wind Power
- Level A, pp. 193–196
- Level B, pp. 197–200
- Level C, p. 201

Advanced students should complete Levels B & C.

 Writing a Lab Report, D12–13

Technology Resources

Customize this student lab as needed or look for an alternative. Print rubrics to assess student lab reports.

 **Lab Generator CD-ROM**

480 Unit 4: **Ecology and Resources**

Content Standard
6.6.a Students know the utility of energy sources is determined by factors that are involved in converting these sources to useful forms and the consequences of the conversion process.

Investigation Standard
6.7.a Develop a hypothesis.

5. Cut the top off the pint carton, as shown. Punch two holes on opposite sides of the carton. Make sure the holes line up and are large enough for the straw to turn easily.

6. Slide the straw through the holes. Tape the string to the end of the straw. Tie a small paper clip (weight) to the other end of the string.

7. Test the model by blowing on the blades. Describe what happens to the weight.

8. Run three trials of the lifting power of the model windmill as you blow on the blades. Keep the amount of force you use constant. Have a classmate use a stopwatch or clock with a second hand to time the trials. Record the results in your data table. Average your results.

9. Vary the strength of the wind by using a small fan at different speeds to turn the windmill's blades. Remember to write a hypothesis explaining what you think will happen in the next two sets of trials.

step 6

Observe and Analyze

Write It Up

1. **MODEL** Draw a picture of the completed windmill. What happens to the weight when the blades turn?
2. **IDENTIFY VARIABLES** What method did you use to increase the wind strength? Add a sketch of this method to your picture to illustrate the experimental procedure.
3. **RECORD OBSERVATIONS** Make sure your data table is completed.
4. **COMPARE** How did the average times it took to raise the weight at different wind strengths differ?

Conclude

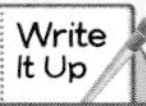

1. **INTERPRET** Answer the question posed under "problem" on page 480.
2. **ANALYZE** Did your results support your hypothesis?
3. **IDENTIFY LIMITS** What limitations or sources of error could have affected your experimental results?
4. **APPLY** Wind-powered turbines are used to generate electricity in some parts of the country. What might limit the usefulness of wind power as an energy source?

INVESTIGATE Further

CHALLENGE How can you get your model windmill to do more work? You might try different weights, or you might build a larger windmill and compare it with your original. Create a new data table. Use a bar graph to compare different weights and wind strengths. How much wind power is needed to lift the additional weight?

Wind Power
Problem
Hypothesize
Observe and Analyze

Table 1. Time to Lift Weight

Wind Force Used	Trial Number	Time (sec)
Student powered	1	
	2	
	3	
	Average	
Fan on low speed	1	
	2	
	3	
	Average	
Fan on high speed	1	
	2	
	3	
	Average	

Conclude

Observe and Analyze

SAMPLE DATA student powered, average time = 5 sec; fan on low speed, average time = 3 sec; fan on high speed, average time = 1 sec

1. *The weight is lifted.*
2. *The method was either using a fan or using two or more people to blow on the windmill. Student sketches should show which method they used to increase wind strength.*
3. *Check student data tables to make sure they are complete.*
4. *Average time decreased as wind strength increased.*

Conclude

1. *Increasing the wind strength increases the lifting power of the windmill.*
2. *Answers will vary, depending upon students' hypotheses.*
3. *using too heavy a weight, bending or distorting the windmill blades, timing inaccurately*
4. *Wind energy requires strong, steady winds; wind farms require a large amount of land. Thus, lack of strong wind or adequate land could limit the use of wind power.*

INVESTIGATE Further

CHALLENGE Test trials on the new models should reflect earlier results—students should see an increase in lifting power as they increase wind strength.

Post-Lab Discussion

Tell students that some relationships between variables are directly proportional (they increase or decrease together), while others are inversely proportional (one increases as the other decreases). Ask: Which variables in the investigation are directly proportional? *wind strength and lifting power* Which variables are inversely proportional? *wind strength and time*

BACK TO

the BIG idea

Tell students to suppose that they had lived in the year 1803. In terms of natural resource use, how would their lives have been different than they are now? *Fossil fuels weren't widely used then, so heat might have come from wood, and lighting from candles. Plastics didn't exist, so many of the items used today wouldn't have been around. Clothes would have been homemade. People would have used horses and boats for travel.*

KEY CONCEPTS SUMMARY

SECTION 13.1

Ask: Is a nonrenewable resource a natural resource or a human-made resource? *natural resource*

Ask: What are renewable resources and nonrenewable resources used for? *energy and products*

SECTION 13.2

Ask: What three uses of copper are illustrated? *electric wiring, piping, sculpture*

Ask: When can minerals form in nature? *Minerals can form when water evaporates, organisms form shells and bones, hot water cools, molten rock cools, and heat and pressure cause changes.*

SECTION 13.3

Ask: What are the recyclable items shown in the photograph, and what are they made of? *aluminum cans and plastic bottles*

Ask: What ways can people conserve resources to reduce the amount of garbage they throw away? *reuse products, donate items to a charity instead of throwing them out, buy products that use less packaging*

SECTION 13.4

Ask: Which one form of energy shown in the diagram is nonrenewable? *nuclear*

Review Concepts

- Big Idea Flow Chart, p. T97
- Chapter Outline, pp. T103–T104

13 Chapter Review

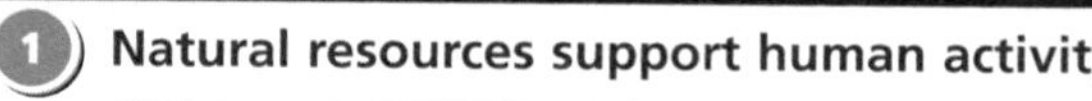

the BIG idea

Society depends on natural resources for energy and materials.

KEY CONCEPTS SUMMARY

1 Natural resources support human activity.

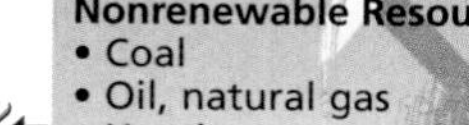

VOCABULARY
natural resource p. 449
renewable resource p. 450
nonrenewable resource p. 450
fossil fuel p. 452

2 Minerals and rocks are nonrenewable resources.

Minerals have many uses.

VOCABULARY
ore p. 462

3 Resources can be conserved and recycled.

People can **conserve** natural resources by reducing waste at the source and reusing products.

Recycling helps people recover materials, reduce the use of fossil fuels, and protect the environment and human health.

VOCABULARY
conservation p. 467
recycling p. 468

4 Resources can be converted to useful forms.

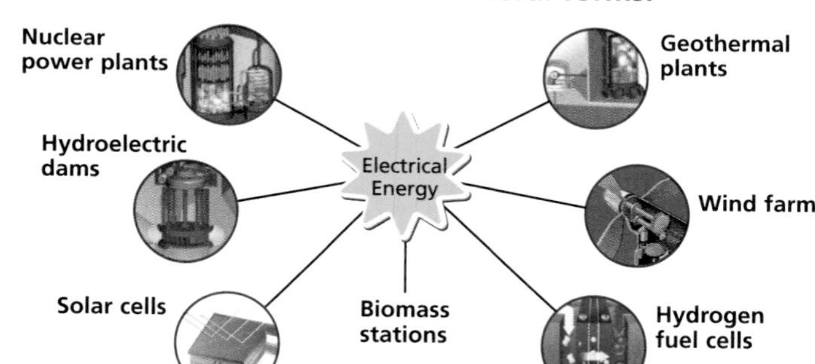

VOCABULARY
hydroelectric energy p. 472
geothermal energy p. 473
solar cell p. 475
biomass p. 476
hydrogen fuel cell p. 476
nuclear energy p. 477

Technology Resources

Have students visit **ClassZone.com** or use the CD-ROM for a cumulative review of concepts.

 **CONTENT REVIEW**

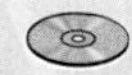 **CONTENT REVIEW CD-ROM**

Engage students in a whole-class interactive review of Key Concepts. Edit content as you wish.

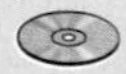 **POWER PRESENTATIONS**

Reviewing Vocabulary

Copy the chart below, and write each word's definition. Use the meaning of the underlined word part to help you.

Word	Meaning of Part	Definition
1. Natural resource	to rise again	
2. Renewable resource	to refresh	
3. Nonrenewable resource	not to refresh	
4. Fossil fuel	material that burns	
5. Nuclear energy	nut or kernel	
6. Geothermal energy	heat	

Reviewing Key Concepts

Multiple Choice *Choose the letter of the best answer.*

7. What makes wind a renewable resource? (6.6.b)
   a. no pollution
   b. varied speeds
   c. no waste products
   d. unlimited supply

8. Which of the following is a nonrenewable resource? (6.6.b)
   a. trees
   b. oil
   c. sunlight
   d. geothermal energy

9. Fossil fuels provide most of the energy used in the United States because they (6.6.a)
   a. are found everywhere in the world
   b. have no harmful byproducts
   c. are easy to transport and burn
   d. can be quickly replaced in nature

10. Diamonds are often used as (6.6.c)
    a. pigments
    b. abrasives
    c. ores
    d. metals

11. Which of the following is not a problem associated with the use of fossil fuels? (6.6.a)
    a. air pollution
    b. explosions
    c. limited supply
    d. radioactivity

12. Which category of products is the most dependent on oil? (6.6.c)
    a. pottery
    b. coins
    c. plastics
    d. paper

13. How do nuclear power plants generate the heat energy to turn water into steam? (6.3.a)
    a. by drawing hot water from Earth's crust
    b. by producing an electric current
    c. by turning a turbine
    d. by splitting uranium atoms

14. Hydroelectric energy is produced by using (6.3.a)
    a. wind
    b. sunlight
    c. moving water
    d. living matter

15. Solar cells produce which of the following? (6.3.a)
    a. heat energy
    b. steam
    c. radioactivity
    d. electricity

16. What limits the use of biomass liquid fuels? (6.6.a)
    a. not enough plant material
    b. too expensive to mass-produce
    c. not enough energy generated
    d. too many harmful byproducts

17. Open-pit mining is used to obtain ores that lie (6.6.a)
    a. under flat land
    b. deep in Earth's crust
    c. near the surface of Earth
    d. in riverbeds

Short Answer *Write a few sentences to answer each question.*

18. Why is it important to find renewable sources of energy? (6.6.b)

19. Why is conservation of natural resources important? (6.6.b)

20. How can recycling help reduce the use of fossil fuels? (6.6.a)

Reviewing Vocabulary

1. any energy resource, organism, or substance found in nature that people use

2. a natural resource that can be replaced in nature at about the same rate it is used

3. a natural resource that exists in a fixed amount or that is used up faster than it can be replaced in nature

4. a nonrenewable energy source made from once-living plants and animals that were buried in Earth's crust for millions of years

5. an alternative energy source that comes from splitting uranium atoms

6. energy that comes from using Earth's heat in the crust

Reviewing Key Concepts

7. d
8. b
9. c
10. b
11. d
12. c
13. d
14. c
15. d
16. b
17. c

18. Supplies of fossil fuels are running out. Also, renewable energy sources will reduce the amount of air, water, and soil pollution released into the environment.

19. It can help make limited resources last longer by reducing waste and reusing products instead of buying new ones.

20. It takes less fossil-fuel generated electricity to make products from recycled materials than to make new products.

ASSESSMENT RESOURCES

ASSESSMENT BOOK
- Chapter Test A, pp. 293–296
- Chapter Test B, pp. 297–300
- Chapter Test C, pp. 301–304
- Alternative Assessment, pp. 305–306

STANDARDS REVIEW AND PRACTICE, pp. 23–24, 51–58, 61–62

Technology Resources

Edit test items and answer choices.

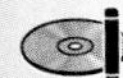

Test Generator CD-ROM

Visit **ClassZone.com** to extend test practice.

Test Practice

Thinking Critically

21. nonrenewable: red, blue, green
    renewable: purple, orange, aqua, yellow
22. Region A: 75%, Region B: 50%
23. Region B because 50% of its energy comes from renewable resources
24. It may have few natural renewable resources and must rely on fossil fuels for most of its energy.
25. Region A: climate is sunny but not windy; Region B: climate is more windy but with fewer sunny days
26. Region B might have rivers
27. Circle graph should show 50% fossil fuels, a small % of solar energy, and the rest divided between biomass and wind energy.

Charting Information

28. fission
29. smog, acid rain, other pollution
30. wind
31. flowing water; none
32. solar cells; none
33. biomass
34. electrons; water, heat

the BIG idea

35. APPLY Students should list ways to obtain energy from renewable and nonrenewable sources.
36. SYNTHESIZE Possible criteria: nonpolluting, renewable, cheap to mass produce, provide a lot of energy, and usable in power plants, homes, and vehicles.
37. APPLY Possible answers: encourage people to reuse products, sponsor flea markets and rummage sales to reuse items, show people how to save energy at home, require carpools.

UNIT PROJECTS

Collect schedules, materials lists, and questions. Be sure dates and materials are obtainable, and questions are focused.

 Unit Projects, pp. 5–10

Thinking Critically

Use the circle graphs below to answer the following questions.

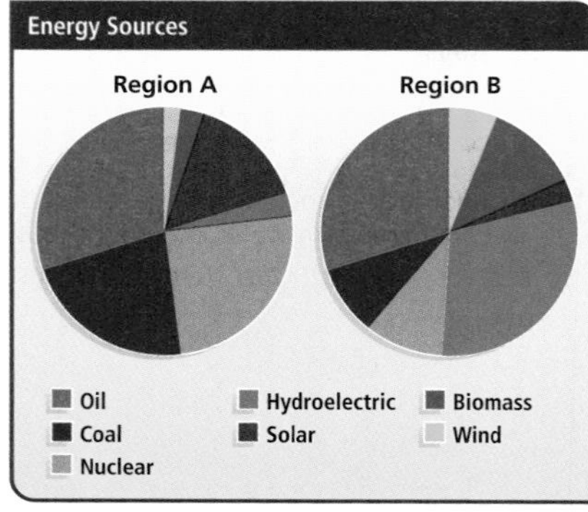

21. **INTERPRET** Which colors represent nonrenewable resources and which ones represent renewable resources? **(6.6.b)**

22. **CALCULATE** Fossil fuels and nuclear energy together represent about what percentage of the total energy resources in region A? in region B? **(6.6.a)**

23. **PREDICT** If the price of nonrenewable energy sources rises sharply, which region is likely to be affected more? Why? **(6.6.b)**

24. **DRAW CONCLUSIONS** What might be one reason that region A uses a greater percentage of fossil fuels and nuclear energy than region B does? **(6.6.a)**

25. **INFER** Look at the renewable energy sources used in each region. What can you infer about the climate in region A compared with the climate in region B? **(6.6.b)**

26. **IDENTIFY CAUSES** Why might region B use so much more hydroelectric energy? **(6.6.a)**

27. **SYNTHESIZE** Region C gets half of its electrical energy from fossil fuels. The region has only 100 days of clear sunlight a year but has abundant plant crops and strong, steady winds. Draw a circle graph for region C, showing the percentage of fossil fuels and the percentage of each renewable energy source the region might use. Explain your choices. **(6.6.b)**

Charting Information

Copy and fill in this chart.

Energy Source	Produces Energy From	Byproducts
28. uranium		radioactive wa
29. fossil fuel	burning oil, coal	
30.	moving air	none
31. river		
32. sunlight		
33.	burning wood	carbon dioxide
34. hydrogen		

the BIG idea

35. **APPLY** Look again at the photograph on pages 446–447. Reread the question on the photograph. Now that you have finished the chapter, what would you add to or change about your answer? **(6.6.b)**

36. **SYNTHESIZE** Imagine that you are a scientist or engineer who is developing a new energy source. What characteristics would you want your energy source to have? List your choices in order of importance, with the most important first—for instance, nonpolluting, inexpensive to mass-produce, and so on. **(6.6.a)**

37. **APPLY** If you were in charge of your town or city, what measures would you take to conserve natural resources? **(6.6.b)**

UNIT PROJECTS

If you need to create graphs or other visuals for your project, be sure you have graph paper, poster board, markers, and other supplies.

MONITOR AND RETEACH

If students have trouble applying the concepts in items 21–27, remind them that

- the United States gets most of its energy from fossil fuel;
- fossil fuels are nonrenewable.

Students may benefit from summarizing one or more sections of the chapter.

 Summarizing the Chapter, pp. 211–212

Standards-Based Assessment

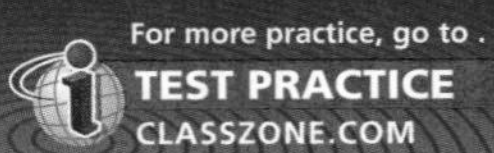

Analyzing a Graph

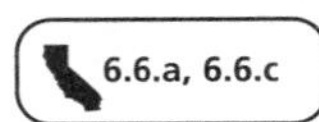

This graph shows what happens to fuels consumed for energy in the United States. Some of this energy is used and some is lost as heat. Use the graph to answer the questions below.

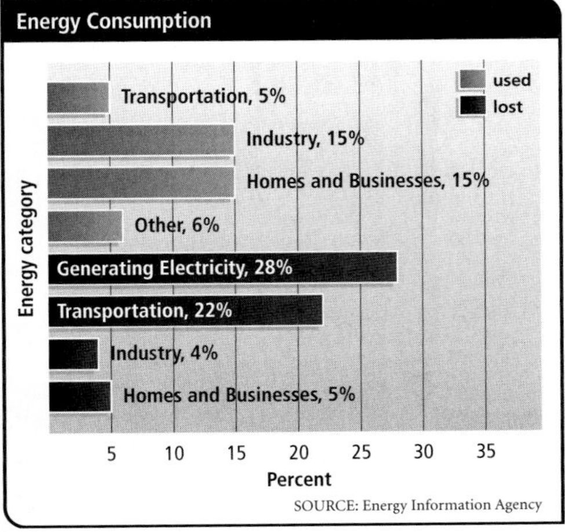

1. How much energy is used for transportation and industry?
   - a. 15 percent
   - b. 20 percent
   - c. 30 percent
   - d. 35 percent
2. What is the total amount of energy used and lost in industry?
   - a. 4 percent
   - b. 15 percent
   - c. 19 percent
   - d. 28 percent
3. What is the largest category of lost energy?
   - a. transportation
   - b. homes and businesses
   - c. generating electricity
   - d. industry
4. Which category would include energy used to heat a grocery store?
   - a. used in homes and businesses
   - b. used in industry
   - c. used in transportation
   - d. used in other ways
5. If cars burned fuel more efficiently, which category would probably be smaller?
   - a. used in homes and businesses
   - b. used in other ways
   - c. lost in transportation
   - d. lost in industry
6. Which statement is true about energy used and lost in transportation?
   - a. The amount lost is greater than the amount used.
   - b. The amount used is greater than the amount lost.
   - c. The amounts used and lost are about the same.
   - d. The amounts used and lost are very low in comparison to the other categories.

Extended Response

Answer the two questions below in detail. Include some of the terms in the word box. In your answers, underline each term you use.

reusing	recycling	conserve	extends
electricity	hot water	factories	

7. Explain the difference between reusing and recycling products. How does each activity help to reduce the use of natural resources?

8. Give three or more examples of ways in which people in the United States use or rely on energy resources every day.

REFLECTING ON THE CHAPTER

Have students answer the following questions in their **Science Notebook:**

1. How did this chapter change your view of natural resources and energy production?
2. Do you think that people in the United States will become better conservationists? Why or why not? Will you? Why or why not?
3. What was the most interesting part of your Unit Project?

California Content Standards

6.6.a Students know the utility of energy sources is determined by factors that are involved in converting these sources to useful forms and the consequences of the conversion process.

6.6.c Students know the natural origin of the materials used to make common objects.

Analyzing a Graph

1. b	*3.c*	*5. c*
2. c	*4. a*	*6. a*

Extended Response

7. RUBRIC

4 points for a response that correctly answers the question and uses the following terms accurately:

- reusing
- recycling
- conserve
- extends

Sample answer: Reusing means using a product more than once, so that fewer products need to be made. This conserves resources, such as oil, wood, and other raw materials. Recycling means recovering materials that would otherwise be thrown away. Less energy is used to make products from recycled materials. Less energy means less fossil fuel or uranium is used, which extends these resources.

3 points correctly answers question and uses three terms accurately
2 points correctly answers question and uses two terms accurately
1 point correctly answers question and uses one term correctly

8. RUBRIC

3 points for a response that correctly answers the question and uses the following terms accurately:

- electricity
- hot water
- factories

Sample answer: Nearly every appliance people use runs on electricity. People depend on a car to get them to work and other places every day. Even hot water can be used as energy in a geothermal plant. Most factories are powered by fossil fuels

2 points correctly answers question and uses two terms correctly
1 point correctly answers question and uses one term correctly

CHAPTER

Human Impact on Ecosystems

Life Science
UNIFYING PRINCIPLES

PRINCIPLE 1
All living things share common characteristics.

PRINCIPLE 2
All living things share common needs.

PRINCIPLE 3
Living things meet their needs through interactions with the environment.

PRINCIPLE 4
The types and numbers of living things change over time.

Unit: Ecology and Resources
BIG IDEAS

CHAPTER 11
Ecosystems and Biomes
Matter and energy together support life within an environment.

CHAPTER 12
Interactions Within Ecosystems
Living things within an ecosystem interact with each other and the environment.

CHAPTER 13
Natural Resources
Society depends on natural resources for energy and materials.

CHAPTER 14
Human Impact on Ecosystems
Humans and human population growth affect the environment.

CHAPTER 14
KEY CONCEPTS

SECTION 1

Human population growth presents challenges.

1. The human population is increasing.
2. Human populations can put pressure on ecosystems.

SECTION 2

Human activities affect the environment.

1. Humans use many resources.
2. Pollution endangers biodiversity.
3. Habitat loss endangers biodiversity.

SECTION 3

People are working to protect ecosystems.

1. Environmental awareness is growing.
2. Conserving resources protects ecosystems.
3. Think globally, act locally.

The Big Idea Flow Chart is available on p. T105 in the **TRANSPARENCY BOOK.**

Previewing Content

SECTION

Human population growth presents challenges. pp. 489–496

1. The human population is increasing.
Earth's human population was 6 billion in 1999 and is expected to be 9 billion by 2050. Part of the reason for growth is longer life spans, and another reason is the high birth rate.

The human population is not following the usual pattern of leveling off at carrying capacity.

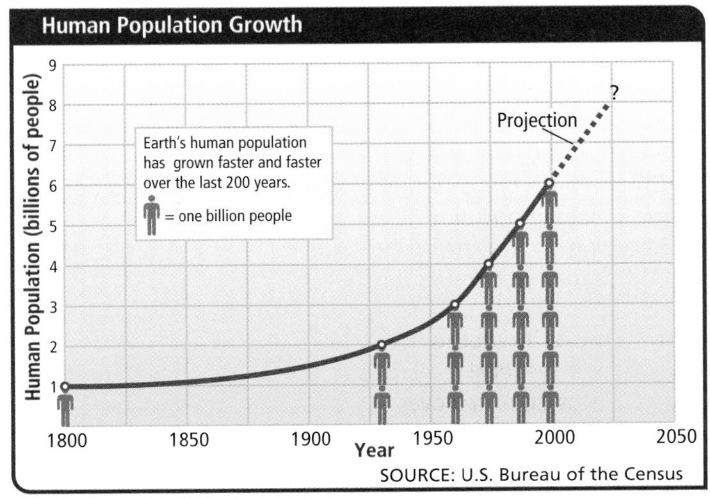

2. Human populations can put pressure on ecosystems.
The pressures humans place on ecosystems arise from waste, resource use, and land-use changes.
- Waste fills up land with toxic garbage. Sewage releases contaminants into the environment.
- Natural resources are not evenly distributed. Much of the world's population lives in Asia and Africa, where natural resources are often exported for commercial interests.
- High demand for water is difficult to meet, especially in arid regions. Water is a finite resource.
- A high **population density** contributes to overuse of resources and disturbance or destruction of natural habitats.

SECTION

Human activities affect the environment. pp. 497–505

1. Humans use many resources.
- Renewable resources include trees, sunlight, and water.
- Nonrenewable resources include fossil fuels (coal, oil, natural gas) and minerals such as copper and gold.

2. Pollution endangers biodiversity.
Biodiversity describes the number and variety of living things in an ecosystem. Ecosystems with a variety of species are healthier and more able to recover from problems such as disease.
- Air and water **pollution** affect entire ecosystems.
- Use of fossil fuels causes acid rain, which destroys trees, kills fish, and damages soil.
- Water pollution is caused by oil spills, soil erosion, wastewater, and chemical and waste runoff from farm fields, animal feedlots, and landfills. Water pollution poisons fish, causes algal blooms, and damages the entire food web.
- Pollution moves across systems.

3. Habitat loss endangers biodiversity.
If living space is limited or a food source is removed, then the number of organisms in a biological community will be reduced. Human actions remove habitat, for example, by clear-cutting forests.

Invasive species change habitat. An invasive species is a nonnative species that is introduced by humans or moves in and supplants native species.

Common Misconceptions

MISCONCEPTION DATABASE
CLASSZONE.COM Background on student misconceptions

POLLUTION Most students hold the misconception that air pollution and water pollution affect a limited area. In fact, air pollution can fall to the ground in precipitation, seep into watersheds, and run into bodies of water. Water pollution can evaporate into the air, all the while being carried to larger and larger areas.

 This misconception is addressed on p. 499.

BIODIVERSITY Students sometimes think that changes in population of an organism may not affect an ecosystem because some organisms are not important. Students also may think that a change in only one population will have limited or no effects on an ecosystem. In fact, all populations are important and affect the entire ecosystem.

 This misconception is addressed on p. 500.

Previewing Content

SECTION

People are working to protect ecosystems. pp. 506–515

1. Environmental awareness is growing.
Awareness of the environment and environmental protection have slowly progressed since the nineteenth century in the United States. Some milestones are these:

- Yellowstone National Park, the first U.S. national park, was established in 1872.
- *Silent Spring,* by Rachel Carson, a book about toxic chemical use published in 1962, raised public awareness about how pollution spreads throughout ecosystems. The author's research on the toxicity of DDT in the environment led to U.S. laws banning its use.
- Citizen efforts to preserve biodiversity have included the founding of the Nature Conservancy and the National Wildlife Federation.
- More recent government efforts to protect ecosystems include the Endangered Species Act, the Clean Air Act, the Clean Water Act, and the National Environmental Policy Act.

Discontinuing DDT use has permitted several raptors to recover from drastically low populations.

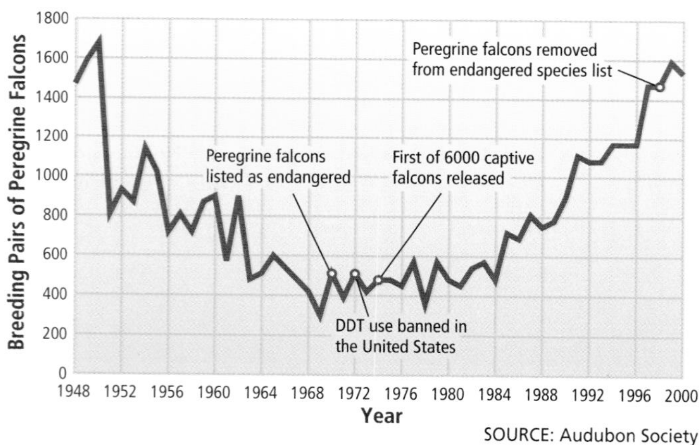

SOURCE: Audubon Society

2. Conserving resources protects ecosystems.
Sustainable practices are ways to use resources without using them up. They include the following established practices:

- U.S. farms practice conservation tillage and use natural fertilizers, such as compost, and natural pest controls, such as ladybugs.
- Forestry practices are changing to strip and selective cutting, which improve regrowth and help prevent erosion.
- Energy companies are exploring alternative sources of energy such as hydropower (energy generated by the force of flowing water), geothermal power (energy from the heat at Earth's core), and wind power (generated from windmills).
- Cutting back on fossil-fuel consumption in cars and homes will decrease pollution.
- Recycling efforts keep glass, aluminum, some plastic, paper, and cardboard out of landfills.

3. Think globally, act locally.
Working at the local level, people are involved in many efforts to help ecosystems recover.

- Prairie recovery projects are taking place in the Midwest.
- The United States and Canada have worked together to clean up Lake Erie, which was heavily polluted by phosphorus.
- River and watershed restoration takes place in areas throughout the United States, largely through local community efforts. Businesspeople, economists, and urban planners are also beginning to look at ecosystems as service providers, with economic value to the community.

Common Misconceptions

MISCONCEPTION DATABASE
CLASSZONE.COM Background on student misconceptions

INVASIVE SPECIES Some students may think that all plant and animal species, including invasive species, benefit the environment. In fact, because invasive species often have no local predators, they can cause decreases in populations of native organisms through competition. They can use up resources and become difficult to remove or control.

 This misconception is addressed on p. 504.

SCIENTIFIC MODELS Middle-school students generally think of the world concretely and often interpret a scientific model too literally. They often believe that scientific models are exact representations of the world. Every model is in some way different from that which it represents.

 This misconception is addressed on p. 515.

Previewing Labs

Lab Generator CD-ROM
Edit these Pupil Edition labs and generate alternative labs.

EXPLORE the BIG idea

How Easily Does Polluted Water Move Through Plants? p. 487 To discover how pollution could affect plants, students observe that dye moves through plants.	**TIME** 10 minutes **MATERIALS** cup of water, food coloring, stalk of celery
Internet Activity: The Environment, p. 487 Students use the Internet to explore how humans can change ecosystems.	**TIME** 20 minutes **MATERIALS** computer with Internet access

SECTION 1

EXPLORE Sharing Resources, p. 489 Students divide objects among members of a group and discover how difficult it is to share unequal resources.	**TIME** 15 minutes **MATERIALS** bag; assorted unlike objects such as pennies, blocks, pencils
INVESTIGATE Water Usage, p. 492 Students determine how much water they use in a week. **ALTERNATIVE:** Reading Activity, URB p. 273 R Water Use Sheet, p. 222	**TIME** 30 minutes **MATERIALS** water use sheet, calculator

SECTION 2

INVESTIGATE Particles in the Air, p. 498 Students collect and observe samples of local air pollution. **ALTERNATIVE:** Teacher Demonstration, URB p. 273	**TIME** 30 minutes **MATERIALS** 2 index cards, marker, hole punch, string, scissors, petroleum jelly, hand lens

SECTION 3

EXPLORE Environmental Impacts, p. 506 Students add water to compressed and uncompressed soil to see how trampling could affect water absorption.	**TIME** 15 minutes **MATERIALS** 2 plant pots with trays, potting soil, measuring cup, stopwatch, water
CHAPTER INVESTIGATION Cleaning Oil Spills, pp. 514–515 Students create and clean up an oil spill, exploring different methods of cleanup. **ALTERNATIVE:** Teacher Modeling, URB p. 273	**TIME** 40 minutes **MATERIALS** small beaker, vegetable oil, turmeric, spoon, aluminum baking pan, sand, large beaker, water, sponge, dish soap, rubbing alcohol, paper towels, cotton balls, cotton rag, cornstarch, yarn, feather, seaweed

R **Additional INVESTIGATION,** Pollutants on the Move, A, B, & C, pp. 262–270; Teacher Instructions, pp. 273–274

Previewing Chapter Resources

CHAPTER 14
Human Impact on Ecosystems

INTEGRATED TECHNOLOGY

CLASSZONE.COM
- eEdition Plus
- EasyPlanner Plus
- Misconception Database
- Content Review
- Test Practice
- Visualization
- Resource Centers
- Internet Activity: The Environment
- Math Tutorial

SCILINKS.ORG

SCILINKS

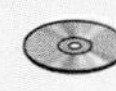
CD-ROMS
- eEdition
- EasyPlanner
- Power Presentations
- Content Review
- Lab Generator
- Test Generator

AUDIO CDS
- Audio Readings
- Audio Readings in Spanish

LABS AND ACTIVITIES

EXPLORE the Big Idea, p. 487
- How Easily Does Polluted Water Move Through Plants?
- Internet Activity: The Environment

UNIT RESOURCE BOOK
Unit Projects, pp. 5–10

Lab Generator CD-ROM
Generate customized labs.

SECTION

Human population growth presents challenges.
pp. 489–496

Lesson Plan, pp. 213–214

- **VISUALIZATION,** Population Growth
- **RESOURCE CENTER,** Urban Expansion

TRANSPARENCY BOOK
- Big Idea Flow Chart, p. T105
- Daily Vocabulary Scaffolding, p. T106
- Note-Taking Model, p. T107
- 3-Minute Warm-Up, p. T108
- "Landfill Cross Section" Visual, p. T110

- EXPLORE Sharing Resources, p. 489
- INVESTIGATE Water Usage, p. 492
- California Close-Up, p. 496

UNIT RESOURCE BOOK
- Water Use Sheet, p. 222
- Datasheet, Water Usage, p. 223

SECTION
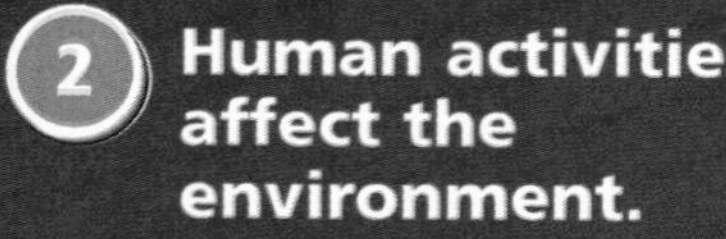
Human activities affect the environment.
pp. 497–505

Lesson Plan, pp. 225–226

- **RESOURCE CENTER,** Natural Resources
- **MATH TUTORIAL**

TRANSPARENCY BOOK
- Daily Vocabulary Scaffolding, p. T106
- 3-Minute Warm-Up, p. T108

- INVESTIGATE Particles in the Air, p. 498
- Math in Science, p. 505

UNIT RESOURCE BOOK
- Datasheet, Particles in the Air, p. 234
- Math Support, p. 251
- Math Practice, p. 252
- Additional INVESTIGATION, Pollutants on the Move, A, B, & C, pp. 262–270

SECTION

People are working to protect ecosystems.
pp. 506–515

Lesson Plan, pp. 236–237

- **RESOURCE CENTER,** Ecosystem Recovery
- **RESOURCE CENTER,** Water Conservation

TRANSPARENCY BOOK
- Big Idea Flow Chart, p. T105
- Daily Vocabulary Scaffolding, p. T106
- 3-Minute Warm-Up, p. T109
- Chapter Outline, pp. T111–T112

- EXPLORE Environmental Impacts, p. 506
- CHAPTER INVESTIGATION, Cleaning Oil Spills, pp. 514–515

UNIT RESOURCE BOOK
CHAPTER INVESTIGATION, Cleaning Oil Spills, A, B, & C, pp. 253–261

KEY TO ICONS

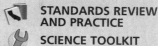

  CD/CD-ROM
 Teacher Edition
 TRANSPARENCY BOOK
 STANDARDS REVIEW AND PRACTICE
 INTERNET
 Pupil Edition
 UNIT RESOURCE BOOK
 ASSESSMENT BOOK
 SCIENCE TOOLKIT

READING AND REINFORCEMENT	ASSESSMENT	STANDARDS
 **Modified Lesson Plans for English Learners,** pp. 51–53  • Magnet Words, B24–25 • Choose Your Own Strategy, C36, C42–43 • Daily Vocabulary Scaffolding, H1–8  **UNIT RESOURCE BOOK** • Vocabulary Practice, pp. 248–249 • Decoding Support, p. 250 • Summarizing the Chapter, pp. 271–272 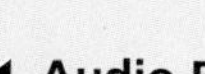 **Audio Readings CD** Listen to Pupil Edition. **Audio Readings in Spanish CD** Listen to Pupil Edition in Spanish.	 • Chapter Review, pp. 517–518 • Standards-Based Assessment, p. 519  **ASSESSMENT BOOK** • Diagnostic Test, pp. 307–308 • Chapter Test, A, B, & C, pp. 312–323 • Alternative Assessment, pp. 324–325 • Unit Test, A, B, & C, pp. 326–337  **STANDARDS REVIEW AND PRACTICE,** pp. 49–58, 61–62, 65–66  **McDougal Littell Assessment System**  **Test Generator CD-ROM** Generate customized and Spanish tests.	California Content Standards 6.5.e, 6.6.a, 6.6.b, 6.6.c, 6.7.a, 6.7.c, 6.7.d, 6.7.e See p. 486 for the standards.
 **UNIT RESOURCE BOOK** • Reading Study Guide, A & B, pp. 215–218 • Spanish Reading Study Guide, pp. 219–220 • Challenge and Extension, p. 221 • Reinforcing Key Concepts, p. 224	 Ongoing Assessment, pp. 490–491, 493–495  Section 14.1 Review, p. 495 **ASSESSMENT BOOK** Section 14.1 Quiz, p. 309	California Content Standards 6.5.e, 6.6.b
UNIT RESOURCE BOOK • Reading Study Guide, A & B, pp. 227–230 • Spanish Reading Study Guide, pp. 231–232 • Challenge and Extension, p. 233 • Reinforcing Key Concepts, p. 235 • Challenge Reading, pp. 246–247	 Ongoing Assessment, pp. 498–503  Section 14.2 Review, p. 504  **ASSESSMENT BOOK** Section 14.2 Quiz, p. 310	California Content Standards 6.5.e, 6.6.a, 6.6.b
 **UNIT RESOURCE BOOK** • Reading Study Guide, A & B, pp. 238–241 • Spanish Reading Study Guide, pp. 242–243 • Challenge and Extension, p. 244 • Reinforcing Key Concepts, p. 245	 Ongoing Assessment, pp. 507–508, 510–512  Section 14.3 Review, p. 513 **ASSESSMENT BOOK** Section 14.3 Quiz, p. 311	California Content Standards 6.5.e, 6.6.a, 6.6.b, 6.6.c, 6.7.a, 6.7.d; 6.7.e

Previewing Resources for Differentiated Instruction

CHAPTER INVESTIGATION

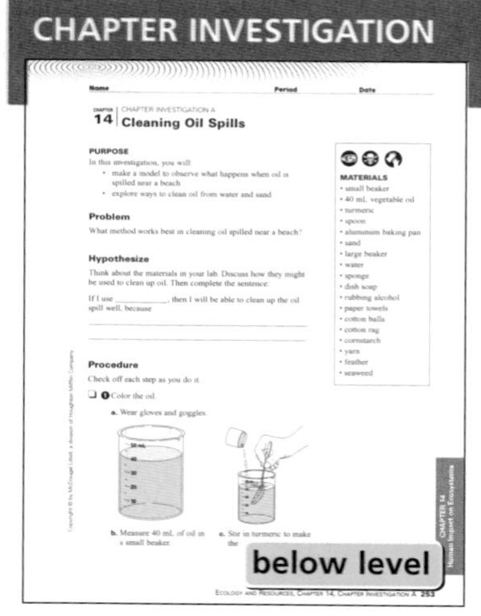

UNIT RESOURCE BOOK, pp. 253–256

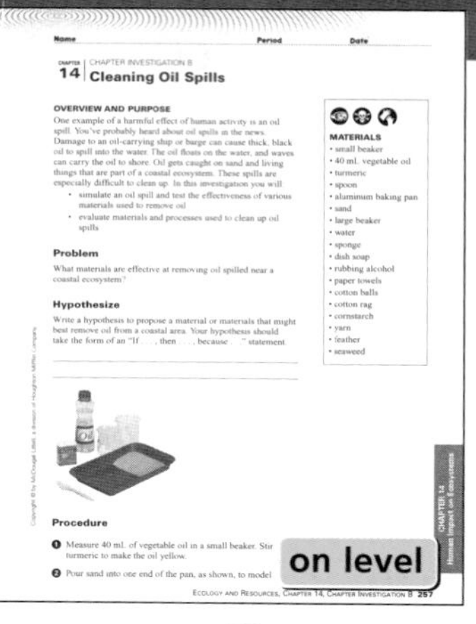

pp. 257–260

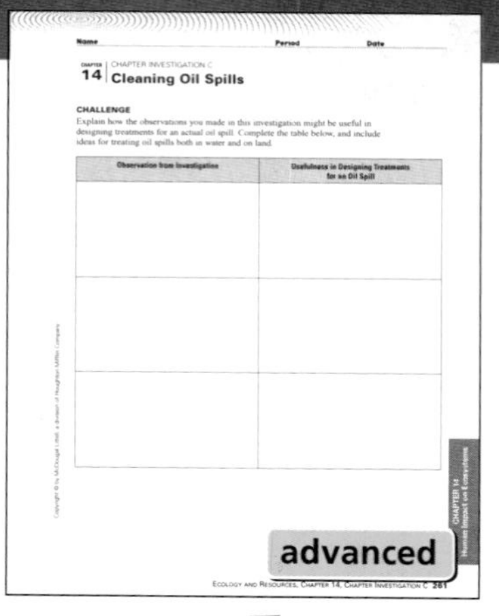

pp. 257–261

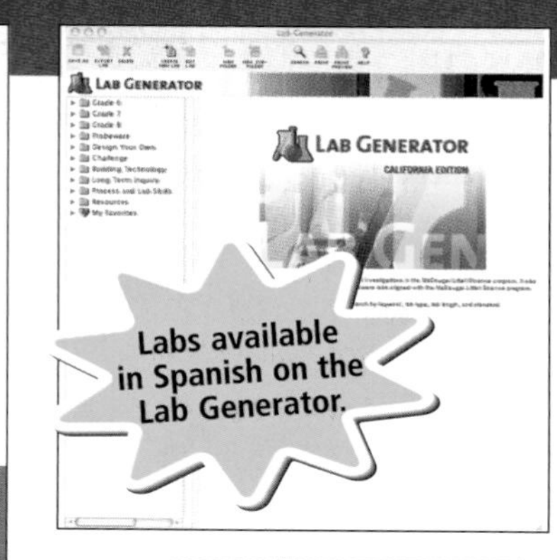

READING STUDY GUIDE

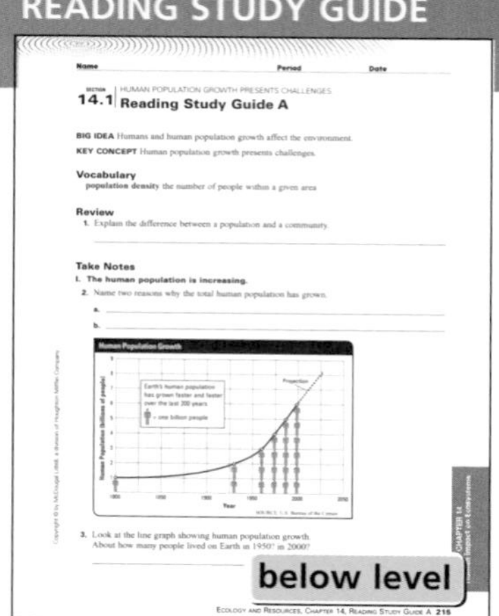

UNIT RESOURCE BOOK, pp. 215–216

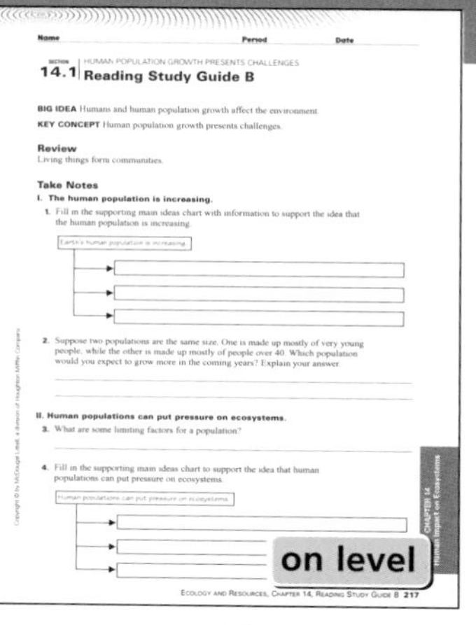

pp. 217–218

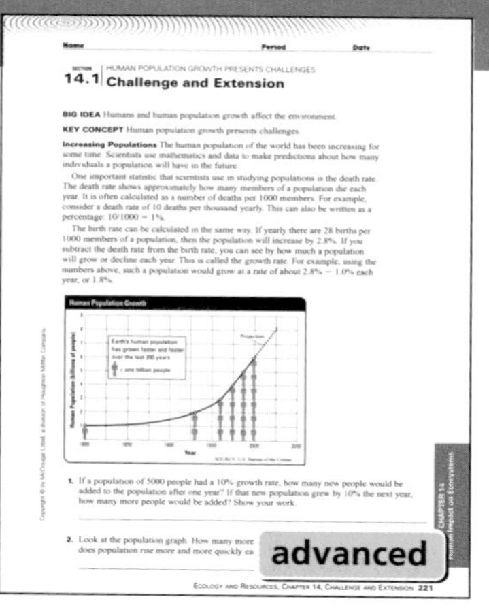

p. 221

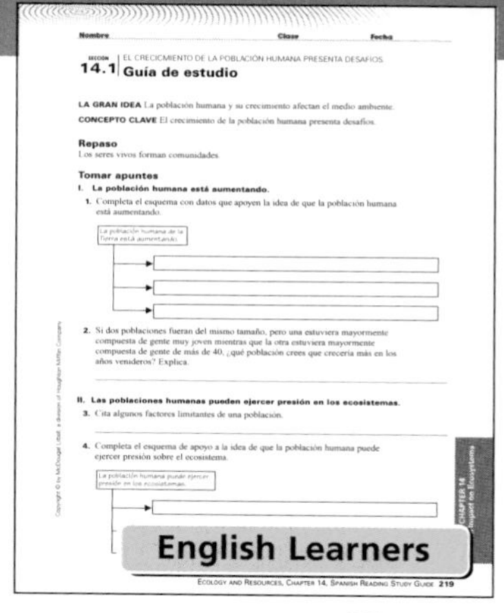

p. 219

CHAPTER TEST

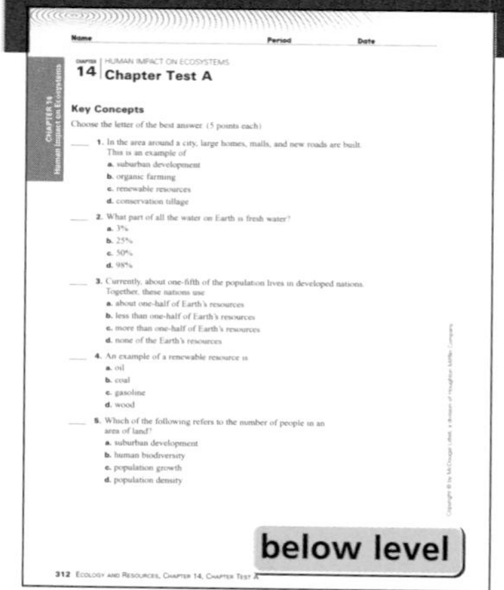

ASSESSMENT BOOK, pp. 312–315

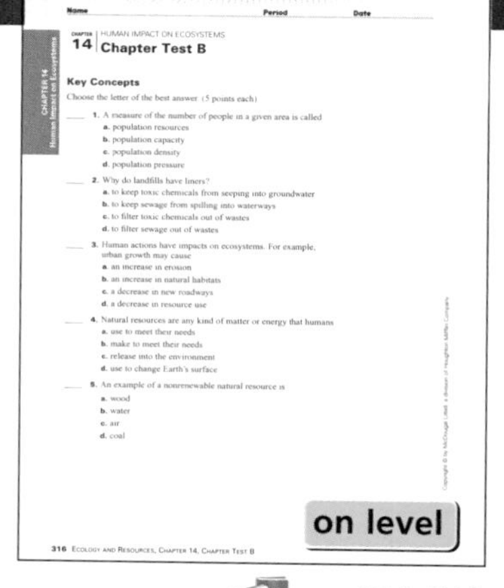

pp. 316–319

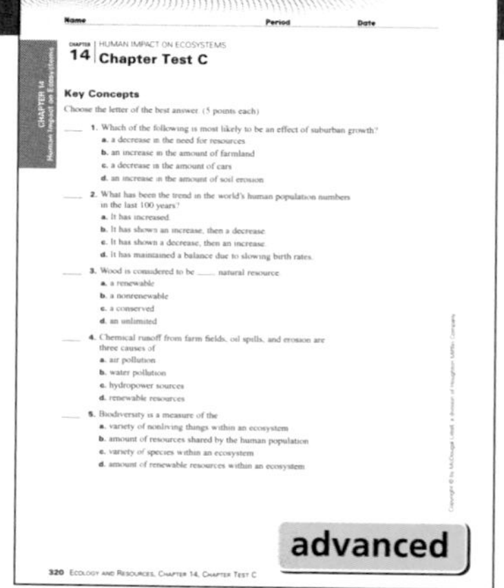

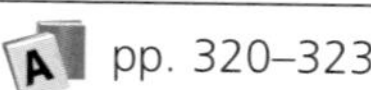
pp. 320–323

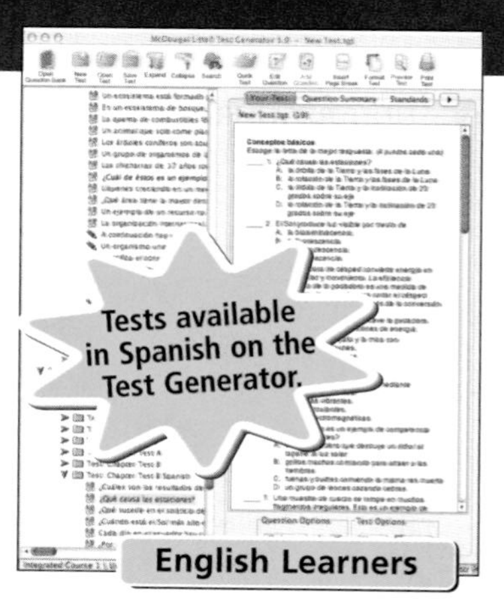

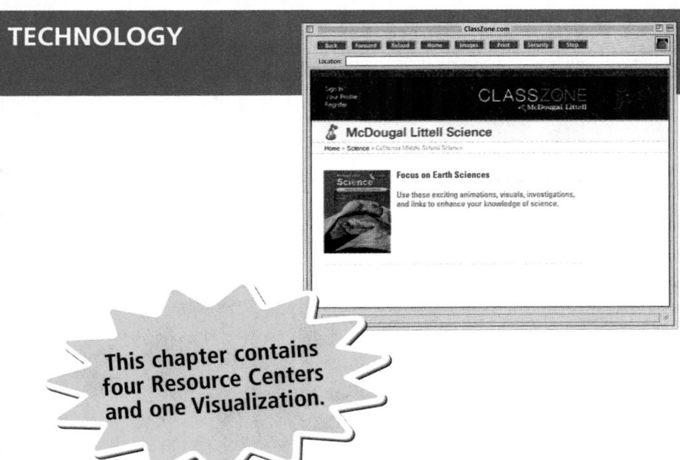

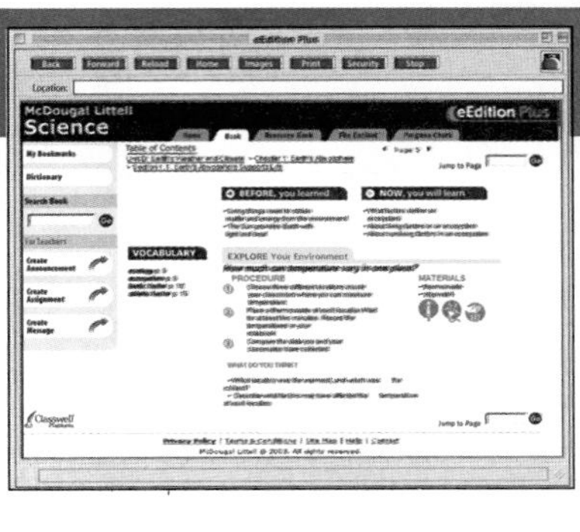

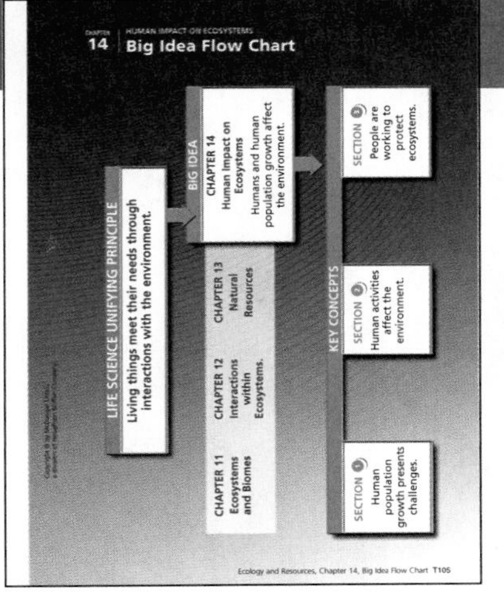

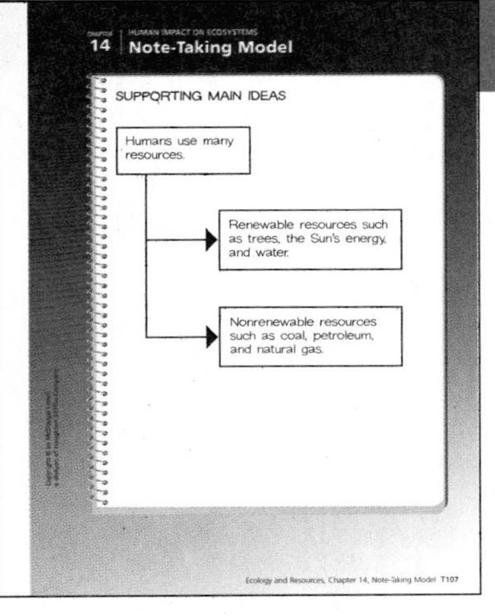

14 Note-Taking Model
SUPPORTING MAIN IDEAS
Humans use many resources.
Renewable resources such as trees, the Sun's energy, and water.
Nonrenewable resources such as coal, petroleum, and natural gas.

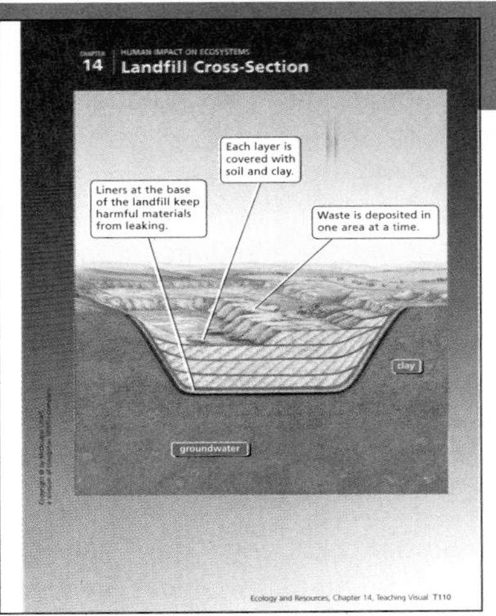

TRANSPARENCY BOOK, p. T105

p. T107

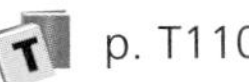
p. T110

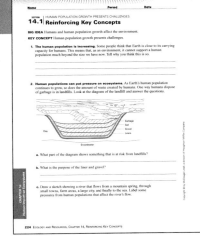

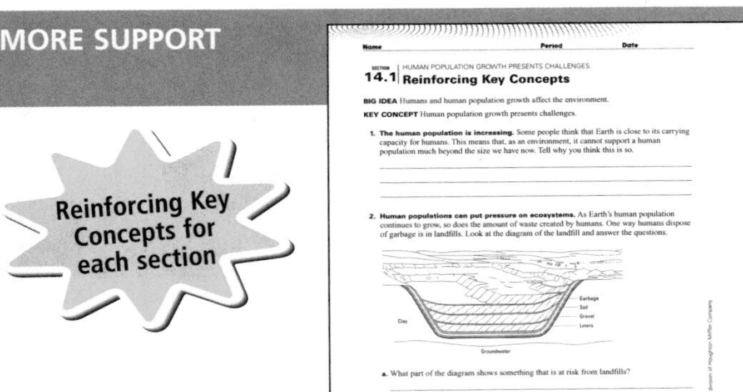

MORE SUPPORT
Reinforcing Key Concepts for each section
14.1 Reinforcing Key Concepts

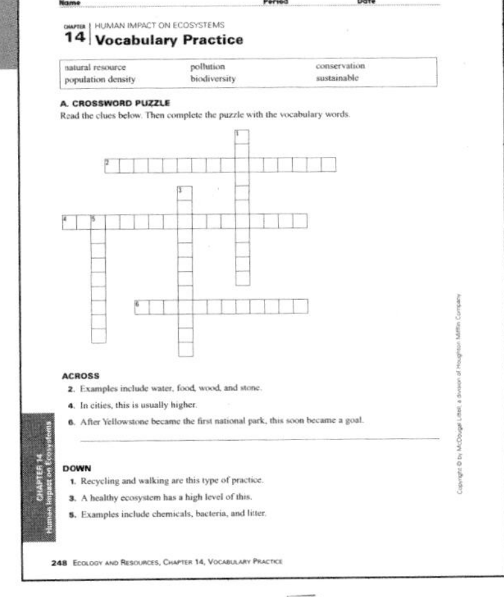

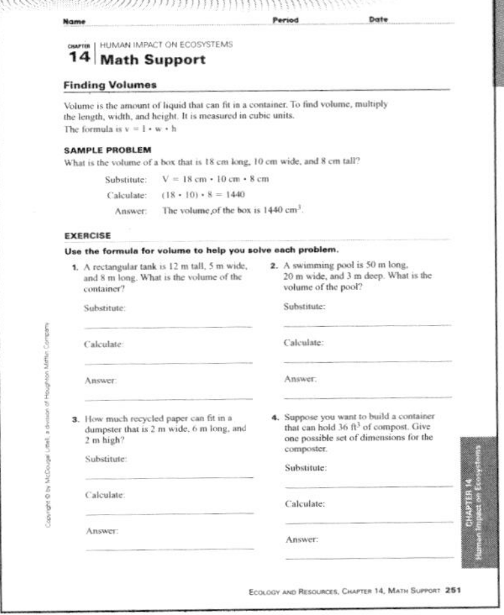

UNIT RESOURCE BOOK, p. 224

pp. 248–249

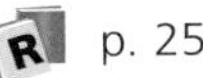
p. 251

CHAPTER

Human Impact on Ecosystems

INTRODUCE

the BIG idea

Have students look at the photograph of cars on a California freeway system and discuss how the question in the box links to the Big Idea:

- What items did humans add to this landscape?
- How do you think humans altered the original landscape?

California Content Standards

6.5.e Students know the number and types of organisms an ecosystem can support depends on the resources available and on abiotic factors, such as quantities of light and water, a range of temperatures, and soil composition.

6.6.a Students know the utility of energy sources is determined by factors that are involved in converting these sources to useful forms and the consequences of the conversion process.

6.6.b Students know different natural energy and material resources, including air, soil, rocks, minerals, petroleum, fresh water, wildlife, and forests, and know how to classify them as renewable or nonrenewable.

6.6.c Students know the natural origin of the materials used to make common objects.

6.7.a Develop a hypothesis.

6.7.c Construct appropriate graphs from data and develop qualitative statements about the relationships between variables.

6.7.e Recognize whether evidence is consistent with a proposed explanation.

CHAPTER

Human Impact on Ecosystems

the BIG idea

Humans and human population growth affect the environment.

Key Concepts

SECTION

Human population growth presents challenges.
Learn how the increasing human population must share land and resources and dispose of its wastes.

SECTION

Human activities affect the environment.
Learn how humans may affect natural resources, air and water quality, and biodiversity.

SECTION

People are working to protect ecosystems.
Learn about federal, local, and scientific efforts to improve resource use and protect ecosystems.

California ClassZone

CLASSZONE.COM

Chapter 14 online resources: Content Review, Visualization, four Resource Centers, Math Tutorial, Test Practice

486 Unit 4: **Ecology and Resources**

How have humans affected this landscape in California?

INTERNET PREVIEW

CLASSZONE.COM For student use with the following pages:

Review and Practice

- Content Review, pp. 488, 516
- Math Tutorial: Finding the Volume of a Cylinder, p. 505
- Test Practice, p. 519

Activities and Resources

- Internet Activity: The Environment, p. 487
- Resource Centers: Urban Expansion p. 494; Natural Resources, p. 498; Ecosystem Recovery, p. 507; Water Conservation, p. 513
- Visualization: Population Growth, p. 490

Population Growth
Code: MDL003

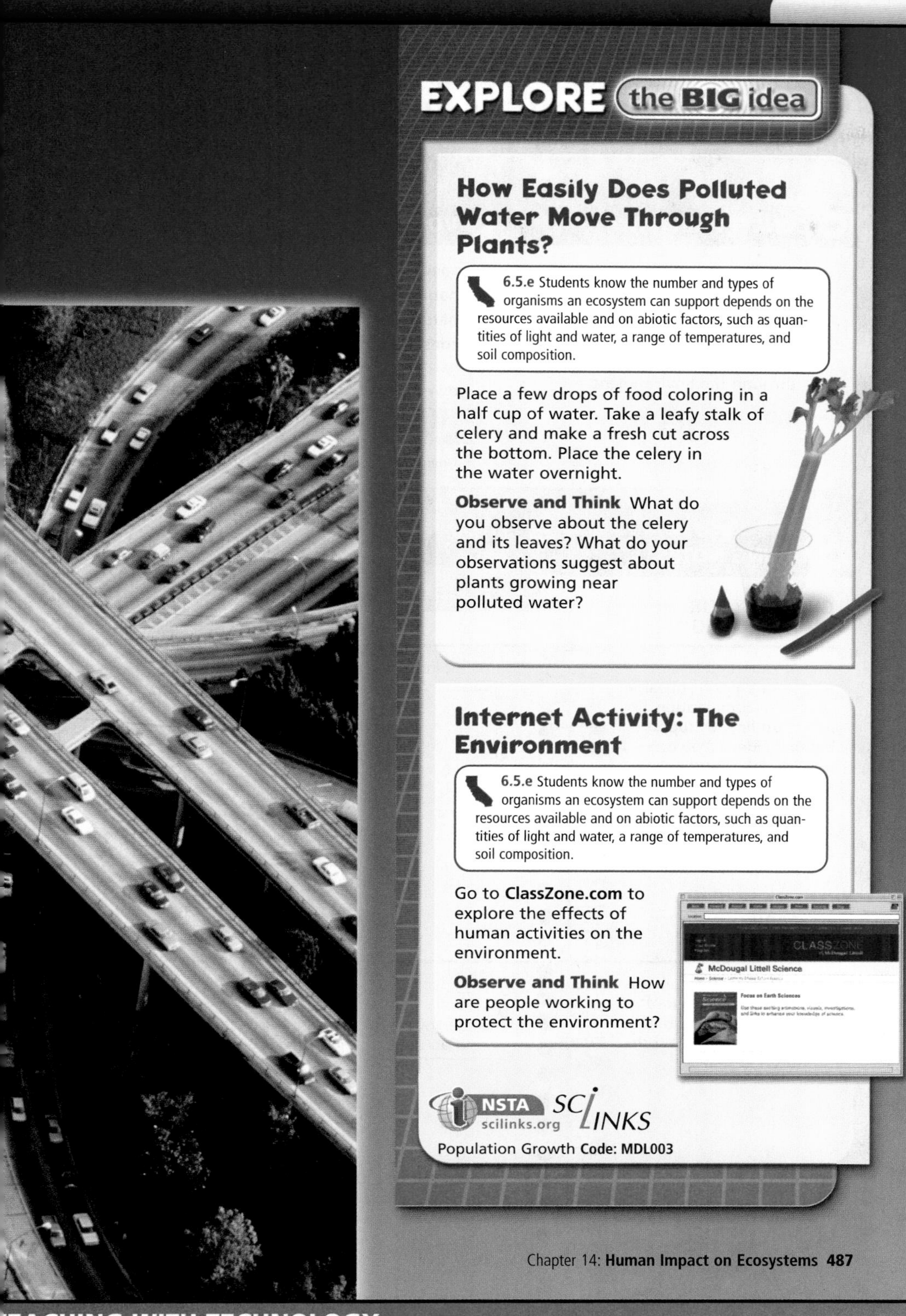

EXPLORE the BIG idea

How Easily Does Polluted Water Move Through Plants?

6.5.e Students know the number and types of organisms an ecosystem can support depends on the resources available and on abiotic factors, such as quantities of light and water, a range of temperatures, and soil composition.

Place a few drops of food coloring in a half cup of water. Take a leafy stalk of celery and make a fresh cut across the bottom. Place the celery in the water overnight.

Observe and Think What do you observe about the celery and its leaves? What do your observations suggest about plants growing near polluted water?

Internet Activity: The Environment

6.5.e Students know the number and types of organisms an ecosystem can support depends on the resources available and on abiotic factors, such as quantities of light and water, a range of temperatures, and soil composition.

Go to ClassZone.com to explore the effects of human activities on the environment.

Observe and Think How are people working to protect the environment?

NSTA scilinks.org SCILINKS
Population Growth Code: MDL003

Chapter 14: Human Impact on Ecosystems 487

EXPLORE the BIG idea

These inquiry-based activities are appropriate for use at home or as a supplement to classroom instruction.

How Easily Does Polluted Water Move Through Plants?

PURPOSE To introduce students to the way plants absorb pollution from water. Students observe how food coloring moves into celery.

TIP *10 min.* Students will not see the liquid moving. Have them wait until the next class period to observe results.

Answer: The food coloring moved up into the celery. Plants near polluted water would take the pollution into their bodies.

REVISIT after p. 500.

Internet Activity: The Environment

PURPOSE To explore how humans can change ecosystems.

TIP *20 min.* Ask students to think about steps they can take to protect the environment.

Sample answer: People are building awareness, passing laws, and conserving resources.

REVISIT after p. 513.

'EACHING WITH TECHNOLOGY

)nline Government Many documents 'howing water use with community resource ata are available at county, city, and town Veb sites. Bookmark these sites or help stuents find them. You can use them as part of 'ne Investigate Water Usage activity on p. 492.

Documentary Film You may wish to introduce the Investigation on p. 514 with a video documentary about a specific oil spill.

PREPARE

CONCEPT REVIEW

Activate Prior Knowledge

- Ask students to list some factors that make up an ecosystem.
- Ask: What would happen if you eliminated light from an ecosystem? if you doubled the light?
- Discuss how changing other factors might affect an ecosystem.

TAKING NOTES

Choose Your Own Strategy

Have students use the Note-Taking Handbook at the back of the textbook to review various note-taking strategies, such as combination notes, outline, and supporting main ideas. Encourage students to use a different strategy for each section.

Vocabulary Strategy

Students can use the magnet word strategy for any word or phrase that poses a challenge to them. They do not need to stay with the listed vocabulary items: The strategy can be especially helpful for students learning English.

Vocabulary and Note-Taking Resources

- Vocabulary Practice, pp. 248–249
- Decoding Support, p. 250

- Daily Vocabulary Scaffolding, p. T106
- Note-Taking Model, p. T107

- Magnet Word, B24–25
- Choose Your Own Strategy, C36, C42–43
- Daily Vocabulary Scaffolding, H1–8

CHAPTER 14

Getting Ready to Learn

CONCEPT REVIEW

- Both living and nonliving factors affect ecosystems.
- Populations can grow or decline over time.
- Matter and energy move through the environment.

VOCABULARY REVIEW

species p. 413
habitat p. 414
natural resource p. 449
conservation p. 467

See Glossary for definitions.
diversity, urban

Review concepts and vocabulary.

TAKING NOTES

CHOOSE YOUR OWN STRATEGY

Take notes using one or more strategies from earlier chapters—**combination notes, outline,** or **supporting main ideas.** You can also use other note-taking strategies that you might already know.

VOCABULARY STRATEGY

Think about a vocabulary term as a **magnet word** diagram. Write terms or ideas related to that term around it.

See the Note-Taking Handbook on pages R45–R51.

SCIENCE NOTEBOOK

Combination Notes

Outline

I. Main Idea
A. Supporting idea
1. Detail
2. Detail
B. Supporting idea

Supporting Main Ideas

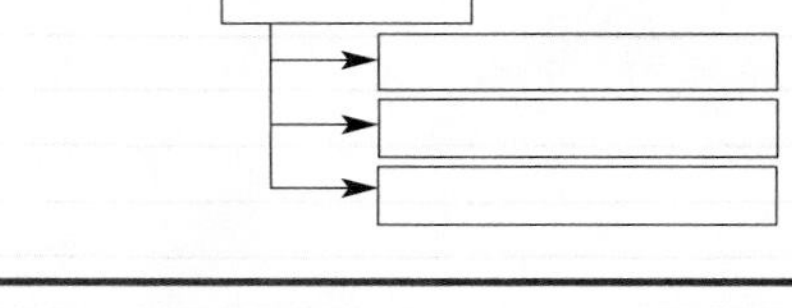

CHECK READINESS

Administer the Diagnostic Test to determine students' readiness for new science content and their mastery of requisite math skills.

 Diagnostic Test, pp. 307–308

Technology Resources

Students needing content and math skills should visit **ClassZone.com.**

- **CONTENT REVIEW**
- **MATH TUTORIAL**

 **CONTENT REVIEW CD-ROM**

KEY CONCEPT

Human population growth presents challenges.

CALIFORNIA Content Standards

6.5.e Students know the number and types of organisms an ecosystem can support depends on the resources available and on abiotic factors, such as quantities of light and water, a range of temperatures, and soil composition.

6.6.b Students know different natural energy and material resources, including air, soil, rocks, minerals, petroleum, fresh water, wildlife, and forests, and know how to classify them as renewable or nonrenewable.

BEFORE, you learned

- Populations have boundaries and are affected by limiting factors
- Living things form communities

NOW, you will learn

- How a growing human population puts pressure on ecosystems
- How sharing resources can be difficult

VOCABULARY

population density p. 494

EXPLORE Sharing Resources (6.6.b)

How can you model resource distribution?

PROCEDURE

1. You will work in a group of several classmates. One member of your group gets a bag of objects from your teacher.
2. Each object in the bag represents a necessary resource. Divide the objects so that each member of the group gets the resources he or she needs.
3. After 10 minutes, you may trade resources with other groups.

MATERIALS

bag containing an assortment of objects

WHAT DO YOU THINK?

- Did you get a fair share of your group's objects?
- Did the objects represent renewable resources or nonrenewable resources?
- Was the job made easier when trading occurred across groups?

NOTE-TAKING STRATEGY
Use a strategy from an earlier chapter to take notes on the main idea: *The human population is increasing.*

The human population is increasing.

The United Nations reported that on October 12, 1999, Earth's human population reached 6 billion. Until 300 years ago, it had never grown beyond a few hundred million people. Only 200 years ago, the population reached 1 billion. So the increase to 6 billion people has occurred in a very short time. About one-third of all humans alive today are 14 years old or younger. Experts predict that Earth's population will keep growing—to 9 billion or more by the year 2050.

14.1 FOCUS

Set Learning Goals

Students will

- Describe how a growing human population puts pressure on ecosystems.
- Explain how sharing resources can be difficult.
- Analyze how much water they use in one week.

3-Minute Warm-Up

Display Transparency 108 or copy this exercise on the board:

Which of the following are populations and which are communities? Write *P* next to a description of a population. Write *C* beside a description of a community.

- group of elephants living in the same grassland *P*
- iguanas and crabs interacting with one another *C*
- group of grasses growing on a prairie *P*
- group of fungi living in a pond *P*

 3-Minute Warm-Up, p. T108

14.1 MOTIVATE

EXPLORE Sharing Resources

PURPOSE To experience the difficulty of sharing unequal resources

TIPS *15 min.* 4–5 students per group is suggested. Representative or symbolic objects can include drinking straws for water, kidney beans for food, birthday candles for fuel, and so on.

WHAT DO YOU THINK? *Sample answers: No; group members could not figure out a fair distribution. (Most groups will be unable to divide the objects fairly throughout the exercise.)*

RESOURCES FOR DIFFERENTIATED INSTRUCTION

Below Level

UNIT RESOURCE BOOK

- Reading Study Guide A, pp. 215–216
- Decoding Support, p. 250

Advanced

UNIT RESOURCE BOOK

Challenge and Extension, p. 221

English Learners

UNIT RESOURCE BOOK

Spanish Reading Study Guide, pp. 219–220

- Audio Readings in Spanish
- Audio Readings (English)

14.1 INSTRUCT

Teach the Standards

Sharing resources 6.5.e

In this section: Make sure students understand that the human population is growing and using up natural resources, especially in densely populated areas.

- **previously taught:** populations, p. 414; limiting factors, p. 432; carrying capacity, p. 433
- **future opportunities:** pollution, p. 502; conserving resources, pp. 510–513

Teach from Visuals

To help students interpret the human population growth graph, ask:

- What is measured on the *x*-axis? *years*
- What is measured on the *y*-axis? *population in billions of people*
- What does the slope of the line tell you? *The human population is growing faster than it used to.*
- What is one problem with using only a mathematical projection for predicting population growth? *A mathematical projection does not account for other factors that might affect future population growth. It only uses the current growth rate.*

Ongoing Assessment

CHECK YOUR READING *Answer: If the population continues to grow rapidly, Earth's carrying capacity may be reached. Some students may add that the population would then level off.*

GRAPH CAPTION Answer: The population will continue to grow at an increasing rate.

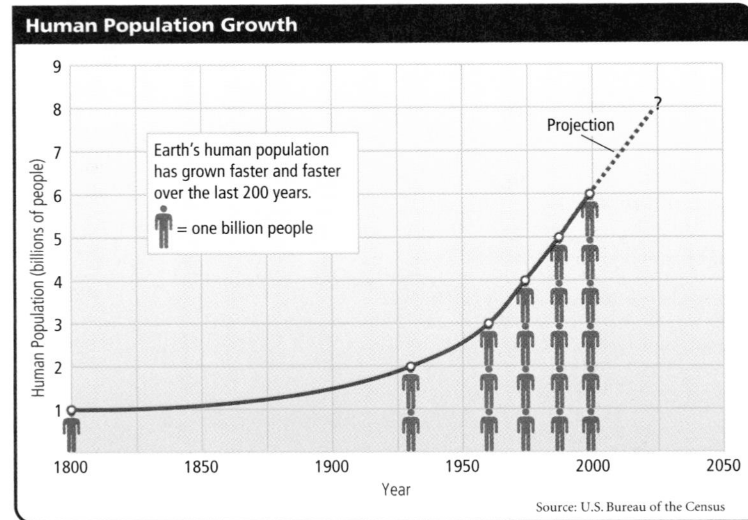

PREDICT The graph shows actual population growth through 2000. Predict how the population will grow in the future.

The graph above shows how the human population has grown in the last 200 years. You can see from the way the line gets much steeper after 1950 how quickly the population increased in the 50 years between 1950 and 2000. It is not only the number of babies being born that contributes to Earth's large human population. People are living longer as a result of improving health care and nutrition.

The dotted line on the graph shows a projection that helps us predict what the population would be if it continues to grow at the rate it is growing today. However, remember that an ecosystem has a carrying capacity for any given population. At some point, Earth will reach its carrying capacity for the human population. Today, many people think that our planet is close to—if not already at—its carrying capacity for humans.

CHECK YOUR READING How might Earth's carrying capacity affect human population growth?

Human populations can put pressure on ecosystems.

VISUALIZATION CLASSZONE.COM

Examine how the human population has grown.

If your family has guests for the weekend, you may find that you run out of hot water for showers or do not have enough milk for everyone's breakfast. The resources that would ordinarily be enough for your family are no longer enough.

DIFFERENTIATE INSTRUCTION

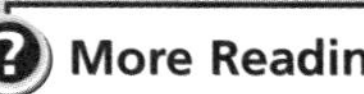

More Reading Support

A Why has the population grown so fast? *longer life spans, high birthrates*

B Why is part of the graph dotted? *It is a prediction.*

English Learners Help English learners realize that *may* and *might* indicate that an event is uncertain, or hypothetical. For example, if guests visit for the weekend, you *might* run out of hot water for showers, or you *might* not have enough milk for everyone's breakfast. Have students practice writing science statements that contain *may* or *might*.

Help English learners undertand the "2200 acres" estimate on p. 491. This area is the same as 8.9 square kilometers or 3.4 square miles.

You read in Chapter 12 that resources such as food, water, and space can be limiting factors for biological populations. These same resources limit Earth's human population. As the human population grows, it uses more resources—just as your guests used more of your home's resources. The activities of the growing human population are putting pressure on Earth's ecosystems.

REMINDER

A limiting factor is something that prevents a population from continuing to grow.

Pressures of Waste Disposal

As Earth's human population grows, so does the amount of waste produced by humans. Humans, like all living things, produce natural waste. Often, the water that carries this waste is treated to remove the waste before being cycled back to the environment. However, some of these materials still make it into lakes, rivers, and oceans. This can harm these ecosystems.

Some of the waste produced by humans is garbage, or food waste. The rest of it is trash, or nonfood waste. In the United States, huge amounts of trash are thrown out each year. Most garbage and trash ends up in landfills.

CALIFORNIA Focus

Californians have been using methods such as recycling and composting to decrease the percentage of solid waste sent to landfills each year. In 1994 the amount of solid waste sent to landfills was 36.3 million tons, or 75 percent of the total. In 2004 the amount sent to landfills was 37 million tons, or 52 percent of the total.

Landfills can take up a lot of space. The Fresh Kills Landfill in Staten Island, New York, is about 69 meters (225 ft) high in some places. It covers 2200 acres. Decomposing trash and garbage can release dangerous gases into the air as well as harmful chemicals into the ground. Liners made of plastic or packed clay are used to keep chemicals from leaking into the surrounding land and water.

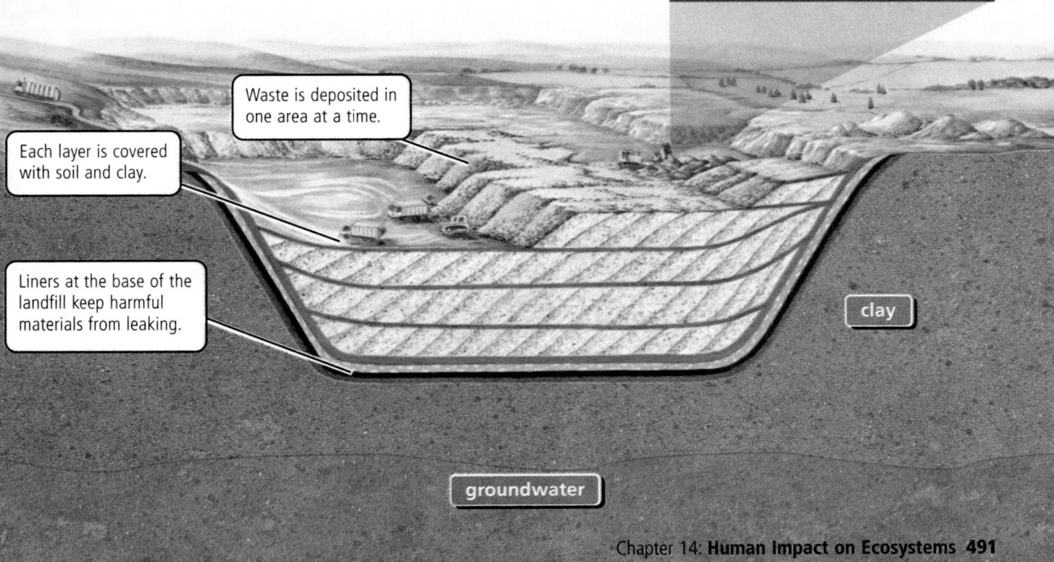

Waste is deposited in one area at a time.
Each layer is covered with soil and clay.
Liners at the base of the landfill keep harmful materials from leaking.
clay
groundwater

DIFFERENTIATE INSTRUCTION

More Reading Support

C What resources limit human population? *food, water, space*

D What is one problem resulting from placing garbage in landfills? *It takes up lots of space.*

Below Level Have students list items that they regularly throw away as trash. Ask them to sort the items or materials in their lists into those that will probably stay in the environment for a long time and those that will break down quickly.

Develop Critical Thinking

EVALUATE To help students evaluate a problem and solution:

- Tell students that landfills do not actually destroy trash and garbage. Why, then, have they become a widely used method of dealing with solid waste? *They provide a place to store solid waste in a restricted area so that it will have the least impact on the environment. Landfills are also designed to provide a barrier between the solid waste and the soil and groundwater.*
- Ask: What problems with destroying solid waste do landfills avoid? *Landfills eliminate the need to burn solid waste, so they eliminate the air pollution that is produced by burning.*
- Ask: What are some drawbacks of landfills? *Pollutants may leak out and contaminate the soil and groundwater. Landfills may also make an area permanently unsuitable for other uses.*

Teach from Visuals

To help students interpret the illustration of a landfill, ask:

- What is used to cover each layer? *soil and clay*
- What prevents chemicals from leaking into the landfill and surrounding areas? *plastic liners*
- What lies between the landfill and the groundwater? *clay*

The visual "Landfill Cross Section" is available as T110 in the Transparency Book.

Ongoing Assessment

Describe how a growing human population puts pressure on ecosystems.

Ask: Why can't the human population just keep growing forever? *Sources of food, water, and space for humans are limited, as is space for human waste.*

INVESTIGATE Water Usage

PURPOSE To have students collect and analyze data about their own use of fresh water, to exercise skills in collecting and totaling data, to realize just how much water they use

TIPS *30 min.* Have students use calculators to analyze their data. Allow students to work in pairs to help each other with the calculations.

INCLUSION
- Remind students to align the decimal points when adding decimals.
- Have students keep track of the number of zeros as placeholders when multiplying by the U.S. population figure.

WHAT DO YOU THINK? *Answers for water use will vary but are likely to include taking showers, taking baths, flushing toilets, or other household use. Ways of reducing water use might include taking shorter showers, filling the tub with less water, installing low-flush toilets, turning off the water while brushing teeth, and watering lawns less and at times of day when less water is lost to evaporation.*

CHALLENGE *Answers will vary but should include the idea that after pure water is used, it will never again exist in that natural state and is therefore nonrenewable; however, the water can be treated in purification systems, making it renewable.*

- Water Use Sheet, p. 222
- Datasheet, Water Usage, p. 223

Technology Resources

Customize this student lab as needed or look for an alternative. Print rubrics to assess student lab reports.

Lab Generator CD-ROM

Teaching with Technology

Water-use documents may be available on your city, town, or county Web site. Show students how this site is set up, and discuss the variety of resources, including how to contact local officials by e-mail.

Another way to get rid of trash and garbage is to incinerate it—to burn it. The problem with incineration is that it releases harmful gases and chemicals into the air. To prevent the release of these harmful substances, incinerator smokestacks have filters. To prevent further environmental contamination, used filters must be disposed of safely.

Pressures on Resources

You have seen that a growing human population puts pressure on ecosystems by the amount of waste it leaves behind. Human populations also put pressure on ecosystems by what they take away. Humans depend on the environment for resources. As you recall, a natural resource is any type of material or energy source that humans use to meet their needs. Natural resources that humans take from their environment include water, food, wood, stone, metal, and minerals.

Clean fresh water is an important resource. Only three percent of Earth's water supply is fresh water—and two-thirds of that small amount is contained in polar ice caps, glaciers, and permanent snow. As the human population grows, sharing this important resource will become more difficult.

INVESTIGATE Water Usage

How much water do you use in a week?

PROCEDURE

1. Write down all the ways you use water in a day. Start with the time you get up in the morning. Include activities such as brushing your teeth, flushing the toilet, using ice, and taking a shower.
2. Look at the Water Use datasheet. Identify other ways that you and others in your household use water.
3. Add up how many liters of water you use in a day, and multiply that by seven. This is how much water you use in a week.

WHAT DO YOU THINK?
- Which of your activities used the most water?
- What are some ways that you could reduce the amount of water you use weekly?

CHALLENGE How is clean drinking water like a nonrenewable resource? a renewable resource?

SKILL FOCUS
Analyzing data (6.6.b)

MATERIALS
- Water Use datasheet
- calculator

TIME
30 minutes

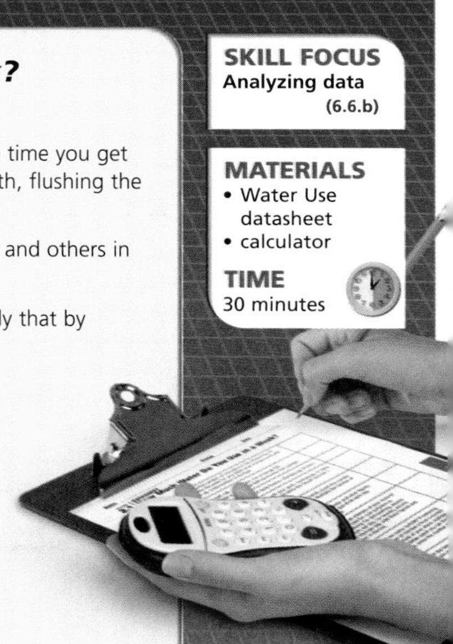

DIFFERENTIATE INSTRUCTION

More Reading Support

E What are problems with burning trash? *harmful gases, chemicals*

F What are examples of natural resources? *water, food, wood, metal*

Inclusion If you and your students obtain documents from local government agencies, ask whether Braille documents are available. Also request the largest format and type size available.

Case Study: The Colorado River

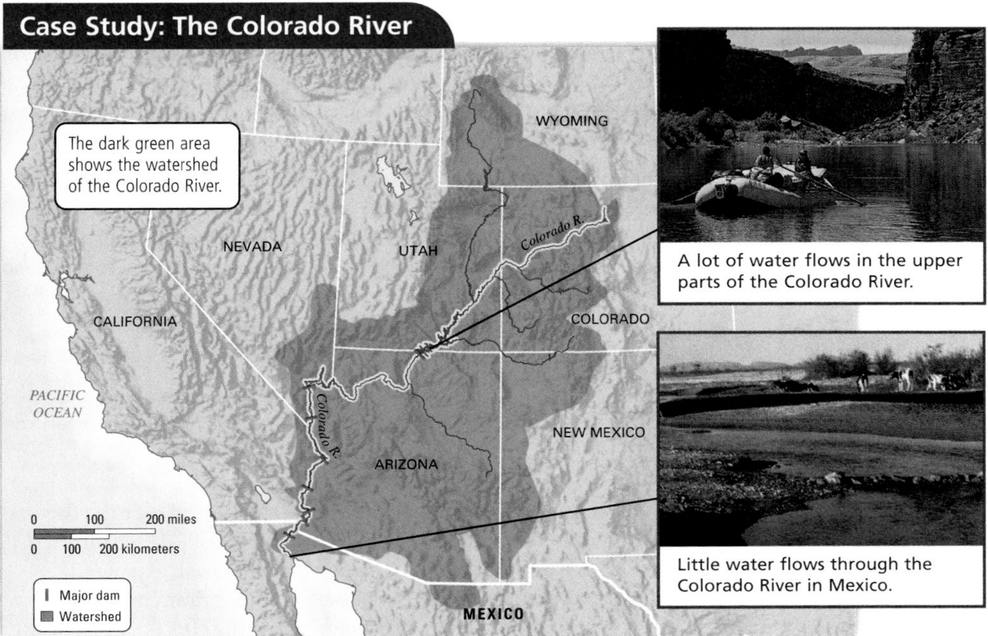

A lot of water flows in the upper parts of the Colorado River.

Little water flows through the Colorado River in Mexico.

A case study that involves the Colorado River shows how a growing human population puts pressures on natural resources. This example also shows that sharing resources isn't easy. The watershed of this major Western river extends into seven U.S. states and parts of Mexico. The watershed includes all the smaller rivers and streams that flow into the Colorado River. In a region where little rain falls each year, these streams and rivers are an important source of water for drinking and agriculture.

READING TIP A watershed is an area of land in which water drains into a stream system. It is also called a drainage basin.

As the West was settled, disagreements about water rights arose between people in the upstream states of Colorado, Utah, Wyoming, and New Mexico and people in the downstream states of California, Arizona, and Nevada. In 1922 the seven states signed an agreement that divided the water between the two groups.

Problems with this agreement soon became apparent. First, the needs of Native American and Mexican populations were not considered. Second, the dams and channels built to prevent floods and transport water harmed river ecosystems. And third, the seven states planned to use more water than the river usually holds. As a result, the river often runs nearly dry at its mouth in Mexico.

 G

CHECK YOUR READING List three problems that developed after people made a plan to share Colorado River water.

DIFFERENTIATE INSTRUCTION

More Reading Support

G What happens to the Colorado River when it reaches Mexico? *It runs nearly dry.*

Advanced Have a student volunteer bring in a cardboard box large enough to hold the paper that is generated in your classroom in one day. Ask the group to figure out the approximate volume of trash that the class generates each day. Have them use the daily total to estimate the volume of waste paper generated in a year. Have students determine how many classrooms the trash would fill.

R Challenge and Extension, p. 221

Teach from Visuals

To help students interpret the map of the Colorado River, ask:

- What is the relationship between the large map and the two inset photographs? *The photographs describe details of the large map.*
- If you trace the Colorado River with your finger, how many states and countries do you move through? *five states, two countries*
- Where does more water flow—in the northern parts or toward Mexico? *The amount of water is much greater in the north.*

Geography Connection

You can assess the learning goals for this section by having students work cooperatively to draft and present a plan for sharing the resources of the Colorado River watershed. Make sure students include the interests of the seven states and Mexico and address ways to solve each of the three problems the original plan encountered.

Ongoing Assessment

Explain how sharing resources can be difficult.

Ask: Why do international treaties regulate water rights, fishing, and land boundaries? *Sample answer: Resources are scarce and people compete for them, and some resources are found in more than one country.*

CHECK YOUR READING *Answer: The agreement ignored the needs of Native Americans and Mexicans, the dams and reservoirs destroyed river ecosystems, and there was not enough water in the river to meet the amounts that each state wanted to withdraw.*

Teach Difficult Concepts

Some students may have a hard time understanding the concept of population density. Ask them to imagine two pictures: twenty cows in a field and twenty cows in a barn. Have them contrast the pictures. Point out that the population density is greater in the barn. To help students understand this concept, you may wish to use the following demonstration.

Teacher Demo

Give students the measurements of the classroom, and ask them to compute the area. Compare the population density of students during class to the population density during lunchtime or another time, when the classroom is mostly empty.

Develop Geometry Skills

Population density is the number of people in a particular area. Students may need a refresher on area calculations.

- Area is expressed in square feet, square miles, square meters, and so forth.
- The area of a square or rectangle equals length times width, or $A = lw$.
- The area of a circle equals πr^2.

Teach from Visuals

To help students interpret the aerial photograph and satellite photographs of Las Vegas:

- Ask: In 1972, about how much of Las Vegas was developed land? *no more than one-third*
- Ask: In 1997, about how much of Las Vegas was developed land? *more than one-half*
- Explain that the largest photograph shows Las Vegas in 2000. Ask students to infer what may have changed for the city between 1997 and 2000. *greater diversity at the city center and outskirts, greater resource use*

Ongoing Assessment

CHECK YOUR READING *Answer: The population density is too high for all needs to be met by resources from the local environment.*

Learn more about urban expansion.

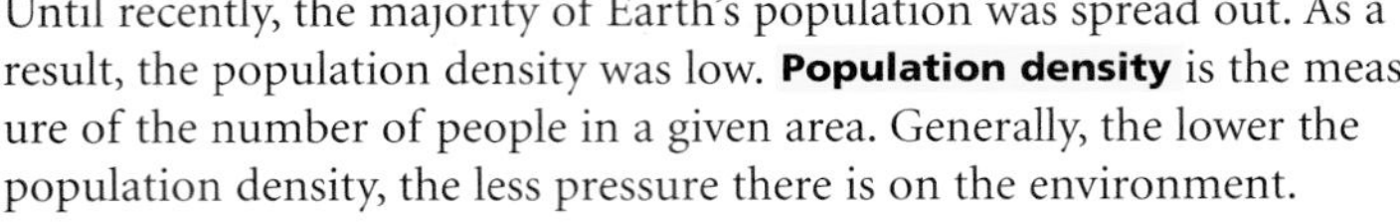

Pressures of Urban Growth

Until recently, the majority of Earth's population was spread out. As a result, the population density was low. **Population density** is the measure of the number of people in a given area. Generally, the lower the population density, the less pressure there is on the environment.

H Today, about half of the world's population lives in urban, or city, areas. People are attracted to these areas to live and to work. Over time, suburban areas around a city develop as more and more people look for a place to live. In cities, buildings are spaced close together, so the population density is high. A large number of people in a small area changes the landscape. The local environment can no longer support the number of people living there, so resources must come from outside the environment.

CHECK YOUR READING Why do people who live in a city need to bring in resources from other areas?

I In recent years, some people have raised concerns over the dramatic growth in and around urban areas. Los Angeles, Houston, Atlanta, and Washington, D.C., are all cities that have expanded rapidly. Another urban area that has experienced dramatic growth is Las Vegas, Nevada. The images below show the effects of increasing

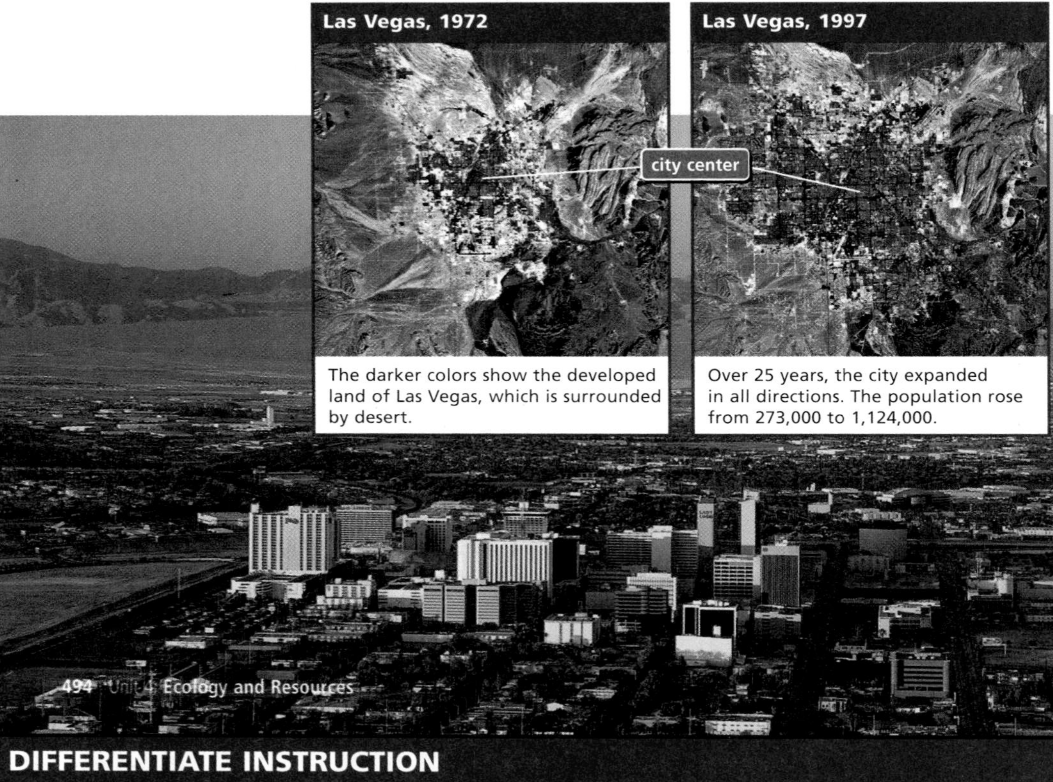

The darker colors show the developed land of Las Vegas, which is surrounded by desert.

Over 25 years, the city expanded in all directions. The population rose from 273,000 to 1,124,000.

494 Unit 4: Ecology and Resources

DIFFERENTIATE INSTRUCTION

More Reading Support

H Where does half of the world's population live? *in cities*

I What has happened to cities in recent years? *Some have grown very fast.*

English Learners Have students write definitions for *population density* and *natural resource* in their Science Word Dictionaries. English learners may not have prior knowledge of the terms *suburban* and *urban*. Use the aerial photograph of Las Vegas to explain these terms. Students may be unfamiliar with the concept of the mouth of a river as discussed on p. 493.

population density around the city between 1972 and 1997. Located in the middle of a desert, Las Vegas depends on the Colorado River for water and electrical energy. As the population grows, so does the need for natural resources.

INFER What do you think this ecosystem looked like a hundred years ago? two hundred years ago?

Pressures of Expanding Land Use

One consequence of urban growth is an increasing demand for resources in a particular area. But as communities around cities expand onto surrounding land, the environment is affected. Natural habitats, such as forests, are destroyed. Because forests cycle carbon through the environment, cutting down trees affects the carbon cycle. Soil that was held in place by tree roots may wash into lakes and rivers.

Another consequence of widespread development is the loss of productive farmland. Development replaces more than 2.2 million acres of farmland each year in the United States. This means less land is available locally to produce food for the growing population. The result is that food must be transported over greater distances.

Unlike city development, suburban development increases the need for residents to have cars. This is because most people in suburban areas live farther from where they work, shop, or go to school. A greater number of cars can decrease the air quality. More cars lead to the construction of more roads, which can interrupt natural habitats and endanger wildlife.

CHECK YOUR READING Describe some ways that development harms natural ecosystems.

14.1 Review

KEY CONCEPTS

1. Identify four pressures placed on ecosystems by an increasing human population. (6.5.e)
2. Give an example that shows how resources can be difficult to share. (6.5.e)

CRITICAL THINKING

3. **Apply** Describe an example of sharing resources that occurs in your school.
4. **Infer** How would a city's population density change if the city increased in area and the number of people in it remained the same?

CHALLENGE

5. **Evaluate** Imagine that you live along the Colorado River. What information would you need to evaluate a water-sharing agreement?

ANSWERS

1. Natural habitats are destroyed, the carbon cycle is affected, erosion and loss of productive farmland occur, air quality decreases, and construction interrupts habitats and can endanger wildlife.

2. The Colorado River case study shows how the use of river water at one location can remove resources from another location.

3. Sample answer: Computer time is a limited resource. Students share by following set time limits for individual computer use.

4. Population density would decrease.

5. Important information would include how many communities depend on one source, how much water is affected by dams, and how much water a town needs.

Ongoing Assessment

Explain how a growing population puts pressure on an ecosystem.

Ask: What happens when the human population grows too fast? *Problems may result from the increased demand for garbage disposal, water, and transport.*

CHECK YOUR READING *Sample answer: Natural habitats disappear, the carbon cycle is interrupted, local climate may change, and erosion occurs.*

PHOTO CAPTION Answer: One hundred years ago there were fewer houses and roads. Two hundred years ago there were probably no houses or roads.

Reinforce the BIG idea

Have students relate the section to the Big Idea.

 Reinforcing Key Concepts, p. 224

14.1 ASSESS & RETEACH

Assess

A Section 14.1 Quiz, p. 309

Reteach

Refer to the graph on p. 490. Have students compare the curve with the moose and wolf graphs on p. 432. Ask:

- How do the graphs differ? *Humans show steady increase, moose and wolf go up and down.*
- Why does the wolf population go down after the moose population does? *The moose provide food for the wolves. When there are too few moose, the wolves do not have enough food.*
- Will the human population have enough or too little food if it continues to grow? *There may be too little.*

Technology Resources

Have students visit **ClassZone.com** for reteaching of Key Concepts.

 **CONTENT REVIEW**

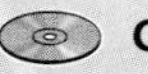 **CONTENT REVIEW CD-ROM**

CALIFORNIA CLOSE-UP
Science in Action in California

Set Learning Goal

To understand how some organisms depend on natural fires to succeed

Present the Science

California fires are often considered disasters, but for giant sequoias, fires are necessary. Fires affect abiotic (nonliving) environmental factors, such as soil condition, space for growth, and heat conditions needed for sequoia seeds to open.

Discussion Questions

Have students share their knowledge and experience with sequoias and John Muir. Then point out the scientific method in this article.

- Ask: What did scientists and rangers learn by experimentation? *Fires are necessary to the reproduction of the giant trees.*
- Ask: How were scientists able to figure this out? *by observing the forest, testing the hypothesis that preventing fires would help trees, and connecting the history of fires shown by tree scars and the health of the forest*
- Ask: What abiotic factors needed by sequoias were affected by fires? *soil condition, temperature, and space for growing*

Make Connections

Show the quarter that honors the state of California, issued by the U.S. Mint in 2005. Have students identify what is pictured on the quarter. *John Muir, Half Dome in Yosemite Valley, a California condor* Discuss why these items were chosen and what they represent about the state of California.

Close

Ask students to name the national parks they have visited. Remind them that John Muir was instrumental in protecting land for the creation of national parks.

ECOSYSTEM MANAGEMENT

Burn On!

6.5.e Students know the number and types of organisms an ecosystem can support depends on the resources available and on **abiotic factors,** such as quantities of light and water, a range of temperatures, and soil composition.

John Muir (right), shown here with President Theodore Roosevelt, spent his life working for the protection of the natural world. He played a key role in forming many of our national parks, including Yosemite, Sequoia, and Mount Rainier National Parks. In the early 1900s, rangers in Sequoia fought forest fires. They thought that eliminating fires would protect and encourage the growth of giant sequoia trees.

Sequoias, or redwoods, are tall evergreen trees native to California and Oregon. For many years forest rangers prevented fires in sequoia groves. Surprisingly, the sequoias failed to reproduce. What went wrong? It turned out that to protect the sequoias, rangers needed to let them burn. Fire is essential to sequoia reproduction. It clears the forest floor of debris and smaller trees, making room for new growth. The heat from the fire causes the sequoia cones to dry out and open, releasing the seeds. Fire also creates the necessary soil conditions for the sequoia seeds to germinate.

Ferns growing in Yosemite after a forest fire

Fire's role in the history of sequoia ecosystems has literally been burned into the trees. Tree rings tell a story of a region's fires, insect attacks, droughts, and floods. Differences in growing conditions cause the widths of rings to vary in size. Fire scars on the tree rings show scientists when fires occurred and how large the fires were.

Today, National Park Service rangers practice a new kind of ecosystem management that includes controlled burns. With knowledge about the past from the tree rings, we can better care for the places that John Muir fought so hard to protect.

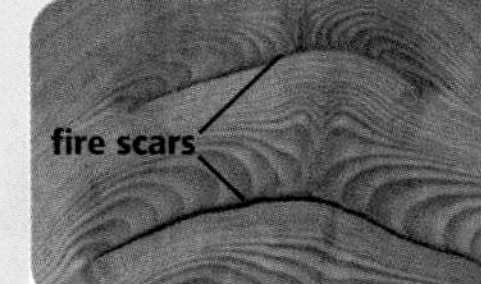

Scientists study tree rings to understand the role that fire plays in forest ecosystems.

WRITING ABOUT SCIENCE

What other challenges do our national parks face today? Choose one problem, such as overcrowding, and research it. Write a description of the problem and propose your solution to it.

496 Unit 4: Ecology and Resources

WRITING ABOUT SCIENCE

Writing Applications 6.2.2 This assignment will give students practice in writing a problem-solution essay. Suggest that partners read each other's solutions and evaluate them in terms of effectiveness and practicality.

The best essays will

- completely describe the problem.
- offer a realistic solution or partial solution.

KEY CONCEPT

Human activities affect the environment.

CALIFORNIA Content Standards

6.6.a Students know the utility of energy sources is determined by factors that are involved in converting these sources to useful forms and the consequences of the conversion process.

6.6.b Students know different natural energy and material resources, including air, soil, rocks, minerals, petroleum, fresh water, wildlife, and forests, and know how to classify them as renewable or nonrenewable.

BEFORE, you learned

- Human populations are increasing
- Human population growth causes problems

NOW, you will learn

- How natural resources are classified
- How pollution affects the environment
- How a loss of diversity affects the environment

VOCABULARY

pollution p. 498
biodiversity p. 498

THINK ABOUT

How do you use water?

Think of the number of times you use water every day. Like all living things, you need water. In fact, more than half of the material that makes up your body is water.

Most of the time when you turn on a faucet, clean water flows out. You use water when you take a shower, brush your teeth, or wash a dish. If you've ever lost water service to your home, you've probably been reminded of how much you depend on it. No doubt about it, people need water.

NOTE-TAKING STRATEGY
Choose a strategy for taking notes about the main idea: *Humans use many resources.*

Humans use many resources.

Throughout history, people around the world have relied on natural resources for survival. Ancient civilizations used stone to create tools and weapons. Wood was an important fuel for cooking and keeping warm. Today, humans continue to rely on the environment and have discovered additional resources to meet their needs. As you read in Chapter 13, people classify these resources into two categories:

- renewable resources
- nonrenewable resources

14.2 FOCUS

Set Learning Goals

Students will

- Classify natural resources.
- Explain how pollution affects the environment.
- Describe how a loss of biodiversity affects the environment.
- Collect and observe air-pollution samples.

3-Minute Warm-Up

Display Transparency 108 or copy this exercise on the board:

Suppose that next week our school had to accept a number of new students that would double the student population. List five changes that would occur, and explain how they would affect you. *Sample answer: The hallways would be much more crowded, so getting to class on time would be harder. Lunchtime would have to last longer to accommodate more students in the same space; I could end up eating lunch at 10:00 in the morning. Classes would be twice as large, and teachers would spend less time with each student. Books and supplies would become scarce and have to be shared. Getting on a sports team would be more competitive.*

 3-Minute Warm-Up, p. T108

14.2 MOTIVATE

THINK ABOUT

PURPOSE To understand the importance of water in everyday life

DISCUSS Have students discuss where water comes from at their home. Ask:

- Where is the water that comes from a faucet stored?
- How does it get into the storage tank?
- Does it come from a well, reservoir, or river?
- Under what circumstances could we run out of clean water?

Sample answer: water heater in basement; from pipes from city water source; reservoir; drought

RESOURCES FOR DIFFERENTIATED INSTRUCTION

Below Level

UNIT RESOURCE BOOK
Reading Study Guide A, pp. 227–228
Decoding Support, p. 250

AUDIO CDS

Advanced

UNIT RESOURCE BOOK
- Challenge and Extension, p. 233
- Challenge Reading, pp. 246–247

English Learners

UNIT RESOURCE BOOK
Spanish Reading Study Guide, pp. 231–232

AUDIO CDS

- Audio Readings in Spanish
- Audio Readings (English)

Additional INVESTIGATION, Pollutants on the Move, A, B, & C, pp. 262–270; Teacher Instructions, pp. 273–274

14.2 INSTRUCT

Teach the Standards

Converting energy sources 6.6.a

In this section: Help students understand that pollution results from converting natural resources into usable energy. Explain that pollution affects air, water, and land and threatens habitats.

- **previously taught:** conservation of resources, pp. 466–467; recycling, pp. 468–469
- **future opportunities:** protecting the environment, pp. 506–510; reducing pollution, pp. 512–513

INVESTIGATE Particles in the Air

PURPOSE To observe air pollution

TIPS *30 min.* The longer each card hangs, the better. Some pollutants take a full week to appear. Premake cards for disabled students.

WHAT DO YOU THINK? *Sample answers: dust, dirt, exhaust, pollen, and so on. Answers will vary depending on the locations from which samples were collected.*

CHALLENGE *Possibilities include better ventilation or air circulation, proximity to sources of pollution, location inside or outside, and number of people who use the area.*

Particles in the Air Datasheet, p. 234

Technology Resources

Customize this student lab as needed or look for an alternative. Print rubrics to assess student lab reports.

Lab Generator CD-ROM

Ongoing Assessment

Classify natural resources. Ask: Into what categories do people classify natural resources? *renewable resources and nonrenewable resources*

RESOURCE CENTER
CLASSZONE.COM
Find out more about natural resources.

As people use natural resources from one part of the Earth system, they affect other parts of the system. As you read in Chapter 13, there are costs as well as benefits to using natural resources. Some of the costs are described below.

Pollution endangers biodiversity.

VOCABULARY
Remember to add magnet word diagrams to your notebook for *pollution* and *biodiversity*.

A
As you walk along a city street, you may smell car exhaust or see litter. These are examples of pollution. **Pollution** is the addition of harmful substances to the environment. Many of the ways humans use natural resources cause pollution to be released into soil, air, and water. Pollutants include chemicals, bacteria, and dirt. Even materials that are ordinarily not harmful can cause pollution when they build up in one location.

B
As pollution becomes common in an ecosystem, living things may be threatened. Plant and animal populations may decrease, and biodiversity may decline. **Biodiversity** is the number and variety of life forms within an ecosystem. Healthy ecosystems support a variety of species. An ecosystem with a variety of organisms can recover more easily from disturbances than an ecosystem that has fewer species.

INVESTIGATE Particles in the Air

SKILL FOCUS
Observing (6.5.e, 6.6.b)

MATERIALS
- 2 index cards
- marker
- hole punch
- string
- scissors
- petroleum jelly
- hand lens

TIME
30 minutes

Where do you find air pollution?

PROCEDURE

1. Use a hole punch to make a hole at one end of each index card. Cut two pieces of string 30 cm long and tie a string to each card.
2. Choose a different location for each card. Mark the card with its location and the date.
3. Spread a thin film of petroleum jelly about the size of your thumb on each card. Hang the cards at the locations you've chosen.
4. Take down the cards after one week and examine them with a hand lens.

WHAT DO YOU THINK?
- Identify the types of particles collected at each location.
- Were all the particles collected the result of pollution?
- Which location had the most pollution?

CHALLENGE Hypothesize why certain locations have more particles in the air than others.

498 Unit 4: **Ecology and Resources**

DIFFERENTIATE INSTRUCTION

More Reading Support

A What is pollution? *any substance that harms air, water, or land*

B What is biodiversity? *the number and variety of species of living things in an ecosystem*

Below Level To help students distinguish between renewable and nonrenewable resources, have them construct a collage for each category. Tell them to use examples that they draw or cut from magazines. Display the collages on posters or a bulletin board.

Air Quality

Air quality affects entire ecosystems. For example, in 1980 Mount St. Helens erupted in Washington state. Hot ash was blown 15 miles up into the air. Three days later some of that ash reached the East Coast. Although natural events like this occasionally release large amounts of air pollutants, human activities pollute every day.

READING TIP
Pollute and *pollutant* are in the same word family as *pollution*.

Motor vehicles, factories, and power plants are the main sources of air pollution in the United States today. The fossil fuels they burn release sulfur dioxide, nitrogen dioxide, and carbon monoxide into the air. These pollutants affect humans and animals and are the main cause of acid rain, a serious problem affecting ecosystems.

CHECK YOUR READING What air pollutants contribute to acid rain problems in the United States?

You read about acid rain in Chapters 3 and 10. Acid rain occurs when air pollutants such as sulfur dioxide and nitrogen dioxide mix with water in the atmosphere to form acid droplets of rain, ice, snow, or mist. Just as wind carried ash from Mount St. Helens, wind can carry these droplets for very long distances before they fall as rain.

Most of the air pollution in urban areas comes from the burning of fossil fuels such as oil, gasoline, and coal. Sunlight causes some of the gases produced by burning fuels to react chemically. The reactions form a type of pollution called smog. Large amounts of smog in the air form a brownish haze. Smog can irritate your eyes, nose, throat, and lungs, and it can cause difficulty in breathing.

Air Quality Smog forms in a layer near the ground. The mountains around Los Angeles help trap smog over the city.

Address Misconceptions

IDENTIFY Ask students to describe or draw the way pollution spreads in water, in air, or on land. If students answer by describing small or isolated areas, they may hold the misconception that air pollution and water pollution affect only limited areas.

CORRECT Demonstrate evaporation by heating a small amount of water on a burner until it boils away. Have students discuss where the water has gone. Pour another pot of water in the sink or on the ground, and discuss where it went.

REASSESS Ask: What is likely to happen to pollutants that enter a lake? *Some pollutants would enter the soil around the lake; others might affect living things in the lake. Other pollutants might enter the water cycle through evaporation, move throughout the atmosphere, and fall back to Earth. Evaporated pollutants would enter the air. Precipitation would bring the pollution back to Earth again.* How would you describe the movement of pollutants through a system? *They move in a cycle from air to water and soil, into bodies of water, and back to air again.*

Technology Resources

Visit **ClassZone.com** for background on common student misconceptions.

 **MISCONCEPTION DATABASE**

Ongoing Assessment

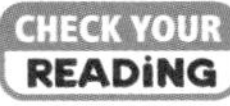 CHECK YOUR READING *Answer: exhaust from motor vehicles, factories, and power plants*

DIFFERENTIATE INSTRUCTION

More Reading Support

C What are some sources of air pollution? *motor vehicles, factories, power plants*

D What is acid rain? *rain that has turned acidic from air pollution*

Additional Investigation To reinforce Section 14.2 learning goals, use the following full-period investigation:

Additional INVESTIGATION, Pollutants on the Move, A, B, & C, pp. 262–270, 273–274
(Advanced students should complete Levels B and C.)

Teach from Visuals

To help students interpret the photographs of chemical pollution, ask:

- Why is the scientist testing the water? *because chemicals were released into the water*
- How does chemical pollution harm fish? *It can kill them.*

Address Misconceptions

IDENTIFY Ask: What types of populations can change without affecting the rest of their ecosystem? If students name any type of organism, they may hold the misconception that some organisms do not affect the health of an ecosystem. On the contrary, each type of organism is important and affects the entire ecosystem.

CORRECT Use one of the students' answers as an example to illustrate the importance of all organisms to an ecosystem. A sudden decrease in the mosquito population, for example, may cause a decrease in the populations of animals that feed on mosquitoes, such as swallows and bats. The effects continue to move up the food chain.

REASSESS Ask: What species can be removed from an ecosystem without affecting it? *None; all species eat or consume something. Even fleas are predators and serve the purpose of thinning host populations.*

Technology Resources

Visit **ClassZone.com** for background on common student misconceptions.

 **MISCONCEPTION DATABASE**

EXPLORE the BIG idea

Revisit "How Easily Does Polluted Water Move Through Plants?" on p. 487. Have students explain how the activity relates to plants near polluted water.

Ongoing Assessment

CHECK YOUR READING *Answer: oil spills, soil erosion, wastewater, chemical runoff*

Water Quality

 E

Water quality is another factor that affects biodiversity in ecosystems. In the 1960s, newspaper headlines announced that Lake Erie was "dead" because of pollution. Almost every living thing in the lake had died. Lake Erie suffered for years from pollution from cities, industries, and farms located along its banks. Rivers that emptied into the lake also carried pollution with them.

The pollution found in Lake Erie is common in communities across the United States. Chemicals or wastes that drain off of farm fields, animal feedlots, and landfills all cause water pollution. So do oil spills, soil erosion, and wastewater from towns and industries.

CHECK YOUR READING Name four different sources of water pollution.

 F

Like air pollution, water pollution affects entire ecosystems. One river that suffers from heavy pollution is the Duwamish River in Washington. Over 600 million gallons of untreated waste and storm water drain off the land into the river each year. As a result, large amounts of bacteria and harmful chemicals contaminate the water, killing fish and putting humans at risk.

When fish and other animals in aquatic ecosystems are exposed to pollution, the entire food web is affected. If fish become scarce, some birds may no longer find enough food. The bird population may decrease as birds die or move to a new habitat. The result is a decrease in biodiversity in the ecosystem.

Water Quality A scientist tests the water of the Duwamish River after chemicals were released into the river.

Water Pollution

Pollution that flows into aquatic ecosystems can harm—even kill—organisms such as these fish.

DIFFERENTIATE INSTRUCTION

More Reading Support

E What killed Lake Erie? *water pollution*

F How much of an ecosystem can water pollution affect? *all of it*

Advanced Tell students that scientists have found amphibians with mutations in aquatic ecosystems. Scientists have identified several possible causes, such as chemical pollution, UV radiation, disease, and parasites. Have students research and debate whether pollution caused the deformities.

Have students who are interested in amphibians with mutations read the following article:

 Challenge Reading, pp. 246–247

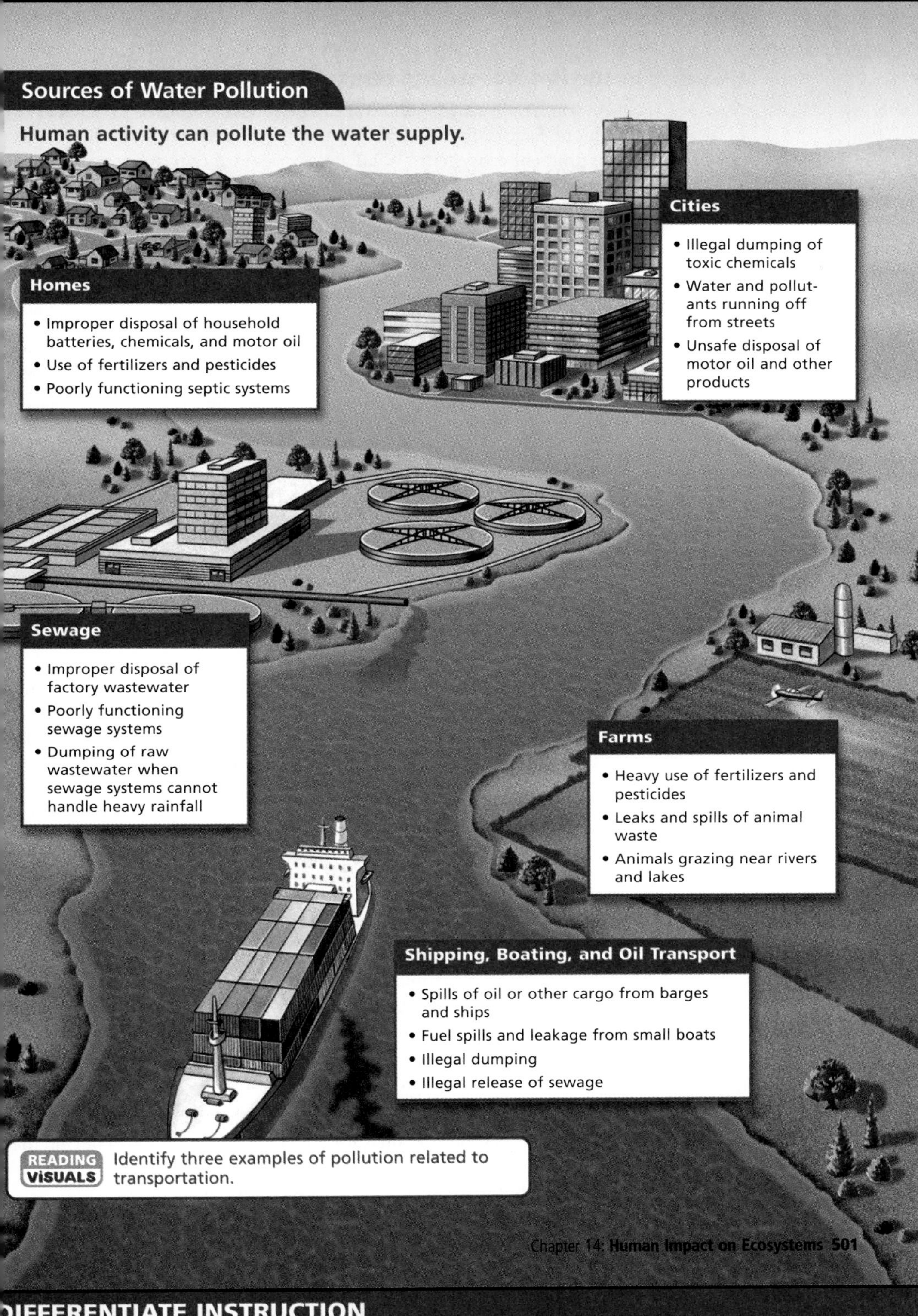

Sources of Water Pollution
Human activity can pollute the water supply.
Homes
• Improper disposal of household batteries, chemicals, and motor oil
• Use of fertilizers and pesticides
• Poorly functioning septic systems
Cities
• Illegal dumping of toxic chemicals
• Water and pollutants running off from streets
• Unsafe disposal of motor oil and other products
Sewage
• Improper disposal of factory wastewater
• Poorly functioning sewage systems
• Dumping of raw wastewater when sewage systems cannot handle heavy rainfall
Farms
• Heavy use of fertilizers and pesticides
• Leaks and spills of animal waste
• Animals grazing near rivers and lakes
Shipping, Boating, and Oil Transport
• Spills of oil or other cargo from barges and ships
• Fuel spills and leakage from small boats
• Illegal dumping
• Illegal release of sewage
READING VISUALS Identify three examples of pollution related to transportation.
Chapter 14: Human Impact on Ecosystems 501

DIFFERENTIATE INSTRUCTION

Below Level Have each student create an illustration to show the five major sources of water pollution. Have students write labels in their own words.

Teach from Visuals

To help students interpret the visual showing sources of water pollution, ask:

- What are five major categories of water pollution sources? *homes (residential); cities (urban); sewage; farms (agriculture); and shipping, boating, and oil transport*
- What causes urban pollution? *illegal dumping of toxic chemicals, runoff from streets, unsafe disposal of motor oil and other products*
- What is the plane doing? *spreading pesticides*
- How is the ship causing water pollution? *Oil or fuel is leaking into the water.*
- Why might a part of the river downstream be more polluted than a part of the river upstream? *Pollution accumulates in the river downstream from various sources upstream.*
- Which sources of pollution have you seen occurring? *Answers will vary. Students may have seen runoff, gasoline leaking from a boat motor, or wastewater coming from a pipe.*

Social Studies Connection

Display a map of your geographic region. Try to find a large-scale map that shows a relatively small area. U.S. Geological Service (USGS) topographic maps work well. Have students locate possible sources of water pollution in your area. Students might first find rivers and lakes on the map, and then locate towns, farmland, and ports along the waterways. Compare these sources with those shown in the visual on this page.

Ongoing Assessment

READING VISUALS *Answers should include spills of oil or other cargo from barges and ships, unsafe disposal of motor oil and other products, and fuel spills and leakage from small boats.*

Teach from Visuals

To help students interpret the diagrams of water and air pollution, ask:

- In the picture on the left, how does pollution move from one place to another? *by water*
- In the picture on the right, how does pollution move from one place to another? *by evaporating into the air*
- How do these pictures suggest a cycle? *The arrows suggest that pollution moves from land to water, and from water to air.*
- What might be the next part of the cycle? *Pollution in the air might return to land with rain or snow.*

Integrate the Sciences

Pollutants can move great distances and end up hundreds or thousands of miles away from their source. This "jumping" from one location to another is sometimes referred to as the grasshopper effect. The pollutants move by water or by air. For example, PCBs and mercury can exist as tiny particles that are carried by winds through Earth's atmosphere. These same pollutants can fall in drops of rain or in snow to Earth's surface, where they can enter streams and lakes. Warm temperatures can cause pollutants in the water to vaporize and return to Earth's atmosphere. The air and the water each represent a different medium that carries the pollutants. This type of interaction is described as cross-media contamination.

Ongoing Assessment

Explain how pollution affects the environment.

Ask: How do air and water pollution affect Earth? *Air pollution causes acid rain, which can damage ecosystems; water pollution poisons fish and other species.*

Pollution Across Systems

As you have learned, pollution can be spread among ecosystems by abiotic factors. For example, wind carried ash from Mount St. Helens to different ecosystems. Wind also carries acid rain to forest ecosystems. Pollution can move between air and water. For example, some chemical pollutants can run off land and into a body of water. These pollutants, like the water itself, can evaporate from the water's surface and cycle into the air, moving into the atmosphere.

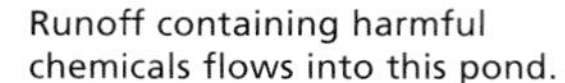

1 Runoff containing harmful chemicals flows into this pond.

2 The chemicals evaporate into the air from the surface of the water.

Habitat loss endangers biodiversity.

Scientists know that an ecosystem with many different species of plants and animals can withstand the effects of flooding, drought, and disease more effectively than an ecosystem with fewer species. But a habitat must be able to support a large number of different species for biodiversity to be maintained. If living space is limited or a food source is removed, then the number of species in a biological community will be reduced.

Removing Habitats

One way human activities affect habitats is by reducing the amounts of natural resources available to other living things. When this occurs, populations that rely on those resources are less likely to survive. For example, if people trim all the dead branches off the trees in a park and remove them, insects that live in rotting wood will not be present in the park. As a result, woodpeckers that may have nested in the area will lose their source of food. By removing this food source, people might affect the biodiversity in the park.

Now consider altering an ecosystem much larger than a park. Instead of removing a single resource, imagine removing a large area of land that is a habitat to many different species. Disturbing habitats removes not only food but space, shelter, and protection for living things.

DIFFERENTIATE INSTRUCTION

More Reading Support

G How does pollution move from land to water? *It dissolves in rainwater or gets eroded in runoff.*

Alternative Assessment Have students design an experiment to test human impact on an ecosystem. Have them study how paving an area can affect soil and water in the region. Refer them to the Nature of Science pp. CA20–CA23. Have students identify the information they will need, the method of measuring results, and the observations they make.

Removing Habitat

A clear-cut forest provides a dramatic example of habitat loss.

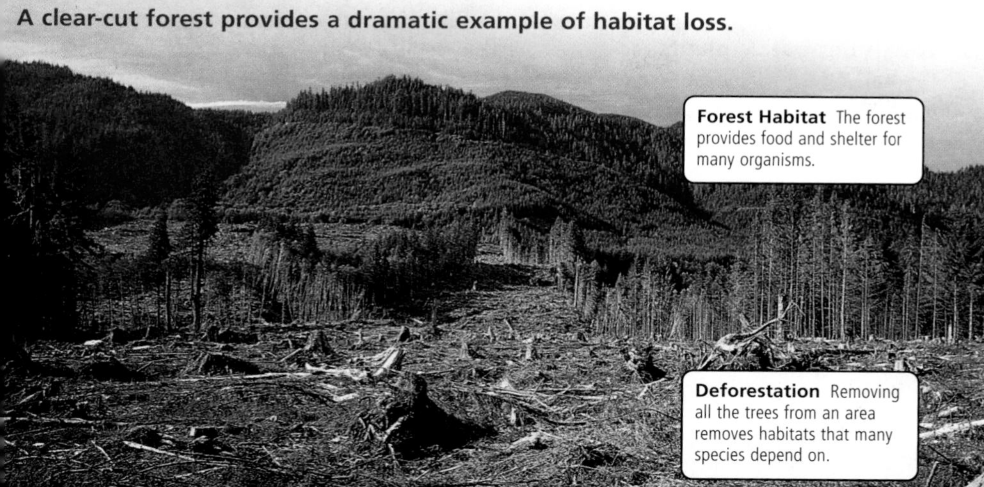

Forest Habitat The forest provides food and shelter for many organisms.

Deforestation Removing all the trees from an area removes habitats that many species depend on.

Because of land development, forests that once stretched for hundreds of miles have been broken apart into small patches. Organisms that depend on trees cannot live in woods that have large areas that have been clear-cut, or removed all at one time. There is a greater risk of attack by predators such as skunks, raccoons, and crows. These animals eat the eggs of forest songbirds, but will not travel deep into large forests. However, they can reach nests more easily when forests are broken into small areas.

CHECK YOUR READING Why is biodiversity important, and how can human activities affect it?

Changing Habitats

Another kind of habitat loss occurs when humans move species into new habitats, either on purpose or by accident. Some species, when released in a new place, successfully compete against the native species and crowd them out. Over time, the new species, called invasive species, may replace the native species.

One example of an invasive plant is purple loosestrife. In the 1800s loosestrife from Europe was brought to the United States to use in gardens and medicines. One loosestrife plant can produce over 2 million seeds a year. These seeds are carried long distances by wind, water, animals, and humans. Loosestrife sprouts in wetlands, where it can fill in an open-water habitat or replace native plants.

Teach from Visuals

To help students interpret the photograph of a clear-cut forest, ask:

- What has happened in the foreground of the picture? *The forest has been clear-cut.*
- How does the light in the background differ from the light in the foreground? *Much more light is in the foreground.*
- How might the ecosystem change from the foreground to the background? *The foreground has dry soil with very little life. The background has a variety of life in and under trees; the soil is not eroded.*

Real World Example

There are many examples of invasive species. Imported red fire ants were accidentally introduced into Alabama in the hold of merchant ships. The ants have spread throughout the South. Fire ants are aggressive, their stings are painful, and their mounds can ruin crops. The kudzu vine, imported from Japan, now runs wild in the South, covering small houses and killing trees. In the Great Lakes region, zebra mussels from Europe cover piers, boats, and machinery, and clog water supply pipes. In Australia, European rabbits have wiped out some native vegetation.

Ongoing Assessment

Describe how a loss of biodiversity affects the environment.

Ask: When land is cleared with a bulldozer, how does loss of diversity affect the environment? *Soil is removed and may become too thin or dry for plants to grow. Plants, insects, and other living things are removed. Many larger animals can no longer live in this habitat. They lose the food and living space they depend on.*

CHECK YOUR READING *Answer: Biodiversity is important because it measures the richness and variety of life in an ecosystem. Human activities can reduce biodiversity by decreasing the amount of land in an ecosystem.*

DIFFERENTIATE INSTRUCTION

More Reading Support

J What is an invasive species? *a species that moves to a new place and replaces native species*

Advanced In the 1950s, Australia's rabbit population had exploded and caused competition with cattle for pasture for grazing. To deal with this problem, officials released a virus that kills rabbits. Rabbit populations then sharply decreased, and native plants and animals rebounded. Ask students to analyze what could go wrong with such a practice. *The virus could affect other organisms, seriously damaging the food web.*

R Challenge and Extension, p. 233

Address Misconceptions

IDENTIFY Ask students to explain why they think ecologists should or should not work to reduce the growth of some plants. Students may think that all species are beneficial to an environment, and that there is no need to control growth of an invasive species.

CORRECT Ask volunteers to add steps to a flow chart on the board that illustrates what might happen to the monarch butterfly if the only food source for its larvae were replaced by an invasive plant species.

REASSESS Explain how the growth of a population of a nonnative species might limit the growth of another species. *through competition or the destruction of a living area*

Reinforce the BIG idea

Have students relate the section to the Big Idea.

 Reinforcing Key Concepts, p. 235

14.2 ASSESS & RETEACH

Assess

 Section 14.2 Quiz, p. 310

Reteach

Create a three-column chart for students titled "Human Activities Affect the Environment." Use these headings:

- Use Resources
- Release Waste and Pollution
- Alter Habitats

Have students cite specific activities under each heading. Discuss the effects on biodiversity and efficiency of the ecosystem. Have students brainstorm activities that minimize impacts.

Technology Resources

Have students visit **ClassZone.com** for reteaching of Key Concepts.

 CONTENT REVIEW

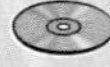 CONTENT REVIEW CD-ROM

Changing Habitat

Habitat loss occurs when purple loosestrife fills in open water or crowds out native plants.

Invasive Species Purple loosestrife fills in wetlands and replaces native species, disturbing organisms that rely on native species for food or living space.

Native Species Goldenrod is a native species that is a food source for many wetland populations.

Most ducks and fish do not feed on purple loosestrife. When the native plants that wetland animals depend on are replaced by loosestrife, the animals disappear too.

Scientists estimate that Earth supports more than 10 million different species. They also estimate that thousands of species are threatened, and hundreds of species of plants and animals become extinct every year. By protecting biodiversity we can help ecosystems thrive and recover more quickly after a natural disturbance such as a hurricane. Biodiversity benefits humans too. Many medications are based on natural compounds from plants that grow only in certain types of ecosystems.

14.2 Review

KEY CONCEPTS

1. List some renewable and nonrenewable resources that you need in order to survive. (6.6.b)
2. Describe two ways in which pollution can move through ecosystems. (6.6.a)
3. Explain what scientists mean by *biodiversity*. (6.6.b)

CRITICAL THINKING

4. **Explain** Under some circumstances, valuable natural resources can be considered pollutants. Explain this statement, giving two examples.
5. **Compare** Identify two natural habitats in your area, one with high biodiversity and one with low biodiversity. Describe the biodiversity of each.

CHALLENGE

6. **Hypothesize** When lakes are polluted by acid rain, the water appears to become clearer, not cloudier. Why do you think this is the case?

ANSWERS

1. renewable: air, water, crops; nonrenewable: oil, coal, minerals, metals

2. Wind can carry acid rain; chemical pollutants run off land into groundwater.

3. number and variety of life forms in an ecosystem

4. Natural resources can be pollutants when they are placed in areas where they don't belong. Examples: when erosion washes soil into streams; when carbon dioxide from a forest fire pollutes the air.

5. Sample: high biodiversity: a forest with a variety of plant and animal life; low biodiversity: grassy field with insects, worms

6. Acidic water slows the growth of producers in the lake. With fewer producers and less food available, the water appears clearer because it contains less life.

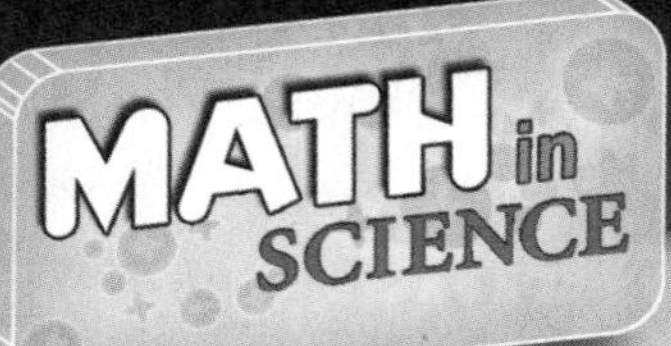

SKILL: FINDING VOLUMES

How Much Water?

When you take a ten-minute shower, you are using about 75 liters of water. How much is that? Liters are a metric unit of volume, the amount of space that matter takes up. One liter is equal to 1000 cubic centimeters.

MATH TUTORIAL
CLASSZONE.COM
Click on Math Tutorial for more help with finding the volume of a cylinder.

Math 6.MG.1.2, 6.MG.1.3
Science 6.6.b

Example

A tank in the shape of a cylinder holds enough water for a 10-minute shower. The tank has a radius of 30 cm and a height of 27 cm. What is the volume of a tank?

Volume = area of the base × height

$V = \pi \times r^2 \times h$

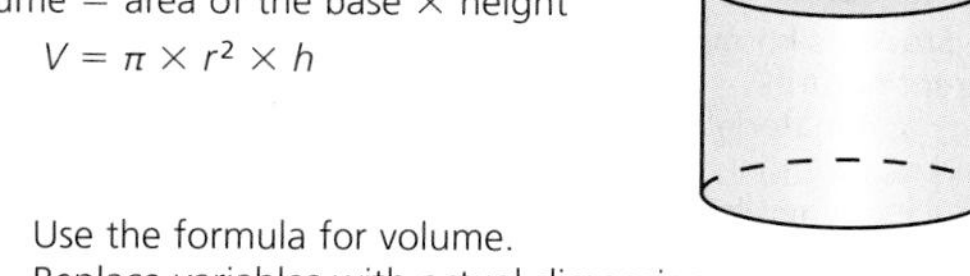

(1) Use the formula for volume.
Replace variables with actual dimensions.
$V = 3.14 \times (30\text{ cm})^2 \times 27\text{ cm}$

(2) Calculate by multiplying.
$3.14 \times 900 \times 27$
$2826 \times 27 = 76{,}302$

(3) Check units:
$\text{cm} \times \text{cm} \times \text{cm} = \text{cm}^3$ (cubic centimeters)

ANSWER $3.14 \times (30\text{ cm})^2 \times 27\text{ cm} = 76{,}302\text{ cm}^3$

Find the following volumes.

1. Brushing your teeth with the water running uses the water in a tank that has a radius of 10 cm and a height of 12 cm. Sketch a tank that holds exactly this amount. Label the dimensions. What is the volume?
2. If you turn off the water while you brush, you use only about half as much water. Sketch a tank that has a radius of 10 cm and a height of 6 cm. Label the dimensions. What is the volume?
3. A toilet flush uses the water in a space with a radius of 10 cm and a height of 37 cm. Find the volume in cubic centimeters. Sketch a model of this volume.

CHALLENGE **There are approximately 5678 cubic meters of water in the water tower shown. How many people could the tower supply with water for one day if each person uses a volume of water that would fill a cylinder that has a radius of 0.4 m and a height of 0.34 m?**

ANSWERS

1. *Tanks should have radius and height labeled correctly; 3768 cm³*
2. *Sample answer:* $3.14 \cdot (10\text{ cm})^2 \cdot 6\text{ cm} = 1884\text{ cm}^3$
3. $3.14 \cdot (10\text{ cm})^2 \cdot 37\text{ cm} = 11{,}618\text{ cm}^3$

CHALLENGE $3.14 \cdot (.4\text{ m})^2 \cdot .34\text{ m} = .17\text{ m}^3;\ \dfrac{5678\text{ m}^3}{.17\text{ m}^3} = 33{,}400$

MATH IN SCIENCE
Math Skills Practice for Science

Set Learning Goal

To calculate volumes for various scenarios of water usage

Math Standards

6.MG.1.2 Know common estimates of π (3.14; 22/7) and use these values to estimate and calculate the circumference and the area of circles; compare with actual measurements.

6.MG.1.3 Know and use the formulas for the volume of triangular prisms and cylinders (area of base × height); compare these formulas and explain the similarity between them and the formula for the volume of a rectangular solid.

Present the Science

From 50 to 90 percent of all living things is water. The basic material of cells, protoplasm, is a solution of water and substances such as fats, proteins, and salts. Water transports, breaks down, and dissolves these substances.

Develop Geometry Skills

- Remind students that volume adds the third dimension to area.
- Have students begin each problem by writing out the $V = \pi \cdot r^2 \cdot h$ equation.

DIFFERENTIATION TIP Have students who have trouble with the formula keep a cylinder (such as a can) on their desks as a reminder that volume takes up space. Remind them to find the area of the base and then multiply by the third dimension, height.

Close

Have students use amounts given in the problems to estimate the volume of water they use in a total day. *Sample answer: 76,302 cm³ for a shower, 5 flushes at 11,618 cm³ per flush, 2 tooth brushings at 1,884 cm³ each Total = 138,160 cm³ per day*

- Math Support, p. 251
- Math Practice, p. 252

Technology Resources

Students can visit **ClassZone.com** for practice in finding volumes.

MATH TUTORIAL

14.3 FOCUS

Set Learning Goals

Students will

- Consider laws that have been passed to help protect the environment.
- Describe the efforts that are being made to conserve natural resources.

3-Minute Warm-Up

Display Transparency 109 or copy this exercise on the board:

Match the definition to the correct term.

Definitions

1. something from the environment that humans use *c*
2. number of people in a given area *b*
3. the addition of harmful substances to the environment *a*

Terms

a. pollution
b. population density
c. natural resource
d. invasive species
e. biodiversity

3-Minute Warm-Up, p. T109

14.3 MOTIVATE

EXPLORE Environmental Impacts

PURPOSE To demonstrate how foot traffic might affect water absorption by soil

TIPS *15 min.* Pots about 4 inches in diameter work well. Any soil will do.

WHAT DO YOU THINK? *The compressed soil took longer to absorb the water; soil that is walked on quite a bit will hold less water, making it more difficult for grass or other plants to get water. Water that is not absorbed by soil could carry pollutants into rivers and streams.*

KEY CONCEPT

14.3 People are working to protect ecosystems.

CALIFORNIA Content Standards

6.6.a Students know the utility of energy sources is determined by factors that are involved in converting these sources to useful forms and the consequences of the conversion process.

6.6.b Students know different natural energy and material resources, including air, soil, rocks, minerals, petroleum, fresh water, wildlife, and forests, and know how to classify them as renewable or nonrenewable.

6.6.c Students know the natural origin of the materials used to make common objects.

BEFORE, you learned

- Human activities produce pollutants
- Human activity is depleting some natural resources

NOW, you will learn

- About local and federal efforts to protect the environment
- About efforts that are being made to conserve natural resources

VOCABULARY

sustainable p. 510

EXPLORE Environmental Impacts (6.5.e)

What happens when soil is compressed?

PROCEDURE

1. Fill two pots with 1 cup each of potting soil.
2. Compress the soil in the first pot by pushing down hard on it with your hand.
3. Pour 1 cup of water into the second pot. Start the stopwatch as soon as you start pouring. Stop the watch as soon as all the water has been absorbed. Record the time.
4. Pour 1 cup of water into the first pot. Again record how long it takes for the water to be absorbed. Wash your hands.

WHAT DO YOU THINK?

- What effect does compressing the soil have on how quickly the water is absorbed?
- What might happen to water that is not absorbed quickly by soil?

MATERIALS

- 2 plant pots with trays
- measuring cup
- potting soil
- water
- stopwatch

NOTE-TAKING STRATEGY Use a strategy of your choosing to take notes on the main idea.

Environmental awareness is growing.

As pioneers moved westward across the grassy plains and steep mountain ranges of North America, many believed that resources were endless. Midwestern prairies were converted to farmland. Forests were clear-cut for lumber. Mines were dug for coal.

By the 1800s, foresters and naturalists began to take an interest in preserving the wild areas they saw rapidly disappearing. In 1872 Yellowstone was established as the world's first national park. It wasn't long before the conservation of wild places became a goal.

506 Unit 4: **Ecology and Resources**

RESOURCES FOR DIFFERENTIATED INSTRUCTION

Below Level

UNIT RESOURCE BOOK

- Reading Study Guide A, pp. 238–239
- Decoding Support, p. 250

AUDIO CDS

Advanced

UNIT RESOURCE BOOK

Challenge and Extension, p. 244

English Learners

UNIT RESOURCE BOOK

Spanish Reading Study Guide, pp. 242–243

AUDIO CDS

- Audio Readings in Spanish
- Audio Readings (English)

As you read in Chapter 13, conservation is the process of saving or protecting a natural resource.

The movement to protect our environment grew rapidly in the 1960s. In 1962 the book *Silent Spring* raised public awareness of the effects of harmful chemicals on the environment. As local efforts for environmental protection grew, the United States government responded. Throughout the 1970s, far-reaching laws were passed to preserve and protect the environment. Today, local and national government efforts, along with groups of concerned citizens, protect America's natural resources.

CHECK YOUR READING List three events in the history of the environmental movement in the United States.

RESOURCE CENTER CLASSZONE.COM

Discover how people help ecosystems recover.

Volunteers work to clean up a stream.

Local Efforts

Maybe you have heard the expression "Think globally, act locally." It urges people to consider the health of the entire planet and to take action in their own communities. Long before federal and state agencies began enforcing environmental laws, people were coming together to protect habitats and the organisms that depend on them. These efforts are often referred to as grassroots efforts. They occur on a local level and are often run by volunteers.

Sometimes the efforts of a few citizens attract the support and interest of so many people that those people form a larger organization. These groups work to bring about change by communicating with politicians, publishing articles, or talking to the news media. Some groups purchase land and set it aside for preservation.

DIFFERENTIATE INSTRUCTION

More Reading Support

A When did the movement to protect the environment catch on in a big way? *1960s*

English Learners Encourage English learners to share environmental issues from their native countries. Also encourage them to discuss any local or community conservation efforts.

14.3 INSTRUCT

Teach the Standards

Renewable and nonrenewable energy sources 6.6.b

In this section: Help students understand that because human use of renewable and nonrenewable energy sources causes pollution and threatens ecosystems, people are practicing conservation to protect the environment. Point out that laws exist to protect ecosystems.

previously taught: solar energy, p. 24; fossil fuels, pp. 452–455; renewable energy resources, pp. 471–477; nuclear power, pp. 477–479

Social Studies Connection

President Theodore Roosevelt is depicted on Mount Rushmore because, more than any other president, he supported conservation. At Roosevelt's urging, Congress created the Forest Service in 1905 to manage federal forests. Roosevelt set aside about 200 million acres as public lands to protect them from commercial exploitation. He designated 150 national forests, the first 51 federal bird reservations, and 5 national parks. He pushed for the Reclamation Act of 1902, which established irrigation and other services for western lands.

History of Science

Rachel Carson wrote four books about the connection between living things and their environment. The most important of these books is *Silent Spring.* Published in 1962, *Silent Spring* exposed the danger of the pesticide DDT. The book explained how DDT entered the food chain and affected entire ecosystems. Carson kept careful notes, and her hard work paid off. Today, *Silent Spring* is credited with starting the environmental movement in the United States.

Ongoing Assessment

CHECK YOUR READING *Answer: creation of first national park (1872), publication of* Silent Spring *(1962), passage of major environmental laws in the 1970s*

Teach from Visuals

To help students interpret the graph of peregrine falcon pairs, ask:

- What was happening to the peregrine falcon population until 1968? *The overall trend was that the population declined.*
- In what year was DDT banned? *1972*
- In what year were the first captive falcons released? *1974*
- What has been happening to the peregrine falcon population since 1985? *The number of breeding pairs has risen steeply.*

Real World Example

DDT was once considered very beneficial. After World War II, it was used heavily throughout the world to control insects that carry life-threatening diseases such as malaria, yellow fever, typhus, and elephantiasis. In the 1950s in India, the use of DDT decreased the number of malaria cases from 75 million to less than 1 million.

By 1962, however, DDT's damaging effects were being identified. Because DDT is a very stable chemical, it accumulated in the birds and fish that ate the insects, poisoning them and causing reproductive problems. Many insects developed resistance to DDT, and these populations grew unchecked while their natural predators were killed. For these reasons, DDT was banned in the United States in 1972 except for use in extreme health emergencies. Developing countries, such as those in Africa, continue to use DDT to control mosquitoes that can carry malaria.

Ongoing Assessment

CHECK YOUR READING *Answer: the National Environmental Policy Act (NEPA), the Endangered Species Act, the Clean Air Act, and the Clean Water Act*

Federal Efforts

 B

You have probably heard of the Endangered Species Act or the Clean Air Act. You might wonder exactly what these laws do. The United States government works with scientists to write environmental laws. The goal of the laws is for companies and individuals to work together to conserve natural resources and maintain healthy ecosystems.

 C

In 1969 the National Environmental Policy Act (NEPA) made the protection of natural ecosystems a national goal. Several important laws followed. For example, the Clean Air Act and Clean Water Act helped control the kinds and amounts of pollutants that can be released into the air and water. The Environmental Protection Agency (EPA) enforces all federal environmental laws.

CHECK YOUR READING Identify two federal environmental laws.

Over the past century, chemical waste from factories has piled up in landfills, and it has polluted water sources. These wastes can threaten ecosystems and human health. In 1980 citizen awareness of the dangers led to the Superfund Program. The goal of the program is to identify dangerous areas and clean up the worst sites.

Helping Endangered Species

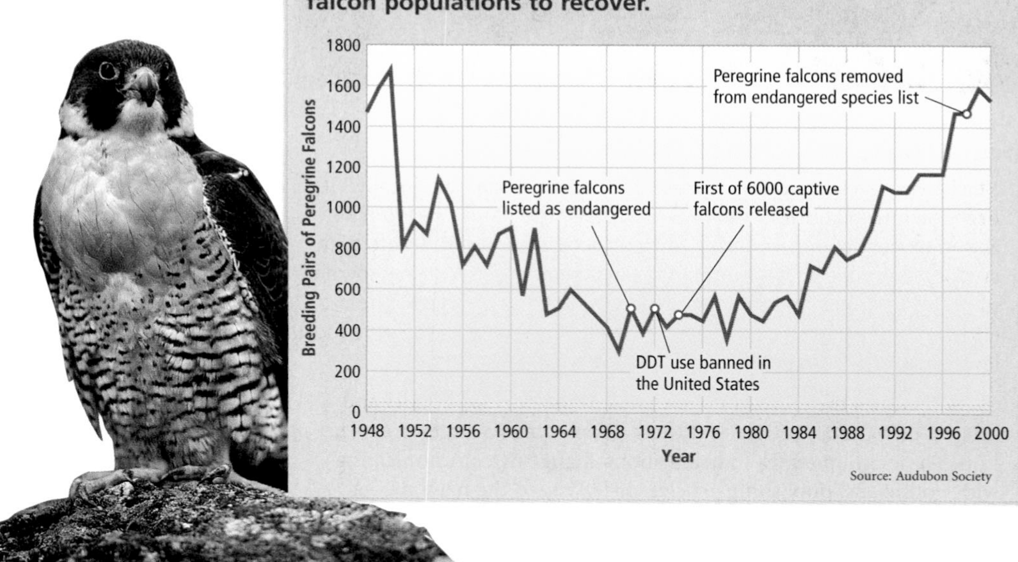

DIFFERENTIATE INSTRUCTION

More Reading Support

B What do the Clean Air and Clean Water Acts do? *allow government to establish pollution controls*

C What does the EPA do? *enforces all federal environmental laws*

Advanced Suggest that students create political cartoons depicting pollution issues and/or government or civilian responses.

 Challenge and Extension, p. 244

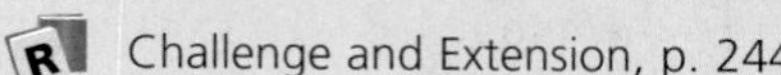

English Learners There are many different types of graphs. Review the graph on endangered species with English learners. Help them understand how the information is arranged and how to interpret it. Encourage them to generate questions that can be answered by the graph.

Ecosystem Recovery

A growing awareness of the importance of healthy ecosystems is inspiring restoration projects.

Wetland

Restoration efforts in Galveston Bay, Texas, focus on bringing back the sea-grass meadows near the coast.

Volunteers help replant sea grass around Galveston Island State Park. Sea grass is a major habitat for birds, fish, and crabs. It helps prevent erosion by holding sediments in place.

Desert

Members of a restoration group work to restore desert plants and soil in Red Rock Canyon State Park, California.

1 A power auger is used to break up very compacted soil and prepare it for planting.

2 Seedlings of native species, such as the saltbush, are grown elsewhere. Once the plants reach a mature size, they are planted in the park.

3 Plastic cones are used to protect plants from severe weather or predators.

Teach from Visuals

Ecosystem recovery projects are underway in many areas, including Galveston Island State Park in Texas and Red Rock Canyon State Park in California.

To help students interpret the photographs of wetland and desert, ask:

- How do the seagrass meadows help the marine ecosystem? *Sea grass holds soil in place and keeps the water clear.*
- What were plastic cones used for? *to protect new plants*
- Why did vegetation need to be restored in Red Rock Canyon? *Soil had been compacted and vegetation stripped by vehicles and mining.*

Real World Example

To restore the Galveston Island sea-grass meadows—which broke up because of shrimp trawling and pumping groundwater for industrial, commercial, and residential use—an offshore oyster reef had to be replaced. The oyster reef had protected the wetlands from the waves. Restorers installed 13,500 feet of geotubes in open water offshore to simulate the reef. Geotubes use a special fabric that contains fill material while allowing water to pass through. Scientists expect that these geotubes will help minimize erosion and improve water clarity.

DIFFERENTIATE INSTRUCTION

Below Level Create a two-column chart on a bulletin board or dry-erase board. Use the column headings "Sustainable Practices" and "Renewable Resources." Have students brainstorm specific examples of each category. Write any "non-examples" off to the side to discuss as a contrast.

Integrate the Sciences

One use for recycled newspapers is cellulose insulation. Newspaper is turned into a pulp, which is then sprayed into walls and under roofs. The pulp fills cavities and so stops air filtration better than fiberglass batting does. Cellulose-insulated buildings may use 20 to 40 percent less energy than do conventionally insulated buildings. Also, it takes less energy to make cellulose insulation than to make fiberglass insulation. Cellulose insulation also increases a building's fire resistance.

Ongoing Assessment

Consider laws that have been passed to help protect the environment.

Ask: What is the goal of the National Environmental Policy Act? *to protect natural ecosystems from damage or destruction*

CHECK YOUR READING *Answer: Sustainable practices use natural resources without using them up.*

PHOTO CAPTION Answer: The worker wears a face mask because the chemicals could harm him.

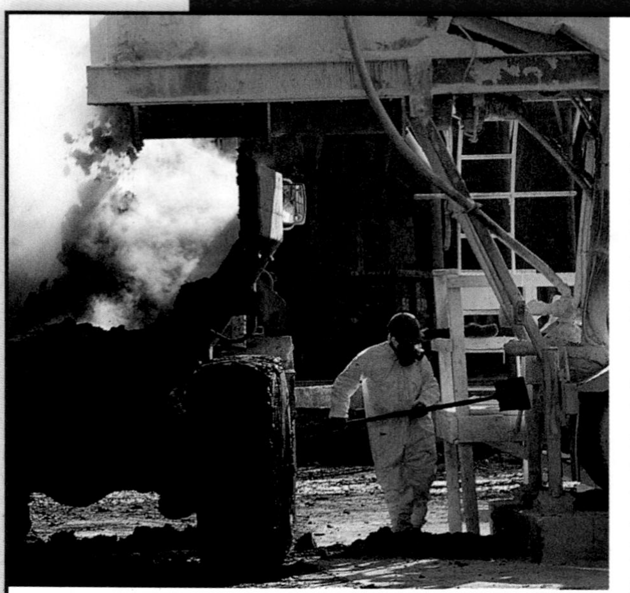

INFER At this Superfund site, the chemical cadmium pollutes the soil. Why does this worker need to wear a face mask?

Federal agencies oversee the Superfund Program and other environmental laws. In addition to federal laws protecting the environment, there are state laws. Companies must follow all the laws that apply in each state where they do business. The same company may need to follow different laws in different states.

The United States is just one of many countries learning to deal with the effects of their human population on the environment. Dozens of countries have already met to discuss concerns about clear-cutting, water pollution, and endangered species. At the international level, the United Nations Environment Programme encourages sound environmental practices worldwide.

Conserving resources protects ecosystems.

Around the world, individuals and companies are expressing more interest in **sustainable** practices—ways of living and doing business that use natural resources without using them up. Sustainable development allows people to enjoy a high quality of life while limiting harm to ecosystems. Developing new technologies, reducing resource use, and creating less waste are three ways to practice sustainability.

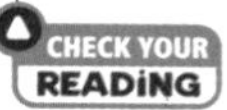

What are sustainable practices?

Improving Resource Use

As you read in Chapter 12, many different interactions take place in ecosystems. Some organisms form close relationships with one another and their environment. Humans are like other organisms. We depend on the environment to help meet our requirements for life. Because many of the resources we rely on are limited, businesses and governments are changing the way they manage farms, forests, and energy resources. They are adopting sustainable practices.

For example, some farmers are practicing sustainable methods that protect soil. Soil conservation is important because soil takes a very long time to form. It can be difficult or impossible to replace once it has been lost. Most soil conservation methods are designed to hold soil in place and keep it fertile. A few of the soil conservation methods that are used by farmers around the world are described on page 511.

DIFFERENTIATE INSTRUCTION

D Describe one sustainable practice. *use fewer resources; reduce waste*

E Name one sustainable practice farmers use to protect soil. *Sample answer: crop rotation*

English Learners English learners may be unfamiliar with words that have multiple meanings. Explain the multiple meanings of the following words in the section. On p. 508, *private* is used to mean nongovernmental. On p. 510, *adopting* is used to indicate something being put to use. On p. 510, *practice* is used to mean a policy or way of doing things. On p. 512, *pool* in *carpooling* is used to mean a group.

Crop rotation is the practice of planting different crops on the same field in different years or growing seasons. Grain crops, such as wheat, use up a lot of the nitrogen—a necessary plant nutrient—in the soil. The roots of bean crops, such as soybeans, contain bacteria that restore nitrogen to the soil. By rotating these crops, farmers can help maintain soil fertility.

Conservation tillage includes several methods of reducing the number of times fields are tilled, or plowed, in a year. The less soil is disturbed by plowing, the less likely it is to be washed or blown away. In one method of conservation tillage, fields are not plowed at all. The remains of harvested crops are simply left on the fields to cover and protect the soil. New seeds are planted in narrow bands of soil.

Terraces are flat, steplike areas built on a hillside to hold rainwater and prevent it from running downhill. Crops are planted on the flat tops of the terraces.

Contour plowing is the practice of plowing along the curves, or contours, of a slope. Contour plowing helps channel rainwater so that it does not run straight downhill, carrying away soil with it. A soil conservation method called strip-cropping is often combined with contour plowing. Strips of grasses, shrubs, or other plants are planted between bands of a grain crop along the contour of a slope. These strips of plants also help slow the runoff of water.

Windbreaks are rows of trees planted between fields to "break," or reduce, the force of winds that can carry off soil.

Terracing

Contour Plowing

READING VISUALS COMPARE Both terracing and contour plowing are soil conservation methods used on sloping land. How does each method help conserve soil?

Develop Critical Thinking

APPLY Tell students that renewable resources are those that can be easily replaced by natural processes, at the same rate at which they are used. Nonrenewable resources take thousands of years to be replaced. Point out that soil is replaced by natural processes. Have students apply this information to what they know about soil. Ask: Would you consider soil a renewable or nonrenewable resource? *Soil is a nonrenewable resource because well-developed soils may take thousands of years to form.*

Ongoing Assessment

READING VISUALS *Answer: Terraces hold rainwater and prevent it from washing soil downhill. Contour plowing helps channel rainwater so that it does not run straight downhill and carry soil away.*

DIFFERENTIATE INSTRUCTION

More Reading Support

F How does crop rotation help preserve soil? *maintains soil fertility*

G What are windbreaks? *rows of trees planted between fields to reduce the force of wind*

Real World Example

Several cities have innovative ways of decreasing traffic and pollution. Singapore created a drivable city center by constructing a ring of tollbooths around the city. The toll that people pay varies with the time during which they are driving and how much pollution is present. It costs more to drive into the city during rush hour than during off-peak periods, and more when pollution is high than when it is low. Licenses for cars also vary in price, depending on how much the car is driven. A license to drive only on weekends costs less than one needed to drive every day. London uses congestion charging, which charges drivers five pounds a day to drive in central London. This policy encourages the use of other modes of transportation, such as buses and trains.

Teach from Visuals

To help students interpret the pie chart, ask:

- Which three activities use the most water? *flushing the toilet, using a washing machine, showering*
- What percentage of the water that people use each day comes from the tap? *12 percent*
- Which two uses make up half of the water used at home each day? *flushing the toilet, and either taking showers or using a washing machine*
- What repair could save 5 percent of the water that people use? *fixing leaking toilets*

Ongoing Assessment

Describe the efforts that are being made to conserve natural resources.

Ask: What are some ways that people conserve fossil fuels in their daily transportation to work and school? *carpooling, mass transit, telecommuting*

CHECK YOUR READING *Answer: Traffic is reduced; there is less air and noise pollution and less use of fossil fuels.*

PHOTO CAPTION Answer: Mass transit reduces traffic congestion and noise. It might take longer for some people to get where they are going if they use mass transit.

INFER What benefits do people get from using mass transit? Why might some people be reluctant to use mass transit?

Reducing Waste and Pollution

Perhaps you take a bus to school. Buses and trains are examples of mass transit, the moving of large groups of people at the same time. When you travel by mass transit, you are working to reduce waste and pollution. The photograph to the left shows a train that carries commuters from downtown Portland, Oregon, to suburbs an hour away. In Portland, mass transit helps reduce traffic congestion, fuel use, air pollution, and noise pollution.

Another way to reduce pollution is by carpooling, or sharing rides. Many states, including California, encourage carpools by reducing tolls or reserving highway lanes for cars carrying more than one person. Traffic is also reduced when workers telecommute, or work from home using computers and telephones. Of course, a telecommuter uses energy at home. But there are many ways to reduce home energy use. You can install compact fluorescent light bulbs, which use less electricity than a regular light bulb. And you can choose energy-efficient appliances.

CHECK YOUR READING How does mass transit benefit the environment?

People can conserve water in three ways. The first way is to use less water. A simple way that some cities reduce water use is by repairing leaks in underground pipes. The second way is to reuse water. Many cities reuse treated wastewater for landscaping. The third method is to use water again for the same purpose. Industries can recycle water used to cool machines back through the same system.

READING TIP The prefix *re-* means "again," so to recycle a resource is to use it again.

The chart below shows how people living in the United States use water in their homes. Note that one way people could conserve water is by repairing leaking toilets.

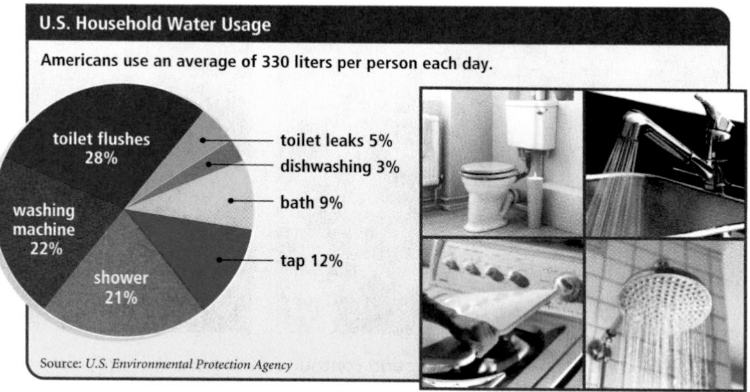

DIFFERENTIATE INSTRUCTION

More Reading Support

H Name some ways to reduce the use of cars. *mass transit, carpool*

I Name one way to conserve water. *use less water*

Below Level Have students review the ways to conserve natural resources on pp. 512–513 and give an example of each way that is practiced in their local neighborhood. Ask for an example of reducing waste (using a lunch box or canvas grocery bag rather than throw-away packaging), recycling (returning bottles), conserving energy use (lowering heat or air-conditioner use), and reducing air pollution (walking or biking).

Other ways that people can conserve water at home include changes in plumbing and in daily habits. Low-flow toilets and showerheads can cut water use in half. People conserve water by turning off the faucet while brushing their teeth, taking shorter showers, and running the dishwasher only when it is full. Leaking pipes and dripping faucets in homes cause huge amounts of water to be wasted. Regular repair and maintenance of plumbing systems can reduce water use greatly.

Learn more about water conservation.

What are three ways in which people can conserve water at home?

Think globally, act locally.

Visitors to an ocean beach may find signs like the one on the right. Such signs remind people that small actions, such as protecting the nests of sandpipers, make a difference in the preservation of ecosystems.

The challenges facing society are great. Providing Earth's growing human population with clean water, clean air, and energy for heating, cooling, and transportation are only some of the many tasks. Scientists continue to learn about the interactions in ecosystems and the importance of ecosystems to humans. As you have read about the interactions in ecosystems, you have probably realized that humans—including you—have a large effect on the natural world.

In the coming years, protecting ecosystems will remain a major challenge. By thinking globally, you will be able to understand the effects of society's decisions about resources, development, and transportation. By acting locally, you can become involved in efforts to reduce the use of limited resources and to restore ecosystems.

14.3 Review

KEY CONCEPTS

1. What is meant by the slogan, "Think globally, act locally"?
2. List at least five ways that you can reduce your use of natural resources. **(6.6.b)**
3. Describe three ways that resources can be managed in a sustainable way. **(6.6.b)**

CRITICAL THINKING

4. **Infer** Controlling air and water pollution and protecting endangered species usually require the involvement of the federal government. Why can't state or local governments do this on their own?
5. **Synthesize** How are sustainable practices related to the use of nonrenewable resources?

CHALLENGE

6. **Apply** Explain how efforts to protect endangered species relate to the restoration of ecosystems.

ANSWERS

1. Consider the health of Earth and take local action.

2. volunteer cleanup, mass transit, sustainable farming, recycling, alternative energy sources

3. Farms can use conservation tillage. Mass transit can reduce fuel use. Taking shorter showers can conserve water.

4. Animals migrate and pollution created in one state can travel, so the federal government needs to be involved to solve problems and set policies.

5. Sustainable practices help prevent nonrenewable resources from being used up.

6. Successful efforts to protect endangered species bring more balance and biodiversity to the ecosystem.

CHECK YOUR READING *Answer: People can use less water by repairing leaks in plumbing, taking shorter showers, and installing low-flow toilets and shower heads.*

EXPLORE the BIG idea

Revisit "Internet Activity: The Environment" on p. 487. Have students explain their results.

Reinforce the BIG idea

Have students relate the section to the Big Idea.

 Reinforcing Key Concepts, p. 245

14.3 ASSESS & RETEACH

Assess

 Section 14.3 Quiz, p. 311

Reteach

Have the class add to a natural resources problem/possible solutions chart. Students can brainstorm actions to be taken in response to the following problems:

- polluted water
- endangered species
- polluted air
- use of nonrenewable energy sources such as fossil fuels

Technology Resources

Have students visit **ClassZone.com** for reteaching of Key Concepts.

 **CONTENT REVIEW**

 **CONTENT REVIEW CD-ROM**

CHAPTER INVESTIGATION

Focus

PURPOSE Hypothesize the effects of various methods for containing and cleaning up an oil spill, and design an experimental model to test the effects of a spill on a beach environment

OVERVIEW Using sand and water, students will construct a model of a beach. They will add oil to their "coastal area" and then use materials and solutions to try to remove the oil. Students will find that cotton balls are most effective for absorbing oil, and that detergent is most effective for breaking down oil. Students will analyze the difference between their models and real oil-spill situations.

Lab Preparation

- Square cake pans work well.
- Before they begin working, have students read through the investigation and prepare their data tables. As an alternative, you may wish to copy and distribute datasheets and rubrics.

 UNIT RESOURCE BOOK, pp. 253–261

 SCIENCE TOOLKIT, F12

Lab Management

- Ensure that all students wear gloves and aprons.
- Spread newspapers to protect desks from spills.
- Students may dampen the sand for the beach so that it stays in place.

Teaching with Technology

You may wish to introduce this activity with a video documentary on cleaning up oil spills.

CHAPTER INVESTIGATION

Cleaning Oil Spills

DESIGN — YOUR OWN —

OVERVIEW AND PURPOSE

One example of a harmful effect of human activity is an oil spill. You've probably heard about oil spills in the news. Damage to an oil-carrying ship or barge can cause thick, black oil to spill into the water. The oil floats on the water, and waves can carry the oil to shore. Oil coats sand and living things that are part of a coastal ecosystem. These spills are especially difficult to clean up. In this investigation you will

- simulate an oil spill and test the effectiveness of various materials used to remove oil
- evaluate materials and processes used to clean up oil spills

Problem

What materials are effective at removing oil spilled near a coastal ecosystem?

Hypothesize

Write a hypothesis to propose a material or materials that might best remove oil from a coastal area. Your hypothesis should take the form of an "If . . . , then . . . , because . . ." statement.

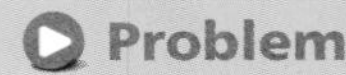

MATERIALS

- small beaker
- 40 mL vegetable oil
- turmeric
- spoon
- aluminum baking pan
- sand
- large beaker
- water
- sponge
- dish soap
- rubbing alcohol
- paper towels
- cotton balls
- cotton rag
- cornstarch
- yarn
- feather
- seaweed

6.6.a, 6.7.a, 6.7.e

Procedure

1. Make a table in your **Science Notebook** like the one shown on the sample notebook page. Record your observations on the effectiveness of each material.
2. Measure 40 mL of vegetable oil in a small beaker. Stir in a small amount of turmeric to make the oil yellow.

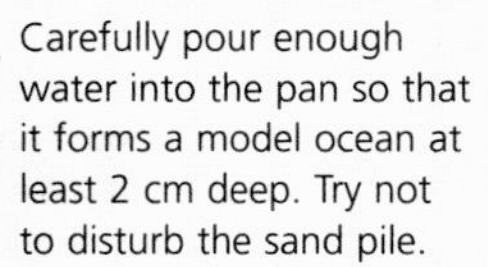

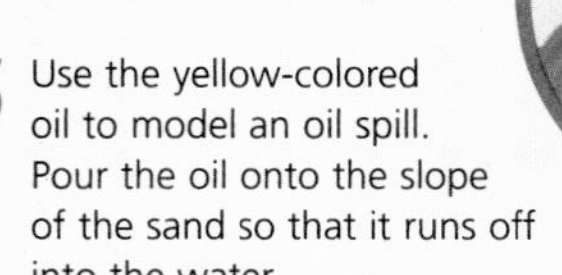

3. Pour sand into one end of the pan, as shown, to model a beach.
4. Carefully pour enough water into the pan so that it forms a model ocean at least 2 cm deep. Try not to disturb the sand pile.
5. Use the yellow-colored oil to model an oil spill. Pour the oil onto the slope of the sand so that it runs off into the water.

step 5

INVESTIGATION RESOURCES

 CHAPTER INVESTIGATION, Cleaning Oil Spills
- Level A, pp. 253–256
- Level B, pp. 257–260
- Level C, p. 261

Advanced students should complete Levels B & C.

 Writing a Lab Report, D12–13

Technology Resources

Customize this student lab as needed or look for an alternative. Print rubrics to assess student lab reports.

 **Lab Generator CD-ROM**

Content Standard
6.6.a Students know the utility of energy sources is determined by factors that are involved in converting these sources to useful forms and the consequences of the conversion process.

Investigation Standard
6.7.a Develop a hypothesis.

6 Test the materials for effectiveness in removing the oil from the sand and the water. Record your observations on the effectiveness of each material.

7 Place the feather and the seaweed on the beach or in the water, where the oil is. Test materials for effectiveness in removing oil from the feather and seaweed. Record your observations.

8 Using your observations from steps 6 and 7, design a process for removing oil from sand and water. This process may involve several materials and require a series of steps.

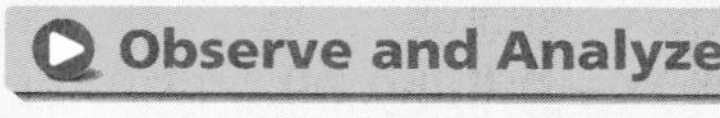

Observe and Analyze

Write It Up

1. **RECORD** Write up your procedure for cleaning oil from sand and water. You may want to include a diagram.
2. **EVALUATE** What, if any, difficulties did you encounter in carrying out this experiment?

Conclude

Write It Up

1. **INTERPRET** How do your results compare with your hypothesis? Answer the problem question.
2. **EVALUATE** Which materials were most useful for cleaning the water? Were they the same materials that were most useful for cleaning the sand?
3. **EVALUATE** Suppose you are trying to clean oil off of a living thing, such as a bird or seaweed. What process would you use?
4. **IDENTIFY LIMITS** In which ways did this demonstration fail to model a real oil spill?

INVESTIGATE Further

CHALLENGE Explain how the observations you made in this investigation might be useful in cleaning up an actual oil spill.

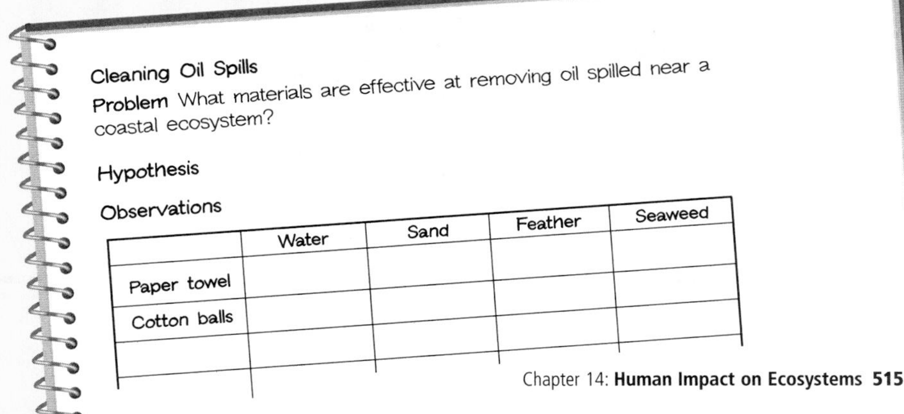
Cleaning Oil Spills
Problem What materials are effective at removing oil spilled near a coastal ecosystem?

Hypothesis

Observations

	Water	Sand	Feather	Seaweed
Paper towel				
Cotton balls				

Post-Lab Discussion

- With modern technology, why are oil spills a problem? *People can't clean up an oil spill completely, and cleanup operations can pollute the environment.*
- During a real oil spill, how do you think bad weather might affect the cleanup? *Bad weather could spread the oil, interfere with cleanup boats, and add to wildlife stress.*
- What might help prevent an oil spill? *safer ships and safety programs for crew members*

Observe and Analyze

Write It Up

1. *Student answers will vary.*
2. *Student answers will vary.*

Conclude

Write It Up

1. *Answers should detail comparisons between hypothesis and results.*
2. *Sample: Cotton balls were most useful for cleaning water. The sand had soaked up most of the oil, so we needed soap to clean the sand.*
3. *Sample: I would remove as much of the oil as possible and then clean the plant or animal. Some animals can be removed from a spill and cleaned immediately.*
4. *Sample: We've created a model of a controlled environment. In real life, oil sinks into the ground and groundwater, making the spill harder to clean up. In a real ecosystem, you must concern yourself with the effects of chemicals like detergents on living things.*

INVESTIGATE Further

CHALLENGE Answer: You need something porous and absorbent to clean oil spills on water. On land, you need to get to the oil as soon as possible before the oil sinks into the soil. Soap or detergent is needed to clean the ground.

Address Misconceptions

IDENTIFY Ask: What can be learned about cleaning real oil spills from making a model? Students may think that the techniques that work in a model would hold true for the real environment. Many students think that scientific models are exact representations.

CORRECT Discuss with students the differences between a real oil spill cleanup and a model oil spill cleanup. Explain that using detergent in a real cleanup could harm living things. Although oil is cleaned from the top layer of sand, oil could seep into lower layers. Also point out that cotton balls and sponges are not available on a large scale.

REASSESS Review students' answers to question 4. Point out that detergent is one method used to clean oil spills, but is much less effective in a real oil spill.

BACK TO

the BIG idea

Use a hypothetical scenario to demonstrate the statement, "Humans and human population growth affect the environment."

Mineral ore is discovered near a small town in the desert. Quickly, companies arrive to mine for and process the ore, bringing their employees to the town. This activity attracts other businesses (stores, gas stations, restaurants, and so on). Explain three ways that these developments will affect the desert ecosystem. *There will be more waste to dispose of. The limited water supply may run out. Expanding land use will destroy habitats.*

KEY CONCEPTS SUMMARY

SECTION 14.1

Ask: What does the steep curve on the graph imply for the challenges posed by population growth? *We might run out of natural resources.*

SECTION 14.2

Ask: How can pollution change systems? *It can make them unfit for inhabitants and fit for new organisms.*

Ask: How do humans cause habitat loss? *by developing pastures and farms, by clear-cutting forests, and by introducing nonnative species*

SECTION 14.3

Ask: What federal laws in the United States protect ecosystems? *NEPA, Clean Air and Clean Water Acts, Superfund Program*

Review Concepts

- Big Idea Flow Chart, p. T105
- Chapter Outline, pp. T111–T112

14 Chapter Review

the BIG idea

Humans and human population growth affect the environment.

CONTENT REVIEW
CLASSZONE.COM

KEY CONCEPTS SUMMARY

Human population growth presents challenges.

As the population continues to grow, there is a greater demand for natural resources. Cities and countries share many resources. Increasing populations put pressure on ecosystems.

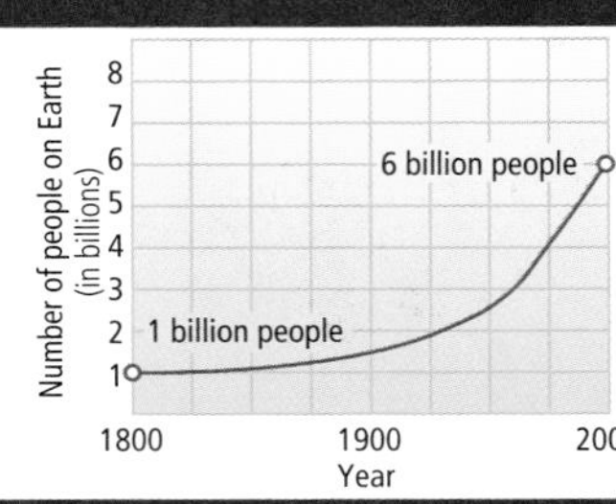

VOCABULARY
population density p. 494

2 Human activities affect the environment.

Pollution and habitat loss make it difficult for plants and animals to survive. Without the necessary resources, biodiversity decreases, and ecosystems become less stable.

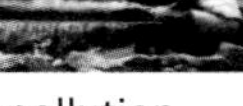

pollution

habitat loss

VOCABULARY
pollution p. 498
biodiversity p. 498

People are working to protect ecosystems.

Working at local and governmental levels, people are helping ecosystems recover.

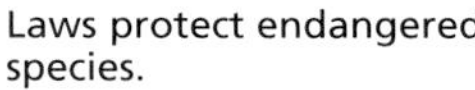

Laws protect endangered species.

People can help clean up the environment.

VOCABULARY
sustainable p. 510

516 Unit 4: Ecology and Resources

Technology Resources

Have students visit **ClassZone.com** or use the CD-ROM for a cumulative review of concepts.

CONTENT REVIEW

CONTENT REVIEW CD-ROM

Engage students in a whole-class interactive review of Key Concepts. Edit content as you wish.

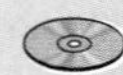

POWER PRESENTATIONS

Reviewing Vocabulary

Place each term at the center of a description wheel diagram. Write some words describing it on the spokes.

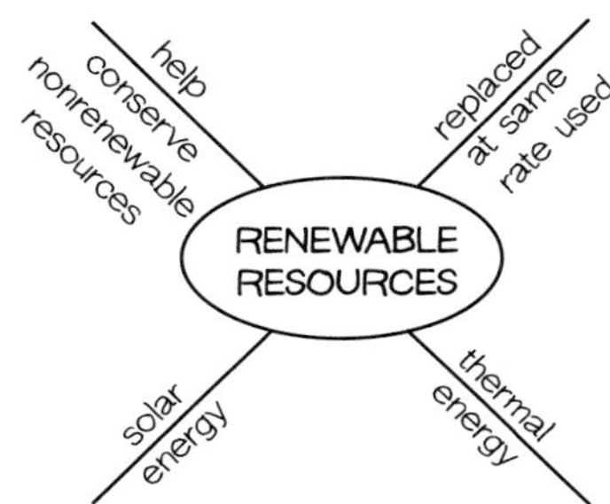

1. population density
2. natural resources
3. pollution
4. biodiversity
5. sustainable
6. conservation

Reviewing Key Concepts

Multiple Choice *Choose the best answer.*

7. What do experts predict will happen to the world population over the next 20 years? (6.5.e)
   - **a.** It will continue to grow rapidly.
   - **b.** It will stay the same.
   - **c.** It will decline sharply.
   - **d.** It will go up and down.

8. Which statement helps explain why Earth's population has grown very rapidly in the last 100 years? (6.5.e)
   - **a.** On average, women are having children at an older age.
   - **b.** People live longer because of improved health care and nutrition.
   - **c.** Global warming has enabled farmers to grow more food.
   - **d.** More land has been developed for housing.

9. Which of the following is an example of increasing biodiversity? (6.6.b)
   - **a.** A forest is clear-cut for its wood, leaving land available for new uses.
   - **b.** New species of animals and plants appear in a wildlife preserve.
   - **c.** A new species of plant outcompetes all of the others around a lake.
   - **d.** A cleared rain forest results in a change to a habitat.

10. Which represents a sustainable practice? (6.6.a)
    - **a.** using conservation tillage and natural fertilizers
    - **b.** removing oil more efficiently
    - **c.** allowing unlimited use of water for higher fees
    - **d.** restocking a lake with fish every year

11. What environmental problem does the Superfund Program address? (6.6.a)
    - **a.** habitat loss
    - **b.** land development
    - **c.** biodiversity
    - **d.** pollution

Short Answer *Write a short answer to each question.*

12. List four ways increased human population density affects ecosystems. (6.5.e)

13. Three ways that humans dispose of waste are landfills, incineration, and wastewater treatment plants. List one advantage and one disadvantage of each. (6.6.a)

14. Write a paragraph to describe how an increase in population density affects land development. (6.5.e)

Reviewing Vocabulary

1–6. Answers will vary, but all of the vocabulary terms listed should be used properly.

Reviewing Key Concepts

7. a

8. b

9. b

10. a

11. d

12. more pollution, greater demand on limited natural resources, destruction of habitats, death of plants and animals

13. Landfill disposal is generally cheap, but trash and materials may stay there for a long time. Incineration reduces the amount of trash and materials that is placed in the ground, but leads to air pollution. Sewage treatment plants clean water that is released into the environment, but the remaining sludge must be disposed of.

14. When a population grows to the point that the local environment becomes stressed, people look for other places to live. Land gets developed—forests, farms, and grasslands are destroyed—as roads and buildings are built to create a place for people to live.

ASSESSMENT RESOURCES

ASSESSMENT BOOK
- Chapter Test A, pp. 312–315
- Chapter Test B, pp. 316–319
- Chapter Test C, pp. 320–323
- Alternative Assessment, pp. 324–325
- Unit Test, A, B, & C, pp. 326–337

STANDARDS REVIEW AND PRACTICE, pp. 49–58, 61–62, 65–66

Technology Resources

Edit test items and answer choices.

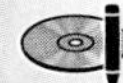 **Test Generator CD-ROM**

Visit **ClassZone.com** to extend test practice.

 **Test Practice**

Thinking Critically

15. *The population of City A in 2000 was 4 million and that of City B was 1.5 million. The rate of growth in City A between 1990 and 2000 was about twice that of City B. At current rates of increase, the population of City B will not grow larger than the population of City A.*
16. *No; area of both cities*
17. *Sample answer: Carrying capacity is higher in City A because available water sources are greater in a temperate forest biome than in a desert.*
18. *More water would be available for Mexican use and for Mexican wildlife near the mouth of the river.*
19. *Trees are generally considered a renewable resource because in a properly managed or natural forest, new growth replaces dead or removed trees. If the land is destroyed or new trees are not planted, trees from a forest are a nonrenewable resource.*
20. *RENEWABLE: water, wood, sunlight; NONRENEWABLE: copper, aluminum, petroleum, coal, soil*
21. *3600 kg less carbon dioxide*

the BIG idea

22. *Answers should show a deeper understanding of not just what was added to the landscape in physical structures, but what was taken away, as well as the pollution and environmental pressures created.*
23. *Answers should list varieties of plants and animals and should include at least four sustainable practices, including conservation of resources and reduction of waste.*

UNIT PROJECTS

Have students present their projects. Use the appropriate rubrics from the Unit Resource Book to evaluate their work.

R Unit Projects, pp. 5–10

Thinking Critically

Use the graph to answer the next three questions.

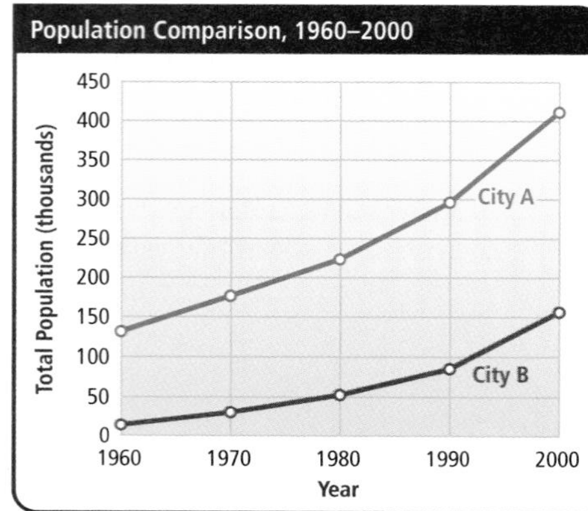

15. **COMPARE AND CONTRAST** Describe the population size and rate of growth for City A and City B. Based on the graph, would you expect the population of City B ever to get bigger than that of City A? **(6.5.e)**

16. **EVALUATE** Is it possible to determine from the data shown whether the population density is higher in City A than in City B? If not, what other information would you need? **(6.5.e)**

17. **CONNECT** City A is located in a temperate-forest biome, and City B is located in a desert biome. How might the characteristics of these biomes affect the carrying capacity of the human populations in these cities? **(6.5.e)**

18. **PREDICT** If the United States used less water from the Colorado River, how would the depth of the river in Mexico be affected? **(6.6.b)**

19. **COMPARE AND CONTRAST** Explain why trees are generally considered a renewable resource. Describe circumstances under which they could be considered a nonrenewable resource. **(6.6.b)**

20. **CLASSIFY** Sort the resources below into the correct categories: **(6.6.b)**

Resource	Renewable	Nonrenewable
Water		
Coal		
Soil		
Wood		
Copper		
Petroleum		
Aluminum		
Sunlight		

21. **CALCULATE** A compact fluorescent bulb uses less energy than a regular incandescent bulb. It is estimated that a coal-burning power plant would release 72 kilograms more carbon dioxide (CO_2) a year to power one regular bulb than it would to power one fluorescent bulb. If you replace five regular bulbs with five compact bulbs, how much less CO_2 would be released in a 10-year period? **(6.6.a)**

the BIG idea

22. **PROVIDE EXAMPLES** Look again at the photograph on pages 486–487. How would you now change or add details to your initial answer to the question on the photograph? **(6.6.a)**

23. **APPLY** Suppose that you live in a community located on a small island. Make a brochure that describes the island habitat. Include information about natural resources, such as water and soil. List the plants and animals that live there. Establish four rules that the community should follow to preserve the local habitat. **(6.6.b)**

UNIT PROJECTS

Evaluate the materials in your project folder. Finish your project and get ready to present it to your class.

MONITOR AND RETEACH

If students have trouble applying the concepts in items 15–17, explain that upward-trending lines in the graph show that the populations of the two cities have increased steadily over the past 40 years. Ask: What does it mean that City B is lower on the graph? *The population numbers are lower.* Review the impacts of population growth.

Students may benefit from summarizing sections of the chapter.

 Summarizing the Chapter, pp. 271–272

Standards-Based Assessment

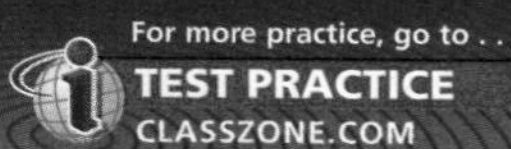

Analyzing Data

6.6.a, 6.7.c

Nowhere is the impact of human population growth more obvious than in the increased size of urban areas. Buildings, parking lots, and roads are replacing forests, farmland, and wetlands. The table below shows the growth of urban areas around 10 cities in the United States over a 20-year period.

Growth in Land Area, 1970–1990

Location	Growth in Land Area (km^2)
Atlanta, GA	1817
Houston, TX	1654
New York City-NJ	1402
Washington, D.C.-MD-VA	1166
Philadelphia, PA-NJ	1068
Los Angeles, CA	1020
Dallas-Fort Worth, TX	965
Tampa-St. Petersburg-Clearwater, FL	929
Phoenix, AZ	916
Minneapolis-Saint Paul, MN	885

Source: U.S. Bureau of Census Data on Urbanized Areas

1. What patterns can you see in the way information is presented from the top of the table to the bottom?

a. Cities are arranged alphabetically.
b. Cities are arranged by growth in population over 20 years.
c. Cities are arranged by the growth in land area over 20 years.
d. Cities are arranged by size of urban area.

2. How many square kilometers around Philadelphia were affected by urbanization between 1970 and 1990?

a. 1020 km^2
b. 1068 km^2
c. 1116 km^2
d. 1166 km^2

3. How would you describe the change in the land around Atlanta between 1970 and 1990?

a. More land was used for farming.
b. More land was used for buildings and roads.
c. More land was covered with forests.
d. Wetland habitats for birds increased.

4. Which type of graph would be best for displaying the data in the table?

a. bar graph
b. circle graph
c. line graph
d. double bar graph

Extended Response

5. Write a paragraph to describe how a rural area would change if the land were developed and the area became more urban. Use the terms below and underline them in your answer.

population density	biodiversity
renewable resources	habitat

6. Suppose that you are an urban designer working for a small city that expected to expand rapidly in the next ten years. What recommendations would you make to the city council on how the land should be developed?

REFLECTING ON THE CHAPTER

Have students answer the following questions in their **Science Notebook:**

1. How has reading the chapter made you think about your own impact on ecosystems?
2. What activity in the chapter posed the greatest challenge? What was important to you about that activity?
3. What have you learned from your research on your Unit Project?

California Content Standards

6.6.a Students know the utility of energy sources is determined by factors that are involved in converting these sources to useful forms and the consequences of the conversion process.

6.7.c Construct appropriate graphs from data and develop qualitative statements about the relationships between variables.

Analyzing Data

1. c *2. b* *3. b* *4. a*

Extended Response

5. RUBRIC

4 points for a response that uses at least three vocabulary words and offers an accurate description of urbanization

Sample: Urban development of a rural area changes the area's natural resources. Clearing trees and other vegetation alters available renewable resources. Many animals would lose their habitat, changing the area's biodiversity. As more people move into the area, population density increases.

3 points description is realistic and uses at least two vocabulary words
2 points description is realistic and uses at least one vocabulary word
1 point attempts to describe the urban area; uses no vocabulary words

6. RUBRIC

4 points for a response that addresses the following topics:

- wildlife and/or ecosystems
- traffic, transportation, and/or development
- sewage and/or water supply
- waste disposal and/or pollution

Sample: Council members should plan to preserve open spaces for wildlife and for people. They should plan to avoid traffic congestion through the use of bike paths, trains, buses, and carpool lanes. Sewage and water supply should not overwork the environment. Recycling should be used to address the extra burden on landfills.

3 points for a response that correctly addresses the question and addresses three of the topics above
2 points for a response that correctly addresses the question and addresses two of the topics above
1 point for a response that attempts to address the question and addresses one of the topics above

520

Student Resource Handbooks

Making Observations

An **observation** is an act of noting and recording an event, characteristic, behavior, or anything else detected with an instrument or with the senses.

Observations allow you to make informed hypotheses and to gather data for experiments. Careful observations often lead to ideas for new experiments. There are two categories of observations:

- **Quantitative observations** can be expressed in numbers and include records of time, temperature, mass, distance, and volume.
- **Qualitative observations** include descriptions of sights, sounds, smells, and textures.

EXAMPLE

A student dissolved 30 grams of Epsom salts in water, poured the solution into a dish, and let the dish sit out uncovered overnight. The next day, she made the following observations of the Epsom salt crystals that grew in the dish.

To determine the mass, the student found the mass of the dish before and after growing the crystals and then used subtraction to find the difference.

The student measured several crystals and calculated the mean length. (To learn how to calculate the mean of a data set, see page R36.)

Table 1. Observations of Epsom Salt Crystals

Quantitative Observations	Qualitative Observations
• mass = 30 g • mean crystal length = 0.5 cm • longest crystal length = 2 cm	• Crystals are clear. • Crystals are long, thin, and rectangular. • White crust has formed around edge of dish. Epsom salt crystals

Photographs or sketches are useful for recording qualitative observations.

MORE ABOUT OBSERVING

- Make quantitative observations whenever possible. That way, others will know exactly what you observed and be able to compare their results with yours.
- It is always a good idea to make qualitative observations too. You never know when you might observe something unexpected.

Predicting and Hypothesizing

A **prediction** is an expectation of what will be observed or what will happen. A **hypothesis** is a tentative explanation for an observation or scientific problem that can be tested by further investigation.

EXAMPLE

Suppose you have made two paper airplanes and you wonder why one of them tends to glide farther than the other one.

1. Start by asking a question.
2. Make an educated guess. After examination, you notice that the wings of the airplane that flies farther are slightly larger than the wings of the other airplane.
3. Write a prediction based upon your educated guess, in the form of an "If . . . , then . . ." statement. Write the independent variable after the word *if,* and the dependent variable after the word *then.*
4. To make a hypothesis, explain why you think what you predicted will occur. Write the explanation after the word *because*.

1. Why does one of the paper airplanes glide farther than the other?

2. The size of an airplane's wings may affect how far the airplane will glide.

3. Prediction: If I make a paper airplane with larger wings, then the airplane will glide farther.

4. Hypothesis: If I make a paper airplane with larger wings, then the airplane will glide farther, because the additional surface area of the wing will produce more lift.

To read about independent and dependent variables, see page R30.

Notice that the part of the hypothesis after *because* adds an explanation of why the airplane will glide farther.

MORE ABOUT HYPOTHESES

- The results of an experiment cannot prove that a hypothesis is correct. Rather, the results either support or do not support the hypothesis.
- Valuable information is gained even when your hypothesis is not supported by your results. For example, it would be an important discovery to find that wing size is not related to how far an airplane glides.
- In science, a hypothesis is supported only after many scientists have conducted many experiments and produced consistent results.

Inferring

An **inference** is a logical conclusion drawn from the available evidence and prior knowledge. Inferences are often made from observations.

SCIENTIFIC THINKING HANDBOOK

EXAMPLE

A student observing a set of acorns noticed something unexpected about one of them. He noticed a white, soft-bodied insect eating its way out of the acorn.

The student recorded these observations.

Observations

- There is a hole in the acorn, about 0.5 cm in diameter, where the insect crawled out.
- There is a second hole, which is about the size of a pinhole, on the other side of the acorn.
- The inside of the acorn is hollow.

Here are some inferences that can be made on the basis of the observations.

Inferences

- The insect formed from the material inside the acorn, grew to its present size, and ate its way out of the acorn.
- The insect crawled through the smaller hole, ate the inside of the acorn, grew to its present size, and ate its way out of the acorn.
- An egg was laid in the acorn through the smaller hole. The egg hatched into a larva that ate the inside of the acorn, grew to its present size, and ate its way out of the acorn.

When you make inferences, be sure to look at all of the evidence available and combine it with what you already know.

MORE ABOUT INFERENCES

Inferences depend both on observations and on the knowledge of the people making the inferences. Ancient people who did not know that organisms are produced only by similar organisms might have made an inference like the first one. A student today might look at the same observations and make the second inference. A third student might have knowledge about this particular insect and know that it is never small enough to fit through the smaller hole, leading her to the third inference.

Identifying Cause and Effect

In a **cause-and-effect relationship,** one event or characteristic is the result of another. Usually an effect follows its cause in time.

There are many examples of cause-and-effect relationships in everyday life.

Cause	Effect
Turn off a light.	Room gets dark.
Drop a glass.	Glass breaks.
Blow a whistle.	Sound is heard.

Scientists must be careful not to infer a cause-and-effect relationship just because one event happens after another event. When one event occurs after another, you cannot infer a cause-and-effect relationship on the basis of that information alone. You also cannot conclude that one event caused another if there are alternative ways to explain the second event. A scientist must demonstrate through experimentation or continued observation that an event was truly caused by another event.

EXAMPLE

Make an Observation

Suppose you have a few plants growing outside. When the weather starts getting colder, you bring one of the plants indoors. You notice that the plant you brought indoors is growing faster than the others are growing. You cannot conclude from your observation that the change in temperature was the cause of the increased plant growth, because there are alternative explanations for the observation. Some possible explanations are given below.

- The humidity indoors caused the plant to grow faster.
- The level of sunlight indoors caused the plant to grow faster.
- The indoor plant's being noticed more often and watered more often than the outdoor plants caused it to grow faster.
- The plant that was brought indoors was healthier than the other plants to begin with.

To determine which of these factors, if any, caused the indoor plant to grow faster than the outdoor plants, you would need to design and conduct an experiment.

See pages R28–R35 for information about designing experiments.

R5

Recognizing Bias

Television, newspapers, and the Internet are full of experts claiming to have scientific evidence to back up their claims. How do you know whether the claims are really backed up by good science?

SCIENTIFIC THINKING HANDBOOK

Bias is a slanted point of view, or personal prejudice. The goal of scientists is to be as objective as possible and to base their findings on facts instead of opinions. However, bias often affects the conclusions of researchers, and it is important to learn to recognize bias.

When scientific results are reported, you should consider the source of the information as well as the information itself. It is important to critically analyze the information that you see and read.

SOURCES OF BIAS

There are several ways in which a report of scientific information may be biased. Here are some questions that you can ask yourself:

1. Who is sponsoring the research?

   Sometimes, the results of an investigation are biased because an organization paying for the research is looking for a specific answer. This type of bias can affect how data are gathered and interpreted.

2. Is the research sample large enough?

   Sometimes research does not include enough data. The larger the sample size, the more likely that the results are accurate, assuming a truly random sample.

3. In a survey, who is answering the questions?

   The results of a survey or poll can be biased. The people taking part in the survey may have been specifically chosen because of how they would answer. They may have the same ideas or lifestyles. A survey or poll should make use of a random sample of people.

4. Are the people who take part in a survey biased?

   People who take part in surveys sometimes try to answer the questions the way they think the researcher wants them to answer. Also, in surveys or polls that ask for personal information, people may be unwilling to answer questions truthfully.

SCIENTIFIC BIAS

It is also important to realize that scientists have their own biases because of the types of research they do and because of their scientific viewpoints. Two scientists may look at the same set of data and come to completely different conclusions because of these biases. However, such disagreements are not necessarily bad. In fact, a critical analysis of disagreements is often responsible for moving science forward.

Identifying Faulty Reasoning

Faulty reasoning is wrong or incorrect thinking. It leads to mistakes and to wrong conclusions. Scientists are careful not to draw unreasonable conclusions from experimental data. Without such caution, the results of scientific investigations may be misleading.

EXAMPLE

Scientists try to make generalizations based on their data to explain as much about nature as possible. If only a small sample of data is looked at, however, a conclusion may be faulty. Suppose a scientist has studied the effects of the El Niño and La Niña weather patterns on flood damage in California from 1989 to 1995. The scientist organized the data in the bar graph below.

The scientist drew the following conclusions:

1. The La Niña weather pattern has no effect on flooding in California.
2. When neither weather pattern occurs, there is almost no flood damage.
3. A weak or moderate El Niño produces a small or moderate amount of flooding.
4. A strong El Niño produces a lot of flooding.

Flood and Storm Damage in California

Estimated damage (millions of dollars)
2000
1500
1000
500
0
1989 1992 1995
Starting year of season (July 1–June 30)
Weak–moderate El Niño
Strong El Niño

SOURCE: *Governor's Office of Emergency Services, California*

For the six-year period of the scientist's investigation, these conclusions may seem to be reasonable. However, a six-year study of weather patterns may be too small of a sample for the conclusions to be supported. Consider the following graph, which shows information that was gathered from 1949 to 1997.

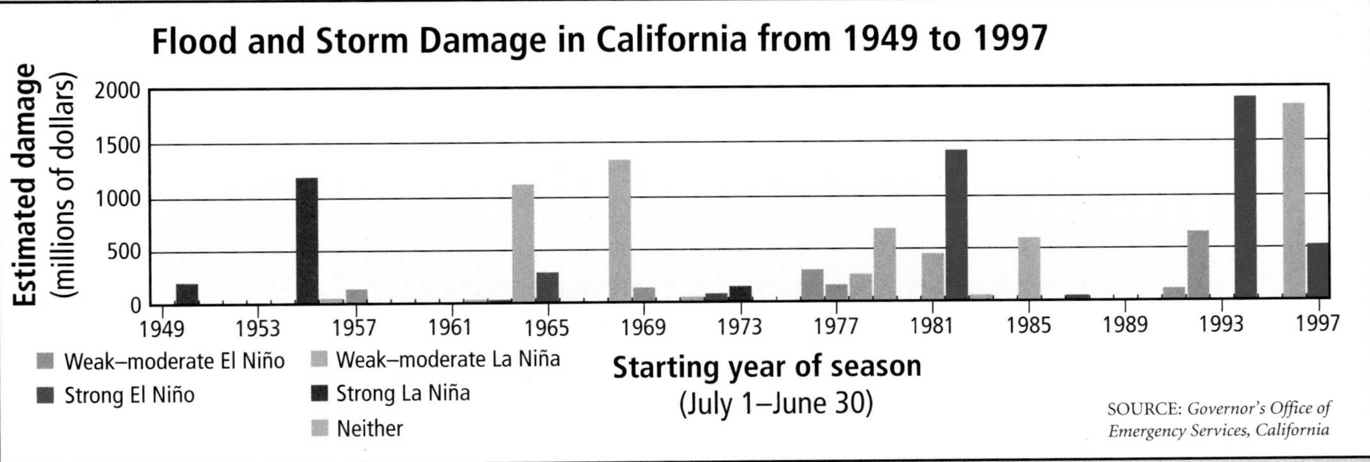

SOURCE: *Governor's Office of Emergency Services, California*

The only one of the conclusions that all of this information supports is number 3: a weak or moderate El Niño produces a small or moderate amount of flooding. By collecting more data, scientists can be more certain of their conclusions and can avoid faulty reasoning.

SCIENTIFIC THINKING HANDBOOK

Analyzing Statements

To **analyze** a statement is to examine its parts carefully. Scientific findings are often reported through media such as television or the Internet. A report that is made public often focuses on only a small part of research. As a result, it is important to question the sources of information.

Evaluate Media Claims

To **evaluate** a statement is to judge it on the basis of criteria you've established. Sometimes evaluating means deciding whether a statement is true.

Reports of scientific research and findings in the media may be misleading or incomplete. When you are exposed to this information, you should ask yourself some questions so that you can make informed judgments about the information.

1. **Does the information come from a credible source?**

   Suppose you learn about a new product and it is stated that scientific evidence proves that the product works. A report from a respected news source may be more believable than an advertisement paid for by the product's manufacturer.

2. **How much evidence supports the claim?**

   Often, it may seem that there is new evidence every day of something in the world that either causes or cures an illness. However, information that is the result of several years of work by several different scientists is more credible than an advertisement that does not even cite the subjects of the experiment.

3. **How much information is being presented?**

   Science cannot solve all questions, and scientific experiments often have flaws. A report that discusses problems in a scientific study may be more believable than a report that addresses only positive experimental findings.

4. **Is scientific evidence being presented by a specific source?**

   Sometimes scientific findings are reported by people who are called experts or leaders in a scientific field. But if their names are not given or their scientific credentials are not reported, their statements may be less credible than those of recognized experts.

Differentiate Between Fact and Opinion

Sometimes information is presented as a fact when it may be an opinion. When scientific conclusions are reported, it is important to recognize whether they are based on solid evidence. Again, you may find it helpful to ask yourself some questions.

1. **What is the difference between a fact and an opinion?**
   A **fact** is a piece of information that can be strictly defined and proved true. An **opinion** is a statement that expresses a belief, value, or feeling. An opinion cannot be proved true or false. For example, a person's age is a fact, but if someone is asked how old they feel, it is impossible to prove the person's answer to be true or false.
2. **Can opinions be measured?**
   Yes, opinions can be measured. In fact, surveys often ask for people's opinions on a topic. But there is no way to know whether or not an opinion is the truth.

HOW TO DIFFERENTIATE FACT FROM OPINION

Human Activities and the Environment

Unfortunately, human use of fossil fuels is one of the most significant developments of the past few centuries. Humans rely on fossil fuels, a nonrenewable energy resource, for more than 90 percent of their energy needs.

This careless misuse of our planet's resources has resulted in pollution, global warming, and the destruction of fragile ecosystems. For example, oil pipelines carry more than one million barrels of oil each day across tundra regions. Transporting oil across such areas can only result in oil spills that poison the land for decades.

Opinions
Notice words or phrases that express beliefs or feelings. The words *unfortunately* and *careless* show that opinions are being expressed.

Opinion
Look for statements that speculate about events. These statements are opinions, because they cannot be proved.

Facts
Statements that contain statistics tend to be facts. Writers often use facts to support their opinions.

SCIENTIFIC THINKING HANDBOOK

Lab Handbook

Safety Rules

Before you work in the laboratory, read these safety rules twice. Ask your teacher to explain any rules that you do not completely understand. Refer to these rules later on if you have questions about safety in the science classroom.

Directions

- Read all directions and make sure that you understand them before starting an investigation or lab activity. If you do not understand how to do a procedure or how to use a piece of equipment, ask your teacher.
- Do not begin any investigation or touch any equipment until your teacher has told you to start.
- Never experiment on your own. If you want to try a procedure that the directions do not call for, ask your teacher for permission first.
- If you are hurt or injured in any way, tell your teacher immediately.

Dress Code

goggles

apron

gloves

- Wear goggles when
  - — using glassware, sharp objects, or chemicals
  - — heating an object
  - — working with anything that can easily fly up into the air and hurt someone's eye
- Tie back long hair or hair that hangs in front of your eyes.
- Remove any article of clothing—such as a loose sweater or a scarf—that hangs down and may touch a flame, chemical, or piece of equipment.
- Observe all safety icons calling for the wearing of eye protection, gloves, and aprons.

Heating and Fire Safety

fire safety

heating safety

- Keep your work area neat, clean, and free of extra materials.
- Never reach over a flame or heat source.
- Point objects being heated away from you and others.
- Never heat a substance or an object in a closed container.
- Never touch an object that has been heated. If you are unsure whether something is hot, treat it as though it is. Use oven mitts, clamps, tongs, or a test-tube holder.
- Know where the fire extinguisher and fire blanket are kept in your classroom.
- Do not throw hot substances into the trash. Wait for them to cool or use the container your teacher puts out for disposal.

Electrical Safety

electrical safety

- Never use lamps or other electrical equipment with frayed cords.
- Make sure no cord is lying on the floor where someone can trip over it.
- Do not let a cord hang over the side of a counter or table so that the equipment can easily be pulled or knocked to the floor.
- Never let cords hang into sinks or other places where water can be found.
- Never try to fix electrical problems. Inform your teacher of any problems immediately.
- Unplug an electrical cord by pulling on the plug, not the cord.

Chemical Safety

chemical safety

poison

fumes

- If you spill a chemical or get one on your skin or in your eyes, tell your teacher right away.
- Never touch, taste, or sniff any chemicals in the lab. If you need to determine odor, waft. Wafting consists of holding the chemical in its container 15 centimeters (6 in.) away from your nose, and using your fingers to bring fumes from the container to your nose.
- Keep lids on all chemicals you are not using.
- Never put unused chemicals back into the original containers. Throw away extra chemicals where your teacher tells you to.
- Pour chemicals over a sink or your work area, not over the floor.
- If you get a chemical in your eye, use the eyewash right away.
- Always wash your hands after handling chemicals, plants, or soil.

Wafting

Glassware and Sharp-Object Safety

sharp objects

- If you break glassware, tell your teacher right away.
- Do not use broken or chipped glassware. Give these to your teacher.
- Use knives and other cutting instruments carefully. Always wear eye protection and cut away from you.

Animal Safety

- Never hurt an animal.
- Touch animals only when necessary. Follow your teacher's instructions for handling animals.
- Always wash your hands after working with animals.

Cleanup

disposal

- Follow your teacher's instructions for throwing away or putting away supplies.
- Clean your work area and pick up anything that has dropped to the floor.
- Wash your hands.

Using Lab Equipment

Different experiments require different types of equipment. But even though experiments differ, the ways in which the equipment is used are the same.

Beakers

- Use beakers for holding and pouring liquids.
- Do not use a beaker to measure the volume of a liquid. Use a graduated cylinder instead. (See page R16.)
- Use a beaker that holds about twice as much liquid as you need. For example, if you need 100 milliliters of water, you should use a 200- or 250-milliliter beaker.

Test Tubes

- Use test tubes to hold small amounts of substances.
- Do not use a test tube to measure the volume of a liquid.
- Use a test tube when heating a substance over a flame. Aim the mouth of the tube away from yourself and other people.
- Liquids easily spill or splash from test tubes, so it is important to use only small amounts of liquids.

Test-Tube Holder

- Use a test-tube holder when heating a substance in a test tube.
- Use a test-tube holder if the substance in a test tube is dangerous to touch.
- Make sure the test-tube holder tightly grips the test tube so that the test tube will not slide out of the holder.
- Make sure that the test-tube holder is above the surface of the substance in the test tube so that you can observe the substance.

LAB HANDBOOK

Test-Tube Rack

- Use a test-tube rack to organize test tubes before, during, and after an experiment.
- Use a test-tube rack to keep test tubes upright so that they do not fall over and spill their contents.
- Use a test-tube rack that is the correct size for the test tubes that you are using. If the rack is too small, a test tube may become stuck. If the rack is too large, a test tube may lean over, and some of its contents may spill or splash.

Forceps

- Use forceps when you need to pick up or hold a very small object that should not be touched with your hands.
- Do not use forceps to hold anything over a flame, because forceps are not long enough to keep your hand safely away from the flame. Plastic forceps will melt, and metal forceps will conduct heat and burn your hand.

Hot Plate

- Use a hot plate when a substance needs to be kept warmer than room temperature for a long period of time.
- Use a hot plate instead of a Bunsen burner or a candle when you need to carefully control temperature.
- Do not use a hot plate when a substance needs to be burned in an experiment.
- Always use "hot hands" safety mitts or oven mitts when handling anything that has been heated on a hot plate.

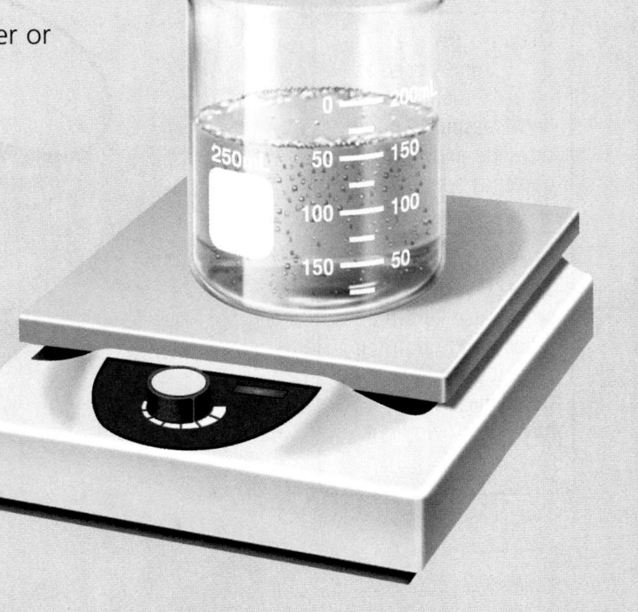

LAB HANDBOOK

Microscope

Scientists use microscopes to see very small objects that cannot easily be seen with the eye alone. A microscope magnifies the image of an object so that small details may be observed. A microscope that you may use can magnify an object 400 times—the object will appear 400 times larger than its actual size.

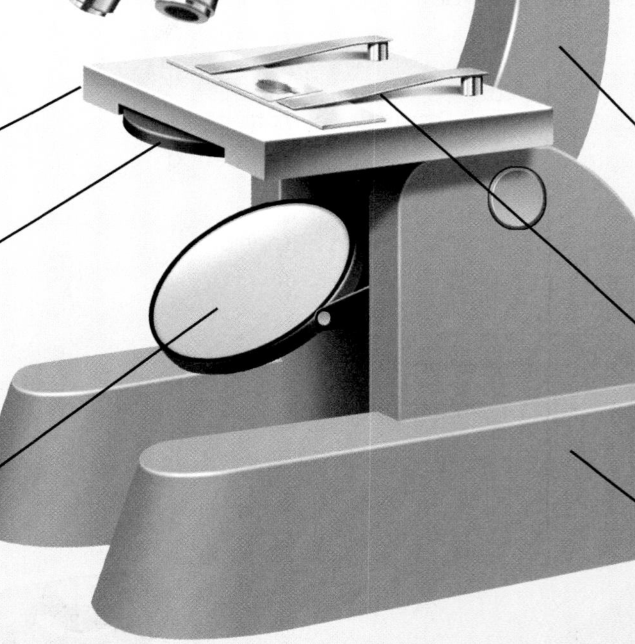

Body The body separates the lens in the eyepiece from the objective lenses below.

Nosepiece The nosepiece holds the objective lenses above the stage and rotates so that all lenses may be used.

High-Power Objective Lens This is the largest lens on the nosepiece. It magnifies an image approximately 40 times.

Stage The stage supports the object being viewed.

Diaphragm The diaphragm is used to adjust the amount of light passing through the slide and into an objective lens.

Mirror or Light Source Some microscopes use light that is reflected through the stage by a mirror. Other microscopes have their own light sources.

Eyepiece Objects are viewed through the eyepiece. The eyepiece contains a lens that commonly magnifies an image 10 times.

Coarse Adjustment This knob is used to focus the image of an object when it is viewed through the low-power lens.

Fine Adjustment This knob is used to focus the image of an object when it is viewed through the high-power lens.

Low-Power Objective Lens This is the smallest lens on the nosepiece. It magnifies an image approximately 10 times.

Arm The arm supports the body above the stage. Always carry a microscope by the arm and base.

Stage Clip The stage clip holds a slide in place on the stage.

Base The base supports the microscope.

VIEWING AN OBJECT

1. Use the coarse adjustment knob to raise the body tube.
2. Adjust the diaphragm so that you can see a bright circle of light through the eyepiece.
3. Place the object or slide on the stage. Be sure that it is centered over the hole in the stage.
4. Turn the nosepiece to click the low-power lens into place.
5. Using the coarse adjustment knob, slowly lower the lens and focus on the specimen being viewed. Be sure not to touch the slide or object with the lens.
6. When switching from the low-power lens to the high-power lens, first raise the body tube with the coarse adjustment knob so that the high-power lens will not hit the slide.
7. Turn the nosepiece to click the high-power lens into place.
8. Use the fine adjustment knob to focus on the specimen being viewed. Again, be sure not to touch the slide or object with the lens.

MAKING A SLIDE, OR WET MOUNT

1 Place the specimen in the center of a clean slide.

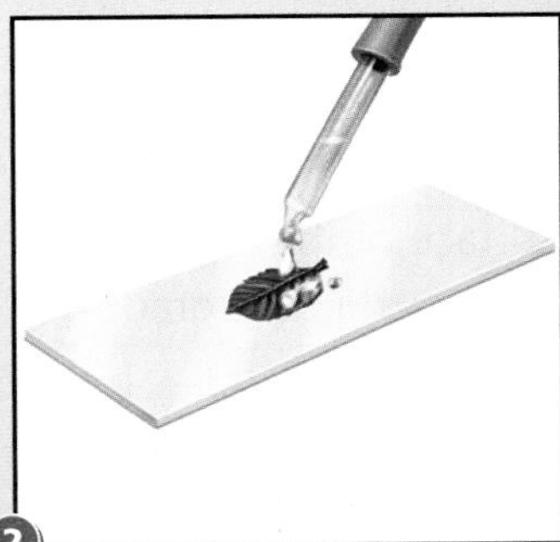

2 Place a drop of water on the specimen.

3 Place a cover slip on the slide. Put one edge of the cover slip into the drop of water and slowly lower it over the specimen.

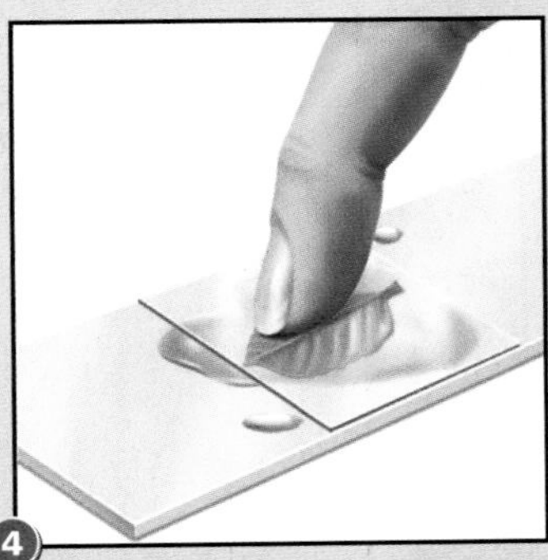

4 Remove any air bubbles from under the cover slip by gently tapping the cover slip.

5 Dry any excess water before placing the slide on the microscope stage for viewing.

R15

Spring Scale (Force Meter)

- Use a spring scale to measure a force pulling on the scale.
- Use a spring scale to measure the force of gravity exerted on an object by Earth.
- To measure a force accurately, a spring scale must be zeroed before it is used. The scale is zeroed when no weight is attached and the indicator is positioned at zero.
- Do not attach a weight that is either too heavy or too light to a spring scale. A weight that is too heavy could break the scale or exert too great a force for the scale to measure. A weight that is too light may not exert enough force to be measured accurately.

Graduated Cylinder

- Use a graduated cylinder to measure the volume of a liquid.
- Be sure that the graduated cylinder is on a flat surface so that your measurement will be accurate.
- When reading the scale on a graduated cylinder, be sure to have your eyes at the level of the surface of the liquid.
- The surface of the liquid will be curved in the graduated cylinder. Read the volume of the liquid at the bottom of the curve, or meniscus (muh-NIHS-kuhs).
- You can use a graduated cylinder to find the volume of a solid object by measuring the increase in a liquid's level after you add the object to the cylinder.

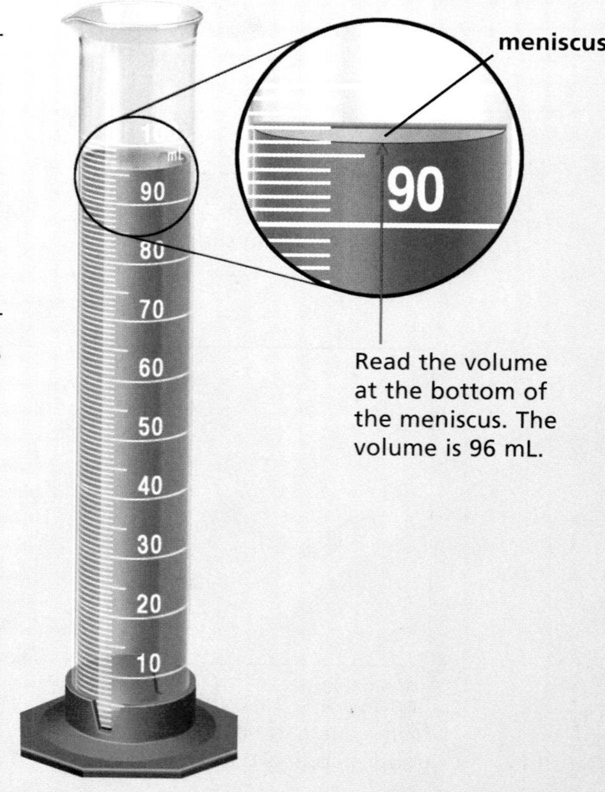

Read the volume at the bottom of the meniscus. The volume is 96 mL.

Metric Rulers

- Use metric rulers or meter sticks to measure objects' lengths.
- Do not measure an object from the end of a metric ruler or meter stick, because the end is often imperfect. Instead, measure from the 1-centimeter mark, but remember to subtract a centimeter from the apparent measurement.
- Estimate any lengths that extend between marked units. For example, if a meter stick shows centimeters but not millimeters, you can estimate the length that an object extends between centimeter marks to measure it to the nearest millimeter.
- **Controlling Variables** If you are taking repeated measurements, always measure from the same point each time. For example, if you're measuring how high two different balls bounce when dropped from the same height, measure both bounces at the same point on the balls—either the top or the bottom. Do not measure at the top of one ball and the bottom of the other.

EXAMPLE

How to Measure a Leaf

1. Lay a ruler flat on top of the leaf so that the 1-centimeter mark lines up with one end. Make sure the ruler and the leaf do not move between the time you line them up and the time you take the measurement.
2. Look straight down on the ruler so that you can see exactly how the marks line up with the other end of the leaf.
3. Estimate the length by which the leaf extends beyond a marking. For example, the leaf below extends about halfway between the 4.2-centimeter and 4.3-centimeter marks, so the apparent measurement is about 4.25 centimeters.
4. Remember to subtract 1 centimeter from your apparent measurement, since you started at the 1-centimeter mark on the ruler and not at the end. The leaf is about 3.25 centimeters long (4.25 cm – 1 cm = 3.25 cm).

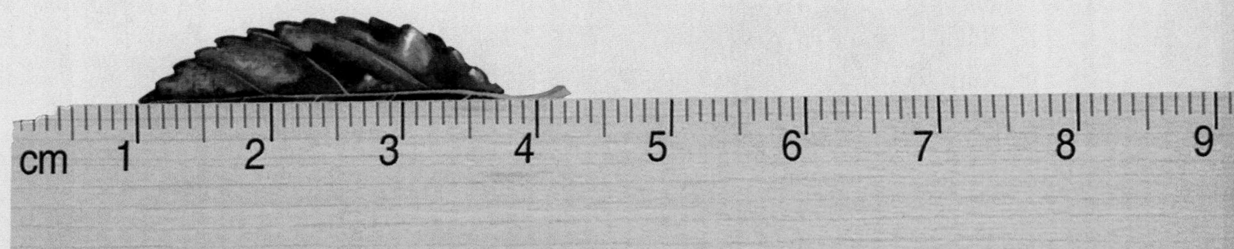

LAB HANDBOOK

Triple-Beam Balance

This balance has a pan and three beams with sliding masses, called riders. At one end of the beams is a pointer that indicates whether the mass on the pan is equal to the masses shown on the beams.

1. Make sure the balance is zeroed before measuring the mass of an object. The balance is zeroed if the pointer is at zero when nothing is on the pan and the riders are at their zero points. Use the adjustment knob at the base of the balance to zero it.
2. Place the object to be measured on the pan.
3. Move the riders one notch at a time away from the pan. Begin with the largest rider. If moving the largest rider one notch brings the pointer below zero, begin measuring the mass of the object with the next smaller rider.
4. Change the positions of the riders until they balance the mass on the pan and the pointer is at zero. Then add the readings from the three beams to determine the mass of the object.

300 g	position of largest rider
90 g	position of middle rider
+ 3 g	position of smallest rider
393 g	mass of beaker

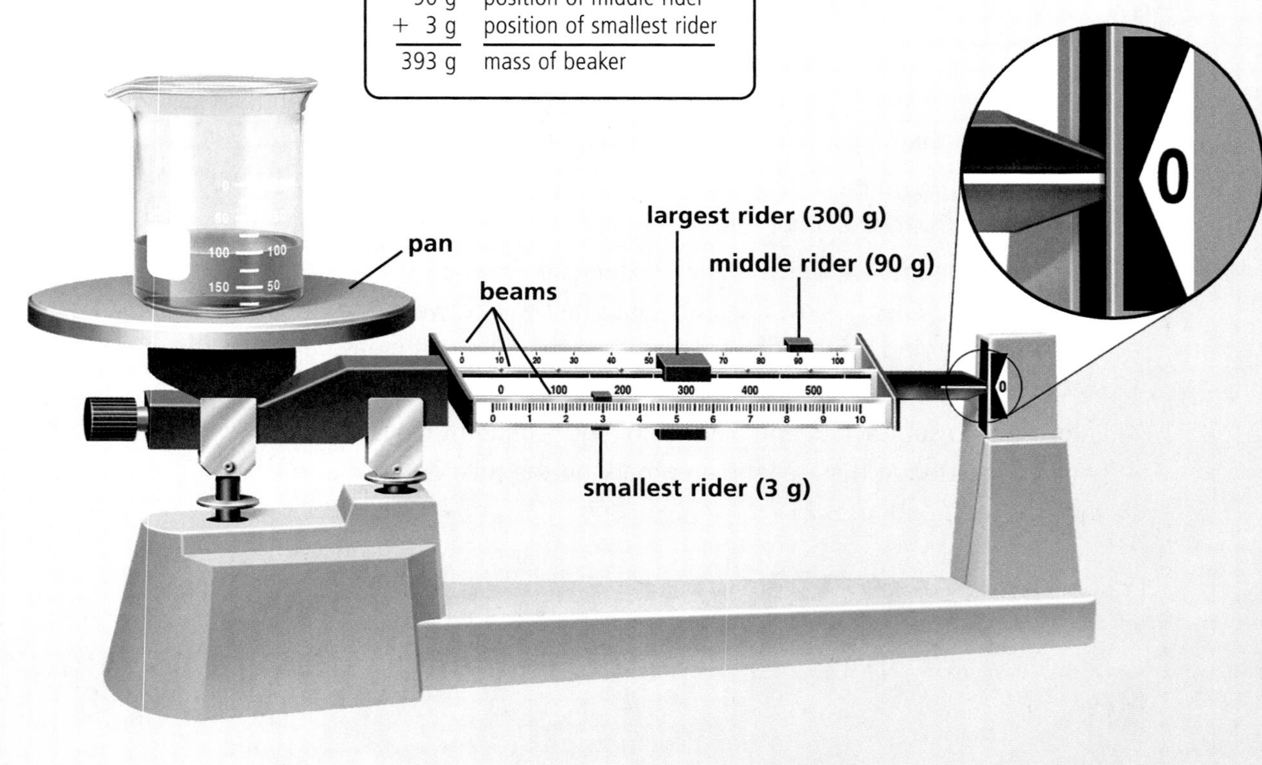

Double-Pan Balance

This type of balance has two pans. Between the pans is a pointer that indicates whether the masses on the pans are equal.

1. Make sure the balance is zeroed before measuring the mass of an object. The balance is zeroed if the pointer is at zero when there is nothing on either of the pans. Many double-pan balances have sliding knobs that can be used to zero them.
2. Place the object to be measured on one of the pans.
3. Begin adding standard masses to the other pan. Begin with the largest standard mass. If this adds too much mass to the balance, begin measuring the mass of the object with the next smaller standard mass.
4. Add standard masses until the masses on both pans are balanced and the pointer is at zero. Then add the standard masses together to determine the mass of the object being measured.

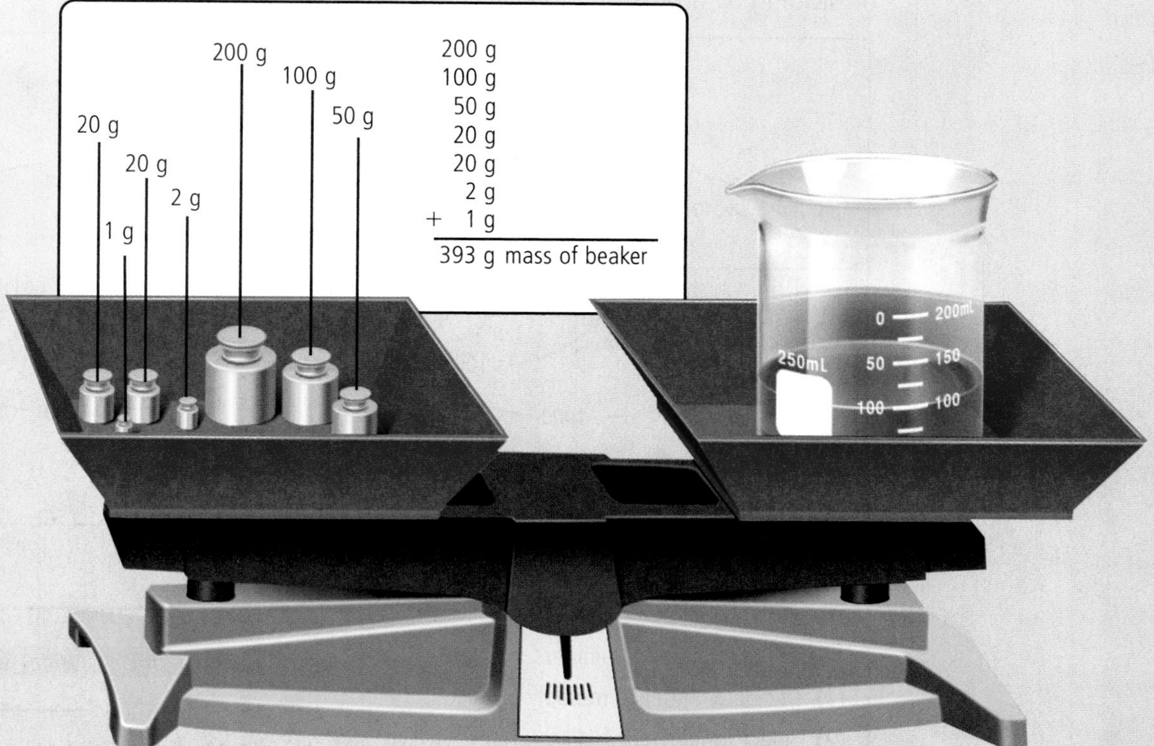

Never place chemicals or liquids directly on a pan. Instead, use the following procedure:

1. Determine the mass of an empty container, such as a beaker.
2. Pour the substance into the container, and measure the total mass of the substance and the container.
3. Subtract the mass of the empty container from the total mass to find the mass of the substance.

LAB HANDBOOK

The Metric System and SI Units

Scientists use International System (SI) units for measurements of distance, volume, mass, and temperature. The International System is based on multiples of ten and the metric system of measurement.

Basic SI Units		
Property	**Name**	**Symbol**
length	meter	m
volume	liter	L
mass	kilogram	kg
temperature	kelvin	K

SI Prefixes		
Prefix	**Symbol**	**Multiple of 10**
kilo-	k	1000
hecto-	h	100
deca-	da	10
deci-	d	0.1 $\left(\frac{1}{10}\right)$
centi-	c	0.01 $\left(\frac{1}{100}\right)$
milli-	m	0.001 $\left(\frac{1}{1000}\right)$

Changing Metric Units

You can change from one unit to another in the metric system by multiplying or dividing by a power of 10.

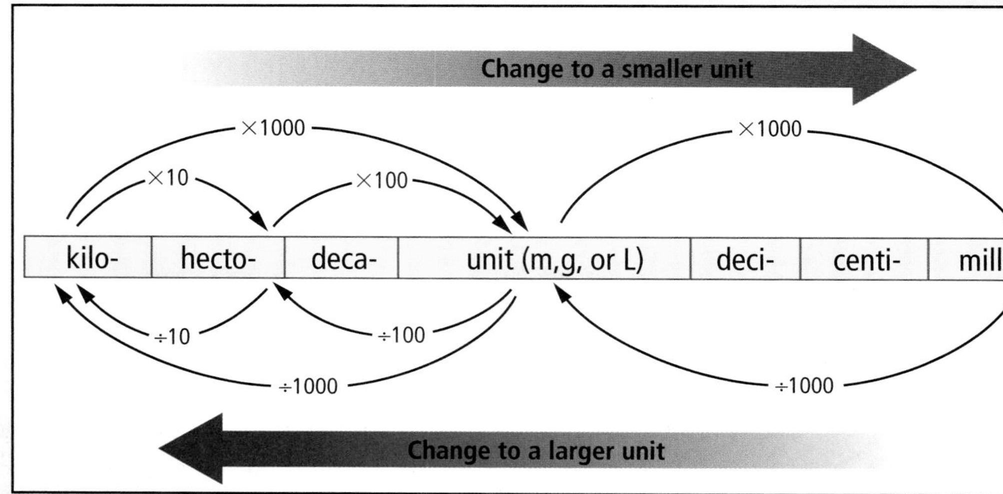

Example

Change 0.64 liters to milliliters.

(1) Decide whether to multiply or divide.

(2) Select the power of 10.

ANSWER 0.64 L = 640 mL

Change to a smaller unit by multiplying.

L —— × 1000 ——→ **mL**

0.64 × 1000 = **640.**

Example

Change 23.6 grams to kilograms.

(1) Decide whether to multiply or divide.

(2) Select the power of 10.

ANSWER 23.6 g = 0.0236 kg

Change to a larger unit by dividing.

kg ←—— ÷ 1000 —— **g**

23.6 ÷ 1000 = **0.0236**

LAB HANDBOOK

Temperature Conversions

Even though the kelvin is the SI base unit of temperature, the degree Celsius will be the unit you use most often in your science studies. The formulas below show the relationships between temperatures in degrees Fahrenheit (°F), degrees Celsius (°C), and kelvins (K).

$$°C = \frac{5}{9}(°F - 32)$$

$$°F = \frac{9}{5}°C + 32$$

$$K = °C + 273$$

See page R42 for help with using formulas.

Examples of Temperature Conversions

Condition	Degrees Celsius	Degrees Fahrenheit
Freezing point of water	0	32
Cool day	10	50
Mild day	20	68
Warm day	30	86
Normal body temperature	37	98.6
Very hot day	40	104
Boiling point of water	100	212

Converting Between SI and U.S. Customary Units

Use the chart below when you need to convert between SI units and U.S. customary units.

SI Unit	From SI to U.S. Customary			From U.S. Customary to SI		
Length	**When you know**	**multiply by**	**to find**	**When you know**	**multiply by**	**to find**
kilometer (km) = 1000 m	kilometers	0.62	miles	miles	1.61	kilometers
meter (m) = 100 cm	meters	3.28	feet	feet	0.3048	meters
centimeter (cm) = 10 mm	centimeters	0.39	inches	inches	2.54	centimeters
millimeter (mm) = 0.1 cm	millimeters	0.04	inches	inches	25.4	millimeters
Area	**When you know**	**multiply by**	**to find**	**When you know**	**multiply by**	**to find**
square kilometer (km^2)	square kilometers	0.39	square miles	square miles	2.59	square kilometers
square meter (m^2)	square meters	1.2	square yards	square yards	0.84	square meters
square centimeter (cm^2)	square centimeters	0.155	square inches	square inches	6.45	square centimeters
Volume	**When you know**	**multiply by**	**to find**	**When you know**	**multiply by**	**to find**
liter (L) = 1000 mL	liters	1.06	quarts	quarts	0.95	liters
	liters	0.26	gallons	gallons	3.79	liters
	liters	4.23	cups	cups	0.24	liters
	liters	2.12	pints	pints	0.47	liters
milliliter (mL) = 0.001 L	milliliters	0.20	teaspoons	teaspoons	4.93	milliliters
	milliliters	0.07	tablespoons	tablespoons	14.79	milliliters
	milliliters	0.03	fluid ounces	fluid ounces	29.57	milliliters
Mass	**When you know**	**multiply by**	**to find**	**When you know**	**multiply by**	**to find**
kilogram (kg) = 1000 g	kilograms	2.2	pounds	pounds	0.45	kilograms
gram (g) = 1000 mg	grams	0.035	ounces	ounces	28.35	grams

Precision and Accuracy

When you do an experiment, it is important that your methods, observations, and data be both precise and accurate.

low precision

precision, but not accuracy

precision and accuracy

Precision

In science, **precision** is the exactness and consistency of measurements. For example, measurements made with a ruler that has both centimeter and millimeter markings would be more precise than measurements made with a ruler that has only centimeter markings. Another indicator of precision is the care taken to make sure that methods and observations are as exact and consistent as possible. Every time a particular experiment is done, the same procedure should be used. Precision is necessary because experiments are repeated several times and if the procedure changes, the results will change.

EXAMPLE

Suppose you are measuring temperatures over a two-week period. Your precision will be greater if you measure each temperature at the same place, at the same time of day, and with the same thermometer than if you change any of these factors from one day to the next.

Accuracy

In science, it is possible to be precise but not accurate. **Accuracy** depends on the difference between a measurement and an actual value. The smaller the difference, the more accurate the measurement.

EXAMPLE

Suppose you look at a stream and estimate that it is about 1 meter wide at a particular place. You decide to check your estimate by measuring the stream with a meter stick, and you determine that the stream is 1.32 meters wide. However, because it is hard to measure the width of a stream with a meter stick, it turns out that you didn't do a very good job. The stream is actually 1.14 meters wide. Therefore, even though your estimate was less precise than your measurement, your estimate was actually more accurate.

Making Data Tables and Graphs

Data tables and graphs are useful tools for both recording and communicating scientific data.

Making Data Tables

You can use a **data table** to organize and record the measurements that you make. Some examples of information that might be recorded in data tables are frequencies, times, and amounts.

EXAMPLE

Suppose you are investigating photosynthesis in two elodea plants. One sits in direct sunlight, and the other sits in a dimly lit room. You measure the rate of photosynthesis by counting the number of bubbles in the jar every ten minutes.

1. Title and number your data table.
2. Decide how you will organize the table into columns and rows.
3. Any units, such as seconds or degrees, should be included in column headings, not in the individual cells.

Table 1. Number of Bubbles from Elodea

Time (min)	Sunlight	Dim Light
0	0	0
10	15	5
20	25	8
30	32	7
40	41	10
50	47	9
60	42	9

Always number and title data tables.

The data in the table above could also be organized in a different way.

Table 1. Number of Bubbles from Elodea

Light Condition	Time (min)						
	0	10	20	30	40	50	60
Sunlight	0	15	25	32	41	47	42
Dim light	0	5	8	7	10	9	9

Put units in column heading.

LAB HANDBOOK

Making Line Graphs

You can use a **line graph** to show a relationship between variables. Line graphs are particularly useful for showing changes in variables over time.

EXAMPLE

Suppose you are interested in graphing temperature data that you collected over the course of a day.

Table 1. Outside Temperature During the Day on March 7

	Time of Day						
	7:00 A.M.	9:00 A.M.	11:00 A.M.	1:00 P.M.	3:00 P.M.	5:00 P.M.	7:00 P.M.
Temp (°C)	8	9	11	14	12	10	6

1. Use the vertical axis of your line graph for the variable that you are measuring—temperature.
2. Choose scales for both the horizontal axis and the vertical axis of the graph. You should have two points more than you need on the vertical axis, and the horizontal axis should be long enough for all of the data points to fit.
3. Draw and label each axis.
4. Graph each value. First find the appropriate point on the scale of the horizontal axis. Imagine a line that rises vertically from that place on the scale. Then find the corresponding value on the vertical axis, and imagine a line that moves horizontally from that value. The point where these two imaginary lines intersect is where the value should be plotted.
5. Connect the points with straight lines.

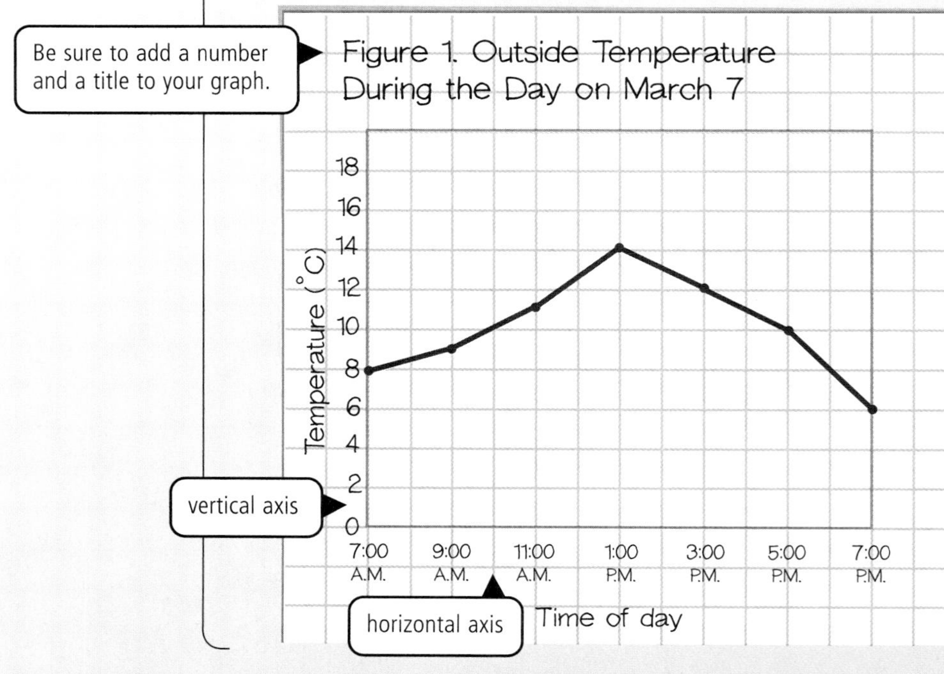

Making Circle Graphs

You can use a **circle graph,** sometimes called a pie chart, to represent data as parts of a circle. Circle graphs are used only when the data can be expressed as percentages of a whole. The entire circle shown in a circle graph is equal to 100 percent of the data.

EXAMPLE

Suppose you identified the species of each mature tree growing in a small wooded area. You organized your data in a table, but you also want to show the data in a circle graph.

1. To begin, find the total number of mature trees.

   $56 + 34 + 22 + 10 + 28 = 150$

2. To find the degree measure for each sector of the circle, write a fraction comparing the number of each tree species with the total number of trees. Then multiply the fraction by 360°.

   Oak: $\frac{56}{150} \times 360° = 134.4°$

3. Draw a circle. Use a protractor to draw the angle for each sector of the graph.
4. Color and label each sector of the graph.
5. Give the graph a number and title.

Table 1. Tree Species in Wooded Area

Species	Number of Specimens
Oak	56
Maple	34
Birch	22
Willow	10
Pine	28

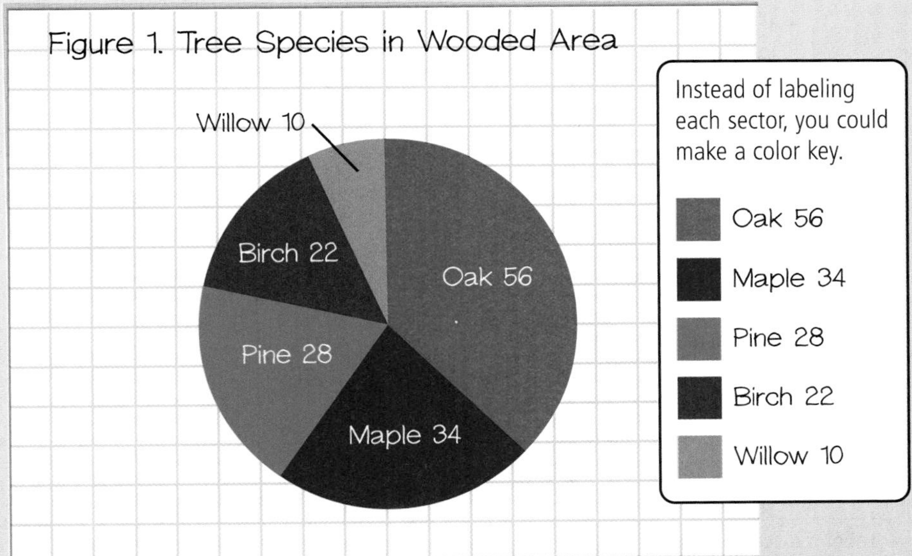

LAB HANDBOOK

Bar Graph

A **bar graph** is a type of graph in which the lengths of the bars are used to represent and compare data. A numerical scale is used to determine the lengths of the bars.

EXAMPLE

To determine the effect of water on seed sprouting, three cups were filled with sand, and ten seeds were planted in each. Different amounts of water were added to each cup over a three-day period.

Table 1. Effect of Water on Seed Sprouting

Daily Amount of Water (mL)	Number of Seeds That Sprouted After 3 Days in Sand
0	1
10	4
20	8

1. Choose a numerical scale. The greatest value is 8, so the end of the scale should have a value greater than 8, such as 10. Use equal increments along the scale, such as increments of 2.
2. Draw and label the axes. Mark intervals on the vertical axis according to the scale you chose.
3. Draw a bar for each data value. Use the scale to decide how long to make each bar.

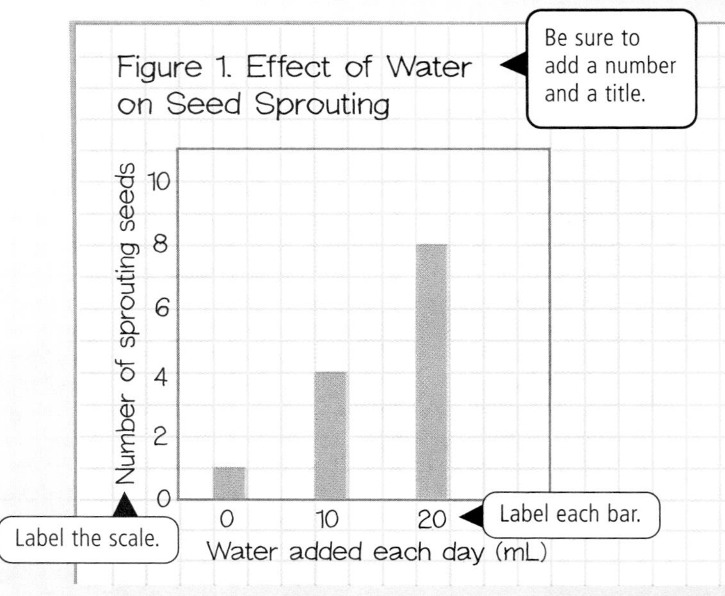

R26

Double Bar Graph

A **double bar graph** is a bar graph that shows two sets of data. The two bars for each measurement are drawn next to each other.

EXAMPLE

The seed-sprouting experiment was done using both sand and potting soil. The data for sand and potting soil can be plotted on one graph.

1. Draw one set of bars, using the data for sand, as shown below.
2. Draw bars for the potting-soil data next to the bars for the sand data. Shade them a different color. Add a key.

Table 2. Effect of Water and Soil on Seed Sprouting

Daily Amount of Water (mL)	Number of Seeds That Sprouted After 3 Days in Sand	Number of Seeds That Sprouted After 3 Days in Potting Soil
0	1	2
10	4	5
20	8	9

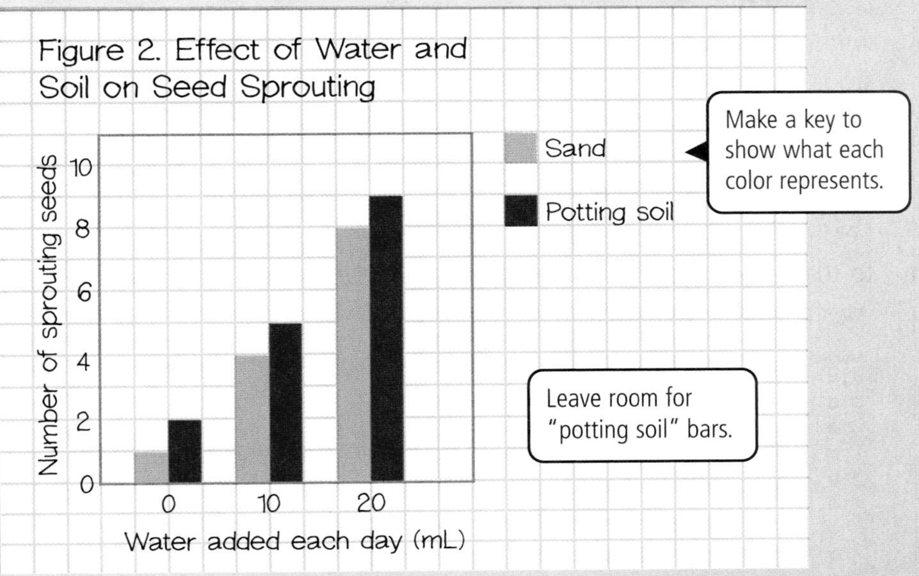

LAB HANDBOOK

Designing an Experiment

Use this section when designing or conducting an experiment.

Determining a Purpose

You can find a purpose for an experiment by doing research, by examining the results of a previous experiment, or by observing the world around you. An **experiment** is an organized procedure to study something under controlled conditions.

Don't forget to learn as much as possible about your topic before you begin.

1. Write the purpose of your experiment as a question or problem that you want to investigate.
2. Write down research questions and begin searching for information that will help you design an experiment. Consult the library, the Internet, and other people as you conduct your research.

EXAMPLE

Middle school students observed an odor near the lake by their school. They also noticed that the water on the side of the lake near the school was greener than the water on the other side of the lake. The students did some research to learn more about their observations. They discovered that the odor and green color in the lake came from algae. They also discovered that a new fertilizer was being used on a field nearby. The students inferred that the use of the fertilizer might be related to the presence of the algae and designed a controlled experiment to find out whether they were right.

Problem

How does fertilizer affect the presence of algae in a lake?

Research Questions

- Have other experiments been done on this problem? If so, what did those experiments show?
- What kind of fertilizer is used on the field? How much?
- How do algae grow?
- How do people measure algae?
- Can fertilizer and algae be used safely in a lab? How?

Research
As you research, you may find a topic that is more interesting to you than your original topic, or learn that a procedure you wanted to use is not practical or safe. It is OK to change your purpose as you research.

Writing a Hypothesis

A **hypothesis** is a tentative explanation for an observation or scientific problem that can be tested by further investigation. You can write your hypothesis in the form of an "If . . . , then . . . , because . . ." statement.

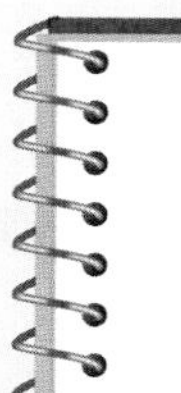

Hypothesis

If the amount of fertilizer in lake water is increased, then the amount of algae will also increase, because fertilizers provide nutrients that algae need to grow.

Hypotheses
For help with hypotheses, refer to page R3.

Determining Materials

Make a list of all the materials you will need to do your experiment. Be specific, especially if someone else is helping you obtain the materials. Try to think of everything you will need.

Materials

- 1 large jar or container
- 4 identical smaller containers
- rubber gloves that also cover the arms
- sample of fertilizer-and-water solution
- eyedropper
- clear plastic wrap
- scissors
- masking tape
- marker
- ruler

Determining Variables and Constants

EXPERIMENTAL GROUP AND CONTROL GROUP

An experiment to determine how two factors are related always has two groups—a control group and an experimental group.

1. Design an experimental group. Include as many trials as possible in the experimental group in order to obtain reliable results.
2. Design a control group that is the same as the experimental group in every way possible, except for the factor you wish to test.

Experimental Group: two containers of lake water with one drop of fertilizer solution added to each

Control Group: two containers of lake water with no fertilizer solution added

Go back to your materials li and make sure you have enough items listed to cove both your experimental grou and your control group.

LAB HANDBOOK

VARIABLES AND CONSTANTS

Identify the variables and constants in your experiment. In a controlled experiment, a **variable** is any factor that can change. **Constants,** or controlled parameters, are all of the factors that are the same in both the experimental group and the control group.

Hypothesis
If the amount of fertilizer in lake water is increased, then the amount of algae will also increase, because fertilizers provide nutrients that algae need to grow.

1. Read your hypothesis. The **independent variable** is the factor that you wish to test and that is manipulated or changed so that it can be tested. The independent variable is expressed in your hypothesis after the word *if*. Identify the independent variable in your laboratory report.
2. The **dependent variable** is the factor that you measure to gather results. It is expressed in your hypothesis after the word *then*. Identify the dependent variable in your laboratory report.

Table 1. Variables and Constants in Algae Experiment

Independent Variable	Dependent Variable	Constants
Amount of fertilizer in lake water	Amount of algae that grow	• Where the lake water is obtained • Type of container used • Light and temperature conditions where water will be stored

Set up your experiment so that you will test only one variable.

MEASURING THE DEPENDENT VARIABLE

Before starting your experiment, you need to define how you will measure the dependent variable. An **operational definition** is a description of the one particular way in which you will measure the dependent variable.

Your operational definition is important for several reasons. First, in any experiment there are several ways in which a dependent variable can be measured. Second, the procedure of the experiment depends on how you decide to measure the dependent variable. Third, your operational definition makes it possible for other people to evaluate and build on your experiment.

EXAMPLE 1

An operational definition of a dependent variable can be qualitative. That is, your measurement of the dependent variable can simply be an observation of whether a change occurs as a result of a change in the independent variable. This type of operational definition can be thought of as a "yes or no" measurement.

Table 2. Qualitative Operational Definition of Algae Growth

Independent Variable	Dependent Variable	Operational Definition
Amount of fertilizer in lake water	Amount of algae that grow	Algae grow in lake water

A qualitative measurement of a dependent variable is often easy to make and record. However, this type of information does not provide a great deal of detail in your experimental results.

EXAMPLE 2

An operational definition of a dependent variable can be quantitative. That is, your measurement of the dependent variable can be a number that shows how much change occurs as a result of a change in the independent variable.

Table 3. Quantitative Operational Definition of Algae Growth

Independent Variable	Dependent Variable	Operational Definition
Amount of fertilizer in lake water	Amount of algae that grow	Diameter of largest algal growth (in mm)

A quantitative measurement of a dependent variable can be more difficult to make and analyze than a qualitative measurement. However, this type of data provides much more information about your experiment and is often more useful.

Writing a Procedure

Write each step of your procedure. Start each step with a verb, or action word, and keep the steps short. Your procedure should be clear enough for someone else to use as instructions for repeating your experiment.

If necessary, go back to your materials list and add any materials that you left out.

Procedure

1. Put on your gloves. Use the large container to obtain a sample of lake water.
2. Divide the sample of lake water equally among the four smaller containers.
3. Use the eyedropper to add one drop of fertilizer solution to two of the containers.

Controlling Variables The same amount of fertilizer solution must be added to two of the four containers.

4. Use the masking tape and the marker to label the containers with your initials, the date, and the identifiers "Jar 1 with Fertilizer," "Jar 2 with Fertilizer," "Jar 1 without Fertilizer," and "Jar 2 without Fertilizer."
5. Cover the containers with clear plastic wrap. Use the scissors to punch ten holes in each of the covers.
6. Place all four containers on a window ledge. Make sure that they all receive the same amount of light.

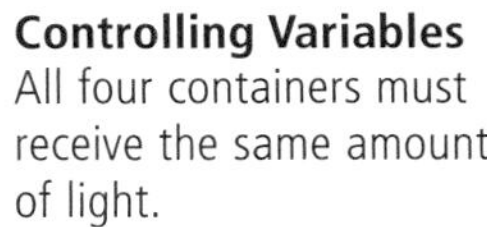

Controlling Variables All four containers must receive the same amount of light.

7. Observe the containers every day for one week.
8. Use the ruler to measure the diameter of the largest clump of algae in each container, and record your measurements daily.

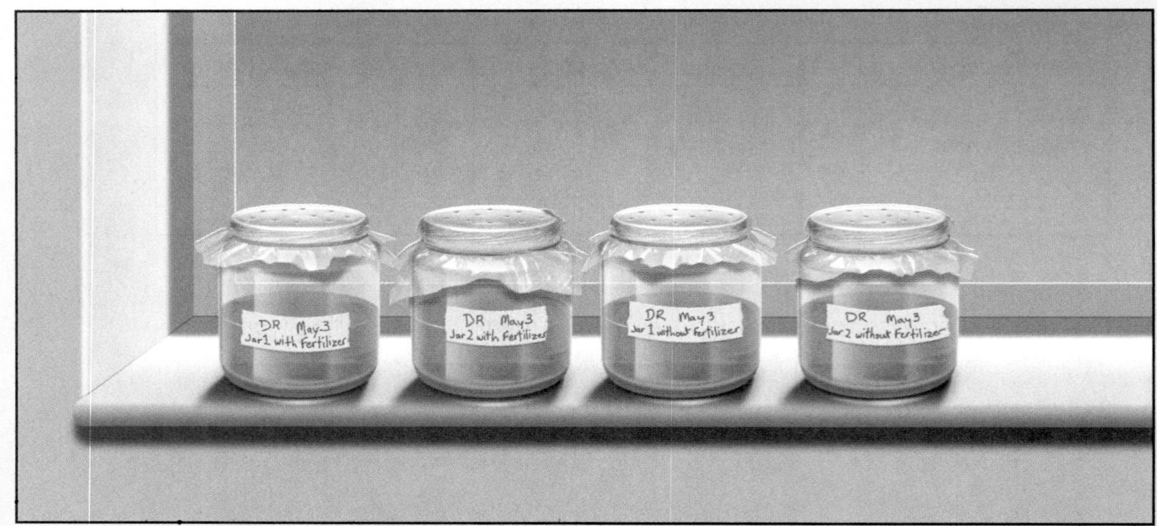

Recording Observations

Once you have obtained all of your materials and your procedure has been approved, you can begin making experimental observations. Gather both quantitative and qualitative data. If something goes wrong during your procedure, make sure you record that too.

Observations
For help with making qualitative and quantitative observations, refer to page R2.

For more examples of data tables, see page R23.

Table 4. Fertilizer and Algae Growth

	Experimental Group		Control Group		
Date and Time	Jar 1 with Fertilizer (diameter of algae in mm)	Jar 2 with Fertilizer (diameter of algae in mm)	Jar 1 without Fertilizer (diameter of algae in mm)	Jar 2 without Fertilizer (diameter of algae in mm)	Observations
5/3 4:00 P.M.	0	0	0	0	condensation in all containers
5/4 4:00 P.M.	0	3	0	0	tiny green blobs in jar 2 with fertilizer
5/5 4:15 P.M.	4	5	0	3	green blobs in jars 1 and 2 with fertilizer and jar 2 without fertilizer
5/6 4:00 P.M.	5	6	0	4	water light green in jar 2 with fertilizer
5/7 4:00 P.M.	8	10	0	6	water light green in jars 1 and 2 with fertilizer and in jar 2 without fertilizer
5/8 3:30 P.M.	10	18	0	6	cover off jar 2 with fertilizer
5/9 3:30 P.M.	14	23	0	8	drew sketches of each container

Notice that on the sixth day, the observer found that the cover was off one of the containers. It is important to record observations of unintended factors because they might affect the results of the experiment.

Drawings of Samples Viewed Under Microscope on 5/9 at 100x

Use technology, such as a microscope, to help you make observations when possible.

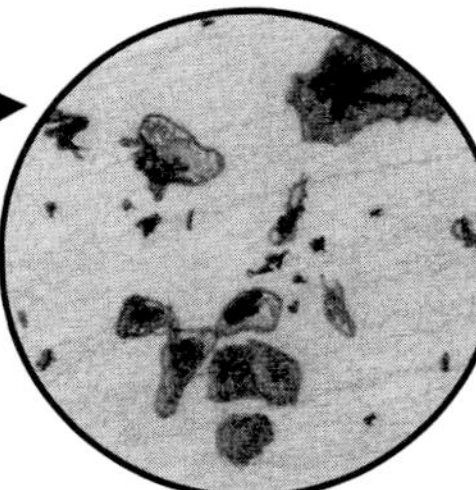
Jar 1 with Fertilizer

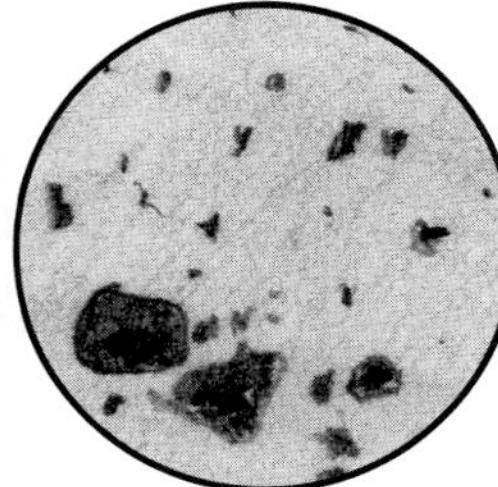
Jar 2 with Fertilizer

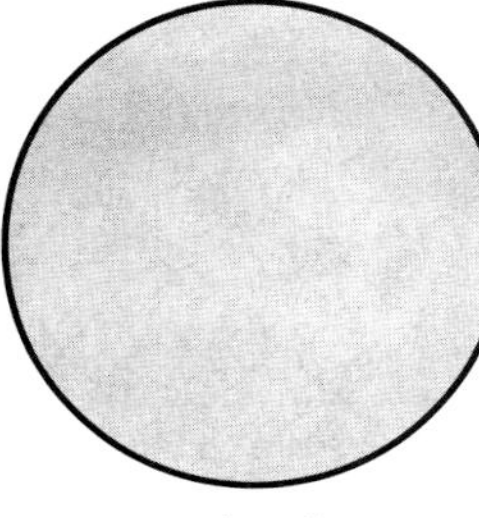
Jar 1 without Fertilizer

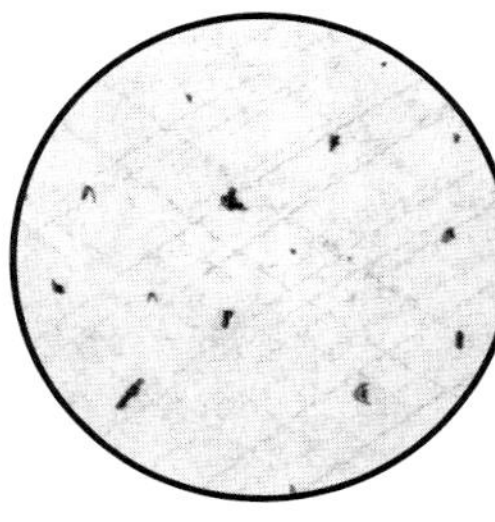
Jar 2 without Fertilizer

R33

Summarizing Results

To summarize your data, look at all of your observations together. Look for meaningful ways to present your observations. For example, you might average your data or make a graph to look for patterns. When possible, use spreadsheet software to help you analyze and present your data. The two graphs below show the same data.

LAB HANDBOOK

EXAMPLE 1

Figure 1. Fertilizer and Algae Growth

Always include a number and a title with a graph.

Diameter of algae (mm)

25
20
15
10
5
0

5/3 5/4 5/5 5/6 5/7 5/8 5/9

Date

Jar 1 with fertilizer
Jar 1 without fertilizer
Jar 2 with fertilizer
Jar 2 without fertilizer

Line graphs are useful for showing changes over time. For help with line graphs, refer to page R24.

EXAMPLE 2

Bar graphs are useful for comparing different data sets. This bar graph has four bars for each day. Another way to present the data would be to calculate averages for the tests and the controls, and to show one test bar and one control bar for each day.

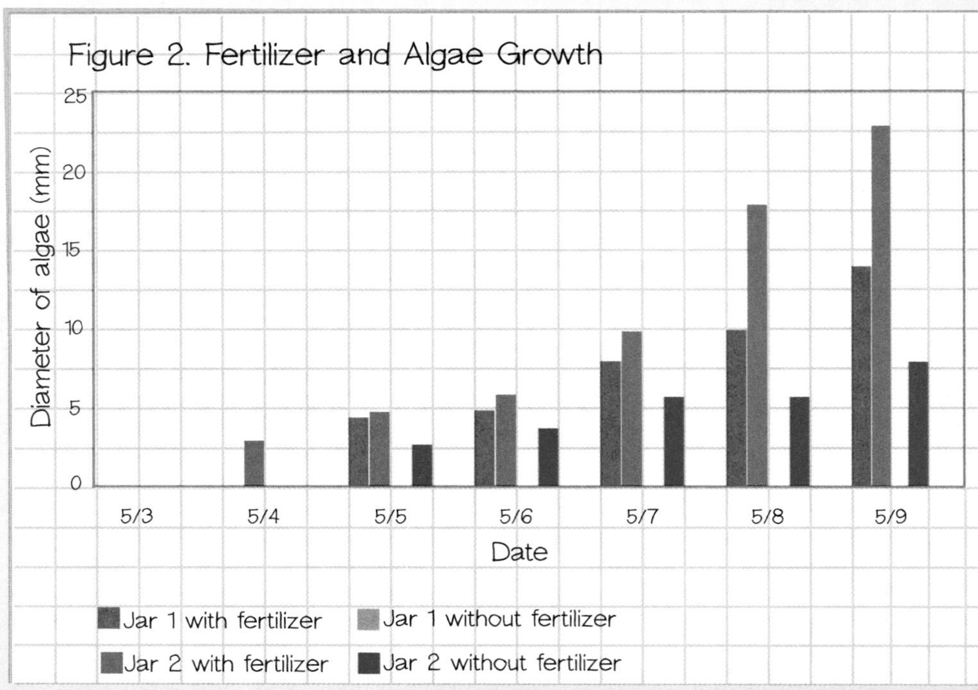

Drawing Conclusions

RESULTS AND INFERENCES

To draw conclusions from your experiment, first write your results. Then compare your results with your hypothesis. Do your results support your hypothesis? Be careful not to make inferences about factors that you did not test.

For help with making inferences, see page R4.

Results and Inferences

The results of my experiment show that more algae grew in lake water to which fertilizer had been added than in lake water to which no fertilizer had been added. My hypothesis was supported. I infer that it is possible that the growth of algae in the lake was caused by the fertilizer used on the field.

Notice that you cannot conclude from this experiment that the presence of algae in the lake was due only to the fertilizer.

QUESTIONS FOR FURTHER RESEARCH

Write a list of questions for further research and investigation. Your ideas may lead you to new experiments and discoveries.

Questions for Further Research

- What is the connection between the amount of fertilizer and algae growth?
- How do different brands of fertilizer affect algae growth?
- How would algae growth in the lake be affected if no fertilizer were used on the field?
- How do algae affect the lake and the other life in and around it?
- How does fertilizer affect the lake and the life in and around it?
- If fertilizer is getting into the lake, how is it getting there?

Describing a Set of Data

Means, medians, modes, and ranges are important math tools for describing data sets such as the following widths of fossilized clamshells.

13 mm 25 mm 14 mm 21 mm 16 mm 23 mm 14 mm

Mean

The **mean** of a data set is the sum of the values divided by the number of values.

Example

To find the mean of the clamshell data, add the values and then divide the sum by the number of values.

$$\frac{13\text{ mm} + 25\text{ mm} + 14\text{ mm} + 21\text{ mm} + 16\text{ mm} + 23\text{ mm} + 14\text{ mm}}{7} = \frac{126\text{ mm}}{7} = 18\text{ mm}$$

ANSWER The mean is 18 mm.

Median

The **median** of a data set is the middle value when the values are written in numerical order. If a data set has an even number of values, the median is the mean of the two middle values.

Example

To find the median of the clamshell data, arrange the values in order from least to greatest. The median is the middle value.

13 mm 14 mm 14 mm 16 mm 21 mm 23 mm 25 mm

ANSWER The median is 16 mm.

Mode

The **mode** of a data set is the value that occurs most often.

Example

To find the mode of the clamshell data, arrange the values in order from least to greatest and determine the value that occurs most often.

13 mm 14 mm 14 mm 16 mm 21 mm 23 mm 25 mm

ANSWER The mode is 14 mm.

A data set can have more than one mode or no mode. For example, the following data set has modes of 2 mm and 4 mm:

2 mm 2 mm 3 mm 4 mm 4 mm

The data set below has no mode, because no value occurs more often than any other.

2 mm 3 mm 4 mm 5 mm

Range

The **range** of a data set is the difference between the greatest value and the least value.

Example

To find the range of the clamshell data, arrange the values in order from least to greatest.

13 mm 14 mm 14 mm 16 mm 21 mm 23 mm 25 mm

Subtract the least value from the greatest value.

13 mm is the least value.
25 mm is the greatest value.

25 mm – 13 mm = 12 mm

ANSWER The range is 12 mm.

MATH HANDBOOK

Using Ratios, Rates, and Proportions

You can use ratios and rates to compare values in data sets. You can use proportions to find unknown values.

Ratios

A **ratio** uses division to compare two values. The ratio of a value a to a nonzero value b can be written as $\frac{a}{b}$.

Example

The height of one plant is 8 centimeters. The height of another plant is 6 centimeters. To find the ratio of the height of the first plant to the height of the second plant, write a fraction and simplify it.

$$\frac{8 \text{ cm}}{6 \text{ cm}} = \frac{4 \times \cancel{2}^{1}}{3 \times \cancel{2}_{1}} = \frac{4}{3}$$

ANSWER The ratio of the plant heights is $\frac{4}{3}$.

You can also write the ratio $\frac{a}{b}$ as "a to b" or as $a\!:\!b$. For example, you can write the ratio of the plant heights as "4 to 3" or as 4:3.

Rates

A **rate** is a ratio of two values expressed in different units. A unit rate is a rate with a denominator of 1 unit.

Example

A plant grew 6 centimeters in 2 days. The plant's rate of growth was $\frac{6 \text{ cm}}{2 \text{ days}}$. To describe the plant's growth in centimeters per day, write a unit rate.

Divide numerator and denominator by 2: $\frac{6 \text{ cm}}{2 \text{ days}} = \frac{6 \text{ cm} \div 2}{2 \text{ days} \div 2}$

Simplify: $= \frac{3 \text{ cm}}{1 \text{ day}}$

You divide 2 days by 2 to get 1 day, so divide 6 cm by 2 also.

ANSWER The plant's rate of growth is 3 centimeters per day.

MATH HANDBOOK

Proportions

A **proportion** is an equation stating that two ratios are equivalent. To solve for an unknown value in a proportion, you can use cross products.

Example

If a plant grew 6 centimeters in 2 days, how many centimeters would it grow in 3 days (if its rate of growth is constant)?

Write a proportion: $\frac{6 \text{ cm}}{2 \text{ days}} = \frac{x}{3 \text{ days}}$

Set cross products: $6 \text{ cm} \cdot 3 = 2x$

Multiply 6 and 3: $18 \text{ cm} = 2x$

Divide each side by 2: $\frac{18 \text{ cm}}{2} = \frac{2x}{2}$

Simplify: $9 \text{ cm} = x$

ANSWER The plant would grow 9 centimeters in 3 days.

Using Decimals, Fractions, and Percents

Decimals, fractions, and percentages are all ways of recording and representing data.

Decimals

A **decimal** is a number that is written in the base-ten place value system, in which a decimal point separates the ones and tenths digits. The values of each place is ten times that of the place to its right.

Example

A caterpillar traveled from point *A* to point *C* along the path shown.

A — 36.9 cm — B — 52.4 cm — C

ADDING DECIMALS To find the total distance traveled by the caterpillar, add the distance from *A* to *B* and the distance from *B* to *C*. Begin by lining up the decimal points. Then add the figures as you would whole numbers and bring down the decimal point.

$$\begin{array}{r} 36.9 \text{ cm} \\ +\ 52.4 \text{ cm} \\ \hline 89.3 \text{ cm} \end{array}$$

ANSWER The caterpillar traveled a total distance of 89.3 centimeters.

Example *continued*

SUBTRACTING DECIMALS To find how much farther the caterpillar traveled on the second leg of the journey, subtract the distance from *A* to *B* from the distance from *B* to *C*.

```
  52.4 cm
– 36.9 cm
---------
  15.5 cm
```

ANSWER The caterpillar traveled 15.5 centimeters farther on the second leg of the journey.

Example

A caterpillar is traveling from point *D* to point *F* along the path shown. The caterpillar travels at a speed of 9.6 centimeters per minute.

D E 33.6 cm F

MULTIPLYING DECIMALS You can multiply decimals as you would whole numbers. The number of decimal places in the product is equal to the sum of the number of decimal places in the factors.

For instance, suppose it takes the caterpillar 1.5 minutes to go from *D* to *E*. To find the distance from *D* to *E*, multiply the caterpillar's speed by the time it took.

```
   9.6        1   decimal place
 × 1.5      + 1   decimal place
 -----      ---
   480
   96
 -----
  14.40       2   decimal places
```

Align as shown.

ANSWER The distance from *D* to *E* is 14.4 centimeters.

DIVIDING DECIMALS When you divide by a decimal, move the decimal points the same number of places in the divisor and the dividend to make the divisor a whole number.

For instance, to find the time it will take the caterpillar to travel from *E* to *F*, divide the distance from *E* to *F* by the caterpillar's speed.

```
9.6 )33.6          Move each decimal point one place to the right.

      3.5
96 )336.           Line up decimal points.
    288
     480
     480
       0
```

ANSWER The caterpillar will travel from *E* to *F* in 3.5 minutes.

MATH HANDBOOK

R40

Fractions

A **fraction** is a number in the form $\frac{a}{b}$, where b is not equal to 0. A fraction is in **simplest form** if its numerator and denominator have a greatest common factor (GCF) of 1. To simplify a fraction, divide its numerator and denominator by their GCF.

Example

A caterpillar is 40 millimeters long. The head of the caterpillar is 6 millimeters long. To compare the length of the caterpillar's head with the caterpillar's total length, you can write and simplify a fraction that expresses the ratio of the two lengths.

Write the ratio of the two lengths: $\frac{\text{Length of head}}{\text{Total length}} = \frac{6 \text{ mm}}{40 \text{ mm}}$

Write numerator and denominator as products of numbers and the GCF: $= \frac{3 \times 2}{20 \times 2}$

Divide numerator and denominator by the GCF: $= \frac{3 \times \overset{1}{\cancel{2}}}{20 \times \underset{1}{\cancel{2}}}$

Simplify: $= \frac{3}{20}$

ANSWER In simplest form, the ratio of the lengths is $\frac{3}{20}$.

Percents

A **percent** is a ratio that compares a number to 100. The word *percent* means "per hundred" or "out of 100." The symbol for *percent* is %.

For instance, suppose 43 out of 100 caterpillars are female. You can represent this ratio as a percent, a decimal, or a fraction.

Percent	Decimal	Fraction
43%	0.43	$\frac{43}{100}$

Example

In the preceding example, the ratio of the length of the caterpillar's head to the caterpillar's total length is $\frac{3}{20}$. To write this ratio as a percent, write an equivalent fraction that has a denominator of 100.

Multiply numerator and denominator by 5: $\frac{3}{20} = \frac{3 \times 5}{20 \times 5}$

$= \frac{15}{100}$

Write as a percent: $= 15\%$

ANSWER The caterpillar's head represents 15 percent of its total length.

MATH HANDBOOK

Using Formulas

A **formula** is an equation that shows the general relationship between two or more quantities.

In science, a formula often has a word form and a symbolic form. The formula below expresses Ohm's law.

Word Form

$$\text{Current} = \frac{\text{voltage}}{\text{resistance}}$$

Symbolic Form

$$I = \frac{V}{R}$$

The term *variable* is also used in science to refer to a factor that can change during an experiment.

In this formula, I, V, and R are variables. A mathematical **variable** is a symbol or letter that is used to represent one or more numbers.

Example

Suppose that you measure a voltage of 1.5 volts and a resistance of 15 ohms. You can use the formula for Ohm's law to find the current in amperes.

Write the formula for Ohm's law: $I = \frac{V}{R}$

***Substitute 1.5 volts for* V *and 15 ohms for* R:** $I = \frac{1.5 \text{ volts}}{15 \text{ ohms}}$

Simplify: $I = 0.1$ amp

ANSWER The current is 0.1 ampere.

If you know the values of all variables but one in a formula, you can solve for the value of the unknown variable. For instance, Ohm's law can be used to find a voltage if you know the current and the resistance.

Example

Suppose that you know that a current is 0.2 amperes and the resistance is 18 ohms. Use the formula for Ohm's law to find the voltage in volts.

Write the formula for Ohm's law: $I = \frac{V}{R}$

***Substitute 0.2 amp for* I *and 18 ohms for* R:** $0.2 \text{ amp} = \frac{V}{18 \text{ ohms}}$

Multiply both sides by 18 ohms: $0.2 \text{ amp} \cdot 18 \text{ ohms} = V$

Simplify: $3.6 \text{ volts} = V$

ANSWER The voltage is 3.6 volts.

MATH HANDBOOK

R42

Finding Areas

The area of a figure is the amount of surface the figure covers.

Area is measured in square units, such as square meters (m^2) or square centimeters (cm^2). Formulas for the areas of three common geometric figures are shown below.

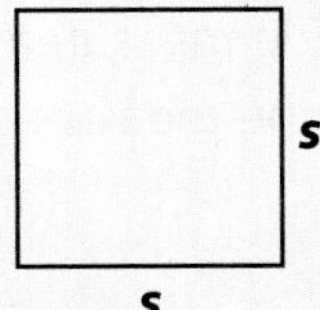

Area = (side length)^2
$A = s^2$

Area = length × width
$A = lw$

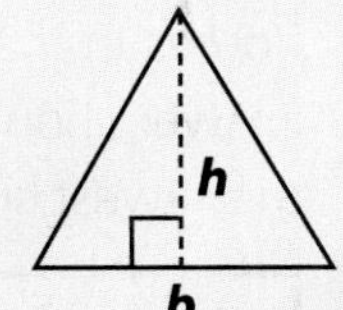

Area = $\frac{1}{2}$ × base × height
$A = \frac{1}{2}bh$

Example

Each face of a halite crystal is a square like the one shown. You can find the area of the square by using the steps below.

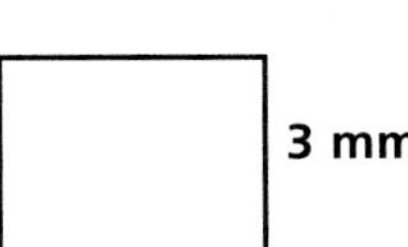

Write the formula for the area of a square: $A = s^2$

Substitute 3 mm for s: $= (3\text{ mm})^2$

Simplify: $= 9\text{ mm}^2$

ANSWER The area of the square is 9 square millimeters.

Finding Volumes

The volume of a solid is the amount of space contained by the solid.

Volume is measured in cubic units, such as cubic meters (m^3) or cubic centimeters (cm^3). The volume of a rectangular prism is given by the formula shown below.

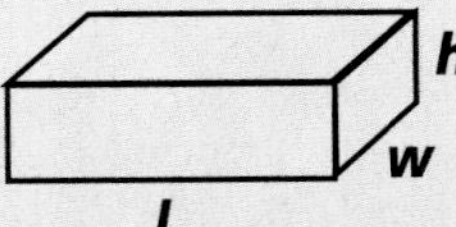

Volume = length × width × height
$V = lwh$

Example

A topaz crystal is a rectangular prism like the one shown. You can find the volume of the prism by using the steps below.

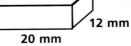

10 mm
12 mm
20 mm

Write the formula for the volume of a rectangular prism: $V = lwh$

Substitute dimensions: $= 20\text{ mm} \times 12\text{ mm} \times 10\text{ mm}$

Simplify: $= 2400\text{ mm}^3$

ANSWER The volume of the rectangular prism is 2400 cubic millimeters.

Using Significant Figures

The **significant figures** in a decimal are the digits that are warranted by the accuracy of a measuring device.

When you perform a calculation with measurements, the number of significant figures to include in the result depends in part on the number of significant figures in the measurements. When you multiply or divide measurements, your answer should have only as many significant figures as the measurement with the fewest significant figures.

Example

Using a balance and a graduated cylinder filled with water, you determined that a marble has a mass of 8.0 grams and a volume of 3.5 cubic centimeters. To calculate the density of the marble, divide the mass by the volume.

Write the formula for density: $\text{Density} = \frac{\text{mass}}{\text{Volume}}$

Substitute measurements: $= \frac{8.0 \text{ g}}{3.5 \text{ cm}^3}$

Use a calculator to divide: $\approx 2.285714286 \text{ g/cm}^3$

ANSWER Because the mass and the volume have two significant figures each, give the density to two significant figures. The marble has a density of 2.3 grams per cubic centimeter.

Using Scientific Notation

Scientific notation is a shorthand way to write very large or very small numbers. For example, 73,500,000,000,000,000,000,000 kg is the mass of the Moon. In scientific notation, it is 7.35×10^{22} kg.

Example

You can convert from standard form to scientific notation.

Standard Form	Scientific Notation
720,000	7.2×10^5
5 decimal places left	Exponent is 5.
0.000291	2.91×10^{-4}
4 decimal places right	Exponent is –4.

You can convert from scientific notation to standard form.

Scientific Notation	Standard Form
4.63×10^7	46,300,000
Exponent is 7.	7 decimal places right
1.08×10^{-6}	0.00000108
Exponent is –6.	6 decimal places left

MATH HANDBOOK

Note-Taking Handbook

Note-Taking Strategies

Taking notes as you read helps you understand the information. The notes you take can also be used as a study guide for later review. This handbook presents several ways to organize your notes.

Content Frame

1. Make a chart in which each column represents a category.
2. Give each column a heading.
3. Write details under the headings.

NAME	GROUP	CHARACTERISTICS	DRAWING
snail	mollusks	mantle, shell	
ant	arthropods	six legs, exoskeleton	
earthworm	segmented worms	segmented body, circulatory and digestive systems	
heartworm	roundworms	digestive system	
sea star	echinoderms	spiny skin, tube feet	
jellyfish	cnidarians	stinging cells	

categories

details

Combination Notes

1. For each new idea or concept, write an informal outline of the information.
2. Make a sketch to illustrate the concept, and label it.

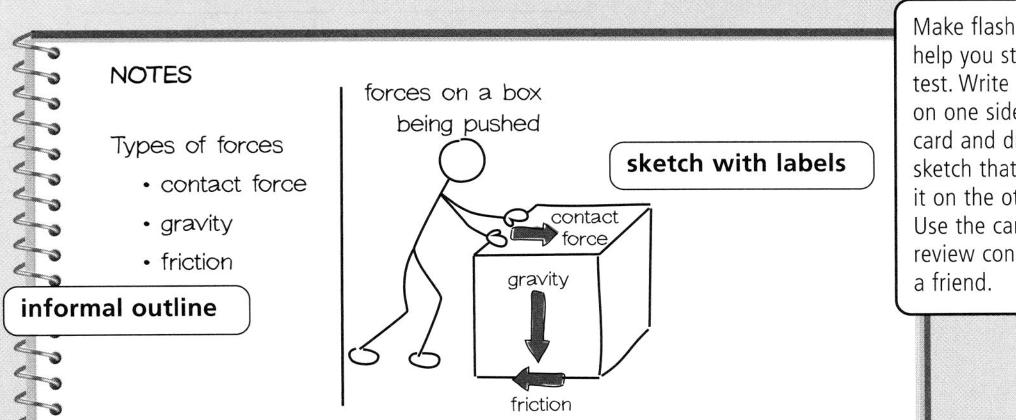

Make flash cards to help you study for a test. Write a concept on one side of each card and draw the sketch that goes with it on the other side. Use the cards to review concepts with a friend.

NOTE-TAKING HANDBOOK

Main Idea and Detail Notes

1. In the left-hand column of a two-column chart, list main ideas. The blue headings express main ideas throughout this textbook.
2. In the right-hand column, write details that expand on each main idea.

You can shorten the headings in your chart. Be sure to use the most important words.

When studying for tests, cover up the detail notes column with a sheet of paper. Then use each main idea to form a question—such as "How does latitude affect climate?" Answer the question, and then uncover the detail notes column to check your answer.

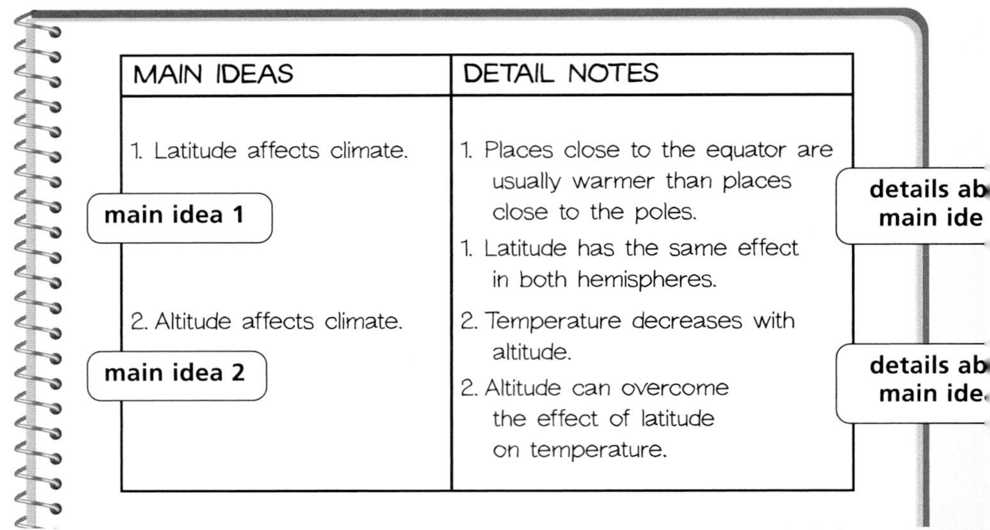

Force is necessary to do work.
The joule is the unit used to measure work.

MAIN IDEAS
DETAIL NOTES
1. Latitude affects climate.
main idea 1
1. Places close to the equator are usually warmer than places close to the poles.
1. Latitude has the same effect in both hemispheres.
details ab
main ide
2. Altitude affects climate.
main idea 2
2. Temperature decreases with altitude.
2. Altitude can overcome the effect of latitude on temperature.
details ab
main ide

Main Idea Web

1. Write a main idea in a box.
2. Add boxes around it with related vocabulary terms and important details.

You can find definitions near highlighted terms.

Work = force · distance

NOTE-TAKING HANDBOOK

Mind Map

1. Write a main idea in the center.
2. Add details that relate to one another and to the main idea.

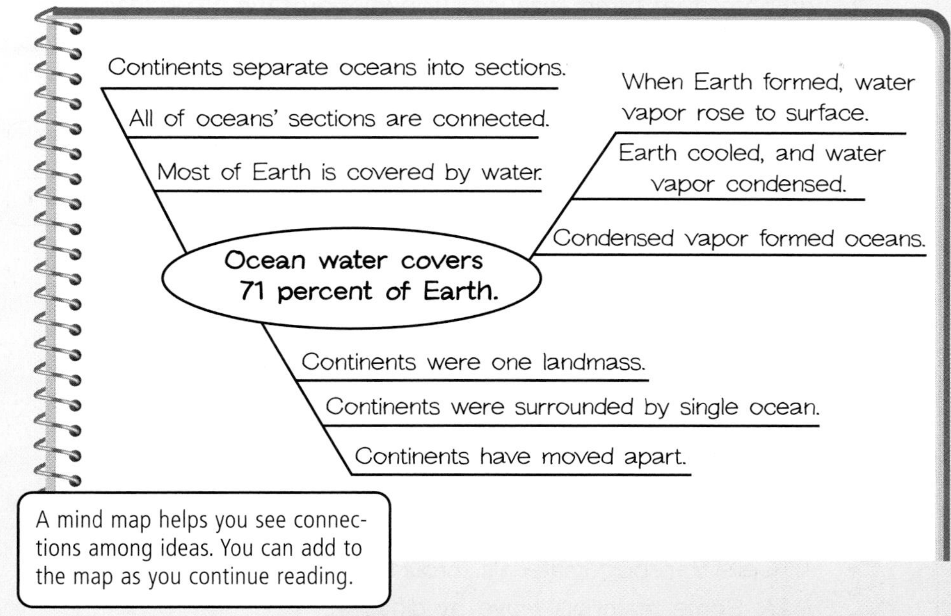

Supporting Main Ideas

1. Write a main idea in a box.
2. Add boxes underneath with information—such as reasons, explanations, and examples—that supports the main idea.

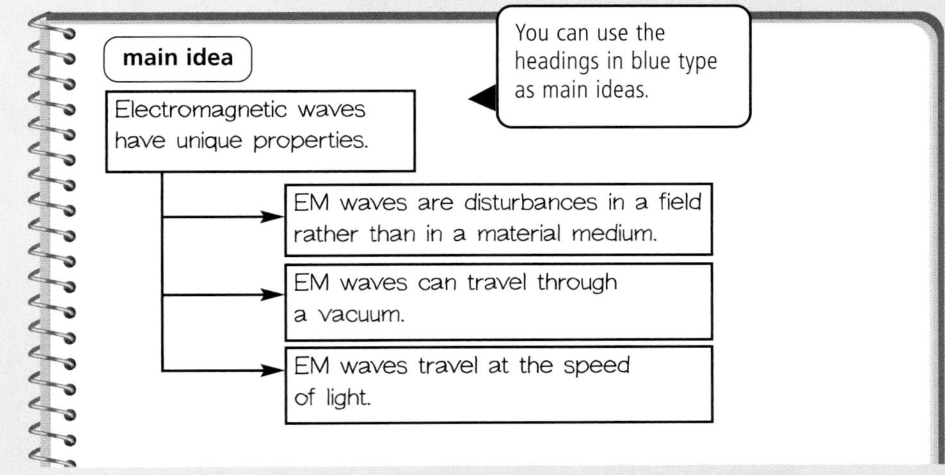

NOTE-TAKING HANDBOOK

Outline

1. Copy the chapter title and headings from the book in the form of an outline.
2. Add notes that summarize in your own words what you read.

Cell Processes

I. Cells capture and release energy. — **1st key idea**
   A. All cells need energy. — **1st subpoint of I**
   B. Some cells capture light energy. — **2nd subpoint of I**
      1. Process of photosynthesis — **1st detail about B**
      2. Chloroplasts (site of photosynthesis) — **2nd detail about B**
      3. Carbon dioxide and water as raw materials
      4. Glucose and oxygen as products
   C. All cells release energy.
      1. Process of cellular respiration
      2. Fermentation of sugar to carbon dioxide
      3. Bacteria that carry out fermentation

II. Cells transport materials through membranes.
   A. Some materials move by diffusion.
      1. Particle movement from higher to lower concentrations
      2. Movement of water through membrane (osmosis)
   B. Some transport requires energy.
      1. Active transport
      2. Examples of active transport

Correct Outline Form

Include a title.

Arrange key ideas, subpoints, and details as shown.

Indent the divisions of the outline as shown.

Use the same grammatical form for items of the same rank. For example, if A is a sentence, B must also be a sentence.

You must have at least two main ideas or subpoints. That is, every A must be followed by a B, and every 1 must be followed by a 2.

Concept Map

1. Write an important concept in a large oval.
2. Add details related to the concept in smaller ovals.
3. Write linking words on arrows that connect the ovals.

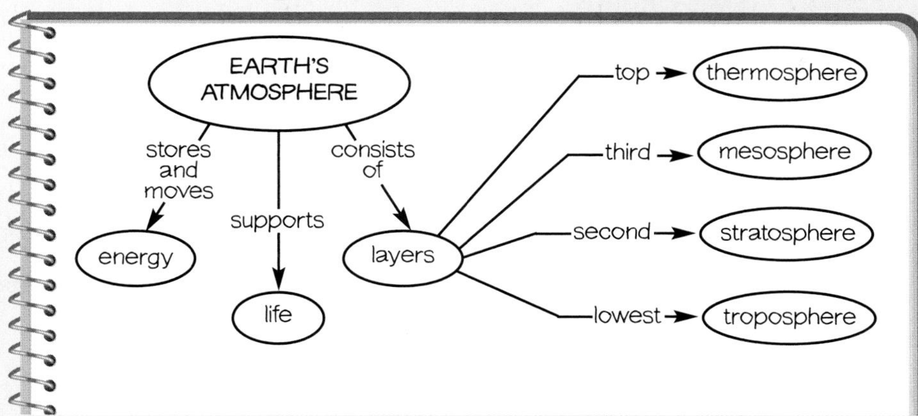

The main ideas or concepts can often be found in the blue headings. An example is "The atmosphere stores and moves energy." Use nouns from these concepts in the ovals, and use the verb or verbs on the lines.

Venn Diagram

1. Draw two overlapping circles, one for each item that you are comparing.
2. In the overlapping section, list the characteristics that are shared by both items.
3. In the outer sections, list the characteristics that are peculiar to each item.
4. Write a summary that describes the information in the Venn diagram.

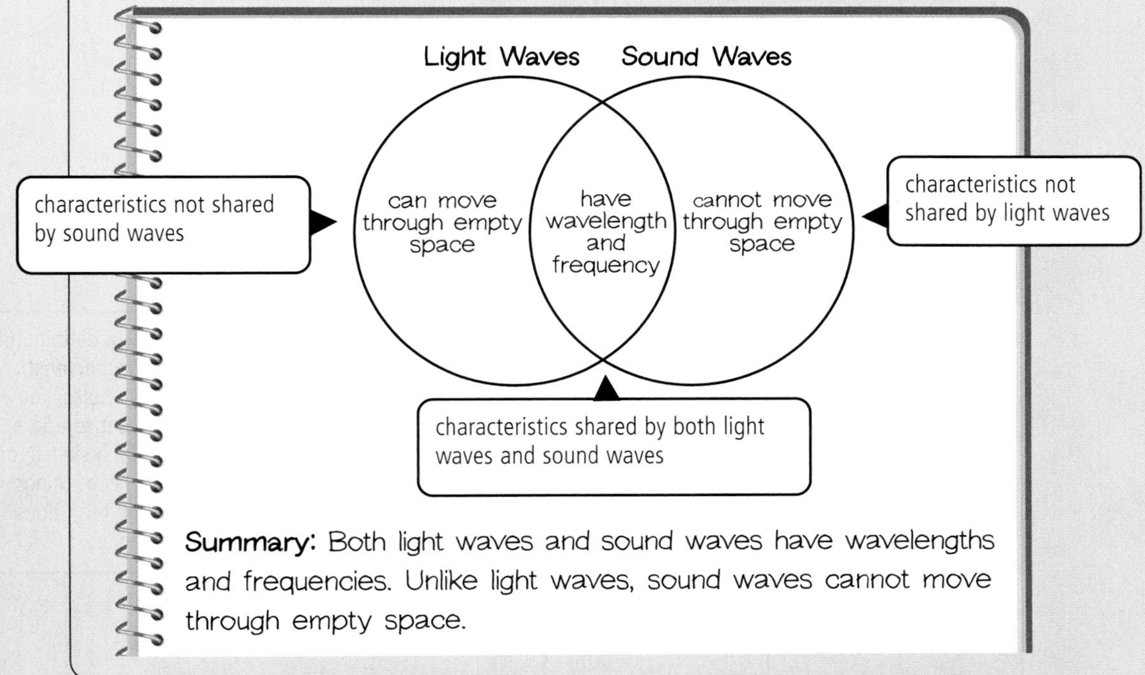

NOTE-TAKING HANDBOOK

Vocabulary Strategies

Important terms are highlighted in this book. A definition of each term can be found in the sentence or paragraph where the term appears. You can also find definitions in the Glossary. Taking notes about vocabulary terms helps you understand and remember what you read.

Description Wheel

1. Write a term inside a circle.
2. Write words that describe the term on "spokes" attached to the circle.

When studying for a test with a friend, read the phrases on the spokes one at a time until your friend identifies the correct term.

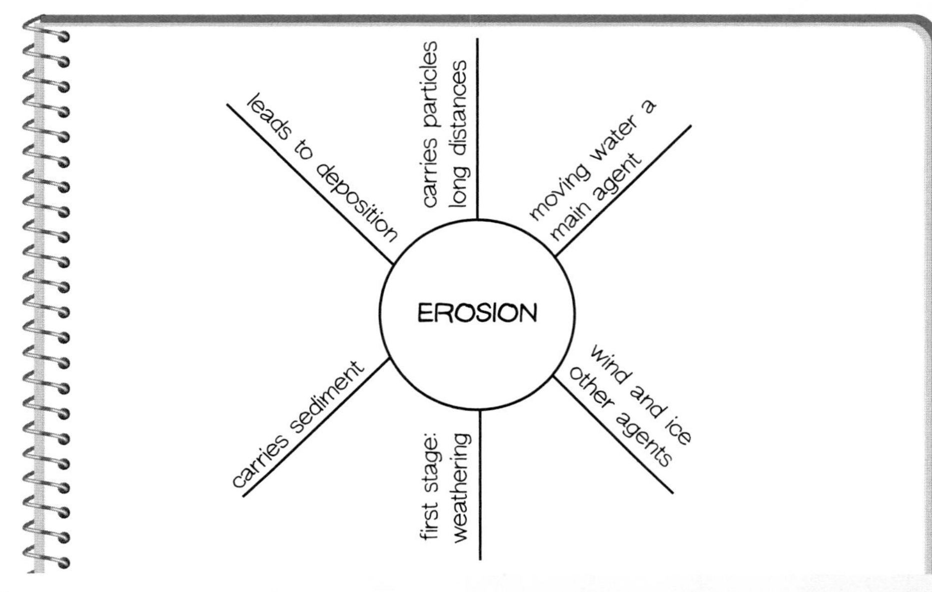

Four Square

1. Write a term in the center.
2. Write details in the four areas around the term.

Definition	Characteristics
any living thing	needs food, water, air; needs energy; grows, develops, reproduces
Examples	**Nonexamples**
dogs, cats, birds, insects, flowers, trees	rocks, water, dirt

ORGANISM

Include a definition, some characteristics, and examples. You may want to add a formula, a sketch, or examples of things that the term does *not* name.

NOTE-TAKING HANDBOOK

Frame Game

1. Write a term in the center.
2. Frame the term with details.

Include examples, descriptions, sketches, or sentences that use the term in context. Change the frame to fit each new term.

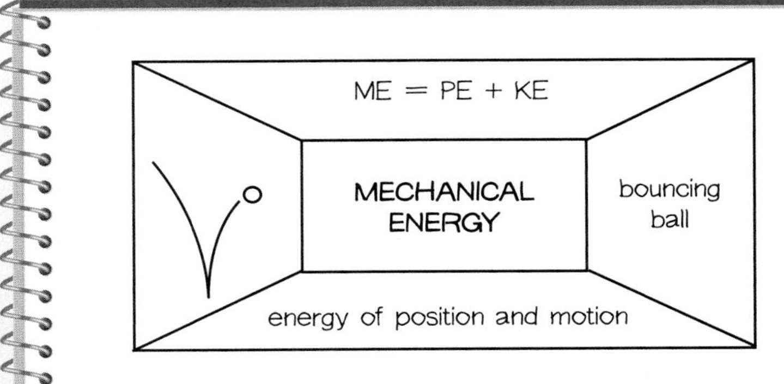

Magnet Word

1. Write a term on the magnet.
2. On the lines, add details related to the term.

You can also use phrases or sentences on the lines.

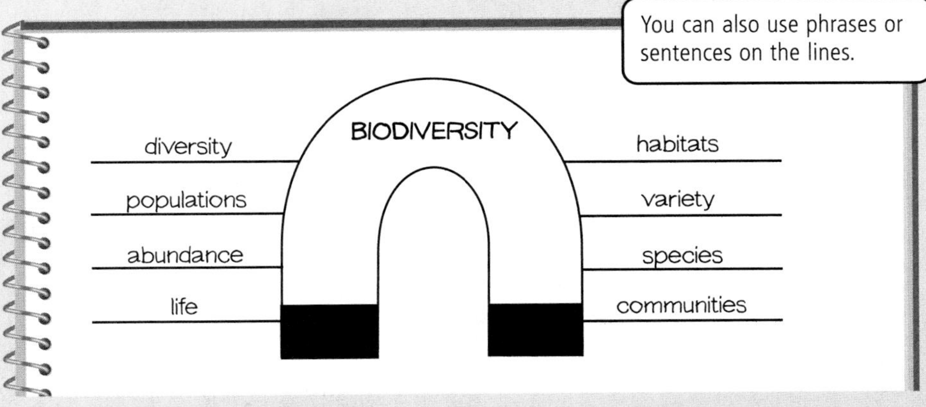

Word Triangle

1. Write a term and its definition in the bottom section.
2. In the middle section, write a sentence in which the term is used correctly.
3. In the top section, draw a small picture to illustrate the term.

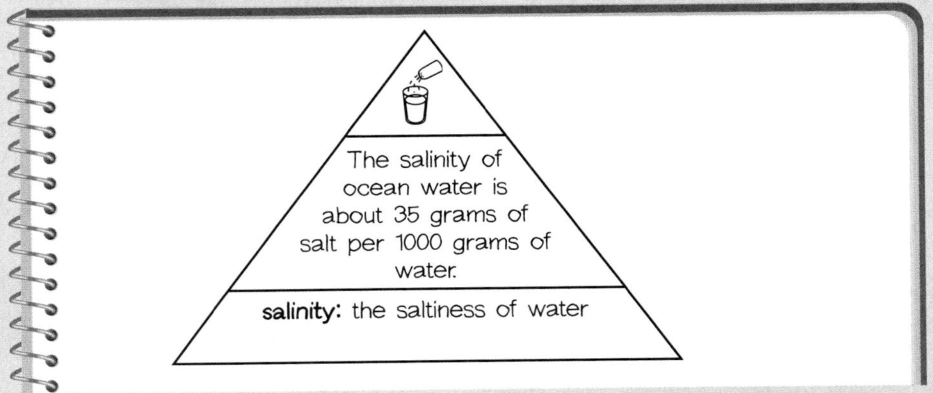

NOTE-TAKING HANDBOOK

Appendix

United States Physical Map

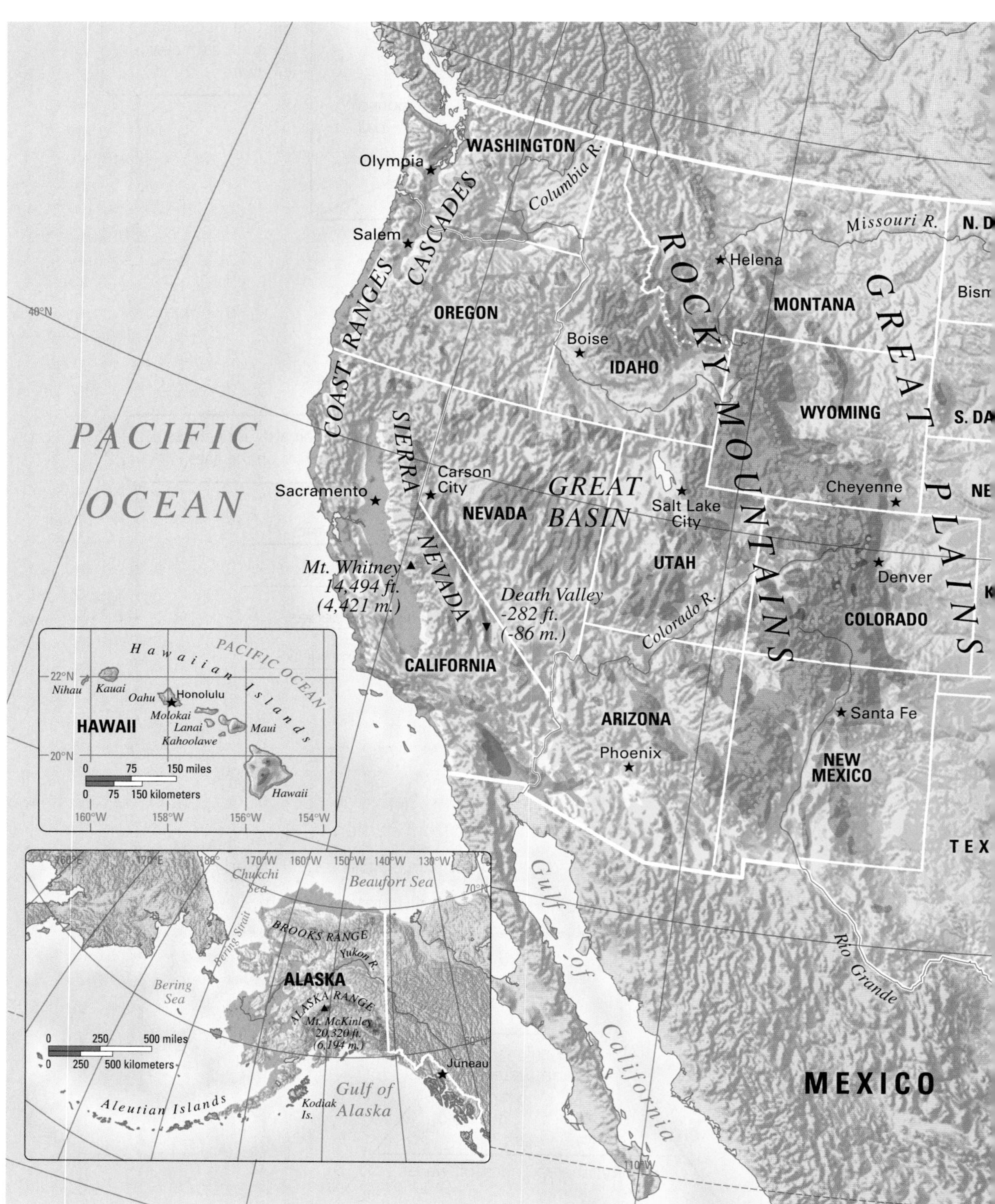

PACIFIC OCEAN
WASHINGTON
Olympia
Columbia R.
CASCADES
Salem
COAST RANGES
OREGON
ROCKY MOUNTAINS
Helena
MONTANA
Missouri R.
N. D
Bism
GREAT PLAINS
Boise
IDAHO
WYOMING
S. DA
SIERRA NEVADA
Carson City
Sacramento
NEVADA
GREAT BASIN
Salt Lake City
Cheyenne
NE
UTAH
Denver
Mt. Whitney 14,494 ft. (4,421 m.)
Death Valley -282 ft. (-86 m.)
Colorado R.
COLORADO
CALIFORNIA
ARIZONA
Phoenix
Santa Fe
NEW MEXICO
TEX
Gulf of California
Rio Grande
MEXICO
40°N
110°W
Hawaiian Islands
PACIFIC OCEAN
22°N
Nihau
Kauai
Oahu
Honolulu
Molokai
Lanai
Kahoolawe
Maui
HAWAII
Hawaii
20°N
0 75 150 miles
0 75 150 kilometers
160°W
158°W
156°W
154°W
Chukchi Sea
Beaufort Sea
BROOKS RANGE
Yukon R.
Bering Strait
Bering Sea
ALASKA
ALASKA RANGE
Mt. McKinley 20,320 ft. (6,194 m.)
0 250 500 miles
0 250 500 kilometers
Juneau
Aleutian Islands
Kodiak Is.
Gulf of Alaska
170°W
160°W
150°W
140°W
130°W
70°N

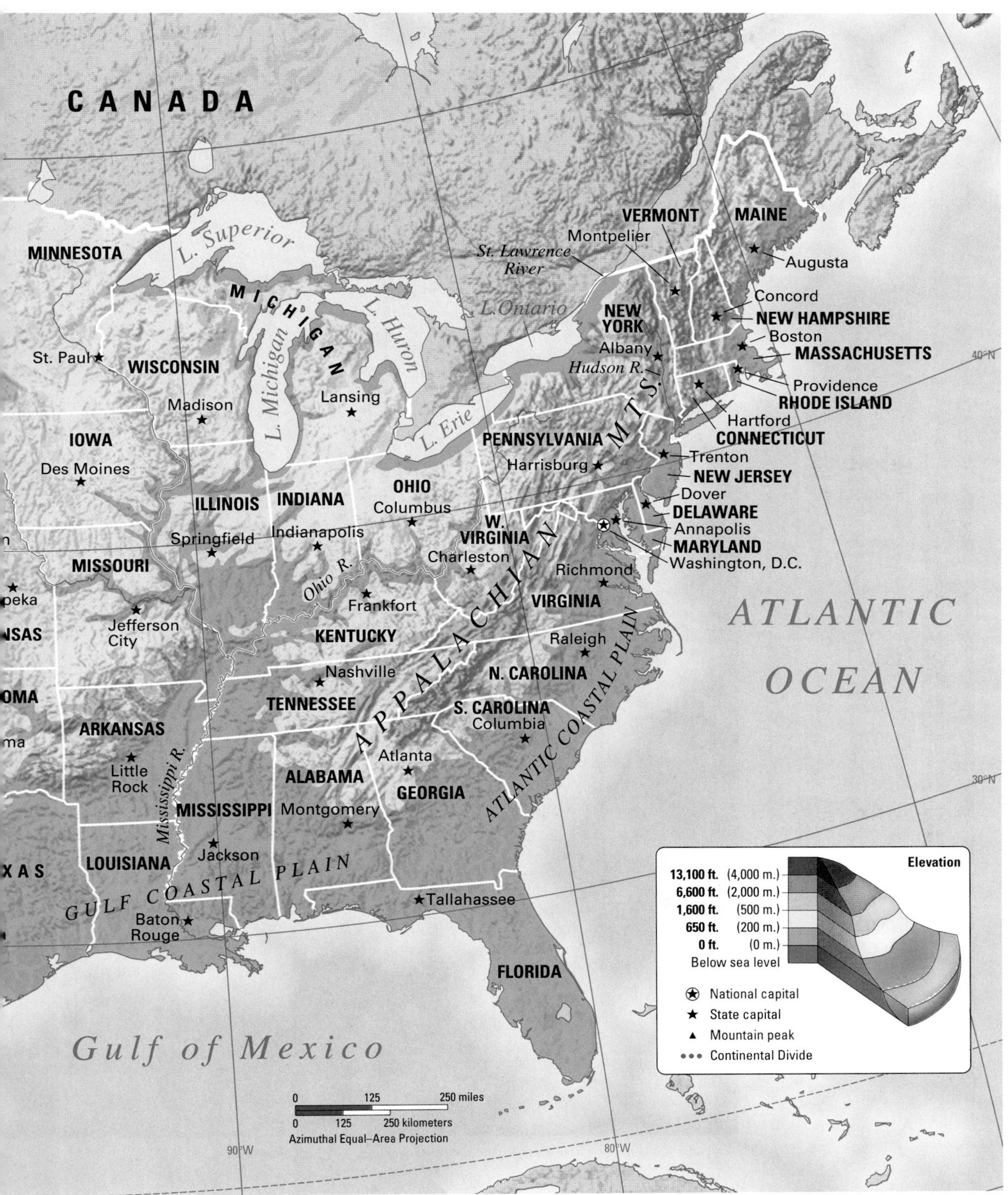
CANADA
L. Superior
MINNESOTA
MICHIGAN
L. Huron
L. Michigan
L. Ontario
L. Erie
St. Lawrence River
VERMONT
MAINE
Montpelier
Augusta
Concord
NEW HAMPSHIRE
NEW YORK
Albany
Hudson R.
Boston
MASSACHUSETTS
Providence
RHODE ISLAND
Hartford
CONNECTICUT
St. Paul
WISCONSIN
Madison
Lansing
IOWA
Des Moines
PENNSYLVANIA
Harrisburg
Trenton
NEW JERSEY
Dover
DELAWARE
Annapolis
MARYLAND
Washington, D.C.
OHIO
Columbus
ILLINOIS
INDIANA
Indianapolis
Springfield
W. VIRGINIA
Charleston
MISSOURI
Jefferson City
Ohio R.
Frankfort
Richmond
VIRGINIA
KENTUCKY
Raleigh
N. CAROLINA
Nashville
TENNESSEE
S. CAROLINA
Columbia
APPALACHIAN MTS.
ATLANTIC COASTAL PLAIN
ATLANTIC OCEAN
ARKANSAS
Little Rock
Mississippi R.
Atlanta
ALABAMA
GEORGIA
MISSISSIPPI
Montgomery
Jackson
LOUISIANA
GULF COASTAL PLAIN
Baton Rouge
Tallahassee
FLORIDA
Gulf of Mexico
40°N
30°N
90°W
80°W
Elevation
13,100 ft. (4,000 m.)
6,600 ft. (2,000 m.)
1,600 ft. (500 m.)
650 ft. (200 m.)
0 ft. (0 m.)
Below sea level
National capital
State capital
Mountain peak
Continental Divide
0 125 250 miles
0 125 250 kilometers
Azimuthal Equal-Area Projection

APPENDIX

World Physical Map

METERS
9000
5000
3500
2000
1000
Sea level
0
–1500
–3000
–5000
–7000
–9000
–11000

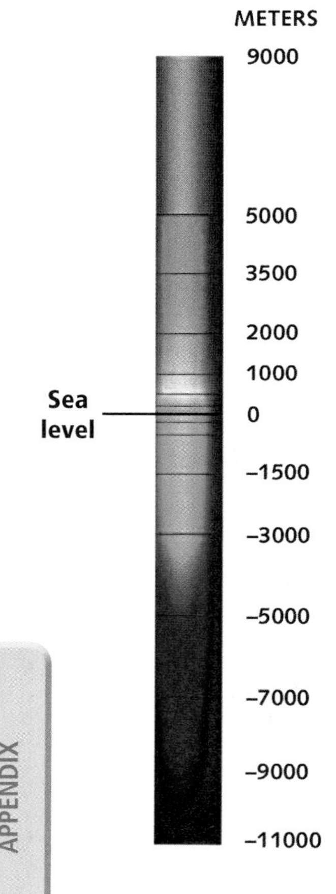

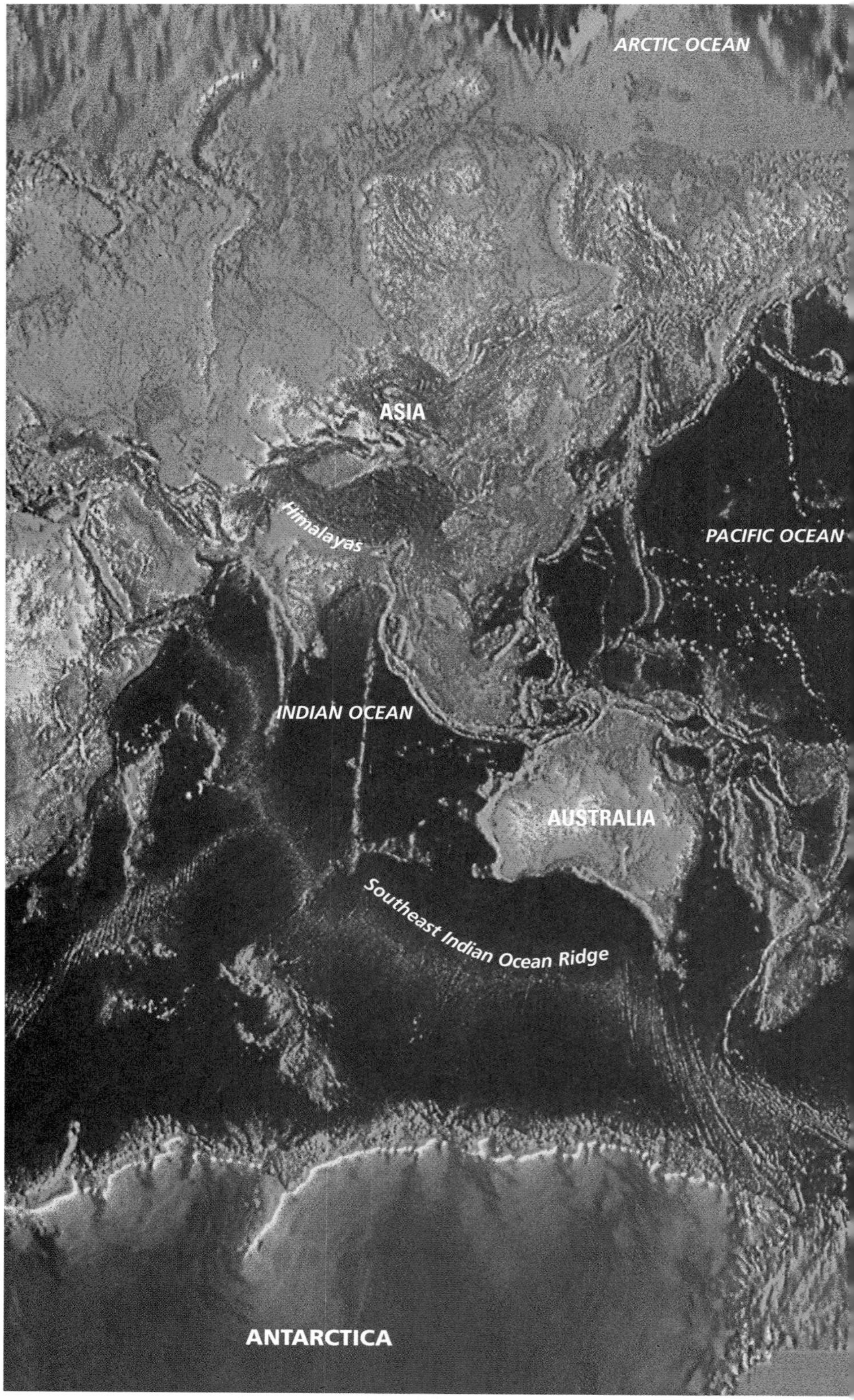

ARCTIC OCEAN
ASIA
Himalayas
PACIFIC OCEAN
INDIAN OCEAN
AUSTRALIA
Southeast Indian Ocean Ridge
ANTARCTICA

This image was generated from a combination of satellite altimetry data, ship-based data, and land-based data.

APPENDIX

R54

GREENLAND
NORTH AMERICA
EUROPE
Rocky Mountains
Appalachian Mts.
Alps
ATLANTIC OCEAN
Atlas Mts.
Mid-Atlantic Ridge
AFRICA
PACIFIC OCEAN
SOUTH AMERICA
INDIAN OCEAN
East Pacific Rise
Andes
Southwest Indian Ocean Ridge
ANTARCTICA
ANTARCTICA

APPENDIX

Tectonic Plates

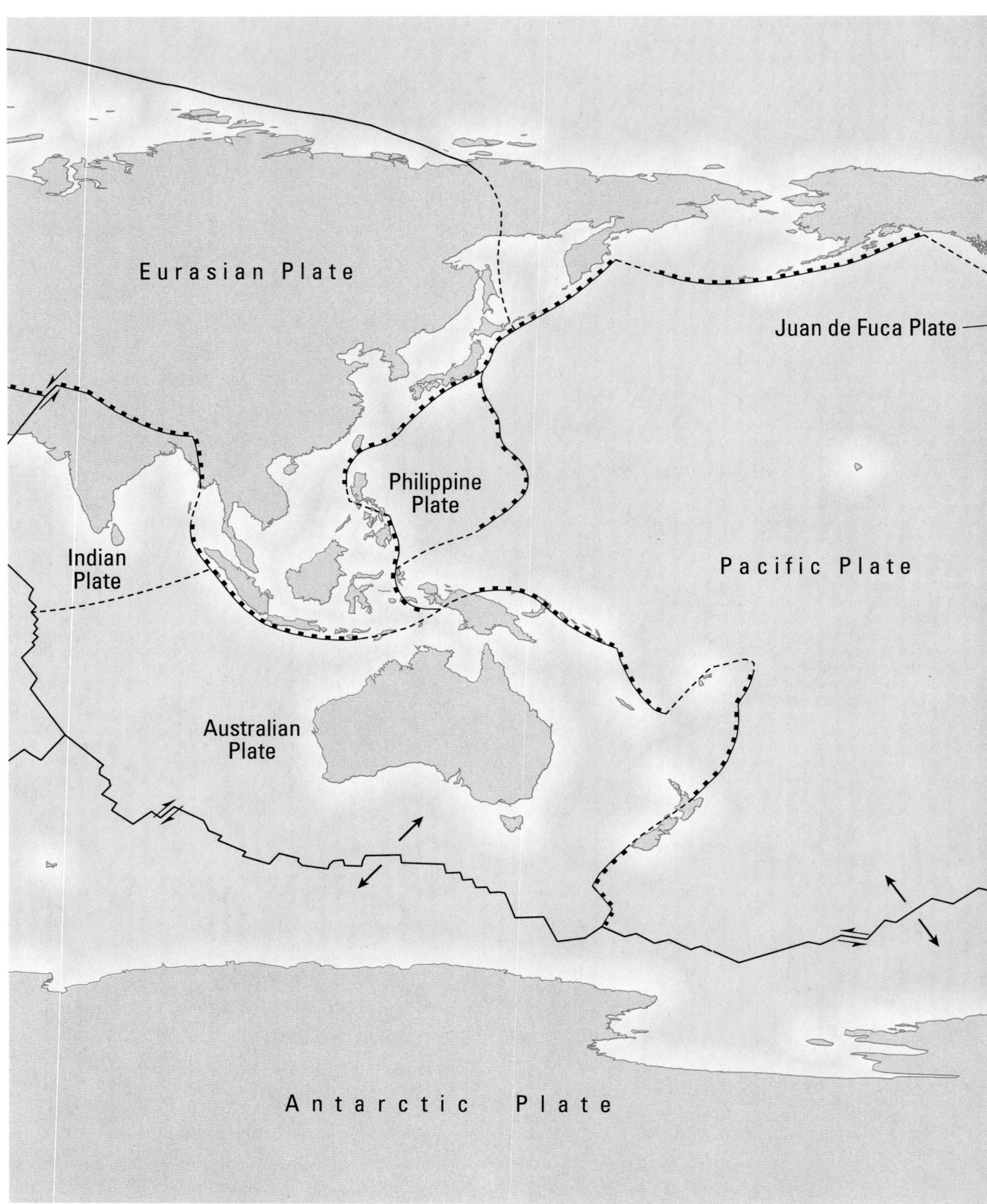

APPENDIX

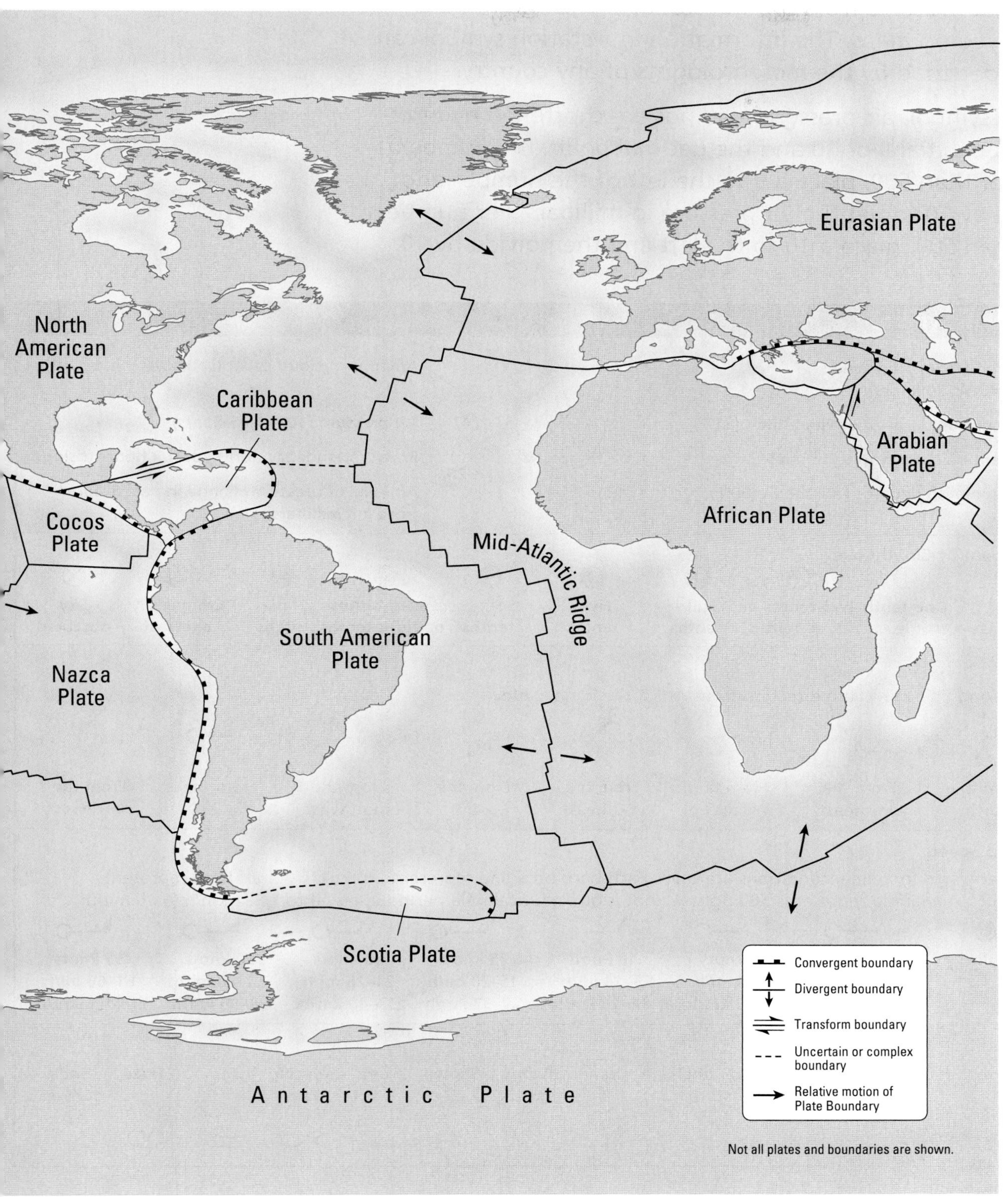

Eurasian Plate
North American Plate
Caribbean Plate
Arabian Plate
African Plate
Cocos Plate
Mid-Atlantic Ridge
South American Plate
Nazca Plate
Scotia Plate
Antarctic Plate
Convergent boundary
Divergent boundary
Transform boundary
Uncertain or complex boundary
Relative motion of Plate Boundary
Not all plates and boundaries are shown.

APPENDIX

Station Symbols

Meteorologists use station symbols to condense the weather data they receive from ground stations. The symbols are displayed on maps. The information in a station symbol can be understood by the meteorologists of any country.

In the symbol, air pressure readings are shortened by omitting the initial 9 or 10 and the decimal point. For numbers greater than 500, place a 9 to the left of the number and divide by 10 to get the air pressure in millibars. For numbers less than 500, place a 10 to the left and then divide by 10.

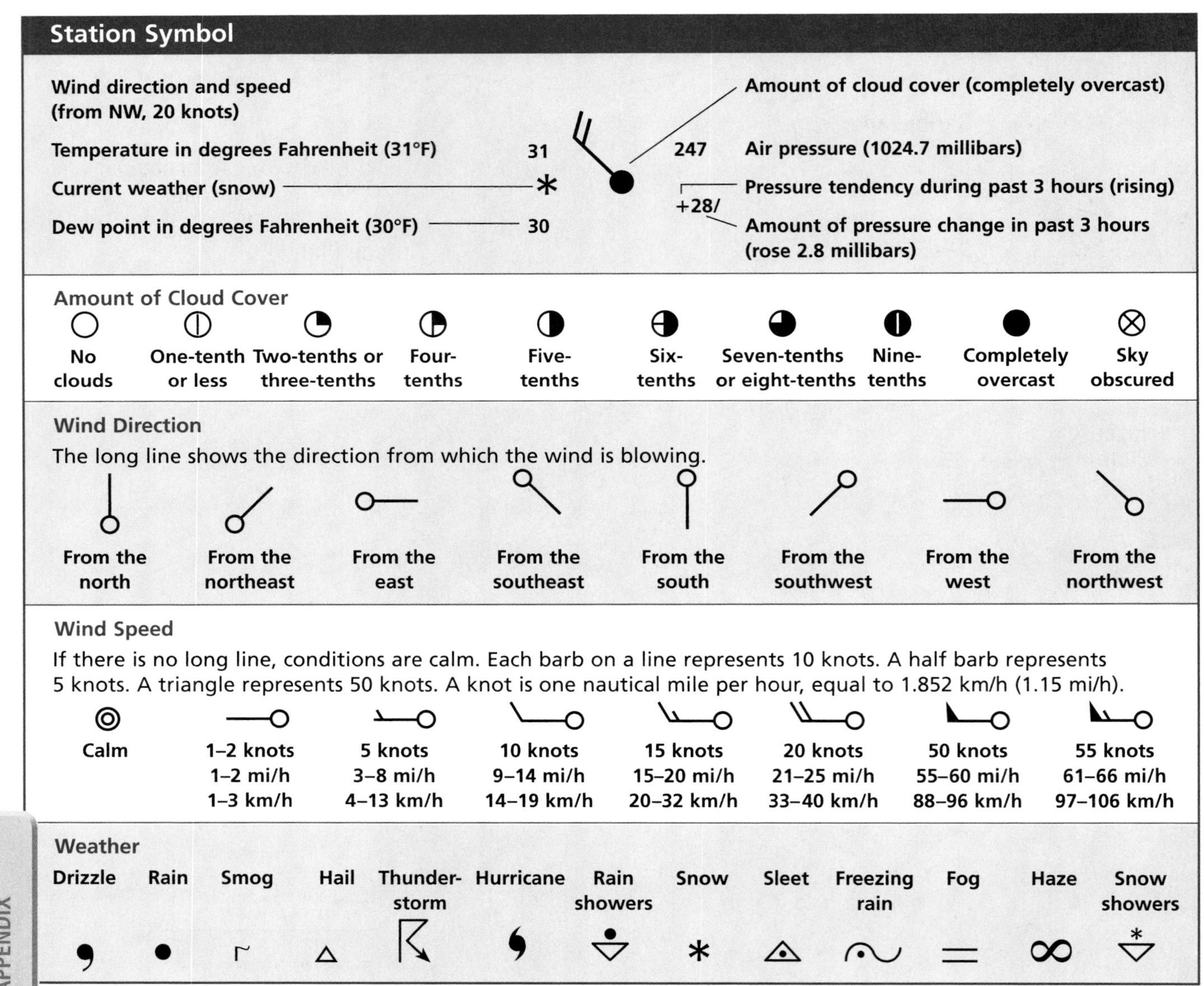

APPENDIX

Relative Humidity

You can find the relative humidity by calculating the difference between the two readings on a psychrometer. First look up the dry-bulb temperature in the left-hand column of the relative humidity chart. Then find in the top line the difference between the wet-bulb temperature and the dry-bulb temperature.

Relative Humidity (%)

Dry-Bulb Temperature (°C)	Difference Between Wet-Bulb and Dry-Bulb Temperatures (°C)															
	0	1	2	3	4	5	6	7	8	9	10	11	12	13	14	15
−20	100	28														
−18	100	40														
−16	100	48														
−14	100	55	11													
−12	100	61	23													
−10	100	66	33													
−8	100	71	41	13												
−6	100	73	48	20												
−4	100	77	54	32	11											
−2	100	79	58	37	20	1										
0	100	81	63	45	28	11										
2	100	83	67	51	36	20	6									
4	100	85	70	56	42	27	14									
6	100	86	72	59	46	35	22	10								
8	100	87	74	62	51	39	28	17	6							
10	100	88	76	65	54	43	33	24	13	4						
12	100	88	78	67	57	48	38	28	19	10	2					
14	100	89	79	69	60	50	41	33	25	16	8	1				
16	100	90	80	71	62	54	45	37	29	21	14	7	1			
18	100	91	81	72	64	56	48	40	33	26	19	12	6			
20	100	91	82	74	66	58	51	44	36	30	23	17	11	5		
22	100	92	83	75	68	60	53	46	40	33	27	21	15	10	4	
24	100	92	84	76	69	62	55	49	42	36	30	25	20	14	9	4
26	100	92	85	77	70	64	57	51	45	39	34	28	23	18	13	9
28	100	93	86	78	71	65	59	53	47	42	36	31	26	21	17	12
30	100	93	86	79	72	66	61	55	49	44	39	34	29	25	20	16

R59

Wind Speeds

Descriptive names, such as *fresh gale,* were used by sailors and other people to describe the strength of winds. Later, ranges of wind speeds were determined. The table below lists the wind speeds and conditions you might observe around you on land.

Beaufort Scale of Wind Speeds

Beaufort Number	Wind Speed	Description
0	0 km/h (0 mi/h)	**Calm or Still** Smoke will rise vertically
1	2–5 km/h (1–3 mi/h)	**Light Air** Rising smoke drifts, weather vane is inactive
2	6–12 km/h (4–7 mi/h)	**Light Breeze** Leaves rustle, can feel wind on your face, weather vane moves
3	13–20 km/h (8–12 mi/h)	**Gentle Breeze** Leaves and twigs move around, lightweight flags extend
4	21–30 km/h (13–18 mi/h)	**Moderate Breeze** Thin branches move, dust and paper raised
5	31–40 km/h (19–24 mi/h)	**Fresh Breeze** Small trees sway
6	41–50 km/h (25–31 mi/h)	**Strong Breeze** Large tree branches move, open wires (such as telegraph wires) begin to "whistle," umbrellas are difficult to keep under control
7	51–61 km/h (32–38 mi/h)	**Moderate Gale** Large trees begin to sway, noticeably difficult to walk
8	62–74 km/h (39–46 mi/h)	**Fresh Gale** Twigs and small branches are broken from trees, walking into the wind is very difficult
9	75–89 km/h (47–54 mi/h)	**Strong Gale** Slight damage occurs to buildings, shingles are blown off of roofs
10	90–103 km/h (55–63 mi/h)	**Whole Gale** Large trees are uprooted, building damage is considerable
11	104–119 km/h (64–72 mi/h)	**Storm** Extensive, widespread damage. These typically occur only at sea, rarely inland.
12	120 km/h or more (74 mi/h or more)	**Hurricane** Extreme damage, very rare inland

Tornado Intensities

The Fujita scale describes the strength of a tornado based on the damage it does. The scale is useful for classifying tornadoes even though it is not exact. For example, a tornado can strengthen and then weaken before it dies out. The wind speeds are estimates of the strongest winds near the ground. Most tornadoes are F0 or F1. One-quarter to one-third of tornadoes are F2 or F3. Only a few percent of tornadoes are F4 or F5.

Fujita Scale for Tornadoes

F-Scale	Wind Speed	Type of Damage
F0	64–116 km/h (40–72 mi/h)	**Light Damage** Some damage to chimneys; branches broken off trees; shallow-rooted trees pushed over; sign boards damaged
F1	117–180 km/h (73–112 mi/h)	**Moderate Damage** Surface peeled off roofs; mobile homes pushed off foundations or overturned; moving autos blown off roads
F2	181–253 km/h (113–157 mi/h)	**Considerable Damage** Roofs torn off frame houses; mobile homes demolished; boxcars overturned; large trees snapped or uprooted; light-object missiles generated; cars lifted off ground
F3	254–332 km/h (158–206 mi/h)	**Severe Damage** Roofs and some walls torn off well-constructed houses; trains overturned; most trees in forest uprooted; heavy cars lifted off the ground and thrown
F4	333–418 km/h (207–260 mi/h)	**Devastating Damage** Well-constructed houses leveled; structures with weak foundations blown away some distance; cars thrown and large missiles generated
F5	419–512 km/h (261–318 mi/h)	**Incredible Damage** Strong frame houses leveled off foundations and swept away; automobile-sized missiles fly through the air in excess of 100 meters (109 yds); trees debarked; incredible phenomena will occur

Geologic Time Scale

Eon	Era		Period	MYA* *Millions of years ago	Epoch
Phanerozoic	Cenozoic "Age of Mammals"		Quaternary	0.01 (10,000 yrs)	Holocene or Rece
				2	Pleistocene
		Tertiary	Neogene	5	Pliocene
				24	Miocene
			Paleogene	34	Oligocene
				55	Eocene
				65	Paleocene
	Mesozoic "Age of Reptiles"		Cretaceous	144	
			Jurassic	206	
			Triassic	248	
	Paleozoic "Age of Invertebrates"		Permian	290	
		Carboniferous	Pennsylvanian	323	
			Mississippian	354	
			Devonian	417	
			Silurian	443	
			Ordovician	490	
			Cambrian	543	
Proterozoic				2,500	
Archean				3,800?	

APPENDIX

MYA	Life	North American Rock Record
0.01 (10,000 yrs)	Humans dominant. Domestic animal species develop.	West Coast uplift continues in U.S.; Great Lakes form.
2	Hominids develop. Elephants flourish in North America, then die out.	Ice Age. Raising of mountains and plateaus in western U.S.
5	Hominids appear. Modern horse, camel, elephant develop. Sequoias decline; tropical trees driven south.	North America joined to South America. Sierras and Appalachians re-elevated by isostatic rebound.
24	Horse migrates to Asia, elephant to America. Grasses, grazing animals thrive.	North America joined to Asia. Volcanism in northwestern U.S., Columbia Plateau.
34	Mammals progress. Cats and dogs develop and diverge. Elephants in Africa.	Volcanism in western U.S. as Alps and Himalayas forming.
55	Pygmy ancestors of modern horse, other mammals. First whales. Diatoms, flowering plants thrive.	Coal forming in western U.S.
65	Many new mammals appear.	Uplift in western U.S. continues.
144	Dinosaurs, ammonites die out. Mammals, birds show new adaptations. Flowering plants, hardwoods rise.	Uplift of Rockies begins. Colorado Plateau raised. Coal swamps in western U.S. Intrusion of Sierra Nevada batholith.
206	Giant dinosaurs. First birds. Conifers and cycads abundant. Earliest mammals.	West-central North America under huge sea. Gulf of Mexico, Atlantic Ocean begin to form.
248	Reptiles thrive. Forests of conifers and cycads.	Volcanism and faulting along East Coast. Palisades of the Hudson River formed.
290	Mass extinction of existing species. Trilobites, seed ferns, scale trees die out. Corals abundant.	Final uplift in Appalachians. Salt-forming deserts in western U.S. while an ice age in South America.
323	First reptiles. Many giant insects. Spore-bearing plants, amphibians flourish.	Great coal-forming swamps in North America (and Europe).
354	Sharks, amphibians, and crinoids flourish. Seed ferns, conifers abundant.	Extensive submergence of continents.
417	First amphibians; fishes abound. First forests.	Mountain building continues in New England and Canada. White Mountains raised.
443	First land plants and animals (spiders, scorpions). Fishes develop; marine invertebrates thrive.	Salt and gypsum deserts forming in eastern U.S.
490	Marine invertebrates thrive: mollusks, trilobites, graptolites.	Beginning of Appalachian mountain building. Taconic and Green Mountains form. Half of North America submerged.
543	First vertebrates (fish). Many marine invertebrates (first trilobites, shelled animals). Many seaweeds.	Extensive deposition of sediments in inland seas.
2,500	No life on land. Simple marine organisms (algae, fungi, worms). Stromatolites dominant. Other life probably existed, but fossil evidence is lacking.	Great volcanic activity, lava flows, metamorphism of rocks. Formation of iron, copper, and nickel ores.
3,800?		Formation of Earth's crust.

APPENDIX

Properties of Rocks and Earth's Interior

Scheme for Sedimentary Rock Identification

TEXTURE	GRAIN SIZE	COMPOSITION	COMMENTS	ROCK NAME	MAP SYMBOL
Clastic (fragmental)	Pebbles, cobbles, and/or boulders embedded in sand, silt, and/or clay	Mostly quartz, feldspar, and clay minerals; may contain fragments of other rocks and minerals	Rounded fragments	Conglomerate	
			Angular fragments	Breccia	
	Sand (0.2 to 0.006 cm)		Fine to coarse	Sandstone	
	Silt (0.006 to 0.0004 cm)		Very fine grain	Siltstone	
	Clay (less than 0.0004 cm)		Compact; may split easily	Shale	

CHEMICALLY AND/OR ORGANICALLY FORMED SEDIMENTARY ROCKS

TEXTURE	GRAIN SIZE	COMPOSITION	COMMENTS	ROCK NAME	MAP SYMBOL
Crystalline	Varied	Halite	Crystals from chemical precipitates and evaporites	Rock Salt	
	Varied	Gypsum		Rock Gypsum	
	Varied	Dolomite		Dolostone	
Bioclastic	Microscopic to coarse	Calcite	Cemented shell fragments or precipitates of biologic origin	Limestone	
	Varied	Carbon	From plant remains	Coal	

Scheme for Metamorphic Rock Identification

TEXTURE		GRAIN SIZE	COMPOSITION	TYPE OF METAMORPHISM	COMMENTS	ROCK NAME	MAP SYMBOL
FOLIATED	MINERAL ALIGNMENT	Fine	MICA, QUARTZ, FELDSPAR, AMPHIBOLE, GARNET, PYROXENE	Regional	Low-grade metamorphism of shale	Slate	
		Fine to medium		(Heat and pressure increase with depth)	Foliation surfaces shiny from microscopic mica crystals	Phyllite	
					Platy mica crystals visible from metamorphism of clay or feldspars	Schist	
	BAND-ING	Medium to coarse			High-grade metamorphism; some mica changed to feldspar; segregated by mineral type into bands	Gneiss	
NONFOLIATED		Fine	Variable	Contact (Heat)	Various rocks changed by heat from nearby magma/lava	Hornfels	
		Fine to coarse	Quartz	Regional or Contact	Metamorphism of quartz sandstone	Quartzite	
			Calcite and/or dolomite		Metamorphism of limestone or dolostone	Marble	
		Coarse	Various minerals in particles and matrix		Pebbles may be distorted or stretched	Metaconglomerate	

APPENDIX

Scheme for Igneous Rock Identification

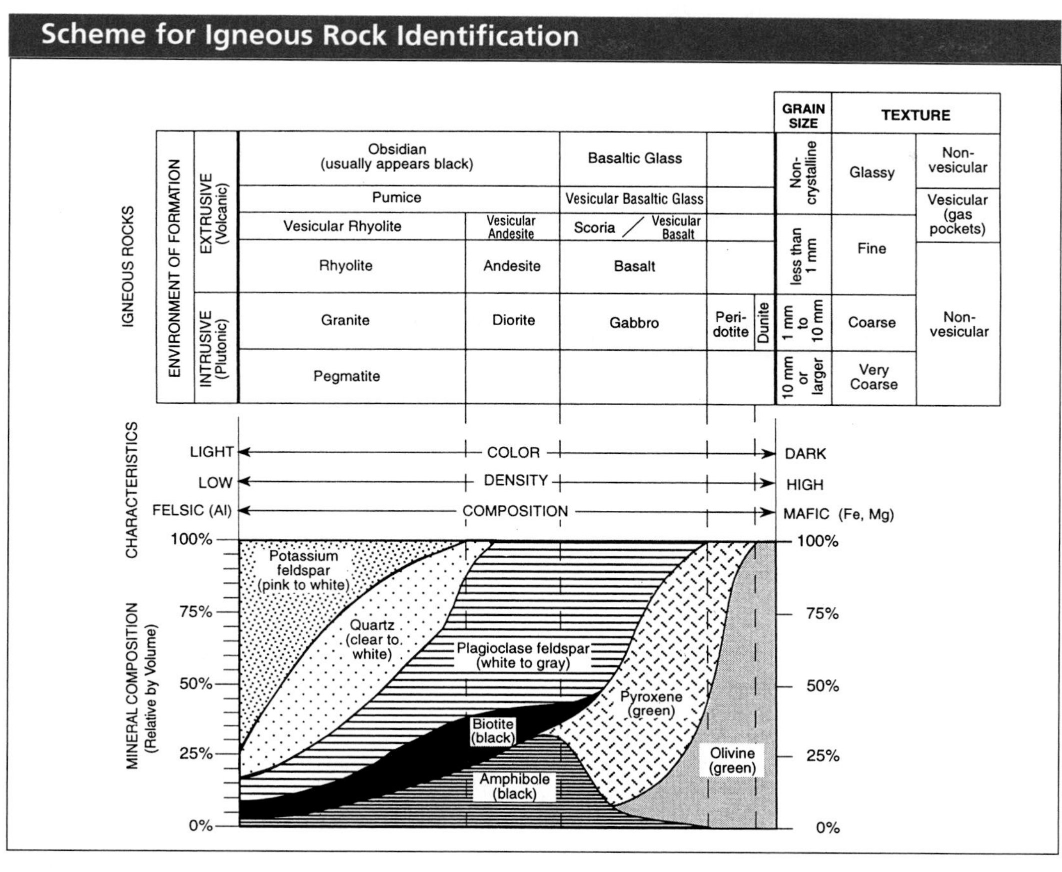

GRAIN SIZE
TEXTURE
IGNEOUS ROCKS
ENVIRONMENT OF FORMATION
EXTRUSIVE (Volcanic)
INTRUSIVE (Plutonic)
Obsidian (usually appears black)
Basaltic Glass
Pumice
Vesicular Basaltic Glass
Vesicular Rhyolite
Vesicular Andesite
Scoria / Vesicular Basalt
Rhyolite
Andesite
Basalt
Granite
Diorite
Gabbro
Peri-dotite
Dunite
Pegmatite
Non-crystalline
less than 1 mm
1 mm to 10 mm
10 mm or larger
Glassy
Fine
Coarse
Very Coarse
Non-vesicular
Vesicular (gas pockets)
Non-vesicular
CHARACTERISTICS
LIGHT
COLOR
DARK
LOW
DENSITY
HIGH
FELSIC (Al)
COMPOSITION
MAFIC (Fe, Mg)
MINERAL COMPOSITION (Relative by Volume)
100%
75%
50%
25%
0%
Potassium feldspar (pink to white)
Quartz (clear to white)
Plagioclase feldspar (white to gray)
Biotite (black)
Amphibole (black)
Pyroxene (green)
Olivine (green)

Inferred Properties of Earth's Interior

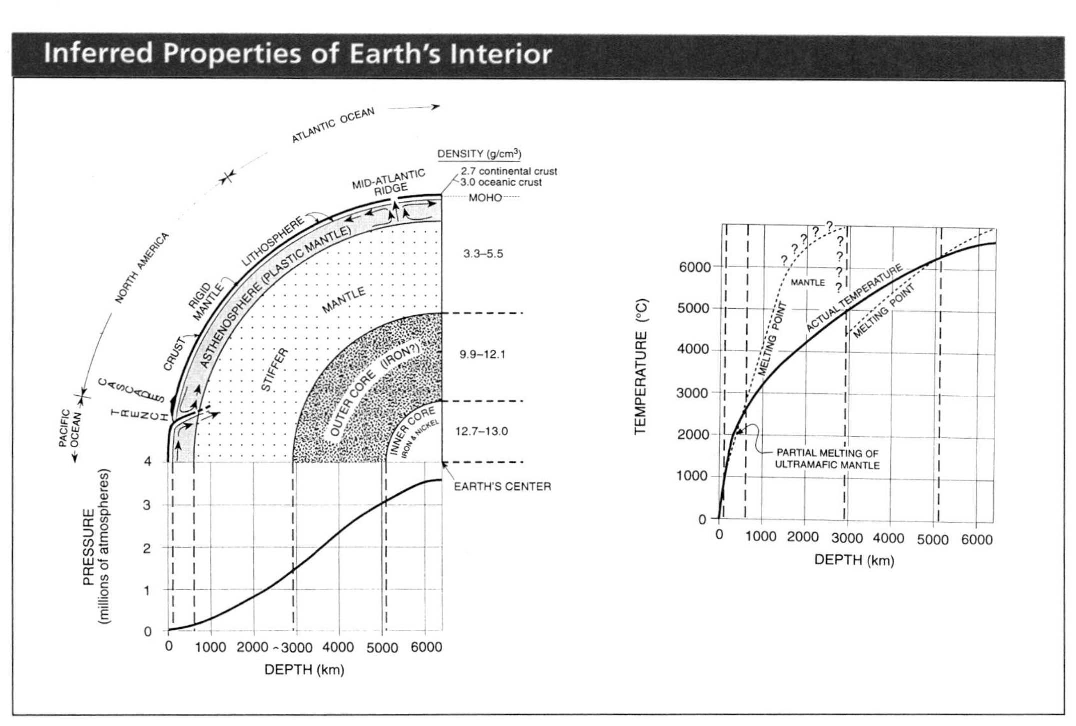

APPENDIX

Properties of Common Minerals

In this table, minerals are arranged alphabetically, and the most useful properties for identification are printed in *italic* type. Most minerals can be identified by means of two or three of the properties listed below. For some minerals, density is important; for others, cleavage is characteristic; and for others, the crystal shapes identify the minerals. The colors listed are the most common for each mineral.

Name	Hardness	Color	Streak	Cleavage	Remarks
Apatite	5	Green, brown	White	Poor in one direction	Nonmetallic (glassy) luster. Sp. gr. 3.1 to 3.2.
Augite	5–6	Dark green to black	Greenish	*Two directions, nearly at 90°*	Nonmetallic (glassy) luster. *Stubby four- or eight-sided crystals.* Common type of pyroxene. Sp. gr. 3.2 to 3.4.
Beryl	7.5–8	*Bluish-green, yellow, pink, colorless*	White	Imperfect in one direction	Nonmetallic (glassy) luster. *Hardness, greenish color, six-sided crystals.* Aquamarine and emerald are gem varieties. Sp. gr. 2.6 to 2.8.
Biotite mica	2.5–3	Black, brown, dark green	White	*Perfect in one direction*	Nonmetallic (glassy) luster. *Thin elastic films peel off easily.* Sp. gr. 2.8 to 3.2.
Calcite	*3*	White, colorless	White	*Perfect, three directions, not at 90° angles*	Nonmetallic (glassy to dull) luster. *Fizzes in dilute hydrochloric acid.* Sp. gr. 2.7.
Chalcopyrite	3.5–4	*Golden yellow*	Greenish black	Poor in one direction	Metallic luster. *Hardness distinguishes from pyrite.* Sp. gr. 4.1 to 4.3.
Chlorite	2–2.5	*Greenish*	Pale green to gray or brown	Perfect in one direction	Nonmetallic (glassy to pearly) luster. *Nonelastic flakes.* Sp. gr. 2.6 to 3.3.
Copper	2.5–3	*Copper red*	Copper	None	*Metallic luster on fresh surface. Dense.* Sp. gr. 8.9.
Corundum	9	Brown, pink, blue	White	None, parting resembles cleavage	Nonmetallic (glassy to brilliant) luster. *Barrel-shaped, six-sided crystals with flat ends.* Sp. gr. 4.0.
Diamond	10	Colorless to pale yellow	White	Perfect, four directions	Nonmetallic (brilliant to greasy) luster. *Hardest of all minerals.* Sp. gr. 3.5.

Sp. gr. = specific gravity

APPENDIX

Name	Hardness	Color	Streak	Cleavage	Remarks
Dolomite	3.5–4	Pinkish, colorless, white	White	*Perfect, three directions, not at 90° angles*	Nonmetallic luster. *Scratched surface fizzes in dilute hydrochloric acid. Cleavage surfaces curved. Sp. gr. 2.8 to 2.9.*
Feldspar (Orthoclase)	*6*	*Salmon pink, red,* white, light gray	White	*Good, two directions, 90° intersection*	Nonmetallic (glassy) luster. *Hardness, color, and cleavage taken together are diagnostic.* Sp. gr. 2.6.
Feldspar (Plagioclase)	6	*White to light gray,* can be salmon pink	White	*Good, two directions, about 90°*	Nonmetallic (glassy to pearly) luster. *If striations are visible, they are diagnostic.* Sp. gr. 2.6 to 2.8.
Fluorite	4	Varies	White	*Perfect, four directions*	Nonmetallic (glassy) luster. In cubes or octahedrons as crystals. Sp. gr. 3.2.
Galena	2.5	*Lead gray*	Lead gray	*Perfect, three directions, at 90° angles*	*Metallic luster.* Occurs as crystals and masses. *Dense.* Sp. gr. 7.4 to 7.6.
Gold	2.5–3	*Gold*	Gold	None	Metallic luster. *Dense.* Sp. gr. 15.0 to 19.3.
Graphite	1–2	*Dark gray to black*	Grayish black	*Perfect in one direction*	Metallic or nonmetallic (earthy) luster. *Greasy feel, marks paper.* This is the "lead" in a pencil (mixed with clay). Sp. gr. 2.2.
Gypsum	*2*	Colorless, white, gray, yellowish, reddish	White	*Perfect in one direction*	Nonmetallic (glassy to silky) luster. *Can be scratched easily by a fingernail.* Sp. gr. 2.3.
Halite	2–2.5	Colorless, white	White	*Perfect, three directions, at 90° angles*	Nonmetallic (glassy) luster. *Salty taste.* Sp. gr. 2.2.
Hematite	5–6 (may appear softer)	*Reddish-brown, gray, black*	*Reddish*	None	Metallic or nonmetallic (earthy) luster. *Dense.* Sp. gr. 5.3.
Hornblende	5–6	*Dark green to black*	Brown to gray	*Perfect, two directions at angles of 56° and 124°*	Nonmetallic (glassy to silky) luster. Common type of amphibole. Long, slender, six-sided crystals. Sp. gr. 3.0 to 3.4.
Kaolinite	2	White, gray, yellowish	White	*Perfect in one direction*	Nonmetallic (dull, earthy) luster. Claylike masses. Sp. gr. 2.6.
Limonite group	4–5.5	*Yellow, brown*	*Yellowish brown*	None	Nonmetallic (earthy) luster. Rust stains. Sp. gr. 2.9 to 4.3.
Magnetite	5.5–6.5	*Black*	Black	None	Metallic luster. Occurs as eight-sided crystals and granular masses. *Magnetic. Dense.* Sp. gr. 5.2.

Sp. gr. = specific gravity

APPENDIX

Properties of Common Minerals *continued*

Name	Hardness	Color	Streak	Cleavage	Remarks
Muscovite mica	2–2.5	Colorless in thin films; silvery, yellowish, and greenish in thicker pieces	*White*	Perfect in one direction	Nonmetallic (glassy to pearly) luster. *Thin elastic films peel off readily.* Sp. gr. 2.8 to 2.9.
Olivine	6.5–7	*Yellowish, greenish*	White	*None*	*Nonmetallic (glassy) luster. Granular.* Sp. gr. 3.3 to 4.4.
Opal	5–6.5	Varies	White	None	*Nonmetallic (glassy to pearly) luster. Conchoidal fracture.* Sp. gr. 2.0 to 2.2.
Pyrite	*6–6.5*	*Brass yellow*	Greenish black	None	Metallic luster. *Cubic crystals* and granular masses. *Dense.* Sp. gr. 5.0 to 5.1.
Quartz	*7*	*Colorless, white; varies*	White	None	Nonmetallic (glassy) luster. *Conchoidal fracture. Six-sided crystals common.* Many varieties. Sp. gr. 2.6.
Serpentine	3–5	*Greenish (variegated)*	White	None or good in one direction, depending on variety	*Nonmetallic (greasy, waxy, or silky) luster. Conchoidal fracture.* Sp. gr. 2.5 to 2.6.
Sphalerite	*3.5–4*	*Yellow, brown, black*	Yellow to light brown	*Perfect, six directions*	*Nonmetallic (brilliant to resinous) luster.* Sp. gr. 3.9 to 4.1.
Sulfur	1.5–2.5	*Yellow*	Yellow	Poor, two directions	Nonmetallic (glassy to earthy) luster. Granular. Sp. gr. 2.0 to 2.1.
Talc	*1*	Apple-green, gray, white	White	Perfect in one direction	Nonmetallic (pearly to greasy) luster. Nonelastic flakes, *greasy feel.* Sp. gr. 2.7 to 2.8.
Topaz	*8*	Varies	White	Perfect in one direction	Nonmetallic (brilliant to glassy) luster. *Crystals commonly striated lengthwise.* Sp. gr. 3.4 to 3.6.
Tourmaline	7–7.5	*Black; varies*	White	None	Nonmetallic (glassy) luster. *Crystals often have triangular cross sections. Conchoidal fracture.* Sp. gr. 3.0 to 3.3.

Sp. gr. = specific gravity

Mineral Identification

To identify a mineral, you need to observe its properties—characteristic features that identify it. Usually it is necessary to observe several different properties of a mineral before being able to determine its identity.

Sometimes the shape of a mineral's crystals can help you identify the mineral. The photographs below show examples of well-formed crystals. But although all minerals have an internal crystal structure, crystals with well-formed outer shapes are not particularly common.

As you begin the process of identifying a mineral, you might look at its color. However, many minerals occur in more than one color. You would need to examine other properties as well. Some of these properties are related to the appearance of the mineral, such as how shiny or dull its surface is. Others, such as hardness and density, are related to the mineral's composition and internal structure.

Crystal Groups

Crystal groups are named by their shapes and the angles formed by imaginary lines through their centers. Crystals take many shapes, but all belong to these six groups.

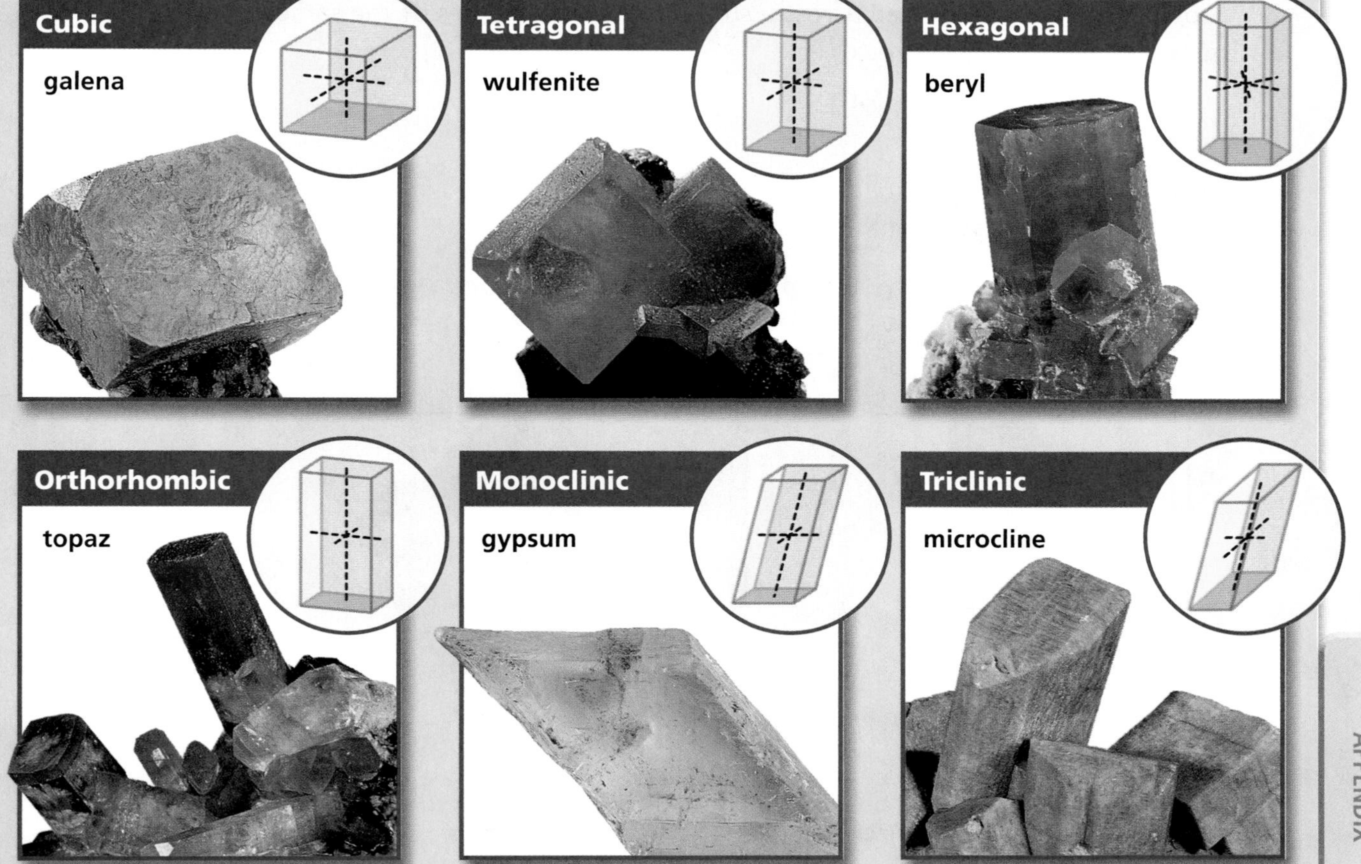

APPENDIX

Color and Streak

Some minerals can be almost any color, but most minerals have a more limited color range. For example, a particular mineral may almost always be brown to black.

Three main factors cause minerals to vary in color. First, a mineral may get its color from tiny amounts of an element that is not part of its normal chemical makeup. For example, a sample of pure quartz is clear and colorless, but tiny amounts of iron can give quartz a violet color. This violet variety of quartz is called amethyst. Second, a mineral's color can change when it is at or near Earth's surface and is in contact with the atmosphere or water. Third, mineral crystals can have defects in their crystal structures that change their color.

Some minerals have a different color when they are ground into a fine powder than when they are left whole. A mineral's streak is the color of the powder left behind when the mineral is scraped across a surface. Geologists use a tile of unglazed porcelain, called a streak plate, as a tool to identify minerals by their streaks. Streak is a better clue to a mineral's identity than surface color is. Look at the photographs of hematite below. Even though the mineral samples are different colors, both leave a reddish brown streak when scraped across a streak plate. All samples of the same mineral have the same streak.

Streak

These samples are of the mineral hematite. They are different colors, but they have the same streak.

This hematite looks dull because it has tiny crystals that reflect light in all directions.

This hematite looks shiny because it has larger crystals.

Luster

A mineral's luster is the way in which light reflects from its surface. The two major types of luster are metallic and nonmetallic. The mineral pyrite has a metallic luster. It looks as if it were made of metal. A mineral with a nonmetallic luster can be shiny, but it does not appear to be made of metal. An example of a nonmetallic luster is the glassy luster of garnet. Compare the lusters of pyrite and garnet in the photographs below.

Pyrite has a metallic luster.

Garnet crystals in this rock have a nonmetallic luster.

Like a mineral's color, its luster may vary from sample to sample. If a mineral has been exposed to the atmosphere or to water, its surface luster can become dull. However, if the mineral is broken to reveal a fresh surface, its characteristic luster can be seen.

The way a mineral breaks helps identify it.

If you hit a piece of calcite with a hammer, the calcite will break into tilted blocks. You can peel off layers of mica because it splits into thin, flat sheets. Each kind of mineral always breaks in the same way, and this property can help identify a mineral. In fact, the way a mineral breaks is a better clue to its identity than are its color and luster.

Cleavage

Cleavage is a tendency to break along flat surfaces.

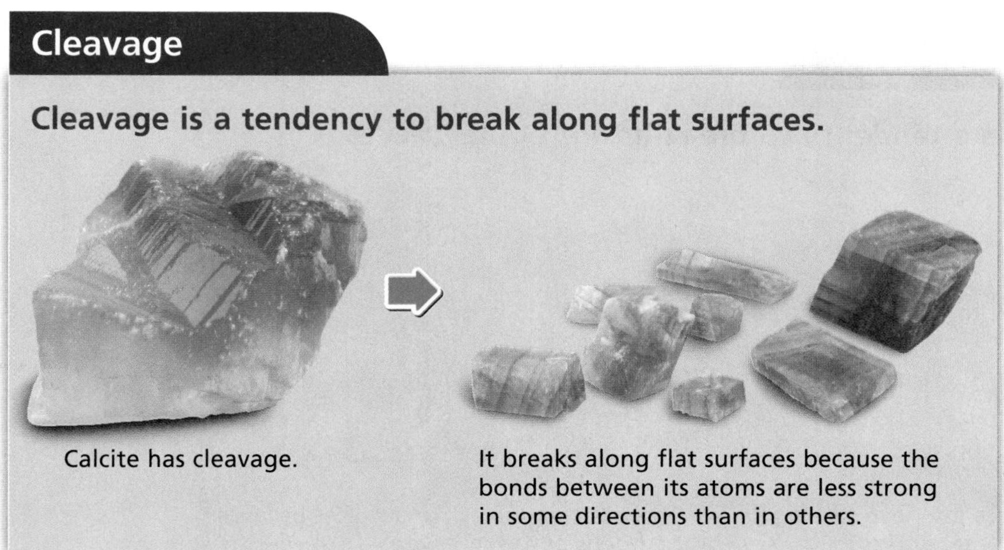

Calcite has cleavage.

It breaks along flat surfaces because the bonds between its atoms are less strong in some directions than in others.

Cleavage

Cleavage is the tendency of a mineral to break along flat surfaces. The way in which a mineral breaks depends on how its atoms are bonded, or joined together. In a mineral that displays cleavage, the bonds of the crystal structure are weaker in the directions in which the mineral breaks.

Carbon Bonds in Graphite

strong bonds within layers

weak bonds between layers

carbon atoms

In graphite, carbon atoms are arranged in layers. Graphite has cleavage because the weak bonds between the layers break easily.

When geologists describe the cleavage of a mineral, they consider both the directions in which the mineral breaks and the smoothness of the broken surfaces. Mica has cleavage in one direction and breaks into sheets. The photographs on page R71 show that calcite has cleavage in three directions and breaks into tilted blocks. Because the broken surfaces of both mica and calcite are smooth, these minerals are said to have perfect cleavage.

Fracture

Fracture is the tendency of a mineral to break into irregular pieces. Some minerals such as quartz break into pieces with curved surfaces, as shown below. Other minerals may break differently—perhaps into splinters or into rough or jagged pieces.

In a mineral that displays fracture, the bonds that join the atoms are fairly equal in strength in all directions. The mineral does not break along flat surfaces because there are no particular directions of weakness in its crystal structure.

Fracture

Fracture is a tendency to break into irregular pieces.

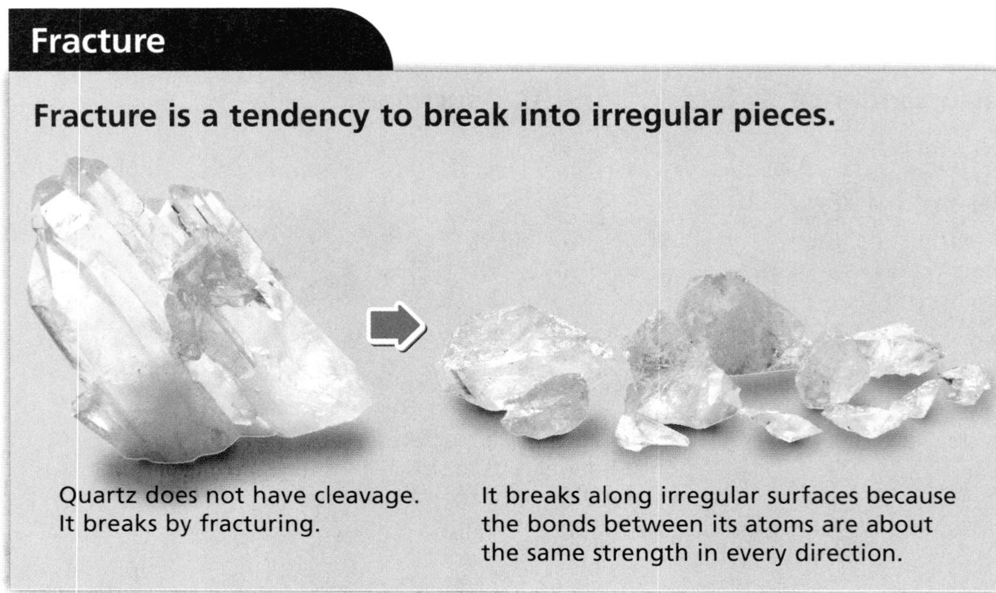

Quartz does not have cleavage. It breaks by fracturing.

It breaks along irregular surfaces because the bonds between its atoms are about the same strength in every direction.

APPENDIX

A mineral's density and hardness help identify it.

A tennis ball is not as heavy or as hard as a baseball. You would be able to tell the two apart even with your eyes closed by how heavy and hard they feel. You can identify minerals in a similar way.

Density

Even though a baseball and a tennis ball are about the same size, the baseball has more mass and so is more dense. A substance's density is the amount of mass in a given volume of the substance. For example, 1 cubic centimeter of the mineral pyrite has a mass of 5.1 grams, so pyrite's density is 5.1 grams per cubic centimeter.

Density is very helpful in identifying minerals. For example, gold and pyrite look very similar. Pyrite is often called fool's gold. However, you can tell the two minerals apart by comparing their densities. Gold is much denser than pyrite. The mass of a piece of gold is almost four times the mass of a piece of pyrite of the same size. A small amount of a very dense mineral, such as gold, can have more mass and be heavier than a larger amount of a less dense mineral, such as pyrite. A mineral's density is determined by the kinds of atoms that make up the mineral, as well as how closely the atoms are joined together. An experienced geologist can estimate the density of a mineral by lifting it. But to get an exact measurement, geologists use special scales.

Comparing Densities

Differences in density can be used to tell minerals apart.

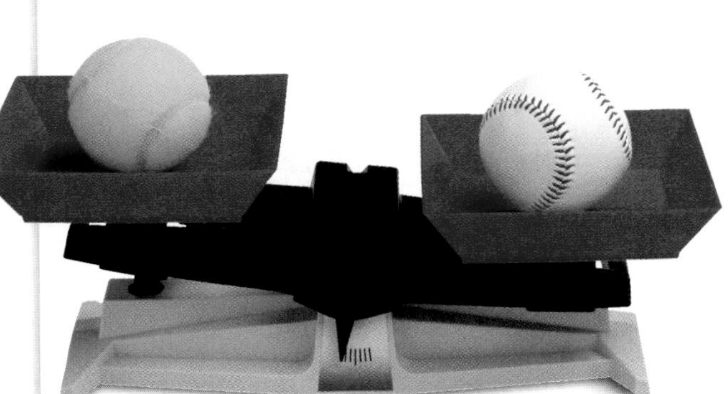

The baseball on the right has more mass, and so is denser, than a tennis ball that is about the same size.

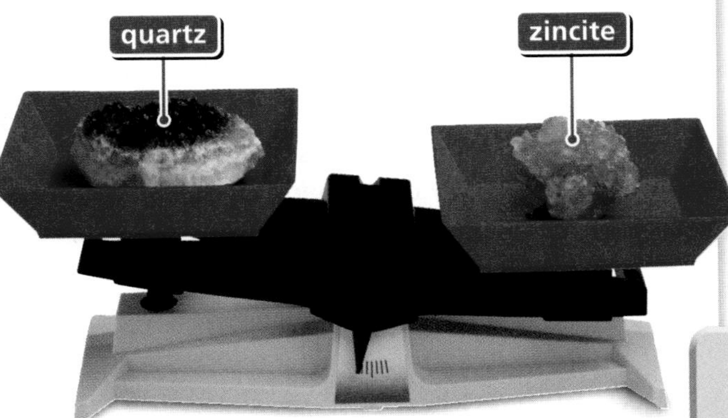

The zincite sample on the right is about twice as dense as the quartz sample.

APPENDIX

Hardness

One way to tell a tennis ball from a baseball without looking at them is to compare their densities. Another way is to test which one is harder. Hardness is another dependable clue to a mineral's identity.

A mineral's hardness is its resistance to being scratched. Like a mineral's cleavage, a mineral's hardness is determined by its crystal structure and the strength of the bonds between its atoms. Harder minerals have stronger bonds.

A scale known as the Mohs scale is often used to describe a mineral's hardness. This scale is based on the fact that a harder mineral will scratch a softer one. As you can see in the chart at the right, ten minerals are numbered in the scale, from softest to hardest. Talc is the softest mineral and has a value of 1. Diamond, the hardest of all minerals, has a value of 10.

A mineral can be scratched only by other minerals that have the same hardness or are harder. To determine the hardness of an unknown mineral, you test whether it scratches or is scratched by the minerals in the scale. For example, if you can scratch an unknown mineral with apatite but not with fluorite, the mineral's hardness is between 4 and 5 in the Mohs scale.

In place of minerals, you can use your fingernail, a copper penny, and a steel file to test an unknown mineral. To avoid damage to the minerals, you can test whether the mineral scratches these items. When using a penny to test hardness, make sure its date is 1982 or earlier. Only older pennies are made mainly of copper, which has a hardness of about 3.

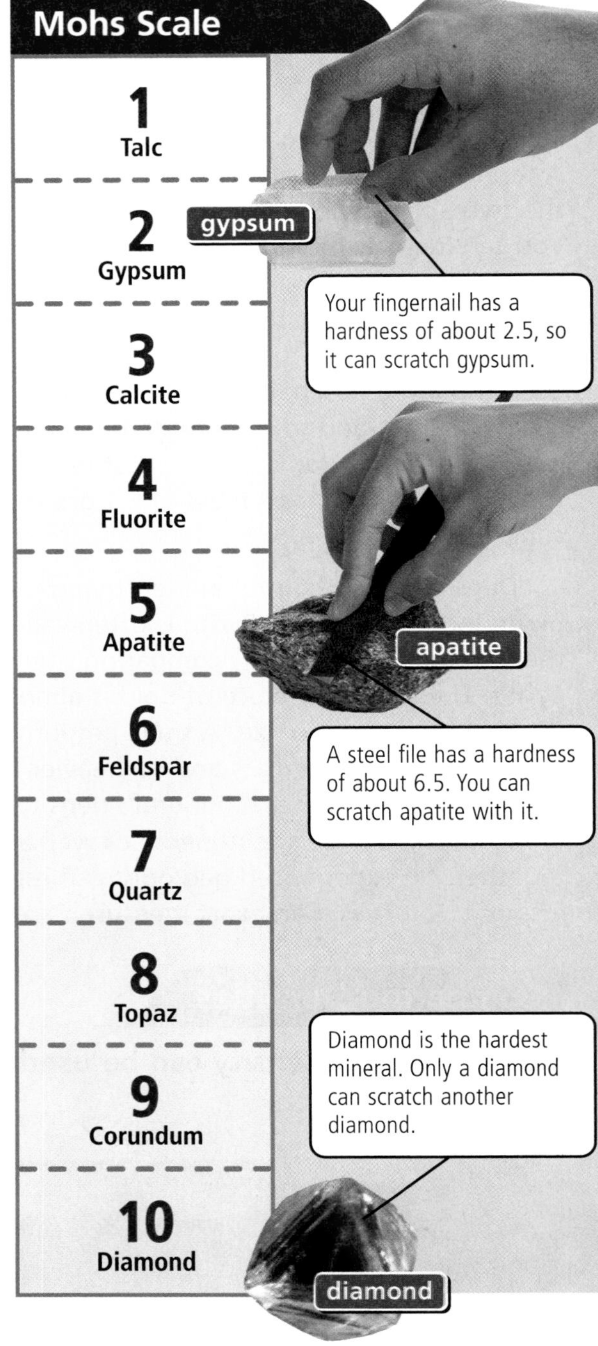
Mohs Scale
1 Talc
2 Gypsum
3 Calcite
4 Fluorite
5 Apatite
6 Feldspar
7 Quartz
8 Topaz
9 Corundum
10 Diamond
gypsum
Your fingernail has a hardness of about 2.5, so it can scratch gypsum.
apatite
A steel file has a hardness of about 6.5. You can scratch apatite with it.
Diamond is the hardest mineral. Only a diamond can scratch another diamond.
diamond

APPENDIX

R74

Some minerals have special properties.

The photographs below show tests that help identify minerals that have unusual properties. Minerals in the carbonate group, such as calcite, react with acid. Chalk is a familiar item that is made up of carbonate minerals. The test consists of putting a drop of a weak solution of hydrochloric acid on a mineral sample. If the acid reacts with the mineral, carbon dioxide gas will form and bubble out of the acid. The bubbles show that the mineral is a carbonate.

Some minerals have a property known as fluorescence (flu-REHS-uhns). Fluorescent minerals glow when they are exposed to ultraviolet (UHL-truh-VY-uh-liht) light. The word *fluorescence* comes from the name of the mineral fluorite, which has this property. Other minerals that display fluorescence include calcite and willemite. Although fluorescence is an interesting and sometimes dramatic property, it has limited value in mineral identification. Different samples of the same mineral may or may not display fluorescence, and they may glow in different colors.

A few minerals respond to magnets. A magnet is pulled toward these minerals. The mineral magnetite strongly attracts magnets, and some other minerals weakly attract magnets. To test a mineral, hold a magnet loosely and bring it close to the mineral. You will be able to notice if there is even a small pull of the magnet toward the mineral. Magnets are commonly used in laboratories and industries to separate magnetic minerals from other minerals.

Some rare minerals have a property known as radioactivity. They contain unstable elements that change into other elements over time. As this happens, they release energy. Geologists can measure this energy and use it to identify minerals that contain unstable elements.

Special Properties

Acid Test

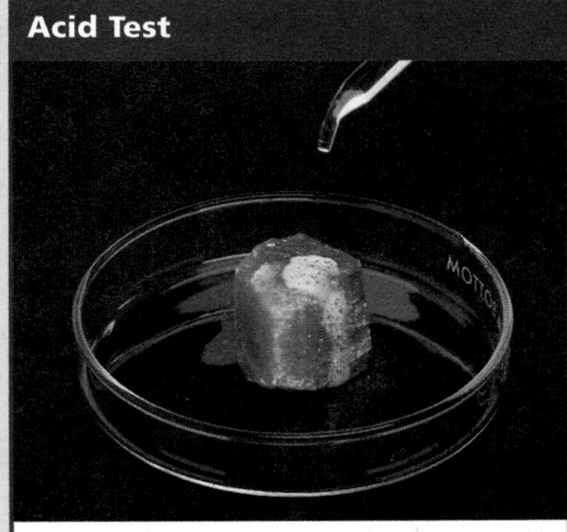

Acid in contact with carbonate minerals, such as calcite, forms bubbles.

Fluorescence

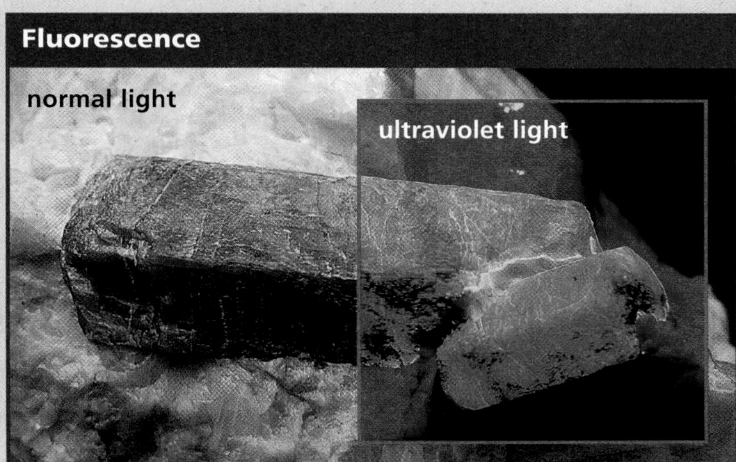

These minerals look ordinary in normal light but display red and green fluorescence under ultraviolet light.

APPENDIX

Topographic Map Symbols

The U.S. Geological Survey uses the following symbols to mark human-made and natural features on all of the topographic maps the USGS produces.

Primary highway, hard surface
Secondary highway, hard surface
Light-duty road, hard or improved surface
Unimproved road
Trail
Railroad: single track
Railroad: multiple track
Bridge
Drawbridge
Tunnel
Footbridge
Overpass—Underpass
Power transmission line with located tower
Landmark line (labeled as to type) TELEPHONE

Dam with lock
Canal with lock
Large dam
Small dam: masonry—earth
Buildings (dwelling, place of employment, etc.)
School—Church—Cemeteries Cem
Buildings (barn, warehouse, etc.)
Tanks; oil, water, etc. (labeled only if water) Water Tank
Wells other than water (labeled as to type) Oil Gas
U.S. mineral or location monument—Prospect
Quarry—Gravel pit
Mine shaft—Tunnel or cave entrance
Campsite—Picnic area
Located or landmark object—Windmill
Exposed wreck
Rock or coral reef
Foreshore flat
Rock: bare or awash

Benchmarks BM ×671 ×672
Road fork—Section corner with elevation 429 + 58
Checked spot elevation × 5970
Unchecked spot elevation × 5970

Source: U.S. Geological Survey

Boundary: national
State
county, parish, municipio
civil township, precinct, town, barrio
incorporated city, village, town, hamlet
reservation, national or state
small park, cemetery, airport, etc.
land grant
Township or range line, U.S. land survey
Section line, U.S. land survey
Township line, not U.S. land survey
Section line, not U.S. land survey
Fence line or field line
Section corner: found—indicated
Boundary monument: land grant—other

Index contour
Intermediate contour
Supplementary cont
Depression contours
Cut—Fill
Levee
Mine dump
Large wash
Dune area
Distorted surface
Sand area
Gravel beach

Glacier
Intermittent streams
Seasonal streams
Aqueduct tunnel
Water well—Spring
Falls
Rapids
Intermittent lake
Channel
Small wash
Sounding—Depth curve 10
Marsh (swamp)
Land subject to controlled flooding
Dry lake bed

Woodland
Mangrove
Submerged marsh
Scrub
Orchard
Wooded marsh
Vineyard
Many buildings
Areas revised since previous edition

APPENDIX

Time Zones

Because Earth rotates, noon can occur in one location at the same moment that the Sun is setting in another location. To avoid confusion in transportation and communication, officials have divided Earth into 24 time zones. Within a time zone, clocks are set to the same time of day.

Time zones are centered on lines of longitude, but instead of running straight, their boundaries often follow political boundaries. The starting point for the times zones is centered on the prime meridian (0°). The time in this zone is generally called Greenwich Mean Time (GMT), but it is also called Universal Time (UT) by astronomers and Zulu Time (Z) by meteorologists. The International Date Line is centered on 180° longitude. The calendar date to the east of this line is one day earlier than the date to the west.

In the map below, each column of color represents one time zone. The color beige shows areas that do not match standard zones. The labels at the top show the times at noon GMT. Positive and negative numbers at the bottom show the difference between the local time in the zone and Greenwich Mean Time.

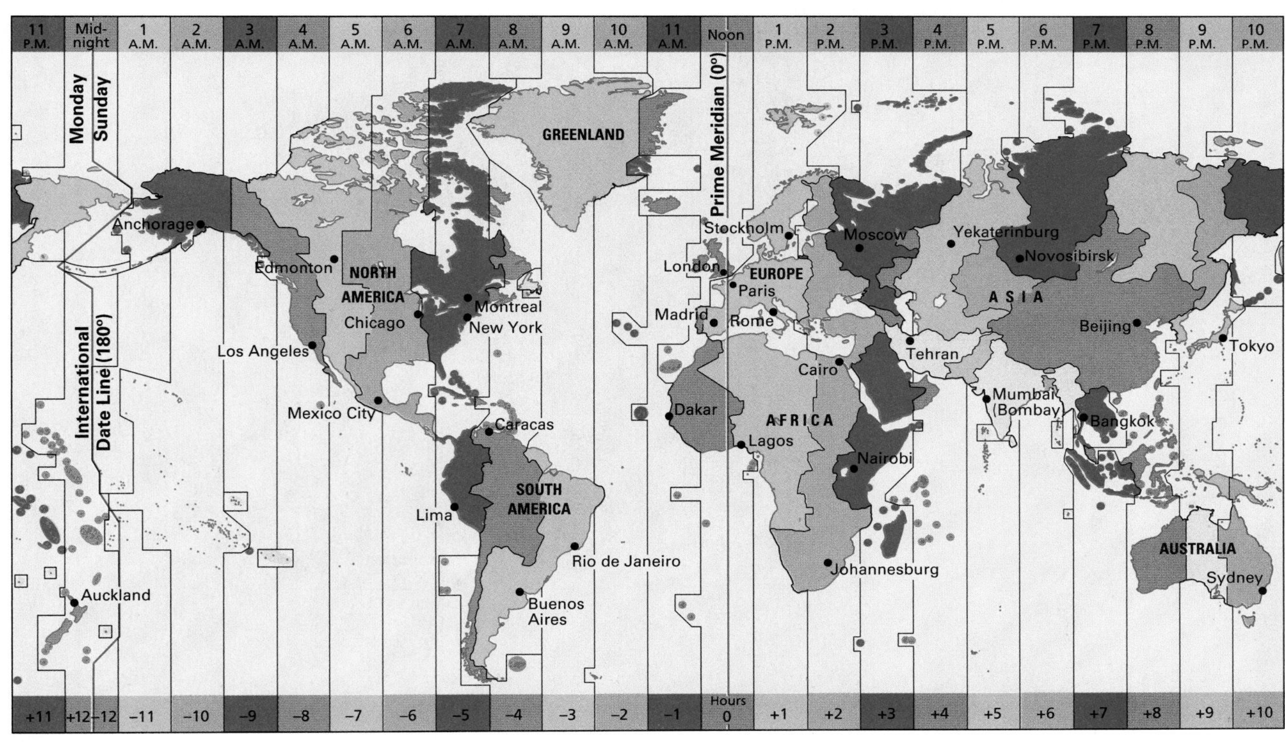

APPENDIX

California Physical Map

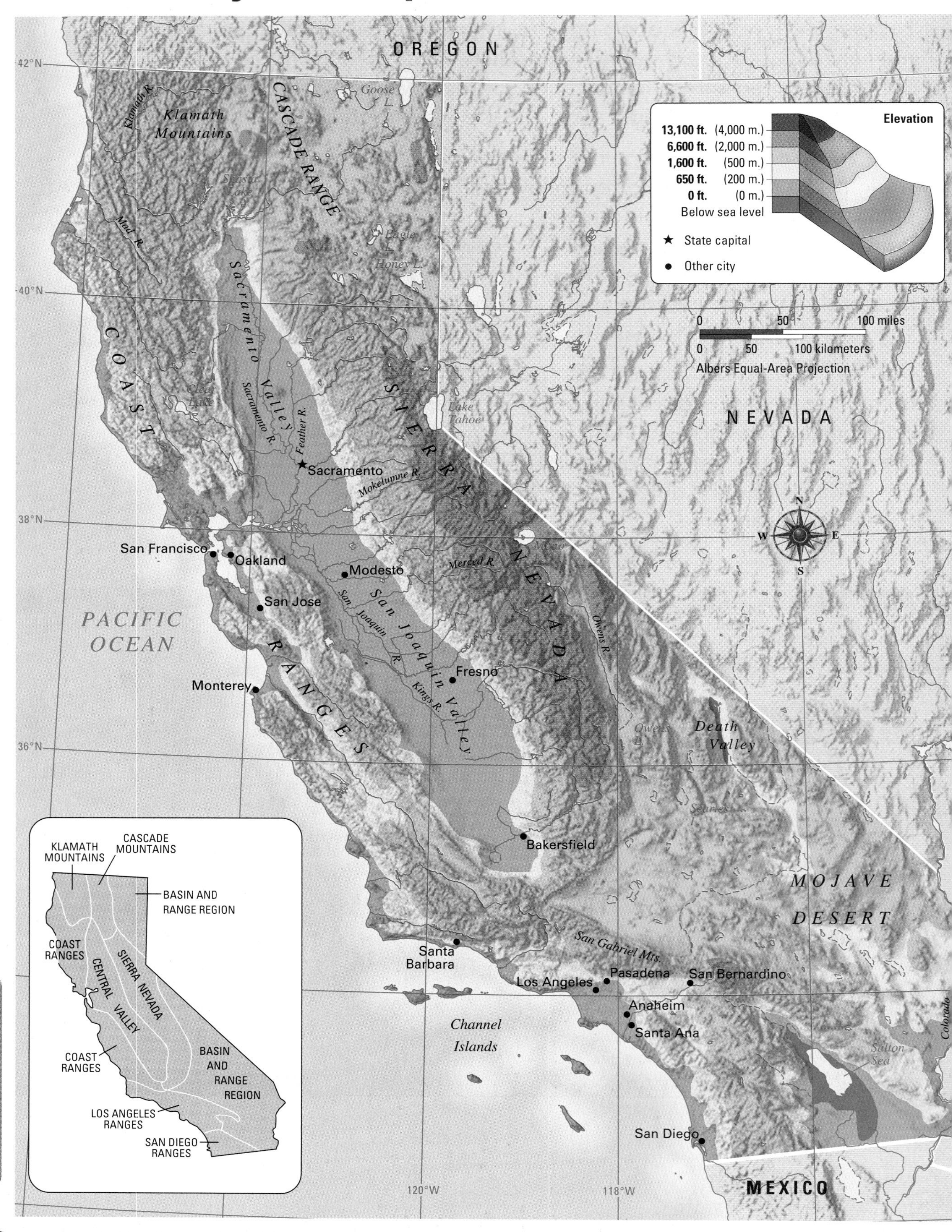

OREGON
NEVADA
MEXICO
42°N
40°N
38°N
36°N
120°W
118°W
Klamath R.
Klamath Mountains
CASCADE RANGE
Goose L.
Shasta Lake
Eagle L.
Honey L.
Mad R.
Sacramento Valley
Sacramento R.
Feather R.
Clear Lake
COAST RANGES
SIERRA NEVADA
Lake Tahoe
Sacramento
Mokelumne R.
Mono L.
Merced R.
San Francisco
Oakland
Modesto
San Jose
San Joaquin R.
San Joaquin Valley
Owens R.
PACIFIC OCEAN
Fresno
Kings R.
Monterey
Owens L.
Death Valley
Searles L.
Bakersfield
MOJAVE DESERT
San Gabriel Mts.
Santa Barbara
Los Angeles
Pasadena
San Bernardino
Anaheim
Santa Ana
Channel Islands
Colorado
Salton Sea
San Diego
Elevation
13,100 ft. (4,000 m.)
6,600 ft. (2,000 m.)
1,600 ft. (500 m.)
650 ft. (200 m.)
0 ft. (0 m.)
Below sea level
★ State capital
● Other city
0 50 100 miles
0 50 100 kilometers
Albers Equal-Area Projection
N
S
E
W
KLAMATH MOUNTAINS
CASCADE MOUNTAINS
BASIN AND RANGE REGION
COAST RANGES
SIERRA NEVADA
CENTRAL VALLEY
COAST RANGES
BASIN AND RANGE REGION
LOS ANGELES RANGES
SAN DIEGO RANGES

APPENDIX

Glossary

A

abiotic factor (AY-by-AHT-ihk)
A nonliving physical or chemical part of an ecosystem. (p. 378)

factor abiótico Una parte física o química sin vida de un ecosistema.

acid rain
Rain that has become more 'acidic' than normal due to pollution. (pp. 106, 360)

lluvia ácida Lluvia que se ha vuelto más ácida de lo normal debido a la contaminación.

adaptation
A characteristic, a behavior, or any inherited trait that makes a species able to survive and reproduce in a particular environment. (p. CA17)

adaptación Una característica, un comportamiento o cualquier rasgo heredado que permite a una especie sobrevivir o reproducirse en un medio ambiente determinado.

aftershock
A smaller earthquake that follows a more powerful earthquake in the same area. (p. 318)

réplica Un terremoto más pequeño que ocurre después de uno más poderoso en la misma área.

air mass
A large volume of air that has nearly the same temperature and humidity at different locations at the same altitude. (p. 115)

masa de aire Un gran volumen de aire que tiene casi la misma temperatura y humedad en distintos puntos a la misma altitud.

air pressure
The force of air molecules pushing on an area. (p. 79)

presión de aire La fuerza de las moléculas de aire empujando sobre un área.

alluvial fan (uh-LOO-vee-uhl)
A fan-shaped deposit of sediment at the base of a slope, formed as water flows down the slope and spreads out at the bottom. (p. 233)

abanico aluvial Un depósito de sedimentos en forma de abanico situado en la base de una pendiente; se forma cuando el agua baja por la pendiente y se dispersa al llegar al pie de la misma.

altitude
The distance above sea level.

altitud La distancia sobre el nivel del mar.

asthenosphere (as-THEHN-uh-SFEER)
The layer in Earth's upper mantle and directly under the lithosphere in which rock is soft and weak because it is close to melting. (p. 267)

astenosfera La capa del manto superior de la Tierra situada directamente bajo la litosfera en la cual la roca es blanda y débil por encontrarse próxima a su punto de fusión.

atmosphere (AT-muh-SFEER)
The outer layer of gases of a large body in space, such as a planet or star; the mixture of gases that surrounds the solid Earth; one of the four parts of the Earth system. (p. CA15)

atmósfera La capa externa de gases de un gran cuerpo que se encuentra en el espacio, como un planeta o una estrella; la mezcla de gases que rodea la Tierra sólida; una de las cuatro partes del sistema terrestre.

atom
The smallest particle of an element that has the chemical properties of that element. (p. CA19)

átomo La partícula más pequeña de un elemento que tiene las propiedades químicas de ese elemento.

axis
An imaginary line about which a turning body, such as Earth, rotates. (pp. 52, 684)

eje Una línea imaginaria alrededor de la cual gira un cuerpo, como lo hace la Tierra.

B

barometer
An instrument that measures air pressure in the atmosphere. (p. 82)

barómetro Un instrumento que mide la presión del aire en la atmósfera.

GLOSSARY

barrier island
A long, narrow island that develops parallel to a coast as a sandbar builds up above the water's surface. (p. 240)

isla barrera Una isla larga y angosta que se desarrolla paralelamente a la costa al crecer una barra de arena hasta rebasar la superficie del agua.

biodiversity
The number and variety of living things found on Earth or within an ecosystem. (p. 498)

biodiversidad La cantidad y variedad de organismos vivos que se encuentran en la Tierra o dentro de un ecosistema.

biomass
Organic matter that contains stored energy from sunlight and that can be burned as fuel. (p. 476)

biomasa Materia orgánica que contiene energía almacenada proveniente de la luz del Sol y que puede ser usada como combustible.

biome (BY-OHM)
A region of Earth that has a particular climate and certain types of plants. Examples are tundra, taiga, desert, grassland, temperate forest, and tropical forest. (p. 398)

bioma Una región de la Tierra que tiene un clima particular y ciertos tipos de plantas. La tundra, la taiga, el desierto, la estepa, la selva tropical y el bosque templado son ejemplos de biomas.

biosphere (BY-uh-SFEER)
All living organisms on Earth in the air, on the land, and in the waters; one of the four parts of the Earth system. (p. CA15)

biosfera Todos los organismos vivos de la Tierra, en el aire, en la tierra y en las aguas; una de las cuatro partes del sistema de la Tierra.

biotic factor (by-AHT-ihk)
A living thing in an ecosystem. (p. 378)

factor biótico Un organismo vivo en un ecosistema.

blizzard
A blinding snowstorm with winds of at least 56 kilometers per hour (35 mi/h), usually with temperatures below –7°C (20°F). (p. 126)

ventisca Una cegadora tormenta de nieve con vientos de por lo menos 56 kilómetros por hora (35 mi/h), usualmente con temperaturas menores a –7°C (20°F).

carbon cycle
The continuous movement of carbon through Earth, its atmosphere, and the living things on Earth. (p. 386)

ciclo del carbono El movimiento continuo del carbono en la Tierra, su atmósfera y todos los seres vivos en ella.

carrying capacity
The maximum sustainable size that a population can reach in an ecosystem. (p. 433)

capacidad de carga El tamaño máximo sostenible que una población puede alcanzar en un ecosistema.

cell
The smallest unit that is able to perform the basic functions of life. (p. CA17)

célula La unidad más pequeña capaz de realizar las funciones básicas de la vida.

chemical weathering
The breakdown or decomposition of rock that takes place when minerals change through chemical processes. (p. 202)

meteorización química La descomposición de las rocas que ocurre cuando los minerales cambian mediante procesos químicos.

climate
The characteristic weather conditions in an area over a long period of time. (p. 65)

clima Las condiciones meteorológicas características de un lugar durante un largo período de tiempo.

commensalism (kuh-MEHN-suh-LIHZ-uhm)
An interaction between two species in which one species benefits without harming the other; a type of symbiosis. (p. 427)

comensalismo Una interacción entre dos especies en la cual una especie se beneficia sin causar daño a la otra; un tipo de simbiosis.

community
All the populations that live and interact with each other in a particular place. The community can live in a place as small as a pond or a park, or it can live in a place as large as a rain forest or the ocean. (p. 416)

comunidad Todas las poblaciones que viven e interactúan entre sí en un lugar. La comunidad puede vivir en un lugar tan pequeño como una laguna o un parque o en un lugar tan grande como un bosque tropical o el océano.

competition
The struggle between two or more living things that depend on the same limited resource. (p. 423)

competencia La lucha entre dos o más organismos vivos que dependen del mismo recurso limitado.

compound
A substance made up of two or more different types of atoms bonded together.

compuesto Una sustancia formada por dos o más diferentes tipos de átomos enlazados.

condensation
The process by which a gas changes into a liquid. (p. 92)

condensación El proceso por el cual un gas se transforma en líquido.

conduction
The process by which energy is transferred from a warmer object to a cooler object by means of physical contact. (p. 27)

conducción El proceso mediante el cual se transfiere energía de un objeto más caliente a un objeto más frío por medio de contacto físico.

coniferous (koh-NIHF-uhr-uhs)
A term used to describe cone-bearing trees and shrubs that usually keep their leaves or needles during all the seasons of the year; examples are pine, fir, and spruce trees. (p. 400)

conífero Un término usado para describir a los árboles y los arbustos que producen conos o piñas y que generalmente conservan sus hojas o agujas durante todas las estaciones del año; el pino, el abeto y la picea son ejemplos de coníferas.

conservation
The process of saving or protecting a natural resource. (p. 467)

conservación El proceso de salvar o proteger un recurso natural.

conservation of energy
A law stating that no matter how energy is transferred or transformed, it continues to exist in one form or another (p. 14)

conservación de la energía Una ley que establece que no importa cómo se transfiere o transforma la energía, toda la energía sigue en alguna forma u otra.

consumer
A living thing that gets its energy by eating other living things in a food chain; consumers are also called heterotrophs. (p. 392)

consumidor Un organismo vivo que obtiene su energía alimentándose de otros organismos vivos en una cadena alimentaria; los consumidores también son llamados heterótrofos.

continental-continental collision
A boundary along which two tectonic plates carrying continental crust push together. (p. 287)

colisión continente-continente Un límite a lo largo del cual dos placas tectónica de corteza continental empujan contra sí.

continental drift
The hypothesis that Earth's continents move on Earth's surface. (p. 270)

deriva continental La hipótesis que postula que los continentes de la Tierra se mueven sobre la superficie del planeta.

contour interval
On a topographic map, the difference in elevation from one contour line to the next. (p. 166)

equidistancia entre curvas de nivel En un mapa topográfico, la diferencia en elevación de una curva de nivel a la siguiente.

contour line
A line on a topographic map that joins points of equal elevation. (p. 165)

curva de nivel Una línea en un mapa topográfico que une puntos de igual elevación.

convection
The transfer of energy from place to place by the motion of heated gas or liquid; in Earth's mantle, convection is thought to transfer energy by the motion of solid rock, which when under great heat and pressure can move like a liquid. (pp. 28, 273)

convección La transferencia de energía de un lugar a otro por el movimiento de un líquido o gas calentado; se piensa que en el manto terrestre la convección transfiere energía mediante el movimiento de roca sólida, la cual puede moverse como un líquido cuando está muy caliente y bajo alta presión.

convection current
A circulation pattern in which material is heated and rises in one area, then cools and sinks in another area, flowing in a continuous loop. (pp. 30, 273)

corriente de convección Un patrón de circulación en el cual el material se calienta y asciende en un área, luego se enfría y se hunde en otra área, fluyendo en un circuito contínuo.

convergent boundary (kuhn-VUR-juhnt)
A boundary along which two tectonic plates push together, characterized either by subduction or a continental collision. (p. 278)

límite convergente Un límite a lo largo del cual dos placas tectónicas se empujan mutuamente; este límite se caracteriza por una zona de subducción o una colisión entre continentes.

GLOSSARY

cooperation
A term used to describe an interaction between two or more living things in which they are said to work together. (p. 425)

cooperación Un término que describe la interacción entre dos or más organismos vivos en la cual se dice que trabajan juntos.

Coriolis effect (KAWR-ee-OH-lihs)
The influence of Earth's rotation on objects that move over Earth. (p. 85)

efecto Coriolis La influencia de la rotación de la Tierra sobre objetos que se mueven sobre la Tierra.

crust
A thin outer layer of rock above a planet's mantle, including all dry land and ocean basins. Earth's continental crust is 40 kilometers thick on average and oceanic crust is 7 kilometers thick on average. (p. 267)

corteza Una delgada capa exterior de roca situada sobre el manto de un planeta que incluye toda la tierra seca y todas las cuencas oceánicas. La corteza continental de la Tierra tiene un grosor promedio de 40 kilómetros y la corteza oceánica tiene un grosor promedio de 7 kilómetros.

crystal
A solid substance in which the atoms are arranged in an orderly, repeating, three-dimensional pattern. (p. 185)

cristal Una sustancia sólida en la cual los átomos están organizados en un patrón tridimensional y ordenado que se repite.

cycle
n. A series of events or actions that repeat themselves regularly; a physical and/or chemical process in which one material continually changes locations and/or forms. Examples include the water cycle, the carbon cycle, and the rock cycle.

v. To move through a repeating series of events or actions. (pp. 44, 384)

ciclo *s.* Una serie de eventos o acciones que se repiten regularmente; un proceso físico y/o químico en el cual un material cambia continuamente de lugar y/o forma. Ejemplos: el ciclo del agua, el ciclo del carbono y el ciclo de las rocas.

data
Information gathered by observation or experimentation that can be used in calculating or reasoning. *Data* is a plural word; the singular is *datum.*

datos Información reunida mediante observación o experimentación y que se puede usar para calcular o para razonar.

deciduous (dih-SIHJ-oo-uhs)
A term used to describe trees and shrubs that drop their leaves when winter comes; examples are maple, oak, and birch trees. (p. 401)

caducifolio Un término usado para describir árboles y arbustos que dejan caer sus hojas cuando llega el invierno; el arce, el roble y el abedul son ejemplos de árboles caducifolios.

decomposer
An organism that feeds on and breaks down dead plant or animal matter. (p. 393)

descomponedor Un organismo que se alimenta de y degrada materia vegetal o animal.

delta
An area of land at the end, or mouth, of a river that is formed by the buildup of sediment. (p. 233)

delta Un área de tierra al final, o en la desembocadura, de un río y que se forma por la acumulación de sedimentos.

density
A property of matter representing the mass per unit volume. (p. 28)

densidad Una propiedad de la materia que representa la masa por unidad de volumen.

deposition (DEHP-uh-ZIHSH-uhn)
The process in which transported sediment is laid down. (p. 225)

sedimentación El proceso mediante el cual se deposita sedimento que ha sido transportado.

dew point
The temperature at which air with a given amount of water vapor will reach saturation. (p. 94)

punto de rocío La temperatura a la cual el aire con una cantidad determinada de vapor de agua alcanzará la saturación.

divergent boundary (dih-VUR-juhnt)
A boundary along which two tectonic plates move apart, characterized by either a mid-ocean ridge or a continental rift valley. (p. 278)

límite divergente Un límite a lo largo del cual dos placas tectónicas se separan; este límite se caracteriza por una dorsal oceánica o un valle de rift continental.

diversity
A term used to describe the quality of having many differences. Biodiversity describes the great variety and many differences found among living things.

diversidad Un término usado para describir la cualidad de tener muchas diferencias. La biodiversidad describe la gran variedad y las muchas diferencias encontradas entre organismos vivos.

divide
A continuous high line of land—or ridge—from which water drains to one side or the other. (p. 231)

línea divisoria de aguas Una línea continua de tierra alta, o un cerro, desde donde el agua escurre hacia un lado o hacia el otro.

drainage basin
An area of land in which water drains into a stream system. The borders of a drainage basin are called divides. (p. 231)

cuenca tributaria Un área de tierra en la cual el agua escurre a un sistema de corrientes. Los límites de una cuenca tributaria se denominan líneas divisorias de aguas.

dune
A mound of sand built up by wind. (p. 241)

duna Un montículo de arena formado por el viento.

E

earthquake
A shaking of the ground caused by the sudden movement of large blocks of rocks along a fault. (p. 301)

terremoto Un temblor del suelo ocasionado por el movimiento repentino de grandes bloques de rocas a lo largo de una falla.

ecology
The scientific study of how living things interact with each other and their environment. (p. 377)

ecología El estudio científico de cómo interactúan los organismos vivos entre sí y con su medio ambiente.

ecosystem
All the living and nonliving things that interact in a particular environment. An ecosystem can be as small as a rotting log or as large as a forest or a desert. (p. 377)

ecosistema Todos los organismos vivos y las cosas que interactúan en un medio ambiente específico. Un ecosistema puede ser tan pequeño como un tronco podrido, o tan grande como un bosque o un desierto.

electromagnetic spectrum
The range of all electromagnetic frequencies, including the following types (from lowest to highest frequency): radio waves, microwaves, infrared light, visible light, ultraviolet light, x-rays, and gamma rays. (p. 21)

espectro electromagnético La gama de todas las frecuencias electromagnéticas, incluyendo los siguientes tipos (de la frecuencia más baja a la más alta): ondas de radio, microondas, luz infrarroja, luz visible, luz ultravioleta, rayos X y rayos gamma.

element
A substance that cannot be broken down into a simpler substance by ordinary chemical changes. An element consists of atoms of only one type. (p. 184)

elemento Una sustancia que no puede descomponerse en otra sustancia más simple por medio de cambios químicos normales. Un elemento consta de átomos de un solo tipo.

elevation
A measure of how high something is above a reference point, such as sea level. (p. 165)

elevación Una medida de lo elevado que está algo sobre un punto de referencia, como el nivel del mar.

energy
The ability to do work or to cause a change. For example, the energy of a moving bowling ball knocks over pins; energy from food allows animals to move and to grow; and energy from the Sun heats Earth's surface and atmosphere, which causes air to move. (p. 9)

energía La capacidad para trabajar o causar un cambio. Por ejemplo, la energía de una bola de boliche en movimiento tumba los pinos; la energía proveniente de su alimento permite a los animales moverse y crecer; la energía del Sol calienta la superficie y la atmósfera de la Tierra, lo que ocasiona que el aire se mueva.

energy pyramid
A model used to show the amount of energy available to living things in an ecosystem. (p. 396)

pirámide de energía Un modelo usado para mostrar la cantidad de energía disponible para organismos vivos en un ecosistema.

R83

environment
Everything that surrounds a living thing. An environment is made up of both living and nonliving factors. (p. CA17)

medio ambiente Todo lo que rodea a un organismo vivo. Un medio ambiente está compuesto de factores vivos y factores sin vida.

epicenter (EHP-ih-SEHN-tuhr)
The point on Earth's surface directly above the focus of an earthquake. (p. 308)

epicentro El punto en la superficie de la Tierra situado directamente sobre el foco sísmico.

equator
An imaginary east-west line around the center of Earth that divides the planet into the Northern Hemisphere and the Southern Hemisphere; a line set at 0° latitude. (p. 158)

ecuador Una línea imaginaria de este a oeste alrededor del centro de la Tierra y que divide al planeta en hemisferio norte y hemisferio sur; la línea está fijada a latitud 0°.

erosion
The process in which sediment is picked up and moved from one place to another. (p. 225)

erosión El proceso en el cual el sedimento es recogido y transportado de un lugar a otro.

estuary
The lower end of a river where it meets the ocean and fresh and salt waters mix. (p. 401)

estuario La parte baja de un río donde desemboca en el océano y donde el agua dulce del río se mezcla con el agua salada del mar.

evaporation
The process by which liquid changes into gas. (p. 92)

evaporación El proceso por el cual un líquido se transforma en gas.

experiment
An organized procedure to study something under controlled conditions. (pp. CA22, R28)

experimento Un procedimiento organizado para estudiar algo bajo condiciones controladas.

extinction
The permanent disappearance of a species. (p. CA17)

extinción La desaparición permanente de una especie.

F

false-color image
A computer image in which the colors are not what the human eye would see. A false-color image can assign different colors to different types of radiation coming from an object to highlight its features. (p. 171)

imagen de color falso Una imagen computacional en la cual los colores no son los que el ojo humano observaría. Una imagen de color falso puede asignar diferentes colores a los diferentes tipos de radiación que provienen de un objeto para hacer destacar sus características.

fault
A fracture in Earth's lithosphere along which blocks of rock move past each other. (p. 301)

falla Una fractura en la litosfera de la Tierra a lo largo de la cual bloques de roca se mueven y pasan uno al lado de otro.

fault-block mountain
A mountain that forms as blocks of rock move up or down along normal faults in areas where the lithosphere is being pulled apart. (p. 342)

montaña de bloques de falla Una montaña que se forma cuando bloques de roca se mueven hacia arriba o hacia abajo a lo largo de fallas normales en las áreas donde la litosfera está siendo separada.

floodplain
A flat area of land on either side of a stream that becomes flooded when a river overflows its banks. (p. 232)

planicie de inundación Un área plana de tierra en cualquier costado de un arroyo que se inunda cuando un río se desborda.

focus
In an earthquake, the point underground where the rocks first begin to move. (p. 308)

foco sísmico En un terremoto, el punto subterráneo donde comienza el movimiento de las rocas.

folded mountain
A mountain that forms as continental crust is compressed and rocks bend into large folds. (p. 340)

montaña plegada Una montaña que se forma cuando la corteza continental es comprimida y las rocas se doblan en grandes pliegues.

food chain
A model used to show the feeding relationship between a single producer and a chain of consumers in an ecosystem. In a typical food chain, a plant is the producer that is eaten by a consumer, such as an insect; then the insect is eaten by a second consumer, such as a bird. (p. 394)

cadena alimenticia Un modelo usado para mostrar la relación de ingestión entre un solo productor y una cadena de consumidores en un ecosistema. En una cadena alimenticia típica, una planta es la productora que es ingerida por un consumidor como un insecto, y luego el insecto es ingerido por un segundo consumidor como un pájaro.

food web
A model used to show a feeding relationship in which many food chains overlap in an ecosystem. (p. 394)

red trófica Red de cadenas alimenticias de un ecosistema.

force
A push or a pull; something that changes the motion of an object. (p. CA12)

fuerza Un empuje o un jalón; algo que cambia el movimiento de un objeto.

fossil
A trace or the remains of a once-living thing from long ago. (p. CA15)

fósil Un rastro o los restos de un organismo que vivió hace mucho tiempo.

fossil fuel
Fuel formed from the remains of prehistoric organisms that is burned for energy. (p. 452)

combustibles fósiles Combustibles formados a partir de los restos de organismos prehistóricos que son consumidos para obtener energía.

freezing rain
Rain that freezes when it hits the ground or another surface and coats the surface with ice. (p. 104)

lluvia helada Lluvia que se congela cuando cae a la tierra o cualquier otra superficie y cubre la superficie con hielo.

friction
A force that resists the motion between two surfaces in contact. (p. CA19)

fricción Una fuerza que resiste el movimiento entre dos superficies en contacto.

front
The boundary between air masses. (p. 118)

frente El límite entre masas de aire.

G

geographic information systems GIS
Computer systems that can store, arrange, and display geographic data in different types of maps. (p. 173)

sistemas de información geográfica Sistemas computarizados que pueden almacenar, organizar y mostrar datos geográficos en diferentes tipos de mapas.

geologic cycle
All the processes by which Earth's features are worn down and built up. (p. 199)

ciclo geológico Todos los procesos por medio de los cuales los rasgos de la Tierra son desgastados y construidos.

geologic map
A type of map that shows the locations of geologic features at and near Earth's surface. (p. 206)

mapa geológico Un tipo de mapa que muestra el lugar de los rasgos geológicos en y cerca de la superficie de la Tierra.

geosphere (JEE-uh-SFEER)
All the features on Earth's surface—continents, islands, and seafloor—and everything below the surface—the inner and outer core and the mantle; one of the four parts of the Earth system. (p. CA15)

geosfera Todas las características de la superficie de la Tierra, es decir, continentes, islas y el fondo marino, y de todo bajo la superficie, es decir, el núcleo externo e interno y el manto; una de las cuatro partes del sistema de la Tierra.

geothermal energy
Heat energy that originates from within Earth and drives the movement of Earth's tectonic plates. Geothermal energy can be used to generate electricity. (p. 473)

energía geotérmica Energía calorífica que se origina en el interior de la Tierra y que impulsa el movimiento de las placas tectónicas de planeta. La energía geotérmica puede usarse para generar electricidad.

geyser
A type of hot spring that shoots water into the air. (p. 361)

géiser Un tipo de fuente termal que dispara agua al aire.

glacier (GLAY-shuhr)
A large mass of ice that exists year-round and moves over land. (p. 245)

glaciar Una gran masa de hielo que existe durante todo el año y se mueve sobre la tierra.

global winds
Winds that travel long distances in steady patterns over several weeks. (p. 84)

vientos globales Vientos que viajan grandes distancias en patrones fijos por varias semanas.

gravity
The force that objects exert on each other because of their mass. (pp. CA13, CA19)

gravedad La fuerza que los objetos ejercen entre sí debido a su masa.

greenhouse effect
The process by which certain gases in a planet's atmosphere absorb and emit infrared radiation, resulting in an increase in surface temperature. (p. 63)

efecto invernadero El proceso mediante el cual ciertos gases en la atmósfera de un planeta absorben y emiten radiación infrarroja, resultando en un incremento de la temperatura superficial del planeta.

H

habitat
The natural environment in which a living thing gets all that it needs to live; examples include a desert, a coral reef, and a freshwater lake. (p. 414)

hábitat El medio ambiente natural en el cual un organismo vivo consigue todo lo que requiere para vivir; ejemplos incluyen un desierto, un arrecife coralino y un lago de agua dulce.

hail
Layered lumps or balls of ice that fall from cumulonimbus clouds. (p. 104)

granizo Trozos de hielo que caen de nubes cumulonimbos.

heat energy
The total energy of the motion of particles in an object; also called thermal energy. (p. 10)

energía calórica La energía total del movimiento de partículas en un objeto, también llamado energía térmica.

heat flow
The movement of heat energy. (p. 11)

flujo de calor El movimiento de energía calórica.

high-pressure system
A generally calm and clear weather system that occurs when air sinks down in a high-pressure center and spreads out toward areas of lower pressure as it nears the ground. (p. 120)

sistema de alta presión Un sistema climático generalmente claro y calmo que se presenta cuando el aire desciende en un centro de alta presión y se esparce hacia áreas de baja presión conforme se acerca al suelo.

hot spot
An area where a column of hot material rises from deep within a planet's mantle and heats the lithosphere above it, often causing volcanic activity at the surface. (p. 283)

punto caliente Un área donde una columna de material caliente surge del interior del manto de un planeta y calienta la litosfera situada sobre él, con frecuencia ocasionando actividad volcánica en la superficie.

humidity
The amount of water vapor in air. (p. 94)

humedad La cantidad de vapor de agua en el aire.

hurricane (HUR-ih-KAYN)
A tropical low-pressure system with sustained winds of 120 kilometers per hour (74 mi/h) or more. (p. 123)

huracán Un sistema tropical de baja presión con vientos sostenidos de 120 kilómetros por hora (74 mi/h) o más.

hydroelectric energy
Electricity that is generated by the conversion of the energy of moving water. (p. 472)

energía hidroeléctrica Electricidad que se genera por la conversión de la energía del agua en movimiento.

hydrogen fuel cell
A device that uses hydrogen and oxygen to produce electricity. The byproducts are heat and water. (p. 476)

celda de combustible de hidrógeno Un aparato que usa hidrógeno y oxígeno para producir electricidad. Los subproductos son calor y agua.

hydrosphere (HY-druh-SFEER)
All water on Earth—in the atmosphere and in the oceans, lakes, glaciers, rivers, streams, and underground reservoirs; one of the four parts of the Earth system. (p. CA15)

hidrosfera Toda el agua de la Tierra: en la atmósfera y en los océanos, lagos, glaciares, ríos, arroyos y depósitos subterráneos; una de las cuatro partes del sistema de la Tierra.

hypothesis
A tentative explanation for an observation or phenomenon. A hypothesis is used to make testable predictions. (p. CA22)

hipótesis Una explicación provisional de una observación o de un fenómeno. Una hipótesis se usa para hacer predicciones que se pueden probar.

I

igneous rock (IHG-nee-uhs)
Rock that forms as molten rock cools and becomes solid. (p. 191)

roca ígnea Roca que se forma al enfriarse la roca fundida y hacerse sólida.

inner core
A solid sphere of metal, mainly nickel and iron, at Earth's center. (p. 266)

núcleo interno Una esfera sólida de metal, principalmente níquel y hierro, que se encuentra en el centro de la Tierra.

interaction
The condition of acting or having an influence upon something. Living things in an ecosystem interact with both the living and nonliving parts of their environment.

interacción La condición de actuar o influir sobre algo. Los organismos vivos en un ecosistema interactúan con las partes vivas y las partes sin vida de su medio ambiente.

isobar (EYE-suh-BAHR)
A line on a weather map connecting places that have the same air pressure. (p. 137)

isobara Una línea en un mapa climático que conecta lugares que tienen la misma presión de aire.

J

jet stream
A fast-moving wind that flows from west to east around Earth generally at altitudes of 10 to 15 kilometers. (p. 88)

corriente de chorro Vientos de alta velocidad que giran alrededor de la Tierra de oeste a este, generalmente a una altitud de 10 a 15 kilómetros.

K

kettle lake
A bowl-shaped depression that was formed as sediment built up around a block of ice left behind by a glacier and later filled with water. (p. 249)

lago de la caldera Una depresión que se formó al acumularse sedimento alrededor de un bloque de hielo que quedó como resultado de una acción glacial. Luego, al derretirse el hielo, la caldera se llena de agua.

L

latitude
The distance in degrees north or south from the equator. (p. 158)

latitud La distancia en grados norte o sur a partir del ecuador.

lava
Molten rock that reaches a planet's surface through a volcano. (pp. 191, 347)

lava Roca fundida que llega a la superficie de un planeta a través de un volcán.

law
In science, a rule or principle describing a physical relationship that always works in the same way under the same conditions. The law of conservation of energy is an example.

ley En las ciencias, una regla o un principio que describe una relación física que siempre funciona de la misma manera bajo las mismas condiciones. La ley de la conservación de la energía es un ejemplo.

lichen (LY-kuhn)
An organism that results from a close association between single-celled algae and fungi.

liquen Un organismo que resulta de una asociación cercana entre algas unicelulares y hongos.

limiting factor
A factor or condition that prevents the continuing growth of a population in an ecosystem. (p. 432)

factor limitante Un factor o una condición que impide el crecimiento contínuo de una población en un ecosistema.

liquefaction
A process in which the shaking of ground causes loose, wet soil to act like a liquid. (p. 318)

licuefacción Un proceso en el cual el temblor del suelo ocasiona que la tierra húmeda y suelta actúe como un líquido.

lithosphere (LIHTH-uh-SFEER)
The layer of Earth made up of the crust and the rigid rock of the upper mantle, averaging about 40 kilometers thick and broken into tectonic plates. (p. 267)

litosfera La capa de la Tierra compuesta por la corteza y la roca rígida del manto superior, con un promedio de 40 kilómetros de grosor y fracturada en placas tectónicas.

GLOSSARY

loess (LOH-uhs)
Deposits of fine-grained, wind-blown sediment. (p. 242)

loess Depósitos de sedimento de grano fino transportado por el viento.

longitude
The distance in degrees east or west of the prime meridian. Longitude lines are numbered from 0° to 180°. (p. 159)

longitud La distancia en grados al este o al oeste del primer meridiano. Las líneas de longitud están numeradas de 0° a 180°.

longshore current
The overall direction and movement of water as waves strike the shore at an angle. (p. 239)

corriente litoral La dirección y el movimiento general del agua conforme las olas golpean la costa en ángulo.

longshore drift
The zigzag movement of sand along a beach, caused by the action of waves. (p. 239)

deriva litoral El movimiento en zigzag de la arena a lo largo de una playa, ocasionado por la acción de las olas.

low-pressure system
A large and often stormy weather system that occurs when air moves around and into a low-pressure center, then moves up to higher altitudes. (p. 121)

sistema de baja presión Un sistema climático grande y usualmente lluvioso que se presenta cuando el aire se mueve alrededor de y hacia un centro de baja presión, y luego se mueve hacia mayores altitudes.

M

magma
Molten rock beneath Earth's surface. (p. 191)

magma Roca fundida que se encuentra bajo la superficie de la Tierra.

magnetic reversal
A switch in the direction of Earth's magnetic field so that the magnetic north pole becomes the magnetic south pole and the magnetic south pole becomes the magnetic north pole. (p. 280)

inversión magnética Un cambio en la dirección del campo magnético de la Tierra, de modo que el polo norte magnético se convierte en el polo sur magnético y el polo sur magnético se convierte en el polo norte magnético.

mantle
The layer of rock between Earth's outer core and crust, in which most rock is hot enough to flow in convection currents; Earth's thickest layer. (p. 267)

manto La capa de roca situada entre el núcleo externo y la corteza de la Tierra, en la cual la mayor parte de la roca es lo suficientemente caliente para fluir en corrientes de convección; la capa más gruesa de la Tierra.

map legend
A chart that explains the meaning of each symbol used on a map; also called a key. (p. 157)

clave del mapa Una tabla que explica el significado de cada símbolo usado en un mapa.

map scale
The comparison of distance on a map with actual distance on what the map represents, such as Earth's surface. Map scale may be expressed as a ratio, a bar scale, or equivalent units. (p. 157)

escala del mapa La comparación de la distancia en un mapa con la distancia real en lo que el mapa representa, como la superficie de la Tierra. La escala del mapa puede expresarse como una azón, una barra de escala o en unidades equivalentes.

mass
A measure of how much matter an object is made of.

masa Una medida de la cantidad de materia de la que está compuesto un objeto.

mass wasting
The downhill movement of loose rock or soil. (p. 227)

movimiento de masa El desplazamiento cuesta abajo de suelo o de roca suelta.

matter
Anything that has mass and volume. Matter exists ordinarily as a solid, a liquid, or a gas. (p. CA13)

materia Todo lo que tiene masa y volumen. Generalmente la materia existe como sólido, líquido o gas.

mechanical weathering
The breakdown of rock into smaller pieces of the same material without any change in its composition. (p. 200)

meteorización mecánica El desmoronamiento de las rocas en pedazos más pequeños del mismo material, sin ningún cambio en su composición.

R88

metamorphic rock (MEHT-uh-MAWR-fihk)
Rock formed as heat or pressure causes existing rock to change in structure, texture, or mineral composition. (p. 194)

roca metamórfica Roca formada cuando el calor o la presión ocasionan que la roca existente cambie de estructura, textura o composición mineral.

meteorologist (MEE-tee-uh-RAHL-uh-jihst)
A scientist who studies weather. (p. 134)

meteorólogo Un científico que estudia el clima.

mid-ocean ridge
A long line of sea-floor mountains where new ocean crust is formed by volcanic activity along a divergent boundary. (p. 272)

dorsal oceánica Una larga línea de montañas en el fondo marino donde se forma nueva corteza oceánica debido a la actividad volcánica a lo largo de un límite divergente.

mineral
A substance that forms in nature, is a solid, has a definite chemical makeup, and has a crystal structure. (p. 184)

mineral Una sustancia sólida formada en la naturaleza, de composición química definida y estructura cristalina.

molecule
A group of atoms that are held together by covalent bonds so that they move as a single unit.

molécula Un grupo de átomos que están unidos mediante enlaces covalentes de tal manera que se mueven como una sola unidad.

monsoon
A wind that changes direction with the seasons. (p. 90)

monzón Un viento que cambia de dirección con las estaciones.

moraine (muh-RAYN)
A deposit of till left behind by a retreating glacier. Moraines can form along a glacier's sides and at its end. (p. 248)

morrena Un depósito de sedimentos glaciares dejado por un glaciar que retrocede. Las morrenas pueden formarse en los costados de un glaciar o en su extremo.

mutualism (MYOO-choo-uh-LIHZ-uhm)
An interaction between two species in which both benefit; a type of symbiosis. (p. 426)

mutualismo Una interacción entre dos especies en la cual ambas se benefician; un tipo de simbiosis.

N

natural resource
Any type of matter or energy from Earth's environment that humans use to meet their needs. (p. 449)

recurso natural Cualquier tipo de materia o energía del medio ambiente de la Tierra que usan los humanos para satisfacer sus necesidades.

niche (nihch)
The role a living thing plays in its habitat. A plant is a food producer, whereas an insect both consumes food as well as provides food for other consumers. (p. 415)

nicho El papel que juega un organismo vivo en su hábitat. Una planta es un productor de alimento mientras que un insecto consume alimento y a la vez sirve de alimento a otros consumidores.

nitrogen cycle
The continuous movement of nitrogen through Earth, its atmosphere, and the living things on Earth. (p. 387)

ciclo del nitrógeno El movimiento continuo de nitrógeno por la Tierra, su atmósfera y los organismos vivos de la Tierra.

nonrenewable resource
A resource that exists in a fixed amount or is used up more quickly than it can be replaced in nature. (p. 450)

recurso no renovable Un recurso que existe en una cantidad fija o se consume más rápidamente de lo que puede reemplazarse en la naturaleza.

nuclear energy
The energy released by a nuclear reaction. (p. 477)

energía nuclear La energía liberada por una reacción nuclear.

nutrient (NOO-tree-uhnt)
A substance that an organism needs to live. Examples include water, minerals, and materials that come from the breakdown of food particles.

nutriente Una sustancia que un organismo necesita para vivir. Ejemplos incluyen agua, minerales y sustancias que provienen de la descomposición de partículas de alimento.

ocean current
A mass of moving ocean water. (p. 62)

corriente oceánica Una masa de agua oceánica en movimiento.

GLOSSARY

oceanic-continental subduction
A boundary along which a tectonic plate carrying oceanic crust sinks beneath a plate with continental crust. (p. 289)

subducción océano-continente Un límite a lo largo del cual una placa tectónica de corteza oceánica se hunde bajo una placa de corteza continental.

oceanic-oceanic subduction
A boundary along which a tectonic plate carrying oceanic crust sinks beneath another plate with oceanic crust. (p. 288)

subducción de placas oceánica-oceánica Un límite a lo largo del cual una placa tectónica de corteza oceánica se hunde bajo otra placa de corteza oceánica.

ore
A rock that contains enough of a valuable mineral to be mined for a profit. (p. 462)

mena Una roca que contiene suficiente mineral valioso para ser extraído con fines lucrativos.

organism
An individual living thing, made up of one or many cells. (p. CA17)

organismo Un individuo vivo, compuesto de una o muchas células.

outer core
A layer of molten metal, mainly nickel and iron, that surrounds Earth's inner core. (p. 266)

núcleo externo Una capa de metal fundido, principalmente níquel y hierro, que rodea al núcleo interno de la Tierra.

P, Q

Pangaea (pan-JEE-uh)
A supercontinent that included all of the landmasses on Earth. It began breaking apart about 200 million years ago. (p. 272)

Pangea Un supercontinente que incluía todas las masas continentales de la Tierra. Empezó a fracturarse aproximadamente hace 200 millones de años.

parasitism (PAR-uh-suh-TIHZ-uhm)
A relationship between two species in which one species is harmed while the other benefits; a type of symbiosis. (p. 427)

parasitismo Una relación entre dos especies en la cual una especie es perjudicada mientras que la otra se beneficia; un tipo de simbiosis.

photosynthesis (FOH-toh-SIHN-thih-sihs)
The process by which green plants and other producers use simple compounds and energy from light to make sugar, an energy-rich compound.

fotosíntesis El proceso mediante el cual las plantas verdes y otros productores usan compuestos simples y energía de la luz para producir azúcares, compuestos ricos en energía.

pioneer species
The first species to move into a lifeless environment. Lichens are typical pioneer species on land. (p. 434)

especie pionera La primera especie que ocupa un medio ambiente sin vida. Los lichens son típicas especies pioneras terrestres.

pollution
The release of harmful substances into the air, water, or land. (p. 498)

contaminación La descarga de sustancias nocivas al aire, al agua o a la tierra.

population
A group of organisms of the same species that live in the same area. For example, a desert will have populations of different species of lizards and cactus plants. (p. 414)

población Un grupo de organismos de la misma especie que viven en la misma área. Por ejemplo, un desierto tendrá poblaciones de distintas especies de lagartijas y de cactus.

population density
A measure of the number of organisms that live in a given area. The population density of a city may be given as the number of people living per square kilometer. (p. 494)

densidad de población Una medida de la cantidad de organismos que viven un área dada. La densidad de población de una ciudad puede expresarse como el número de personas que viven en un kilómetro cuadrado.

precipitation
Any type of liquid or solid water that falls to Earth's surface, such as rain, snow, or hail. (p. 93)

precipitación Cualquier tipo de agua líquida o sólida que cae a la superficie de la Tierra, como por ejemplo lluvia, nieve o granizo.

predator
An animal that hunts other animals and eats them. (p. 423)

predador Un animal que caza otros animales y se los come.

prey
An animal that other animals hunt and eat. (p. 423)

presa Un animal que otros animales cazan y se comen.

prime meridian
An imaginary north-south line that divides the planet into the Eastern Hemisphere and the Western Hemisphere. The prime meridian passes through Greenwich, England. (p. 159)

primer meridiano Una línea imaginaria de norte a sur que divide al planeta en hemisferio oriental y hemisferio occidental. El primer meridiano pasa a través de Greenwich, Inglaterra.

producer
An organism that captures energy from sunlight and transforms it into chemical energy that is stored in energy-rich carbon compounds. Producers are a source of food for other organisms. (p. 391)

productor Un organismo que capta energía de la luz solar y la transforma a energía química que se almacena en compuestos de carbono ricos en energía. Los productores son una fuente de alimento para otros organismos.

projection
A representation of Earth's curved surface on a flat map. (p. 160)

proyección Una representación de la superficie curva de la Tierra en un mapa plano.

pyroclastic flow (PY-roh-KLAS-tihk)
A dense cloud of superheated gases and rock fragments that moves quickly downhill from an erupting volcano. (p. 348)

corriente piroclástica Una nube densa de gases sobrecalentados y fragmentos de rocas que desciende rápidamente de un volcán en erupción.

R

radiation (RAY-dee-AY-shuhn)
Energy that travels across distances as electromagnetic waves. (p. 18)

radiación Energía que viaja a través de la distancia en ondas electromagnéticas.

recrystallization
The process by which bonds between atoms in minerals break and re-form in new ways during metamorphism. (p. 195)

recristalización El proceso mediante el cual los enlaces entre los átomos de los minerales se rompen y se vuelven a formar de diferentes maneras durante el metamorfismo.

recycling
The reusing of materials that people would otherwise throw away, such as paper, glass, plastics, and certain metals. (p. 468)

reciclaje El reutilizar los materiales que la gente de otra forma desecharía, como el papel, el vidrio, los plásticos y ciertos metales.

relative humidity
The comparison of the amount of water vapor in air with the maximum amount of water vapor that can be present in air at that temperature. (p. 94)

humedad relativa La comparación entre la cantidad de vapor de agua en el aire y la cantidad máxima de vapor de agua que puede estar presente en el aire a esa temperatura.

relief
In geology, the difference in elevation between an area's high and low points. (p. 165)

relieve En geología, la diferencia en elevación entre los puntos altos y bajos de un área.

relief map
A map that shows the differences in elevation in an area. Relief maps can show elevations through the use of contour lines, shading, colors, and, in some cases, three-dimensional materials. (p. 156)

mapa de relieve Un mapa que muestra las diferencias en elevación de un área. Los mapas de relieve pueden mostrar elevaciones mediante del uso de curvas de nivel, sombreado, colores y, en algunos casos, materiales tridimensionales.

remote sensing
A method of using scientific equipment to gather information about something from a distance. Most remote-sensing methods make use of different types of electromagnetic radiation. (p. 170)

teledetección Un método de reunir información sobre algo a distancia usando equipo científico. La mayoría de los métodos de sensoramiento remoto hacen uso de diferentes tipos de radiación electromagnética.

R91

renewable resource
A natural resource that can be replaced in nature at about the same rate as it is used. (p. 450)

recurso renovable Un recurso natural que puede reemplazarse en la naturaleza casi al mismo ritmo al que es utilizado.

respiration
The physical and chemical processes by which a living thing exchanges gases with the environment. In cellular respiration, cells take in oxygen and release the energy stored in carbon compounds.

respiración Los procesos físicos y químicos mediante los cuales un organismo vivo toma oxígeno y libera energía. En la respiración celular, las células absorben oxígeno y liberan la energía almacenada en compuestos de carbono.

rift valley
A deep valley formed as tectonic plates move apart, such as along a mid-ocean ridge. (p. 279)

valle de rift Un valle profundo formado cuando las placas tectónicas se separan, como a lo largo de una dorsal oceánica.

rock
A naturally formed solid that is usually made up of one or more types of minerals. (p. 187)

roca Un sólido formado de manera natural y generalmente compuesto de uno o más tipos de minerales.

rock cycle
The set of natural, repeating processes that form, change, break down, and re-form rocks. (p. 196)

ciclo de las rocas La serie de procesos naturales y repetitivos que forman, cambian, descomponen y vuelven a formar rocas.

S

sandbar
A ridge of sand built up by the action of waves and currents. (p. 240)

barra de arena Una colina de arena que se forma por la acción de las olas y las corrientes.

satellite
An object that orbits a more massive object.

satélite Un objeto que orbita un objeto de mayor masa.

saturation
A condition of the atmosphere in which the rates of evaporation and condensation are equal. (p. 94)

saturación Una condición de la atmósfera en la cual las tasas de evaporación y condensación son iguales.

sediment
Solid materials such as rock fragments, plant and animal remains, or minerals that are carried by water or by air and that settle on the bottom of a body of water or on the ground.

sedimento Materiales sólidos como fragmentos de rocas, restos de plantas y animales o minerales que son transportados por el agua o el aire y que se depositan en el fondo de un cuerpo de agua o en el suelo.

sedimentary rock (SEHD-uh-MEHN-tuh-ree)
Rock formed as pieces of older rocks and other loose materials get pressed or cemented together or as dissolved minerals re-form and build up in layers. (p. 192)

roca sedimentaria Roca que se forma cuando los pedazos de rocas más viejas y otros materiales sueltos son presionados o cementados o cuando los minerales disueltos vuelven a formarse y se acumulan en capas.

seismic wave (SYZ-mihk)
The vibrations caused by an earthquake. (p. 307)

onda sísmica Las vibraciones ocasionadas por un terremoto.

seismograph (SYZ-muh-GRAF)
An instrument that constantly records ground movements. (p. 312)

sismógrafo Un instrumento que registra constantemente los movimientos del suelo.

sensor
A mechanical or electronic device that receives and responds to a signal, such as light. (p. 171)

sensor Un dispositivo mecánico o electrónico que recibe y responde a una señal, como la luz.

sinkhole
An open basin that forms when the roof of a cavern becomes so thin that it falls in. (p. 235)

sumidero Una cuenca abierta que se forma cuando el techo de una caverna se vuelve tan delgado que se desploma.

sleet
Small pellets of ice that form when rain passes through a layer of cold air and freezes before hitting the ground. (p. 104)

aguanieve Pequeñas bolitas de hielo que se forman cuando la lluvia pasa a través de una capa de aire frío y se congela antes de caer al suelo.

R92

slope
A measure of how steep a landform is. Slope is calculated as the change in elevation divided by the distance covered. (p. 165)

pendiente Una medida de lo inclinada de una formación terrestre. La pendiente se calcula dividiendo el cambio en la elevación por la distancia recorrida.

soil
The top layer of Earth's surface, consisting of rock and mineral particles mixed with organic matter.

suelo La capa superior de la superficie de la Tierra, que consiste de rocas y partículas minerales mezcladas con material orgánico.

solar cell
A device that converts the energy of sunlight into electrical energy. (p. 475)

celda solar Un aparato que convierte la energía de la luz del Sol en energía eléctrica.

species
A group of living things so closely related that they can breed with one another and produce offspring that can breed as well. (p. 413)

especie Un grupo de organismos que están tan estrechamente relacionados que pueden aparearse entre sí y producir crías que también pueden aparearse.

storm surge
A rapid rise in water level in a coastal area that occurs when a hurricane pushes a huge mass of ocean water, often leading to flooding and widespread destruction. (p. 125)

marea de tormenta Un rápido aumento del nivel del agua en un área costera que ocurre cuando un huracán empuja una gran masa de agua oceánica, muchas veces provocando inundaciones y destrucción extensa.

stress
The force applied by an object pressing on, pulling on, or pushing against another object. (p. 301)

tensión La fuerza aplicada por un objeto que presiona, jala o empuja contra otro objeto.

subduction
The process by which an oceanic tectonic plate sinks under another plate into Earth's mantle. (p. 286)

subducción El proceso mediante el cual una placa tectónica oceánica se hunde bajo otra placa y entra al manto de la Tierra.

succession (suhk-SEHSH-uhn)
A natural process that involves a gradual change in the plant and animal communities that live in an area. (p. 434)

sucesión Un proceso natural que involucra un cambio gradual en las comunidades de plantas y animales que viven en un área.

sustainable
A term that describes the managing of certain natural resources so that they are not harmed or used up. Examples include maintaining clean groundwater and protecting topsoil from erosion. (p. 510)

sostenible Un término que describe el manejo de ciertos recursos naturales para que no se deterioren o se terminen. Ejemplos incluyen mantener limpia el agua subterránea y proteger de la erosión a la capa superficial del suelo.

symbiosis (SIHM-bee-OH-sihs)
The interaction between individuals from two different species that live closely together. (p. 426)

simbiosis La interacción entre individuos de dos especies distintas que viven en proximidad.

system
A group of objects or phenomena that interact. A system can be as simple as a rope, a pulley, and a mass. It also can be as complex as the interaction of energy and matter in the four parts of the Earth system. (p. 41)

sistema Un grupo de objetos o fenómenos que interactúan. Un sistema puede ser algo tan sencillo como una cuerda, una polea y una masa. También puede ser algo tan complejo como la interacción de la energía y la materia en las cuatro partes del sistema de la Tierra.

T

technology
The use of scientific knowledge to solve problems or engineer new products, tools, or processes.

tecnología El uso de conocimientos científicos para resolver problemas o para diseñar nuevos productos, herramientas o procesos.

tectonic plate (tehk-TAHN-ihk)
One of the large, moving pieces into which Earth's lithosphere is broken and which commonly carries both oceanic and continental crust. (p. 268)

placa tectónica Una de las grandes piezas en movimiento en las que la litosfera de la Tierra se rompe y que comúnmente lleva corteza oceánica y continental.

GLOSSARY

temperature
A measure of the average amount of the energy of motion of the particles in an object. (p. 10)

temperatura Una medida de la cantidad promedio de energía de movimiento de las partículas en un objeto.

theory
In science, a set of widely accepted explanations of observations and phenomena. A theory is a well-tested explanation that is consistent with all available evidence.

teoría En las ciencias, un conjunto de explicaciones de observaciones y fenómenos que es ampliamente aceptado. Una teoría es una explicación bien probada que es consecuente con la evidencia disponible.

theory of plate tectonics
A theory stating that Earth's lithosphere is broken into huge plates that move and change in size over time. (p. 274)

teoría de la tectónica de placas Una teoría que establece que la litosfera de la Tierra está formada por enormes placas que se mueven y cambian de tamaño con el tiempo.

thunderstorm
A storm with lightning and thunder. (p. 128)

tormenta eléctrica Una tormenta con relámpagos y truenos.

till
Sediment of different sizes left directly on the ground by a melting, or retreating, glacier. (p. 248)

sedimentos glaciares Sedimentos de diferentes tamaños depositados directamente en el suelo por un glaciar que se derrite o retrocede.

topography
All natural and human-made surface features of a particular area. (p. 164)

topografía Todas las características de superficie de origen natural y humano en un área particular.

tornado
A violently rotating column of air stretching from a cloud to the ground. (p. 131)

tornado Una columna de aire que gira violentamente y se extiende desde una nube hasta el suelo.

transform boundary
A boundary along which two tectonic plates scrape past each other, and crust is neither formed nor destroyed. (p. 278)

límite transcurrente Un límite a lo largo del cual dos placas tectónicas se rozan y no se forma corteza ni se destruye.

tropical storm (TRAHP-ih-kuhl)
A low-pressure system that starts in the tropics with winds of at least 65 kilometers per hour (40 mi/h) but less than 120 kilometers per hour (74 mi/h). (p. 123)

tormenta tropical Un sistema de baja presión que inicia en los trópicos con vientos de por lo menos 65 kilómetros por hora (40 mi/h) pero menores a 120 kilómetros por hora (74 mi/h).

tsunami (tsu-NAH-mee)
A water wave caused by an earthquake, volcanic eruption, or landslide. (p. 318)

tsunami Una ola de agua ocasionada por un terremoto, erupción volcánica o derrumbe.

U

urban
A term that describes a city environment.

urbano Un término que describe el medio ambiente de una ciudad.

V

variable
Any factor that can change in a controlled experiment, observation, or model.

variable Cualquier factor que puede cambiar en un experimento controlado, en una observación o en un modelo.

volcano
An opening in the crust through which molten rock, rock fragments, and hot gases erupt; a mountain built up from erupted materials. (p. 346)

volcán Una abertura en la corteza a través de la cual la roca fundida, fragmentos de roca y gases calientes hacen erupción; una montaña formada a partir de los materiales que surgen de una erupción.

volume
An amount of three-dimensional space, often used to describe the space that an object takes up.

volumen Una cantidad de espacio tridimensional; a menudo se usa este término para describir el espacio que ocupa un objeto.

W, X, Y, Z

water cycle
The continuous movement of water on Earth, through its atmosphere, and in the living things on Earth. (p. 60)

ciclo del agua El movimiento continuo de agua sobre la Tierra, por su atmósfera y dentro de los organismos vivos de la Tierra.

wave
A disturbance that transfers energy from one place to another. (p. 19)

onda Una perturbación que transfiere energía de un lugar a otro.

wavelength
The distance from one wave crest to the next crest; the distance from any part of one wave to the identical part of the next wave. (p. 20)

longitud de onda La distancia de una cresta de onda a la siguiente cresta; la distancia de cualquier parte de una onda a la parte idéntica de la siguiente onda.

weather
The condition of Earth's atmosphere at a particular time and place. (pp. 62, 83)

estado del tiempo La condición de la atmósfera terrestre en un lugar y momento particular.

weathering
The process by which natural processes break down rocks. (p. 199)

meteorización El proceso por el cual los procesos naturales fragmentan las rocas.

wind
The horizontal movement of air caused by differences in air pressure. (p. 83)

viento El movimiento horizontal de aire provocado por diferencias en la presión de aire.

work
The use of force to move an object over a distance. (p. 15)

trabajo El uso de fuerza para mover un objeto una distancia.

R95

Index

Note: The page numbers for definitions are printed in **boldface** type.
The page numbers for illustrations, maps, and charts are printed in *italic* type.

A

B

INDEX

C

INDEX

INDEX

R99

D

INDEX

E

INDEX

F

INDEX

G

INDEX

H

I

INDEX

J, K

L

INDEX

INDEX

R107

M

N

INDEX

O

INDEX

P

INDEX

R111

INDEX

Q

R

INDEX

S

INDEX

R115

INDEX

T

INDEX

U

V

INDEX

R11

X, Y, Z

Acknowledgments

Photography

Cover © Garry Black/Masterfile; **i** © Garry Black/Masterfile; **iii** *top to bottom left* Photograph of James Trefil by Evan Cantwell; Photograph of Rita Ann Calvo by Joseph Calvo; Photograph of Linda Carnin by Amilcar Cifuentes; Photograph of Sam Miller by Samuel Miller; *top to bottom right* Photograph of Kenneth Cutler by Kenneth A. Cutler; Photograph of Donald Steely by Marni Stamm; Photograph of Vicky Vachon by Redfern; **v** *left top to bottom* © William M. Bruce; © Jack Castro; Dr. Bernice Filerman - ; © Mark Handwerker; ca-s6pe-000000-009 **004–v** Sandy Steinburg - ; **viii** AP/Wide World Photos; **x** © Steve Starr/ Stock Boston Inc./PictureQuest; **xii** © Orion Press/Corbis; **xiv** © William Stevenson/Alamy Images; **xx, xxi** Photograph by Sharon Hoogstraten; **CA12–CA13** © Roger Ressmeyer/Corbis; **CA14–CA15** AP/Wide World Photos; **CA16–CA17** © Ron Sanford/ Corbis; **CA18–CA19** © Galen Rowell/Corbis; **CA20** © Vince Streano/Corbis; **CA21** © Roger Ressmeyer/Corbis; **CA22** *top left* University of Florida Lightning Research Laboratory; *center* © Roger Ressmeyer/Corbis; **CA23** *center* © Mauro Fermariello/Science Researchers; *bottom right* © Alfred Pasieka/Photo Researchers; **CA24–CA25** *background* © Stocktrek/Corbis; *center* NOAA; **CA25** *left* © Alan Schein; *center right* Vaisala Oyj, Finland.

Unit 1

1 © Bill Ross/Corbis; **2–3** © Bruce Byers/Getty Images; **3** *top right* © The Chedd-Angier Production Company; *bottom left* © D. Faulkner/Photo Researchers; **4** *top left* © Luiz C. Marigo/Peter Arnold, Inc.; *top center* Image courtesy Norman Kuring/ SeaWiFS Project, NASA; *top right* © Norbert Wu; *bottom* © The Chedd-Angier Production Company; **6–7** AP/Wide World Photos; **7** Photograph by Sharon Hoogstraten; **9** © Peter J. Bryant/Biological Photo Service; **10** *top* © Patrick Ward/Corbis; *bottom* © H. David Seawell/Corbis; **12** © Larry Lee Photography/ Corbis; **14** Photograph by Frank Siteman; **15** © Digital Vision; **16** *top* © Grant Klotz/Alaska Stock Images/PictureQuest; *bottom* Photograph by Sharon Hoogstraten; **17, 18** Photograph by Sharon Hoogstraten; **20** *left* © Jeremy Hoare/Alamy Images; *center* © Mark Clarke/Science Photo Library/Photo Researchers; *right* © Russ Widstrand/Alamy Images; **21** © Alfred Pasieka/Science Photo Library/Photo Researchers; **23** Photograph by Sharon Hoogstraten; **24** © Sally A. Morgan/Ecoscene/Corbis; **25** *left* © Pulse Productions/SuperStock/PictureQuest; **26** Photograph by Sharon Hoogstraten; **27** © Brand X Pictures/Alamy; **28, 29** Photograph by Sharon Hoogstraten; **32** © SuperStock; **33** *top left* © Jeremy Samuelson/FoodPix; *right* © Martin Jacobs/FoodPix; *bottom left* © William Reavell/StockFood Munich/StockFood; **38–39** hanglider - © Joson/Getty Images; **39, 41** Photograph by Sharon Hoogstraten; **42–43** NASA; **42** *left* © David Parker/ Photo Researchers; *right* © Chuck Davis/Getty Images; **43** *bottom center* © Dr. Neville Winchester/University of Victoria, British Columbia, Canada; *bottom right* © Peter and Georgina Bowater/Stock Connection/ PictureQuest; **44** © Carol Polich/Lonely Planet Images; **45** Photograph by Sharon Hoogstraten; **46** AP/Wide World Photos; **47** *left* AP/Wide World Photos; *right* © Sue Ellen Hirschfeld/Department of Geological Sciences, California State Unviversity, East Bay; **48** © David Young-Wolff/ PhotoEdit; **49** © Joson/Corbis; **50** *top* © Lauri Nykopp/Alamy Images; *bottom* © Sergio Pitamitz/ Alamy Images; **51** Photograph by Sharon Hoogstraten; **55** © Thomas Hallstein/Alamy Images; **56** *top* © Michael Kevin Daly/Corbis; *bottom* Photograph by Sharon Hoogstraten; **58** © Martin Rietze/Alamy Images; **61** © MedioImages/Alamy Images; **63** © AFP/ Corbis; **65** Photo by Sharon Hoogstraten; **67** *left* © Simon Fraser/Mauna Loa Observatory/Photo Researchers; *bottom right* Photograph by Sharon Hoogstraten; **72** © Don Farrall/Getty Images; **73** *top left* © Sheila Terry/Photo Researchers; *top right, center* © Dorling Kindersley; *bottom* © SEF/Art Resource, New York; **74** *top left* Mary Evans Picture Library; *top right, bottom* © Dorling Kindersley; **75** *right* © Mark Wiens/ Masterfile; *left* © 1913 Debris Yearbook, Purdue University; **76–77** AP/Wide World Photos; **77, 79, 81, 83, 85** Photograph by Sharon Hoogstraten; **90** Earth Vistas; **91** *left* © Lester Lefkowitz/Corbis; *inset* NASA/Corbis; **92** *center right* Photograph by Sharon Hoogstraten; *bottom left* © Japack Company/Corbis; **93** © Kristi Bressert/Index Stock Imagery/PictureQuest; **95** *bottom right* Photograph by Sharon Hoogstraten; **96** © Grant Heilman/Grant Heilman Photography, Inc.; **98** *top* © John Mead/Photo Researchers; *center* © Corbis; *bottom* © Fred Whitehead/Animals Animals/Earth Scenes; **99** © Mark E. Gibson/Corbis; **100** *top* © Gunter Marx Photography/Corbis; *bottom* Photograph by Sharon Hoogstraten; **102** *top* © Stockbyte/PictureQuest;

105 *left* © Larry West/Photo Researchers; *right* © Astrid & Hanns-Frieder Michler/Photo Researchers, Inc.; **106** © Will McIntyre/Photo Researchers; **107** *left* ©1990 Warren Faidley/Weatherstock; *right* Global Atmospherics, Inc; **110** © Dorling Kindersley; **112–113** AP/Wide World Photos; **113, 115, 117** Photograph by Sharon Hoogstraten; **119** © Photodisc/Getty Images; **120** *bottom right* University of Wisconsin-Madison Space Science and Engineering Center; **122** © Stephen J. Krasemann/Photo Researchers; **123** Photograph by Sharon Hoogstraten; **124** NASA Goddard Space Flight Center/Image by Marit Jentoft-Nilsen; **125** © Smiley N. Pool/The Dallas Morning News/Corbis; **126** Photograph by Sharon Hoogstraten; **127** AP/Wide World Photos; **128** © William James Warren/Corbis; **130** *top* Photograph by Sharon Hoogstraten; *bottom* © Photodisc/Getty Images; **131** © David K. Hoadley; **132** © Reuters/Corbis; **133** *top left inset, top right* © Fletcher & Baylis/Photo Researchers; *background* © Waite Air Photos, Inc.; **134** Used with permission © January 9, 2003 Chicago Tribune Company, Chicago, Illinois. Photograph by Sharon Hoogstraten; **136, 137, 138** Provided by the Space Science and Engineering Center, University of Wisconsin-Madison; **139** Courtesy Bob Werner/ WSBT-TV, South Bend, Indiana; **140** *top left* © Mary Kate Denny/PhotoEdit; *bottom* Photograph by Sharon Hoogstraten; **140–141** Photograph by Sharon Hoogstraten; **142** *center* NASA Goddard Space Flight Center/Image by Marit Jentoft-Nilsen; *bottom* Provided by the Space Science and Engineering Center, University of Wisconsin-Madison; **144** Used with permission © January 9, 2003 Chicago Tribune Company, Chicago, Illinois. Photograph by Sharon Hoogstraten.

Unit 2

147 © Per Breiehagen/Getty Images; **148–149** Courtesy of NASA/Jet Propulsion Lab/Caltech; **149** *top* NASA/Carla Thomas; *bottom* Courtesy Diamonds North Resources, Ltd.; **150** *top* NASA/Carla Thomas; *bottom* © The Chedd-Angier Production Company; **151** © William Whitehurst/Corbis; **152–153** NASA; **153** *top left* National Air & Space Museum, Smithsonian Institution, Washington, D.C.; *top right* Courtesy of L. Sue Baugh; *center left* NASA/Goddard Space Flight Center/SeaWiFS Project; *bottom left* National Air & Space Museum, Smithsonian Institution, Washington, D.C.; *bottom right* NASA/Goddard Space Flight Center; **155** Photograph by Sharon Hoogstraten; **156** U.S. Geological Survey; **159** © David Parker/Photo Researchers; **160** Photograph by Sharon Hoogstraten; **163** © Jerry Driendl/Getty Images; **164** Photograph by Sharon Hoogstraten; **165** *top* © Stan Osolinski/Getty Images; *bottom* U.S. Geological Survey; **166** U.S. Geological Survey; **168** *top left* U.S. Geological Survey; *center, bottom* Photograph by Sharon Hoogstraten; **170** © Space Imaging; **171** *top* © Space Imaging; *bottom background* © Paul Morrell/Stone/Getty Images; *left, inset* National Oceanic and Atmospheric Administration/Department of Commerce; **172** NASA/MODIS Land Rapid Response Team; **174** © 1997 John D. Rogie; **175** *background* NASA/Goddard Space Flight Center/SeaWiFS Project and ORBIMAGE; *top inset* Library of Congress; *right* NASA/Jet Propulsion Lab/National Imagery and Mapping Agency; **176** *center* U.S. Geological Survey; *bottom left* © Paul Morrell/Stone/Getty Images; *inset* National Oceanic and Atmospheric Administration/ Department of Commerce; **178** U.S. Geological Survey; **179** © National Park Service; **180–181** Panning for gold - © Steve Starr/Stock Boston Inc./PictureQuest; **181** *center* Photograph by Sharon Hoogstraten; *bottom* Courtesy of L. Sue Baugh; **183** Photograph by Sharon Hoogstraten; **185** *center* © Charles D. Winters/Photo Researchers; *bottom* © Astrid & Hanns-Freider/Photo Researchers; **186** Photograph by Sharon Hoogstraten; **187** © Andrew J. Martinez/Photo Researchers; **188** *top left* © Dorling Kindersley; *top right, bottom right* © Doug Martin/Photo Researchers; **189** *left* © Joyce Photographics/ Photo Researchers; *right* © Dorling Kindersley; **190** Photograph by Sharon Hoogstraten; **191** © James Lyon/Lonely Planet Images; **192** *center* © Arthur R. Hill/Visuals Unlimited; *bottom* © Mark Schneider/ Visuals Unlimited; **194** Photograph by Sharon Hoogstraten; **195** *top to bottom* © Gerald & Buff Corsi/Visuals Unlimited; © 1995 Andrew J. Martinez/ Photo Researchers; The Boltin Picture Library; © Breck P. Kent; © 1996 Andrew J. Martinez/Photo Researchers; **196** *top left, bottom left* © Andrew J. Martinez/Photo Researchers; *right* © Arthur R. Hill/Visuals Unlimited; **198** *background* © Nobert Wu/Norbert Wu Productions/PictureQuest; *inset* National Oceanic and Atmospheric Administration *right* © Corbis; **199** Photograph by Sharon Hoogstraten; **201** *background* © Photodisc/Getty Images; *top right* © Susan Rayfield/ Photo Researchers; *center right*, *bottom left* Photograph courtesy of Sara Christopherson; *bottom right* © Kirkendall-Spring Photographers; **202** © Cheyenne Rouse/Visuals Unlimited; **204** *top* © image100/Alamy Images; *bottom* Photograph by Sharon Hoogstraten; **206** © Richard Cummins/ SuperStock; **209** *background* © PhotoBliss/Alamy Images; *center right* © Alamy Images; *bottom left* © W. Perry Conway/Corbis; *bottom right* © Ruaridh Stewart/ZUMA/Corbis; **212** U.S. Geological Survey;

213 *background* AP/Wide World Photos; *left* © Science Photo Library/Photo Researchers; *right* The Granger Collection, New York; **214** *right, center* © Andrew J. Martinez/Photo Researchers; *left* © Arthur R. Hill/ Visuals Unlimited; **218** *top* The Granger Collection; *bottom* © Tom Bean/Corbis; **219** *top* © Gianni Dagli Orti/Corbis; *center* The Natural History Museum, London; *bottom* Courtesy British Geological Survey; **220** *top* © Sally A. Morgan/Ecoscene/ Corbis; *bottom* © James King-Holmes/Photo Researchers; **221** *top* © Sherwin Crasto/Corbis; *center* © Mark A. Klinger/ Carnegie Museum of Natural History; *bottom* © The Field Museum; **222–223** © A.C. Waltham/Robert Harding Picture Library/Alamy Images; **223** *top* Photograph by Mike Mulligan; *bottom* Photograph by Sharon Hoogstraten; **225** © Bernhard Edmaier/Photo Researchers; **226** Photograph by Sharon Hoogstraten; **227** AP/Wide World Photos; **228** *top* Photograph by L.M. Smith, Waterways Experiment Station, U.S. Army Corps of Engineers. Courtesy, U.S. Geological Survey; *bottom* © Thomas Rampton/Grant Heilman Photography, Inc.; **229** © Troy and Mary Parlee/Alamy Images; **230** Photograph by Sharon Hoogstraten; **231** © Bill Ross/Corbis; **232** *top* © Kevin Horan/Stock Boston/ PictureQuest; *bottom* © Yann Arthus-Bertrand/Corbis; **233** *top* © 1992 Tom Bean; **234** © Charles Kennard/ Stock Boston/PictureQuest; **235** *top* © Reuters/Corbis; **236** *top* © Peter Bowater/Alamy Images; *bottom* Photograph by Sharon Hoogstraten; **238** © Craig Lovell/Corbis; **239** © Robert Perron; **240** Photograph by Sharon Hoogstraten; **241** © Tim Barnwell/Picturesque/ PictureQuest; **242** © John Shaw/Bruce Coleman, Inc.; **243** *top* © 1994 Tom Bean; *bottom* © Goodshoot/Alamy Images; **244** *background* © ImageState/ PictureQuest; *inset* © Santa Barbara County Flood Control District; **245** Photograph by Sharon Hoogstraten; **247** *left* © Bernard Edmaier/Photo Researchers; *right* © ImageState-Pictor/PictureQuest; **248** *top* © Norman Barett/Bruce Coleman, Inc.; *bottom* © Jim Wark/Airphoto; ca-s6pe-020704=007 **249** *top* © 1990 Tom Bean; *bottom* Photograph by Sharon Hoogstraten; **250** Mapquest-Source: U.S. Army Corps of Engineers/Great Lakes Commission; **251** © Chuck Pefley/Alamy Images; **252** *top* © Bernhard Edmaier/Photo Researchers; *center* © Craig Lovell/Corbis; *bottom* © John and Lisa Merrill/Getty Images; **254** © Tom Bean.

Unit 3

257 © Roger Ressmeyer/Corbis; **258–259** © Stephen and Donna O'Meara/Photo Researchers; **259** NASA Goddard Space Flight Center/METI/ERSDAC/JAROS, and U.S./Japan ASTER Science Team; **260** *top left* Photograph by T. Miller/U.S. Geological Survey; *inset* U.S. Geological Survey; *bottom* © The Chedd-Angier Production Company; **261** NASA Goddard Space Flight Center/METI/ERSDAC/JAROS, and U.S./Japan ASTER Science Team; **262–263** © Tony Waltham/Geophotos; **263, 265, 268, 270** Photograph by Sharon Hoogstraten; **271** © 1995–2002 Geoclassics. All rights reserved.; **276** *top* © Worldsat International/ Photo Researchers; *bottom* Photograph by Sharon Hoogstraten; **278, 281** Photograph by Sharon Hoogstraten; **283** *top* © Christophe Ratier/NHPA/Photo Researchers; *bottom* © NASA/Photo Researchers; ca-s6pe-0308mf=001 **285** *left* © Dr. John Brackenbury/Photo Researchers; *right* NASA; **286** Photograph by Sharon Hoogstraten; **287** © John Coletti/Stock Boston/PictureQuest; **289** Photograph by Sharon Hoogstraten; **290** © Lloyd Cluff/Corbis; **291** © Paul Chesley/Getty Images; **293** *left* © Albrecht G. Schaefer/ Corbis; *right* © Mitch Diamond/Index Stock/PictureQuest; **298–299** AP/Wide World Photos; **299, 301, 303** Photograph by Sharon Hoogstraten; **304** *top, bottom* © Martin Miller/University of Oregon, Eugene, Oregon; **305** NOAA/National Geophysical Data Center; **306** *top* U.S. Geological Survey; *bottom* © Bettmann/Corbis; **307, 309** Photograph by Sharon Hoogstraten; **315** AP Wide World Photos; **316** Photograph by Sharon Hoogstraten; **317** © Mark Downey; **318** U.S. Geological Survey; **319** © AFP/Getty Images; **322** © Roger Ressmeyer/Corbis; **324** *top* © Michael S. Yamashita/Corbis; *bottom* Photograph by Sharon Hoogstraten; **325** Photograph by Sharon Hoogstraten; **330** *top* © Chris Butler/Photo Researchers; *bottom* © Detlev van Ravenswaay/Photo Researchers; **331** *top* © Jim Brandenburg/Minden Pictures; *center* Courtesy of J.W. Schopf/University of California, Los Angeles; *bottom* Japan Meteorological Agency; **332** *top left* © Simon Fraser/Photo Researchers; *top right* © Chase Studio/Photo Researchers; *bottom* Courtesy of the Ocean Drilling Program; **333** *top left* NASA/Goddard Space Flight Center; *top right* © Brooks Kraft/Corbis; *bottom* NASA/ STS-113 Shuttle Crew; **334–335** Volcanic Eruptions - © Douglas Peebles; **335, 337** Photograph by Sharon Hoogstraten; **338** U.S. Department of the Interior; **339, 340** © Martin Miller/University of Oregon, Eugene, Oregon; **341** © Tim Hauf Photography/Visuals Unlimited; **342** Photograph by Sharon Hoogstraten; **343** © Martin Miller/University of Oregon, Eugene, Oregon; **344** © Phil Schermeister/Corbis; **345** © William Ervin/Photo Researchers; **346, 348** Photograph by Sharon Hoogstraten; **350** © G.R. Roberts Photo Library; **351** *left* © Tom Bean/Corbis; *right* © Krafft-Explorer/SS/Photo Researchers; **352** © F. Gohier/Photo Researchers;

R123

353 NASA/Carnegie Mellon University; **354** *top* © Krafft-Explorer/Photo Researchers; *bottom* Photograph by Sharon Hoogstraten; **356** *top* © James A. Sugar/Corbis; *bottom* © Mark E. Gibson/Corbis; **357** *top* © Stephen and Donna O'Meara/Volcano Watch International/Photo Researchers; *bottom* © Sid Balatan/Black Star Publishing/PictureQuest; **358** U.S. Geological Survey; **360** © The Image Bank/Getty Images; **361** © Simon Fraser/Photo Researchers; **362** © Peter Ryan/Photo Researchers; **363** *background* © Russ Bishop/Age Fotostock; *left* © Hulton-Deutsch Collection/Corbis; *right* © QT Luong/terragalleria.com; *right inset* © Dave G. Houser/Corbis; **364** *left* © Sid Balatan/Black Star Publishing/PictureQuest; *center* © The Image Bank/Getty Images; *right* © Simon Fraser/Photo Researchers; **366** © Roger Ressmeyer/Corbis.

Unit 4

370–371 © Mark Thiessen/National Geographic Image Collection; **371** *top* © Frank Oberle/Getty Images; *bottom* © Hal Horwitz/Corbis; **372** *top left, top right* © Lawrence J. Godson; *bottom* © Chedd-Angier Production Company; **374–375** © William Stevenson/Alamy Images; **375, 377** Photograph by Ken O'Donoghue; **378** © Mark Allen Stack/Tom Stack & Associates; **379** *left* © Jim Brandenburg/Minden Pictures; *right* © Ted Kerasote/Photo Researchers, Inc.; **380** © Grant Heilman Photography; **381** © Frans Lemmens/Getty Images; **382** *top* © Larry Lefever/Grant Heilman Photography, Inc.; *bottom* Photograph by Sharon Hoogstraten; **384** Photograph by Ken O'Donoghue; **387** Photograph by Frank Siteman; **389** © Randy Wells/Corbis; **390** Photograph by Frank Siteman; **391** *left* © Eric Crichton/Corbis; *top right* © E.R. Degginger/Color-Pic, Inc.; *bottom right* © T.E. Adams/Visuals Unlimited; **392** © Anthony Mercieca Photo/Photo Researchers, Inc.; **393** *top* © Fred Bruemmer/DRK Photo; *bottom* Photograph by Ken O'Donoghue; **395** *background* © Raymond Gehman/Corbis; **397** *left* © Arthur Gurmankin and Mary Morina/Visuals Unlimited; *right* © Carmela Leszczynski/Animals Animals; **398** © Charles Melton/Visuals Unlimited; **399** © Michio Hoshino/Minden Pictures; **400** *top left* © Tom Bean; *top right* © E.R. Degginger/Color-Pic, Inc.; *bottom* © Joe McDonald/Visuals Unlimited; **401** *left* © David Wrobel/Visuals Unlimited; *right* © Tom Bean; **402** *left* © Owaki-Kulla/Corbis; *right* © Frans Lanting/Minden Pictures; **403** *top* Photograph by Sharon Hoogstraten; *bottom* © Stephen Dalton/Photo Researchers, Inc.; **404** *left* © Aaron Horowitz/Corbis; *center* © Hans Pfletschinger/Peter Arnold, Inc.; *right* © Arthur Gurmankin and Mary Morina/Visuals Unlimited; **405** *left* © Paul Rezendes; *center* © Richard Herrmann/Visuals Unlimited; *right* © Norbert Wu; **410–411** © Wolcott Henry/National Geographic Image Collection; **411** Photograph by Frank Siteman; **413** © Kevin Schafer/Corbis; **414** *left, center* © Frans Lanting/Minden Pictures; *right* © Robin Karpan/Visuals Unlimited; **418** © Walt Anderson/Visuals Unlimited; **419** © Alan & Linda Detrick/Photo Researchers, Inc.; **420** *top* © Frank Awbrey/Visuals Unlimited; *bottom* Photograph by Sharon Hoogstraten; **422** © Spencer Grant/PhotoEdit; **423** © Gary Braasch; **424** *top* © Joe McDonald/Visuals Unlimited; *bottom* © Stephen J. Krasemann/Photo Researchers, Inc.; **425** *top* Photograph by Ken O'Donoghue; *bottom* © Michael Fogden/Bruce Coleman, Inc.; **426** © Michael & Patricia Fogden/Minden Pictures; **427** © Bradley Sheard; **428** *top left* © Phil Degginger/Color-Pic, Inc.; *top center* © S.J. Krasemann/Peter Arnold, Inc.; *top right* © Ray Coleman/Visuals Unlimited; *center* © Astrid & Hanns-Frieder Michler/Science Photo Library; *bottom left* © Dwight R. Kuhn; *bottom right* © E.R. Degginger/Color-Pic, Inc.; **429** © Arthur Morris/Visuals Unlimited; **430** *background* © Kevin Fleming/Corbis; *top* © David M. Dennis/Animals Animals; **431** Photograph by Ken O'Donoghue; **432** *top* © Shin Yoshino/Minden Pictures; *bottom* © Tim Fitzharris/ Minden Pictures; **433** Photograph by Frank Siteman; **434** © Leo Collier/Getty Images; **435** © David R. Frazier/Getty Images; **437** © A. & J. Visage/Peter Arnold, Inc.; **438** © Frans Lanting/Minden Pictures; **442** *left* Denver Public Library, Western History Collection, call # F-4659; *top right* © James Randklev/Getty Images; *bottom right* Library of Congress, Prints and Photographs Division; **443** *top left* © H.H. French/Corbis; *top right* © Bill Ross/Corbis; *center left* The Bancroft Library, University of California, Berkeley; *center right* © Corbis; *bottom* © Michael Sewell/Peter Arnold, Inc.; **444** *top* © Tom Bean/DRK Photo; *center left* © Alfred Eisenstaedt/Getty Images; *center right* © David Muench/Corbis; *bottom left* © Kevin Schafer/Corbis; *bottom right* Habitat Quality for San Joaquin Kit Fox on Managed and Private Lands reprinted from ESRI Map Book, Vol. 16 and used herein with permission. Copyright © 2001 ESRI. All rights reserved.; **445** *top left* © Tom Soucek/AlaskaStock.com; *top right* © Ohio State University; *bottom* © Richard Galosy/Bruce Coleman, Inc.; **446–447** © Richard Folwell/Photo Researchers; **447** Photograph by Sharon Hoogstraten; **449** © Corbis; **451** *top* © SuperStock; *bottom* © Gunter Marx Photography/Corbis; **455** Photograph by Sharon Hoogstraten; **456** *left* Diane Moore/Icon SMI; *top right* © Corbis; *bottom right* © Photodisc/Getty Images; **457** *background* © Pauline Horton/Corbis; *left* © Craig Aurness/Corbis; *right* © Peter Essick/Getty Images; **458** Photograph by Sharon Hoogstraten; **459** *top left* © Geoff Tompkinson/Photo Researchers; *top right* © Charles Falco/

Photo Researchers; *center left* © A.J. Copely/ Visuals Unlimited; *center right* © Dorling Kindersley; *bottom left* © Charles D. Winters/Photo Researchers; *bottom right* © Dorling Kindersley; **461** *top* © Mark A. Schneider/ Photo Researchers; *center left* © Mark A. Schneider/Photo Researchers; *center right* © Andrew J. Martinez/ Photo Researchers; *bottom* © M. Claye/ Photo Researchers; **463** *top* © Mervyn P. Lawes/Corbis; *bottom* Photograph by Sharon Hoogstraten; **464** Courtesy of Newmont Mining Corp.; **465** *top left, center left, bottom left* © Dorling Kindersley; *right* © Louis Goldman/Photo Researchers; **466, 467** Photograph by Sharon Hoogstraten; **468** *top* Photograph by Sharon Hoogstraten; *bottom* © David Young-Wolff/PhotoEdit; **469** © Jose Azel/Aurora; **470** *left, inset* © Lowell Georgia/Corbis; **471** © Donald C. & Priscilla Alexander Eastman/Lonely Planet Images; **472** © Beth Davidow/Visuals Unlimited; **473** © James Stilling/Getty Images; **474** © Lynne Ledbetter/Visuals Unlimited; **475** © Martin Bond/Photo Researchers; **476** Andrew Carlin/ Tracy Operators; **477** © California Fuel Cell Partnership; **479** © Steve Allen/Brand X Pictures/PictureQuest; **480** *top* © M.L. Sinibald/Corbis; *bottom* Photograph by Sharon Hoogstraten; **481** Photograph by Sharon Hoogstraten; **482** *upper left-top* © SuperStock; *upper left, bottom* © Gunter Marx Photography/Corbis; *center* © Jose Azel/Aurora; *bottom left* © Astrid & Hanns-Freider/ Photo Researchers; *bottom right, top to bottom* © Photodisc/Getty Images; © Dorling Kindersley; © Photodisc/ Getty Images; **486–487** highways © Alex Maclean/Photonica; **487** Photograph by Ken O'Donoghue; **489** Photograph by Frank Siteman; **491** © Ray Pfortner/Peter Arnold, Inc.; **492** Photograph by Ken O'Donoghue; **493** *top* © John Elk III; *bottom* © Ted Spiegel/Corbis; **494** *top left, top right* U.S. Geological Survey/EROS Data Center; *bottom* © ChromoSohm/ Sohm/Photo Researchers, Inc.; **495** © Mark E. Gibson/Visuals Unlimited; **496** *background* © John M. Roberts/Corbis; *left inset* © Bettmann/Corbis; *top right* © Dewitt Jones/Corbis; *bottom right* © Dr. Henri Grissno-Mayer, Department of Geography, University of Tennessee; **497** © David Young-Wolff/ PhotoEdit; **498** Photograph by Ken O'Donoghue; **499** *left* © Jenny Hager/The Image Works; *right* © Tom Bean/DRK Photo; **500** *left* © Natalie Fobes/Corbis; *right* © Natalie Fobes/Getty Images; **503** © Kent Foster Photgraphs/ Visuals Unlimited; **504** *top* © Andrew J. Martinez/Photo Researchers, Inc.; *inset* © D. Cavagnaro/Visuals Unlimited; **505** © Tom Edwards/Visuals Unlimited; **506** *top* Photograph by Ken O'Donoghue; *bottom* Photograph by Frank Siteman; **507** © Frank Pedrick/The Image Works; **508** © Joe McDonald/Visuals Unlimited; **509** *background* © Tom Bean/Corbis; *top left inset* © Jim Wark/Airphoto; *top right inset* © Scott Williams/U.S. Fish and Wildlife Service; *bottom insets* Courtesy of San Diego State University, Soil Ecology and Restoration Group; **510** © Melissa Farlow/National Geographic Image Collection; **511** *top left* © Charles O'Rear/Corbis; *top right* © Larry Lefever/Grant Heilman Photography, Inc.; **512** *top* © Janis Miglavs; *bottom, clockwise from top left* © Digital Vision; © Bob Melnychuk/ Getty Images; © Digital Vision; © Photodisc/Getty Images; **513** © Kevin Schafer/Corbis; **514** *top* © Tom Myers/ Photo Researchers, Inc.; *bottom* Photograph by Frank Siteman; **515** Photograph by Frank Siteman; **516** *top left* © Natalie Fobes/Corbis; *top right* © Kent Foster Photographs/Visuals Unlimited; *bottom left* © Joe McDonald/Visuals Unlimited; *bottom right* © Klein/Hubert/Peter Arnold, Inc.; **R54–R55** NOAA/National Geophysical Data Center; **R69** *top left* © Charles D. Winters/Photo Researchers; *top right* Photograph by Malcolm Hjerstedt. Courtesy of F. John Barlow/SANCO Publishing; *center* © Charles D. Winters/Photo Researchers; *bottom left* © Biophoto Associates/ Photo Researchers; *bottom center* © Dorling Kindersley; *bottom right* © Phil Degginger/ Color-Pic, Inc.; **R70** Photograph by Sharon Hoogstraten; **R71** *top left* © Charles D. Winters/Photo Researchers; *top right* © Mark A. Schneider/Photo Researchers; *bottom* Photograph by Sharon Hoogstraten; **R72, R73** Photograph by Sharon Hoogstraten; **R74** *top left, top right,* Photograph by Sharon Hoogstraten; *top center* © Mark A. Schneider/Visuals Unlimited; *center right* Photograph by Sharon Hoogstraten; *bottom right* © Thomas Hunn/Visuals Unlimited.

R125

Illustration and Maps

Accurate Art, Inc. **145, 255**
Ampersand Design Group **33, 502**
Argosy **66, 82, 474, 475**
Richard Bonson/Wildlife Art Ltd. **60, 70, 80, 108, 266, 267, 294, 296, 328, 339, 341, 343, 347, 361, 364, 396, 415, 417, 428, 438**
Peter Bull **135, 142, 240, 242, 247, 249, 252, 273, 308, 314, 326, 501**
Steve Cowden **11**
Sandra Doyle/Wildlife Art Ltd. **395**
Stephen Durke **13, 59, 64, 185, 280, 321, 323, 326, R72**
Chris Forsey **195, 311**
Luigi Galante **434, 435, 438**
David A. Hardy **44**
Garry Hincks **84, 87, 197, 229, 233, 279, 280, 282, 284, 287, 288, 290, 291, 294, 350–351, 364, 385, 386, 388, 404, 482, 491**
Mapquest.com, Inc. **50, 53, 54, 62, 85, 88, 90, 91, 103, 116, 119, 120, 121, 122, 124, 129, 133, 138, 157, 158, 159, 161, 162, 163, 174, 176, 207, 209, 210, 211, 231, 235, 246, 269, 271, 272, 275, 279, 283, 284, 287, 291, 292, 294, 302, 313, 319, 320, 326, 332, 338, 341, 349, 359, 399, 415, 462, 493, R52–R53, R56–R57**
Martin Macrae/nbIllustration.co.uk **380**
Janos Marffy **193, 453**
Laurie O'Keefe **397**
Precision Graphics **89, 95, 108, 304, 305, 326, 352, 454**
Mike Saunders **97, 105, 108, 201, 203, 214**
SlimFilms **452, 472, 473, 478**
Raymond Turvey **119, 142, 239**
NOAA/National Geophysical Data Center **R54–R55**
Rob Wood/Wood Ronsaville Harlin **201, 234, 252**

ACKNOWLEDGMENTS